THE CATALOG OF CATALOGS

By Edward L. Palder

CATALOGS III

The Complete Mail-Order Directory

WOODBINE HOUSE   1993

Published by Woodbine House, 5615 Fishers Lane, Rockville, MD 20852.
301/468–8800; 800/843–7323.

Library of Congress Cataloging-in-Publication Data

Palder, Edward L.
    The catalog of catalogs III : the complete mail-order directory / by Edward L. Palder. — 3rd ed.
      p.   cm.
    Rev. ed. of: The catalog of catalogs II.
    Includes index.
    ISBN 0–933149–59–X (pbk.) : $19.95
    1. Catalogs, Commercial—United States—Directories. 2. Mail-order business—United States—Directories. I. Palder, Edward L. Catalog of catalogs II. II. Title.
HF5466.P35 1993
381'.142'029473—dc20
                                                   92–46160
                                                    CIP

Manufactured in the United States of America

10 9 8 7 6 5 4 3

To my wife, who put up with all the hours I spent writing this book.

■ HELP WANTED ■

Dear Reader:

I am planning to periodically update **The Catalog of Catalogs.** To do this, I need your help.

If you know of a company that you think should be included in the next edition, or if you are dissatisfied, for any reason, with the response you receive from a company, please let me know. I will closely evaluate all your recommendations for the next edition of **The Catalog of Catalogs.**

I would also like to invite merchants or manufacturers who would like to be considered for a listing in the next edition, or whose address or telephone number has changed, to send their mailing address and telephone number, along with a copy of their latest catalog(s) to:

> The Catalog of Catalogs
> P.O. Box 6590
> Silver Spring, MD 20916-6590

To those readers of the previous editions who took the time to write me suggesting subjects and companies to be added or deleted—thanks a million. And I thank all of you in advance for your help in making future editions of **The Catalog of Catalogs** as complete as possible.

Happy catalog shopping!

> Sincerely,
> Edward L. Palder

TABLE OF CONTENTS

■ INTRODUCTION ■

It's a buyer's market. If you have the money, then the chances are that someone, somewhere sells exactly what you want. The problem is knowing where to look.

Provided you have the time and patience, you can phone around and try to explain to a succession of harried store clerks just what it is you're looking for. Or you can get in your car and drive from store to store and comb the shelves yourself. But what if you have other, more pressing demands on your time, are unable to leave your home, or simply hate to shop? And what if the stores in your area just don't offer the product you are after in the size, color, or model you want or at a price you can afford? Are the only alternatives to do without or settle for second best?

Not if you have **The Catalog of Catalogs III.** With **The Catalog of Catalogs III,** you can order almost anything you could possibly need—at any hour of the day or night—from the comfort of your own home. You can also send away for free or low-cost recipes and request specialized information such as lists of nearby dealers who carry particular brands of merchandise.

By opening up the world of catalog shopping, **The Catalog of Catalogs III** will enable you to choose merchandise from some of the largest possible selections. Retail stores order their inventories from many of the same sources whose catalogs are listed in this book, but stores only have room to display a few items. When you browse through a catalog, you get to see all the possibilities. What's more, you can often save yourself a bundle in the process. First, if you don't live in the state where the mail-order company is based, you don't have to pay sales tax. And second, since mail-order houses don't have to pay for fancy window displays or expensive floor space, they often pass their savings on to you, the catalog shopper.

This new edition of **The Catalog of Catalogs** contains listings for approximately 12,000 retailers, wholesalers, and manufacturers grouped into over 650 subject areas. As in the previous edition, companies that offer a diverse line of products are sometimes listed in more than one category. This time around, however, double listings of this nature have been kept to a minimum, so that as many different catalog suppliers as possible could be included. Another change is the elimination of the section on travel information sources—once again, to make room for more product listings. As a consequence, there is a larger selection of catalogs than ever to choose from—especially in those categories that reflect the way people live today. For instance, the sections on Recycled and Environmentally Safe Products, Baby Care, Computers, Running, Jogging, and Walking, and Electronic Toys and Games have all been expanded since the second edition.

Making *The Catalog of Catalogs III* Work for You

The Catalog of Catalogs III is a directory for obtaining catalogs and information, not an order catalog. The information given in each listing is intended to help you decide whether you'd like to order a particular catalog and to tell you how to do so if the answer is "yes."

Many of the catalogs, brochures, price lists, and information packets in **The Catalog of Catalogs III** are free. You can request free information simply by calling the phone number in the catalog description or by sending in a postcard. Some mail-order companies ask that a business-sized, self-addressed, stamped envelope (SASE) accompany requests for catalogs or other information. When this is the case, you'll find the notation immediately following the address in the catalog listing. If there's a charge for a catalog, you'll also find this information right after the address—with information about how much of the charge, if any, is refundable after you place an order.

No matter how little the charge for a catalog is, *never send cash through the mail.* Pay by money order or personal check. That way, if you don't receive the information you requested, you'll have proof of your payment. Not that this is likely to happen. In compiling this new edition of **The Catalog of Catalogs,** I reviewed all the listings in the second edition to verify they were still in business, and that their addresses hadn't changed. New listings were verified by making hundreds of phone calls and sending thousands of letters. But because merchants *do* go out of business, change their names, combine with other companies, or move to new addresses without notifying the Post Office, I apologize in advance should any of your requests for information go unanswered. I'm continually updating the information in **The Catalog of Catalogs III,** so if any of your catalog requests are returned as undeliverable, I invite you to send me the returned correspondence and any other information available. If I have a more recent address, I'll send it to you. Your requests for this information should be sent to: Edward L. Palder, The Catalog of Catalogs, P.O. Box 6590, Silver Spring, MD 20906-6590.

One final note about ordering catalogs: try to be patient. Catalogs are usually mailed fourth class, and can take from two to three weeks for delivery. Possible delays can occur when companies are revising or reprinting their catalogs, and some companies process catalog requests only once or twice a month.

Finding the Catalogs You Need

Catalogs in **The Catalog of Catalogs III** are grouped according to subject matter. For example, all computer catalogs are listed in the *Computer* section, and all food catalogs appear in the *Foods* section. Long sections are further divided into subsections. In the *Computer* section, for example, catalogs featuring dust covers & cases; computer manufacturers; computer retailers; printers, peripherals & accessories; software (public domain); software publishers; software retailers; and supplies are grouped together. In the *Foods* section, catalogs featuring cakes & cookies, cheese, maple syrup, meats, and other types of food are grouped together.

Within **The Catalog of Catalogs III,** subjects are listed alphabetically, from *Air Compressors* to *Yoga.* Within each subject area, I've listed catalogs alphabetically by company name. *Narco Avionics* comes before *Northstar Avionics,* and so on. Please note that when a company name begins with a personal name, it's alphabetized by last name, instead of first name. For example, *Earl May Seeds & Nursery Company* is alphabetized as though it began with an "M" instead of an "E"; the *Douglas M. Harding Rare Book & Print Center* is alphabetized as if it began with an "H." Also, names that include numerals are alphabetized as though the numberals were spelled out.

You can find catalogs within **The Catalog of Catalogs III** one of two ways—either by a company's name or by the type of products it sells. To locate the catalog of a company whose name you already know, simply turn to the Corporate Index near the end of the book. This index lists the names of every source of product information described in **The Catalog of Catalogs III,** alphabetized according to the rules outlined above. Sometimes a company is listed more than once because it carries several different types of products. To locate catalogs that offer a specific type of product, check the Table of Contents first. Like the book as a whole, the Table of Contents is arranged alphabetically by subject. So, if you were looking for catalogs of pet supplies, you'd flip to the "P's" in the Table of Contents to find the page number you needed. If you can't find exactly what you're looking for in the Table of Contents, turn to the Subject Index at the very back of the book. Here I've listed topics under as many alternative names as I could think of—for example, the words "dishes" and "plates" will refer you to the pages listing suppliers of china. Through cross references ("See also's") the Subject Index can also direct you to related topics you might otherwise overlook. For instance, the listing for *Greeting Cards* instructs you to see also *Birth Announcements* and *Wedding Invitations.*

Your Mail-Order Rights

Although shopping by mail can be fun and adventuresome, it's not entirely without its hassles. Although I made every effort to ensure that **The Catalog Catalogs III** includes only reputable merchants, sometimes your catalog orders may be damaged in transit, fail to live up to your expectations, take too long to be delivered, or never arrive. Fortunately, in each of these instances, you can take steps to get a refund, repairs, or replacement.

Packages Damaged in Transit

Let's start with the simplest situation. If something you've ordered arrives with obvious damage to the package, write "refused" on the wrapper and return it unopened. Don't sign for it if it arrives insured, registered, certified, or C.O.D., or you'll have to pay the return postage. If you don't discover that your merchandise is damaged until you've opened the package, repackage it with a note describing the problem. Then mail it back by certified or insured mail and wait for the company to send you a free replacement.

Unsatisfactory Merchandise

If something you ordered breaks soon *after* it arrives, or is unsatisfactory for other reasons (it's the wrong size, shoddily made, or completely different from the description in the catalog), your next step depends on the exchange policy of the company you ordered from. Many companies allow you to return unsatisfactory merchandise within thirty days after purchase; others offer unconditional money-back guarantees for the lifetime of their products. Check a company's warranty policies *before you buy:* a bargain is no bargain if it comes without a guarantee. Consult the catalog for the company's return policies and for any special procedures to be followed when returning merchandise for a replacement or refund. If the company has no stated returns policy, don't give up. Noted consumer activist David Horowitz recommends that you send back the unsatisfactory item with a letter explaining why you're disappointed, a copy of your proof of purchase (cancelled check, money order, or credit card statement), and a copy of the original ad. If you don't receive a reply within two weeks, place a collect call to the president of the company to ask what action he or she intends to take. (Horowitz notes that you may not get through to the president, but should at least find out his or her name.) If your phone call doesn't resolve your problem, write a letter to the president informing him that you'll contact the deputy chief postal inspector in his region if you don't get a refund or replacement in seven days. Then do what you said you would. Bring copies of your letters and proof of purchase to the local post office and fill out a Consumer Service form. Your postmaster will turn the matter over to the postal inspectors and the Post Office Consumer Advocate for investigation of possible fraud.

Delayed or Missing Orders

What if your order never arrives? What if you wait days or weeks longer than the delivery time promised in the catalog and still no package? Under the Mail-Order Rule of the Federal Trade Commission, you can take immediate recourse. The Mail-Order Rule requires a company to ship your order within the time promised in its ad or within thirty days of receiving your order and payment. In case of delay, the merchant must notify you of the new shipment date. If the new date is more than thirty days later than the original date, you can cancel your order (in writing) for a full refund. If the new date is less than thirty days later, you can still cancel for a refund, but if you don't respond, it means that you accept the new date. In either case, it is advisable to send your reply by registered or certified mail so you have a return receipt to show your letter was delivered.

The merchant must refund your money within ten days of receiving your cancellation (or notify your credit card company within one billing cycle to credit your account). If the merchant does not give you a refund, credit, or the merchandise, take a copy of your letter and proof of payment to your local postmaster to initiate an investigation for fraud. You can also send a copy of your letter to: Mail-Order Action Line, Direct Marketing Association, 6 E. 42nd St., New York, NY 10017-4646. If the merchant is a member of the DMA, the Association can pressure the merchant to refund your money.

Preventing and Reducing Problems

I hope you don't run into any of the problems described above, but on the off chance that you might, there are several precautions that can make resolution of problems easier. First, remember that any offer that sounds too good to be true should first be checked. When in doubt about a product, contact the merchant *before you buy* for information about warranties, exchange policies, missing facts, or unbelievable claims. Second, make sure you fill out the order form accurately and completely, and enclose all shipping and handling charges requested by the company. And finally, always pay by check, money order, or credit card so you have proof of payment. Keep a record of the name and address of the company, the merchandise ordered, the date you placed the order, the name of the publication in which the merchandise was described, and the number of your money order or check.

Let the World Come to You

Now that you know the ground rules of mail-order shopping **The Catalog of Catalogs** way, why not take a moment to glance through the Table of Contents and Subject Index. I hope you will not only find what you are looking for, but also hundreds of other teasers you'll want to send away for. Don't resist the urge! Ordering by mail is by far the easiest, most convenient, and most cost-effective way I know of to shop. It can also be highly addictive, as the long-suffering civil servant who delivers all my catalogs and packages can attest. But don't worry. In the unlikely event you ever want to break the habit of catalog shopping, you can have your name removed from many merchants' mailing lists by contacting the Direct Marketing Association at the address given above. (They can also *add* your name to more mailing lists, if you desire.) So, sit back and take advantage of all **The Catalog of Catalogs III** has to offer you. Send away for what you want, and let the world come to you.

AIR COMPRESSORS

Campbell Hausfeld, 100 Production Dr., Harrison, OH, 45030: Free information ■ Air compressors. 800–634–4793.

DeVilbiss, 213 Industrial Dr., Jackson, TN 38301: Free information ■ Air compressors. 901–423–7000.

Sanborn Manufacturing Company, 118 W. Rock St., P.O. Box 206, Springfield, MN 56087: Free information ■ Air compressors. 800– 533–0365.

Stanley-Bostitch, Inc., One Feltloc Ln., East Greenwich, RI 02818: Free information ■ Air compressors. 800–556–6696.

AIR CONDITIONERS & CONTROLS

Cal-K, Inc., 7411 Laurel Canyon Blvd., North Hollywood, CA 91605: Free information ■ Programmable setback thermostats. 818–764–3288.

Carrier Corporation, P.O. Box 4808, Syracuse, NY 13221: Free information ■ Combination gas/electric heating and cooling system, gas and electric furnaces, heat pumps, and air conditioners. 800–CARRIER.

Friedrich Air Conditioning & Refrigeration Company, P.O. Box 1540, San Antonio, TX 78295: Free information ■ Through-the-wall air conditioners. 512–225–2000.

G.E. Appliances, 4700 Allmond Ave, Louisville, KY 40209: Free information ■ Packaged terminal air conditioners and heat pumps. 800–626–2000.

Hunter Fan Company, 2500 Fisco Ave., Memphis, TN 38114: Brochure $1 ■ Electronically programmable thermostat for heating and air conditioning systems, ceiling fans, lighting fixtures, and dehumidifiers. 901–745–9287.

Jameson Home Products, 2820 Thatcher Rd., Downers Grove, IL 60515: Free information ■ Programmable, electronic thermostats. 708–963–2850.

Sears, Roebuck & Company, Catalog Division, 925 S. Homan Ave., Chicago, IL 60607: Free catalog ■ Heating and cooling equipment (Catalog also available from local stores.) 312–875–2500.

Thomas Industries, Inc., 1419 Illinois Ave., Sheboygan, WI 53082: Free information ■ Air conditioners. 414–457–4891.

AIRCRAFT

Aircraft Kits

Advanced Aviation, Inc., 323 N. Ivey Ln. Orlando, FL 32811: Information package $3 (specify model) ■ One- and two-person high-wing amphibians Includes the Cobra Model B, King Cobra Model B, Highcraft Buccaneer SX, Buccaneer II, Carrera, Carrera 150, Carrera 180/182, and Explorer Sierra. 407–294–6700.

Adventure Air, P.O. Box 579, Barstow, CA 92312: Information package $10 ■ Two person high-wing, monoplane with optional tailwheel or retractable amphibian landing gear: Adventurer. 619–257–3816.

Aero Composite Technology, Inc., RD 3, Somerset, PA 15501: Information package $10 ■ Two-person amphibian with optional trigear or retractable amphibian landing gear: Sea Hawker. 814–445–8608.

Aero Visions International, Rt. 2, Box 282, South Webster, OH 45682: Brochure $3 (specify model) ■ High-wing monoplanes with tandem seating: Culite Culex and Celebrity Horizon. 614–778–3185.

Bushby Aircraft, Inc., 674 Rt. 52, Minooka, IL 60447: Brochure $5 (specify model) ■ One- and two-person low-wing monoplanes: Midget Mustang and Mustang II. 815–467–2346.

Carlson Aircraft, Inc., 50643 SR 14, P.O. Box 88, East Palestine, OH 44413: Information package $15 (specify model) ■ One- and two-person high-wing monoplanes: Sparrow Ultralight, Sparrow II, Sparrow Sport Special Skycycle '87, and Sparrowette. 216–426–3934.

CGS Aviation, Inc., P.O. Box 41007, Brecksville, OH 44141: Information package $5 ■ One- and two-person high-wing monoplanes. Includes the CGS Hawk, CGS Hawk II, and CGS Ag-Hawk. 216–632–1424.

Circa Reproductions, 8027 Argyll Rd., Edmonton, Alberta, Canada T6C 4A9: Information package $5 (specify model) ■ One- and two-person biplanes: Nieuport 11 EXP, Nieuport 11 UL, and Nieuport 12 EXP. 403–469–2692.

Coldfire Systems, Inc., 2235 1st St., Simi Valley, CA 93065: Information package $15 (specify model ■ One- and two-person kits: Buckeye Powered Parachute and Buckeye Powered Parachute-B. 805–583–3085.

Co-Z Development, 2046 N. 63rd Pl., Mesa, AZ 85205: Information package $10 ■ Four-person, pusher-type powered airplane: Cozy Mark IV. 602–981–6401.

Denney Aerocraft Company, 100 N. Kings Rd., Nampa, ID 83687: Information package $10 ■ Two-person high-wing monoplane: Kitfox. 208–466–1711.

Diehl Aero-Nautical, 1855 N. Elm, Jenks, OK 74037: Information package $3 ■ One-person mid-wing canard amphibian: XTC. 918–299–4445.

Earthstar Aircraft, Inc., Star Rt., Box 313, Santa Margarita, CA 93453: Information package $2 (specify model) ■ One- and two-person aircraft kits: Laughing Gull (LG1), Laughing Gull (LG1H), Ultra Gull (U1H), Thunder Gull (J), and Thunder Gull (JX). 805–438–5235.

Eipper Aircraft, P.O. Box 1572, Temecula, CA 92390: Free information package (specify model) ■ One- and two-person monoplanes: Quicksilver MX Sprint, Quicksilver GT–400, and Quicksilver MXL. 714–676–6886.

Falconar Aviation, Ltd., 19 Airport Rd., Edmonton, Alberta, Canada T5G 0W7: Information package $10 (specify model) ■ One- and two-person low-wing monoplanes: Falconar Jodel F Series and Falconar SAL Mustang P51 and a cabin model, the Flying Flea Series Cubmajor. 403–454–7272.

Fisher Flying Products, Inc., P.O. Box 468, Edgeley, ND 58433: Information package $5 (specify model) ■ One- and two-person high-wing monoplanes. Includes the FP–101, FP–202, FP–303, FP–404, FP–404 EXP, FP–505, FP–606, and a two-person biplane, the Sky Baby Classic. 701–493–2286.

Flightworks Corporation, 4211 Todd Ln., Austin, TX 78744: Information package $5 (specify model) ■ One- and two-person high-wing monoplanes: Capella and Capella XS (dual seat). 512–441–8844.

Hipp's Superbird's, Inc., P.O. Box 266, Saluda, NC 28773: Information package $4 (specify model) ■ One-person high-wing monoplanes: Kitten, Super Kitten, Sportster,

Super Sportster, Reliant, Reliant SX, and Reliant II. 704–749–9134.

Historical Aircraft Corporation, P.O. Box 2218, Durango, CO 81302: Information package $18.95 (specify model) ■ One-person low-wing monoplanes: AU–1 Corsair, P–51D and P–51B Mustang, and P–40C Tomahawk. 303–259–1037.

Jurca Plans, 1733 Kansas, Flint, MI 48506: Information package $5 (specify model) ■ One- and two-person monoplanes: MJ–2 Tempete, MJ–5 Sirocco, MJ–7 Gnatsun P–51, MJ–77 Mustang, MJ–9 ME109, MJ–10 Spitfire, MJ–12 P–40, and MJ–90 ME109. 313–232–5395.

Kolb Company, Inc., RD 3, Box 38, Phoenixville, PA 19460: Information package $5 ■ One- or two-person high-wing monoplane: Firestar Mark III. 215–948–4136.

Leading Edge Airfoils, Inc., 331 S. 14th St., Colorado Springs, CO 80904: Information package $5 (specify model) ■ Biplanes: Nieuport 11 UL and Nieuport 11 EXP. 719–632–4959.

Light Miniature Aircraft, Opa Locka Airport, Building 411, Opa Locka, FL 33054: Information package $5 (specify model) ■ One- and two-person high-wing monoplanes: LM–1, LM–1U, LM–1X, LM–2U, LM–2X, LM–3X, and LM–2X–2P. 305–681–4068.

Loehle Aviation, Inc., 380 Shipmans Creek Rd., Wartrace, TN 37183: Information package $5 ■ One-person low-wing monoplane: 5151 Mustang RG Replica. 615–857–3419

Macair Industries, Inc., Box 1000, Baldwin, Ontario, Canada L0E 1A0: Information package $5 ■ Two-person high-wing monoplane with optional tailwheel, floats, or ski-floats landing gear: Merlin. 416–722–3411.

Maxair Aircraft Corporation, P.O. Box 5345, Valdosta, GA 31603: Information package $10 (specify model)* One- and two-person high-wing monoplanes: ARV Drifter 277, ARV Drifter 377, ARV 582 Drifter, and ARV 503 Drifter. 912–333–9606.

Merganser Aircraft Corporation, P.O. Box 8, Annapolis, MD 21404: Information package $7.50 ■ Two-seater low-wing canard with optional trigear or retractable amphibian landing gear: Merganser. 410–741–5075.

Mosler Airframes & Powerplants, 140 Ashwood Rd., Hendersonville, NC 28739: Information package $15 (specify model) ■ One- and two-person high-wing monoplanes: N3 Pup UL, SP, N3–2, Pup, and Super Pup. 704–692–7713.

Murphy Aviation, Ltd., 8880 Young Rd. South, Chilliwack, British Columbia, Canada V2P 4P5: Information package $15 (specify model) ■ Two-seater tandem biplanes: Renegade II and Renegade Spirit Rebel. 604–792–5855.

Neico Aviation, Inc., 2244 Airport Way, Redmond, OR 97756: Information package $15 (specify model) ■ Low-wing monoplanes: four-person Lancair IV, and two-person Lancair 235 and Lancair 320. 503–923–2244.

Barney Oldfield Aircraft Company, P.O. Box 228, Needham, MA 02192: Information package $10 (specify model) ■ One- and two-person biplanes: Baby Lakes, Buddy Baby Lakes, and Super Baby Lakes. 617–444–5480.

Osprey Aircraft, 3741 El Ricon Way, Sacramento, CA 95825: Information package $12 (specify model) ■ Two-person monoplanes: Osprey–2 and GP–4. 916–483–3004.

Phantom Aircraft Corporation, 1800 Goetz Rd., Perris, CA 92370: Free information package (specify model) ■ One- and two-person high-wing monoplanes: Phantom I and Phantom II. 714–943–9445.

Powers Bashforth Aircraft Corporation, 4700 188th St. NE, Arlington, WA 98223: Information package $15 (specify model) ■ One- and two-person high-wing monoplanes: B1–RD, B1–RD, Amateur Built Silverwing, and Custom Mini Master. 206–435–4356.

ProTech Aircraft, 24215 FM 1093, Richmond, TX 77469: Information package $10 ■ Two-person high-wing monoplane: PT–2. 713–341–9712.

Quad City Aircraft Corporation, 3610 Coaltown Rd., Moline, IL 61265: Information package $10 (specify model) ■ One- and two-person high-wing monoplanes: Challenger U/L, Special Challenger II, and Challenger II Special. 309–764–3515.

Quicksilver Enterprises, P.O. Box 1572, Temecula, CA 92390: Information package $3 (specify model) ■ One- and two-person

high-wing monoplanes: Quicksilver MX Sprint, Quicksilver MX Sport, Quicksilver MXII Sprint, Quicksilver MXII Sport, Quicksilver GT 400, and Quicksilver GT 500. 714–676–6886.

Rand Robinson Engineering, Inc., 15641 Product Ln., Huntington Beach, CA 92649: Information package $8 (specify model) ■ One- and two-person low-wing monoplanes: KR–1, KR–1B, KR–2, and KR–100. 714–898–3811.

Rans Company, 1104 E. Hwy. 40 Bypass, Hays, KS 67601: Information package $10 (specify model) ■ One- and two-person high-wing monoplanes: RANS Coyote, RANS S–9 Chaos, RANS S–7 Courier, RANS S–10 Sakota, RANS S–6 Coyote II, and RANS S–12 Airaile. 913–625–6346.

W. W. Redfern, 26009 Silverwood Ln., Athol, ID 83801: Information package $6 (specify model) ■ One-person biplanes: Redfern Nieuport 17 or 24, Redfern DH–2, and Redfern Fokker DR–1. 208–683–2264.

Ron Sands, Inc., RD 1, Box 341, Mertztown, PA 19539: Information package $15 (specify model) ■ One-person triplanes: Fokker DR–1 and Fokker D VIII. 215–682–6788.

Seabird Aviation, Inc., Terminal One, 4920 E. 5th Ave., Columbus, OH 43219: Information package $10 ■ Two-person side-by-side seating seaplane with land capability: Petrel. 614–236–0475.

Sierra Delta Systems, 1702 W. McNair St., Chandler, AZ 85224: Information package $9 ■ Two-person high-performance airplane: E-Racer. 602–491–1548.

S.N.A. Aircraft, Inc., Box 607, Kimberton, PA 19442: Information package $25 ■ Four-person amphibian: Seawind. 215–983–3377.

Sorrell Aircraft Company, Inc., 16525 Tilley Rd., South Tenino, WA 98589: Information package $15 (specify model) ■ One- and two- person biplanes: Hiperlight SNS–8, EXP–SNS–8, EXP II SNS–9, Guppy SNS–2, and Hiperbipe SNS–7. 206–264–2866.

Steen Aero Lab, 1210 Airport Rd., Marion, NC 28752: Information package $10 ■ Two-person open cockpit biplane: Steen Skybolt. 704–652–7382.

Stoddard-Hamilton Aircraft, Inc., 18701 58th Ave. NE, Arlington, WA 98223: Information package $20 (specify model) ■ Two-person low-wing monoplanes: Glasair II–S

TD, Glasair II–S FT, Glasair II–S RG, Glasair III, and Glasair III Turbo. 206–435–8533.

Stolp Starduster Corporation, 4301 Twining St., Riverside, CA 95209: Information package $5 (specify model) ■ One- and two-person biplanes: V-Star SA–900, Starlet SA–500, Starduster Too SA–300, Acroduster Too SA–750, and Super Starduster SA–101. 714–686–7943.

Sunrise Ultralight Manufacturing Company, Rt. 4, Box 336, New Caney, TX 77357: Information package $8 (specify model) ■ One- and two-person high-wing monoplanes: Clipper UL, Super Sport Clipper, Spitfire UL, Spitfire Super Sport, Spitfire II UTV, and Spitfire Elite. 713–354–1348.

TEAM, Inc., Box 338, Bradyville, TN 37026: Information package $3 (specify model) ■ One-person mid-wing monoplanes: HI-MAX and MiniMAX. 615–765–5397.

Teenie Company, Box 625, Coolidge, AZ 85228: Information package $10 ■ One-person low-wing monoplane: Teenie Two. 602–723–5660.

Van's Aircraft, Inc., P.O. Box 160, North Plains, SD 97133: Information package $8 ■ One- and two-person low-wing monoplanes: RV–3, RV–4, RV–6, and RV–6A. 503–647–5117.

War Aircraft Replica, Inc., 348 S. 8th St., Santa Paula, CA 93060: Information package $12 (specify model) ■ One-person low-wing monoplanes: Focke-Wulf 190, F–4U Corsair, Hawker Sea Fury, P–47 Thunderbolt, and P–51D Mustang. 805–525–8212.

Western Aircraft Supplies, 623 Markerville Rd. NE, Calgary, Alberta, Canada T2E 5X1: Information package $5 ■ Two-person low-wing monoplane: PGK–1 Hirondelle. 403–275–3513.

Zenith Aircraft Company, P.O. Box 650-K, Mexico, MO 65265: Information package $15 (specify model) ■ One- and two-person low-wing monoplanes: Zodiac CH–600, Zenith CH–200, Zenith CH–250, TRi-Z CH–300, and Zenair STOL CH–701. 314–581–9000.

Avionics Equipment

Aircraft Spruce & Specialty, 201 W. Truslow Ave., Box 424, Fullerton, CA 92632: Free information ■ Avionics equipment and accessories for homebuilt and experimental aircraft. 800–824–1930.

Bendix/King General Aviation Avionics Division, 400 N. Rogers Rd., Olathe, KS 66062: Free information ■ Avionics equipment and accessories for homebuilt and experimental aircraft. 913–782–0400.

Eventide Avionics, One Alsan Way, Little Ferry, NJ 07643: Free information ■ Avionics equipment and accessories for homebuilt and experimental aircraft. 800–446–7878.

Foster Air Data Systems, 7020 Huntley Rd., Columbus, OH 43229: Free information ■ Avionics equipment and accessories for homebuilt and experimental aircraft. 614–885–9502.

ICOM America, 2380 116th Ave. NE, Bellevue, WA 98004: Free information ■ Avionics equipment and accessories for homebuilt and experimental aircraft. 800–999–9877.

II Morrow, P.O. Box 23939, Portland, OR 97223: Free information ■ Avionics equipment and accessories for homebuilt and experimental aircraft. 800–742–0077.

Narco Avionics, 2825 Laguna Canyon Rd., Laguna Beach, CA 92652: Free information ■ Avionics equipment and accessories for homebuilt and experimental aircraft. 800–223–3636.

Northstar Avionics, 30 Sudbury Rd., Acton, MA 01720: Free information ■ Avionics equipment and accessories for homebuilt and experimental aircraft. 800–628–4487.

Terra Avionics, 3520 Pan American Freeway NE, Albuquerque, NM 87107: Free information ■ Avionics equipment and accessories for homebuilt and experimental aircraft. 505–884–2321.

Gliders

Rotec Engineering, P.O. Box 124, Duncanville, TX 75116: Photo brochure $5 ■ Power hang gliders, kits, and accessories. 214–298–2505.

Schweizer Aircraft Corporation, P.O. Box 147, Elmira, NY 14902: Free list ■ Glider pilot equipment, accessories, and books. 607–739–3821.

Gyro Aircraft Kits

Barnett Rotorcraft, 4307 Olivehurst Ave., Olivehurst, CA 95961: Information package $15 (specify model) ■ One-person gyroplane: Barnett J4B and Barnett J4B-2; two-person gyroplane: Barnett J4B–2. 916–742–7416.

Ken Brock Manufacturing, 11852 Western Ave., Stanton, CA 90680: Information package $7 (specify model) ■ One-person gyroplanes: Brock KB–2 and Brock KB–3. 714–898–4366.

B W Rotor Company, Inc., P.O. Box 391, Tonowanda, KS 67144: Information package $5 ■ One- and two-person jet-powered helicopters and gyroplanes.

DRL Technologies, P.O. Box 5102, Vandenburg Air Force Base, CA 93437: Brochure $10 ■ One-person ultralight helicopter.

Gyro-2000, P.O. Box 8434, Santa Fe, NM 87504: Information package $10 ■ One-person gyroplane.

Helicraft, Inc., P.O. Box 50, Riderwood, MD 21139: Information package $10 ■ Home-built helicopter kits. 410–583–6366.

Moshier Technologies, 334 State St., Ste. 106, Los Altos, CA 94022: Information package $20 ■ Two-person co-axial helicopter with twin counter-rotating rotors.

Bill Parsons Gyros, 2965 Carrier Ave., Sanford, FL 32773: Free information ■ Two-person gyroplane: Rotocraft. 407–323–2372.

Rotary-Air Force, Inc., Ponoka Industrial Airport, Hanger #3, Box 1205, Ponoka, Alberta, Canada T0C 2H0: Information package $12 ■ Cross-country gyroplane: RAF 2000. 403–783–8484.

Rotorway International, 300 S. 25th Ave., Phoenix, AZ 85009: Information package $15 ■ Two-person helicopter for sport flying. 602–278–8899.

Sno-Bird Aircraft, Inc., 13007 122nd Ave. NW, Gig Harbar, WA 98335: Information package $25 (specify model) ■ One- and two-person gyroplanes: SnoBird 503, Sno-Bird 582, and SnoBird 636. 206–857–3200.

Star Aviation, Inc., 821 Lone Star Dr., New Braunfels, TX 78130: Information package $15 ■ An easy-to-build helicoper kit: Lone-Star Sport Helicopter.

4

Ultralight Aircraft, 39416 264th Ave. SE, Enumclaw, WA 98022: Information package $10 (specify model) ■ One-person gyroplanes: Sno-Bird and Sno-Bird XL. 206–825–3782.

Vancraft Copters, 7246 N. Mohawk, Portland, OR 97203: Information package $25 (specify model) ■ One- and two person gyroplanes: Rotorlightning Sport Copter and Vancraft Copter. 503–286–5462.

Parts & Tools

A & S International Marketing Company, Inc., P.O. Box 672, Brentwood, NY 11717: Free catalog ■ Aircraft equipment, accessories and components, ground support equipment, avionics, and electronics. 516–435–2999.

The Aeroplane Store, Kampel Airport, 8930 Carlisle Rd., Wellsville, PA 17365: Free catalog ■ Aircraft-building supplies and accessories. Includes Sitka spruce, aircraft plywood, Randolph finishing supplies, and hardware. 717–432–9688.

Aircraft Spruce & Specialty, 201 W. Truslow Ave., Box 424, Fullerton, CA 92632: Catalog $5 ■ Tools, construction materials and supplies, accessories, instruments, engines, fabrics, pilot supplies and equipment, and books. 800–824–1930.

Airparts, Inc., 31 N. 7th St., Kansas City, KS 66101: Free information ■ Aircraft-building supplies and components Includes aluminum and alloys of various types and sizes. 913–321–3280.

Alexander Aeroplane Company, Inc., P.O. Box 909, Griffin, GA 30224: Free catalog ■ Aircraft building supplies. Includes covering systems, presewn fabrics, custom and presewn interiors, tubing and sheet metal, composite materials, hardware, and aircraft plywood, fir, and spruce. 800–831–2949; 404–228–3815 (in GA).

B & F Aircraft Supply, Inc., 9524 W. Gulfstream Rd., Frankfort, IL 60423: Catalog $4 (refundable with $30 order) ■ Accessories, components, and supplies for building and maintaining aircraft. 815–469–2473.

California Power Systems, Inc., 790 139th Ave., San Leandro, CA 94578: Catalog $6.95 ■ Supplies and parts for ultralight aircraft. 510–357–2403.

EMG Engineering Company, P.O. Box 1368, Hesperia, CA 92345: Free brochure ■ Pressure jet engine for homebuilt helicopters, planes, and gliders. Available as a complete engine, kit, or plans. 619–247–8519.

Flight Suits, Ltd., 1675 Pioneer Way, El Cajon, CA 92020: Free catalog ■ Flight suits, helmets, boots, jackets, communication equipment and accessories, and other services. 619–440–6976.

J.A. Air Center/Joliet Avionics, Inc., Dupage Airport, West Chicago, IL 60185: Free information: Avionics equipment. 312–584–3200.

Leading Edge Airfoils, Inc., 331 S. 14th St., Colorado Springs, CO 80904: Catalog $5 ■ Building materials and accessories for sport aircraft. Includes hardware, accessories, tools, engines and propellers, fabric and finishes, and books. 719–632–4959.

Wil Neubert Aircraft Supply, 403 3rd Ave., Watervliet, NY 12189: Catalog $5 (refundable) ■ Avionics equipment, engines and parts, radios and antennas, timers and clocks, wheels and brakes, custom fuel tanks, custom engine mounts, hardware, batteries, and other accessories. 800–831–7527; 518–273–2327 (in NY).

R.O.A.R. Products, 7612 S. Marquette, Chicago, IL 60649: Free information ■ Metal rotor blades for homebuilt helicopters. 312–734–6135.

Stits Poly-Fiber Aircraft Coatings, P.O. Box 3084, Riverside, CA 92519: Free catalog ■ Aircraft covering materials. 714–684–4280.

Superflite Aircraft Supplies, 2149 E. Pratt Blvd., Elk Grove Village, IL 60007: Catalog $5 ■ Aircraft supplies and accessories. 800–323–0611.

Univair Aircraft Corporation, 2500 Himalaya Rd., Aurora, CO 80011: Free information ■ Parts and accessories for antique and classic aircraft. 303–375–8882.

Val Avionics, Ltd., P.O. Box 13025, Salem, OR 97309: Free information ■ Avionics equipment. 503–370–9429.

Wag-Aero, Inc., 1216 North Rd., Lyons, WI 53148: Free information with long SASE ■ Avionics equipment, engines, tools, and accessories. 800–766–1216.

Watkins Aviation, Inc., 15770 Midway Rd., Hanger #6, Dallas, TX 75244: Free catalog ■ Flying suits, jackets, emblems and insignia, helmets, parachutes, communications services, survival gear, gloves, and other supplies. 214–934–0033.

Wicks Aircraft Supply, 410 Pine St., Highland, IL 62249: Catalog $6 ■ Tools, construction materials and supplies, accessories, instruments, fabric, engines, and propellers. 800–221–8425.

Pilot Supplies & Equipment

LDT Pilot Equipment, 9375 Dielman Industrial Dr., St. Louis, MO 63132: Free information ■ Hand-held electronic information systems. 800–274–0949; 314–997–1150 (in OH).

Sporty's Pilot Shop, Chermont Airport, Batavia, OH 45132: Free catalog ■ Pilot supplies and equipment. 800–543–8633.

AIR PURIFIERS

AirXchange, Inc., 401 VFW Dr., Rockland, MA 02370: Free information ■ Home air filters. 617–871–4816.

Altech Energy Corporation, 7009 Raywood Rd., Madison, WI 53713: Free information ■ Home air filters.

Carrier Corporation, P.O. Box 4808, Syracuse, NY 13221: Free information ■ Electronic air cleaners. 800–CARRIER.

Enviracaire, 747 Bowman Ave., Hagerstown, MD 21740: Free brochure ■ Air cleaners for tobacco smoke, fumes, pollen, bacteria, animal dander, dust, and dust-mite allergens.

Honeywell, Inc., Residential Division, 1985 Douglas Dr. North, Golden Valley, MN 55422: Free information ■ Electronic air cleaners. 800–468–1502.

National EnviroAlert Company, 297 Lake St., Waltham, MA 02154: Free brochure ■ Environmental air systems and water filtration units for home and office. 617–891–7484.

Newtron Products, Inc., 3874 Virginia Ave., Cincinnati, OH 45227: Free information ■ Electrostatic air cleaners.

Nortec Industries, Box 698, Ogdensburg, NY 13669: Free information ■ Home air filters. 315–425–1255.

4

Purity Home Products, Inc., Box 397, Millersport, OH 43046: Free information ■ Home air filters. 614–837–2109.

Sanyo Electric, 200 Riser Rd., Little Ferry, NJ 07643: Free information with long SASE ■ Electrostatic air cleaner/ionizer with an automatic smoke sensor. 201–641–2333.

ALARM SYSTEMS

A & S International Marketing Company, Inc., P.O. Box 672, Brentwood, NY 11717: Free catalog ■ Home intercom systems, security systems, visual call systems, visual signal systems, and audio-visual call systems. 516–435–2999.

ABCO Supply Company, 387 Canal St., New York, NY 10013: Free information ■ Install-it-yourself burglar alarm kits for stores, factories, autos, boats, apartments, and homes. 212–431–5066.

ADT Security Systems, 300 Interpace Pkwy., Parsippany, NJ 07054: Free guide ■ Burglar alarm systems and accessories. 800–238–4636.

Advanced Security, 2964 Peachtree St., Atlanta, GA 30305: Catalog $1 ■ Burglar and fire alarm systems. 800–241–0267.

Alarm Controls Corporation, 19 Brandywine Dr., Deer Park, NY 11729: Free information ■ Electronic security and fire protection units. 516–586–4220.

ATV Research, Inc., 1301 Broadway, Dakota City, NE 68731: Catalog $3 ■ Closed circuit surveillance television systems for homes. 402–987–3771.

Black & Decker Home Protector, Box 5259, Clifton, NJ 07012: Free information ■ Wireless security system. Options include a 24-hour telephone monitoring service and direct notification of police.

Burle Industries, Inc., 1000 New Holland Ave., Lancaster, PA 17601: Free information ■ Lighting systems that turn on when someone approaches a secured area and turn off when they leave. 717–295–6000.

CCTV Corporation, 315 Hudson St., New York, NY 10013: Free information ■ Closed circuit cameras that play on television sets. 800–221–2240; 212–989–4433 (in NY).

Direct Sales Center, P.O. Box 1074, Moorhead, MN 56561: Catalog $5 (refundable) ■

Security, alarm, and surveillance/counter-surveillance systems. 701–232–5107.

Espion, Inc., 137 California St., Newton, MA 02158: Free information ■ Motion detector alarm systems for the home. 800–548–7313.

Falcon Eye, Inc., 3130 Marquita, Fort Worth, TX 76116: Free information ■ Indoor and outdoor sensor-operated, plug-in, and direct-wire automatic light units. 800–541–3507.

Fyrnetics, Inc., 1021 Davis Rd., Elgin, IL 60123: Free information ■ Burglar alarm and smoke alarm systems with selective control options. 708–742–0282.

Heath Company, P.O. Box 8589, Benton Harbor, MI 49023: Free catalog ■ Easy-to-install home security, entertainment, and automation equipment. 800–44–HEATH.

Home Control Concepts, 9353 Activity Rd., Ste. C, San Diego, CA 92126: Free catalog ■ Security and home automation equipment. 619–693–8887.

Intelectron, 21021 Corsair Blvd., Hayward, CA 94545: Free information ■ Motion detector alarm system for homes. 510–732–6790.

Interactive Technologies, Inc., 2266 2nd St. North, St. Paul, MN 55109: Free information ■ Telephone-based security systems for the home. 800–777–5485.

JDS Technologies, 17471 Plaza Otonal, San Diego, CA 92128: Free information ■ Telephone-based home security systems. 619–487–8787.

Mountain West Alarm Supply Company, Alpha Omega Security Group, Inc., 9420 E. Doubletree Ranch Rd., Scottsdale, AZ 85258: Catalog $1 ■ Burglar and fire-protection security systems. 800–528–6169; 602–971–1200 (in AZ).

Nalcor, American Builders Hardware, 13344 S. Main St., Los Angeles, CA 90061: Free information ■ Easy-to-install wireless burglar alarm.

New Century, 1422 Boswell, Crete, NE 68333: Free brochure with long SASE ■ Automatic/remote control house monitoring systems. 800–728–4155.

NuTone, Inc., Madison & Red Bank Rds., Cincinnati, OH 45227: Free information ■ Video door-answering system with voice transmission over telephone and wireless

security system that can be zone programmed. 513–527–5100.

Phonetics, Inc., 101 State Rd., Media, PA 19063: Free information ■ Telephone-based home security systems. 215–565–8520.

Premier Communications Company, Inc., P.O. Box 1513, High Point, NC 27261: Free brochure ■ Easy-to-install burglar alarms. Modular units available for future expansion. 919–841–4355.

Quam Products, Box 130, Elk Point, SD 57025: Free information ■ Driveway alarm system that announces when someone enters or leaves your home, driveway, or other location. 605–356–2772.

Radio Shack, Division Tandy Corporation, 1500 One Tandy Center, Fort Worth, TX 76102: Free product information ■ Easy-to-install burglar and fire alarm system for home use. Will work with an automatic message dialer. 817–390–3700.

Spectre Security Systems, 843 Dumont Pl., #22, Rochester Hills, MI 48063: Free information ■ Home and automotive security systems and accessories. 313–652–8117.

Techmart, 2745 Winnetka Ave. North, Ste. 139, Minneapolis, MN 55427: Free brochure ■ Honeywell security and alarm devices, night lights, timers, safety products, dimmers, and other security and safety controls. 800–688–1280.

ANTIQUES & REPRODUCTIONS

Mark & Marjorie Allen, RD 1, Box 13, Putnam Valley, NY 10579: Free information ■ English and continental Delftwares, early brass, and other antiques. 914–528–8989.

Antique Christmas Memorabilia, 7027 Limekiln Pike, Philadelphia, PA 19138: Free information ■ Antique Christmas memorabilia. 215–794–3210.

Antique Imports Unlimited, P.O. Box 2978, Covington, LA 70434: Catalog $2 ■ Imported antiques and jewelry. 504–892–0014.

Asian House, 888 7th Ave., New York, NY 10106: Free information ■ Authentic Oriental art, furniture, lamps, screens, and carpets, jewelry, antique porcelain, gifts, and decor accessories. 212–581–2294.

Baker's Antiques & Collectibles, P.O. Box 558, Oakdale, NY 11769: Catalog $12 and long SASE ■ Antique and collectible toys. 516–567–9295.

Benedikt & Salmon Record Rarities, 3020 Meade Ave., San Diego, CA 92116: Free catalogs, indicate choice of (1) autographs and rare books; (2) classical; (3) jazz, big bands, and blues; and (4) personalities, soundtracks, and country music ■ Early phonographs and cylinders, autographed memorabilia and rare books in music and the performing arts, and hard-to-find phonograph recordings from 1890 to date. 619–281–3345.

Ruth Bigel Antiques, 743 Madison Ave., New York, NY 10021: Free information ■ Country furniture, samplers, quilts, weather vanes, and other antiques. 212–734–3262.

Warren Blake, Old Science Books, 308 Hadley Dr., Trumbull, CT 06611: Free catalog ■ Hard-to-find astronomy books and prints. 203–459–0820.

Chinese Porcelain Company, 25 E. 77th St., 3rd Floor, New York, NY 10021: Free information ■ Chinese porcelain antiques. 212–628–4101.

Cinnamon Hill, Inc., 105 High Meadow Dr., Franklin, TN 37064: Free information ■ American furniture and accessories, from the 18th- and early 19th-century. 615–790–0833.

Collector's Gallery at Kentshire, 37 E. 12th St., New York, NY 10003: Free information ■ Antique jewelry. 212–673–6644.

Darr Antiques & Interiors, Main St., P.O. Box 130, Sheffield, MA 01257: Free brochure ■ American, English, and Oriental 18th-and 19th-century antiques. 413–229–7773.

Chuck Darrow's Fun Antiques, 309 E. 61st St., New York, NY 10021: Free information with long SASE ■ Collectible and antique toys. 212–838–0730.

Doll Emporium, P.O. Box 1000, Studio City, CA 91604: Free information with long SASE ■ Antique dolls. 818–763–5937.

Dunbar's Gallery, 76 Havenn St., Milford, MA 01757: Free brochure ■ Advertising nostalgia, Americana, folk art, pottery, comic character toys, mechanical and still banks, and other antiques. 508–634–TOYS.

Bill Egleston, Inc., 509 Brentwood Rd., Marshalltown, IA 50158: Catalog $5 ■ Collectible cloisonne, ivory, netsuke, stone, and oriental items. 800–798–4579.

Fine Tool Journal, Iron Horse Antiques, Inc., P.O. Box 4001, Poultney, VT 05764: Annual subscription $15 ■ Antique tools. 802–287–4050.

N. Flayderman & Company, Inc, P.O. Box 2446, Fort Lauderdale, FL 33303: Catalog $10 ■ Antique guns, swords, knives, and other western, nautical, and militaria antiques and collectibles. 305–761–8855.

Gallery of Antique Rugs & Tapestries, Marvin Kagan, Inc., 991 Madison Ave., New York, NY 10021: Free information ■ Antique rugs. 212–535–9000.

Games People Played, P.O. Box 1540, Pinedale, WY 82925: Brochure $2 ■ Antique replica game boards. 307–367–2502.

Gasoline Alley, 6501 20th NE, Seattle, WA 98115: Free information with long SASE ■ Baseball and football collectibles; vintage toys, from 1875 to 1975. 206–524–1606.

Gem Antiques, 1088 Madison Ave., New York, NY 10028: Free information ■ European and American ceramics. 212–535–7399.

The Gemmary, P.O. Box 816, Redondo Beach, CA 90277: Free information ■ Antique scientific instruments and rare books. 310–372–5969.

Hake's Americana, P.O. Box 1444, York, PA 17405: Catalogs, 4-issue subscription $20 ■ Americana and other collectibles. 717–848–1333.

Hillman-Gemini Antiques, 927 Madison Ave., New York, NY 10021: Free information ■ Antique toys and banks, folk art, and Americana. 212–734–3262.

Historical Technology, Inc., 6 Mugford St., Marblehead, MA 01945: Catalog $12 ■ Antique scientific instruments and books. 617–631–2275.

Jacques Noel Jacobsen, 60 Manor Rd., Ste. 1000, Staten Island, NY 10310: Catalog $10 ■ Military insignia, weapons, photos and paintings, band instruments, and Indian and western items. 718–981–0973.

James II Galleries, Ltd., 15 E. 57th St., New York, NY 10022: Free information ■ Decorative art from the 19th-century. 212–355–7040.

Jukebox Junction, P.O. Box 1081, Des Moines, IA 50311: Price list $2.50 ■ Antique jukeboxes. 515–981–4019.

Kemble's Antiques, 55 N. Sundale, Norwich, OH 43767: Free information ■ Period American furniture. 614–872–3507.

Kinder Haus, Box 560, Cherry Valley, IL 61016: Free information ■ Dolls, toys, and other antiques. 815–544–6330.

Lake Forest Antiquarians, P.O. Box 841, Lake Forest, IL 60045: Free catalog ■ English and Continental silver and other antiques. 708–234–1990.

Leonard's Reproductions & Antiques, 600 Taunton Creek, Seekonk, MA 02771: Catalog $4 ■ Original and reproduction antique beds. 508–336–8585.

Becky & Jay Love Antiques, P.O. Box 5206, Lancaster, PA 17601: Free information ■ Antique toys. 717–396–9879.

Sandy & Don Madden, 1315 Shanessey Rd., El Cajon, CA 92019: List $2 ■ Windup, battery-operated, and Disneyana toys. 619–444–8531.

Clarence & Betty Maier, P.O. Box 432, Montgomeryville, PA 18936: Free information ■ Victorian art glass. 215–855–5388.

Mandarin Antiques, Ltd., 812 W. Pine St., P.O. Box 428, Farmville, NC 27828: Free information ■ Chinese and Japanese antique porcelains, screens, scrolls, jardinieres, furniture, chandeliers, and lamps. 919–753–3324.

Mechanick's Workbench, P.O. Box 668, Marion, MA 02738: Free information with long SASE ■ Antique woodworking tools. 508–748–1680.

Mill House Antiques, Rt. 6, Woodbury, CT 06798: Free information ■ English and French antique furniture and accessories. 203–263–3446.

The Museum of Historical Arms, Inc., P.O. Box 190898, Miami, FL 33119: Catalog $10 ■ Antique guns and knives.

Nautical Antiques, P.O. Box 785, Kennebunkport, ME 04046: Catalog $3 ■ American paintings, scrimshaw, and nautical antiquities. 207–967–3218.

Nelson Rarities, Inc., One City Center, Portland, ME 04101: Free catalog ■ Rare stones, cameos, and other jewelry from estates and collections. 207–775–3150.

Neon Etc., Robert Newman, 10809 Charnock Rd., Los Angeles, CA 90034: Free information ■ Neon signs, gas pumps, coke machines, neon clocks, wood telephone booths, auto couches, and other restored antique mechanical memorabilia. 213–559–0539.

Old Friends Antiques, P.O. Box 754, Sparks, MD 21152: Annual subscription to lists $10 ■ Steiff bears and other animals in mint condition. 410–472–4632.

Philadelphia Print Shop, Ltd., 8441 Germantown Ave., Philadelphia, PA 19118: Catalog $4 ■ Antique maps, prints, and books. 215–242–4750.

Wayne Pratt Antiques, 257 Forest St., Marlboro, MA 01752: Free information ■ American antiques. 508–481–2917.

C. L. Prickett, 930 Stony Hill Rd., Yardley, PA 19067: Free information ■ Authenticated American antiques. 215–493–4284.

Quester Gallery, On the Green, P.O. Box 446, Stonington, CT 06378: Free information ■ Marine art and antiques. 203–535–3860.

Eugene & Ellen Reno, Box 191, Lawrence, MA 01842: Free information ■ Cut glass, depression glass, dolls and toys, miniatures, jewelry, sterling silver, glassware, china items, and other collectibles. 603–898–7426.

John Rinaldi Antiques, Box 765, Kennebunkport, ME 04046: Catalog $3 ■ Marine antiquities. 207–967–3218.

James Robinson, 15 E. 57th St., New York, NY 10022: Free information ■ Antique English silver, jewelry, porcelains, glass collectibles, and other antiques. 212–752–6166.

Donald R. Sack, P.O. Box 132, Buck Hill Falls, PA 18323: Free information ■ American antiques. 717–595–7567.

Israel Sack, Inc., 15 E. 57th St., New York, NY 10022: Catalog $10 ■ Furniture, antique clocks and watches, and other collectibles. 212–753–6562.

The Sadagursky's, 15 Hawthorne Ct., Centerport, NY 11721: Free information ■ Antique mechanical toys. 516–757–5598.

St. Jame's House Company, 4742 W. Peterson, Chicago, IL 60646: Catalog $5 ■ Antique scientific instruments and clocks. 312–545–0011.

Samurai Antiques, 229 Santa Ynez Ct., Santa Barbara, CA 93103: Free information ■ Japanese antique Samurai, Emperor, and Empress dolls. 805–965–9688.

S. J. Shrubsole, 104 E. 57th St., New York, NY 10022: Free information ■ American and English antique silver, jewelry, art objects, gold boxes, and other antiques. 212–753–8920.

Kate Smalley's Antique Dolls, P.O. Box 945, Branford, CT 06405: Free list with long SASE ■ Antique dolls and other items. 203–481–8163.

Southampton Antiques, 172 College Hwy., Rt. 10, Southampton, MA 01073: Catalog $25 ■ Antique American oak and Victorian furniture. 413–527–1022.

Spencertown Art & Antique Company, Rt. 203, Spencertown, NY 12165: Free information ■ Oriental rugs, American and European paintings, and sculpture from the 19th- and early 20th-century. 518–392–4442.

Tesseract, Box 151, Hastings-On-Hudson, NY 10706: Catalog $5 ■ Antique medical and scientific instruments and books. 914–478–2594.

Edith Weber & Company, Place des Antiquaries, 125 E. 57th St., New York, NY 10022: Free information ■ Antique jewelry. 212–688–4331.

Michael B. Weisbrod, Inc., 987 Madison Ave., New York, NY 10021: Free information ■ Oriental works of art. 212–734–6350.

Richard Wright Antiques, Flowing Springs & Hollow Roads, Birchrunville, PA 19421: Free information ■ Antique dolls. 215–827–7442.

APPLIANCES
Manufacturers

Amana Refrigeration, Inc., Amana, IA 52204: Free information ■ Standard refrigerators and side-by-side units with optional in-the-door ice and water dispensers. 800–843–0304.

Andi Company Appliances, 65 Campus Plaza, Raritan Center, Edison, NJ 08837: Free information ■ Electric and gas cooktop stoves, dishwashers, and ranges. 800–344–0043.

Black & Decker, 6 Armstrong Rd., Shelton, CT 06484: Free information ■ Small appliances and accessories. 203–926–3000.

Braun Appliances, 66 Broadway, Rt. 1, Lynnefield, MA 01940: Free information ■ Small appliances and accessories. 800–272–8622.

Caloric Corporation, Amana Refrigeration, Amana, IA 52204: Free information ■ Microwave ovens, ranges, refrigerators, and freezers. 319–622–5800.

Frigidaire Company, 6000 Perimeter Rd., Dublin, OH 43017: Free information with long SASE ■ Refrigerators, freezers, and dishwashers. 800–451–7007.

G. E. Appliances, 4700 Allmond Ave., Louisville, KY 40209: Free information ■ Electric cooktop stoves, microwave ovens, dishwashers, free-standing full-size ranges, refrigerators, freezers, washers and dryers, and small appliances. 800–626–2000.

Hotpoint, Appliance Park, Louisville, KY 40225: Free information ■ Dishwashers, microwave ovens, refrigerators, freezers, and other appliances. 800–626–2000.

In-Sink-Erator, Emerson Electric Company, 4700 21st St., Racine, WI 53406: Free information ■ Dishwashers and other appliances. 800–558–5712.

Jenn-Air Company, 3035 Shadeland Ave., Indianapolis, IN 46226: Brochure $1 ■ Cooktop stoves, dishwashers, ranges, range hoods, and other appliances. 317–545–2271.

Kelvinator, 6000 Perimeter Dr., Dublin, OH 43017: Free information ■ Appliances for the home. 800–323–7773.

KitchenAid, Inc., 701 Main St., St. Joseph, MI 49805: Free information ■ Cooktop stoves, dishwashers, range hoods, refrigerators, washers and dryers, small appliances and accessories, wall ovens, washing machines and dryers, and refrigerators. 800–422–1230.

Magic Chef, 740 King Edward Ave., Cleveland, TN 37311: Free information ■ Electric cooktop stoves, wall ovens, refrigerators, and dishwashers. 800–332–4432.

Menumaster, Inc., 600 E. 54th North, Sioux Falls, SD 57104: Free information ■ Microwave ovens. 605–336–2222.

Miele Appliance, Inc., 22D Worlds Fair Dr., Somerset, NJ 08873: Free information ■ Electric and gas cooktop stoves, dishwashers, ranges, washers and dryers, and wall ovens. 800–289–MIELE.

Modern Maid Company, Amana Refrigeration, Amana, IA 52204: Free information ■ Electric and gas cooktop stoves, range hoods, refrigerators, dishwashers, small appliances, and wall ovens. 319–622–5800.

Panasonic, Panasonic Way, Secaucus, NJ 07094: Free information ■ Microwave ovens. 201–348–7000.

Regal Ware, Inc., Marketing Communications, 1675 Reigle Dr., Kewaskum, WI 53040: Free information ■ Small appliances. 414–626–2121.

Sanyo Electric, 200 Riser Rd., Little Ferry, NJ 07643: Free information ■ Under-the-counter refrigerators, microwave ovens, portable laundry washers and dryers, and other appliances. 201–641–2333.

Sears, Roebuck & Company, Catalog Division, 925 S. Homan Ave., Chicago, IL 60607: Free catalog ■ Appliances for the home (Catalog also available from local stores.). 312–875–2500.

Sharp Electronics, Sharp Plaza, Mahwah, NJ 07430: Free information ■ Microwave ovens. 800–BE–SHARP.

Speed Queen Company, Shepard St., P.O. Box 990, Ripon, WI 54971: Free information from local sources ■ Washers and dryers. 414–748–3121.

Tappan, 6000 Perimeter Dr., Dublin, OH 43017: Free information ■ Electric cooktop stoves, ranges, dishwashers, and other appliances. 800–537–5530.

Thermador/Waste King, 5119 District Blvd., Los Angeles, CA 90040: Free information ■ Electric and gas cooktop stoves, ranges, wall ovens, and other appliances. 800–366–6836.

Vent-A-Hood Company, 1000 N. Greenville Ave., Richardson, TX 75080: Free information ■ Range hoods. 214–235–5201.

Viking Range Corporation, P.O. Box 956, Greenwood, MS 38930: Free information ■

Gas ranges, range hoods, cooktops, and other appliances. 601–455–1200.

Waring Products, Rt. 44, New Hartford, CT 06057: Free information ■ Small appliances and accessories. 203–379–0731.

West Bend, 400 Washington St., West Bend, WI 53095: Free information ■ Small appliances and accessories. 414–334–2311.

Whirlpool Corporation, 2000 M63 North, Benton Harbor, MI 49022: Free information ■ Electric cooktop stoves, wall ovens, dishwashers, refrigerators, freezers, and other appliances. 800–253–1301.

Retailers

Bernie's Discount Center, Inc., 821 6th Ave., New York, NY 10001: Free information with long SASE ■ Save up to 50 percent on audio and video equipment, telephones and answering machines, large appliances, small kitchen appliances, and personal care appliances. 212–564–8758.

Bondy Export Corporation, 40 Canal St., New York, NY 10002: Free information ■ Large and small appliances, cameras, video and television equipment, office machines and typewriters, and luggage. 212–925–7785.

Cole's Appliance & Furniture Company, 4026 Lincoln Ave., Chicago, IL 60618: Free information with long SASE ■ Furniture, audio and video equipment, television sets, and kitchen appliances. 312–525–1797.

E.B.A. Wholesale Corporation, 2361 Nostrand Ave., Brooklyn, NY 11210: Free information ■ Save up to 40 percent on large appliances and electronics. 718–252–3400.

Focus Electronics, Inc., 4523 13th Ave., Brooklyn, NY 11219: Catalog $4 ■ Save from 20 to 50 percent on appliances, computers and accessories, audio and video equipment, and television sets. 718–436–4646.

Foto Electric Supply Company, 31 Essex St., New York, NY 10002: Free information ■ Save up to 30 percent on appliances. 212–673–5222.

Harry's Discounts & Appliance Corporation, 8701 18th Ave., Brooklyn, NY 11214: Free information with long SASE ■ Electronics and appliances. 718–236–5150.

Percy's, Inc., 19 Glennie St., Worcester, MA 01605: Free information ■ Save up to

50 percent on appliances and electronics. 508–755–5334.

Irv Wolfson Company, 3221 W. Irving Park Rd., Chicago, IL 60618: Free information with long SASE ■ Appliances and electronics, vacuum cleaners, personal care appliances, electric blankets, and kitchen aids that operate on 220-volt/50-cycles. 312–267–7828.

APPLIQUES

Badhir Trading, Inc., 8429 Sisson Hwy., Eden, NY 14057: Catalog $2.50 (refundable) ■ Beaded, sequined, and jeweled appliques, trims and fringes for dresses, costumes, and bridal fashions. 800–654–9418.

Craftways, 4118 Lakeside Dr., Richmond, CA 94806: Catalog $2 ■ Designs for appliques, quilts, and cross stitching. 510–223–3144.

Freed Company, 415 Central NW, P.O. Box 394, Albuquerque, NM 87103: Brochure $1 ■ Custom hand-sewn beaded and sequined appliques. 505–247–9311.

Made to Order, P.O. Box 621149, Littleton, CO 80162: Catalog $2 ■ Iron-on velour appliques.

Quintessence, P.O. Box 723544, Atlanta, GA 30339: Catalog $3 ■ Beaded appliques; exotic animal and reptile skins that include snakeskin, fishskin, and lambskin; and beads, rhinestones, handcarved sea shells, and other notions. 404–264–1759.

Sunflower & Sunshine Company, 127 W. 30th St., Hutchinson, KS 67502: Free price list ■ Applique pattern packets and wheat weaving supplies, that include books, tools, weaving materials, kits, and painting supplies. 316–665–6256.

Timberline Design, 2185 S. Larsen Pkwy., Provo, UT 84606: Free information ■ Velour and glitter iron-ons. 801–377–2717.

Winslow Stitchery, 908 Winslow, West St. Paul, MN 55118: Catalog $1 (refundable) ■ Stitchery patterns for appliques. 612–457–8624.

ARCHERY & BOW HUNTING

Aimpoint, 203 Elder St., Herndon, VA 22070: Free information ■ Archery equipment and supplies.

Alpine Archery, Inc., P.O. Box 319, Lewiston, ID 83501: Free information ■ Archery equipment and supplies.

American Archery, P.O. Box 200, Florence, WI 54121: Free information ■ Archery bows and accessories. 800–255–4939; 715–528–3000 (in WI).

Amsec International Ammo Depot, 1849-B Candy Ln. SW, Marietta, GA 30060: Catalog $10 (refundable) ■ Archery, camping, hunting, and ammunition supplies. 800–622–1121.

Anderson Archery, Box 130, Grand Ledge, MI 48837: Free catalog ■ Archery equipment and supplies. 517–627–3251.

Arizona Archery, 2781 N. Valley View Dr., P.O. Box 25387, Prescott Valley, AZ 86312: Free information ■ Arrows and supplies.

Barnett International, Inc., P.O. Box 934, Odessa, FL 33556: Free information ■ Arrow holders, bow cases, quivers, wax, bows and accessories, and sights. 800–237–4507; 813–920–2241 (in FL).

Bear Archery Company, 4600 SW 41st Blvd., Gainesville, FL 32601: Free information ■ Arrows and arrow-making components, bows and accessories, sights, and targets. 800–874–4603; 800–342–4751 (in FL).

Beman Archery Corporation, 3065 N. Rockwell St., Chicago, IL 60618: Free information ■ Arrows and supplies.

Bohning Company, Ltd., 7361 N. Seven Mile Rd., Lake City, MI 49651: Free information ■ Archery equipment, arrows, and arrow-making components. 616–229–4247.

Bowhunter Supply, Inc., 1158 46th St., P.O. Box 5010, Vienna, WV 26105: Free information ■ Arrows and arrow-making components, bows and accessories, sights, and targets. Other equipment includes game calls, targets, camouflage clothing, and camping equipment. 800–624–1923; 800–642–2638 (in WV).

Bowhunter's Warehouse, Inc., 1045 Ziegler Rd., Wellsville, PA 17365: Free catalog ■ Equipment and supplies for hunting, bow hunting, and archery. Includes rifles, game calls, targets, camouflage clothing, and camping equipment. 717–432–8611.

Bonnie Bowman, Inc., 2511 W. Winton Ave., Hayward, CA 94545: Free information ■ Arm guards, arrow holders, bow cases, bow stabilizers, bow strings, gloves, quivers, tabs, tools, bows and accessories, sights, and arrows and arrow-making components. 800–227–1532; 510–785–2500 (in CA).

Broward Shooter's Exchange, 250 S. 60th Ave., Hollywood, FL 33023: Catalog $8 ■ Equipment and supplies for shooting, reloading, and muzzleloading; hunting; and archery. 800–554–9002.

Browning Company, Dept. C006, Morgan, UT 84050: Catalog $2 ■ Arm guards, arrow holders, bow cases, bow stabilizers, bow strings, gloves, point sharpeners, scents and lures, quivers, tabs, wax, bows and accessories, arrows and arrow-making components, and sights. 800–333–3288.

Buckeye Sports Supply, John's Sporting Goods, 2655 Harrison Ave. SW, Canton, OH 44706: Free information ■ Archery equipment and supplies. 800–533–8691.

Darton Archery, 3540 Darton Rd., Hale, MI 48739: Free information ■ Bow hunting equipment and supplies. 517–728–4231.

Feline Archery, Inc., 229 Rt. 30 West, Ligonier, PA 15658: Free information ■ Arrows and arrow-making components, bows and accessories, sights, and targets. 412–238–3673.

Gander Mountain, Inc., P.O. Box 248, Gander Mountain, Wilmot, WI 53192: Free catalog ■ Archery equipment. 800–558–9418.

Golden Eagle Archery, 1111 Corporate Dr., Farmington, NY 14425: Free information ■ Bow cases, bow stabilizers, bow strings, quivers, scents and lures, slings, bows and accessories, and sights. 716–924–1880.

Hoyt USA, 475 N. Neil Armstrong Rd., Salt Lake City, UT 84116: Free information ■ Bow cases, bow stabilizers, bow strings, quivers, slings, bows and accessories, sights, and arrows and arrow-making. 801–363–2990.

Kolpin Manufacturing, Inc., P.O. Box 107, Fox Lake, WI 53933: Free information ■ Arm guards, arrow holders, bow cases, gloves, tabs, and arrow-making components. 414–928–3118.

McPherson Archery Company, Inc., RR 4, Box 12, Austin, MN 55912: Free information ■ Archery equipment and supplies.

Martin Archery, Inc., Rt. 5, Box 127, Walla Walla, WA 99362: Free information ■ Arrows and arrow-making components, bows and accessories, sights, and targets. 509–529–2554.

O. H. Mullen Sales, Inc., RR 2, Oakwood, OH 45873: Free information ■ Arm guards, arrow holders, bow cases, bow stabilizers, bow strings, brush buttons, clips, gloves, nock locks, point sharpeners, quivers, racks, scents and lures, slings, tabs, arrows and arrow-making components, bows and accessories, sights, and targets. 800–258–6625; 800–248–6625 (in OH).

Oneida Labs, Inc., P.O. Box 366, Syracuse, NY 13202: Free information ■ Bow hunting equipment and supplies. 315–474–1876.

Oregon Bow Company, 250 E. 10th Ave., Junction City, OR 97448: Free information ■ Bow hunting equipment and supplies. 503–998–2504.

Ben Pearson Archery, Inc., P.O. Box 7465, Pine Bluff, AR 71611: Free information ■ Bows and accessories, sights, arrows and arrow-making components, and targets. 800–621–2724.

Pilgrim Archery Products, 3706 Clear Falls, Kingwood, TX 77339: Free information ■ Targets.

Premier Archery, P.O. Box 132, Ocono Falls, WI 54154: Free information ■ Archery equipment and supplies.

Pro Line Company, 1675 Gun Lake Rd., Hastings, MI 49058: Free information ■ Arrows and arrow-making components, bows and accessories, and sights. 800–356–9695; 616–948–8026 (in MI).

P.S.E. Archery, Inc., 2727 N. Fairview, P.O. Box 5487, Tucson, AZ 85703: Free information ■ Arrows and arrow-making components, bows and accessories, sights, and targets. 602–884–1479.

Robin Hood Archery, P.O. Box 806, Fort Smith, AR 72902: Free information ■ Archery equipment and supplies.

Ryva Tackle Company, Inc., 13023 Old Hwy. 11, Sturtevant, WI 53177: Free information ■ Arm guards, bow cases, bow stabilizers, bow strings, brush buttons, clips, gloves, nock locks, point sharpeners, quivers, racks, scents and lures, slings, tabs, tools, bows and accessories, and arrow-making components. 414–886–4452.

Saunders Archery Company, P.O. Box 476, Columbus, NE 68601: Free information ■ Arm guards, arrow holders, bow cases, bow stabilizers, bow strings, brush buttons, clips, gloves, nock locks, point sharpeners, quivers, scents and lures, slings, tabs, tools, arrows and arrow-making components, sights, and targets. 800–228–1408; 402–564–7176 (in NE).

Southern Archery, P.O. Box 204, Louisville, MS 39339: Free information ■ Archery equipment and supplies.

Sport Shop, P.O. Box 340, Grifton, NC 28530: Free catalog ■ Archery, bow hunting, and fishing equipment 919–524–4571.

Springer Archery Supply, Inc., 12731 Huron River Dr., P.O. Box 338, Romulus, MI 48174: Free information ■ Arrows and arrow-making components, bows and accessories, sights, and targets. 800–521–7766; 313–941–6010 (in MI).

York Archery, Woodcraft Equipment Company, P.O. Box 110, Independence, MO 64051: Free information ■ Arm guards, bow cases, bow strings, gloves, point sharpeners, quivers, tabs, wax, arrows and arrow-making components, bows and accessories, sights, and targets. 800–526–5040; 816–252–9612 (in MO).

ART SUPPLIES & EQUIPMENT

Graphic Art Supplies

The AAZ-DAR Company, 1087 Branch St., Chicago, IL 60622: Free catalog ■ Graphic art and silk-screening supplies. 312–943–8338.

Accent Products Division, Borden, Inc., 300 E. Main St., Lake Zurich, IL 60047: Free information ■ Acrylic paints. 800–323–0079.

Aiko's Art Materials Import, 3347 N. Clark St., Chicago, IL 60657: Catalog $1.50 ■ Japanese handmade paper, Oriental art supplies, fabric dyes and equipment, and other supplies. 312–404–5600.

Aldy Graphic Supply, Inc., 1115 Hennepin Ave., Minneapolis, MN 55403: Free information ■ Easy-to-use projector that enlarges and reduces opaque compositions, photographs, or drawings. 800–289–2539.

William Alexander Art Supplies, P.O. Box 20250, Salem, OR 97305: Catalog $1 ■ Painting kits, supplies, and books. 800–547–8747.

Alvin & Company, Inc., P.O. Box 188, Bloomfield, CT 06002: Catalog $1.50 ■ Art supplies and equipment for artists, draftsmen, engineers, and surveyors. 800–444–ALVIN; 203–243–8991 (in CT).

Anco Wood Specialties, Inc., 71-08 80th St., Glendale, NY 11385: Free information ■ Easels. 800–262–6963; 718–326–2023 (in NY).

Applied Arts International, 22313 Meekland Ave., Hayward, CA 94541: Free information ■ Etching press that can be used with most printmaking processes associated with a roller type press. 510–537–9773.

Art Essential of New York, Ltd., 3 Cross St., Suffern, NY 10901: Free information ■ Gold, silver, and other metal leaf in sheets and rolls, other supplies and tools, how-to videos, and instructional publications. 800–283–5323.

Art Express, P.O. Box 21662, Columbia, SC 29221: Free catalog ■ Art supplies, equipment, and accessories 800–535–5908.

Artisan/Santa Fe Art Supplies, Inc., 717 Canyon Rd., Santa Fe, NM 87501: Free catalog ■ Soft pastels and sets; crayons and pastel pencils; oil pastels and sets; fixatives, stomps and tortillons; pastepaper in sheets, rolls, and pads; and pastel canvasses and boxes. 800–331–6375.

Art Mart, 533 Seabright Ave., Santa Cruz, CA 95062: Free catalog ■ Art supplies, equipment, and accessories. 800–688–5798.

Artograph, Inc., 13205 16th Ave. North, Minneapolis, MN 55441: Free information ■ Projector that enlarges and reduces opaque compositions, photographs, drawings, and other art. 800–328–4653.

Art Supply Warehouse, Inc., 360 Main Ave., Norwalk, CT 06851: Free catalog ■ Oil and acrylic paints, pigments and fixatives, other coloring mediums, solvents, chalks, pencils, inks, papers, canvasses, easels, canvas stretchers, storage boxes,

palette knives, brushes, and pastels. 800–243–5038; 203–846–2279 (in CT).

Artway Crafts, Box 699, Tombean, TX 75489: Catalog $1 (refundable) ■ Acrylics, oil paints, watercolors, canvasses, brushes, charcoal pastels, paper, palettes, and other art supplies. 903–546–6755.

Badger Air-Brush Company, 9128 W. Belmont Ave., Franklin Park, IL 60131: Free brochure ■ Air brushes. 708–678–3104.

Barclay Leaf Imports, Inc., 21 Wilson Terrace, Elizabeth, NJ 07208: Free information ■ Gold leaf and supplies. 908–353–5522.

Dick Blick Company, P.O. Box 1267, Galesburg, IL 61401: Catalog $2 ■ Printing, drafting, display arranging, and commercial art supplies, tools, and accessories. 800–447–8192.

Arthur Brown & Bros., Inc., P.O. Box 7820, Maspeth, NY 11378: Catalog $3 ■ Art supplies and equipment. 800–772–7367; 718–628–0600 (in NY).

Stan Brown's Arts & Crafts, Inc., 13435 NE Whitaker Way, Portland, OR 97230: Catalog $3.50 ■ Art supplies, equipment, and books. 503–257–0559.

Chaselle, Inc., 9645 Gerwig Ln., Columbia, MD 21046: Catalog $4 ■ Art software and books, brushes and paints, tempera colors, acrylics and sets, pastels, ceramic molds and kilns, sculpture equipment, silk-screen painting supplies, and other arts and crafts supplies. 800–242–7355.

Chatham Art Distributors, 11 Brookside Ave., Chatham, NY 12037: Catalog $3 (refundable) ■ Acrylics, brushes, canvasses, oils, milk paint, tin supplies, wooden items, and books. 800–822–4747; 518–392–6300 (in NY).

Conrad Machine Company, 1525 S. Warner, Whitehall, MI 49461: Free information ■ Etching and lithography presses. 616–893–7455.

Co-Op Artists' Materials, P.O. Box 53097, Atlanta, GA 30355: Catalog $2 (refundable) ■ Art supplies and accessories. 800–877–3242.

Createx Colors, 14 Airport Park Rd., East Granby, CT 06026: Free information ■ Coloring agents for most surfaces. Includes pearlescents, iridescents, acrylics, fabric colors, liquid permanent dyes, and pure pigments. 800–243–2712; 203–653–5505 (in CT).

Crescent Bronze Powder Company, 3400 N. Avondale Ave., Chicago, IL 60618: Free information with long SASE ■ Metallic colors, liquids for mixing glitter and tinsel applications, diamond dust, and other crafts supplies. 312–539–2441.

Crown Art Products, Inc., 90 Dayton Ave., Passaic, NJ 07055: Free catalog ■ Silk-screening supplies. 201–777–6010.

Dalverwood Art Products, 6820 Orangethorpe Ave., Buena Park, CA 90620: Free information ■ Art supplies. 800–654–2581.

Decart, Inc., P.O. Box 309, Morrisville, VT 05661: Free brochure ■ Fabric paints and dyes for use with air brushes, and water-based enamels and paints for transfer techniques, glass crafting, silk-screening, and other crafts. 802–888–4217.

Delta Technical Coatings, 2550 Pellissier Pl., Whittier, CA 90601: Free information ■ Acrylics, oils, casein paints, and paint sticks. 800–423–4135; 213–686–0678 (in CA).

Dharma Trading Company, P.O. Box 916, San Rafael, CA 94902: Free brochure ■ Fabric painting and batik-making supplies. 800–542–5227.

Dickerson Press Company, P.O. Box 8, South Haven, MI 49090: Free information ■ Etching and lithography presses in manual and electric models and a press that prints intaglio, relief, lithographs, stone, plate, and other medias. 616–637–4251.

Duncan, 5673 E. Shields Ave., Fresno, CA 93727: Free information ■ Fabric paints, outline writers, and dispensers for applying glitter. 209–291–4444.

Dutch Door, Inc., P.O. Box 21662, Columbia, SC 29221: Free catalog ■ Art supplies. 800–750–1492; 803–798–8441 (in SC).

Ebersole Lapidary Supply, 11417 West Hwy. 54, Wichita, KS 67209: Free information ■ Brushes and paints, paper, canvasses, glue, varnishes, pencils, charcoal, and books, shells, lapidary equipment, jewelry-making supplies, clock-making supplies and equipment, and calligraphy supplies. 316–722–4771.

Fairgate Rule Company, Inc., 22 Adams Ave., P.O. Box 278, Cold Spring, NY 10516: Free catalog ■ Rulers, other measuring devices, stencils, and drawing aids. 800–431–2180; 914–265–3677 (in NY).

The Fine Gold Leaf People, Three Cross St., Suffern, NY 10901: Free information ■ Genuine, imitation, and variegated sheets and rolls of metallic foil, brushes, other supplies, and books. 800–283–5323.

Flax Artist Materials, 1699 Market St., P.O. Box 7216, San Francisco, CA 94120: Catalog $2.50 ■ Supplies and accessories for artists, architects, draftsmen, and sign painters. 800–547–7778.

Fletcher-Lee & Company, P.O. Box 626, Elk Grove Village, IL 60009: Free information ■ Acrylic paints and other supplies. 800–I–LUV–ART.

Foster Manufacturing Company, 414 N. 13th St., Philadelphia, PA 19108: Free catalog ■ Equipment, supplies, storage cabinets, and accessories for graphic artists. 800–523–4855; 215–625–0500 (in PA).

A. I. Friedman Art Supplies, 44 W. 18th St., New York, NY 10011: Free catalog ■ Art supplies and accessories. 212–243–9000.

Gamblin, P.O. Box 625, Portland, OR 97207: Color chart $2 ■ Artist oils. 503–228–9763.

Gill Mechanical Company, P.O. Box 7247, Eugene, OR 97401: Free information ■ Tube wringers to end the waste of half-used tubes. 503–686–1606.

Gold Leaf & Metallic Powders, 74 Trinity Pl., Ste. 1807, New York, NY 10006: Free information ■ Genuine and composition leaf in rolls, sheets, and books, and other supplies and tools. 800–322–0323; 212–267–4900 (in NY).

Graphic Art Mart, Inc., 321 Dekalb Ave., Brooklyn, NY 11205: Free catalog ■ Art supplies and equipment. 718–789–9219.

Graphic Chemical & Ink Company, P.O. Box 27, Villa Park, IL 60181: Free catalog ■ Print-making supplies for etching, making block prints, lithography, and other reproduction processes. 708–832–6004.

J. L. Hammett Company, 30 Hammett Pl., Braintree, MA 02184: Free catalog ■ Art supplies and accessories. 800–672–1932; 617–848–1000 (in MA).

Hearlihy & Company, 714 W. Columbia St., Springfield, OH 45504: Free catalog ■ Furniture and art supplies for drafting and designing. 800–622–1000.

Heritage Brushes, 511 NW Service Rd., Warrenton, MO 63383: Free information ■ Brushes and tools for ceramics and crafts. 314–456–2500.

Hobby Game Distributors, Inc., 3710 W. Tuohy, Skokie, IL 60076: Free information ■ Art supplies and accessories. Other items include computer games and software. 800–621–6419.

Hofcraft, P.O. Box 1791, Grand Rapids, MI 49501: Catalog $3 ■ Save up to 40 percent on how-to books, brushes, dyes, paints, and handcrafted wood items. 800–828–0359.

HK Holbein, Inc., Box 555, Williston, VT 05495: Free information ■ Art supplies, equipment, and accessories.

The Italian Art Store, P.O. Box 300, Millington, NJ 07946: Free catalog ■ Oils, acrylics, watercolors, dry pigments, air brush colors, and other supplies. 201–644–2717.

Jerry's Artarama, Inc., P.O. Box 1105, New Hyde Park, NY 11040: Catalog $2.50 ■ Art supplies. 800–U–ARTIST; 516–328–6633 (in NY).

Kaufman Supply, Rt. 1, Centertown, MO 65023: Free catalog ■ Supplies and equipment for sign painters. 314–893–2124.

Koh-I-Noor Rapidograph, Inc., 100 North St., Bloomsbury, NJ 08804: Free catalog ■ Art materials and drawing aids. 800–631–7646.

Krylon, 6830 Cochran Rd., Solon, OH 44139: Free information ■ Textured paints that make wood, metal, plastic, ceramic, and painted surfaces look like stone. 800–247–3270.

MaDaNa Manufacturing, 947 N. Cole Ave., Los Angeles, CA 90038: Free catalog ■ Genuine gold leaf and composition metal leaf, accessories, and other supplies. 213–469–0856.

Marx Brush Manufacturing Company, Inc., 400 Commercial Ave., Palisades Park, NJ 07650: Free information ■ Paint brushes for artists and crafters. 800–654–6279.

Michael's Artist Supplies, 314 Sutter St., San Francisco, CA 94108: Catalog $3 ■ Equipment, supplies, and accessories for graphic artists. 415–421–1576.

Store, 1041 Lincoln
: Free catalog ■ Art
)6.

Naz-Dar Company, 1087 Branch St., Chicago, IL 60622: Free catalog ■ Graphic arts and silk-screening equipment and supplies. 312–943–8338.

Nova Color, 5894 Blackwelder St., Culver City, CA 90232: Free price list ■ Acrylic paints that include pearls and metallics. 213–870–6000.

OAS Art Supplies, 10181 Crailet Dr., Huntington, Beach, CA 92646: Free catalog ■ Supplies and materials for Chinese brush painting. Includes brushes, rice paper, ink, Chinese colors, and books. 714–962–5189.

Paasche Airbrush Company, 7440 W. Lawrence Ave., Harwood Heights, IL 60656: Free catalog ■ Airbrushing and spraying equipment and accessories. 708–867–9191.

Pearl Paint, 308 Canal St., New York, NY 10013: Free catalog ■ Art supplies, tools, equipment, and paints. 800–221–6845; 212–431–7932 (in NY).

Perma Color Division, 226 E. Tremont, Charlotte, NC 28203: Free price list ■ All-media dry pigments. 704–333–9201.

Plaid Enterprises, Box 7600, Norcross, GA 30091: Free information ■ Acrylic paints and other supplies.

Pyramid of Urbana, 2107 N. High Cross Rd., Urbana, IL 61801: Free catalog ■ Art supplies, crafts supplies, office accessories and supplies, and school equipment. 217–328–3099.

Sargent Art, Inc., 100 E. Diamond Ave., Hazleton, PA 18201: Free information ■ Crayons, powdered tempera, liquid tempera, water colors, and finger paints. 717–454–3596.

Heinz Scharff Brushes, P.O. Box 746, Fayetteville, GA 30214: Free catalog ■ Brushes for tole, chinaware, and decorative painting. 404–461–2200.

Sepp Leaf Products, Inc., 381 Park Ave. South, New York, NY 10016: Free information ■ Gold and palladium leaf, rolled gold, tools, and kits. 212–683–2840.

Daniel Smith Art Supplies, Inc., 4130 1st Ave. South, Seattle, WA 98134: Catalog $3 ■ Art supplies, books, framing supplies,

studio equipment, and furniture. 206–223–9599.

M. Swift & Sons, Inc., 10 Love Ln., Hartford, CT 06141: Free booklet ■ Silver, palladium, aluminum, and composite gold leaf for decorating and restoring art and other surfaces. 800–262–9620.

Technical Papers Corporation, 29 Franklin St., Needham Heights, MA 02194: Free information ■ Handmade rice paper in prints, solid colors, and multi-colors. Available in sheets and rolls. 617–449–1300.

Testrite Instrument Company, Inc., 133 Monroe St., Newark, NJ 07105: Free catalog ■ Lightweight aluminum and chrome steel easels, portable light boxes, lighting and photography equipment, and opaque projectors. 201–589–6767.

Thayer & Chandler, P.O. Box 711, Libertyville, IL 60048: Free brochure ■ Air brushes. 708–816–1611.

Tole Americana, Inc., 5750 NE Hassalo, Portland, OR 97213: Free information ■ Brushes, oils, acrylics and fabric paints, sealers, mediums, varnishes, tole supplies, unfinished wood products, and books for decorative art and tole painting. 800–547–8854; 800–452–8663 (in OR).

Tricon Colors, Inc., 16 Leliarts Ln., Elmwood Park, NJ 07407: Free information ■ Dry pigments. 201–794–3800.

Leo Uhlfelder Company, 420 S. Fulton Ave., Mt. Vernon, NY 10553: Free information ■ Custom natural hair brushes for painting and lettering and synthetic brushes for working in oils, acrylics, sign painting, and crafts. 914–664–8701.

United Art Supply Company, Box 9219, Fort Wayne, IN 46899: Catalog $3 ■ Art supplies and equipment. 800–322–3247.

Utrecht Art & Drafting Supply, 33 35th St., Brooklyn, NY 11232: Free catalog ■ Save 25 to 50 percent on art, sculpture, and print-making supplies. 718–768–2525.

Visual Systems Company, Inc., 1596 Rockville Pike, Rockville, MD 20852: Free catalog ■ Art and drawing supplies and equipment. 800–368–2803; 301–770–0500 (in MD).

Wally R Company, 5029 Calmview Ave., Baldwin Park, CA 91706: Free information ■ Acrylic paints. 800–368–2803.

World Frame Distributors, 107 Maple St., Denton, TX 76201: Free brochure ■ Canvasses and miscellaneous supplies and traditional ready-made frames and gallery ornates. 817–382–3442.

Ziegler Art & Craft Supply, Inc., P.O. Box 50037, Tulsa, OK 74150: Catalog $2 (refundable) ■ Art supplies and materials. 918–584–2217.

Modeling & Casting Supplies

ADA Village Candle, 3572 Roger B. Chaffee, Grand Rapids, MI 49508: Catalog 50¢ ■ Macrame supplies, dough art modeling mediums, candle-making supplies, and books. 616–247–8353.

American Art Clay Company, Inc., 4717 W. 16th St., Indianapolis, IN 46222: Free catalog ■ Modeling clay, self-hardening clay, paper mache products, casting compounds, modeling dough, mold-making materials, acrylics, finishing supplies, fabric dyes, fillers and patching compounds, wood stains, and metallic finishes. 800–428–3239.

Apoxie Clay, AES Studio, Box 344, River Falls, WI 54022: Free information ■ Easy-to-use permanent, self-hardening, waterproof clay. 715–386–9097.

Chaselle, Inc., 9645 Gerwig Ln., Columbia, MD 21046: Catalog $4 ■ Art software and books, brushes and paints, tempera colors, acrylics and sets, pastels, ceramic molds and kilns, sculpture equipment, silk-screen painting supplies, and other art supplies. 800–242–7355.

The Clay Factory of Escondido, 525 N. Andreasen, P.O. 1270, Escondido, CA 92025: Free information ■ Modeling materials. 800–243–3466.

Concrete Machinery Company, P.O. Box 99, Hickory, NC 28603: Catalog $10 ■ Supplies for making ornamental concrete items. 704–322–7710.

Craft Time Catalog, 211 S. State College Blvd., #341, Anaheim, CA 92806: Catalog $2 (refundable) ■ Ready-to-paint figurines.

Creative Paperclay Company, 1800 S. Robertson Blvd., Ste. 907, Los Angeles, CA 90035: Soft, fine-textured modeling material that air dries light-weight. 310–839–0466.

Lynnette Company, Inc., 6251 Mentor Park, Mentor, OH 44060: Free information ■ Plaster casting molds.

ARTWORK

Posters, Paintings & Prints

Jeffrey Allon, Bayard Rd., Apt. 919, Pittsburgh, PA 15213: Free information ■ Personalized handcrafted works of art. Includes ketubahs for Jewish weddings and anniversaries. 412–683–8838.

America Gallery, 83647 N. Pacific Hwy., Creswell, OR 97426: Catalog $5 ■ Civil War art. 503–895–26.

American Arts & Graphics, Inc., P.O. Box 2067, Everett, WA 98203: Free catalog ■ Art, photo, and movie posters; fun posters for kids; aerodynamic, all-star pinup, and sports posters; and humorous, animal, scenic, art, and photo calendars. 800–524–3900.

American Print Gallery, P.O. Box 4477, Gettysburg, PA 17325: Information $1 ■ Military art prints and note cards. 800–448–1863.

Around the Corner, 5135 Pheasant Ridge Rd. Fairfax, VA 22030: Catalog $5 ■ American, European, Victorian, and traditional posters, prints, and canvas replicas. 800–999–3083; 703–631–3227 (in VA).

Art Poster Company, 29555 Northwesterrn Hwy., Southfield, MI 48034: Catalog $2 ■ Prints and posters with contemporary, traditional abstract, art deco, classical, Oriental, botanical, photographic, children's, and other themes. Framing available. 313–569–5555.

Artrock Posters, 45 Sheridan St., San Francisco, CA 94103: Catalog $2 ■ Original rock concert posters. 415–255–7390.

Associated American Artists, 20 W. 57th St., New York, NY 10019: Catalog $1 ■ Prints of original works of art. 212–359–5510.

Carl Bach & Associates, P.O. Box 5144, High Point, NC 27262: Free information ■ Paintings from the 17th- to 19th-century. 919–883–9789.

J.N. Bartfield Galleries, 30 W. 57th St., 3rd Floor, New York, NY 10019: Catalog $5 ■ American and European 19th- and 20th-century paintings; sculptures, original oils, bronzes, and watercolors. 212–245–8890.

Hank Baum Gallery, P.O. Box 26689, San Francisco, CA 94126: Free information ■ Contemporary paintings, watercolors, col-lages, prints, drawings, and vintage photographs. 415–752–4336.

Mitchell Beja, 1180 E. 92nd St., Brooklyn, NY 11236: Free information ■ Fine art posters. 718–649–1617.

John & Lynne Bolen Fine Arts, P.O. Box 5654, Huntington Beach, CA 92615: Free information ■ American paintings, prints, and sculptures from the 19th- and 20th-century. 714–968–0806.

Breedlove Enterprises, 1527 Amherst Rd., Massillon, OH 44648: Free information ■ Limited edition, numbered and signed Civil War lithographs. 216–837–8845.

Brooks Galleries, Inc., 77 Middle Neck Rd. Great Neck, NY 11021: Free catalog ■ Cels, drawings, backgrounds, layouts, and model sheets from movie studios. 800–541–2278; 516–487–355.

Brush Strokes, Box 8045, South Bend, IN 46637: Brochure $3 ■ Signed and numbered, limited edition reproduction prints of original oil paintings. Framing available. 219–277–5414.

Buck Hill Associates, 23 Catallon Dr., Waterford, NY 12188: Catalog 50¢ ■ Reproduction collectible posters, prints, and handbills. 518–583–1166.

Michael Campbell Fine Art, 7824 E. Lewis Ave., Scottsdale, AZ 85251: Free information ■ Contemporary and Latin American paintings, sculptures, graphics, pre-Columbian art, Spanish paintings, and out-of-print art books. 602–947–5399.

Cel-ebration, P.O. Box 123, Little Silver, NJ 07739: Free catalog ■ Animation art. 908–842–8489.

Ralph M. Chait Galleries, Inc., 12 E. 56th St., New York, NY 10022: Free information ■ Chinese art. 212–319-0471.

Chandler Mill Editions, P.O. Box 77, North Pembroke, MA 02358: Free information ■ Limited edition lithographs. 617–294–1687.

Merril Chase Art Galleries, 835 N. Michigan Ave., Chicago, IL 60602: Free catalog ■ Prints, paintings, and other art collectibles from the 19th-century.

Cherokee National Museum Gift Shop, P.O. Box 515, TSA-LA-GI, Tahlequah, OK 74464: Free price list with long SASE ■ Original paintings, prints, sculptures, and craft items that include baskets, Indian art, and weapons. 918–456–6007.

Cincinnati Art Museum, Eden Park, Cincinnati, OH 45202: Free catalog ■ Color reproductions of posters and postcards, and other collectibles. 513–721–5204.

Collector Military Art, Inc., 3118 Barcelona St., Tampa, FL 33629: Free information ■ Military art. 813–831–9517.

The Cricket Gallery, 529 Covington Pl., Wyckoff, NJ 07481: Free catalog ■ Vintage and contemporary animation cels, drawings, and Disney backgrounds. 800–BUY–CELS; 201–848–9567 (in NJ).

Dance Mart, P.O. Box 48, Homecrest Station, Brooklyn, NY 11229: Free catalog with long SASE ■ Books, prints, music, autographs, and collectibles on dance. 718–627–0477.

Michael Dunev Gallery, 77 Geary St., San Francisco, CA 94108: Free information ■ European and American contemporary paintings and prints. 415–398–7300.

Dyansen Gallery of SoHo, 122 Spring St., New York, NY 10012: Catalog $5 ■ Sculptures, paintings, and graphics. 800–348–2787.

E.H.G. Art, Ltd., 4201 N. Marshall Way, Scottsdale, AZ 85251: Catalog $2.50 ■ Art prints, posters, and graphics. 602–941–9348.

Wally Findlay Gallery, 814 N. Michigan Ave., Chicago, IL 60602: Free information ■ Original paintings. 312–649–1500.

Fine Art Impressions, P.O. Box 613, Wayzata, MN 55391: Free brochure ■ Impressionist art recreations on canvas. Available framed and unframed. 800–279–4–ART; 612–377–0166 (in MN).

Fine Art World, 3798 NW 19th St., Fort Lauderdale, FL 33311: Free information ■ Original oils, watercolors, mixed media, graphics, sculptures, and tapestries. 305–739–5340.

Framing Fox Art Gallery, P.O. Box 679, Lebanon, NJ 08833: Free information with long SASE ■ Civil War prints. 908–236–6077.

Fredericksburg Historical Prints, 829 Caroline St., Fredericksburg, VA 22401: Free information ■ Civil War prints, engravings, other prints, books, bronze sculptures, and paintings. 703–373–1861.

Gallerie Robin, 6808 Pennywell Dr., Nashville, TN 37205: Free information ■ Limited edition art prints. 800–635–8279.

Gallery Graphics, Inc., 227 Main St., P.O. Box 502, Noel, MO 64854: Catalog $5 (refundable) ■ Great art masterpiece reproductions. Includes antique prints, note cards, and Christmas cards. 417–475–6116.

Gallery Lainzberg, 200 Guaranty Bldg., Cedar Rapids, IA: Free catalog ■ Animation art from most major studios. Includes classic and modern production cels, limited editions, and serigraphs. 800–678–4608.

Gallery 3, 3819 N. 3rd St., Phoenix, AZ 85012: Free information ■ Contemporary paintings, graphics by Southwestern artists, and sculptures. 602–277–9540.

Gifted Images Gallery, P.O. Box 34, Baldwin, NY 11510: Free catalog ■ Animation art. 800–726–6708; 516–536–6886 (in NY).

Godel & Company Fine Art, Inc., 969 Madison Ave., New York, NY 10021: Catalog $10 ■ Folk art, Hudson River School art, marine scenes, American impressionism, still lifes, and other art collectibles. 212–288–7272.

Graphic Encountering, Inc., 4621 W. Washington Blvd., Los Angeles, CA 90016: Free information ■ Hand-cast paper sculptures, hand-painted acrylics, and mixed media serigraphs. 800–472–7445; 213–930–2410 (in CA).

The Greenwich Workshop, Inc., 30 Liondeman Dr., Trumbull, CT 06611: Free information ■ Limited edition prints that include fantasy, wilderness, Old West, exotic lands, and aviation themes. 800–243–4246; 203–371–6568 (in CT).

Grunewald Folk Art, P.O. Box 721, Wauconda, IL 60084: Catalog $2 ■ Limited edition lithographs of pen-and-ink folk drawings in color. Includes animals and people in rural American settings. Signed, titled, and numbered by the artist. 708–526–1417.

Guarisco Gallery, 2828 Pennsylvania Ave. NW, Washington, DC 20007: Catalog $10 ■ European, British, and American 19th-century paintings. 202–333–8533.

Habitat Gallery, 400 Galleria, Ste. 400, Southfield, MI 480340: Free catalog ■ Custom framed art posters and prints. Includes contemporary, children, lifestyle, scenic, fine art, and photography themes. 800–477–3300.

Harvest Gallery, Inc., 1527 Beverly Dr., Wichita Falls, TX 76309: Free brochure ■ Limited edition prints. 800–545–8231.

Hefner Galleries, 1020 Madison Ave., 5th Floor, New York, NY 10021: Free information ■ Contemporary oil paintings from The People's Republic of China. 212–861–1700.

Heritage Art, 125 Kemp Ln., P.O. Box 1587, Easton, MD 21601: Free information ■ Limited edition signed prints and boxed note card assortments. 800–727–6006.

Historical Art Prints, Ltd., P.O. Box 660, Drawer B, Southbury, CT 06488: Free information ■ Military art. 203–262–6680.

Icart Graphics, 8568 W. Pico Blvd., Los Angeles, CA 90035: Catalog $3.50 ■ Icart art deco posters. 310–659–1023.

Incredible Arts, P.O. Box 342, Carmel, CA 93921: Catalog $4 ■ Reprints of 19th-century lithographs and famous drawings. 408–372–0873.

Kasumi-mono, 1594 Rydalmount, Cleveland, OH 44118: Catalog $2 (refundable) ■ Japanese prints. Includes original Kasumi renditions from the satire, Urban Samurai, and modern Japanese culture. 216–932–9475.

Kennedy Galleries, 40 W. 57th St., New York, NY 10019: Catalog $5 ■ Prints and other art collectibles. 212–541–9600.

Coe Kerr Gallery, 49 E. 82nd St., New York, NY 10028: Free information ■ American art from the 19th- and 20th-century. 212–628–1340.

Kruckmeyer & Cohn, P.O. Box 967, Evansville, IN 47706: Free catalog ■ Paintings, lithographs, and collectible art glass. 812–464–9111.

J.J. Lally & Company, 42 E. 57th St., New York, NY 10022: Free information ■ Oriental art. 212–371–3380.

Leslie Levy Fine Art, 7142 Main St., Scottsdale, AZ 85262: Free information ■ Contemporary American paintings, drawings, and sculptures. 800–765–2787; 602–947–0937 (in AZ).

Liros Gallery, Inc., P.O. Box 946, Blue Hill, ME 46140: Free catalog ■ Art prints and paintings. 207–374–5370.

Lublin Graphics, 95 E. Putnam Ave., Greenwich, CT 06830: Catalog $2 ■ Original graphics by contemporary American and European artists. 800–243–4004; 203–622–8777 (in CT).

Kenneth Lux Gallery, 1021 Madison Ave., New York, NY 10021: Free information ■ American paintings from the 19th- and early 20th-century. 212–861–6839.

Makk Art Studios, 250 N. Robertson Blvd., Beverly Hills, CA 90211: Free information ■ Contemporary impressionist oils, watercolors, prints, and sculptures. 310–273–6768.

The Masters' Collection, Box 317540, Newington, CT 05131: Catalog $5 ■ On-canvas replicas of original oil painting masterpieces. 800–2–CANVAS.

The Masters Portfolio, 2049 N. Fremont St., Chicago, IL 60614: Free information ■ Drawings and paintings from the 1880s to 1960s. 312–248–8074.

Melanin Graphics, 1131 S. Howard St., Baltimore, MD 21230: Free information ■ African-American art. 410–783–0259.

Metropolitan Museum of Art, Special Service Office, Middle Village, NY 11381: Catalog $1 ■ Original lithographs, prints, and other graphics from around the world. Other items include porcelain, ceramics and glass; silver, brass, and pewter jewelry; scarves, shawls and neckties; needlework pillow kits; and books. 800–468–7386.

Monarch Studios, 119 Colony Square, Williamsburg, VA 23185: Free brochure ■ Original contemporary posters and prints. 800–545–9060; 804–221–0112 (in VA).

The Moss Portfolio, 2878 Hartland Rd., Falls Church, VA 22043: Catalog $10 ■ Prints for decor settings and collecting. 703–849–0845.

Museum Editions of New York, Ltd., 12 Harrison St., 3rd Floor, New York, NY 10013: Catalog $5 ■ Reproductions of contemporary to modern posters by famous artists. 212–431–1913.

National Archives & Records Administration, National Archives Books, Washington, DC 20408: Free brochure ■ Historic, patriotic posters and postcards. 202–523–3164.

Native American Arts, P.O. Box 2103, Ada, OK 74820: Free price list with long SASE ■ Original paintings, jewelry, bronze pieces, and sculptures. 405–436–5506.

Nostalgia Decorating Company, P.O. Box 1312, Kingston, PA 18704: Brochure $2 ■ Color reproductions of turn-of-the century prints of old ads, magazine covers, and pictures of children. Available framed or unframed. 717–472–3764.

The Old Print Gallery, 1220 31st St. NW, Washington, DC 20007: Catalog $3 ■ Prints and maps from the 18th- and 19th-century. 202–965–1818.

Opus Art Studios, 1810 Ponce De Leon Blvd., Coral Gables, FL 33134: Free information ■ Contemporary paintings, graphics, and sculptures. 305–448–8976.

Original Print Collectors Group, Ltd., 611 Broadway, Ste. 426, New York, NY 10012: Free catalog ■ Numbered and signed, original and framed limited-edition prints, serigraphs, etchings, and lithographs. 800–556–6200.

Park South Gallery, 885 7th Ave., New York, NY 10019: Free information ■ Contemporary posters, Icart etchings, rare Chagall posters, and original art nouveau deco posters. 212–246–5900.

Poster Originals, 330 Hudson St., New York, NY 10021: Catalog $10 ■ Art posters and billboards. Framing available. 212–620–0522.

Poster Service, 255 Northland Blvd., Cincinnati, OH 45246: Catalog $2 ■ Imported and domestic music, psychedelic, movie, and art posters.

Posters of Santa Fe, 111 E. Palace Ave., Santa Fe, NM 87501: Catalog $3 ■ Art posters. 800–827–6745; 505–982–6645 (in NM).

Steven S. Raab, 2033 Walnut St., Philadelphia, PA 19103: Free catalog ■ Autographs, signed books and photos, historic newspapers, World War I posters, and other historic memorabilia. 215–446–6193.

Red Lancer, P.O. Box 8056, Mesa, AZ 85214: Catalog $6 ■ Original 19th-century military art, rare books, Victorian era campaign medals and helmets, old toy soldiers, and other collectibles. 602–964–9667.

Norman Rockwell Museum, 601 Walnut St., Philadelphia, PA 19106: Brochure $1 (refundable) ■ Norman Rockwell prints, posters, and canvas art. 215–922–4345.

Ronin Gallery, 605 Madison Ave., New York, NY 10022: Catalog $6 ■ Japanese prints. 212–688–0188.

Rosenbaum Fine Art, 5181 NE 12th Ave., Fort Lauderdale, FL 33334: Free information ■ Original, limited editions of paintings, sculptures, water colors, and other works of art. 800–344–2787; 305–772–1386 (in FL).

Connie Seaborn Studio, P.O. Box 23795, Oklahoma City, OK 73132: Free information with long SASE ■ Original paintings, drawings, and hand-pulled prints. 405–728–3903.

Silver Image Gallery, 92 S. Washington St., Seattle, WA 98104: Catalog $4 (refundable) ■ Posters made using different mediums alone or in combination with graphic design, offset lithography, photography, or typography. 206–623–8119.

Spencertown Art & Antique Company, Rt. 203, Spencertown, NY 12165: Free information ■ Oriental rugs and American and European paintings and sculpture, from the 19th- and early 20th-century. 518–392–4442.

A. Strader Folk Art, 100 S. Montgomery St., Union, OH 45322: Catalog $2 ■ Primitive-style prints from the 17th- and 18th-century, and handcrafted country crafts that include fireboards, miniature chests, custom oils, and other collectibles. 513–836–6308.

Syracuse Cultural Workers, P.O. Box 6367, Syracuse NY 13217: Free Catalog ■ Posters designed to "enhance and inspire a world of peace, justice, economic equality, liberation and environmental harmony." 315–474–1132.

Taggart & Jorgensen Gallery, 3241 P St. NW, Washington, DC 20007: Free information ■ American paintings from the 19th- and 20th-century. 202–298–7676.

Tai Chi Arts Studio, Box 7591, Athens, GA 30604: Information $2 ■ Original Sumi art. Includes large and miniature scrolls and miniature screens. 404–613–0328.

Treasures Art, P.O. Box 5605, Columbus, GA 31906: Free catalog ■ Antique Chinese porcelain art. 404–322–4606.

Ursus Prints, 981 Madison Ave., New York, NY 10021: Free information ■ Antique prints, drawings, and watercolors. 212–772–8787.

Vestal Press, Ltd., P.O. Box 97, Vestal, NY 13851: Catalog $2 ■ Posters, books, and recordings that relate to museum antiquities and the theater. Includes carousels, music boxes, player pianos and other music machines, antique radios and phonographs, theater pipe organs, reed organs, early movie theater and film stars, and radio personalities. 607–797–4872.

Vladimir Arts U.S.A., Inc., 6125 Sprinkle Rd., Portage, MI 49001: Free information ■ Original oils, acrylics, watercolors, and graphics. 800–678–VLAD.

Wild Wood Gallery, 502 Factory Ave., Box 300, Syracuse, NY 13205: Catalog $1 ■ Decorative accessories for the home. Includes pictures, mirrors, wall plaques, decor groupings, and other items. 315–469–8098.

Sculptures & Carvings

Arrow Gems & Minerals, P.O. Box 9068, Phoenix, AZ 85068: Free catalog ■ Pewter figurines. 602–997–6373.

Ballard Designs, 1670 DeFoor Ave. NW, Atlanta, GA 30318: Catalog $3 ■ Sculptured castings, furniture, lamps, decor accessories, garden and landscaping pieces, fireplace accessories, frames, pictures, and pillows. 404–351–5099.

John & Lynne Bolen Fine Arts, P.O. Box 5654, Huntington Beach, CA 92615: Free information ■ American paintings, prints, and sculptures, from the 19th- and 20th-century. 714–968–0806.

Henry Bonnard Bronze Company & Associates, 4305 S. Hwy. 17-92, Casselberry, FL 32707: Free catalog ■ Collectible bronze statuary. Marble bases available. 800–521–3179; 407–339–9103 (in FL).

Boone Trading Company, 562 Coyote Rd., Brinnon, WA 98320: Catalog $3 ■ Genuine ivory, scrimshaw tusks and netsuke, Oriental and Eskimo carvings, fossilized walrus, and mammoth ivory tusks and pieces. 206–796–4330.

Michael Campbell Fine Art, 7824 E. Lewis Ave., Scottsdale, AZ 85251: Free information ■ Contemporary and Latin American paintings, sculptures, graphics, pre-Columbian art, Spanish paintings, and out-of-print art books. 602–947–5399.

Carol's Gift Shop, 17601 S. Pioneer Blvd., Artesia, CA 90701: Free information ■ Sculptures, figurines, and display cabinets. 310–924–6335.

Cherokee National Museum Gift Shop, P.O. Box 515, TSA-LA-GI, Tahlequah, OK 74464: Free price list with long SASE ■ Original paintings, prints, sculptures, baskets, other Indian art, and weapons. 918–456–6007.

Churchills, Twelve Oaks Mall, Novi, MI 48377: Free information ■ Art collectibles and plates. 800–388–1141.

Cirrus Gallery, 542 S. Alameda St., Los Angeles, CA 90037: Free information ■ Contemporary art and other works from nationally known artists. 213–680–3473.

Duncan Royale, 1141 S. Acacia Ave., Fullerton, CA 92631: Free information ■ Sculptured figurines from the Ebony Collection. 800–366–4646.

Dyansen Gallery of SoHo, 122 Spring St., New York, NY 10012: Catalog $5 ■ Sculptures, paintings, and graphics. 800–348–2787.

Eleganza, Ltd., 3217 W. Smith, Ste. 170, Seattle, WA 98199: Catalog $3 ■ Sculptures made from oxolyte that resembles Carrara marble. 206–283–0609.

Enesco Corporation, One Enesco Plaza, Elk Grove Village, IL 60007: Free information ■ Figurines, musical sculptures, ornaments, bells, and other sculptures. 800–323–0636; 800–824–5959 (in IL).

European Imports & Gifts, 7900 N. Milwaukee Ave., Niles, IL 60648: Free information ■ Art collectibles. 800–227–8670; 708–967–5253 (in IL).

Fine Art World, 3798 NW 19th St., Fort Lauderdale, FL 33311: Free information ■ Original oils, mixed media, watercolors, graphics, sculptures, and tapestries. 305–739–5340.

The Front Parlor, Inn on the Square, 3 Montgomery St., Oakland, IL 61943: Free information ■ David Winter cottages, including retired items. 217–346–3533.

Gallery 3, 3819 N. 3rd St., Phoenix, AZ 85012: Free information ■ Contemporary paintings, graphics by Southwestern artists, and sculptures. 602–277–9540.

Gifts & Such, 3626 Walton Way Ext., Augusta, GA 30909: Free information ■ Art collectibles. 800–828–3445; 404–738–4574 (in GA).

Giust Gallery, 1920 Washington St., Boston, MA 02118: Catalog $2 ■ Reproductions of classical sculptures in major European museums. 617–445–3800.

Bill Glass Studio, Star Route South, Box 39B, Locust Grove, OK 74352: Free information with long SASE ■ Original stoneware sculpture and pottery. Some stone carvings and bronzes. 918–479–8884.

Goebel, Inc., Goebel Plaza, P.O. Box 10, Pennington, NJ 08534: Free information ■ Sculptured miniatures of characters from Walt Disney's animated film classics. 800–366–4632.

Kelley Haney Art Gallery, P.O. Box 103, Seminole, OK 74868: Free brochure with long SASE ■ Original Indian paintings, sculpture, jewelry, baskets, and pottery. 405–382–3915.

Historical Sculptures, P.O. Box 141, Cairo, NY 12413: Free information ■ Historical Civil War sculptures in cold-cast bronze. 518–622–3508.

Honk 'N Quax, Ltd., 1500 Main St., P.O. Box 15155, Springfield, MA 01115: Catalog $2 ■ Handcrafted carvings, ready for sanding and finishing. Available finished and signed by the artist. 413–525–4980.

The Huntington Bronze Collection, 401 E. Cypress, Visalia, CA 93277: Free catalog ■ Over 300 lost wax bronze sculptures. 800–777–8126.

Imagine That, 5903 Queens Chapel, Hyattsville, MD 20782: Free information ■ Sculptures, figurines, and other art collectibles. 800–722–2227.

The Kittyhawk Gallery, 915 Broadway, New York, NY 10010: Free catalog ■ Authentic handcarved and handpainted aircraft models. 212–529–1144.

Kruckmeyer & Cohn, P.O. Box 867, Evansville, IN 47706: Free catalog ■ Handmade sculptures with a "Merry Olde England" theme. 812–464–9111.

Leslie Levy Fine Art, 7142 Main St., Scottsdale, AZ 85262: Free information ■ Contemporary American paintings, drawings, and sculptures. 800–765–2787; 602–947–0937 (in AZ).

Makk Art Studios, 250 N. Robertson Blvd., Beverly Hills, CA 90211: Free information ■ Contemporary impressionist oils, watercolors, prints, and sculptures. 310–273–6768.

Munyon & Sons, 1119 Waverly Hills Dr., Thousand Oaks, CA 91360: Free catalog ■ Full-size museum-quality reproductions of Remington bronzes. 800–289–2850.

Native American Arts, P.O. Box 2103, Ada, OK 74820: Free price list with long SASE ■ Original paintings, jewelry, bronzes, and sculptures.

Opus Art Studios, 1810 Ponce De Leon Blvd., Coral Gables, FL 33134: Free information ■ Contemporary paintings, graphics, and sculptures. 305–448–8976.

Bob Parker's Sports Collectibles, P.O. Box 2141, Union, NJ 07083: Free newsletter ■ Collectible sports statues and plates. 800–543–7794.

Rostand Fine Jewelers, 8349 Foothill Blvd., Sunland, CA 91040: Free information ■ Lladro collectibles. 800–222–9208; 818–352–7814 (in CA).

Schmid Woodcarvings, 55 Pacella Park Dr., Randolph, MA 02368: Free information ■ Registered woodcarvings. Limited editions are numbered. 617–961–3000.

Shorebird Decoys, Inc., 124 Forest Ave., Hudson, MA 01749: Brochure $1 ■ Authentic reproductions of works by early carvers. 508–562–7841.

Someone Special, Street Road Plaza, 2635 Street Rd., Bensalem, PA 19020: Free catalog ■ American Civil War sculptures in pewter and other fine metals. 215–245–0919.

Treasure Chest, 1221 E. Powell, Gresham, OR 97030: Free information ■ Art collectibles. 800–228–1297; 503–667–2999 (in OR).

Van Der Waay Jewelers, 834 S. Federal Hwy., Deerfield Beach, FL 33441: Free catalog ■ Lladro and Hummel collectibles. 305–421–5114.

Wolf Chief Graphics, 907 C Ave. NW, Great Falls, MT 59404: Free price list with long SASE ■ Original watercolor paintings, alabaster and bronze sculptures, hand pulled serigraphs, bone chokers, and other art. 406–452–4449.

Wood Carvings by Ted Nichols, P.O. Box 1050, Salisbury, MD 21802: Catalog $1 ■ Handcarved and painted woodcarvings. 301–546–9522.

World Treasures, 23016 Del Lago Dr., Laguna Hills, CA 92653: Catalog $6 ■ Handmade replicas of famous museum pieces. 714–768–0353.

ASTRONOMY

Astrophotography

Santa Anita Camera & Optical Company, 1031 S. Baldwin Ave., Arcadia, CA 91007: Free information ■ Astrophotography equipment and binoculars. 818–447–1854.

Sky Scientific, 28578 Hwy. 18, P.O. Box 184, Skyforest, CA 91335: Catalog $1 ■ Astrophotography equipment. 714–337–3440.

Spectra Astro Systems, 6631 Wilbur Ave., Ste. 30, Reseda, CA 91335: Free catalog ■ Astrophotography equipment. 818–343–1352.

Observatories & Planetariums

Ace Dome, 3186 Juanita, Las Vegas, NV 89102: Free brochure ■ Portable domes ready-to-use or in easy-to-assemble kits. 702–873–5790.

Ash Manufacturing Company, Inc., Box 312, Plainfield, IL 60544: Free brochure ■ Mechanical or electrical observatory domes from 10 to 36 feet in diameter. 815–436–9403.

Learning Technologies, Inc., 59 Walden St., Cambridge, MA 02140: Free catalog ■ Portable planetarium system with a projector and accessories. 800–537–8703; 617–547–7724 (in MA).

Observa-Dome Laboratories, Inc., 371 Commerce Park Dr., Jackson, MS 39213: Free catalog ■ Domes for amateur astronomers, professional tracking, research, communications, and defense systems. 800–647–5364; 601–982–3333 (in MS).

Research 2000, 386 Nahant Rd., Nahant, MA 01908: Free catalog ■ Observatories for amateurs and institutions. 617–592–1422.

Radio Astronomy

Bob's Electronic Service, 7605 Deland Ave., Fort Pierce, FL 33451: Catalog $3 ■ Radio astronomy equipment. 407–464–2118.

Noctilume, P.O. Box 63, Harbor City, CA 90710: Free brochure ■ Radio astronomy equipment. 310–325–7827.

Software

Andromeda Software, Inc., P.O. Box 1361, Williamsville, NY 14231: Free catalog ■ Astronomy software for IBM, Apple, and Commodore computers. 716–691–4510.

Archive PC Specialists, P.O. Box 59, Flanders, NJ 07836: Free catalog ■ Astronomy software. 908–850–4414.

A.R.C. Software, P.O. Box 1974, Loveland, CO 80539: Free literature ■ Astronomy simulation software for IBM personal computers. 303–663–3223.

Carina Software, 830 Williams St., San Leandro, CA 94577: Free information ■ Astronomy software for Macintosh computers. 510–352–7328.

Deltron, 155 Deer Hill Rd., Lebanon, NJ 08833: Free information ■ Astronomy software. 908–236–2928.

Diamond Computer Solutions, 4607 Beacon Hill Ct., Eagan, MN 55122: Free information ■ Astronomy software for IBM personal computers. 612–452–7940.

GAO Associates, P.O. Box 60333, Florence, MA 01060: Free information ■ Orbital simulation and display programs for IBM personal computers. 413–586–3999.

Lewis-Michaels Engineering, 48 Delemere Blvd., Fairport, NY 14450: Free catalog ■ Astronomy software and telescope-making supplies. 716–425–3470.

Planet Mac, P.O. Box 186, Stillwater, ME 04489: Catalog $1 ■ Astronomy software for Macintosh computers.

Picoscience, 41512 Chadbourne Dr., Fremont, CA 94539: Astronomy software for IBM computers. 510–498–1095.

Software Bisque, 912 12th St., Golden, CO 80401: Free information ■ Astronomy software for IBM computers. 303–278–4478.

Southwest Astronomy, 4242 Roma NE, Albuquerque, NM 87108: Free catalog ■ Astronomy software.

Telescopes & Accessories

Adorama, 42 W. 18th St., New York, NY 10011: Catalog $1 ■ Telescopes and accessories, telescope-making supplies, cameras and photographic equipment, astronomy audio-visual aids, mounts, lenses, filters, eyepieces, charts and star maps, books, and binoculars. 212–741–0052.

Advance Camera Corporation, 15 W. 46th St., New York, NY 10036: Free information ■ Telescopes and accessories, telescope-making supplies, astronomy audio-visual aids, cameras and photographic equipment, lenses, filters, eyepieces, charts and star maps, and binoculars. 212–944–1410.

Aries Optics, Rt. 1, Box 143G, Palouse, WA 99161: Catalog $3 ■ Telescopes, eyepieces, and accessories. 509–878–1713.

Astronomics, 2401 Tee Cir., Ste. 106, Norman, OK 73069: Free information with long SASE ■ Astronomy equipment. 800–422–7876.

The Astronomy Shoppe, 15836 N. Cave Creek Rd., Phoenix, AZ 85032: Free literature with long SASE ■ Telescopes and accessories, maps and star charts, and books. 602–971–3170.

Astro-Tech, 222 W. Main, P.O. Box 2001, Ardmore, OK 73402: Catalog $1 ■ Telescopes and accessories, binoculars, books, electro-optical equipment, filters, telescope mounts, science equipment, star maps, and atlases. 405–226–3074.

Astro-Track Engineering, 9811 Brentwood Dr., Santa Ana, CA 92704: Free information ■ Equatorial mounts that will hold up to 20-inch telescopes. 714–289–0402.

Astro World, 5126 Belair Rd., Baltimore, MD 21206: Free price list with long SASE ■ Telescopes and accessories, telescope-making supplies, astronomy audio-visual aids, photographic equipment and accessories, mounts, lenses, filters, eyepieces, charts and star maps, domes, books, binoculars, used equipment, and coating and repair services. 410–483–5100.

Berger Brothers Camera Exchange, 209 Broadway, Amityville, NY 11701: Free information ■ Telescopes and accessories, telescope-making supplies, astronomy audio-visual aids, photographic equipment and accessories, mounts, lenses, filters, eyepieces, charts and star maps, books, and binoculars. 800–262–4160.

Black Forest Observatory, 12815 Porcupine Ln., Colorado Springs, CO 80908: Free information with long SASE ■ Telescopes, binoculars, books, cameras, computers and software, eyepieces and filters, mirrors and lenses, star maps and atlases, and science equipment. 719–495–3828.

Bushnell Optical, Bausch & Lomb, 300 N. Lone Hill Ave., San Dimas, CA 91773: Free literature ■ Telescopes and accessories. 714–592–8072.

California Telescope Company, P.O. Box 1338, Burbank, CA 91507: Catalog $5 ■ Telescopes and accessories, telescope-making supplies, audio-visual aids, photographic equipment, computer software, lenses, filters, eyepieces, charts and star maps, books, and binoculars. 818–505–8424.

Celestron International, 2385 Columbia St., Torrance, CA 90503: Catalog $2 ■ Telescopes and accessories. 310–328–9560.

Chicago Optical & Supply Company, Box 1361, Morton Grove, IL 60053: Free catalog ■ Telescopes and accessories, view finders, filters, and camera equipment. 708–827–4846.

Cosmic Connections, Inc., P.O. Box 7, Aurora, IL 60505: Catalog $2 ■ Telescopes and accessories, telescope-making supplies, photographic equipment, mounts, lenses, filters, eyepieces, charts and star maps, domes, books, and binoculars. 800–634–7702; 708–844–0268 (in IL).

Cosmos, Ltd., 9215 Waukegan Rd., Morton Grove, IL 60053: Free catalog ■ Ultra widefield telescopes and accessories. 708–827–4846.

Coulter Optical Company, P.O. Box K, Idyllwild, CA 92349: Free information ■ Telescopes and accessories, mirrors, and mounts. 714–659–4621.

D & G Optical, 6490 Lemon St., East Petersburg, PA 17520: Catalog $1 ■ Ready-to-use tube assemblies with objective lens, 2–inch focusing lens, 50-mm finderscope, dewcap, and dustcover. 717–560–1519.

Davilyn Corporation, 13406 Saticoy St., North Hollywood, CA 91605: Free catalog ■ Star drives and declination motors. 800–235–6222; 818–787–3334 (in CA).

DFM Engineering, Inc., 1035 Delaware Ave., Unit D, Longmont, CO 80501: Brochure $4 ■ Computer controlled telescopes. 303–678–8143.

Dobbins Instrument Company, 5168 Lynd Ave., Lyndhurst, OH 44124: Catalog $2 ■ Telescope mounts and refractors.

Eagle Optics, 6109 Odana Rd., Madison, WI 53719: Free price list ■ Telescopes and accessories, photographic equipment, books, and binoculars. 608–271–4751.

Edmund Scientific Company, Edscorp Building, Barrington, NJ 08007: Free catalog ■ Telescopes, telescope-making supplies, astronomy audio-visual aids, photographic equipment, mounts, lenses, filters, eyepieces, charts and star maps, domes, books, and binoculars. 609–573–6260.

Effonscience, Inc., 3350 Dufferin St., Toronto, Ontario, Canada M6A 3A4: Free information with long SASE ■ Telescopes, telescope-making supplies, mounts, electro-optical equipment, audio-visual aids, books, cameras, computers and software, eyepieces, filters, mirrors and lenses, and planetariums. 416–787–4581.

Epoch Instruments, 2331 American Ave., Hayward, CA 94545: Free catalog ■ Telescope mounts, clock drives, setting circles, telescopes and accessories, and other optical instruments. 510–784–0391.

Focus Camera, 4419 13th Ave., Brooklyn, NY 11219: Catalog $3 ■ Telescopes and accessories, astronomy audio-visual aids, photographic equipment, lenses, filters, eyepieces, and binoculars. 718–871–7608.

Fort Davis Astronomical Supply, P.O. Box 922, Fort Davis, TX 79734: Free information ■ Telescopes and accessories. 800–874–3806; 915–426–3008 (in TX).

Galaxy Optics, P.O. Box 2045, Buena Vista, CO 81211: Catalog $1 ■ Telescope-making supplies and Newtonian telescope optics. 719–395–8242.

A. Jaegers Optical Supply Company, 6915 Merrick Rd., Lynbrook, NY 11563: Catalog 25¢ ■ Telescopes and accessories, telescope-making supplies, photographic equipment, mounts, lenses, filters, eyepieces, books, and binoculars. 516–599–3167.

Jim's Mobile, Inc., 1960 County Rd. 23, Evergreen, CO 80493: Catalog $3 ■ Precision astronomy equipment that includes dedicated computers with object databases, telescope-to-PC links, focusing motors, push-on and snap-on declination motors, drive controls, locking easels, telescopes, and software. 303–277–0304.

Jupiter Telescope Company, 810 Saturn St., Ste. 16, Jupiter, FL 33477: Free brochure ■ Portable equatorial telescopes. 407–694–1154.

Kenmore Camera, P.O. Box 82467, Kenmore, WA 98028: Free information with long SASE ■ Telescopes, binoculars, audio-visual aids, books, photographic equipment, computers and software, eyepieces and filters, mirrors and lenses, planetariums, and binoculars. 206–485–7447.

Khan Scope Center, 3243 Dufferin St., Toronto, Ontario, Canada M6A 2T2: Catalog $3 ■ Telescopes and accessories, telescope-making supplies, binoculars, mounts, audio-visual aids, books, photographic equipment, computers and software, eyepieces and filters, mirrors and lenses, and planetariums. 800–668–2067.

Los Angeles Optical Company, P.O. Box 4868, North Hollywood, CA 91617: Free information ■ Telescopes and accessories, lenses, eyepieces, books, maps and charts, filters, and photographic equipment. 818–762–2206.

Lumicon, 2111 Research Dr., Livermore, CA 94550: Free catalog ■ Telescopes, binoculars, eye pieces and filters, mirrors and lenses, mounts, star maps and atlases, computers and software, and photographic equipment. 510–447–9570.

Mardiron Optics, 4 Spartan Cir., Stoneham, MA 02180: Free brochure with two 1st class stamps ■ Telescopes, accessories, and binoculars. 617–938–8339.

Martin's Star Tracker, 633 S. Broadway, Boulder, CO 80301: Free information ■ Telescopes and accessories, telescope-making supplies, photographic equipment, charts and star maps, clothing and jewelry, lens coating services, domes, meteorites, mounts, lenses, filters, eyepieces, books, binoculars, antique instruments, and other science equipment. 303–449–0805.

Thomas Mathis Company, 830 Williams St., San Leandro, CA 94577: Free information ■ Telescope mounts and drives. 510–483–3090.

Meade Instruments Corporation, 1675 Toronto Way, Costa Mesa, CA 92626: Catalog $3 ■ Telescopes and accessories, spotting scopes, and telephoto lenses. 714–556–2291.

F.C. Meichsner Company, 182 Lincoln St., Boston, MA 02111: Free information ■ Telescopes and accessories, antique instruments, photographic equipment, mounts, lenses, filters, eyepieces, charts and star maps, books, and binoculars. 800–321–8439.

MMI Corporation, 2950 Wyman Pkwy., P.O. Box 19907, Baltimore, MD 21211: Catalog $2 ■ Portable planetariums, 35mm slides, videos, celestial globes, computer software, laser disks, teaching manuals, and telescopes. 410–366–1222.

National Camera Exchange, 9300 Olson Memorial Hwy., Golden Valley, MN 55427: Free information ■ Telescopes and accessories, astronomy audio-visual aids, photographic equipment, lenses, filters, eyepieces, charts and star maps, books, and binoculars. 800–624–8107; 612–546–6831 (in MN).

New England Astro-Optics, Inc., P.O. Box 834, Simsbury, CT 06070: Catalog $2 ■ Telescopes, and accessories, photographic equipment, and books. 203–658–0701.

New Jersey Telescope Headquarters, 770 Rt. 17 North, Paramus, NJ 07652: Free information ■ Telescopes and accessories. 800–631–7111; 201–444–7367 (in NJ).

Kenneth F. Novak & Company, Box 69, Ladysmith, WI 54848: Free catalog ■ Telescopes and accessories, mounts, and books. 715–532–5102.

Optica b/c Company, 4100 MacArthur Blvd., Oakland, CA 94619: Catalog $3 ■ Telescopes and accessories, telescope-making supplies, mounts, binoculars, audio-visual aids, books, photographic equipment, computers and software, eyepieces and filters, mirrors and lenses, and planetariums. 510–530–1234.

Optical Glass Fabrication, Inc., 3164 El Camino Real, Atascadero, CA 93422: Free information ■ Custom optical components. 805–461–9402.

Optron Systems, 15840 E. Alta Vista Way, San Jose, CA 95127: Free information ■ Telescopes and accessories, lenses, binoculars, and other optical equipment. 408–923–6800.

Orion Telescope Center, 2450 17th Ave., P.O. Box 1158, Santa Cruz, CA 95061: Free catalog ■ Telescopes and accessories, photographic equipment, charts and star maps, lenses, filters, eyepieces, books, other science equipment, and binoculars. 800–447–1001; 800–443–1001 (in CA).

Parks Optical Company, 270 Easy St., Simi Valley, CA 93065: Free catalog ■ Telescopes, accessories, and other optical equipment. 805–522–6722.

Pauli's Wholesale Optics, 29 Kingswood Rd., Danbury, CT 06811: Catalog $10 ■ Telescopes and accessories, telescope-making supplies, photographic equipment, mounts, lenses, filters, eyepieces, computer software, other science equipment, books, and binoculars. 203–746–3579.

Perceptor, Brownsville Junction Plaza, Box 38, Ste. 201, Schomberg, Ontario, Canada L0G 1T0: Free information ■ Telescopes, telescope-making supplies, mounts, audio-visual aids, books, cameras, computers and software, eyepieces and filters, mirrors and lenses, planetariums, and binoculars. 416–939–2313.

Purus Astro-Mechanism, P.O. Box 123, Escalon, CA 95320: Free catalog ■ Equatorial mounts. 209–838–1259.

Quasar Optics, 7220 Fairmount Dr. SE, Calgary, Alberta, Canada T2H 0X7: Catalog $4 ■ Telescopes and accessories, telescope-making supplies, photographic equipment, lenses, filters, eyepieces, other science equipment, books, and binoculars. 403–255–7633.

Questar, P.O. Box 59, New Hope, PA 18938: Catalog $3 ■ Telescopes and accessories. 215–862–5277.

Redlich Optical, 711 W. Broad St., Falls Church, VA 22046: Free information with long SASE ■ Telescopes, telescope-making equipment, binoculars, books, cameras, photographic equipment, computers and software, eyepieces and filters, mirrors and lenses, star maps, and atlases. 703–241–4077.

Rowlab Science Center, Inc., 1650 Art Museum Dr., Jacksonville, FL 32207: Free information with long SASE ■ Telescopes, telescope-making supplies, binoculars, mounts, electro-optical equipment, audio-visual aids, books, cameras, computers and software, eyepieces and filters, mirrors and lenses, and planetariums. 904–399–8036.

R.V.R. Optical, P.O. Box 62, Eastchester, NY 10709: Catalog $5 ■ All sizes of telescopes up to 2 meters. 914–337–4085.

S & S Optika, 5174 S. Broadway, Englewood, CO 80110: Free information ■ Telescopes and accessories, binoculars, eyepieces, and other optical equipment. 303–789–1089.

Science Education Center, 125 S. Hillside, Wichita, KS 67211: Free information with long SASE ■ Telescopes and accessories, mounts, audio-visual aids, star maps and atlases, eyepieces, and filters. 316–682–1921.

Scope City, P.O. Box 440, Simi Valley, CA 93065: Free catalog ■ Telescopes and accessories, telescope-making supplies, photographic equipment, mounts, lenses, filters, eyepieces, books, and binoculars. 805–522–6701.

Shutan Camera & Video, 312 W. Randolph, Chicago, IL 60606: Catalog $1 ■ Telescopes and accessories, telescope-making supplies, photographic equipment, charts and star maps, lenses, filters, eyepieces, books, binoculars, video equipment, and other electronics. 800–621–2248; 312–332–2000 (in IL).

Sky Designs, 4100 Felps, Ste. C, Colleyville, TX 76034: Free information ■ Portable telescopes. 817–656–4326.

Sky Scientific, 28578 Hwy. 18, P.O. Box 184, Sky Forest, CA 92385: Catalog $1 ■ Telescopes, accessories, and supplies. 714–337–3440.

Star-Liner Company, 1106 S. Columbus, Tucson, AZ 85711: Catalog $5 ■ Telescopes, from 6-inch amateur units to observatory research equipment. 602–795–3361.

Sunwest Space Systems, P.O. Box 20500, St. Petersburg, FL 33742: Free information ■ Telescopes and accessories. 813–577–0629.

Tele-Vue Optics, 100 Rt. 59, Suffern, NY 10901: Catalog $3 ■ Telescopes and accessories, and other optical equipment. 914–357–9522.

Texas Nautical Repair Company, 2129 Westheimer, Houston, TX 77098: Free catalog ■ Portable camera mounting and tracking systems, telescopes, eyepieces and filters, mirrors and lenses, other science equipment, star maps, and atlases. 713–529–3551.

Thousand Oaks Optical, P.O. Box 5044–289, Thousand Oaks, CA 91359: Free brochure ■ Solar filters and astronomy equipment and accessories. 805–491–3642.

Roger W. Tuthill, Inc., Box 1086, Mountainside, NJ 07092: Free catalog ■ Telescopes and accessories, astronomy audio-visual aids, telescope-making supplies, photographic equipment, mounts, lenses, filters, eyepieces, books, and binoculars. 800–223–1063; 908–232–1786 (in NJ).

Unitron, Inc., 175 Express St., Plainview, NY 11803: Free catalog ■ Telescopes, spotting scopes, binoculars, and other optical instruments. 516–822–4601.

University Optics, P.O. Box 1205, Ann Arbor, MI 48106: Free catalog ■ Telescopes and accessories. 800–521–2828.

VERNONscope & Company, 5 Ithaca Rd., Candor, NY 13743: Catalog $3 ■ Portable telescopes. 607–659–7000.

Vista Instrument Company, P.O. Box 1919, Santa Maria, CA 93456: Free brochure ■ Precision camera tracker with optional accessories. 805–925–1240.

Vogel Enterprises, Inc., 38150 Hickory Ct., Batavia, IL 60510: Free catalog ■ Quartz controlled drive correctors. 800–457–8725; 708–879–8725 (in IL).

Ward's Natural Science, P.O. Box 92912, Rochester, NY 14692: Free information with long SASE ■ Telescopes, telescope-making supplies, binoculars, audio-visual aids, books, computers and software, eyepieces and filters, planetariums, and meteorites. 716–359–2502.

Wholesale Optics of Pennsylvania, North Pocono Village, RR 6, Box 6329, Moscow, PA 18444: Free information ■ Astronomy equipment and accessories, binoculars, sighting scopes, telescope-making supplies, charts and star maps, photographic equipment, and books. 717–842–1500.

Willmann-Bell, Inc., P.O. Box 35025, Richmond, VA 23235: Free catalog ■ Telescopes, accessories, and books. 804–320–7016.

Wilson's Camera Sales, 3144 E. Camelback Rd., Phoenix, AZ 85016: Free information with long SASE ■ Telescopes, telescope-making equipment, mirrors and lenses, filters, mounts, star maps and atlases, books, audio-visual aids, binoculars, and cameras. 602–955–6773.

AUTOGRAPHS

American Historical Guild, 130 Circle Dr., Ste. 200, Roslyn Heights, NY 11577: Catalog $2 ■ Original letters and documents by famous Americans, world leaders, scientists, authors, composers, artists, and others. 516–621–3051.

America West Archives, Box 100, Cedar City, UT 84720: Catalog $3 ■ Autographs and collectible letters, stock certificates, bonds, checks, and other documents.

Ray Anthony Autograph Company, 9016 Wilshire Blvd., Ste. 448, Beverly Hills, CA 90211: Catalog $3 ■ Autographed letters, documents, albums, books, and photographs. 310–826–0915.

The Autograph Alcove, 6909 W. North Ave., Wauwatosa, WI 53213: Free catalog ■ Historical Americana, autographs from all fields, manuscripts, and other collectible documents. 414–771–7844.

Autograph Outlet, Susan Sanders Wadopian, 3 Ellenwood Dr., Asheville, NC 28804: Free catalog with long SASE ■ Autographed items from many areas of interest. 704–253–5202.

Catherine Barnes Autographs, P.O. Box 30117, Philadelphia, PA 19103: Free catalog ■ Letters, documents, manuscripts, signed books and photographs, and other collectibles. 215–854–0175.

Robert F. Batchelder, 1 W. Butler Ave., Ambler, PA 19002: Free catalog ■ Letters, documents, and manuscripts from all fields of interest. Includes history, literature, science, military, presidents and politics, music, and others. 215–643–1430.

Benedikt & Salmon Record Rarities, 3020 Meade Ave., San Diego, CA 92116: Free catalogs, indicate choice of (1) autographs and rare books, (2) classical, (3) jazz, big bands, and blues, and (4) personalities, soundtracks, and country music ■ Autographed memorabilia and rare books in music and the performing arts, hard-to-find rare phonograph recordings, from 1890 to date, and antique phonographs and cylinders for collectors. 619–281–3345.

Walter R. Benjamin, Autographs, Box 255, Hunter, NY 12442: Catalog subscription $10 (refundable with $50 order) ■ Letters and documents with historical, literature, musical, and scientific interest. 518–263–4133.

Edward N. Bomsey Autographs, Inc., 7317 Farr St., Annandale, VA 22003: Annual catalog subscription $10 (refundable) ■ Autographs from black movement leaders, and American and international military and political history, sports and entertainment, science, music, literature, aviation, space, science and inventor, fine arts personalities. 703–642–2040.

Book City Collectibles, 6631 Hollywood Blvd., Hollywood, CA 90028: Free information ■ Autographs from the early days of Hollywood to the present. Includes signed photographs, letters, contracts, and other items by movie and music stars, writers, directors, and producers. 800–4–CINEMA; 213–962–7411 (in CA).

Celebrity Access, 20 Sunnyside Ave., Mill Valley, CA 94941: Catalog $2 ■ Autographed rarities. 415–389–8133.

Cinema City, Box 1012, Muskegon, MI 49443: Catalog $3 ■ Posters, photos, autographs, scripts, and other movie memorabilia. 616–722–7760.

Classic Rarities & Company, Inc., P.O. Box 29109, Lincoln, NE 68529: Free catalog ■ Autographed rarities. 402–467–2948.

Dance Mart, P.O. Box 48, Homecrest Station, Brooklyn, NY 11229: Free catalog with long SASE ■ Books, prints, music, autographs, and other collectibles on dance. 718–627–0477.

Eileen Delaney Autographs, 1593 Monrovia, Newport Beach, CA 92663: Catalog $10 (refundable) ■ Autographed historic rarities from Hollywood stars, presidents, scientists and inventors, and other personalities. 800–966–7448.

18th Century Collectibles, Edward J. Craig, 41 3rd St., Newport, RI 02840: Free catalog ■ Early American autographs, postal history, fiscal paper, slavery and Judaica memorabilia, and other collectibles. 401–847–6498.

Elmer's Nostalgia, Inc., 3 Putnam St., Sanford, ME 04073: Free catalog with long SASE and two 1st class stamps ■ Entertainment, political, historical, literary, and pop culture autographs and memorabilia. 207–324–2166.

Golden Age Autographs, P.O. Box 20408, Park West Finance Station, New York, NY 10025: Catalog $2 ■ Autographs and signed photographs from a variety of fields, specializing in entertainers. 212–866–5626.

Golden State Autographs, P.O. Box 24066, Los Angeles, CA 90024: Free information with long SASE ■ Autographs from all fields. 310–444–9663.

Jerry Granat/Manuscripts, P.O. Box 92, Woodmere, NY 11596: Free information with long SASE ■ Letters and autographs from famous people. 516–374–7809.

Mike Gutierrez, c/o Superior Galliery, 9478 W. Olympic Blvd., Beverly Hills, CA 90212: Free catalog ■ Autographed photographs and letters. 310–203–9855.

Adam L. Harwood, P.O. Box 5083, Newport, RI 02841: Free information ■ Signed photos and autographs, letters, first day covers, and other memorabilia from American astronauts. 401–848–7907.

Jim Hayes, Box 12557, James Island, SC 29412: Catalog $6 ■ Autographs from all fields of interest. Includes the Civil and Revolutionary war periods. 803–795–0732.

Hollywood Legends, The Autograph Store, 6621 Hollywood Blvd., Hollywood, CA 90028: Free information ■ Autographs and signed memorabilia from the early days of Hollywood to the present. 213–962–7411.

Howling Moon, P.O. Box 9050, Austin, TX 78766: Free catalog ■ Autographs and paper collectibles. Includes cartoon and celebrity art. 512–499–8504.

Jeanne Hoyt Autographs, P.O. Box 1517, Rohnert Park, CA 94927: Free information with long SASE and 52¢ postage ■ Autographs from all areas, including entertainers. 707–584–4077.

J.D. & Bob's Autographs, P.O. Box 115, Champaign, IL 61824: Free catalog with long SASE ■ Autographs from entertainers. 217–356–2486.

Mark R. Jordan, Inc. 1600 Airport Freeway, Ste. 506, Bedford, TX 76022: Free catalog ■ Autographs by college and pro football players, and past and present entertainment personalities. 800–888–3784.

Robert A. LeGresley, P.O. Box 1199, Lawrence, KS 66044: Free catalog with long SASE ■ Autographs and signed letters, photographs, and original comic art. 913–749–5458.

Abraham Lincoln Book Shop & Gallery, 357 W. Chicago Ave., Chicago, IL 60610: Free information with long SASE ■ New and used books, autographed letters, documents, original prints, and photographs. 312–944–3085.

Linda's Autographs, Box 1, Umpqua, OR 97486: Catalog $1.50 ■ Autographs by musicians, television and movie entertainers, political figures, poets, authors, and other personalities. 503–459–4730.

William Linehan Autographs, Box 1203, Concord, NH 03301: Free catalog ■ Movie costumes of the stars and their autographs. 800–346–9827.

Lone Star Autographs, P.O. Box 500, Kaufman, TX 75142: Free catalog ■ Autographed letters, documents, and photographs, from the Civil War, movies, scientific community, literature, music, space, aviation, military, and politics, and books signed or owned by Presidents and First Ladies. 214–563–2115.

Luckett's Autographs, P.O. Box 436057, Louisville, KY 40243: Free catalog ■ Autographs and signed memorabilia from entertainers, sport figures, military persons, and astronauts. 502–244–8959.

Judi McMahon Autographs, 7 Park Ave., New York, NY 10016: Free information ■ Autographs and signed memorabilia. 212–679–8011.

Joseph M. Maddalena, 9440 Santa Monica Blvd., Ste. 704, Beverly Hills, CA 90210: Free information ■ Letters, photos, documents, and signed books. Other collectibles include memorabilia from presidents, statesmen, movie stars, scientists, authors, inventors, architects, musicians, composers, and others. 800–942–8856; 800–942–8855 (in CA).

J.B. Muns, Bookseller, 1162 Shattuck Ave., Berkeley, CA 94707: List $1 ■ Autographs by classical singers, musicians, and composers. 510–525–2420.

Nate's Autographs, 1015 Gayley Ave., Los Angeles, CA 90024: Catalog subscription $10 ■ Autographs and autographed memorabilia by entertainers, presidents and other historic personalities, music stars, air space and science figures, and sports greats. 310–575–3851.

North Shore Manuscript Company, Inc., P.O. Box 458, Roslyn Heights, NY 11577:

Free catalog ■ Autographed memorabilia. 516–484–6826.

Odyssey Group, Bill Miller/Darrell Talbert, 510 S. Corona Mall, Corona, CA 91720: Free newsletter ■ Autographed letters, manuscripts, photos, and documents in all fields of interest. 714–371–7137.

Oregon State Autograph Company, P.O. Box 1, Umpqua, OR 97486: Free sample catalog ■ Autographs, signed letters, documents, photographs, and books by movie stars and entertainers, political figures and statesmen, presidents, literary greats, sports figures, and others. 503–459–4730.

Tom Peper, 32 Shelter Cove Lane, #109, Hilton Head Island, SC 29928: Price list $1 ■ Autographs, lobby cards and posters, original comic art, animation art and cels, and other collectibles. 800–628–7497.

Personalities Plus, 254 N. Paseo Campo, Anaheim Hills, CA 92807: Free information with long SASE ■ Autographs of entertainment and sports celebrities. 714–998–2659.

A Piece of History, 2899 Agoura Rd., Ste. 522, Westlake Village, CA 91361: Free information ■ Autographed photos, letters, and documents from the World War II era. 818–707–3706.

Tom & Cordelia Platt, 1598 River Rd., Belle Mead, NJ 08052: Catalog subscription $10 (refundable) ■ Autographs in all categories. 908–359–7959.

Robert L. Polk, 4728 N. LaVergne Ave., Chicago, IL 60630: Free list ■ Autographs of entertainers, astronauts, sports figures, writers, military individuals, world leaders, political figures, and others. 312–286–4543.

R & R Enterprises, P.O. Box 2000, Amherst, NH 03031: Catalog $3 ■ Autographs of movie, television, sport, music, and history personalities. 800–443–4461.

Steven S. Raab, 2033 Walnut St., Philadelphia, PA 19103: Free catalog ■ Autographs, signed books and photos, historic newspapers, World War I posters, and other historic memorabilia. 215–446–6193.

Kenneth W. Rendell, Inc., 125 E. 57th St., New York, NY 10022: Free information with long SASE ■ Autographs and documents by famous persons, from early American history to the present. Includes authors, presidents, statesmen, scientists, musicians, military, and world leaders. 800–447–1007; 212–935–6767 (in NY).

Paul C. Richards, Autographs, High Acres, Templeton, MA 01468: Free information ■ Letters, manuscripts, documents, and signed photographs. 800–637–7711.

Rivendell Rarities, Ltd., P.O. Box 238, Bayside, NY 11361: Catalog subscription $6 (refundable) ■ Original letters, documents, and signatures of famous people. 718–217–1612.

Rock & Roll Autographs, Rick Barrett, P.O. Box 66262, Houston, TX 77266: Free list with three 1st class stamps ■ Signed records, photographs, rock memorabilia, and other autographed music-related items.

Safka & Bareis, Autographs, P.O. Box 886, Forest Hills, NY 11375: Free catalog ■ Signed photos, letters, and other autographed items, from opera, music, and movie entertainers. 718–897–7275.

St. Louis Baseball Cards, 5456 Chatfield, St. Louis, MO 63129: Free information ■ Sports cards and memorabilia, autographs, uniforms, press pins, advertising pieces, and other collectibles. 314–892–4737.

H. Drew Sanchez, 19863 Shoshonee Rd., Apple Valley, CA 92307: Free catalog ■ Autographs from the entertainment field and cartoon art. 619–242–9092.

Seaport Autographs, 6 Brandon Ln., Mystic, CT 06355: Free catalog ■ Autographed letters, manuscripts, and documents covering many areas of collecting interest. 203–572–8441.

Searle's Autographs, P.O. Box 849, Woodbine, GA 31569: Free catalog ■ Signed items by artists, authors, politicians, movie stars, and military leaders, and original comic art. 912–576–5094.

Stampede Investments, Scott G. Kalcik, 1533 River Rd., Wisconsin Dells, WI 53965: Free information ■ Autographs, historical documents, old stocks and bonds, and other collectibles. 608–254–7751.

Georgia Terry, Autographs, 840 NE Cochran Ave., Gresham, OR 97030: Free catalog ■ Autographs from the entertainment industry. 503–667–0950.

Theme Prints, Ltd., P.O. Box 123, Bayside, NY 11361: Free brochure ■ Books, antique arms, historic documents, letters and autographs from the Revolutionary War era to early Hollywood. 718–225–4067.

Louis Trotter, Autographs, P.O. Box 732, Port Richey, FL 34673: Free catalog ■ Autographs from all areas of interest. 813–842–3522.

Mark Vardakis Autographs, P.O. Box 408, Coventry, RI 02816: Free information with long SASE ■ Autographs, paper Americana, pre–1900 stocks, bonds and checks, and other items. 800–342–0301; 401–823–8440 (in RI).

Yours Truly Autographs, 1807 Washington St. South, Ste. 106, Naperville, IL 60565: Free information ■ Animation and cartoon art, and autographs from entertainent, sports, history, political, and military figures. 708–420–1162.

AUTOMOTIVE PARTS & ACCESSORIES

Automotive Art & Gifts

Atlanta Gallery of Automotive Art, P.O. Box 420024, Atlanta, GA 30342: Free information ■ Lithographs of automotive art. 404–351–9100.

Auto Dimensions, P.O. Box 133, Mountain Lakes, NJ 07046: Free information with long SASE ■ T-shirts, posters, and other gifts for automobile buffs. 201–625–4388.

Automobilia, 44 Glendale Rd., Park Ridge, NJ 07656: Free information ■ Die-cast and pewter automotive miniatures by Polistil, Brumm, Collectors Case, and others, and car badges, cruise ship models, and toy cars of the 1950s. 201–573–0173.

Auto Motif, Inc., 2968 Atlanta Rd., Smyrna, GA 30080: Catalog $1 ■ Books, prints, puzzles, models, candy, office accessories, lamps, original art, posters, and other gifts with an automotive theme. 404–435–5025.

Automotive Emporium, 100 Turtle Creek Village, Dallas, TX 75219: Free information with long SASE ■ Automotive books and original literature, art and memorabilia, miniatures, and bronze sculptures. 214–521–1930.

Car Collectables, P.O. Box 221, Madison, CT 06443: Free brochure ■ Christmas cards, note cards, and gifts, with an automotive theme. 203–245–2242.

Carswell's Creations, 3476 Alward Rd., Pataskala, OH 43062: Catalog $1 ■ Buttons, magnets, mirrors, bumper stickers, rubber

stamps, note cards, award certificates, and other automotive gifts. 614–927–5224.

Cobweb Collectibles, 9 Walnut Ave., Cranford, NJ 07016: Free information with long SASE ■ Automotive memorabilia that includes books, postcards, toys, pins, factory badges, and other collectibles. 201–272–5777.

Gee Gee Studios, Inc., 6636 S. Apache Dr., Littleton, CO 80120: Catalog $1 (refundable) ■ Original pen and ink drawings and numbered lithographs of famous cars. Available framed or unframed. 303–794–2788.

Knoxgun International, 301 N. Cedar St., Abingdon, IL 61410: Free information with long SASE ■ Watches, clocks, jewelry, desk sets, and other gifts with an automotive theme. 309–462–3248.

Narcon Imports, Inc., 6 Madison Ave., Kearney, NJ 07032: Catalog $6 ■ Antique and international car badges, automotive accessories, and other gifts. 201–998–2994.

Pelham Prints, 1619 N. 6th St., Clinton, IA 52732: Free literature ■ Note cards, antique and classic automotive art, and pen and ink drawings. 319–242–0280.

Universal Tire Company, 987 Stony Battery Rd., Lancaster, PA 17601: Free catalog ■ Collector car accessories. Includes Lucas electric parts, wheel hardware, moldings, and antique and classic tires. 800–233–3827.

Weber's Nostalgia Supermarket, 1121 S. Main, Fort Worth, TX 76104: Catalog $4 (refundable with $10 order) ■ Gas globes, gas pump restoration supplies, porcelain sides, car models, photographs, posters, and other automotive gifts. 817–335–3833.

Body Repair Parts

Auto Body Specialties, Inc., Rt. 66, Middlefield, CT 06455: Catalog $5 ■ Reproduction and original quarter panels, fenders, repair panels, grills, bumpers, and carpets for 1950 to 1986 American and foreign cars, pickups, and vans. 203–346–4989.

Bill's Speed Shop, 13951 Millersburg Rd. SW, Navarre, OH 44662: Free information ■ Hard-to-find panels for older cars and current models. 216–832–9403.

Made-Rite Auto Body Products, Inc., 869 E. 140th St., Cleveland, OH 44110: Free information ■ Steel replacement panels for cars, pickups, and vans. 216–681–2535.

Mill Supply, 3241 Superior Ave., Cleveland, OH 44114: Catalog $4 ■ Steel replacement panels, tools, and body shop equipment for most United States cars, vans, pickups, and foreign cars. 800–888–5072.

Rootlieb, Inc., P.O. Box 1829, Turlock, CA 95381: Free catalog ■ Hoods, fenders, running boards, splash aprons, and other parts for older Ford and Chevrolet cars. 209–632–2203.

Scarborough Faire, 1151 Main St., Pawtucket, RI 02860: Free information ■ Body repair panels for most cars. 401–724–4200.

Howard Whitelaw, 60678 Richmond Rd., Solon, OH 44139: Free information ■ N.O.S. fenders and quarter panels for 1933 to 1976 Chrysler, Dodge, De Soto, and Plymouth cars. 216–721–6755.

Books

Albion Scott Book Distributors, 48 E. 50th St., New York, NY 10022: Catalog $4 ■ Automotive books. 212–980–1929.

Automotive Information Clearinghouse, P.O. Box 1746, La Mesa, CA 92041: Free information with long SASE ■ Original automobile service manuals. 619–447–7200.

Auto World Books, P.O. Box 562, Camarillo, CA 93011: Free information with long SASE ■ Automobile, truck, and motorcycle books, service manuals, and back issues of magazines. 805–987–5570.

Aztex Corporation, P.O. Box 50046, Tucson, AZ 85703: Free list with long SASE ■ Books on transportation and how-to automotive subjects. 602–882–4656.

Francis Burley, Rt. 7, P.O. Box 1281, Moultrie, GA 31768: Free information with long SASE ■ Automobile shop manuals, parts catalogs, and owner's manuals. 912–985–6860.

Car Books, 1099 W. Royal Oaks Dr., Shoreview, MN 55126: Free information ■ Automotive books. 800–642–3289.

Chewning's Auto Literature, Ltd., 123 Main St., P.O. Box 727, Broadway, VA 22815: Free information with long SASE (specify year and model of car) ■ Shop and owner's manuals, and parts and sales catalogs. 703–896–6838.

Chilton Book Company, One Chilton Way, Radnor, PA 19089: Free catalog ■ Books on automotive mechanics and repair. 215–964–4000.

Classic Motorbooks, P.O. Box 1, Osceola, WI 54020: Free catalog ■ Books and manuals for all types of cars. Includes collector guides, repair guides, driving manuals, buying guides, and technical information resource books. 800–826–6600.

Crank'en Hope Publications, 461 Sloan Alley, Blairsville, PA 15717: Free information with long SASE ■ Original and reprinted shop manuals, owner's manuals, parts books, and sales literature. 412–459–8853.

Dragich Discount Auto Literature, 1660 93rd Ln. NE, Minneapolis, MN 55434: Free information ■ Original and reproduction automotive books and manuals. 612–786–3925.

Haynes Publications, Inc., 861 Lawrence Dr., Newbury Park, CA 91320: Free catalog ■ Automotive and motorcycle repair manuals. 818–889–5400.

Ernie Hemmings, Bookseller, P.O. Box 3906, Quincy, IL 62305: Free catalog ■ Hard-to-find books on the Ford Model T and A. 217–224–1670.

Walter Miller, 6710 Brooklawn Pkwy., Syracuse, NY 13211: Free information ■ Original repair manuals, owner's manuals, sales brochures, and parts books for domestic and foreign cars. 315–432–8282.

Schiff European Automotive Literature, Inc., 1 Cambria Ct., Pawtucket, RI 02860: Free information with long SASE ■ European automotive publications. 401–722–7367.

Clothing

Donovan Uniform Company, 171 Parkhouse, Dallas, TX 75207: Free information ■ Caps, goggles, and dusters for men and women. 214–741–3971.

Exhaust Systems & Mufflers

Kanter Auto Parts, 76 Monroe St., Boonton, NJ 07005: Free catalog ■ Heavy-duty replacement exhaust systems for most cars, from 1909 to 1970. 201–334–9575.

John Kepich, 16270 Old U.S. 41 South, Fort Myers, FL 33912: Free information ■ Heavy-duty stainless steel exhaust systems.

Will custom manufacture special orders. 813–433–1150.

King & Queen Mufflers, Box 423, Plumsteadville, PA 18949: Free information ■ N.O.S. exhaust system parts for cars and trucks, 1926 and later. 215–766–8699.

Never Rust Exhaust Systems, 4279 Ohio River Blvd., Pittsburgh, PA 15202: Free information with long SASE ■ Stainless steel exhaust systems. 412–766–7775.

Stainless Steel Muffler Corporation, 3032 Genessee, Buffalo, NY 14225: Free information ■ Stainless steel mufflers for foreign cars. 716–893–2116.

Glass

Buchingers, P.O. Box 66114, Chicago, IL 60666: Free information ■ Windshields, side glass, and back windows for 1940 to 1970 cars. 312–678–6140.

Diamond Auto Glass Corporation, 105 Emjay Blvd., Brentwood, NY 11717: Free information with long SASE ■ Automotive glass for domestic and foreign cars and trucks. 800–235–4311.

Iowa Glass Depot, P.O. Box 122, Cedar Rapids, IA 52406: Free information ■ Hard-to-find windshields for most pre–1960 cars. 800–553–8134; 800–332–5402 (in IA).

Lo-Can Glass International, 693 McGrath Hwy., P.O. Box 45248, Somerville, MA 02145: Free information ■ Hard-to-find glass for old and new cars. 800–345–9595; 617–396–9595 (in MA).

Headlights & Headlight Covers

Extang Corporation, 2298 S. Industrial Hwy., Ann Arbor, MI 48104: Free brochure ■ Headlight covers for most American cars, from 1980 and later. 313–665–5270.

Headlight Headquarters, 35 Timson St., Lynn, MA 01902: Catalog $2 ■ Headlight units, lenses, and parts for 1914 to 1939 American cars, except Fords. 617–598–0523.

License Plates

Richard Diehl, 5965 W. Colgate Pl., Denver, CO 80227: Free list with long SASE ■ License plates from United States, Canada, and foreign countries.

License Plate Restorations, 746 N. Greenbrier Dr., Orange, CT 06477: Free information ■ Restores antique license and city plates and political tags. 201–795–6434.

Bob Lint Motor Shop, P.O. Box 87, Danville, KS 67036: Free inventory list ■ Old license plates for collectors. 316–962–5247.

Locks & Keys

Aero Locksmith, Inc., P.O. Box 16434, Memphis, TN 38186: Free information with long SASE ■ Keys for original or replacement locks on domestic and foreign automobiles. 901–398–8708.

Bill's Lock Shop, 3358 W. Alexis Rd., Toledo, OH 43623: Free information with long SASE ■ Locks and keys for most old cars, and Lincoln, Cadillac, Ford, and Mopar key blanks. 419–473–3090.

Key Shop-Locksmiths, 144 Crescent Dr., Akron, OH 44301: Free information ■ N.O.S. keys and locks for antique, classic, and modern cars. Repairs locks, makes keys by code or duplication, and changes codes. 216–724–3822.

Paint & Touch-Up Supplies

Automotive Paints Unlimited, Rt. 1, Roxboro, NC 27573: Free information ■ Acrylic enamel and lacquer finishes for 1904 to present automobiles. 919–599–5155.

Bill Hirsch, 396 Littleton Ave., Newark, NJ 07103: Free information ■ High-temperature engine enamels for spray or brush application. 201–642–2404.

Mark Auto Company, Inc., Layton, NJ 07851: Catalog $3 ■ Paints, chemicals, and restoration supplies for antique and classic cars. 201–948–4157.

Seelig's Custom Finishes, 10456 Santa Monica Blvd., Los Angeles, CA 90025: Catalog $2 ■ Specializes in custom finishes. Gold leaf and pin striping supplies and 60 colors of pearl available. 213–475–1111.

Parts for All Makes & Models

A. Aabel Used Auto Parts, Inc., 228 E. Arlington Ave., St. Paul, MN 55117: Free information ■ Parts for 1934 to 1988 cars. 612–487–1386.

A.C. Auto, Inc., Rt. 1, Webster, WI 54893: Free information with long SASE ■ Automobile parts for most cars, from 1970 to 1986. 715–866–7660.

Alley Auto Parts, Rt. 2, Box 551, Immokalee, FL 33934: Free information ■ Parts for cars and trucks, from 1948 to 1975. 813–657–3541.

Antique Auto Parts Cellar, P.O. Box 3, South Weymouth, MA 02190: Free information with long SASE ■ N.O.S. and reproduction mechanical parts for most cars, from 1909 to 1965. 617–335–1579.

A–1 Auto Wrecking, 13818 Pacific Ave., Tacoma, WA 98444: Free information ■ Parts for old cars. Includes brake drums, axles, transmission parts, and wheels. 206–537–3445.

Arnold's Auto Parts, 1484 Crandall Rd., Tiverton, RI 02878: Free information ■ Parts for American cars and trucks, from 1930 to 1970. 401–624–6936.

Auto Body Specialties, Inc., Rt. 66, Middlefield, CT 06455: Catalog $5 ■ Reproduction and original quarter panels, fenders, repair panels, grills, bumpers, and carpets for 1950 to 1986 American and foreign cars, pickups, and vans. 203–346–4989.

Auto World Motorsports, 701 N. Keyser Ave., Scranton, PA 18508: Catalog $3 ■ Accessories and performance parts and racing equipment for vintage and current sports and performance cars. 717–344–7258.

Bartnik Sales & Service, 6524 Van Dyke, Cass City, MI 48726: Free information ■ Parts for cars and trucks, from 1960 to 1970. 517–872–3541.

B & C Used Cars, 2600 Broadway SE, Albuquerque, NM 87102: Free information with long SASE ■ Parts for Thunderbirds, Cadillacs, and Lincolns, 1960 and later; Mustangs, 1965 and later. 505–242–0101.

B.C. Automotive, Inc., 2809 Damascus, Zion, IL 60099: Free information with long SASE ■ Parts and accessories for 1960 to 1982 domestic cars, and 1970 to 1984 foreign cars. 708–746–8056.

Big Ben's Used Cars & Salvage, Hwy. 79 North, Fordyce, AR 71742: Free information with long SASE ■ Used parts for 1975 and older cars. 501–352–7423.

Bob's Auto Parts, 6390 N. Lapeer Rd., Fostoria, MI 48435: Free information with long SASE ■ Parts for most 1930 to 1970 cars. 313–793–7500.

Bradley Auto, Inc., 2026 Hwy. A, West Bend, WI 53095: Free information with long

SASE ■ Parts for American cars, imports, and light duty trucks, 1975 and later. 414–334–4653.

Bryant's Auto Parts, RR 1, Westville, IL 61883: Free information with long SASE ■ Parts for most 1939 to 1988 cars. 217–267–2124.

California Discount Warehouse, 2320 E. Artesia Blvd., Long Beach, CA 92802: Catalog $4 ■ High-performance automobile parts and accessories. 310–423–4346.

Canfield Motors, 22–24 Main, New Waverly, IN 46961: Inventory list $4 ■ Parts for American cars, 1940 and later. 219–722–3230.

Cedar Auto Parts, 1100 Syndicate St., Jordan, MN 55352: Free information with long SASE ■ Parts and accessories for cars, from 1949 to current models. 800–755–3266; 612–492–3300 (in MN).

Cherry Auto Parts, 5650 N. Detroit Ave., Toledo, OH 43612: Free brochure ■ Used and rebuilt parts for foreign cars. 419–476–7222.

Chesaning Auto Salvage, 10572 Baldwin Rd., Chesaning, MI 48435: Free information with long SASE ■ Parts and accessories for most cars. 517–845–3076.

Competition Sales, 7702 Long Point, Houston, TX 77055: Free information ■ High-performance automobile parts and accessories. 713–686–7611.

Del-Car Auto Parts, Rt. 441 North, P.O. Box 1686, Lake City, FL 32055: Free information with long SASE ■ Parts for 1930 to 1986 cars. 904–752–1014.

East End Auto Parts, 75 10th Ave. E, Box 183, Dickinson, ND 58601: Catalog $5 ■ Parts for 1940 to 1980 Chevrolets, Fords, Dodges, and foreign cars. 701–225–4206.

E & J Used Auto & Truck Parts, 315 31st Ave., P.O. Box 1316, Rock Island, IL 61201: Free information ■ Parts for 1940 to 1987 American and foreign cars and trucks. 309–788–7686.

Easy Jack Welsh Antique Auto Parts, RD 3, Box 87, Junction City, KS 66441: Free information with long SASE ■ Used parts, from 1912 to 1982. 913–238–7541.

Egge Machine Company, 8403 Allport, Santa Fe Springs, CA 90670: Catalog $2 ■

Parts for older American cars. 800–866–EGGE; 310–945–3419 (in CA).

Faggelli's Auto Parts, 5850 Oakland Rd., Sykesville, MD 21784: Free information ■ Parts for domestic cars and trucks, from late 1940 to the present. 410–795–3007.

Fast Freddy's, 2604 S. Harbor Blvd., Santa Ana, CA 92704: Free information ■ High-performance automobile parts and accessories. 714–540–3801.

Ferrill's Auto Parts, Inc., 18306 Hwy. 99, Lynwood, WA 98037: Free information ■ Parts for domestic cars, from 1970 to 1985. 206–778–3147.

Fitz Auto Parts, 24000 Woodinville-Snohomish Rd., Woodinville, WA 98072: Free information with long SASE ■ Parts and accessories for Ford, General Motors, Chrysler, AMC, and some European and Japanese cars. 206–483–1212.

Fleetline Automotive, 153 Orchard Dr., Wallkill, NY 12589: Free information with long SASE ■ Parts and accessories for Chevrolet cars and trucks, Corvairs, Novas, Camaros, Chevelles, Buicks, Pontiacs, Cadillacs, and Oldsmobiles. 914–895–2381.

Hidden Valley Auto Parts, 21046 N. Rio Bravo Rd., Maricopa, AZ 85239: Free information with long SASE ■ Used antique and classic parts for older American and foreign cars. 602–568–2945.

Hy-Way Auto Parts, Inc., Box 76, Wadsworth, IL 60083: Free inventory list ■ Parts for foreign and American cars. 708–395–7600.

J & B Auto Parts, Inc., 17105 E. Hwy. 50, Orlando, FL 32820: Free information with long SASE ■ Parts for most makes and models of American and foreign cars and trucks. 305–568–2131.

J & M Vintage Auto, P.O. Box 297, Goodman, MO 64843: Free information with long SASE ■ Parts and accessories for 1930 to 1968 cars. 417–364–7203.

Jeg's High Performance Mail Order, 751 E. 11th Ave., Columbus, OH 43211: Free catalog ■ Automotive parts, accessories, and tools. 614–294–5050.

Ingwald Johnson Auto Parts, US 31 South, P.O. Box 52, Plymouth, IN 46563: Free information with long SASE ■ Parts and accessories for late model cars. 219–936–3333.

Kalend's Auto Wrecking, 7237 East Hwy. 26, Stockton, CA 95205: Free information with long SASE ■ Parts and accessories for 1978 to 1988 foreign and domestic cars. 209–931–0929.

Kanter Auto Parts, 76 Monroe St., Boonton, NJ 07005: Free information ■ Automotive parts and accessories. 201–334–9575.

Kelsey Auto Salvage, Rt. 2, Iowa Falls, IA 50126: Free information ■ Parts for 1948 to 1981 American cars. 515–648–3066.

Meier Auto Salvage, RR 1, Box 6L, Sioux City, IA 51108: Free information with long SASE ■ Automotive parts, from 1935 to 1988. 712–239–1344.

Steve Millen Sports Cars, 1627 S. Boyd, Santa Ana, CA 92705: Catalog $5 ■ Parts and accessories for sports cars. 714–258–0633.

Gus Miller, Box 634, Heyworth, IL 61745: Free information with long SASE ■ Parts for 1940 to 1950 cars. 309–473–2979.

Minot Wrecking & Salvage Company, 1123 Valley St., P.O. Box 566, Minot, ND 58701: Free information with long SASE ■ Parts and accessories for most domestic and foreign cars, from 1925 to the present. 800–533–5904.

Morgan Auto Parts, 722 Kennie Rd., Pueblo, CO 81001: Free information ■ Parts and accessories for most cars. 303–545–1702.

Nash Auto Parts, RD 2, Jordan, NY 13080: Free information ■ Parts for 1920 to 1975 cars. Includes some N.O.S. parts. 800–272–6274.

Northern Tire & Auto Sales, North 8219 Hwy. 51, Irma, WI 54442: Free information with long SASE ■ Parts for most cars, from the 1920s to the 1970s. 715–453–5050.

Old Car City USA, 3098 Hwy. 411 NE, White, GA 30184: Free information ■ Parts for cars before 1969. 404–382–6141.

Pacific Auto Accessories, 5882 Machine Dr., Huntington Beach, CA 92649: Brochure $3 ■ Easy-to-install ground effect styling parts and accessories for most cars, trucks, and sport utility vehicles. 800–854–7685; 714–891–3669 (in CA).

Pearson's Auto Dismantling & Used Cars, 2343 Hwy. 49, Mariposa, CA 95338: Free

information ■ Parts and accessories for 1940 to 1960 cars. 209–742–7442.

Performance Automotive Wholesale, 21050 Lassen St., Chatsworth, CA 91311: Catalog $5 ■ High-performance automobile parts and accessories. 818–998–6000.

Petry's Junk Yard, Inc., 800 Gorsuch Rd., Westminster, MD 21157: Free information with long SASE ■ Parts and accessories for most cars, from 1940 to 1970. 410–876–3233.

Philbates Auto Wrecking, Inc., Rt. 1, P.O. Box 88, New Kent, VA 23124: Free information with long SASE ■ Parts and accessories for most cars, from 1940 to 1982. 804–843–9787.

Pine River Salvage, Hwy. 371 North, Pine River, MN 56474: Free information with long SASE ■ Parts and accessories for cars, from 1940 and 1980. 218–587–2700.

Porter Auto Repair & Salvage, Rt. 1, Park River, ND 58270: Free information ■ Parts for Ford, Chevrolet, Dodge, Oldsmobile, Buick, Pontiac cars, and pickups and trucks, from 1950 and 1975. 701–284–6517.

Reliable Motoring Accessories, 1751 Spruce St., Riverside, CA 92505: Catalog $3 ■ Parts and equipment for automotive repairs and changes. 800–854–4770; 714–781–0261 (in CA).

Rick's Auto Wrecking, 12526 Aurora North, Seattle, WA 98133: Free information with long SASE ■ Parts for cars, from the 1950s, 1960s, 1970s, and 1980s. 206–363–6800.

Ron's Auto Salvage, RR 2, Box 54, Allison, IA 50602: Free information with long SASE ■ Parts and accessories for most cars, from 1949 to 1977. 319–267–2871.

Seward Auto Salvage, Inc., Rt. 2, Milton, WI 53563: Free information with long SASE ■ Parts for American and foreign cars, from 1946 to 1986. 608–752–5166.

Bill Shank Auto Parts, 14648 Promise Rd., Noblesville, IN 46060: Free information with long SASE ■ Parts and accessories for 1948 to 1988 cars. 317–776–0080.

Sil's Foreign Auto Parts, Inc., 1498 Spur Dr. South, Islip, NY 11751: Free information with long SASE ■ Parts and accessories for late European and Japanese cars. 516–581–7624.

Sleepy Eye Salvage Company, RR 4, Box 60, Sleepy Eye, MN 56085: Free information with long SASE ■ Parts and accessories for 1937 to 1977 cars. 507–794–6673.

Gale Smyth Antique Auto, 8316 East A.J. Hwy., Whitesburg, TN 37891: Inventory list $5 ■ Parts and accessories for 1935 to 1972 American cars. 615–235–5221.

Lynn H. Steele Rubber Products, 1601 Hwy. 150 East, Denver, NC 28037: Catalog $2 ■ Reproduction rubber parts for Cadillacs, Pontiacs, Buicks, Chevrolets, Chryslers, Oldsmobiles, Packards, and GM trucks. 800–544–8665; 704–483–9343 (in NC).

Summit Racing Equipment, 580 Kennedy Rd., Akron, OH 44305: Free information ■ High-performance automobile parts and accessories. 216–798–9440.

Sunrise Auto Sales & Salvage, Rt. 3, Box 6, Lake City, FL 32055: Free information with long SASE ■ Parts for most cars, from the 1950s through early 1970s. 904–755–1810.

Vander Haag's, Inc., Sanborn, IA 51301: Free information ■ Parts for 1975 and older cars; and for trucks, 1946 and later. 712–262–7000.

Van's Auto Salvage, Rt. 2, Box 164, Waupun, WI 53963: Free information with long SASE ■ Parts and accessories for most cars, from 1947 to 1976. 414–324–2481.

West 29th Auto, Inc., 3200 W. 29th St., Pueblo, CO 81003: Free information ■ Old and new parts and accessories for most cars. 719–543–4247.

J.C. Whitney & Company, 1917–19 Archer Ave., P.O. Box 8410, Chicago, IL 60680: Free catalog ■ Automotive parts, accessories, tools, and specialized equipment. 312–431–6102.

Leo Winakor & Sons, Inc., Forsyth Rd., Salem, CT 06415: Free information ■ Parts for most cars, from 1930 through 1981. 203–859–0471.

Windy Hill Auto Parts, 9200 240th Ave. NE, New London, MN 56273: Free information with long SASE ■ Parts for American cars and trucks, from 1915 to 1990, with most parts pre–1968. 612–354–2201.

Winnicks Auto Sales & Parts, Rt. 61, P.O. Box 476, Shamokin, PA 17872: Free information with long SASE ■ Parts for

American and imported cars and trucks, and Ford and Chevrolet engines. 717–648–6857.

Wiseman's Auto Salvage, 900 W. Cottonwood Ln., Casa Grande, AZ 85222: Free information with long SASE ■ Parts and accessories for 1930 to 1970 cars. 602–836–7960.

Woller Auto Parts, Inc., 8227 Rd. SS, Lamar, CO 81052: Free information ■ Parts for 1955 to 1984 domestic cars and pickups. 719–336–2108.

Parts for Specific Makes & Models

ACURA

A & H Motorsport, 472 Blair Mill Rd., Hatboro, PA 19040: Free catalog ■ Performance parts and accessories. 215–957–6144.

Acura of Bedford Hills, 531 Bedford Rd., Bedford Hills, NY 10507: Free information with long SASE ■ Acura parts and accessories. 914–666–2120.

HKS USA, Inc., 20312 Gramercy Pl., Torrance, CA 90501: Catalog $8 (specify car and model) ■ Performance parts and accessories. 310–328–8100.

Jackson Racing, 16291 Gothard St., Huntington Beach, CA 92647: Catalog $5 ■ High-performance and styling accessories. 714–841–3001.

MSO Parts, 1543 Easton Rd., Roslyn, PA 19001: Free catalog ■ Genuine Acura factory parts. 800–628–0817; 215–657–8423 (in PA).

ALFA ROMEO

Alfa Ricambi, 6644 San Fernando Rd., Glendale, CA 91201: Free information ■ Alfa Romeo stock, high performance, and competition parts. 818–956–7933.

Bobcor Motors, 120 Passaic St., Hackensack, NJ 750760 Catalog $6 ■ Alfa Romeo performance parts and accessories. 800–526–0337.

Europarts Connection, 2022½ Hyperion Ave., Los Angeles, CA 90027: Free information ■ Mechanical, body and interior parts and accessories for the Alfa Romeo. 213–665–6863.

International Auto Parts, Inc., Rt. 29 North, Box 9036, Charlottsville, VA 22906:

Catalog $2 ■ Alfa Romeo parts and accessories. 804–973–0555.

Shankle Engineering, 9135 Alabama Ave., Chatsworth, CA 91311: Catalog $5 ■ High performance engine, drive train, suspension parts, and accessories. 818–709–6155.

AMX

Byers Jeep-Eagle, 390 E. Broad St., P.O. Box 16513, Columbus, OH 43216: Free catalog ■ Original factory parts. 614–221–9181.

Year One, Inc., Box 2023, Tucker, GA 30085: Catalog $5 ■ New, used, and reproduction AMX restoration parts. 404–493–6568.

ANTIQUE & CLASSIC CARS

A–1 Auto Wrecking, 818 Pacific Ave., Tacoma, WA 98444: Free information ■ Parts for old cars. Includes brake drums, axles, transmission parts, and wheels. 206–537–3445.

Burchill Antique Auto Parts, 4150 24th Ave., Port Huron, MI 48060: Free information with long SASE ■ Parts and accessories for early vintage passenger and commercial vehicles. 313–385–3838.

Egge Machine Company, 8403 Allport, Santa Fe Springs, CA 90670: Catalog $2 ■ Parts for old cars. 800–866–EGGE; 213–945–3419 (in CA).

Bob Lint Motor Shop, P.O. Box 87, Danville, KS 67036: Free inventory list ■ Parts for early models of Fords, Chevrolets, Pontiacs, Plymouths, Dodges, and Buicks, and collectible license plates. 316–962–5247.

OlCar Bearing Company, 5101 Fedora, Troy, MI 48098: Free information ■ Bearings and seals for antique, classic and special interest cars, trucks, and tractors. 313–879–7916.

PRO Antique Auto Parts, 50 King Spring Rd., Windsor Locks, CT 06096: Catalog $2 ■ Restoration supplies and parts for antique cars. 203–623–0070.

Rick's Antique Auto Parts, P.O. Box 662, Shawnee Mission, KS 66201: Free catalog ■ Antique car parts and accessories. 800–228–5657.

Zimp's Enterprises, 2800 S. Montana, Butte, MT 59701: Free inventory list ■ Antique car parts. 406–782–5674.

AUBURN

W.H. Lucarelli, 14 Hawthorne Ct., Wheeling, WV 26003: Free information ■ Parts for 1931 to 1933 and 1935 to 1936 Auburns. 304–232–8906.

AUDI

Discount Auto Parts, 4703 Broadway SE, Albuquerque, NM 87105: Free information with long SASE ■ Audi parts. 505–877–6782.

Europarts, 620 Venture St., Escondido, CA 92025: Free information with long SASE ■ Audi parts and accessories. 619–743–3377.

Mathieu Parts & Accessories, 209th & Hilltop, Chicago Heights, IL 60411: Free catalog ■ Audi, Porsche, and Mercedes-Benz parts and accessories. 708–481–3114.

Parts Hotline, 10325 Central Ave., Montclair, CA 91763: Free information with long SASE ■ Audi parts. 800–637–4662; 714–625–4888 (in CA).

AUSTIN HEALEY

Moss Motors, Ltd., 7200 Hollister Rd., P.O. Box 847, Goleta, CA 93116: Free catalog ■ Hard-to-find Austin Healey parts. 800–235–6954.

Scotland Yard British Cars, Ltd., 3101 E. 52nd Ave., Denver, CO 80216: Free information with long SASE ■ New, used, and remanufactured Austin Healey parts. 800–222–1415; 800–328–8716 (in CO).

Sports & Classics, 512 Boston Post Rd., Darien, CT 06820: Catalog $5 ■ Restoration, engine, electrical, body parts and accessories for the Austin Healey. 203–655–8731.

AVANTI

Newman & Altman, Inc., P.O. Box 4276, South Bend, IN 46634: Catalog $5 ■ Avanti parts and accessories. 800–722–4295.

Nostalgic Motor Cars, 47400 Avante Dr., Wixom, MI 48393: Free information with long SASE ■ New and used 1963 to 1985 Avanti parts. 313–624–4210.

Penn Auto Sales, 7115 Leesburg Pike, Falls Church, VA 22043: Free information with long SASE ■ Avanti parts, from 1963 to 1989. 703–538–4388.

Southwest Avanti, 21824 N. 19th Ave., Phoenix, AZ 85027: Free information with long SASE ■ Avanti parts, from 1963 to 1989. 602–943–6970.

BENTLEY

Foreign Parts Connection, Inc., 2028 Cotner Ave., Westwood, CA 90025: Catalog $3 ■ Used postwar parts for the Bentley. 213–473–7773.

Lou Fusz Auto Parts Network, 10725 Manchester, St. Louis, MO 63122: Catalog $3 ■ Bentley and Rolls-Royce parts and accessories. 800–392–1372.

George Haug Company, Inc., 517 E. 73rd St., New York, NY 10021: Free information ■ Bentley parts and accessories. 800–955–4284; 212–288–0176 (in NY).

Rolls-Royce Obsolete Parts, Inc., P.O. Box 796, Anna Maria, FL 34216: Free information with long SASE ■ Bentley and Rolls-Royce parts, accessories, and literature. 813–778–7270.

BMW

Bavarian Auto Service, Inc., 44 Exeter St., Newmarket, NH 03857: Catalog $3 ■ BMW parts and accessories. 800–535–2002.

BMP Design, 5100 Old Bullard, Tyler, TX 75703: Catalog $5 ■ BMW parts and accessories. 800–648–7278.

Campbell/Nelson Volkswagon, P.O. Box 220, Edmonds, WA 98020: Free information ■ Used BMW parts and accessories. 206–771–4931.

Electrodyne, Inc., 4750 Eisenhower Ave., P.O. Box 9670, Alexandria, VA 22304: Catalog $3 ■ BMW parts and accessories. 800–658–8850; 703–823–0202 (in VA).

Europarts, 620 Venture St., Escondido, CA 92025: Free information with long SASE ■ BMW parts and accessories. 619–743–3377.

MSO Parts, 1543 Easton Rd., Roslyn, PA 19001: Free catalog ■ Genuine factory parts for the BMW. 800–628–0817; 215–657–8423 (in PA).

Noble Foreign Auto Parts, 355 Federal Rd., Brookfield, CT 06804: Catalog $5 ■ BMW parts and accessories. 800–327–6302.

Perfect Plastics Industries, Inc., 14th St., New Kensington, PA 15068: Free information ■ BMW body parts. 800–245–6520.

Sportformance, Inc., 1559 N. Main St., Waterbury, CT 06704: Free information ■ New and used BMW parts and accessories. 203–753–6051.

The Ultimate Source, 94 W. Woodhull Rd., Huntington, NY 11743: Catalog $3 ■ BMW parts and accessories. 800–537–8248.

XKSS, P.O. Box 4857, Thousand Oaks, CA 91359: Free brochures ■ Interiors for the BMW. Includes seat upholstery, carpet sets, headliners, and horsehair pads. 800–922–XKSS; 800–222–XKSS (in CA).

Zygmunt Motors, 70 Green St., Doylestown, PA 18901: Catalog $5 ■ BMW parts and accessories. 215–348–3121.

BRITISH SPORTS CARS

Atlanta Imported British Auto Parts, 5383 Buford Hwy., Doraville, GA 30340: Catalog $1 (refundable) ■ New, used, and imported Leyland parts. 404–451–4411.

British Auto, 703 Penfield Rd., Macedon, NY 14502: Free information ■ Parts for the Austin Healey, MG, Triumph, Jensen, Lotus, and Jaguar after 1950. 315–986–3097.

British Car Specialists, 2060 N. Wilson Way, Stockton, CA 95205: Free information with long SASE ■ MG, Jaguar, Triumph, and Austin Healey parts and accessories. 209–948–8754.

British Restoration Parts, 1808 Oak, Kansas City, MO 64108: Catalog $3 ■ Restoration parts and accessories for the Austin Healey, Triumph, Jaguar, Sunbeam, MG, and Triumph. 800–821–3767; 800–892–3250 (in MO).

FASPEC British Parts, 1036 SE Stark St., Portland, OR 97214: Catalogs $2 each (refundable). Specify if for MGA/MGB, Sprite-Midget, or Austin-Healey ■ New and used parts. 800–547–8788; 503–232–1232 (in OR).

Mini Mania, 31 Winsor St., Milpitas, CA 95035: Free catalog ■ Parts and accessories for the Morris Minor, Mini Cooper, Austin Sprite, and MG Midget. 408–9421–5595.

Moss Motors, Ltd., 7200 Hollister Rd., P.O. Box 847, Goleta, CA 93116: Free catalog ■ Hard-to-find parts for British sports cars. 800–235–6954.

Perfect Plastics Industries, Inc., 14th St., New Kensington, PA 15068: Free information ■ Body parts for MGA, MGB, Midget,

Austin Healey, Triumph TR–4, and TR–6. 800–245–6520.

Scarborough Faire, 1151 Main St., Pawtucket, RI 02860: Free MGB catalog (specify year and model); MGA catalog $3; Austin-Healey and Sprite catalog $2 ■ Parts for the MGB, MGA, Austin-Healey, and Sprite. 401–724–4200.

Sports & Classics, 512 Boston Post Rd., Darien, CT 06820: Catalog $5 ■ Restoration parts, engine and electrical parts, body parts, and accessories. 203–655–8731.

TS Imported Automotive, Pandora, OH 45877: Catalog $2 (refundable) ■ New, used, and N.O.S. parts for British cars. 800–543–6648.

Very British Car Parts, 99 Midline Rd., Amsterdam, NY 12010: Free information ■ New, used, and N.O.S. parts. 518–843–1358.

Victoria British, Ltd., P.O. Box 14991, Lenexa, KS 66215: Free information ■ Original and reproduction parts, plus accessories for the Austin Healey and other British sports cars. 800–255–0088.

BRONCO

Bill Alprin, 184 Rivervale Rd., Rivervale, NJ 07675: Free information ■ N.O.S. parts for the Bronco. 201–666–3975.

BUICK

B & B Used Auto Parts, Rt. 1, Box 691, Big Pine Key, FL 33043: Free information ■ Parts for Buicks, 1950 and later. 305–872–9761.

Bob's Automobilia, Box 2119, Atascadero, CA 93423: Catalog $3 ■ Parts, supplies, rubber, literature, upholstery fabrics, and hardware for 1919 to 1953 Buicks. 805–434–2963.

Buick Farm, Cloverdale Rd., RD 2, Box 102, Swedesboro, NJ 08085: Information $2 ■ Parts for post-war Buicks, 1950 to 1975. 609–467–1883.

Cars, Pearl St., Neshanic, NJ 08853: Catalog $2 (specify year and model) ■ New, used, and reproduction parts for 1935 to 1975 Buicks. 201–369–3666.

Classic Buicks, Inc., 4632 Riverside Dr., Chino, CA 91710: Catalog $4 ■ New, used, and reproduction parts for 1946 to 1973 Buicks. 714–591–0283.

Fannaly's Auto Exchange, 701 Range Rd., P.O. Box 23, Ponchatoula, LA 70454: Free information ■ Parts and accessories for 1939 to 1975 Buicks. 504–386–3714.

PRO Antique Auto Parts, 50 King Spring Rd., Windsor Locks, CT 06096: Catalog $2 ■ New parts for 1929 to 1964 Buicks. 203–623–0070.

Speedway Automotive, 2300 Broadway, Phoenix, AZ 85041: Free information with long SASE ■ Buick parts, from 1961 to 1987. 602–276–0090.

Bill Stevenson, P.O. Box 5368, Kent, WA 98064: Free information with long SASE ■ New, N.O.S., used, and reproduction 1946 to 1960 Buick parts. 206–852–0584.

Terrill Machine, Inc., Rt. 2, Box 61, DeLeon, TX 76444: Free information with long SASE ■ Engine overhaul parts for Buicks, from 1937 to 1958. 817–893–2610.

Terry's Auto Parts, Box 131, Granville, IA 51022: Free information ■ Parts for 1940 to 1984 Buicks, including 1963 to 1984 Rivieras. 712–727–3273.

CADILLAC

Aabar's Cadillac & Lincoln Salvage, 9700 NE 23rd, Oklahoma City, OK 73141: Free information ■ Cadillac and Lincoln parts, from 1939 on. 405–769–3318.

All Cadillacs of the 40's, 12811 Foothill Blvd., Sylmar, CA 91342: Free information with long SASE ■ Used and reproduction parts, from 1940 to 1950. 818–361–1140.

Automotive Obsolete, 1023 E. 4th St., Santa Ana, CA 92701: Catalog $3 ■ New parts for Cadillacs, from 1926 to 1970. 714–541–5167.

B & B Used Auto Parts, Rt. 1, Box 691, Big Pine Key, FL 33043: Free information ■ Cadillac parts, from 1950 and later. 305–872–9761.

Caddy Shack Cadillac, 2410 Harvard St., Sacramento, CA 95815: Catalog $3 ■ New, rebuilt, and used mechanical and auto body parts. 916–921–2575.

Cadillac King, Inc., 9840 San Fernando Rd., Pacoima, CA 91331: Free information with long SASE ■ New, used, and rebuilt Cadillac parts. 800–322–1077; 818–890–0621 (in CA).

CR Auto, P.O. Box 237, Hay Lakes, Alberta, Canada T0B 1W0: Free information ■ N.O.S. Cadillac parts, from 1947 to 1978, and original owner and shop manuals. 403–878–3263.

Fannaly's Auto Exchange, 701 Range Rd., P.O. Box 23, Ponchatoula, LA 70454: Free information ■ Parts for 1939 to 1974 Cadillacs. 504–386–3714.

Global Auto Parts Connection, P.O. Box 15548, Phoenix, AZ 86060: Free information ■ Parts for most Cadillacs. 602–376–5896.

Piru Cads, 402 Via Fustero Rd., Box 227, Piru, CA 93040: Free information with long SASE ■ Used parts for 1937 to 1956 Cadillacs. 805–521–1741.

PRO Antique Auto Parts, 50 King Spring Rd., Windsor Locks, CT 06096: Catalog $2 ■ New parts for 1929 to 1964 Cadillacs. 203–623–0070.

Robinson's Auto Sales, 200 New York Ave., New Castle, IN 47362: Free information ■ Parts for 1960 to 1970 models. 317–529–7603.

Lynn H. Steele Rubber Products, 1601 Hwy. 150 East, Denver, NC 28037: Catalog $1 (Specify model) ■ Reproduction rubber parts for Cadillacs and LaSalles. 800–544–8665; 704–483–9343 (in NC).

Terrill Machine, Inc., Rt. 2, Box 61, DeLeon, TX 76444: Free information with long SASE ■ Engine overhaul parts for Cadillacs, from 1936 to 1962. 817–893–2610.

Vintage Tin Auto Parts, 4550 Scotty Ln., Hutchinson, KS 67502: Free information with long SASE ■ Cadillac parts and accessories, from 1940 to 1970. 316–669–8449.

CAMARO

Auto Accessories of America, Box 427, Rt. 322, Boalsburg, PA 16827: Catalog $5 ■ Parts, accessories, interiors, and fiberglass components for the Camaro. 800–458–3475.

Auto Dynamics, 7218 NE Sandy, Portland, OR 97213: Catalog $4 ■ Performance accessories for Camaros, 1982 and later.

Auto Heaven, 103 W. Allen St., Bloomington, IN 47401: Free information ■ Parts for 1967 to 1969 models. 812–332–9401.

California Classic Chevy Parts, 13545 Sycamore Ave., San Martin, CA 95046: Free information ■ New, used, and reproduction parts for 1967 to 1969 Camaros. 408–683–2531.

Camaro Connection, 34 Cleveland Ave., Bay Shore, NY 11706: Free information with long SASE ■ N.O.S. and reproduction parts for the 1967 to 1988 Camaro, and sheet metal, interiors, electrical items, and decals. 800–835–8301.

Camaro Country, Inc., 18591 Centennial Rd., Marshall, MI 49068: Catalog $3 ■ New, used, and reproduction parts. 616–781–2906.

Chicago Camaro & Firebird Parts, 900 S. 5th Ave., Maywood, IL 60153: Free information ■ Sheet metal, interiors, carpets, and new, used, and reproduction parts for 1967 to 1969 Camaros. 708–681–2187.

Classic Camaro, 17832 Gothard St., Huntington Beach, CA 92647: Catalog $4 ■ Parts, equipment, and accessories. 800–854–1280.

Harmon's Chevrolet Restoration Parts, Hwy. 27 North, Geneva, IN 46740: Catalog $3 ■ Camaro restoration parts and accessories, from 1967 to 1980. 219–368–7221.

Luttys Chevys, RD 2, Box 61, Cheswick, PA 15024: Catalog $1 ■ New, used, and reproduction parts and accessories. Includes carpets, interiors, weatherstripping, moldings, sheet metal, and replacement panels. 412–265–2988.

Martz Classic Chevy Parts, RD 1, Box 199, Thomasville, PA 17364: Catalog $1 ■ N.O.S. and reproduction parts, from 1967 to 1969. 717–225–1655.

Musclecar Specialties, 1 Coach Lantern Dr., Hopewell, NY 12533: Free information with long SASE ■ New, N.O.S., and used parts and accessories for the 1962 to 1972 Camaro. 914–227–6837.

National Parts Depot, 3101 SW 40th Blvd., Gainesville, FL 32608: Free catalog ■ Genuine GM parts for Camaros. 904–378–2473.

Obsolete Chevrolet Parts Company, 524 Hazel Ave., P.O. Box 68, Nashville, GA 31639: Catalog $2.50 ■ Parts and reproduction accessories for the 1929 to 1972 Camaro. 912–686–5227.

The Paddock, Inc., P.O. Box 30, Knightstown, IN 46148: Catalog $1 ■

Camaro parts and accessories. 317–345–2131.

Rick's Camaros, 120 Commerce Blvd., Bogart, GA 30622: Catalog $3 ■ New, used, and reproduction parts for 1967 to 1969 Camaros. 706–546–9217.

Super Sport Restoration Parts, Inc., 7138 Maddox Rd., P.O. Box 7, Lithonia, GA 30058: Free information ■ Parts for the Camaro, Chevy II, Nova, and Chevelle. 404–482–9219.

Tom's Obsolete Chevy Parts, 14 Delta Dr., Pawtucket, RI 02860: Catalog $1 ■ Camaro parts, from 1955 to 1972. 401–723–7580.

CAPRI

Bill Alprin, 184 Rivervale Rd., Rivervale, NJ 07675: Free information ■ N.O.S. parts for the Capri. 201–666–3975.

Dobi Capri Catalog, 320 Thor Pl., Brea, CA 92621: Catalog $2 ■ Capri parts. 714–529–1977.

Racer Walsh Company, 5906 Macy, Jacksonville, FL 32211: Catalog $3 ■ Engines, suspensions, and other parts for the Capri. 800–334–0151; 904–743–8253 (in FL).

CHEVELLE

Ausley's Chevelle Parts, 300 S. Main St., Graham, NC 27253: Catalog $3 (specify year and model) ■ Parts for 1964 to 1972 Chevelles. 919–228–6701.

Chevelle Classics, 17832 Gothard St., Huntington Beach, CA 92647: Free catalog ■ Chevelle parts. 800–CHEVELLE; 714–841–5363 (in CA).

Chevelle Parts & Accessories, Inc., 17892 Gothard St., Huntington Beach, CA 92647: Free catalog ■ Reproduction and original GM parts for the Chevelle. 714–841–5363.

Chevy Craft, 3414 Quirt, Lubbock, TX 79404: Catalog $5 ■ New and used parts and accessories, for 1955 and later Chevelles. 806–747–4848.

Danchuk Manufacturing, Inc., 3201 S. Standard Ave., Santa Ana, CA 92705: Catalog $3 (refundable) ■ Parts for 1964 to 1972 Chevelles. 800–854–6911; 714–751–1957 (in CA).

Harmon's Chevrolet Restoration Parts, Hwy. 27 North, Geneva, IN 46740: Catalog

$3 ■ Chevelle restoration parts and accessories, from 1964 to 1972. 219–368–7221.

John's N.O.S. Chevelle Parts, Box 1445, Salem, NH 03079: Catalog $3 ■ Chevelle N.O.S. and reproduction parts, chrome, emblems, grilles, and rubber. 603–898–9366.

Luttys Chevys, RD 2, Box 61, Cheswick, PA 15024: Catalog $1 ■ New, used, and reproduction parts and accessories. Includes carpets, interiors, weatherstripping, moldings, sheet metal, and replacement panels. 412–265–2988.

Martz Classic Chevy Parts, RD 1, Box 199, Thomasville, PA 17364: Catalog $1 ■ Chevelle N.O.S. and reproduction parts, from 1964 to 1972. 717–225–1655.

Musclecar Specialties, 1 Coach Lantern Dr., Hopewell, NY 12533: Free information with long SASE ■ New, N.O.S., and used parts and accessories for 1962 to 1972 Chevelles. 914–227–6837.

Obsolete Chevrolet Parts Company, 524 Hazel Ave., P.O. Box 68, Nashville, GA 31639: Catalog $2.50 ■ Parts and reproduction accessories for the 1929 to 1972 Chevelle. 912–686–5227.

The Paddock, Inc., P.O. Box 30, Knightstown, IN 46148: Catalog $1 ■ Chevelle parts and accessories. 317–345–2131.

Super Sport Restoration Parts, Inc., 7138 Maddox Rd., P.O. Box 7, Lithonia, GA 30058: Free information ■ Parts for the Chevelle, Chevy II, Nova, and Camaro. 404–482–9219.

Tom's Obsolete Chevy Parts, 14 Delta Dr., Pawtucket, RI 02860: Catalog $1 ■ Chevelle parts, from 1955 to 1972. 401–723–7580.

Tri County Auto Parts, 7625 Marsh Rd., Marine City, MI 48039: Free inventory list ■ Parts for 1966 to 1967 Chevelles. 313–765–3114.

CHEVETTE

Year One, Inc., Box 2023, Tucker, GA 30085: Catalog $5 ■ New, used, and reproduction restoration parts. 404–493–6568.

CHEVROLET

Adler's Antique Autos, Inc., 562 Main St., Stephentown, NY 12168: Free information with long SASE ■ Parts for Chevrolet cars and trucks, from 1940 to 1970. 518–733–5749.

Allchevy Auto Parts, 4999 Vanden Rd., Vacaville, CA 95668: Free information ■ Parts for 1955 to 1988 Chevrolet cars and trucks. 707–437–5466.

Antique Cars-Trucks & Parts, 526 E. 2nd, Blue Springs, NE 68318: Free information with long SASE ■ Chevrolet parts, from 1925 to 1948. 402–645–3546.

Automotive Obsolete, 1023 E. 4th St., Santa Ana, CA 92701: Catalog $3 ■ Parts for Chevrolet cars and trucks, from 1914 to 1964. 714–541–5167.

B & B Used Auto Parts, Rt. 1, Box 691, Big Pine Key, FL 33043: Free information ■ Parts for the Chevrolet, from 1950 and on. 305–872–9761.

C & P Chevy Parts, Box 348, Kulpsville, PA 19443: Catalog $1 ■ Restoration supplies and new parts for 1955 to 1957 Chevrolet cars. 215–721–4300.

California Classic Chevy Parts, 13545 Sycamore Ave., San Martin, CA 95046: Free information ■ New, used, and reproduction parts for 1955 to 1957 Chevrolets. 408–683–2531.

C.A.R.S., Inc., 1964 W. 11 Mile Rd., P.O. Box 721187, Berkley, MI 48072: Catalog $4 ■ Parts and accessories for the 1955 to 1972 Bel-Air, Impala, Camaro, Nova, and Chevelle. 313–398–7100.

Chev's of the 40's, 18409 NE 28th St., Vancouver, WA 98682: Catalog $3.75 ■ Chevrolet parts and accessories, from 1937 to 1954. 206–254–2438.

Danchuk Manufacturing, Inc., 3201 S. Standard Ave., Santa Ana, CA 92705: Catalog $4 ■ Parts for 1955 to 1957 Chevrolets. 800–854–6911; 714–751–1957 (in CA).

Dick's Chevy Parts, 1821 Columbus Ave., Springfield, OH 45503: Catalog $3 (specify year) ■ Chevrolet parts, from 1928 to 1972. Includes rubber, chrome, moldings, interiors, and emblems. 513–325–7861.

Howard Dobuck Chevrolet Parts, 3841 S. Ridgeland Ave., Berwyn, IL 60402: Free information ■ New, used, and reproduction parts and accessories for 1955 to 1957 Chevrolets. 708–788–1955.

Doug's Auto Parts, Hwy. 59 North, Box 811, Marshall, MN 56258: Free information with long SASE ■ Chevrolet parts and accessories, from 1955 to 1961. 507–537–1487.

Mike Drago Chevrolet Parts, 141 E. Saint Joseph St., Easton, PA 18042: Free catalog ■ N.O.S., reproduction, and used Chevrolet parts, from 1955 to 1957. 215–252–5701.

Drake Restoration, 4504 Del Amo Blvd., Torrance, CA 90503: Catalog $1 ■ Reproduction and rubber parts, manuals, emblems, weatherstrips, and interiors, for 1955 to 1957 Chevrolets. 310–370–0080.

Edmonds Old Car Parts, 105 Union St., P.O. Box 303, McLouth, KS 66054: Free information with long SASE ■ Chevrolet parts, from 1928 to 1957. 913–796–6415.

Fiberglass & Wood Company, Rt. 3, Box 811, Nashville, GA 31639: Catalog $3 (specify year) ■ Chevrolet parts, from 1927 to 1957. 912–686–3838.

The Filling Station, 853 Main St., Lebanon, OR 97355: Catalog $5 ■ Reproduction parts for the 1929 to 1954 Chevrolet, and 1929 to 1972 trucks. 503–258–2114.

Fleetline Automotive, 153 Orchard Dr., Wallkill, NY 12589: Free information ■ Parts for 1935 to 1975 Chevrolet cars and trucks. 914–895–2381.

Lou Fusz Auto Parts Network, 10725 Manchester, St. Louis, MO 63122: Catalog $3 ■ Chevrolet and Geo parts and accessories and other General Motors products. 800–451–7783.

Harmon's Chevrolet Restoration Parts, Inc., Hwy. 27 North, Geneva, IN 46740: Catalog $3 ■ Chevrolet restoration parts and accessories, from 1965 to 1967. 219–368–7221.

Jim's Chevrolet Parts, 112567 Coloma Rd., Rancho Cordova, CA 95670: Free catalog (specify year and model) ■ Chevrolet parts for 1955 to 1972 Chevrolets. 916–635–8790.

Lakeview Vintage Distributing, 1410 E. Genesee, Skaneateles, NY 13152: Free information ■ Reproduction parts for 1928 to 1948 Chevrolets. 315–685–7414.

Lange's Classics, P.O. Box 2039, Scotia, NY 12302: Catalog $5 ■ Parts and accessories for 1955, 1956, and 1957 Chevrolet cars. 518–372–5024.

Martz Classic Chevy Parts, RD 1, Box 199, Thomasville, PA 17364: Catalog $1 ■ N.O.S. and reproduction 1955 to 1967 Chevrolet parts. 717–225–1655.

Musclecar Specialties, 1 Coach Lantern Dr., Hopewell, NY 12533: Free information with long SASE ■ New, N.O.S., and used parts and accessories for 1929 to 1961 Chevrolets. 914–227–6837.

New England Old Car Barn, US Rt. 1, Box 608, North Hampton, NH 03862: Catalog $3 (refundable) ■ Chevrolet parts, books, and memorabilia. 603–964–7100.

Norm's Antique Auto Supply, 1921 Hickory Grove Rd., Davenport, IA 52804: Free information with long SASE ■ Parts and accessories for 1923 to 1953 Chevrolets. 319–322–8388.

North Yale Auto Parts, Rt. 1, Box 707, Sperry, OK 74073: Free information with long SASE ■ Chevrolet parts, from the 1960s to 1980s. 918–288–7218.

Obsolete Chevrolet Parts Company, 524 Hazel Ave., P.O. Box 68, Nashville, GA 31639: Catalog $2.50 ■ Parts and reproduction accessories for 1929 to 1972 Chevrolet cars. 912–686–5227.

Ol' 55 Chevy Parts, 4154–A Skyron Dr., Doylestown, PA 18901: Catalog $4 ■ Chevrolet parts and accessories, from 1955, 1956, and 1957. 215–348–5568.

Out of the Past Parts, 3720 SW 23rd St., Gainesville, FL 32601: Free information with long SASE ■ Chevrolet parts and accessories, 1935 and later. 904–377–4079.

Petro's Classic Automotive, RD 3, Box 297B, Catawissa, PA 17820: Free information ■ New and used 1955, 1956, and 1957 Chevrolet parts. 717–799–5205.

PRO Antique Auto Parts, 50 King Spring Rd., Windsor Locks, CT 06096: Catalog $2 ■ New parts for 1923 to 1964 Chevrolets. 203–623–0070.

R & B Classics, 10014 Old Lincoln Trail, Fairview Heights, IL 62208: Free catalog ■ Chevrolet parts, from 1955 to 1957. 618–398–3477.

Schuster Auto Wrecking, 406 Benton, Box 31, Wathena, KS 66090: Free information with long SASE ■ Chevrolet parts, from 1938 to 1982. 913–989–4719.

Specialized Auto Parts, 7130 Capitol, Houston, TX 77011: Catalog $4 ■ Chevrolet parts for 1916 to 1948 models. 613–928–3707.

Super Sport Restoration Parts, Inc., 7138 Maddox Rd., P.O. Box 7, Lithonia, GA 30058: Free information ■ Parts for the Chevy II, Nova, Chevelle, and Camaro. 404–482–9219.

Terrill Machine, Inc., Rt. 2, Box 61, De-Leon, TX 76444: Free information with long SASE ■ Engine overhaul parts for Chevrolets, from 1929 to 1951. 817–893–2610.

Volunteer State Chevy Parts, Hwy. 41 South, Greenbrier, TN 37073: Catalog $3 ■ Obsolete Chevrolet parts and accessories. 615–643–4583.

Winnicks Auto Sales & Parts, Rt. 61, P.O. Box 476, Shamokin, PA 17872: Free information with long SASE ■ Parts for American and imported cars and trucks, and Ford and Chevrolet engines. 717–648–6857.

CHRYSLER

B & B Used Auto Parts, Rt. 1, Box 691, Big Pine Key, FL 33043: Free information ■ Parts for Chrysler cars, 1950 and up. 305–872–9761.

Andy Bernbaum Auto Parts, 315 Franklin St., Newton, MA 02158: Catalog $4 ■ Chrysler parts and accessories. 617–244–1118.

Big Ben's Used Cars & Salvage, Hwy. 79 North, Fordyce, AR 71742: Free information with long SASE ■ Parts and accessories for most cars, from the 1960s to 1970s. 501–352–7423.

Find-A-Part, Box 358, Ridgeland, MS 39158: Free information with long SASE ■ Chrysler N.O.S. parts, automotive literature, signs, and calendars. 601–856–7214.

Lou Fusz Auto Parts Network, 10725 Manchester, St. Louis, MO 63122: Catalog $3 ■ Chrysler parts and accessories. 800–325–9584.

Ken's Auto Wrecking, 5051 Coppersage St., Las Vegas, NV 89115: Free information ■ Chrysler parts, 1956 to 1980. 702–643–1771.

Lasiter's Cars & Parts, Rt. 2, Box 39, Wilmar, AR 71675: Free information ■ Parts for 1949 to 1976 models. 501–469–5453.

Mike's Auto Parts, Box 358, Ridgeland, MS 39157: Free information with long SASE ■ Chrysler parts and accessories. 601–856–7214.

Mitchell Motor Parts, Inc., 2467 Jackson Pike, Columbia, OH 43223: Free information with long SASE ■ Chrysler parts and accessories, from 1928 to the present. 614–875–4919.

Norm's Antique Auto Supply, 1921 Hickory Grove Rd., Davenport, IA 52804: Free information with long SASE ■ Chrysler parts and accessories, from 1929 to 1955. 319–322–8388.

North Yale Auto Parts, Inc., Rt. 1, Box 707, Sperry, OK 74073: Free information with long SASE ■ Parts and accessories for Chrysler cars, 1977 and later. 918–288–7218.

PRO Antique Auto Parts, 50 King Spring Rd., Windsor Locks, CT 06096: Catalog $2 ■ New parts for 1929 to 1964 Chrysler cars. 203–623–0070.

Roberts Motor Parts, 17 Prospect St., West Newbury, MA 01985: Catalog $4 ■ Parts for Chrysler cars. 508–363–5407.

Terrill Machine, Inc., Rt. 2, Box 61, De-Leon, TX 76444: Free information with long SASE ■ Engine overhaul parts for Chryslers, from 1937 to 1954. 817–893–2610.

Vintage Tin Auto Parts, 4550 Scotty Ln., Hutchinson, KS 67502: Free information with long SASE ■ Chrysler parts and accessories, from 1940 to 1970. 316–669–8449.

CITROEN

B & B Used Auto Parts, Rt. 1, Box 691, Big Pine Key, FL 33043: Free information with long SASE ■ Parts for Citroens, 1968 and later. 305–872–9761.

COBRA

Cobra Restorers, 3099 Carter, Kenesaw, GA 30144: Catalog $3 ■ Parts for restoring Cobra cars. 404–427–0020.

Contemporary Classic Motor Car Company, Inc., 115 Hoyt Ave., Mamaroneck, NY 10543: Catalog $4 ■ Cobra parts. 914–381–5678.

COMET

Bill Alprin, 184 Rivervale Rd., Rivervale, NJ 07675: Free information ■ N.O.S. parts for the Comet. 201–666–3975.

City Motor Company, P.O. Box 526, Clarkston, WA 99403: Catalog $2 ■ New original and reproduction parts for the 1964 to 1967 Comet. 509–758–6262.

Bob Cook Classic Auto Parts, P.O. Box 190, Hazel, KY 42049: Catalog $6 (specify year and model) ■ Reproduction parts for the 1956 to 1972 Comet. 502–492–8166.

FTC Enterprises, 213 E. 4th St., Unit 2, Loveland, CO 80537: Free parts list (specify year) with long SASE ■ Reproduction, N.O.S., and used parts for 1962 to 1971 Comets. 303–663–6862.

King & Wesley Obsolete Parts, Inc., P.O. Box A, Courthouse Square, Liberty, KY 42539: Free information ■ Comet N.O.S. and reproduction parts. Includes sheet metal, moldings, hubcaps, grilles, and suspension parts. 606–787–5031.

Northwest Classic Falcons, 1964 NW Pettygrove, Portland, OR 97209: Parts list $2 ■ Used, new, reproduction, and N.O.S. Comet parts, from 1960 to 1970. 503–241–9454.

CORD

J.K. Howell, 465 N. Grace St., Lombard, IL 60148: Catalog $1 ■ Cord parts. 708–495–1949.

CORVAIR

Clark's Corvair Parts, Inc., Rt. 2, Shelburne Falls, MA 01370: Catalog $4 ■ Corvair parts. 510–625–9776.

Robinson's Auto Sales, 200 New York Ave., New Castle, IN 47362: Free information ■ Parts for 1960 to 1970 models. 317–529–7603.

CORVETTE

Auto Accessories of America, Rt. 322, Box 427, Boalsburg, PA 16827: Catalog $5 ■ Corvette parts, accessories, interiors, and fiberglass components. 800–458–3475.

Blue Ribbon Products, Ltd., 4965 Old House Trail NE, Atlanta, GA 30342: Free catalog ■ Corvette parts and accessories, from 1956 to 1967. 404–843–8414.

Chevy Craft, 3414 Quirt, Lubbock, TX 79404: Catalog $5 ■ New and used parts and accessories for the Corvette, 1955 and later. 806–747–4848.

Chicago Corvette Supply, 7322 S. Archer Ave., Justice, IL 60458: Free information with long SASE ■ New and reproduction parts. 708–839–5671.

Corvette Central, 16 Sawyer Rd., Sawyer, MI 49125: Free information with long SASE ■ New, used, and reproduction parts for 1953 to 1982 Corvettes. 616–426–3342.

Corvette Rubber Company, 10640 W. Cadillac Rd., Cadillac, MI 49601: Free catalog (specify year) ■ Rubber parts for Corvettes. 616–779–2888.

Corvette Stop, Rural Rt. 07, El Dorado Hills, CA 95630: Free information ■ Hard-to-find new and used 1953 to 1972 obsolete and N.O.S. Corvette parts. 916–939–4400.

Howard's Corvettes, RR 3, Box 162, Sioux Falls, SD 57106: Free inventory list ■ Parts for 1968 to 1986 Corvettes. 605–743–5233.

J.B.'s Corvette Supplies, 1992 White Plains Rd., Bronx, NY 10462: Catalog $3 ■ Corvette parts and accessories. 212–931–2599.

Legendary Corvette, Inc., 903 Easton Rd., Warrington, PA 18976: Free information ■ Corvette parts and stock and custom body panels. 800–346–2426; 215–343–2424 (in PA).

Mid America Corvette Supplies, 1519 E. 1st Ave., Milan, IL 61264: Free information with long SASE ■ Corvette parts, supplies, and accessories. 309–787–5119.

Mid America Designs, Inc., P.O. Box 1368, Effingham, IL 62401: Catalog $3 (refundable) ■ Corvette replacement and performance parts and accessories. 217–347–5591.

Stoudt Auto Sales, Warren & Carbon, Reading, PA 19601: Free catalog ■ Corvette parts, from 1953 to 1987. 800–523–8485.

Vette Products of Michigan, 2330 W. Clarkston, Lake Orion, MI 48035: Free catalog (specify year and model) ■ Corvette parts and accessories. 313–693–1907.

Zip Products, 1250 Commercial Centre, Mechanicsville, VA 23111: Catalog $2 (refundable) ■ Parts for restoring and maintaining Corvettes. 804–746–2290.

COUGAR

Bill Alprin, 184 Rivervale Rd., Rivervale, NJ 07675: Free information ■ N.O.S. parts for the Cougar. 201–666–3975.

Auto Krafters, Inc., P.O. Box 6, Broadway, VA 22815: Catalog $1 (specify year and model) ■ New, used, and reproduction parts and accessories. 703–896–5910.

City Motor Company, P.O. Box 526, Clarkston, WA 99403: Catalog $2 ■ New original and reproduction parts for the 1967 to 1973 Cougar. 509–758–6262.

Colorado Mustang Specialists, Inc., 19900 E. Colfax, Aurora, CO 80011: Free inventory list ■ Parts for 1967 to 1973 Cougars. 303–343–7024.

Bob Cook Classic Auto Parts, P.O. Box 190, Hazel, KY 42049: Catalog $6 (specify year and model) ■ Reproduction parts for 1965 to 1973 Cougars. 502–492–8166.

Ken's Falcon Parts, 1799 E. Alosta, Glendora, CA 91740: Catalog $2 (specify model) ■ New, used, and reproduction parts for the 1967 to 1973 Cougar, 1960 to 1970 Falcon, and 1965 to 1973 Mustang. 818–963–5905.

King & Wesley Obsolete Parts, Inc., P.O. Box A, Courthouse Square, Liberty, KY 42539: Free information ■ N.O.S. and reproduction parts. Includes sheet metal, moldings, hubcaps, grilles, and suspension parts. 606–787–5031.

CUTLASS

Mid-Atlantic Performance, P.O. Box 333, Simpsonville, MD 21150: Catalog $1 ■ Cutlass 4–4–2 parts. 914–735–7203.

Year One, Inc., Box 2023, Tucker, GA 30085: Catalog $5 ■ New, used, and reproduction Cutlass restoration parts. 404–493–6568.

DATSUN

Auto Accessories of America, Rt. 322, Box 427, Boalsburg, PA 16827: Catalog $5 ■ Parts, accessories, interiors, and fiberglass components. 800–458–3475.

Autoshow, 2326 E. 44th St., Indianapolis, IN 46205: Catalog $3 (refundable) ■ Parts and accessories for the Datsun Z and other models. 800–428–2200; 317–545–6223 (in IN).

Dobi Datsun Catalog, 320 Thor Pl., Brea, CA 92621: Catalog $2 ■ Replacement parts for the Datsun Z, 200SX, and 510. 714–529–1977.

Lou Fusz Auto Parts Network, 10725 Manchester, St. Louis, MO 63122: Catalog $3 ■ Datsun and other Nissan parts and accessories. 800–325–1587.

HKS USA, Inc., 20312 Gramercy Pl., Torrance, CA 90501: Catalog $8 (specify year and model) ■ Performance accessories for the Datsun. 310–328–8100.

Motorsport Auto, 1139 W. Collins Ave., Orange, CA 92667: Catalog $4 ■ Parts for the Datsun Z. 800–633–6331; 714–639–2620 (in CA).

Perfect Plastics Industries, Inc., 14th St., New Kensington, PA 15068: Free information ■ Body parts for Datsun Z. 800–245–6520.

Bob Sharp Racing/Accessories, Danbury Rd., Rt. 7, Wilton, CT 06897: Catalog $1 ■ Parts, accessories, styling, and racing parts for the Datsun. 203–544–8386.

DELOREAN

Delorean Service & Parts, 10728 N. 96th Ave., Peoria, AZ 85345: Free information with long SASE ■ Delorean parts and service. 602–979–2673.

J.P. Enterprises, 95 Seawanhaka Ave., Lake Grove, NY 11755: Free information with long SASE ■ DeLorean parts. 516–467–4438.

DE SOTO

Andy Bernbaum Auto Parts, 315 Franklin St., Newton, MA 02158: Catalog $4 ■ Parts and accessories for the De Soto. 617–244–1118.

Mike's Auto Parts, Box 358, Ridgeland, MS 39157: Free information with long SASE ■ De Soto parts and accessories. 601–856–7214.

PRO Antique Auto Parts, 50 King Spring Rd., Windsor Locks, CT 06096: Catalog $2 ■ New parts for 1929 to 1964 De Sotos. 203–623–0070.

Roberts Motor Parts, 17 Prospect St., West Newbury, MA 01985: Catalog $4 ■ Parts and accessories for De Sotos. 508–363–5407.

Terrill Machine, Inc., Rt. 2, Box 61, De-Leon, TX 76444: Free information with long SASE ■ Engine overhaul parts for De Sotos, from 1937 to 1954. 817–893–2610.

Vintage Tin Auto Parts, 4550 Scotty Ln., Hutchinson, KS 67502: Free information with long SASE ■ De Soto parts and accessories. 316–669–8449.

DODGE

Andy Bernbaum Auto Parts, 315 Franklin St., Newton, MA 02158: Catalog $4 ■ Parts and accessories for Dodge cars. 617–244–1118.

Antique Cars-Trucks & Parts, 526 E. 2nd, Blue Springs, NE 68318: Free information with long SASE ■ Dodge parts, from 1920 to 1926. 402–645–3546.

Lou Fusz Auto Parts Network, 10725 Manchester, St. Louis, MO 63122: Catalog $3 ■ Dodge parts and accessories and other Chrysler products. 800–325–9584.

Mike's Auto Parts, Box 358, Ridgeland, MS 39157: Free information with long SASE ■ Dodge parts and accessories. 601–856–7214.

Out of the Past Parts, 3720 SW 23rd St., Gainesville, FL 32601: Free information with long SASE ■ Dodge parts and accessories, 1935 and later. 904–377–4079.

PRO Antique Auto Parts, 50 King Spring Rd., Windsor Locks, CT 06096: Catalog $2 ■ New parts for 1929 to 1964 Dodge cars. 203–623–0070.

Roberts Motor Parts, 17 Prospect St., West Newbury, MA 01985: Catalog $4 ■ Dodge parts and accessories. 508–363–5407.

Terrill Machine, Inc., Rt. 2, Box 61, De-Leon, TX 76444: Free information with long SASE ■ Engine overhaul parts for Dodges, from 1937 to 1954. 817–893–2610.

Vintage Tin Auto Parts, 4550 Scotty Ln., Hutchinson, KS 67502: Free information with long SASE ■ Dodge parts and accessories, from 1940 to 1970. 316–669–8449.

Year One, Inc., Box 2023, Tucker, GA 30085: Catalog $5 ■ New, used, and reproduction Dodge restoration parts. 404–493–6568.

EAGLE

Lou Fusz Auto Parts Network, 10725 Manchester, St. Louis, MO 63122: Catalog $3 ■ Eagle parts and accessories. 800–325–9584.

EDSEL

Beckers Auto Salvage, Hwy. 30 West, Atkins, IA 52206: Free information ■ Parts for Edsel cars. 319–446–7141.

Bob Cook Classic Auto Parts, P.O. Box 190, Hazel, KY 42049: Catalog $6 (specify year and model) ■ Reproduction parts for 1958 to 1960 Edsels. 502–492–8166.

LeMance Autoworks, 914 Mill Rd., P.O. Box 449, Wartburg, TN 37887: Free information ■ Parts for 1958 to 1959 Edsels. 615–346–3194.

EL CAMINO

Ausley's Chevelle Parts, 300 S. Main St., Graham, NC 27253: Catalog $3 (specify year and model) ■ El Camino parts for 1964 to 1972 models. 919–228–6701.

Chevelle Classics, 17892 Gothard St., Huntington Beach, CA 92647: Free catalog ■ El Camino parts. 800–CHEVELLE; 714–841–5363 (in CA).

Chevelle Parts & Accessories, Inc., 17892 Gothard St., Huntington Beach, CA 92647: Free catalog ■ Reproduction and original GM parts for the El Camino. 714–841–5363.

Danchuk Manufacturing, Inc., 3201 S. Standard Ave., Santa Ana, CA 92705: Catalog $3 (refundable) ■ Parts for the 1964 to 1972 El Camino. 800–854–6911; 714–751–1957 (in CA).

John's N.O.S. Chevelle Parts, Box 1445, Salem, NH 03079: Catalog $3 ■ El Camino N.O.S. and reproduction parts, chrome, emblems, grilles, and rubber. 603–898–9366.

ENGLISH FORD

Dave Bean Engineering, Inc., 636 E. Saint Charles St., San Andreas, CA 95249: Catalog $6 ■ Parts and accessories for the English Ford. 209–754–5802.

ESCORT

Racer Walsh Company, 5906 Macy, Jacksonville, FL 32211: Catalog $3 ■ Engines,

suspensions, and other parts for Escorts. 800–334–0151; 904–743–8253 (in FL).

FAIRLANE

Bill Alprin, 184 Rivervale Rd., Rivervale, NJ 07675: Free information ■ N.O.S. parts for the Fairlane. 201–666–3975.

Auto Krafters, Inc., P.O. Box 6, Broadway, VA 22815: Catalog $1 (specify year and model) ■ New, used, and reproduction parts and accessories for 1962 to 1971 Fairlanes. 703–896–5910.

City Motor Company, P.O. Box 526, Clarkston, WA 99403: Catalog $2 ■ New original and reproduction parts for the 1962 to 1971 Fairlane. 509–758–6262.

Bob Cook Classic Auto Parts, P.O. Box 190, Hazel, KY 42049: Catalog $6 (specify year and model) ■ Reproduction parts for 1960 to 1972 Fairlanes. 502–492–8166.

Ford Parts Store, P.O. Box 226, Bryan, OH 43506: Catalog $2 ■ Fairlane parts and accessories. 419–636–2475.

FTC Enterprises, 213 E. 4th St., Unit 2, Loveland, CO 80537: Free parts list with long SASE (specify year) ■ Reproduction, N.O.S., and used parts for 1962 to 1971 Fairlanes. 303–663–6862.

Joblot Automotive, Inc., 98–11 211th St., Queens Village, NY 11429: Free catalog ■ Parts for the Fairlane. 212–468–8585.

King & Wesley Obsolete Parts, Inc., P.O. Box A, Courthouse Square, Liberty, KY 42539: Free information ■ N.O.S. and reproduction parts. Includes sheet metal, moldings, hubcaps, grilles, and suspension parts. 606–787–5031.

Obsolete Ford Parts Company, P.O. Box 787, Nashville, GA 31639: Catalog $2 ■ N.O.S. and reproduction parts for the 1949 to 1964 Fairlane. 912–686–2470.

Obsolete Ford Parts, Inc., 6601 S. Shields, Oklahoma City, OK 73149: Catalog $3 (specify year and model) ■ Parts for 1960 to 1972 Fairlanes. 405–631–3933.

FALCON

Bill Alprin, 184 Rivervale Rd., Rivervale, NJ 07675: Free information ■ N.O.S. parts for the Falcon. 201–666–3975.

Auto Krafters, Inc., P.O. Box 6, Broadway, VA 22815: Catalog $1 (specify year and model) ■ New, used, and reproduction parts and accessories for 1960 to 1965 Falcons. 703–896–5910.

Dennis Carpenter Ford Reproductions, P.O. Box 26398, Charlotte, NC 28221: Catalog $2 ■ Rubber parts for 1960 to 1965 Falcons. 704–786–8139.

City Motor Company, P.O. Box 526, Clarkston, WA 99403: Catalog $2 ■ New original and reproduction parts for the 1960 to 1966 Falcon. 509–758–6262.

Bob Cook Classic Auto Parts, P.O. Box 190, Hazel, KY 42049: Catalog $6 (specify year and model) ■ Reproduction parts for 1960 to 1972 Falcons. 502–492–8166.

Joblot Automotive, Inc., 98–11 211th St., Queens Village, NY 11429: Free catalog ■ Falcon parts. 212–468–8585.

Ken's Falcon Parts, 1799 E. Alosta, Glendora, CA 91740: Catalog $2 (specify model) ■ New, used, and reproduction parts for 1960 to 1970 Falcon, 1967 to 1973 Cougar, and 1965 to 1973 Mustang. 818–963–5905.

King & Wesley Obsolete Parts, Inc., P.O. Box A, Courthouse Square, Liberty, KY 42539: Free information ■ N.O.S. and reproduction parts. Includes sheet metal, moldings, hubcaps, grilles, and suspension parts. 606–787–5031.

Northwest Classic Falcons, 1964 NW Pettygrove, Portland, OR 97209: Parts list $2 ■ Hard-to-find new, used, and reproduction 1960 to 1970 Falcon parts. 503–241–9454.

Obsolete Ford Parts Company, P.O. Box 787, Nashville, GA 31639: Catalog $2 ■ N.O.S. and reproduction parts for 1960 to 1970 Falcons. 912–686–2470.

Obsolete Ford Parts, Inc., 6601 S. Shields, Oklahoma City, OK 73149: Catalog $3 (specify year and model) ■ Parts for 1960 to 1972 Falcons. 405–631–3933.

FERRARI

Alfa Ricambi, 6644 San Fernando Rd., Glendale, CA 91201: Free information ■ Parts for the Ferrari. 818–956–7933.

International Auto Parts, Inc., Rt. 29 North, P.O. Box 9036, Charlottesville, VA 22906: Catalog $2 (refundable) ■ Ferrari parts and accessories. 804–973–0555.

J.P. Enterprises, 95 Seawanhaka Ave., Lake Grove, NY 11755: Free brochure ■ Ferrari parts. 516–467–4438.

FIAT

Asian Italian Auto Parts, 3736 Buford Hwy., Duluth, GA 30136: Free information ■ New and used Fiat parts and accessories. 404–476–2279.

Bayless, Inc., 1111 Via Bayless, Marietta, GA 30060: Catalog $4 ■ High performance accessories and replacement parts. 404–928–1446.

Celiberti Motors, 615 Oak St., Santa Rosa, CA 95404: Free information ■ Fiat parts and accessories. 800–USA–FIAT.

International Auto Parts, Inc., Rt. 29 North, P.O. Box 9036, Charlottesville, VA 22906: Catalog $2 (refundable) ■ Replacement and restoration parts and performance accessories. 804–973–0555.

Perfect Plastics Industries, Inc., 14th St., New Kensington, PA 15068: Free information ■ Body parts for the FIAT. 800–245–6520.

FIREBIRD

Ames Performance Engineering, Marlborough, NH 03455: Catalog $2 ■ Firebird parts and accessories. 603–876–4514.

Auto Accessories of America, Rt. 322, Box 427, Boalsburg, PA 16827: Catalog $5 ■ Firebird parts, accessories, interiors, and fiberglass components. 800–458–3475.

Auto Heaven, 103 W. Allen St., Bloomington, IN 47401: Free information ■ Parts for 1967 to 1969 Firebirds. 812–332–9401.

Chicago Camaro & Firebird Parts, 900 S. 5th Ave., Maywood, IL 60153: Free information ■ New, used, and reproduction parts, from 1967 to 1969, and sheet metal, interiors, other options, and carpets. 708–681–2187.

Firebird/Trans Am America, Rt. 322, Box 427, Boalsburg, PA 16827: Free information with long SASE ■ Parts for 1967 to 1987 Firebirds. 800–458–3475.

The Paddock, Inc., P.O. Box 30, Knightstown, IN 46148: Catalog $1 ■ Parts and accessories. 317–345–2131.

Year One, Inc., Box 2023, Tucker, GA 30085: Catalog $5 ■ New, used, and reproduction Firebird restoration parts. 404–493–6568.

FORD

Bill Alprin, 184 Rivervale Rd., Rivervale, NJ 07675: Catalog $5 (specify year and model) ■ Trim, sheet metal, mechanical, steering, and transmission parts for 1932 to 1979 Fords. 201–666–3975.

B & B Used Auto Parts, Rt. 1, Box 691, Big Pine Key, FL 33043: Free information ■ Ford parts, from 1950 and later. 305–872–9761.

C & G Early Ford Parts, 165 Balboa St., San Marcos, CA 92069: Catalog $6 ■ Reproduction parts for 1932 to 1956 Ford cars and trucks. 619–744–0470.

Dennis Carpenter Ford Reproductions, P.O. Box 26398, Charlotte, NC 28221: Catalog $2 ■ Rubber parts for 1932 to 1964 Fords. 704–786–8139.

Concours Parts & Accessories, 3563 Numancia St., P.O. Box 1210, Santa Ynez, CA 93460: Catalog $4 ■ Ford parts, from 1949 to 1966. 805–688–7795.

Bob Cook Classic Auto Parts, P.O. Box 190, Hazel, KY 42049: Catalog $6 ■ New, obsolete, and reproduction parts for 1960 to 1972 Fords. Other items include carpet and sheet metal. 502–492–8166.

Doug's Auto Parts, Hwy. 59 North, Box 811, Marshall, MN 56258: Free information with long SASE ■ Ford parts and accessories, from 1932 to 1948. 507–537–1487.

Early Ford Parts, 2948 Summer Ave., Memphis, TN 38112: Catalog $4 ■ New parts for 1928 to 1969 Fords. 901–323–2179.

Find-A-Part, Box 358, Ridgeland, MS 39158: Free information with long SASE ■ Ford N.O.S. parts, automotive literature, signs, and collectible calendars. 601–856–7214.

Ford Parts Store, P.O. Box 226, Bryan, OH 43506: Catalog $2 ■ Ford parts and accessories. 419–636–2475.

Lou Fusz Auto Parts Network, 10725 Manchester, St. Louis, MO 63122: Catalog $3 ■ Ford parts and accessories. 800–533–2175.

Garton's Auto Ford Parts & Accessories, 5th & Vine, Millville, NJ 08332: Free information with long SASE (specify make and model of car) ■ Genuine 1932 to 1960 Ford parts. Includes fenders, grilles, trim, ornaments, and mechanical and chassis parts. 609–825–3618.

King & Wesley Obsolete Parts, Inc., P.O. Box A, Courthouse Square, Liberty, KY 42539: Free information ■ N.O.S. and reproduction parts. Includes sheet metal, moldings, hubcaps, grilles, and suspension parts. 606–787–5031.

Lakeview Vintage Distributing, 1410 E. Genesee, Skaneateles, NY 13152: Free information ■ Reproduction parts for 1928 to 1948 Ford cars. 315–685–7414.

Lasiter's Cars & Parts, Rt. 2, Box 39, Wilmar, AR 71675: Free information ■ Parts for 1949 to 1979 Fords, including trucks. 501–469–5453.

McDonald Ford Parts Company, RR 3, Box 94, Rockport, IN 47635: Catalog $5 (specify year and model) ■ Parts for 1932 to 1982 Fords. 812–359–4965.

Medicine Bow Motors, Inc., 5120 Hwy. 93 South, Missoula, MT 59801: Free information ■ Parts for 1928 to 1948 Fords. 406–251–2244.

New England Old Car Barn, US Rt. 1, Box 608, North Hampton, NH 03862: Catalog $3 (refundable) ■ Ford V–8 parts, books, and memorabilia. 603–964–7100.

Norm's Antique Auto Supply, 1921 Hickory Grove Rd., Davenport, IA 52804: Free information with long SASE ■ Ford parts and accessories, from 1917 to 1969. 319–322–8388.

North Yale Auto Parts, Inc., Rt. 1, Box 707, Sperry, OK 74073: Free information with long SASE ■ Parts and accessories for 1977 and later Fords. 918–288–7218.

Obsolete Ford Parts Company, P.O. Box 787, Nashville, GA 31639: Catalog $2 ■ N.O.S. and reproduction parts for 1949 to 1964 Fords. 912–686–2470.

Obsolete Ford Parts, Inc., 6601 S. Shields, Oklahoma City, OK 73149: Catalog $3 (specify year and model) ■ Ford parts, from 1928 to 1932. 405–631–3933.

Out of the Past Parts, 3720 SW 23rd St., Gainesville, FL 32601: Free information

with long SASE ■ Ford parts and accessories, 1935 and later. 904–377–4079.

Papke Enterprises, 17202 Gothard St., Huntington Beach, CA 92647: Free information with long SASE ■ Parts and accessories for 1949 to 1951 Fords. Some 1952 to 1953 parts available. 714–843–6969.

PRO Antique Auto Parts, 50 King Spring Rd., Windsor Locks, CT 06096: Catalog $2 ■ New parts for 1928 to 1964 Fords. 203–623–0070.

Schuster Auto Wrecking, 406 Benton, Box 31, Wathena, KS 66090: Free information with long SASE ■ Ford parts, from 1938 to 1982. 913–989–4719.

Specialized Auto Parts, 7130 Capitol, Houston, TX 77011: Catalog $4 ■ Parts for 1909 to 1948 Fords. 713–928–3707.

T-Bird Nest, P.O. Box 1012, Grapevine, TX 76051: Free information ■ New parts for 1928 to 1959 Fords. 817–481–1776.

Tee-Bird Products, Inc., Exton, PA 19341: Parts list $2 ■ Ford passenger car parts, from 1955 and 1956. 215–363–1725.

Valley Ford Parts, 11610 Van Owen St., North Hollywood, CA 91605: Free information ■ New and used parts for 1928 to 1970 Fords. 818–982–5303.

Vintage Tin Auto Parts, 4550 Scotty Ln., Hutchinson, KS 67502: Free information with long SASE ■ Ford parts and accessories, 1940 to 1970. 316–669–8449.

Winnicks Auto Sales & Parts, Rt. 61, P.O. Box 476, Shamokin, PA 17872: Free information with long SASE ■ Ford and Chevrolet engines, and parts for American and imported cars and trucks. 717–648–6857.

FRAZER

Wayne's Auto Salvage, RR 3, Box 41, Winner, SD 57580: Free information ■ Frazer parts. 605–842–2054.

GALAXIE

Bill Alprin, 184 Rivervale Rd., Rivervale, NJ 07675: Free information ■ N.O.S. parts for the Galaxie. 201–666–3975.

City Motor Company, P.O. Box 526, Clarkston, WA 99403: Catalog $2 ■ New original and reproduction parts for the 1960 to 1966 Galaxie. 509–758–6262.

Bob Cook Classic Auto Parts, P.O. Box 190, Hazel, KY 42049: Catalog $6 (specify year and model) ■ Reproduction parts for 1960 to 1972 Galaxies. 502–492–8166.

GRAHAM

Graham Factory Service, 1919 S. Wayne, Auburn, IN 46706: Free catalog ■ Original engines, chassis, body parts, and instruments. 219–925–2210.

GRANADA

Bill Alprin, 184 Rivervale Rd., Rivervale, NJ 07675: Free information ■ N.O.S. parts for the Granada. 201–666–3975.

GTO

Ames Performance Engineering, Marlborough, NH 03455: Catalog $2 ■ GTO parts and accessories. 603–876–4514.

The Paddock, Inc., P.O. Box 30, Knightstown, IN 46148: Catalog $1 ■ GTO parts and accessories. 317–345–2131.

Year One, Inc., Box 2023, Tucker, GA 30085: Catalog $5 ■ New, used, and reproduction restoration parts. 404–493–6568.

HONDA

A & H Motorsport, 472 Blair Mill Rd., Hatboro, PA 19040: Free catalog ■ Honda parts and accessories. 215–957–6144.

A-T Engineering, 2 Candlewood Rd., New Milford, CT 06776: Catalog $4 ■ Honda parts and accessories. 203–355–1579.

Dobi Honda Catalog, 320 Thor Pl., Brea, CA 92621: Catalog $2 ■ Honda parts and accessories. 714–529–1977.

HKS USA, Inc., 20312 Gramercy Pl., Torrance, CA 90501: Catalog $8 (specify year and model) ■ Performance parts and accessories for the Honda. 310–328–8100.

Ide Honda, 875 Panoma, Rochester, NY 14625: Free information ■ Factory parts and accessories. 800–362–9012.

Jackson Racing, 16291 Gothard St., Huntington Beach, CA 92647: Catalog $5 ■ High performance and styling accessories for the Honda. 714–841–3001.

MSO Parts, 1543 Easton Rd., Roslyn, PA 19001: Free catalog ■ Genuine factory parts for the Honda. 800–628–0817; 215–657–8423 (in PA).

Plaza Honda, 2722 Nostrand Ave., Brooklyn, NY 11210: Free catalog ■ Honda parts and accessories. 718–253–6939.

Shankle Engineering, 9135 Alabama Ave., Chatsworth, CA 91311: Free brochure (specify car, model, and year) ■ Engine and suspension parts and accessories. 818–709–6155.

HUDSON

American Motor Haven, 1107 Campbell Ave., San Jose, CA 95126: Free information ■ Obsolete and hard-to-find Hudson parts. 408–246–0957.

Twin H Ranch, 16593 Arrow Blvd., Fontana, CA 92335: Free information with long SASE ■ New, used, and reproduction Hudson parts. 714–823–9168.

Vintage Tin Auto Parts, 4550 Scotty Ln., Hutchinson, KS 67502: Free information with long SASE ■ Hudson parts and accessories. 316–669–8449.

Wayne's Auto Salvage, RR 3, Box 41, Winner, SD 57580: Free information ■ Hudson parts. 605–842–2054.

IMPALA

Chevy Craft, 3414 Quirt, Lubbock, TX 79404: Catalog $5 ■ New and used parts and accessories for the Impala, 1955 and later. 806–747–4848.

Musclecar Specialties, 1 Coach Lantern Dr., Hopewell, NY 12533: Free information with long SASE ■ New, N.O.S., and used parts and accessories for the 1962 to 1972 Impala. 914–227–6837.

Tom's Obsolete Chevy Parts, 14 Delta Dr., Pawtucket, RI 02860: Catalog $1 ■ Impala parts, from 1955 to 1972. 401–723–7580.

ISUZU

Lou Fusz Auto Parts Network, 10725 Manchester, St. Louis, MO 63122: Catalog $3 ■ Isuzu parts and accessories. 800–451–1471.

JAGUAR

G.W. Bartlett Company, 1912 Granville Ave., P.O. Box 1673, Muncie, IN 47308: Free catalog ■ Interior restoration parts for

Jaguars. 800–338–8034; 317–289–1586 (in IN).

Bassett's Jaguar, Inc., P.O. Box 245, Wyoming, RI 02898: Free information with long SASE ■ Jaguar parts and supplies. 401–539–7218.

Bluff City British Cars, 1810 Getwell, Memphis, TN 38111: Free information ■ Parts and accessories for Jaguars. 800–621–0227; 901–743–4422 (in TN).

British Auto/USA, 92 Londonberry Tpke., Manchester, NH 03104: Catalog $3.50 ■ Jaguar upholstery parts and accessories, and hard-to-find chrome, electrical, mechanical, and brake system parts. 603–622–1050.

British Motorsports, Inc., 1143 Dell Ave., Campbell, CA 95008: Free information with long SASE ■ New, used, and rebuilt Jaguar parts. 408–370–7174.

British Parts Northwest, 4105 SE Lafayette Hwy., Dayton, OR 97114: Catalog $2.50 ■ Jaguar parts and accessories. 503–864–2001.

British Restoration Parts, 1808 Oak, Kansas City, MO 64108: Catalog $3 ■ Restoration parts and accessories for the Jaguar, Austin Healey, Sunbeam, MG, and Triumph. 800–821–3767; 800–892–3250 (in MO).

Classic Automobiles, 1974 Charles St., Costa Mesa, CA 92627: Catalog $5 ■ Jaguar parts, maintenance aids, books, and owner's manuals. 714–646–6293.

Engel Imports, Inc., 5850 Stadium Dr., Kalamazoo, MI 49009: Free information with long SASE ■ Parts for all models, 1953 to present. Includes many discontinued, obsolete, and "dealer only" items. 800–253–4080; 800–452–4520 (in MI).

Exotic Car Parts, 923 N. Central Ave., Upland, CA 91786: Free information ■ Parts for Jaguar XK120 and MKVII to XXJ6 and XJS. 800–231–3588.

Falvey Automotive, P.O. Box 130, Troy, MI 48099: Free brochure ■ Parts and accessories for the Jaguar. 800–832–5839; 313–643–7894 (in MI).

Genuine Classic Brakes, 341 Knickerbocker Ave., Bohemia, NY 11716: Free catalog ■ Jaguar brakes and parts. Includes wheel cylinders, calipers, power boosters, and master and slave cylinders. 800–541–8347; 516–567–8108 (in NY).

George Haug Company, Inc., 517 E. 73rd St., New York, NY 10021: Free information ■ Jaguar parts. 800–955–4284; 212–288–0176 (in NY).

Jaguar Heaven, 1433 Tillie Lewis Dr., Stockton, CA 95206: Free information ■ Used Jaguar parts and accessories. 209–942–4JAG.

J.P. Enterprises, 95 Seawanhaka Ave., Lake Grove, NY 11755: Free information with long SASE ■ Jaguar parts. 516–467–4438.

Luttys Chevys, RD 2, Box 61, Cheswick, PA 15024: Catalog $1 ■ New, used, and reproduction parts, and accessories. Includes carpets, interiors, weatherstripping, moldings, sheet metal, and replacement panels. 412–265–2988.

Moss Motors, Ltd., 7200 Hollister Rd., P.O. Box 847, Goleta, CA 93116: Free catalog ■ Hard-to-find parts for Jaguars. 800–235–6954.

Regency Motors, Bloomfield Ave. & Valley Rd., Montclair, NJ 07042: Free information with long SASE ■ Jaguar parts and accessories. 201–746–4500.

Scotland Yard British Cars, Ltd., 3101 E. 52nd Ave., Denver, CO 80216: Free information with long SASE ■ New, used, and re-manufactured parts for the Jaguar. 800–222–1415; 800–328–8716 (in CO).

Special Interest Car Parts, 1340 Hartford Ave., Johnston, RI 02919: Free catalog ■ Parts and accessories for 1948 to 1988 Jaguars. 800–556–7496; 401–831–8850 (in RI).

Terry's Jaguar Parts, 117 E. Smith St., Benton, IL 62812: Free information with long SASE ■ High-performance Jaguar parts and accessories. 800–447–4587.

XK's Unlimited, 850 Fiero Ln., San Luis Obispo, CA 93401: Catalog $6 ■ Parts and service for Jaguars, from 1948 and later. 800–445–JAGS.

JAVELIN

Byers Jeep-Eagle, 390 E. Broad St., P.O. Box 16513, Columbus, OH 43216: Free catalog ■ New original parts. 614–221–9181.

JEEP

American Motor Haven, 1107 Campbell Ave., San Jose, CA 95126: Free information

■ Obsolete and hard-to-find parts for the Jeep. 408–246–0957.

Byers Jeep-Eagle, 390 E. Broad St., P.O. Box 16513, Columbus, OH 43216: Free catalog ■ New original parts. 614–221–9181.

Find-A-Part, Box 358, Ridgeland, MS 39158: Free information with long SASE ■ Jeep N.O.S. parts, automotive literature, signs, and calendars. 601–856–7214.

Lou Fusz Auto Parts Network, 10725 Manchester St., St. Louis, MO 63122: Catalog $3 ■ Jeep parts and accessories. 800–325–9584.

MidAmerica Parts & Equipment Company, 1212 E. 19th St., Kansas City, MO 64108: Free catalog ■ New, surplus, and OEM replacemnt parts for Willys Jeeps, from 1940 to present day American Motors Jeeps. 816-221-4232.

Mike's Auto Parts, Box 358, Ridgeland, MS 39157: Free information with long SASE ■ Jeep parts and accessories. 601–856–7214.

Obsolete Jeep & Willys Parts, Division Florida 4–Wheel Drive & Truck Parts, 6110 17th St. East, Bradenton, FL 34203: Free information ■ New, used, rebuilt, and N.O.S. parts. 813–756–7844.

Quadratec, 108 Plant Ave., Wayne, PA 19087: Free information ■ Mechanical and performance parts and accessories for Jeep Wranglers. 800–745–5337.

Sports & Classics, 512 Boston Post Rd., Darien, CT 06820: Catalog $5 ■ Restoration parts, engine and electrical parts, body parts, and accessories. 203–655–8731.

Willys & Jeep Parts, 572 Ramtown Rd., Howell, NJ 07731: Free information ■ Hard-to-find mechanical and body parts, convertible tops, wire harnesses, hub caps, and parts books. 908–458–3966.

JENSEN

Dave Bean Engineering, Inc., 635 E. Saint Charles St., San Andreas, CA 95249: Catalog $6 ■ Parts and accessories for the Jensen. 209–754–5802.

Delta Motorsports, Inc., 2724 E. Bell Rd., Phoenix, AZ 85032: Free information with long SASE ■ Jensen factory parts and accessories. 602–265–8026.

KAISER-FRAZER

Fannaly's Auto Exchange, 701 Range Rd., P.O. Box 23, Ponchatoula, LA 70454: Free information ■ A limited selection of Kaiser-Fraser parts. 504–386–3714.

Wayne's Auto Salvage, RR 3, Box 41, Winner, SD 57580: Free information ■ Kaiser parts. 605–842–2054.

Zeug's K-F Parts, 1449 E. Uppingham Dr., Thousand Oaks, CA 91360: Parts list $2 ■ N.O.S. and used Kaiser-Frazer, Henry J, and Kaiser-Darrin parts. 805–492–5895.

LAMBORGHINI

J.P. Enterprises, 95 Seawanhaka Ave., Lake Grove, NY 11755: Free information with long SASE ■ Lamborghini parts. 516–467–4438.

LANCIA

Alfa Ricambi, 6644 San Fernando Rd., Glendale, CA 91201: Free information ■ Parts for the Lancia. 818–956–7933.

Bayless, Inc., 1111 Via Bayless, Marietta, GA 30060: Catalog $4 ■ Accessories and replacement parts. 404–928–1446.

Celiberti Motors, 615 Oak St., Santa Rosa, CA 95404: Free information ■ Lancia parts and accessories. 800–USA–FIAT.

International Auto Parts, Inc., Rt. 29 North, P.O. Box 9036, Charlottesville, VA 22906: Catalog $2 (refundable) ■ Replacement, restoration, and performance parts for the Lancia. 804–973–0555.

LASALLE

Automotive Obsolete, 1023 E. 4th St., Santa Ana, CA 92701: Catalog $3 ■ New parts for 1926 to 1970 Lasalle cars. 714–541–5167.

Out of the Past Parts, 3720 SW 23rd St., Gainesville, FL 32601: Free information with long SASE ■ Parts and accessories for 1935 and later LaSalles. 904–377–4079.

Piru Cads, 402 Via Fustero Rd., Box 227, Piru, CA 93040: Free information with long SASE ■ Used parts for 1937 to 1956 La-Salles. 805–521–1741.

LEYLAND

Atlanta Imported British Auto Parts, 5383 Buford Hwy., Doraville, GA 30340:

Catalog $1 (refundable) ■ New, used, and imported Leyland parts. 404–451–4411.

LINCOLN

Aabar's Cadillac & Lincoln Salvage, 9700 NE 23rd, Oklahoma City, OK 73141: Free information ■ Lincoln and Cadillac parts, from 1939 and later. 405–769–3318.

Bill Alprin, 184 Rivervale Rd., Rivervale, NJ 07675: Free information ■ N.O.S. parts for the Lincoln Mark II to Mark VII, and for the Continental. 201–666–3975.

Classic Cars Unlimited, P.O. Box 242, Lakeshore, MS 39558: Catalog $3 (specify year & model) ■ Lincoln parts, from 1960 to 1976. 800–543–8691; 601–467–9633 (in MS).

Bob Cook Classic Auto Parts, P.O. Box 190, Hazel, KY 42049: Catalog $6 (specify year & model) ■ Reproduction parts for 1960 to 1972 Lincolns. 502–492–8166.

Fannaly's Auto Exchange, 701 Range Rd., P.O. Box 23, Ponchatoula, LA 70454: Free information ■ Parts for 1946 to 1956 Lincolns. 504–386–3714.

Lou Fusz Auto Parts Network, 10725 Manchester, St. Louis, MO 63122: Catalog $3 ■ Lincoln parts and accessories. 800–533–2175.

Lincoln Land, 1928 Sherwood St., Clearwater, FL 34625: Free information with long SASE ■ Parts for 1961 to 1979 Lincoln Continentals. 813–531–5351.

Narragansett Reproductions, 107 Woodville Rd., P.O. Box 51, Wood River Junction, RI 02894: Free catalog ■ Parts for 1936 to 1948 Lincolns, 1956 to 1957 Lincoln Continentals, and the Lincoln Zephyr. 401–364–3839.

Reliable Motoring Accessories, 1751 Spruce St., Riverside, CA 92505: Catalog $1 ■ New and reproduction Continental Mark II parts. 800–854–4770; 714–781–0261 (in CA).

Rowland's Antique Auto Parts, P.O. Box 387, Zillah, WA 98953: Free information with long SASE ■ Lincoln parts, from 1939 to 1957. 509–829–5026.

LOTUS

Dave Bean Engineering, Inc., 635 E. Saint Charles St., San Andreas, CA 95249:

Catalog $6 ■ Parts and accessories for the Lotus. 209–754–5802.

British Motorsports, Inc., 1143 Dell Ave., Campbell, CA 95008: Free information with long SASE ■ New, used, and rebuilt parts. 408–370–7174.

J.P. Enterprises, 95 Seawanhaka Ave., Lake Grove, NY 11755: Free information with long SASE ■ Lotus parts. 516–467–4438.

Kampena Motors, 140 S. Linden Ave., South San Francisco, CA 94080: Free information with long SASE ■ Lotus parts and accessories. 415–583–5480.

R.D. Enterprises, Ltd., 5090 Durham Rd., P.O. Box 239, Gardenville, PA 18926: Free information with long SASE ■ Parts and accessories for the Lotus. 215–766–0460.

Tingle's Lotus Center, 1615 Shawsheen St., Tewksbury, MA 01876: Free information with long SASE ■ Lotus parts and accessories. 508–851–8370.

MASERATI

International Auto Parts, Inc., Rt. 29 North, P.O. Box 9036, Charlottsville, VA 22906: Catalog $2 ■ Maserati parts and accessories. 804–973–0555.

J.P. Enterprises, 95 Seawanhaka Ave., Lake Grove, NY 11755: Free information with long SASE ■ Maserati parts. 516–467–4438.

MAVERICK

Bill Alprin, 184 Rivervale Rd., Rivervale, NJ 07675: Free information ■ N.O.S. parts for the Maverick. 201–666–3975.

MAZDA

Autoshow, 2326 E. 44th St., Indianapolis, IN 46205: Catalog $3 (refundable) ■ Parts and accessories for the Mazda RX-7. 800–428–2200; 317–545–6223 (in IN).

Dobi Mazda Catalog, 320 Thor Pl., Brea, CA 92621: Catalog $2 ■ Parts and accessories for the Mazda RX-7 and GLC. 714–529–1977.

Lou Fusz Auto Parts Network, 10725 Manchester, St. Louis, MO 63122: Catalog $3 ■ Mazda parts and accessories. 800–341–5935.

HKS USA, Inc., 20312 Gramercy Pl., Torrance, CA 90501: Catalog $5 (specify year & model) ■ Performance parts and accessories for the Mazda. 310–328–8100.

MSO Parts, 1543 Easton Rd., Roslyn, PA 19001: Free catalog ■ Genuine factory parts for the Mazda. 800–628–0817; 215–657–8423 (in PA).

Bob Sharp Racing/Accessories, Danbury Rd., Rt. 7, Wilton, CT 06897: Catalog $1 ■ Mazda parts and accessories that include racing and styling components. 203–544–8386.

MERCEDES-BENZ

Adsit MB Supply, 7401 State Rd. 3, Muncie, IN 47303: Free information ■ New parts and accessories for the Mercedes-Benz. 800–521–7650; 317–282–1593 (in IN).

ATVM Automotive Parts, 97 Mount Royal Ave., Aberdeen, MD 21001: Free information with long SASE ■ Mercedes-Benz parts, from 1934 to 1972. 410–272–2252.

C.A.R.S., Inc., 1964 W. 11 Mile Rd., P.O. Box 721187, Berkley, MI 48072: Catalog $4 ■ Parts for 1976 to 1985 Mercedes-Benz cars. 313–398–7100.

Embee Parts, 4000 Lee Rd., Smyrna, GA 30080: Free information ■ Parts for 1934 to 1988 Mercedes-Benz. 404–434–5686.

Europarts, 620 Venture St., Escondido, CA 92025: Free information with long SASE ■ Mercedes-Benz parts and accessories. 619–743–3377.

IMPCO, Inc., 909 Thompson St., Houston, TX 77077: Free catalog ■ Save up to 30 percent on original 1977 to 1985 diesel Mercedes-Benz parts and accessories. 713–868–1638.

Mathieu Parts & Accessories, 209th & Hilltop, Chicago Heights, IL 60411: Free catalog ■ Mercedes-Benz, Audi, and Porsche parts and accessories. 708–481–3114.

MERCURY

Bill Alprin, 184 Rivervale Rd., Rivervale, NJ 07675: Catalog $5 (specify year & model) ■ Trim, sheet metal, mechanical, steering, and transmission parts for 1939 to 1979 Mercury cars. 201–666–3975.

Bob Cook Classic Auto Parts, P.O. Box 190, Hazel, KY 42049: Catalog $6 (specify year & model) ■ Reproduction Mercury

parts for the 1956 to 1972 Mercury. 502–492–8166.

Lou Fusz Auto Parts Network, 10725 Manchester, St. Louis, MO 63122: Catalog $3 ■ Mercury parts and accessories. 800–533–2175.

McDonald Ford Parts Company, RR 3, Box 94, Rockport, IN 47635: Catalog $5 (specify year and model) ■ Parts for 1932 to 1982 Mercury cars. 812–359–4965.

Mercury Research Company, 639 Glankler St., Memphis, TN 38112: Catalog $4 ■ New parts for 1949 to 1959 Mercury cars.

Papke Enterprises, 17202 Gothard St., Huntington Beach, CA 92647: Free information with long SASE ■ Parts and accessories for 1949 to 1951 Mercury cars. 714–843–6969.

PRO Antique Auto Parts, 50 King Spring Rd., Windsor Locks, CT 06096: Catalog $2 ■ New parts for 1928 to 1964 models. 203–623–0070.

Rowland's Antique Auto Parts, P.O. Box 387, Zillah, WA 98953: Free information with long SASE ■ Parts for the 1939 to 1957 Mercury. 509–829–5026.

METEOR

Bob Cook Classic Auto Parts, P.O. Box 190, Hazel, KY 42049: Catalog $6 (specify year & model) ■ Reproduction parts for the 1956 to 1964 Meteor. 502–492–8166.

MG

British Miles, 222 Grove, Morrisville, PA 19067: Free information ■ Reconditioned and new MG parts. 215–736–9300.

British Restoration Parts, 1808 Oak, Kansas City, MO 64108: Catalog $3 ■ Restoration parts and accessories for the MG. 800–821–3767; 800–892–3250 (in MO).

Burnett's Garage, Inc., 60 Maple St., Wenham, MA 01984: Free information ■ MG parts. 508–468–4011.

Dobi MGB Catalog, 320 Thor Pl., Brea, CA 92621: Catalog $2 ■ Parts and accessories for MGB cars. 714–529–1977.

Engel Imports, Inc., 5850 Stadium Dr., Kalamazoo, MI 49009: Free information with long SASE ■ Parts for MG cars, 1953 to present. Includes discontinued, obsolete, and "dealer only" items. 800–253–4080; 800–452–4520 (in MI).

George Haug Company, Inc., 517 E. 73rd St., New York, NY 10021: Free information ■ MG parts. 800–955–4284; 212–288–0176 (in NY).

M & G Vintage Auto, 265 Rt. 17, Box 226, Tuxedo Park, NY 10987: Free information ■ Parts and accessories for the MGA, MGB, and MGT. 800–631–8990; 914–753–5900 (in NY).

MG Bits & Spares, 105 Azalea Ln., P.O. Box 864, Jonesboro, AR 72401: Free information ■ Parts for the MGB and MGB-GT. 501–932–7150.

New England Old Car Barn, US Rt. 1, Box 608, North Hampton, NH 03862: Free information with long SASE ■ MG parts, books, and memorabilia. 603–964–7100.

Northwest Import Parts, 10915 SW 64th Ave., Portland, OR 97219: Free information ■ Parts for the MGB, MGA, and Midget. 503–245–3806.

Scarborough Faire, 1151 Main St., Pawtucket, RI 02860: Free list ■ MGB body repair parts and panels. 401–724–4200.

Scotland Yard British Cars, Ltd., 3101 E. 52nd Ave., Denver, CO 80216: Free information with long SASE ■ New, used, and remanufactured parts for the MG. 800–222–1415; 800–328–8716 (in CO).

Sports & Classics, 512 Boston Post Rd., Darien, CT 06820: Catalog $5 ■ Restoration, engine and electrical, body parts, and accessories. 203–655–8731.

Victoria British, Ltd., P.O. Box 14991, Lenexa, KS 66215: Free information ■ Original, replacement, and reproduction parts and accessories for the MG and other British sports cars. 800–255–0088.

Vintage Specialists, P.O. Box 772, Hobe Sound, FL 33475: Catalog $2 ■ New and used MG parts, supplies, and accessories. 407–546–3177.

MIDGET

King Midget Auto Works, P.O. Box 549, Westport, IN 47283: Free parts list ■ Parts for the Midget. 812–591–2719.

MITSUBISHI

Lou Fusz Auto Parts Network, 10725 Manchester, St. Louis, MO 63122: Catalog $3 ■ Mitsubishi parts and accessories. 800–528–2525.

HKS USA, Inc., 20312 Gramercy Pl., Torrance, CA 90501: Catalog $5 (specify year & model) ■ Performance parts and accessories for the Mitsubishi. 310–328–8100.

MODEL A & MODEL T FORDS

Antique Cars-Trucks & Parts, 526 E. 2nd, Blue Springs, NE 68318: Free information with long SASE ■ Ford Model A and T parts, from 1917 to 1931. 402–645–3546.

Bob's Antique Auto Parts, 7826 Forest Hills Rd., P.O. Box 2523, Rockford, IL 61132: Catalog $1 ■ Ford Model T parts. 815–633–7244.

Bratton's Antique Ford Parts, 9410 Watkins Rd., Gaithersburg, MD 20879: Free information ■ Parts for the Model A Ford. 301–253–1929.

BSIA Mustang Supply, 303 Brighton St., LaPorte, IN 46350: Free information with long SASE ■ Model A Ford parts, from 1928 to 1931; mid–1964 to 1973 Mustang parts. 219–326–1300.

C.A.R. Distributors, 12375 New Holland St., Holland, MI 48072: Free information with long SASE ■ Ford Model A parts and accessories. 616–399–6783.

Carlin Manufacturing & Distributor, Inc., 1250 Gulf St., Beaumont, TX 77701: Catalog $2 ■ Parts and accessories for Ford Model T, A, and V8 cars. Includes wood, sheet metal, seat springs, engine and chassis parts, and some custom parts. 409–833–9757.

Cars & Parts, Rt. 1, Dyer, TN 38330: Free information with long SASE ■ Parts for Ford Model A and T cars. 901–643–6448.

Connecticut Antique Ford Parts, 985 Middlesex Tpk., Old Saybrook, CT 06475: Free information ■ Model A Ford parts. 203–388–5872.

Gaslight Auto Parts, Inc., 1445 S. State Rt. 68, P.O. Box 291, Urbana, OH 43078: Catalog $2 ■ Replacement parts for Ford Model A and T cars. 513–652–2145.

Joblot Automotive, Inc., 98–11 211th St., Queens Village, NY 11419: Free catalog ■

Ford Model A and Model T parts. 718–468–8585.

LeBaron Bonney Company, 6 Chestnut St., Amesbury, MA 01913: Information and price list $1 ■ Interiors and tops, seat upholstery, panels and headlining, top kits, and top assemblies for 1928 to 1931 Fords. 508–388–3811.

Mac's Antique Auto Parts, 1051 Lincoln Ave., Lockport, NY 14094: Catalog $5 ■ Parts for 1928 to 1931 Model A Fords, and 1909 to 1927 Model T Fords. 800–828–7948; 800–777–0948 (in NY).

Mal's A Sales, 4966 Pacheco Blvd., Martinez, CA 94553: Free catalog ■ New parts for Fords, from 1909 to 1931. 510–228–8180.

Masonville Garage, Box 57, Masonville, IA 50654: Catalog $2 (refundable) ■ Model A parts. 319–927–4290.

New England Old Car Barn, US Rt. 1, Box 608, North Hampton, NH 03862: Free information with long SASE ■ Ford Model A and Model T parts, books, and memorabilia. 603–964–7100.

Newood Products, 1404 Broadway, P.O. Box 128, Monett, MO 65708: Free price list ■ Wood body parts for 1923 to 1925 Model T Fords and 1928 to 1931 Model A Fords. 417–235–5872.

Obsolete Ford Parts, Inc., 6601 E. Shields, Oklahoma City, OK 73149: Catalog $3 (specify year & model) ■ Model A parts and Model T parts. 405–631–3933.

Rootlieb, Inc., P.O. Box 1829, Turlock, CA 95381: Free information ■ Sheet metal parts for early vintage Ford cars. 209–632–2203.

Sacramento Vintage Ford Parts, Inc., 4675 Aldona Ln., Sacramento, CA 95841: Catalog $1 ■ Model T parts, from 1909 to 1927; Model A parts, from 1928 to 1931. 916–489–3444.

Smith & Jones Antique Parts, 1 Biloxi Square, Columbia Airport, West Columbia, SC 29170: Catalog $2.50 ■ Reproduction Model A and Model T Ford parts. 803–822–8502.

Snyder's Antique Auto Parts, New Springfield, OH 44443: Catalog $1 ■ Model T parts, 1909 to 1927 and Model A parts, 1928 to 1931. 216–519–5313.

Vintage Auto Parts, 11318 Beach Blvd., Stanton, CT 90680: Free information with long SASE ■ New parts for Ford Model A and Model T cars. 714–894–5464.

MONTE CARLO

Chevrolet Specialties, 4335 S. Highland Ave., Butler, PA 16001: Catalog $3 ■ Monte Carlo parts, from 1970 to 1977. 412–482–2670.

CJ Auto, Rt. 5, Box 116, Littleton, NC 27850: Free information with long SASE ■ Used, new, and reproduction Monte Carlo parts, from 1970 to 1972. 919–586–6233.

MONTEGO

Bill Alprin, 184 Rivervale Rd., Rivervale, NJ 07675: Free information ■ N.O.S. parts for the Montego. 201–666–3975.

Bob Cook Classic Auto Parts, P.O. Box 190, Hazel, KY 42049: Catalog $6 (specify year & model) ■ Reproduction parts for the 1965 to 1972 Montego. 502–492–8166.

Monte Carlo Exclusive, P.O. Box 1368, Huntington Beach, CA 92647: Free catalog ■ Monte Carlo parts, from 1962 to 1970. Includes interiors, moldings, body parts, and body panels. 800–72–CARLO.

MUSTANG

Bill Alprin, 184 Rivervale Rd., Rivervale, NJ 07675: Free information ■ N.O.S. parts for the Mustang. 201–666–3975.

American Mustang Parts, 8345 Sunrise Blvd., Rancho Cordova, CA 95670: Free information ■ Mustang restoration parts. Includes interiors, exterior sheet metal, rust repair panels, and chrome interior and exterior accessories. 916–635–7271.

American Pony Parts, 18121 Alderwood Mall Blvd., Lynnwood, WA 98037: Catalog $3 ■ Mustang parts and accessories, from 1965 to 1973. 206–771–4447.

Arizona Mustang Parts, 9153 W. Utopia Rd., Phoenix, AZ 85382: Free brochure ■ Mustang parts and accessories. 602–566–8777.

Auto Krafters, Inc., P.O. Box 6, Broadway, VA 22815: Free information with long SASE (specify year & model) ■ New, used, and reproduction parts and accessories for 1965 to 1973 Mustangs. 703–896–5910.

BSIA Mustang Supply, 303 Brighton St., LaPorte, IN 46350: Free information with long SASE ■ Mustang parts, from mid–1964 to 1973; Model A Fords, from 1928 to 1931. 219–326–1300.

California Mustang Parts & Accessories, 18435 Valley Blvd., La Puenta, CA 91744: Catalog $3 ■ Parts and accessories for Mustangs. Includes upholstery, body panels, engine and transmission parts, and electrical accessories. 818–964–0911.

Canadian Mustang, 3311 Oak St., Victoria, British Columbia, Canada V8X 1P9: Catalog $3 ■ Mustang parts and accessories, from 1965 to 1973. 604–385–7161.

C.A.R. Distributors, 12375 New Holland St., Holland, MI 48072: Free information with long SASE ■ Mustang parts and accessories. 616–399–6783.

Circle City Mustang, Rt. 1, Box 27, Midland City, AL 36350: Free information with long SASE ■ Mustang parts and literature. 205–983–5450.

City Motor Company, P.O. Box 526, Clarkston, WA 99403: Catalog $2 ■ New original and reproduction parts for the 1965 to 1973 Mustang. 509–758–6262.

Classic Auto Air Mfg. Company, 2020 W. Kennedy Blvd., Tampa, FL 33606: Free catalog ■ Complete air conditioning systems and parts for mid–1964 to 1966 Mustangs. 813–251–4994.

Colorado Mustang Specialists, Inc., 19900 E. Colfax, Aurora, CO 80011: Free inventory list ■ Parts for 1965 to 1987 Mustangs. 303–343–7024.

Bob Cook Classic Auto Parts, P.O. Box 190, Hazel, KY 42049: Catalog $6 (specify year & model) ■ Reproduction parts for 1964 to 1973 Mustangs. 502–492–8166.

Crossroads Classic Mustang, 12421 Riverside Ave., Mira Loma, CA 91752: Free information ■ Parts for mid–1964 and later Mustangs. 800–GIODY–UP.

Ken's Falcon Parts, 1799 E. Alosta, Glendora, CA 91740: Catalog $2 (specify model) ■ New, used, and reproduction parts for the 1965 to 1973 Mustang, 1967 to 1973 Cougar, and 1960 to 1970 Falcon. 818–963–5905.

King & Wesley Obsolete Parts, Inc., P.O. Box A, Courthouse Square, Liberty, KY 42539: Free information ■ N.O.S. and

reproduction Mustang parts. Includes sheet metal, moldings, hubcaps, grilles, and suspension parts. 606–787–5031.

Larry's Thunderbird & Mustang Parts, 511 S. Raymond Ave., Fullerton, CA 92631: Free catalog ■ New and used parts for 1965 to 1973 Mustangs and replacement upholstery. 714–871–6432.

Mid County Mustang, Rt. 100, P.O. Box 189, Eagle, PA 19480: Free information with long SASE ■ Mustang parts, from 1964 to 1973. 215–458–8083.

Mr. Mustang, Inc., 5088 Wolf Creek Pike, Dayton, OH 45426: Free information with long SASE ■ Mustang parts and accessories, from mid–1964 to 1972. 513–275–7439.

Mostly Mustang's, Inc., 55 Alling St., Hamden, CT 06517: Free price list ■ New, used, and reproduction Mustang parts. 203–562–8804.

Muscle Car Corral, RR 3, Box 218, Paris, IL 61944: Catalog $2 ■ Parts for 1965 to 1968 Mustangs. 217–465–8386.

Mustang Corral, Rt. 6, Box 242, Edwardsville, IL 62065: Free information with long SASE ■ New and used parts and supplies for 1965 to 1973 Mustangs. 800–327–2897.

Mustang Headquarters, 1080 Detroit Ave., Concord, CA 94518: Catalog $1 ■ Mustang parts and upholstery and interior fittings for 1965 to 1969 models. 800–227–2174.

Mustang Mart, Inc., 655 McGlincey Ln., Campbell, CA 95008: Catalog $3 (refundable) ■ New, used, and reproduction parts. 408–371–5771.

Mustang Parts Corral of Texas, 3533 S. Ledbetter, Dallas, TX 75236: Free catalog ■ Mustang parts and accessories. 214–296–5130.

Mustang Parts of Oklahoma, 6505 S. Shields, Oklahoma City, OK 73149: Catalog $5 ■ Mustang parts and accessories. 405–631–1400.

National Parts Depot, 3101 SW 40th Blvd., Gainesville, FL 32608: Free information ■ Parts, upholstery, and restoration supplies for 1965 to 1973 Mustangs. 904–378–2473.

Obsolete Ford Parts Company, P.O. Box 787, Nashville, GA 31639: Catalog $2 ■ N.O.S. and reproduction parts for 1960 to 1970 Mustangs. 912–686–2470.

The Paddock, Inc., P.O. Box 30, Knightstown, IN 46148: Catalog $1 ■ Mustang parts and accessories. 317–345–2131.

Pennsylvania Mustang, P.O. Box 660, Riegelsville, PA 18077: Catalog $2 ■ Mustang parts and accessories, from 1969 to 1970. 215–749–0411.

Racer Walsh Company, 5906 Macy, Jacksonville, FL 32211: Catalog $3 ■ Engines, suspensions, and other Mustang parts. 800–334–0151; 904–743–8253 (in FL).

Stilwell's Obsolete Car Parts, 1617 Wedeking Ave., Evansville, IL 47711: Catalog $3 ■ Hard-to-find new and reproduction Mustang parts. 812–425–4794.

Texas Mustang Parts, Rt. 6, Box 996, Waco, TX 76706: Free catalog ■ New and reproduction parts for 1965 to 1973 Mustangs. 800–527–1588; 817–662–2790 (in TX).

Valley Ford Parts, 11610 Van Owen St., North Hollywood, CA 91605: Free information ■ New and used parts for 1965 to 1973 Mustangs. 818–982–5303.

NASH

American Motor Haven, 1107 Campbell Ave., San Jose, CA 95126: Free information ■ Obsolete and hard-to-find parts for the Nash. 408–246–0957.

Blaser's Auto, 3200 48th Ave., Moline, IL 61265: Free information with long SASE ■ Nash parts and accessories. 309–764–3571.

Vintage Tin Auto Parts, 4550 Scotty Ln., Hutchinson, KS 67502: Free information with long SASE ■ Nash parts and accessories. 316–669–8449.

Wayne's Auto Salvage, RR 3, Box 41, Winner, SD 57580: Free information ■ Nash parts. 605–842–2054.

NOVA

Chevrolet Specialties, 4335 S. Highland Ave., Butler, PA 16001: Catalog $3 ■ Nova parts, from 1962 to 1974. 412–482–2670.

Harmon's Chevrolet Restoration Parts, Hwy. 27 North, Geneva, IN 46740: Catalog $3 ■ Nova restoration parts and accessories, from 1964 to 1972. 219–368–7221.

Luttys Chevys, RD 2, Box 61, Cheswick, PA 15024: Catalog $1 ■ New, used, and reproduction parts and accessories. Includes carpets, interiors, weatherstripping, moldings, sheet metal, and replacement panels. 412–265–2988.

Martz Classic Chevy Parts, RD 1, Box 199, Thomasville, PA 17364: Free catalog ■ N.O.S. and reproduction parts, from 1955 to 1967. 717–225–1655.

Musclecar Specialties, 1 Coach Lantern Dr., Hopewell Junction, NY 12533: Free information with long SASE ■ New, N.O.S., and used parts and accessories for 1962 to 1972 Novas. 914–227–6837.

Super Sport Restoration Parts, Inc., 7138 Maddox Rd., P.O. Box 7, Lithonia, GA 30058: Free information ■ Parts for the Nova, Chevy II, Chevelle, and Camaro. 404–482–9219.

Tom's Obsolete Chevy Parts, 14 Delta Dr., Pawtucket, RI 02860: Catalog $1 ■ Nova parts, from 1955 to 1972. 401–723–7580.

OLDSMOBILE

Automotive Obsolete, 1023 E. 4th St., Santa Ana, CA 92701: Catalog $3 ■ New parts for 1926 to 1970 Oldsmobiles. 714–541–5167.

Fusick Automotive Products, P.O. Box 655, East Windsor, CT 06088: Catalog $3 (specify model) ■ Parts for Oldsmobiles, 1937 to 1960, 1961–1972; Cutlass, 1961 to 1972; and Toronados, 1988 and later. 203–623–1589.

Musclecar Specialties, 1 Coach Lantern Dr., Hopewell Junction, NY 12533: Free information with long SASE ■ New, N.O.S., used parts, and accessories for the 1958 to 1969 Oldsmobile. 914–227–6837.

Out of the Past Parts, 3720 SW 23rd St., Gainesville, FL 32601: Free information with long SASE ■ Oldsmobile parts and accessories, 1935 and later. 904–377–4079.

PRO Antique Auto Parts, 50 King Spring Rd., Windsor Locks, CT 06096: Catalog $2 ■ New parts for 1929 to 1964 Oldsmobiles. 203–623–0070.

Terrill Machine, Inc., Rt. 2, Box 61, De-Leon, TX 76444: Free information with long SASE ■ Engine overhaul parts for Oldsmobiles, from 1937 to 1960. 817–893–2610.

Vintage Tin Auto Parts, 4550 Scotty Ln., Hutchinson, KS 67502: Free information with long SASE ■ Oldsmobile parts and ac-cessories, from 1940 to 1970. 316–669–8449.

OPEL

Opeleo Automotive Parts, 15822 11th Ave. NE, Seattle, WA 98155: Free information with long SASE ■ Parts for 1957 to 1975 Opel cars. 206–367–6360.

PACKARD

Brinton's Antique Auto Parts, 6826 SW McVey Ave., Redmond, OR 97756: Free information with long SASE ■ Parts for 1920 to 1932 Packards. 503–548–3483.

Fannaly's Auto Exchange, 701 Range Rd., P.O. Box 23, Ponchatoula, LA 70454: Free information ■ Parts for 1946 to 1956 Packards. 504–386–3714.

Kanter Auto Parts, 76 Monroe St., Boonton, NJ 07005: Free information ■ Used and reproduction parts for rebuilding Packards. 201–334–9575.

Norm's Antique Auto Supply, 1921 Hickory Grove Rd., Davenport, IA 52804: Free information with long SASE ■ Packard parts and accessories, from 1935 to 1952. 319–322–8388.

Packard Farm, 97 N. 150 West, Greenfield, IN 46140: Free information ■ Engine and transmission parts and exhaust systems. 317–462–3124.

Steve's Studebaker-Packard, 2287 2nd St., Napa, CA 94559: Free information with long SASE ■ Packard parts, from 1951 to 1956. 707–255–8945.

Terrill Machine, Inc., Rt. 2, Box 61, De-Leon, TX 76444: Free information with long SASE ■ Engine overhaul parts for 1935 to 1956 Packards. 817–893–2610.

Vintage Tin Auto Parts, 4550 Scotty Ln., Hutchinson, KS 67502: Free information with long SASE ■ Packard parts and accessories, from 1940 to 1970. 316–669–8449.

PANTERA

Mostly Mustang's, Inc., 55 Alling St., Hamden, CT 06517: Free price list ■ New, used, and reproduction Pantera parts. 203–562–8804.

PEUGEOT

French Car Connection, 1885 Clairmont Rd., Decatur, GA 30033: Free information ■

Parts and accessories for the Peugeot. 800–255–9870; 404–321–6661 (in GA).

PINTO

Bill Alprin, 184 Rivervale Rd., Rivervale, NJ 07675: Free information ■ N.O.S. parts for the Pinto. 201–666–3975.

Racer Walsh Company, 5906 Macy, Jacksonville, FL 32211: Catalog $3 ■ Engines, suspensions, and other parts and accessories. 800–334–0151; 904–743–8253 (in FL).

PLYMOUTH

Andy Bernbaum Auto Parts, 315 Franklin St., Newton, MA 02158: Catalog $4 ■ Parts and accessories for Plymouth cars. 617–244–1118.

Mike's Auto Parts, Box 358, Ridgeland, MS 39157: Free information with long SASE ■ Plymouth parts and accessories. 601–856–7214.

Mr. Plymouth, 452 Newton, Seattle, WA 98109: Catalog $1 ■ Hard-to-find parts and accessories for Plymouth cars, 1946 to 1954. 206–285–6534.

Out of the Past Parts, 3720 SW 23rd St., Gainesville, FL 32601: Free information with long SASE ■ Plymouth parts and accessories, 1935 and later. 904–377–4079.

PRO Antique Auto Parts, 50 King Spring Rd., Windsor Locks, CT 06906: Catalog $2 ■ New parts for 1929 to 1934 Plymouths. 203–623–0070.

Neil Riddle, 452 Newton, Seattle, WA 98109: Free information ■ Parts for 1946 to 1954 Plymouths. 206–285–6534.

Roberts Motor Parts, 17 Prospect St., West Newbury, MA 01985: Catalog $4 ■ Parts and accessories for Plymouth cars. 508–363–5407.

Terrill Machine, Inc., Rt. 2, Box 61, DeLeon, TX 76444: Free information with long SASE ■ Engine overhaul parts for Plymouths, from 1933 to 1952. 817–893–2610.

Vintage Tin Auto Parts, 4550 Scotty Ln., Hutchinson, KS 67502: Free information with long SASE ■ Parts and accessories for 1940 to 1970 Plymouths. 316–669–8449.

Year One, Inc., Box 2023, Tucker, GA 30085: Catalog $2 ■ New, used, and

reproduction Plymouth restoration parts. 404–493–6568.

PONTIAC

Ames Performance Engineering, Marlborough, NH 03455: Catalog $2 ■ Pontiac parts and accessories. 603–876–4514.

Lou Fusz Auto Parts Network, 10725 Manchester, St. Louis, MO 63122: Catalog $3 ■ Pontiac parts and accessories and other General Motors products. 800–325–1492.

Musclecar Specialties, 1 Coach Lantern Dr., Hopewell Junction, NY 12533: Free information with long SASE ■ New, N.O.S., and used parts and accessories for the 1929 to 1961 Pontiac. 914–227–6837.

Out of the Past Parts, 3720 SW 23rd St., Gainesville, FL 32601: Free information with long SASE ■ Parts and accessories, 1935 and later Pontiacs. 904–377–4079.

PRO Antique Auto Parts, 50 King Spring Rd., Windsor Locks, CT 06096: Catalog $2 ■ New parts for 1929 to 1964 Pontiacs. 203–623–0070.

Terrill Machine, Inc., Rt. 2, Box 61, DeLeon, TX 76444: Free information with long SASE ■ Engine overhaul parts for Pontiacs, from 1937 to 1956. 817–893–2610.

Vintage Tin Auto Parts, 4550 Scotty Ln., Hutchinson, KS 67502: Free information with long SASE ■ Pontiac parts and accessories, from 1940 to 1970. 316–669–8449.

PORSCHE

Allchevy Auto Parts, 4999 Vanden Rd., Vacaville, CA 95688: Free information ■ New and reproduction parts for 1953 to 1986 Porsches. 707–437–5466.

Automobile Atlanta, 504 Clay St., Marietta, GA 30060: Porsche catalog $3 ■ New and used parts for the Porsche 914 and 924/944. 404–427–2844.

Automotion, 3535 Kifer Rd., Santa Clara, CA 95051: Catalog $4 (refundable) ■ Porsche parts and accessories. 800–777–8881.

Best Deal Porsche, 8171 Monroe, Stanton, CA 90680: Free information ■ New, used, and reproduction parts for 1953 to 1986 models. 714–995–0081.

Campbell/Nelson Volkswagon, P.O. Box 220, Edmonds, WA 98020: Free information

■ Used Porsche parts and accessories. 206–771–4931.

Europarts, 620 Venture St., Escondido, CA 92025: Free information with long SASE ■ Porsche parts and accessories. 619–743–3377.

LeMance Autoworks, 914 Mill Rd., P.O. Box 449, Wartburg, TN 37887: Free information ■ Parts for the Porsche 914. 615–346–3194.

Mathieu Parts & Accessories, 209th & Hilltop, Chicago Heights, IL 60411: Free catalog ■ Porsche, Audi, and Mercedes-Benz parts and accessories. 708–481–3114.

914 Ltd., 220 Park St., Morgantown, WV 26505: Free information ■ Used parts for the Porsche 914. 304–292–4546.

Par-Porsche Specialists, 206 S. Broadway, Yonkers, NY 10705: Free information ■ New and used Porsche parts. 914–476–6700.

Parts Hotline, 10325 Central Ave., Montclair, CA 91763: Free information with long SASE ■ Porsche parts and accessories. 800–637–4662; 714–625–4888 (in CA).

Performance Products, 16129 Leadwell, Van Nuys, CA 91406: Catalog $4 ■ Parts, accessories, and tools for Porsche cars. 800–423–3173; 818–787–7500 (in CA).

Sportformance, Inc., 1559 N. Main St., Waterbury, CT 06704: Free information ■ New and used parts and accessories. 203–753–6051.

Stoddard Imported Cars, Inc., 38845 Mentor Ave., Willoughby, OH 44094: Catalog $7 ■ Restoration parts for the Porsche. 800–342–1414; 216–951–1040 (in OH).

Troutman Porsche, 3198 Airport Loop Dr., Costa Mesa, CA 92626: Catalog $3 ■ Porsche parts and accessories. 714–979–3295.

RAMBLER

Blaser's Auto, 3200 48th Ave., Moline, IL 61265: Free information with long SASE ■ Rambler parts and accessories. 309–764–3571.

Byers Jeep-Eagle, 390 E. Broad St., P.O. Box 16513, Columbus, OH 43216: Free catalog ■ New, factory original parts. 614–221–9181.

LeMance Autoworks, 914 Mill Rd., P.O. Box 449, Wartburg, TN 37887: Free information ■ Parts for 1963 to 1964 Rambler classics. 615–346–3194.

Vintage Tin Auto Parts, 4550 Scotty Ln., Hutchinson, KS 67502: Free information with long SASE ■ Rambler parts and accessories. 316–669–8449.

RENAULT

French Car Connection, 1885 Clairmont Rd., Decatur, GA 10033: Free information ■ Parts and accessories for the Renault. 800–255–9870; 404–321–6661 (in GA).

Lou Fusz Auto Parts Network, 10725 Manchester, St. Louis, MO 63122: Catalog $3 ■ Renault parts and accessories, 800–325–9584.

ROLLS-ROYCE

Albers Rolls-Royce, 190 W. Sycamore, Zionsville, IN 46077: Free information ■ Rolls-Royce parts. 317–873–2360.

Foreign Parts Connection, Inc., 2028 Cotner Ave., Westwood, CA 90025: Free information ■ Used postwar parts for the Rolls-Royce. 213–473–7773.

Lou Fusz Auto Parts Network, 10725 Manchester, St. Louis, MO 63122: Catalog $3 ■ Rolls-Royce and Bentley parts and accessories. 800–392–1372.

George Haug Company, Inc., 517 E. 73rd St., New York, NY 10021: Free information ■ Rolls-Royce parts. 800–955–4284; 212–288–0176 (in NY).

Rolls-Royce Obsolete Parts, Inc., P.O. Box 796, Anna Maria, FL 34216: Free information with long SASE ■ Rolls-Royce and Bentley parts, accessories, and literature. 813–778–7270.

Vintage Garage, North Brookfield, MA 01535: Free information ■ Hard-to-find parts for the Rolls-Royce. 508–867–2892.

ROVER

Atlantic British Parts Ltd. of California, P.O. Box 620, Lewiston, CA 96052: Catalog $4 ■ Parts and accessories for the Rover. 916–778–3922.

Bluff City British Cars, 1810 Getwell, Memphis, TN 38111: Free information ■ Parts and accessories for the Range Rover. 800–621–0227; 901–743–4422 (in TN).

British Motorsports, Inc., 1143 Dell Ave., Campbell, CA 95008: Free information with long SASE ■ New, used, and rebuilt parts. 408–370–7174.

Engel Imports, Inc., 5850 Stadium Dr., Kalamazoo, MI 49009: Free information with long SASE ■ Parts for models, 1953 to present. Includes discontinued, obsolete, and "dealer only" items. 800–253–4080; 800–452–4520 (in MI).

Rover Parts Unlimited, Hwy. 96, Box 790, Hoopa, CA 95546: Free catalog ■ New and used Rover parts. 916–625–4727.

Rovers West, 4060 E. Michigan, Tucson, AZ 85714: Free information ■ Parts and accessories for the Rover Sedan, Range Rover, and Land Rover. 602–748–8115.

SAAB

Falvey Automotive, P.O. Box 130, Troy, MI 48099: Free brochure ■ Parts and accessories for the SAAB. 800–832–5839; 313–643–7894 (in MI).

SATURN

Lou Fusz Auto Parts Network, 10725 Manchester, St. Louis, MO 63122: Catalog $3 ■ Saturn parts and accessories. 800–524–5400.

SHELBY

Cobra Restorers, 3099 Carter, Kenesaw, GA 30144: Catalog $3 ■ Parts and accessories for the Shelby. 404–427–0020.

Mostly Mustang's, Inc., 55 Alling St., Hamden, CT 06517: Free price list ■ New, used, and reproduction Shelby parts. 203–562–8804.

Valley Ford Parts, 11610 Van Owen St., North Hollywood, CA 91605: Free information ■ New and used parts for the 1965 to 1973 Shelby. 818–982–5303.

SPITFIRE

British Parts Northwest, 4105 SE Lafayette Hwy., Dayton, OR 97114: Catalog $2.50 ■ Spitfire parts and accessories. 503–864–2001.

STERLING

Bluff City British Cars, 1810 Getwell, Memphis, TN 38111: Free information ■

Parts and accessories for the Sterling. 800–621–0227; 901–743–4422 (in TN).

Falvey Automotive, P.O. Box 130, Troy, MI 48099: Free brochure ■ Parts and accessories for the Sterling. 800–832–5839; 313–643–7894 (in MI).

STUDEBAKER

Beckers Auto Salvage, Hwy. 30 West, Atkins, IA 52206: Free information ■ Parts for Studebakers. 319–446–7141.

Phil Brown Studebaker, 818 Berlin St., Mishawaka, IN 46544: Free information with long SASE ■ N.O.S. and used parts for 1947 to 1966 Studebakers. 219–255–3916.

Jim's Auto Sales, Rt. 2, Inman, KS 67546: Free information with long SASE ■ Studebaker parts and accessories, from 1935 to 1966. 316–585–6648.

Newman & Altman, Inc., P.O. Box 4276, South Bend, IN 46634: Catalog $5 ■ Studebaker parts and accessories. 800–722–4295.

Packard Farm, 97N 150 West, Greenfield, IN 46140: Free information ■ Studebaker engine and transmission parts, and exhaust systems. 317–462–3124.

Steve's Studebaker-Packard, 2287 2nd St., Napa, CA 94559: Free information with long SASE ■ Studebaker parts, from 1953 to 1966. 707–255–8945.

Tucker's Auto Salvage, RD 1, Box 170, Burke, NY 12917: Free information with long SASE ■ Studebaker N.O.S. and used parts and accessories. 518–483–5478.

Wayne's Auto Salvage, RR 3, Box 41, Winner, SD 57580: Free information ■ Studebaker parts. 605–842–2054.

SUBARU

Lou Fusz Auto Parts Network, 10725 Manchester, St. Louis, MO 63122: Catalog $3 ■ Subaru parts and accessories. 800–451–1471.

Parts Hotline, 10325 Central Ave., Montclair, CA 91763: Free information with long SASE ■ Subaru parts and accessories. 800–637–4662; 714–625–4888 (in CA).

SUNBEAM

British Restoration Parts, 1808 Oak, Kansas City, MO 64108: Catalog $3 ■ Restoration parts and accessories for the Sunbeam and other British sports cars. 800–821–3767; 800–892–3250 (in MO).

Moss Motors, Ltd., 7200 Hollister Rd., P.O. Box 847, Goleta, CA 93116: Free catalog ■ Parts for the Sunbeam. 800–235–6954.

Sunbeam Specialties, P.O. Box 771, Los Gatos, CA 95031: Free catalog ■ Parts and restoration aids for 1959 to 1968 Tigers and Alpines. 408–371–1642.

SUZUKI

Lou Fusz Auto Parts Network, 10725 Manchester, St. Louis, MO 63122: Catalog $3 ■ Suzuki parts and accessories. 800–451–1471.

THUNDERBIRD

Bill Alprin, 184 Rivervale Rd., Rivervale, NJ 07675: Free information ■ Thunderbird N.O.S. parts. 201–666–3975.

Bob's Bird House, 124 Watkins Ave., Chadds Ford, PA 19317: Catalog $3 ■ New and used parts and accessories for 1958 to 1978 Thunderbird cars. 215–358–3420.

Dennis Carpenter Ford Reproductions, P.O. Box 26398, Charlotte, NC 28221: Catalog $2 ■ Rubber parts for 1958 to 1966 Thunderbirds. 704–786–8139.

Classic Auto Supply Company, Inc., 795 High St., P.O. Box 810, Coshocton, OH 43812: Free catalog ■ Parts for 1955 to 1957 Thunderbird cars. 614–622–8561.

Concours Parts & Accessories, 3563 Numancia St., P.O. Box 1210, Santa Ynez, CA 93460: Catalog $4 ■ Thunderbird 1955 to 1957 parts. 805–688–7795.

Bob Cook Classic Auto Parts, P.O. Box 190, Hazel, KY 42049: Catalog $6 (specify year & model) ■ Reproduction parts for 1958 to 1960, 1961 to 1964, 1965 to 1966, and 1967 to 1972 Thunderbirds. 502–492–8166.

Dave's Classic T-Bird Parts, 37 Jewett St., Newton, MA 02158: Free information with long SASE ■ Thunderbird parts and accessories, from 1958 to 1976. 617–965–3567.

Joblot Automotive, Inc., 98–11 211th St., Queens Village, NY 11429: Free catalog ■ Thunderbird parts and accessories. 718–468–8585.

Larry's Thunderbird & Mustang Parts, 511 S. Raymond, Fullerton, CA 92631: Free catalog ■ New and used parts, and upholstery, for 1955 to 1957 cars. 714–871–6432.

LeBaron Bonney Company, 6 Chestnut St., Amesbury, MA 01913: Information and price list $1 ■ Thunderbird parts and accessories. 508–388–3811.

National Parts Depot, 3101 SW 40th Blvd., Gainesville, FL 32608: Free information with long SASE ■ Parts, upholstery, and restoration supplies for 1955 to 1957 Thunderbirds. 904–378–2473.

Obsolete Ford Parts, Inc., 6601 S. Shields, Oklahoma City, OK 73149: Catalog $3 (specify year & model) ■ Parts for 1949 to 1959 and 1960 to 1972 Thunderbirds. 405–631–3933.

Prestige Thunderbird, Inc., 10215 Greenleaf Ave., Santa Fe Springs, CA 90670: Catalog $1 ■ Parts, upholstery, and accessories. 310–944–6237.

Quality Thunderbird Parts & Products, 1501 Reistertown Rd., Baltimore, MD 21208: Free catalog ■ Used, re-chromed, refinished, and N.O.S. parts for 1964, 1965, and 1966 Thunderbirds.

T-Bird Connection, 728 E. Dunlap, Phoenix, AZ 85020: Catalogs $3 each (specify year & model) ■ New and used parts for 1958–1960, 1961–1963, 1964–1966, and 1967–1971 Thunderbirds. 602–997–9285.

T-Bird Nest, P.O. Box 1012, Grapevine, TX 76051: Free information ■ Thunderbird parts and accessories, from 1958 to 1966. 817–481–1776.

The T-Bird Sanctuary, 7849 SW Cirrus Dr., Beaverton, OR 97005: Free information with long SASE ■ Catalog $5 ■ Parts and accessories for 1958 to 1972 Thunderbirds. 503–641–0556.

Tee-Bird Products, Inc., Exton, PA 19341: Parts list $2 ■ Parts for 1955 to 1957 Thunderbirds. 215–363–1725.

Thunderbird Center, 23610 John R., Hazel Park, MI 48030: Free catalog ■ New, used, N.O.S., and reproduction parts for 1956 to 1957 Thunderbirds. Includes upholstery, accessories, sheet metal, and weatherstripping. 313–548–3033.

Thunderbird Headquarters, 1080 Detroit Ave., Concord, CA 94518: Catalog $3 ■ Thunderbird parts and accessories, from 1955 to 1957. 800–227–2174; 510–825–9550 (in CA).

Thunderbird Parts & Restoration, 5844 Goodrich Rd., Clarence Center, NY 14032: Free information ■ N.O.S., reproduction, used, and remanufactured parts and accessories. 800–289–2473; 716–741–2866 (in NY).

Thunderbirds East, Lenni Rd. at Chester Creek, Lenni, PA 19052: Free information ■ Used and restoration parts, engine and body parts, tops, and chrome trim, for 1955 to 1957 Thunderbirds. 215–358–1021.

Thunderbirds USA Parts Supply, 3621 Resource Dr., Tuscaloosa, AL 35401: Free catalog ■ N.O.S., used, and reproduction parts; 1955 to 1957 Thunderbird upholstery, decals, radios, books, and accessories. 205–758–5557.

TORINO

Bill Alprin, 184 Rivervale Rd., Rivervale, NJ 07675: Free information ■ N.O.S. parts for the Torino. 201–666–3975.

Auto Krafters, Inc., P.O. Box 6, Broadway, VA 22815: Free information with long SASE ■ New, used, and reproduction parts and accessories for 1962 to 1971 Torinos. 703–896–5910.

Bob Cook Classic Auto Parts, P.O. Box 190, Hazel, KY 42049: Catalog $6 (specify year & model) ■ Reproduction parts for 1960 to 1972 Torino cars. 502–492–8166.

Ford Parts Store, P.O. Box 226, Bryan, OH 43506: Catalog $2 ■ Torino parts and accessories. 419–636–2475.

FTC Enterprises, 213 E. 4th St., Unit 2, Loveland, CO 80537: Free parts list ■ Reproduction, N.O.S., and used parts for 1962 to 1971 Torinos. 303–663–6862.

Obsolete Ford Parts Company, P.O. Box 787, Nashville, GA 31639: Catalog $2 ■ N.O.S. and reproduction parts for 1949 to 1964 Torino cars. 912–686–2470.

TOYOTA

Dobi Toyota Catalog, 320 Thor Pl., Brea, CA 92621: Catalog $2 ■ Replacement parts for the Toyota Celica and Corolla. 714–529–1977.

Falvey Automotive, P.O. Box 130, Troy, MI 48099: Free brochure ■ Parts and accessories for the Toyota. 800–832–5839; 313–643–7894 (in MI).

Lou Fusz Toyota, 10725 Manchester, St. Louis, MO 63122: Catalog $3 ■ Toyota parts and accessories. 800–325–9581.

HKS USA, Inc., 20312 Gramercy Pl., Torrance, CA 90501: Catalog $5 (specify year & model) ■ Toyota performance parts and accessories. 310–328–8100.

Impact Parts, Glen Wild Rd., Glen Wild, NY 12738: Catalog $1 ■ Parts and accessories for the Toyota. 800–431–3400.

Russel Toyota, 6700 Baltimore National Tnpk., Baltimore, MD 21208: Free information ■ Toyota parts and accessories. 800–638–8401.

Bob Sharp Racing/Accessories, Danbury Rd., Rt. 7, Wilton, CT 06897: Catalog $1 ■ Toyota parts and accessories. Includes racing and styling components. 203–544–8386.

Toy Store, 452 Van Houten Ave., Passaic, NJ 07055: Catalog $3 ■ Toyota parts and accessories. 201–473–2446.

TRANS AM

Auto Accessories of America, Rt. 322, Box 427, Boalsburg, PA 16827: Catalog $5 ■ Parts, accessories, interiors, and fiberglass components. 800–458–3475.

Firebird/Trans Am America, Rt. 322, Box 427, Boalsburg, PA 16827: Free information with long SASE ■ Trans Am parts, from 1967 to 1987. 800–458–3475.

TRIUMPH

British Miles, 222 Grove, Morrisville, PA 19067: Free information ■ Reconditioned and new Triumph parts. 215–736–9300.

British Motorsports, Inc., 1143 Dell Ave., Campbell, CA 95008: Free information with long SASE ■ New, used, and rebuilt parts. 408–370–7174.

British Parts Northwest, 4105 SE Lafayette Hwy., Dayton, OR 97114: Catalog $2.50 ■ Triumph parts and accessories. 503–864–2001.

British Restoration Parts, 1808 Oak, Kansas City, MO 64108: Catalog $3 (specify model) ■ Restoration parts and accessories

for the Triumph. 800–821–3767; 800–892–3250 (in MO).

EightParts, 4060 E. Michigan, Tucson, AZ 85714: Free information ■ Parts and accessories for 8–cylinder Triumphs. 602–748–8115.

Engel Imports, Inc., 5850 Stadium Dr., Kalamazoo, MI 49009: Free information with long SASE ■ Parts for models, 1953 to present. Includes discontinued, obsolete, and "dealer only" items. 800–253–4080; 800–452–4520 (in MI).

George Haug Company, Inc., 517 E. 73rd St., New York, NY 10021: Free information ■ Triumph parts. 800–955–4284; 212–288–0176 (in NY).

Moss Motors, Ltd., 7200 Hollister Rd., P.O. Box 847, Goleta, CA 93116: Free catalog ■ Hard-to-find parts for the Triumph. 800–235–6954.

New England Old Car Barn, US Rt. 1, Box 608, North Hampton, NH 03862: Free information with long SASE ■ Triumph parts, books, and memorabilia. 603–964–7100.

Roadster Factory, P.O. Box 332, Armagh, PA 15920: Free catalog ■ Parts and accessories for the Triumph, TR2 through TR8, Spitfire, and GT6. 800–678–8764.

Scotland Yard British Cars, Ltd., 3101 E. 52nd Ave., Denver, CO 80216: Free information with long SASE ■ New, used, and re-manufactured parts for the Triumph. 800–222–1415; 800–328–8716 (in CO).

Sports & Classics, 512 Boston Post Rd., Darien, CT 06820: Catalog $5 ■ Restoration parts, engine and electrical parts, body parts, and accessories. 203–655–8731.

Victoria British, Ltd., P.O. Box 14991, Lenexa, KS 66215: Free information ■ Original, replacement, and reproduction parts and accessories for the Triumph and other British sports cars. 800–255–0088.

VOLKSWAGON

Discount Auto Parts, 4703 Broadway SE, Albuquerque, NM 87105: Free information with long SASE ■ Volkswagon parts. 505–877–6782.

Europarts, 620 Venture St., Escondido, CA 92025: Free information with long SASE ■ Volkswagon parts and accessories. 619–743–3377.

GMP Automotive Parts, 1830 Tomworth Dr., Charlotte, NC 28201: Catalog $1 ■ Performance parts and accessories for the Rabbit, Fox, and Scirroco cars. 704–525–0941.

Johnny's Speed Chrome, 6411 Beach Blvd., Buena Park, CA 90620: Catalog $3 ■ Parts and accessories for the Volkswagon. 800–854–3411.

West Coast Metric, Inc., 24002 Frampton Ave., Harbor City, CA 91320: Catalog $3 ■ Hard-to-find parts and accessories. Includes body replacement parts for the Bug, Bus, Type 3, and Ghia. 805–247–3202.

VOLVO

B & B Used Auto Parts, Rt. 1, Box 691, Big Pine Key, FL 33043: Free information with long SASE ■ Parts for the Volvo, 1968 and later. 305–872–9761.

Beechmont Volvo, 8639 Beechmont Ave., Cincinnati, OH 45255: Free information ■ Volvo parts. 800–255–3601.

Brentwood Volvo, 7700 Manchester Rd., St. Louis, MO 63143: Free information ■ Volvo parts and accessories. 800–844–9502.

Impact Parts, Glen Wild Rd., Glen Wild, NY 12738: Catalog $1 ■ Parts and accessories for the Volvo. 800–431–3400.

Import Motors Volvo, Inc., 6375 Hwy. 290 East, Austin, TX 78723: Free information ■ Volvo parts and accessories. 800–880–2101.

Strandberg's Auto, 615 Polk, P.O. Box 430, Centuria, WI 54824: Free information with long SASE ■ Parts for 1957 to 1989 Volvos. 715–646–2388.

Voluparts, 751 Trabert Ave., Atlanta, GA 30318: Free information ■ New and used Volvo parts. 404–352–3402.

WILLYS

American Motor Haven, 1107 Campbell Ave., San Jose, CA 95126: Free information ■ Hard-to-find parts for the Willys. 408–246–0957.

Obsolete Jeep & Willys Parts, Division Florida 4–Wheel Drive & Truck Parts, 6110 17th St. East, Bradenton, FL 34203: Free information ■ New, used, rebuilt, and N.O.S. parts. 813–756–7844.

Plating

Classic Chrome, 2430 Washington St., Boston, MA 02119: Free information ■ Copper, nickel, chrome, and gold plating. 617–444–4974.

CustomChrome Plating, Inc., 963 Mechanic St., P.O. Box 125, Grafton, OH 44044: Free information ■ Polishing, buffing, and electroplating in chrome, brass, nickel, copper, and black chrome. 216–926–3116.

Duncan Electroplating, Inc., 2459 County Line Rd., York Springs, PA 17372: Free information with long SASE ■ Nickel, chrome, and gold plating of antique car parts. 717–432–9873.

Gary's Plastic Chrome Plating, Inc., 39312 Dillingham, Westland, MI 48185: Free information with long SASE ■ Plating of car parts using the original vacuum metalizing process. 313–326–158.

Graves Plating Company, Industrial Park, P.O. Box 1052, Florence, AL 35631: Free information ■ Automobile parts plating in chrome, nickel, brass, and gold. 205–764–9487.

Martin's of Philadelphia, 7327 State Rd., Philadelphia, PA 19136: Free information ■ Metal finishing and plating. 215–331–5565.

Paul's Chrome Plating, Inc., 198 Mars-Valencia Rd., Mars, PA 16046: Free information ■ Custom plating and pot metal restoration. 800–245–8679.

Plastic Chrome Plating, Inc., 39312 Dillingham, Westland, MI 48185: Free brochure and price list with long SASE ■ Professional plating of GM, Ford, Mopar, and AMC interior plastic parts. 313–326–1858.

Pot Metal Restorations, 4794 Woodlane Cir., Tallahassee, FL 32303: Free brochure ■ Pot metal chrome plating with a smooth "show chrome" finish. 904–562–3847.

Qual Krom, 301 Florida Ave., Fort Pierce, FL 33450: Free information ■ Restoration plating of metals in chrome, brass, silver, gold, and copper. Other services include welding and repair, pot metal restoration, wire wheel restoration, cloisonne services, and engraving. 305–465–7900.

Swirin Plating Service, 535 Indian Rd., Wayne, NJ 07470: Free information ■ Chrome, brass, nickel, copper, and gold plat-ing for antique and classic autos, boats, and motorcycles. 201–839–6580.

Radar Detectors (Manufacturers)

Audiovox, 150 Marcus Blvd., Hauppage, NY 11788: Free information ■ Mini and standard-size radar detectors. 516–436–6200.

Cincinnati Microwave, One Microwave Plaza, Cincinnati, OH 45296: Free information ■ Micro and standard-size radar detectors. 800–543–1608.

Cobra, 6500 W. Cortland St., Chicago, IL 60635: Free information ■ Micro, remote, and standard-size radar detectors. 312–889–8870.

Craig, 13845 Artesia Blvd., Cerritos, CA 90701: Free information ■ Standard-size radar detectors. 310–926–9944.

Early Warning, 30 Congress Dr., Moonachie, NJ 07074: Free information ■ Remote, mini, and standard-size radar detectors. 201–440–5006.

Fox Electronics, 4518 Taylorsville Rd., Dayton, OH 45424: Free information ■ Wireless remote, micro, and standard-size radar detectors. 513–236–3591.

Fultron, 122 Gayoso, Memphis, TN 38103: Free information ■ Pocket-size and standard models of radar detectors. 901–525–5711.

Gul Industries, 23970 Craftsman Rd., Calabasas, CA 91302: Free information ■ Mini, remote, and standard-size radar detectors. 818–716–5335.

K–40 Electronics, 1500 Executive Dr., Elgin, IL 60123: Free information ■ Remote radar detectors. 708–888–7200.

Kraco, 505 E. Euclid Ave., Compton, CA 90224: Free information ■ Standard-size and micro radar detectors. 800–421–1910.

Maxon Electronics, 10828 NW Airworld Dr., Kansas City, MO 64153: Free information ■ Micro and standard-size radar detectors. 816–891–6320.

Radio Shack, Division Tandy Corporation, 1500 One Tandy Center, Fort Worth, TX 76102: Free information ■ Mini, remote, and standard-size models of radar detectors. 817–390–3700.

Uniden, 4700 Amon Carter Blvd., Fort Worth, TX 76155: Free information ■ Stand-ard-size models of radar detectors. 817–858–3300.

Whistler, 5 Liberty Way, Westford, MA 01886: Free information ■ Remote and standard-size radar detectors. 800–531–0004.

Radar Detectors (Retailers)

ComputAbility Consumer Electronics, P.O. Box 17882, Milwaukee, WI 53217: Free information ■ Radar detectors. 800–558–0003; 414–357–8181 (in WI).

Controlonics Corporation, 5 Lyberty Way, Westford, MA 01886: Free information ■ Radar units for motorcycles.

FotoCell, Inc., 49 W. 23rd St., New York, NY 10010: Free information ■ Radar detectors, mounting systems, and car radios. 212–924–7474.

Radar U.S.A., 1749 Golf Rd., Mt. Prospect, IL 60056: Free information ■ Radar detectors and accessories. 800–777–6570; 708–350–0201 (in IL).

Radar World, 210 S. Milwaukee, Wheeling, IL 60090: Free information ■ Radar detectors. 800–521–4211.

S.B.H. Enterprises, 1678 53rd St., Brooklyn, NY 11204: Free information ■ Radar detectors. 800–451–5851; 718–438–1027 (in NY).

SECA Design Corporation, P.O. Box 1165, Maple Grove, MN 55369: Free information ■ Radar detectors, scanners, and accessories. 800–322–7322.

Replica & Conversion Kits

ALLARD

Hardy Motors, Inc., P.O. Box 1132, Ramona, CA 92065: Free information ■ Reproduction car kits. 619–789–9977.

APOLLO VERONA

Apollo Motor Cars, 1321 8th St., Berkeley, CA 94710: Free information ■ Reproduction car kits. 510–644–4228.

ARCHER

Archer Coachworks, 865 N. 360 West, Val-paralso, IN 46383: Information package $4 ■ Reproduction car kits. 219–762–1978.

AUBURN

The Classic Factory, 1454 E. 9th St., Pomona, CA 91766: Information package $3 ■ Replica car kits. 714–629–5968.

Elegant Motors, Inc., P.O. Box 30188, Indianapolis, IN 46230: Free information ■ Reproduction car kits. 317–253–9898.

AUSTIN HEALEY

Classic Roadsters, Ltd., 1617 Main Ave., Fargo, ND 58103: Free brochure ■ Reproduction car kits. 800–767–2277.

BRADLEY GT

Sun Ray Products Corporation, 8017 Ranchers Rd., Fridley, MN 55432: Free parts list $4 ■ Replica car kits. 813–887–5885.

BUGATTI

Ironsmith, Inc., 9621 189th St., Forest Lake, MN 55025: Free information ■ Replica car kits. 612–464–2331.

CABRIOLET/GRIFFIN

Gatsby Productions, 1801 Almaden Rd., San Jose, CA 95125: Brochure $5 ■ Replica car kits. 408–267–0900.

CAMARO

AutoTek Unlimited, 2476 S. Stone Mountain/Lithonia Rd., Lithonia, GA 30058: Information package $2 with long SASE ■ Replica car accessories. 404–482–8327.

CHEETAH

Elegant Motors, Inc., P.O. Box 30188, Indianapolis, IN 46230: Free information ■ Reproduction car kits. 317–253–9898.

COBRA

Ace Auto Services (USA), Ltd., 6825 Tampa Ave., Reseda, CA 91335: Brochure $5 ■ Reproduction car kits. 818–705–3643.

Advanced Chassis, 2435 Blanding Ave., Alameda, CA 94501: Information package $10 ■ Replica car kits. 510–769–8019.

Component Craft, Inc., 10728 S. Pipeline Rd., Hurst, TX 76053: Free information ■ Replica car kits. 817–283–7656.

Contemporary Classic Motor Car Company, 115 Hoyt Ave., Mamaroneck, NY 10543: Brochure $4 ■ Replica car kits. 914–381–5678.

Copy Cars, Inc., 1980 Rt. 30, Sugar Grove, IL 60554: Free brochure ■ Replica car kits. 708–466–7540.

Elegant Motors, Inc., P.O. Box 30188, Indianapolis, IN 46230: Free information ■ Reproduction car kits. 317–253–9898.

E.R.A. Replica Automobiles, 608 E. Main St., New Britain, CT 06051: Information Package $10 ■ Replica car kits. 203–229–7968.

Everett-Morrison Motorcars, 5137 W. Clifton St., Tampa, FL 33634: Information $5 ■ Replica car kits. 813–887–5885.

Frank's Classic Autos, Inc., 3700 Dundee Rd., Winterhaven, FL 33884: Information package $5 ■ Replica car kits. 813–324–8485.

John's Custom Fabrication, 1515 Newmark, Coos Bay, OR 97420: Information package $5 ■ Reproduction car kits. 503–888–9313.

Mid States Classic Cars & Parts, 835 W. Grant, P.O. Box 427, Fremont, NE 68025: Catalog $4 ■ Replica car kits. 402–654–2772.

North American Fiberglass, 202 S. Price Rd., Ste, 101, Tempe, AZ 85281: Brochure $3 ■ Replica car kits. 602–966–9906.

S.C. Motorcar Company, P.O. Box 9, Eucha, OK 74342: Brochure $5 ■ Replica car kits. 918–253–4175.

Shell Valley Motors, Rt. 1, Platte Center, NE 68653: Free information ■ Replica car kits. 402–246–2355.

Southern Roadcraft USA, 102 New Haven Ave., Milford, CT 06460: Free information ■ Reproduction car kits. 203–878–7352.

Unique Motorcars, Inc., 230 E. Broad St., Gadsden, AL 35903: Free information ■ Reproduction car kits. 205–546–3708.

West Coast Cobra, 6785 16 Mile Rd., Sterling Heights, MI 48077: Information $5 ■ Replica car kits. 519–258–1096.

CORD

Elegant Motors, Inc., P.O. Box 30188, Indianapolis, IN 46230: Free information ■ Reproduction car kits. 317–253–9898.

CORSAIR

Roaring 20's Motor Car Company, 21005 Van Dyke, Addison, IL 60101: Information $3 ■ Modified replica car kits. 708–543–0696.

CORVETTE

Beck Development, 1531 W. 13th St., Upland, CA 91786: Free information ■ Replica car kits. 714–981–3840.

Exotic Illusions, P.O. Box 38, North Pembroke, MA 02359: Information $5 ■ Replica car kits. 617–826–4196.

ESCORT

AutoTek Unlimited, 2476 S. Stone Mountain/Lithonia Rd., Lithonia, GA 30058: Information package $2 with long SASE ■ Replica car accessories. 404–482–8327.

FERRARI

Corson Motorcars, Ltd., P.O. Box 41396, Phoenix, AZ 85080: Brochure $5 ■ Replica car kits. 602–375–2544.

B.P. Jakes & Associates, 2176 Bywood Dr., Biloxi, MS 39532: Information package $5 ■ Replica car kits. 601–388–8435.

Rowley Corvette Supply, 357 Main St., Rowley, MA 01969: Free information ■ Reproduction car kits. 508–948–7730.

Special Interest Autos & Components, P.O. Box 508, Alviso, CA 95002: Free information ■ Reproduction car kits. 408–275–7742.

FIERO

American Fiberglass, 821 Prospect Rd., Fort Lauderdale, FL 33309: Free information ■ Fiero reproduction kits. 305–491–6495.

AutoTek Unlimited, 2476 S. Stone Mountain/Lithonia Rd., Lithonia, GA 30058: Information package $2 with long SASE ■ Replica car accessories. 404–482–8327.

Barnett Design, Inc., 5995 120th Ave., Kenosha, WI 53142: Free brochure ■ Conversion car kits. 4124–658–4358.

Canadian Sportcars International, Inc., 12 Woods Rd., Nobel, Ontario, Canada P0G 1G0: Information package $12 ■ Conversion car kits. 705–721–1032.

V–8 Archie, Inc., 1307 Lykins Ln., Niles, MI 49120: Information package $10 ■ Conversion car kits. 616–683–3227.

Westar, 2899 Agoura Rd., #355, Westlake Village, CA 91361: Free information ■ Fiero conversion kits.

FIREBIRD

AutoTek Unlimited, 2476 S. Stone Mountain/Lithonia Rd., Lithonia, GA 30058: Information package $2 with long SASE ■ Replica car accessories. 404–482–8327.

FORD

Classic Motor Carriages, 16650 NW 27th Ave., Miami, FL 33054: Information $2 ■ Replica car kits. 800–252–7742.

JAGUAR

Antique & Collectible Autos, Inc., 35 Dole St., Buffalo, NY 14210: Free brochure ■ Replica car kits. 800–245–1310.

California Convertible Company, Inc., 28720 Roadside Dr., Ste. 225, Agoura Hills, CA 91301: Free information ■ Conversion car kits. 818–706–3919.

Classic Roadsters, Ltd., 1617 Main Ave., Fargo, ND 58103: Free brochure ■ Reproduction car kits. 800–767–2277.

Eagle Coach Works, Inc., 760 Northland Ave., Buffalo, NY 14211: Brochure $3 ■ Replica car kits. 716–897–4292.

G-T Motorsports, 6893 Root Rd., North Ridgeville, OH 44039: Literature $5 ■ Reproduction car kits. 216–327–6451.

LAMBORGHINI

Exotic Dream Machines, P.O. Box 69, Rancho Cordova, CA 95741: Free information ■ Reproduction car kits. 916–635–9695.

Prova Designs USA, 824 W. Hyde Park Blvd., Inglewood, CA 90302: Free information ■ Reproduction car kits. 818–905–9984.

LOTUS

HS Engineering, 3735 Transport Rd., Ventura, CA 93003: Catalog $5 ■ Reproduction car kits. 805–658–2500.

MACHIAVELLI-MAX

Machiavelli Motors, P.O. Box 490237, Key Biscayne, FL 33149: Brochure $5 ■ Replica car kits. 800–FAST–MAX; 305–361–0620 (in FL).

MERCEDES-BENZ

Classic Motor Carriages, 16650 NW 27th Ave., Miami, FL 33054: Brochure $1 ■ Replica car kits. 800–252–7742.

Classic Roadsters, Ltd., 1617 Main Ave., Fargo, ND 58103: Free brochure ■ Reproduction car kits. 800–767–2277.

Classics International, Ltd., P.O. Box 9338, Fargo, ND 58106: Brochure $5 ■ Replica car kits. 800–927–8229.

Fiberfab International, Inc., 6807 Wayzata Blvd., Minneapolis, MN 55426: Free brochure ■ Replica car kits. 800–328–5671; 612–546–7336 (in MN).

Heritage Motor Cars, 16500 NW 7th Ave., Miami, FL 33169: Free information ■ Reproduction car kits. 305–623–2900.

Southern Classic Roadsters, Inc., 212 S. Brookswood Rd., Sherwood, AR 72116: Free information ■ Reproduction car parts and replica kits. 501–834–2000.

MG

British Coach Works, Ltd., Arnold, PA 15068: Information $3 ■ Replica car kits. 800–245–1369; 412–339–3541 (in PA).

Classic Motor Carriages, Inc., 16650 NW 27th St., Miami, FL 33054: Free information ■ Reproduction car kits. 800–252–7742.

Classic Roadsters, Ltd., 1617 Main Ave., Fargo, ND 58103: Free brochure ■ Reproduction car kits. 800–767–2277.

Fiberfab International, Inc., 6807 Wayzata Blvd., Minneapolis, MN 55426: Free brochure ■ Replica car kits. 800–328–5671; 612–546–7336 (in MN).

PACKARD

Gibbon Fiberglass Reproductions, Inc., P.O. Box 490, Gibbon, NE 68840: Catalog $4 ■ Replica car kits. 308–468–6178.

2nd Chance Classics, Inc., P.O. Box 520, Gibbon, NE 68840: Brochure $7 ■ Replica car kits. 308–468–5885.

PORSCHE

Beck Development, 1531 W. 13th St., Upland, CA 91786: Free information ■ Reproduction car kits. 714–981–3840.

Classic Motor Carriages, Inc., 16650 NW 27th St., Miami, FL 33054: Free information ■ Reproduction car kits. 800–252–7742.

Fiberfab International, Inc., 6807 Wayzata Blvd., Minneapolis, MN 55426: Brochure $1 ■ Replica car kits. 800–328–5671; 612–546–7336 (in FL).

SEBRING

Classic Roadsters, Ltd., 1617 Main Ave., Fargo, ND 58103: Free brochure ■ Reproduction car kits. 800–437–4342.

SPECIALTY CARS

Arizona Z Car, 2110 W. Devonshire St., Mesa, AZ 85201: Free information ■ Conversion car kits. 602–844–9677.

Carter's Conversions, P.O. Box 245, Imlay City, MI 48444: Free information ■ Conversion car kits. 313–724–2333.

Convette Corporation, 4104 Preston Hwy., Louisville, KY 40213: Free information ■ Conversion car kits.

Dion Sportscars, 28 Loma Ave., Long Beach, CA 90803: Free information ■ Conversion car kits. 310–438–1085.

Fiberfab International, Inc., 6807 Wayzata Blvd., Minneapolis, MN 55426: Free information ■ Specialty conversion car kits. 800–328–5671; 612–546–7336 (in MN).

Innovations, P.O. Box 60642, Phoenix, AZ 85082: Free information ■ Conversion car kits. 602–377–0104.

Marauder & Company, RR 2, Potomac, IL 61865: Free information ■ Replica car kits.

Spectre/BGW, Ltd., 2534 Woodland Park Dr., Delafield, WI 53018: Free information ■ Conversion car kits. 414–646–4884.

ZMC, Inc., 11530 Firestone Blvd., Norwalk, CA 90650: Free information ■ Specialty conversion car kits. 213–929–8484.

STUTZ BEARCAT

D.H. Aircraft, Inc., 02381 State Rt. 18, Hicksville, OH 43526: Information package $5 ■ Replica car kits.

THUNDERBIRD

Dofral Distributing, Inc., 116 Turnpike Rd., Minneapolis, MN 55416: Information $5 ■ Conversion car kits. 612–546–3510.

Phoenix T-Bird, 6957 NW Hwy. 10, Ramsey, MN 55303: Brochure $6 ■ Reproduction car kits.

TOYOTA

Aeroform, 6300 St. John Ave., Kansas City, MO 64123: Information kit $5 ■ Reproduction car kits. 800–345–2376.

TRANS AM

AutoTek Unlimited, 2476 S. Stone Mountain/Lithonia Rd., Lithonia, GA 30058: Information package $2 with long SASE ■ Replica car accessories. 404–482–8327.

Rubber Parts

Dennis Carpenter Ford Reproductions, P.O. Box 26398, Charlotte, NC 28221: Catalog $2 ■ Rubber parts for 1932 to 1964 Fords; 1958 to 1966 Thunderbirds; and 1960 to 1965 Falcons. 704–786–8139.

Metro Moulded Parts, Inc., 11610 Jay St., P.O. Box 33130, Minneapolis, MN 55433: Catalog $3 ■ Rubber reproduction parts for most American and foreign cars and trucks, from 1929 to 1970. 612–757–0310.

Lynn H. Steele Rubber Products, 1601 Hwy. 150 East, Denver, NC 28037: Catalog $1 (specify make of car) ■ Reproduction rubber parts for Cadillac, Packard, Chrysler, Chevrolet, Buick, Oldsmobile, and Pontiac cars, and Chevrolet trucks. 800–544–8665; 704–483–9343 (in NC).

Seat & Body Covers

Anything Car Covers, Ltd., 11431 Santa Monica, West Los Angeles, CA 90025: Free information ■ Custom car covers for small, medium, and large cars, and most vans and trucks. 800–445–4048.

Auto Stand Fine Motoring Gifts & Accessories, 281 S. Beverly Dr., Beverly Hills, CA 90212: Free information ■ Ready-fit and custom car covers, with cable and lock options. 800–334–4196.

Beverly Hills Motoring Accessories, 200 S. Robertson Blvd., Beverly Hills, CA 90211: Catalog $3 ■ Covers for most makes and models of cars. 800–421–0911; 213–657–4800 (in CA).

Boulevard Seat Covers, 14321 Ventura Blvd., Sherman Oaks, CA 91423: Free information ■ Sheepskin seat covers. 800–325–0022; 818–718–9111 (in CA).

California Car Cover Company, 15430 Cabrito Rd., Van Nuys, CA 91406: Free information ■ Car covers in 100 percent cotton, flannel lined cotton, and multi-layered quilted material. 800–423–5525.

Canvas Shoppe, Inc., 3198 S. Dye Rd., Flint, MI 48507: Free information ■ Lined, water-resistant custom car covers in cotton, twill, or flannel. 800–345–3670.

Classic Motoring Accessories, 146 W. Pomona Ave., Monrovia, CA 91016: Catalog $3 ■ Custom car covers. 800–327–3045; 818–357–8264 (in CA).

Jean Seat International, P.O. Box 7798, Hollywood, FL 33021: Free information ■ Custom seat covers in polyester/cotton. 800–881–0509.

Kanter Auto Parts, 76 Monroe St., Boonton, NJ 07005: Free information ■ Custom-fitted seat cover upholstery kits for most United States cars, from 1932 to 1980. 201–334–9575.

Multisheep, 646 S. Hauser Blvd., Los Angeles, CA 90036: Free information ■ Custom sheepskin seat covers for most cars. 800–532–1222.

New England Auto Accessories, Inc., 2984 E. Main St., Waterbury, CT 06705: Brochure $3 ■ Custom car covers, sheepskin seat covers, and other automotive accessories. 800–732–2761.

Quality Sheepskin, 10726 Sepulveda Blvd., Mission Hills, CA 31345: Free information ■ Custom sheepskin seatcovers, floor mats, and car covers. 800–852–4293.

Reliable Motoring Accessories, 1751 Spruce St., Riverside, CA 92505: Catalog $3 (refundable) ■ Car and seat covers. 800–854–4770; 714–781–0261 (in CA).

Sickafus Sheepskins, Rt. 78, Exit 7, Strausstown, PA 19559: Free catalog ■ Custom sheepskin seat covers. 215–488–1782.

J.C. Whitney & Company, 1917–19 Archer Ave., P.O. Box 8410, Chicago, IL 60680: Free information ■ Custom car covers for American and imported models. 312–431–6102.

Seats

Keiper-Recaro, Inc., 905 W. Maple Rd., Clawson, MI 48017: Free information ■ Orthopedically designed car seats. 800–873–2276.

ProAm, The Seat Warehouse, 6125 Richmond, Houston, TX 77057: Catalog $2 ■ Car seats. 800–847–5712.

Relaxo-Back, Inc., 319 E. California, P.O. Box 812, Gainesville, TX 76240: Free information ■ Form-fitting auxiliary seat that can be used to relieve lower back pain. 800–527–5496; 817–665–6601 (in TX).

Security Systems Manufacturers

ABCO Supply Company, 387 Canal St., New York, NY 10013: Free information ■ Do-it-yourself burglar alarm kits for autos, stores, lofts, factories, boats, apartments, and private homes. 212–431–5066.

Alpine Electronics of America, 19145 Gramercy Pl., Torrance, CA 90505: Free information ■ Automotive security systems. 213–326–8000.

Audiovox, 150 Marcus Blvd., Hauppage, NY 11788: Free information ■ Automotive security systems. 516–436–6200.

Auto Page, 1815 W. 205th St., Torrance, CA 90501: Free information ■ Automotive security systems. 800–423–6687.

Auto Security, 6136 S. Dixie Hwy., Miami, FL 33143: Free information ■ Automotive security systems with optional design features. 305–662–2052.

C & A Control Systems, 7117 Commercial Park Dr., Knoxville, TN 37918: Free information ■ Automotive security systems. 615–922–2148.

Calrad, 819 N. Highland Ave., Los Angeles, CA 90038: Free information ■ Automotive security systems. 213–465–2131.

Chapman Security Industries, 100 Eastern Ave., Bensenville, IL 60106: Free information ■ Automotive security systems. 708–766–4060.

Code-Alarm Security Systems, 32021 Edward, Madison Heights, MI 48071: Free information ■ Automotive security systems with optional design features. 313–583–9620.

Coustic Company, 4260 Charter St., Vernon, CA 90058: Free information ■ Automotive security systems. 213–582–2832.

Ever-Gard Vehicle Security Systems, Inc., P.O. Box 124, Mamaroneck, NY 10543: Free information ■ Easy-to-install automotive alarm systems. 800–782–6644.

Excalibur, 8757 S. Flatrock Rd., Douglasville, GA 30134: Free information ■ Automotive security systems. 404–942–9876.

Fultron, 122 Gayoso, Memphis, TN 38103: Free information ■ Automotive security systems. 901–525–5711.

Kenwood, Box 22745, Long Beach, CA 90801: Free information ■ Automotive security systems. 310–639–9000.

KTK Engineering, 820 S. Palm Ave., Ste. 21, Alhambra, CA 91803: Free information ■ Automotive security systems. 213–639–2200.

Magnum Auto Security Systems, 21822 Lassen St., Chatsworth, CA 91311: Free information ■ Automotive security systems. 818–700–2728.

Paragon Security Systems, 10 Taylor St., Freeport, NY 11520: Free information ■ Automotive security systems. 408–546–0855.

Pentron Products Company, 1560 Montague Expressway, San Jose, CA 95131: Free information ■ Automotive security systems. 408–432–7500.

Radio Shack, Divsion Tandy Corporation, 1500 One Tandy Center, Fort Worth, TX 76102: Free information ■ Automotive security systems. 817–390–3700.

Ranger Vehicle Security Systems, 1 Naclerio Plaza, Bronx, NY 10466: Free information ■ Automotive security systems. 212–324–9111.

Sansui Electronics, 1290 Wall St. West, Lyndhurst, NJ 07071: Free information ■

Automotive security systems. 201–460–9710.

Seco-Larm, 17811 Sky Park Cir., Irvine, CA 92714: Free information ■ Automotive security systems. 714–261–2999.

Techne Electronics, 1916 Commercial St., Palo Alto, CA 94303: Free information ■ Automotive security systems. 415–856–8646.

Vocalarm, 6860 Canby Ave., Reseda, CA 91335: Free information ■ Automotive security systems. 818–856–8646.

Security Systems Retailers

Dometic/A & E Systems, Inc., 3100 W. Segerstrom, Santa Ana, CA 92704: Free information ■ Wireless recreational vehicle alarm system. 714–540–6444.

Spectre Security Systems, 843 Dumont Pl., #22, Rochester Hills, MI 48063: Free information ■ Home and automotive security systems and accessories. 313–652–8117.

Stereo Equipment Manufacturers

Aiwa, 800 Corporate Dr., Moonachie, NJ 07430: Free information ■ Stereo receivers and accessories. 201–512–3600.

Alpine Electronics of America, 19145 Gramercy Pl., Torrance, CA 90501: Free information ■ Sound systems and tuners. 213–326–8000.

Audiovox, 150 Marcus Blvd., Hauppage, NY 11788: Free information ■ Stereo receivers and accessories. 516–436–6200.

Blaupunkt, Robert Bosch Company, 2800 S. 25th Ave., Broadview, IL 60153: Free information ■ Stereo receivers and accessories. 800–866–2022.

Clarion Corporation of America, 661 W. Redondo Beach Blvd., Gardena, CA 90246: Free information ■ Audio/stereo sound systems. 310-327-9100.

Coustic Company, 4260 Charter St., Vernon, CA 90058: Free information ■ Radios and cassette tuners. 213–582–283.

Craig, 13845 Artesia Blvd., Cerritos, CA 90701: Free information ■ Stereo receivers and accessories. 310–926–9944.

Denon America, 222 New Rd., Parsippany, NJ 07054: Free information ■ Stereo receivers and accessories. 201–575–7810.

Fujitsu America, 1100 E. Campbell Rd., Richardson, TX 75081: Free information ■ Stereo receivers and accessories. 214–690–9660.

Harmon Kardon, 240 Crossways Pk., Woodbury, NY 11797: Free information ■ Audio/stereo sound systems. Includes in-dash receivers, in-dash cassette tuners, automotive amplifiers, and crossovers. 516–496–3400.

Hitachi Sales Corporation, 401 W. Artesia Blvd., Compton, CA 90220: Free information ■ Stereo receivers and accessories. 310–537–8383.

Jensen, 25 Tri-State International Office Center, Lincolnshire, IL 60069: Free information ■ Stereo receivers and accessories. 800–323–0707.

JVC, 41 Slater Dr., Elmwood Park, NJ 07407: Free information ■ Stereo receivers and accessories. 201–794–3900.

Kenwood, Box 22745, Long Beach, CA 90801: Free information ■ Audio/stereo sound systems. 310–639–9000.

Marantz, 1150 Feehanville Dr., Mt. Prospect, IL 60056: Free information ■ Stereo receivers and accessories. 708–299–4000.

Mitsubishi Electronics, 57 Plaza Dr., Cypress, CA 90630: Free information. Stereo receivers and accessories. 714–220–2500.

Panasonic, Panasonic Way, Secaucus, NJ 07094: Free information ■ Stereo receivers and accessories. 201–348–7000.

Pioneer Electronics, 5000 Airport Plaza Dr., Long Beach, CA 90810: Free information ■ Stereo receivers. 310–420–5700.

Proton Corporation, 5630 Cerritos Ave., Cypress, CA 90630: Free information ■ Stereo receivers and other cassette receivers that play the sound from television shows. 714–952–6900.

Radio Shack, Division Tandy Corporation, 1500 One Tandy Center, Fort Worth, TX 76102: Free information ■ Stereo receivers. Includes models that can be easily removed. 817–390–3700.

Sansui Electronics, 1290 Wall St. West, Lyndhurst, NJ 07071: Free information ■ Audio/stereo sound system and removable cassette receivers. 201–460–9710.

Sanyo Electronics, 1200 W. Artesia Blvd., Compton, CA 90220: Free information ■ Stereo receivers and accessories. 310–537–5830.

Sears, Roebuck & Company, Catalog Division, 925 S. Homan Ave., Chicago, IL 60607: Free information ■ Audio/stereo sound systems. (Catalog also available from local stores.) 312–875–2500.

Sharp Electronics, Sharp Plaza, Mahwah, NJ 07430 Free information ■ Stereo receivers and accessories. 800–BE–SHARP.

Sherwood, 14830 Alondra Blvd., La Mirada, CA 90638: Free information ■ Stereo receivers. 800–962–3203.

Sony Consumer Products, Sony Dr., Park Ridge, NJ 07656: Free information ■ Stereo receivers. 201–930–1000.

Technics, One Panasonic Way, Secaucus, NJ 07094: Free information ■ Stereo receivers and accessories. 201–348–7000.

Toshiba, 82 Totowa Rd., Wayne, NJ 07470: Free information ■ Stereo receivers and accessories. 201–628–8000.

Vector Research, 1230 Calle Suerte, Camarillo, CA 93010: Free information ■ Stereo receivers and accessories. 805–987–1312.

Yamaha, 6660 Orangethorpe Ave., Buena Park, CA 90620: Free information ■ Audio and stereo receivers. 714–522–9105.

Stereo Equipment Retailers

Crutchfield, 1 Crutchfield Park, Charlottesville, VA 22906: Free catalog ■ Stereo equipment. 800–336–5566.

Crystal Sonics, 1638 S. Central Ave., Glendale, CA 91204: Catalog $2 ■ Stereo equipment and accessories. 800–545–7310; 818–240–7310 (in CA).

FotoCell, Inc., 49–51 W. 23rd St., New York, NY 10010: Free information ■ Radios, radar detectors, and mounting systems. 212–924–7474.

Sound Reproduction, 237 Bloomfield Ave., Bloomfield, NJ 07003: Free catalog ■ Automotive and home audio equipment. 800–932–0087.

Tires

Belle Tire Industries, Inc., 3500 Enterprise Dr., Allen Park, MI 48101: Free catalog ■ Save up to 35 percent on tires. 313–271–9400.

Coker Tires, 1317 Chestnut St., Chattanooga, TN 37402: Free information ■ Tires for antique cars. 800–251–6336; 615–265–6368 (in TN).

Euro-Tire, Inc., 567 Rt. 46, Fairfield, NJ 07006: Free catalog ■ European tires, light alloy wheels, and shock absorbers. 800–631–0080; 201–575–0080 (in NJ).

FasTire, P.O. Box 23055, Cincinnati, OH 45223: Free information ■ Tires, wheels, and car covers. 800–327–8473; 800–522–TIRE (in OH).

Kelsey Tire, Inc., Box 564, Camdenton, MO 65020: Free information ■ Tires and tubes for vintage automobiles. 800–325–0091.

Lucas Automotive, 2141 W. Main St., Springfield, OH 45504: Free information ■ Antique and classic tires. 513–324–1773.

Teletire, 17622 Armstrong Ave., Irvine, CA 92714: Free catalog ■ Automotive tires. Includes performance-rated steel-belted tires. 800–835–8473; 714–250–9141 (in CA).

Tire America, One Bryan Dr., Wheeling, WV 26003: Free information with long SASE ■ RV and high-performance tires and high-performance wheels. 800–443–8473.

Tire Rack, 771 W. Chippewa Ave., South Bend, IN 46614: Brochures $3 (specify car) ■ Tires and wheels for most domestic and imported cars. 800–428–8355; 219–287–2316 (in IN).

Tire-riffic, 9375 US Rt. 1, Laurel, MD 20723: Free information with long SASE ■ Tires for British sports cars. 800–638–9048.

Universal Tire Company, 987 Stony Battery Rd., Lancaster, PA 17601: Free catalog ■ Antique and classic car tires, wheel hardware, moldings, and accessories. 800–233–3827.

Wallace W. Wade Wholesale Tires, 4303 Irving Blvd., Dallas, TX 75247: Free information ■ Antique and classic automobile tires. 800–666–TYRE.

Willies Antique Tires, 5257 W. Diversey Ave., Chicago, IL 60639: Free price list ■ New tires for antique cars. 312–622–4037.

Tools

A & I Supply, 2125 Court St., Pekin, IL 61554: Free information ■ Power and hand tools, air powered and special use tools, welders, compressors, and supplies. 309–353–3002.

Accurate Tool Supply, 1675 Shoreline, P.O. Box 274, Hartland, MI 48029: Free brochure ■ Hand tools and accessories. 313–632–7504.

Eastwood Company, 580 Lancaster Ave., Box 296, Malvern, PA 19355: Free catalog ■ Panel welders and welders, spot welders, rust removers, sand blasting equipment, body repair tools, pin striping equipment, and buffing supplies. 215–644–4412.

Lions Automotive, P.O. Box 229, Bldg. 167, Lyons, IL 50534: Free information ■ Tools and restoration supplies. 708–484–2229.

Pratco, Inc., 1401 Business Center Dr., Conyers, GA 30207: Free information ■ Air tools, spray guns, and accessories. 800–241–0701.

Sonic Technology Products, 120 Richardson St., Grass Valley, CA 95945: Free information ■ Diagnostic listening tool for pinpointing problems in engines, motors, compressors, and other mechanical equipment. 800–247–5548.

Tip Sandblast Equipment, P.O. Box 649, Canfield, OH 44406: Free catalog ■ Sandblasting equipment. 216–533–3384.

Trailers

Atwood Mobile Products, 4750 Hiawatha Dr., Rockford, IL 61101: Free information ■ Boat trailers and accessories. 815–877–7461.

Calkins Manufacturing Company, Spokane Industrial Park, P.O. Box 14527, Spokane, WA 99214: Free information ■ Boat trailers and accessories. 509–928–7420.

Central Manufacturing, 6848 Southeast Blvd., Derby, KS 67037: Free information ■ Jet ski trailers. 316–788–3331.

Coachmen Recreational Vehicle Company, P.O. Box 30, Middlebury, IN 46540: Free information ■ Fifth wheels and travel trailers. 219–825–5821.

Correct Craft, 6100 S. Orange Ave., Orlando, FL 32809: Free information ■ Boat trailers and accessories. 800–346–2092; 407–855–4141 (in FL).

Eastern Marine, 931 S. Chapel St., Newark, DE 19713: Free catalog ■ Boat trailers, electronic equipment for boats, bimini tops, boat covers, and other accessories. 800–622–2628.

Ezee Tow Trailers, Ltd., Hwy. 59 North, P.O. Box 3, Marshall, MN 56258: Free information ■ Stainless steel tandem boat trailers. 507–537–1431.

Gooseneck Trailer Manufacturing Company, Inc., Box 832, Bryan, TX 77806: Free information ■ Horse-carryall and dressing room combination trailers. 409–778–0034.

Hi–Lo Trailer Company, 145 Elm St., Butler, OH 44822: Free information ■ Travel trailers that fold for transporting. 419–883–3000.

Horizon Trailer, 7100 NW 77th Ct., Miami, FL 33166: Free information ■ Boat trailers and accessories. 305–591–1292.

Jensen Enterprises, Ltd., 1301 9th Ave. North, Humboldt, IA 50548: Free literature ■ Custom enclosed car trailers, utility trailers, and open trailers. 515–332–5963.

Loadfast Trailers, 1420 Meylert Ave., Scranton, PA 18509: Free information ■ Boat trailers and accessories. 717–346–0705.

Midwest Industries, Hwy. 59 & 175, P.O. Box 235, Ida Grove, IA 51445: Free information ■ Boat trailers and accessories. 712–364–3365.

Owens Classic Trailers, P.O. Box 628, Sturgis, MI 49091: Free information ■ Open car trailers and accessories. 616–651–9319.

Pierce Sales, Expressway 287, Henrietta, TX 76365: Catalog $1 ■ Cargo carriers, runabouts, horse and stock trailers, and truck beds. 817–538–5646.

QQ's Trailers, Inc., Rt. 15, P.O. Box 166, Lafayette, NJ 07848: Free information ■ Open and enclosed trailers. 201–579–1223.

S & H Trailer Manufacturing Company, 800 Industrial Dr., Madill, OK 73446: Free information ■ Horse, cargo, equipment, stock, RV, utility, and carryall trailers with optional features. 405–795–5577.

Scamp Eveland's, Inc., Box 2, Backus, MN 56435: Free brochure ■ Trailers. 800–346–4962; 800–432–3749 (in MN).

Shoreline Products, P.O. Box 848, Arlington, TX 76004: Free information ■ Boat trailers and accessories. 800–873–6061; 817–465–1351 (in TX).

Sooner Trailers, P.O. Box 1323, Duncan, OK 73534: Free brochure ■ Horse trailers. 405–255–6979.

Target Trailer, P.O. Box 520963, Miami, FL 33152: Free information ■ Boat trailers and accessories. 305–592–6613.

Tommy's Trailers, Inc., 1505 W. 29th St., Ada, OK 74820: Free brochure ■ Single car haulers. 405–332–7785.

Trailer World, P.O. Box 1687, Bowling Green, KY 42102: Free information with long SASE ■ Enclosed and open car trailers, vendor trailers, and parts. 502–843–4587.

Trail-et, 107 Tower Rd., Waupaca, WI 54981: Free brochure ■ All-aluminum horse trailers. 715–258–8565.

Trailex, 60 Industrial Park Dr., P.O. Box 553, Canfield, OH 44406: Free information ■ Boat trailers and accessories. 216–533–6814.

Trail-Rite Boat Trailers, 3100 W. Central, Santa Ana, CA 92704: Free information ■ Boat trailers. 714–556–4540.

VM Boat Trailers, 5200 S. Peach, Fresno, CA 93725: Free information ■ Jet ski trailers. 209–486–0410.

Truck Parts

Alley Auto Parts, Rt. 2, Box 551, Immokalee, FL 33934: Free information ■ Parts for cars and trucks, from 1948 to 1975. 813–657–3541.

Arnold's Auto Parts, 1484 Crandall Rd., Tiverton, RI 02878: Free information ■ Parts for American cars and trucks, from 1930 to 1970. 401–624–6936.

Bartnik Sales & Service, 6524 Van Dyke, Cass City, MI 48726: Free information ■ Parts for trucks and cars, from 1960 to 1970. 517–872–3541.

C & P Chevy Parts, Box 348, Kulpsville, PA 19443: Catalog $1 ■ Restoration supplies for 1955 to 1959 Chevrolet trucks. 215–721–4300.

Dennis Carpenter Ford Reproductions, P.O. Box 26398, Charlotte, NC 28221: Price list, 1932 to 1947 parts $1; 1948 to 1966 parts catalog $2 ■ Parts for Ford pickups. 704–786–8139.

Jim Carter, 1500 E. Alton, Independence, MO 64055: Free catalog with long SASE and two 1st class stamps ■ Chevrolet and GMC truck parts, from 1930 to 1950. 816–833–1913.

Chev's of the 40's, 18409 NE 28th St., Vancouver, WA 98682: Catalog $3.75 ■ Parts and accessories for Chevrolet trucks, from 1937 to 1954. 206–254–2438.

Chuck's Used Auto Parts, 4722 St. Barnabas Rd., Marlow Heights, MD 20748: Free information with long SASE ■ Parts for General Motors early and late model cars and trucks. 800–462–0123; 301–423–0007 (in MD).

Concours Parts & Accessories, 3563 Numancia St., P.O. Box 1210, Santa Ynez, CA 93460: Catalog $4 ■ Parts for 1948 to 1966 Ford trucks. 805–688–7795.

E & J Used Auto & Truck Parts, 315 31st Ave., P.O. Box 1316, Rock Island, IL 61201: Free information ■ Parts for most American and foreign cars and trucks, from 1940 to 1987. 309–788–7686.

Fiberglass & Wood Company, Rt. 3, Box 800, Nashville, GA 31639: Catalog $3 (specify year and model) ■ Chevrolet and GMC truck parts, from 1931 to 1973. 912–686–3838.

Golden State Pickup Parts, 618 E. Gutierrez St., Santa Barbara, CA 93103: Free information with long SASE ■ Chevy/GMC parts for pickup and panel trucks. 805–564–2020.

Heavy Chevy Pickup Parts, P.O. Box 650, Siloam Springs, AR 72761: Catalog $2 ■ Parts for 1948 to 1959 GMC and Chevrolet trucks. 501–524–4873.

Lawrence Auto Body, 306 W. Grand River, Brighton, MI 48116: Free information ■ Parts for 1947 to 1955 pickups. Includes front fenders, rear fenders, running boards, and splash shields. 313–227–9444.

Obsolete Ford Parts Company, P.O. Box 787, Nashville, GA 31639: Catalog for 1948 to 1956 parts $2; 1957 to 1972 parts $2 ■ Ford truck parts. 912–686–2470.

Roberts Motor Parts, 17 Prospect St., West Newbury, MA 01985: Catalog $4 ■ Chevrolet and GMC truck parts. 508–363–5407.

The Truck Shop, 102 W. Marion Ave., P.O. Box 5035, Nashville, GA 31639: Catalog $4 ■ Parts for 1927 to 1972 Chevrolet and GMC trucks. 912–686–3833.

Vander Haag's, Inc., Sanborn, IA 51301: Free information ■ Parts for 1946 and later trucks, and 1975 and later cars. 712–262–7000.

Upholstery & Carpets

ABC Auto Upholstery, 1634 Church St., Philadelphia, PA 19124: Free information ■ N.O.S. upholstery for 1951 to 1966 Fords. 215–289–0555.

AFTCO Upholstery, P.O. Box 278, Isanti, MN 55040: Catalog $5 ■ Upholstery for older cars. 612–742–4025.

Auto Custom Carpets, Inc., 308 J St., P.O. Box 1167, Anniston, AL 36202: Free information ■ Original-style carpets for General Motors, Chrysler, and Ford cars and trucks. 800–633–2358.

Bob's T-Birds's, 4421 NW 9th Ave., Fort Lauderdale, FL 33309: Free information ■ Upholstery for T-Birds, from 1955 to 1957. 305–491–6652.

Cladella Enterprises, Inc., 3757 E. Broadway Rd., Ste. 4, Phoenix, AZ 85044: Catalog $3 ■ Chevrolet upholstery kits for most 1953 to 1972 models. 602–968–4179.

Hampton Coach, 70 High St., P.O. Box 665, Hampton, NH 03842: Free information ■ Top and interior kits for 1922 to 1954 Chevrolet cars. 603–926–6341.

LeBaron Bonney Company, 6 Chestnut St., Amesbury, MA 01913: Catalog $1 ■ Upholstery materials for antique, classic, and special-interest cars. 508–388–3811.

Midland Automotive Products, 33 Woolfolk Ave., Midland City, AL 36350: Free literature ■ Chevrolet carpeting, truck mats, landau tops, and convertible top pads. 205–983–1212.

USA–1 Interiors, P.O. Box 691, Williamstown, NJ 08094: Catalog $2 ■ Upholstery, parts, and accessories. 800–872–USA–1; 609–629–4334 (in NJ).

Wheels & Hub Caps

Agape Auto, 2825 Selzer, Evansville, IN 47712: Free information ■ Wheel covers from 1949 to 1980 and fender skirts from 1935 to 1972. 812–423–7332.

Appleton Garage, 781 Main St., P.O. Box 425, Rockland, ME 04841: Free information with long SASE ■ Wheel covers for 1955 and later models. 207–594–2062.

Calimers Wheel Shop, 30 E. North St., Waynesboro, PA 17268: Free information ■ Custom hickory-spoke wheels for antique cars. 717–762–5056.

Dayton Wheel Products, 1147 Broadway St., Dayton, OH 45408: Free information ■ Custom wire wheels. Repairs and restores damaged wheels. 513–461–1707.

Al Gruhler Hubcaps, 1401 W. Hatcher Rd., Phoenix, AZ 85021: Free information with long SASE ■ Hubcaps and wheel covers, from the 1940s to the 1950s.

House of Hubcaps, 20034 Pacific Hwy. South, Seattle, WA 98198: Free information with long SASE ■ Hubcaps. 206–824–5040.

Hub Cap Annie, 6905 Atlantic Blvd., Jacksonville, FL 32211: Free information ■ Save from 40 to 70 percent on new and used hub caps. 800–624–7179.

Jeff's Custom, 5432 Royal Palm, Tucson, AZ 85705: Free information with long SASE ■ Hubcaps, from 1940 to 1980. 602–888–6329.

Radio & Wheelcover World, 2718 Koper Dr., Sterling Heights, MI 48310: Free information ■ Wheel covers, from the 1950s to the 1980s. 313–977–7979.

Robinson's Auto Sales, 200 New York Ave., New Castle, IN 47362: Free information ■ Hub caps and wheel covers for late 1940 to 1986 model cars. 317–529–7603.

Tire Rack, 3300 W. Sample, South Bend, IN 46619: Brochures $3 (specify car) ■ Tires and wheels for most domestic and imported cars. 800–428–8355; 219–287–2316 (in IN).

Wheel Repair Service, Inc., 317 Southbridge St., Auburn, MA 01501: Catalog $2 (no checks) ■ Hub caps and wheel covers for most cars, street rods, and replicas; wire spoke, alloy, and steel disc wheels. 508–832–4949.

AWARDS & TROPHIES

A & A Trophy Manufacturing Company, 11523 Harry Hines, Dallas, TX 75229: Free information ■ Trophies, plaques, medals, and pins. 214–241–3211.

Advertising Gifts, Inc., 313 W. 37th St., New York, NY 10018: Free information ■ Trophies, trophy cases, plaques, medals, pins, and ribbons. 212–695–4567.

Ames & Rollinson Studio, 20 W. 22nd St., New York, NY 10010: Free brochure ■ Hand-lettered award scrolls and printed certificates with custom scroll art and calligraphy. 212–473–7000.

Award Company of America, 2200 Rice Mine Rd. NE, Tuscaloosa, AL 35403: Free brochure ■ Walnut-finished plaques. 205–349–2990.

Award Products, Inc., 4830 N. Front St., Philadelphia, PA 19120: Free information ■ Trophies, trophy cases, plaques, medals, pins, and ribbons. 215–324–0414.

Chicago Trophy & Award Company, 3255 N. Milwaukee Ave., Chicago, IL 60618: Free information ■ Trophies, plaques, favors, and novelties. 312–685–8200.

Classic Medallics, 2–15 Borden Ave., Long Island City, NY 11101: Free information ■ Medals, pins, cups and trophies, plaques, ribbons, flatware, gavels, and trophy cases. 718–392–5410.

Classic Trophy Company, 3901 N. Portland, Oklahoma City, OK 73112: Free information ■ Trophies, trophy cases, plaques, medals, pins, and ribbons. 405–943–8541.

Cornette Ribbon & Trophy Company, 850 Dunbar Ave., Oldsmar, FL 34677: Free catalog ■ Ribbons, awards, and trophies. 800–237–8930; 800–422–1273 (in FL).

Dinn Brothers, Inc., 68 Winter St., Holyoke, MA 01040: Free catalog ■ Trophies, plaques, ribbons, silverware, medals, and desk sets. 413–536–3816.

Emblem & Badge, Inc., P.O. Box 6226, Providence, RI 02940: Free information ■ Trophies, trophy cases, plaques, medals, pins, and ribbons. 800–556–7466; 401–331–5444 (in RI).

Ferul Corporation, Inc., 33 Redfern Ave., Inwood, NY 11696: Free information ■

Cups, wood and metal plaques, and medals. 516–239–4030.

Fox's Glass Works, P.O. Box 1177, Damariscotta, ME 04543: Catalog $1 ■ Engraved glass trophies with free-hand calligraphy. 207–563–1474.

Freeman Products, Inc., 86 State Hwy. No. 4, Englewood, NJ 07631: Free information ■ Trophies, cups, wood plaques, ribbons, and medals. 201–871–0750.

Hodges Badge Company, Inc., 18 Schoolhouse Ln., Portsmouth, RI 02871: Free catalog ■ Ribbons, athlete and spectator identification badges, award certificates, brass medals available with gold, silver, and copper/bronze finish, and rosettes. Will custom-design logos. 800–556–2440; 401–683–3836 (in RI).

Ira K. Medals & Awards, Inc., 4140 Austin Blvd., Island Park, NY 11558: Free information ■ Trophies, plaques, medals, pins, and ribbons. 516–431–2131.

Jo So Co Trophy Company, 1115 Mercantile St., Oxnard, CA 93030: Free information ■ Gavels, cups and trophies, plaques, medals, pins, and ribbons. 800–243–3428; 800–821–9734 (in CA).

McCormick Engraving, 501 Jefferson, Amarillo, TX 79105: Free information ■ Awards, plaques, and castings for recognition programs. Engraving services available. 806–373–2521.

Music Stand, 1 Rockdale Plaza, Lebanon, OH 03766: Free catalog ■ Trophies, plaques, and certificates. 802–295–9222.

New England Pewter Company, Inc., 417 Roosevelt Ave., Box 1302, Central Falls, RI 02862: Free catalog ■ Custom awards. Includes bonded bronze and pewter animal and bird castings, reproduction automobile models, aerospace items, historical reproductions, signed paintings, wildlife reproductions, medals, and medallions. 401–728–9710.

Rudig Trophies, 213 N. Broadway, Milwaukee, WI 53202: Free information ■ Trophies, plaques, medals, and ribbons. 414–224–4999.

Taylor Graphics, P.O. Box 492, Greencastle, IN 46135: Free catalog ■ Award and recognition plaques, deskplates and doorplates, paperweights, brass identification plates, photo charm products,

nameplates, card cases, and luggage tags. 800–777–1836; 317–653–8481 (in IN).

Tempo Trophy Manufacturing, Inc., 727 E. Ash St., P.O. Box 718, Piqua, OH 45356: Free information ■ Trophies and plaques. 513–773–6613.

Tower Ribbons & Products, P.O. Box 540, Topeka, IN 46571: Free information ■ Cups, plaques, medals, and ribbons. 219–593–2103.

Triple S. Trophies, P.O. Box 31411, Charleston, SC 29407: Free information ■ Trophies and plaques. 803–795–1520.

Tropar Manufacturing Company, Inc., 5 Vreeland Rd., Florham Park, NJ 07932: Free information ■ Cups, plaques, and trophies. 201–822–2400.

Trophyland USA, Inc., 7001 W. 20th Ave., Hialeah, FL 33014: Free catalog ■ Awards for incentive programs, athletic events, and other occasions. 305–823–4830.

Trophy Supply, 1 Odell Plaza, Yonkers, NY 10701: Free information ■ Trophies, plaques and medals, club awards, around-the-neck medals and ribbons, and pins and badges. 800–227–1557; 914–237–9500 (in NY).

Victory Trophies, 2600 N. Clybourn, Chicago, IL 60614: Free information ■ Trophies, plaques, and medals. 312–327–5577.

Volk Corporation, 23936 Industrial Park Dr., Farmington Hills, MI 48024: Free information ■ Award ribbons. 800–521–6799; 313–477–6700 (in MI).

W & E Baum Bronze Tablet Corporation, 200 60th St., Brooklyn, NY 11220: Free information ■ Laminated, metal, and wood plaques. 718–439–3311.

Walnut Miniatures, P.O. Box 245, Barnegat Light, NJ 08006: Free brochure ■ Trophies and gifts. 609–494–2096.

Yarborough Time & Awards Etc., 1 Southside Ave., Hastings-On-Hudson, N.Y. 10706: Free information ■ Plaques, medals, pins, and ribbons. 914–478–1277.

AWNINGS & PATIO COVERS

European Energy Savers, 14315 Troy Way, Magalia, CA 95954: Free information

■ Retractable patio covers, roll shutters, and window awnings. 916–873–2662.

Inter Trade, Inc., 3175 Fujita St., Torrance, CA 90505: Free literature ■ Indoor-operated, custom patio covers and awnings for security and protection from heat, sun, cold, rain, and noise. 310–515–7177.

Pease Industries, Inc., P.O. Box 14–8001, Fairfield, OH 45014: Information 50¢ ■ Retractable-arm awning. Options include a wind sensor for automatic closing and a sun sensor that opens the awning. 800–543–1180.

BABY CARE

After the Stork, 1501 12th St. NW, Albuquerque, NM 87104: Catalog $1 ■ Children's natural fiber clothing, records, tapes, books, and toys, from birth to age 7. 800–333–5437.

A-Plus Products, Inc., P.O. Box 4057, Santa Monica, CA 90405: Free catalog ■ Bath cushions, support rings, inflatable potty, rattles, table and crib clip-on trays, and storage aids. 800–359–9955.

Baby Biz, 1840 Commerce, Unit E, Boulder, CO 80301: Free brochure ■ Nikky covers, Di-D-Klips, and all-in-one Curity Diaper Covers. 800–444–3988.

Baby Dreams, P.O. Box 3338, Gaithersburg, MD 20878: Catalog $1 (refundable) ■ Cotton and cotton-blend quilted covers for strollers, booster seats, car seats, diaper bags, head-support pillows, and changing pads. 800–638–5965.

The Baby's Gallerie, P.O. Box 458, Whitesboro, NY 13492: Free catalog ■ Feeding time, nursery, baby care, playtime, wearing, and travel accessories. 800–446–5951.

Babysling, Inc., 1 Mason, Irvine, CA 92718: Free brochure ■ Over-the-shoulder padded sling for carrying the baby in front. 714–770–5095.

Ben's Babyland, 81 Avenue A, New York, NY 10009: Free information with long SASE ■ Baby walkers, strollers, furniture, and other items. 212–674–1353.

Best Selection, Inc., 2626 Live Oak Hwy., Yuba City, CA 95991: Catalog $2 ■ Baby feeding aids, safety kits, furniture, walkers and strollers, bath aids, and swings.

Biobottoms, P.O. Box 6009, Petaluma, CA 04953: Free catalog ■ Cotton diapers and wool diaper covers. 800–766–1254; 707–778–7152 (in CA).

Borlin Industries, 11960 Wilshire Blvd., Los Angeles, CA 90025: Free catalog ■ Non-ecotoxic and biodegradable household cleaners and detergents, baby care products, and natural body care products. 800–825–4540.

Cuddlers Cloth Diapers, 3020 Cheyenne Dr., Woodward, OK 73801: Free catalog ■ Velcro-fitted all-cotton diapers. 405–254–3518.

Diap-Air, P.O. Box 103, Upton, NY 11973: Free brochure ■ Velcro-fitted Gore-Tex diaper covers and flannel and terry-cloth diapers.

Diaperaps, P.O. Box 3050, Granada Hills, CA 91394: Free brochure ■ Cotton outer layer, polyfoam-protected diaper covers. 800–477–3424.

Hand in Hand, Rt. 26, RR 1, Box 1425, Oxford, ME 04270: Free catalog ■ Products to help nurture, teach, and protect children. Includes books, toys and games, car seat time occupiers, furniture and other play accessories, bathroom accessories, car seats and other comfort items, housewares and hardware, and health aids. 800–872–9745.

Happy Endings, 12391 SE Indian River Dr., Hobe Sound, FL 33455: Free information ■ Contoured cloth diapers. 407–283–1042.

Heir Affair, 625 Russell Dr., Meridian, MS 39301: Catalog $2 ■ Strollers, car seats, high chairs, swings, nursery monitors, and bathing aids. 800–332–4347; 601–484–4323 (in MS).

Ingi Baby Care, 7207 Chagrin Rd., P.O. Box 45, Chagrin Falls, OH 44022: Free catalog ■ Baby carriages, bassinets, bath tables, travel beds, high chairs, clothing, and matching layettes for bedding and bath. 800–338–4644.

MaxiMoms, 5482 Complex St., Ste. 108, San Diego, CA 92123: Free catalog ■ Nursery room furniture, car seats and baby carriers, soft toys, health and safety aids, nursing accessories, toilet trainers, children's furniture, soft toys, trampolines, and educational toys. 619–278–8909.

Metrobaby, P.O. Box 1572, New York, NY 10013: Free brochure ■ Clothing, cotton

diapers, bedding, and bumpers. 212–966–2075.

Mother's Wear Diapers, Box 114, Northampton, MA 01061: Free brochure ■ Contour-shaped diapers and covers. 800–322–2320; 310–455–1426 (in MA).

The Natural Baby Company, RD 1, Box 160, Titusville, NJ 08560: Free brochure ■ Contour-shaped diapers and covers. 609–737–2895.

Natural Lifestyle Supplies, 16 Lookout Dr., Asheville, NC 28804: Free catalog ■ Natural baby care and body care products; food products that include cereals and grains, prepared foods, nuts and seeds, seasonings, condiments, oils, and other natural foods. 800–752–2775.

One Step Ahead, P.O. Box 46, Deerfield, IL 60015: Free catalog ■ Baby items for use when travelling, feeding, bath time, and security. 800–950–5120.

Parent Care, Ltd., 25 Independence Ct., P.O. Box 417, Folcroft, PA 19032: Catalog $2 ■ Video tapes for parents on child care, health and safety, and making learning fun. 800–334–3889.

J.C. Penney Company, Inc., Catalog Division, Milwaukee, WI 53263: Free catalog ■ Nursery furniture, bedding, strollers, car seats, and other items. 800–222–6161.

Peg Perego U.S.A., Inc., 3625 Independence Dr., Fort Wayne, IN 46818: Free information ■ Perego Quattro strollers with high fashion European fabrics and easy-to-handle maneuverability. 219–482–8191.

Perfectly Safe, 7245 Whipple Ave. NW, North Canton, OH 44720: Free catalog ■ Safety products for children age 3 to 6. Includes bathroom, kitchen, car items, and books. 216–494–4366.

Pleasant Company, P.O. Box 998, Middleton, WI 53562: Free catalog ■ Bassinets, diaper bags, bunting, and knits for newborns and infants. 800–845–0005.

Right Start Catalog, Right Start Plaza, 5334 Sterling Center Dr., Westlake Village, CA 91361: Catalog $2 ■ Car seats, clothing, educational toys, and shopping carts that convert into strollers. 800–548–8531.

Rubens & Marble, Inc., P.O. Box 14900, Chicago, IL 60614: Free brochure with long

SASE ■ Stretch stay-up diapers with elastic ends. 312–348–6200.

Sears, Roebuck & Company, Catalog Division, 925 S. Homan Ave., Chicago, IL 60607: Free catalog ■ Clothing for infants and children, toys and games, tricycles, nursery room furniture and supplies, cribs and swings, playpens, and strollers. (Catalog also available from local store.) 312–876–2500.

Wooly Bottoms, 322 Wilson St., Albany, CA 94710: Free information ■ Wool diaper covers. 510–525–9355.

BADGES

Badge-A-Minit, Ltd., 348 N. 30th Rd., Box 800, LaSalle, IL 61301: Free catalog ■ Badge-A-Minit machine for making badges and pin-back buttons with personalized slogans. Includes a starter kit for beginners. 800–223–4103.

Mr. Button Products, P.O. Box 68355, Indianapolis, IN 46268: Free information ■ All-metal button-making system that makes two sizes of buttons. 317–872–7000.

N.G. Slater Corporation, 220 W. 19th St., New York, NY 10011: Free catalog ■ Equipment and supplies for making all kinds of buttons. 212–924–3133.

BADMINTON

Bard Sports Corporation, 14516 SW 119th St., Miami, FL 33186: Free information ■ Racquets and strings. 800–433–1022.

Buckeye Sports Supply, John's Sporting Goods, 2655 Harrison Ave. SW, Canton, OH 44706: Free information ■ Nets, posts, presses, racquets, sets, shuttlecocks, and strings. 216–456–2758.

Cannon Sports, Inc., P.O. Box 11179, Burbank, CA 91510: Free information ■ Nets, posts, racquets and strings, shuttlecocks, and equipment sets. 800–223–0064; 818–503–9570 (in CA).

Douglas Industries, Inc., P.O. Box 393, Eldridge, IA 52748: Free information ■ Nets, posts, and equipment sets. 800–553–8907; 319–285–4162 (in IA).

Edwards Sports Products, Division Brownell & Company, 429 E. Haddam, Moodus, CT 06469: Free information ■ Nets, posts, and equipment sets. 800–243–2512.

Franklin Sports Industries, Inc., 17 Campanelli Pkwy., P.O. Box 508, Stoughton, MA 02072: Free information ■ Nets, posts, racquets, strings, shuttlecocks, and equipment sets. 617–344–1111.

General Sportcraft Company, Ltd., 140 Woodbine St., Bergenfield, NJ 07621: Free information ■ Nets, posts, equipment sets, racquets and strings, and shuttlecocks. 201–384–4242.

Indian Industries, Inc., 817 Maxwell, P.O. Box 889, Evansville, IN 47711: Free information ■ Nets, posts, racquets, strings, shuttlecocks, and equipment sets. 812–426–2281.

Dick Martin Sports, Inc., 185 River Rd., P.O. Box 931, Clifton, NJ 07014: Free information ■ Nets, posts, racquets and strings, and equipment sets. 800–221–1993; 201–473–0757 (in NJ).

Nelson/Weather-Rite Products, Inc., Fuqua Sports, 14760 Santa Fe Trail Dr., Lenexa, KS 66215: Free information ■ Nets, posts, shuttlecocks, and equipment sets. 800–255–6061; 913–452–3200 (in KS).

Park & Sun, Inc., 2065 W. Amherst Ave., Morrison, CO 80110: Free information ■ Nets, posts, and equipment sets. 303–781–1770.

Porter Athletic Equipment Company, 9555 W. Irving Park Rd., Schiller Park, IL 60176: Free information ■ Nets, posts, racquets, sets, and shuttlecocks. 708–671–0110.

Rackets International, 24572 La Cienega Blvd., Laguna Hills, CA 92653: Free information ■ Racquets and strings, shuttlecocks, cases, covers, grips, and presses. 714–831–8913.

Rashied International, P.O. Box 930125, Norcross, GA 30093: Free information ■ Racquets, strings, and shuttlecocks. 404–446–3030.

Regent Sports Corporation, 45 Ranick Rd., Hauppage, NY 11787: Free information ■ Nets, posts, racquets and strings, shuttlecocks, cases, covers, grips, presses, and equipment sets. 516–234–2948.

Spalding & Brothers, 425 Meadow St., P.O. Box 901, Chicopee, MA 01201: Free information ■ Nets, posts, racquets and strings, shuttlecocks, cases, covers, grips, presses, and equipment sets. 413–536–1200.

Sport Fun, Inc., 4621 Sperry St., P.O. Box 39150, Los Angeles, CA 90039: Free infor-

mation ■ Nets, posts, racquets and strings, shuttlecocks, and equipment sets. 800–423–2597; 818–240–6700 (in CA).

Sunstar International, Ltd., Sunsport Sporting Goods, 24–16 Queens Plaza South, Long Island City, NY 11101: Free information ■ Nets, posts, racquets and strings, shuttlecocks, and equipment sets. 718–706–0611.

Trans Global Sports Company, 13104 S. Avalon Blvd., Los Angeles, CA 90061: Free information ■ Nets, posts, racquets and strings, shuttlecocks, and equipment sets. 213–321–9714.

Winston Sports Corporation, 200 5th Ave., New York, NY 10010: Free information ■ Nets, posts, presses, racquets, sets, shuttlecocks, and strings. 212–255–6870.

Yonex Corporation, 350 Maple Ave., Torrance, CA 90503: Free information ■ Racquets and strings, and shuttlecocks. 800–992–6639; 800–772–5522 (in CA).

BALLOONS

Airtime Manufacturing, Inc., 2978 Teagarden St., San Leandro, CA 94577: Free information ■ Foil and latex balloons and accessories. 510–895–8373.

Anagram International, Inc., 7625 Cahill Rd., Minneapolis, MN 55435: Free information ■ Silver balloons with birthday messages and one-of-a-kind designs. Call for names of local distributors. 800–841–8629; 612–944–9600 (in MN).

Ashland Rubber Products, Sherman at 7th St., Ashland, OH 44805: Free catalog ■ Balloons and accessories for party decorations and clowns. 800–323–0405.

Balloon Box, 2416 Ravendale Ct., Kissimmee, FL 32758: Free information ■ Regular balloons, balloons for making sculptures, accessories, and books. 407–933–8888.

Balloon Enterprises, 5897 Pony Express Trail, Pollock Pines, CA 95726: Free information ■ Custom imprinted latex balloons. 916–644–6700.

Balloon Wholesalers International, 1735 E St., Ste. 104, Fresno, CA 93706: Free catalog ■ Balloons. 800–444–9891.

The Entertainers Supermarket, 21 Carol Pl., Staten Island, NY 10303: Free brochure ■ Supplies and props for balloon sculpturists, clowns, magicians, jugglers,

face painters, stilt walkers, and other entertainers. 718–494–6232.

Evergreen Midwest Company, 335 E. 200th St., Euclid, OH 44119: Free information ■ Balloon inflators and accessories. 216–531–3358.

Flowers & Balloons, Inc., 322 Commerce Blvd., Bogart, GA 30622: Free catalog ■ Balloons and gift items. 800–241–2094; 800–241–2096 (in GA).

Gayla Balloons, P.O. Box 920800, Houston, TX 77292: Free catalog ■ Balloons for the balloon artist. 800–327–9513.

La Rock's Fun & Magic Outlet, 2123 Central Ave., Charlotte, NC 28205: Free information ■ Balloons, clown and balloon books, clown and magic supplies, and balloon sculpture kits. 704–333–3434.

Mecca Magic, Inc., 49 Dodd St., Bloomfield, NJ 07003: Free brochure ■ Balloons, theatrical make-up, clown equipment, magic, costumes and wigs, puppets, ventriloquism accessories, custom props, and juggling supplies. 201–429–7597.

Morris Costumes, 3108 Monroe Rd., Charlotte, NC 28205: Catalog $15 + $1.98 (postage) ■ Balloons, costumes, clown props, masks, joke items, magic tricks and special effects, novelties, and books. 704–333–4653.

NameMaker Corporation, P.O. Box 25068, Tamarac, FL 33320: Free price list ■ Custom screen printed balloons. 305–748–1356.

N & D Novelty Company, 13 Hamden Park Dr., Hamden, CT 06517: Free information ■ Inflatable toys and balloons, advertising specialties, official licensed sports souvenirs, stuffed plush toys, carnival supplies, circus items, and plastic toys. Custom silk-screening available. 203–287–9990.

National Balloon Imprinters, 1514 E. Edinger, Ste. G, Santa Ana, CA 92705: Free information ■ Custom imprinted balloons. 714–568–0522.

Novelties Unlimited, 410 W. 21st St., Norfolk, VA 23517: Free list ■ Balloons; clown supplies, props, and gags; magic; party decorations; make-up; and other supplies. 804–622–0344.

Pioneer Balloon Company, 555 N. Woodlawn Ave., Wichita, KS 67208: Free information ■ Balloons and accessories. Call for names of local distributors. 316–685–2266.

Suburban Balloon & Helium, 31535 Vine St., Willowick, OH 44094: Free information ■ Remote and stationary helium or nitrogen filling stations, with hose, connectors, and crimping tool. 800–572–0100.

Toy Balloon Corporation, 204 E. 38th St., New York, NY 10016: Free price list with long SASE ■ Balloons, accessories and equipment, pumps, seal-off clips, string, ribbons, and custom printing. 212–682–3803.

BANKS

Apple Patch Toys, Rd. 6, Box 338, Branchville, NJ 07826: Free price list ■ Banks. 201–702–0008.

Roy L. Baker, 1215 S. Owasso Ave., Tulsa, OK 74120: Free information with long SASE ■ Cast-iron banks for collectors. 918–582–5986.

N. Bowers, 1916 Cleveland, Evanston, IL 60601: Free information ■ Buys, sells, and trades collectible banks. Includes still and mechanical banks, and Schoenhut items. 708–866–6175.

Clive Devenish, P.O. Box 907, Orinda, CA 94563: Free information ■ Mechanical and still penny banks. 510–254–8383.

G & J Toys & Clocks, 28780 Front St., Temecula, CA 92590: Free price list with long SASE ■ Ertl coin banks. 714–676–5508.

Doug Harman, P.O. Box 9146, Winnetka, IL 60093: Free list with long SASE ■ Collectible banks. Buys collections and single banks. 708–446–8354.

BARBECUE GRILLS

Bobby-Q's Bar-B-Q/Smoker, Box 125, Peabody, KS 66866: Free information ■ Four models of barbecue smokers, each in three sizes. 800–237–3657.

Bradley's, P.O. Box 1300, Columbus, GA 31993: Free catalog ■ Gas and charcoal barbecue grills and accessories. 800–241–8981; 404–324–5617 (in GA).

Char-Broil, P.O. Box 1300, Columbus, GA 31993: Free catalog ■ Grills and accessories; outdoor furniture; seasonings, spices, and condiments; and barbecue cookers. 800–252–8248.

Charmglow Industries, 500 S. Madison, Du Quoin, IL 62832: Free information ■ Gas-operated barbecue grills, motor driven spits, and accessories. 800–558–5502; 800–654–5810 (in IL).

Christen Charcoal Starter & Lighter, 59 Branch St., St. Louis, MO 63147: Free information with long SASE ■ Easy and safe-to-use starter for igniting briquettes. 314–241–7033.

Contempra Industries, 651 New Hampshire Ave., Lakewood, NJ 08701: Free information ■ Almost smokeless, electric barbecue grill for indoor use. 908–363–9400.

Hart-Bake Charcoal Ovens, 6229 E. 61st St., Tulsa, OK 74136: Free brochure ■ Multipurpose outdoor charcoal ovens. 800–426–6836; 918–496–3408 (in OK).

Henkel, Inc., P.O. Box 1322, Hammond, LA 70404: Free information ■ Easy-to-operate outdoor cooker that barbecues, grills, broils, roasts, and bakes. 504–345–1016.

Pachinko House, 3410 Clairmont Rd., Atlanta, GA 30319: Free brochure ■ Kamado firebrick smoker and barbecue grill. 404–321–4568.

Weber-Stephen Products, 200 E. Daniels Rd., Palatine, IL 60067: Free information ■ Permanent-mounted gas barbecues, with cooking chambers, side burners, and warmers. 708–934–5700.

BASEBALL & SOFTBALL

Clothing

Action Sports Gear, Inc., 150 N. Farms Rd., Northampton, MA 01060: Free information ■ Shoes. 413–586–8844.

Active Knitting, Ltd., 89 Tycos Dr., Toronto, Ontario, Canada M6B 1W3: Free information ■ Uniforms and socks. 416–789–1101.

Advantage Uniforms, Inc., 115 W. Main, P.O. Box 186, Manchester, MI 48158: Free information ■ Uniforms and undershirts. 313–428–8522.

Apex One, Inc., 900A Corporate Ct. South, Plainfield, NJ 07080: Free information ■ Caps and ready-made uniforms. Will custom make uniforms. 908–757–8800.

Apsco, Inc., 1st Ave. & 50th St., Building 57, Brooklyn, NY 11232: Free information ■ Caps, uniforms, and socks. 718–965–9500.

Betlin Manufacturing, 1445 Marion Rd., Columbus, OH 43207: Free information ■ Uniforms and undershirts. 614–443–0248.

Bike Athletic Company, Kazmaier Associates, Inc., 2801 Red Dog Dr., P.O. Box 666, Knoxville, TN 37901: Free information ■ Uniforms and undershirts. 800–251–9230; 615–546–4703 (in TN).

Bomark Sportswear, Bomark Group, 5804 S. Rice, Houston, TX 77081: Free information ■ Caps and uniforms. 800–231–5351; 800–392–0616 (in TX).

Tom Byrd Warehouse, Tom Byrd Athletic Sales Company, Ltd., 346 N. Justine St., Chicago, IL 60607: Free information ■ Caps and ready-made uniforms. Will custom make uniforms. 312–243–8383.

California Athletic, Ltd., Division Cali Fame of Los Angeles, 2800 E. 11th St., Los Angles, CA 90023: Free information ■ Uniforms and caps. 213–268–3566.

Champion Products, Inc., 3141 Monroe Ave., Rochester, NY 14618: Free information ■ Uniforms, undershirts, and footwear. 716–385–3200.

De Long, 733 Broad St., P.O. Box 189, Grinnell, IA 50112: Free information ■ Uniforms, caps, and undershirts. 800–733–5664; 515–236–3106 (in IA).

Dreier Company, 375 Turnpike Rd., East Brunswick, NJ 08816: Free information ■ Caps, shoes, and socks. 908–257–0400.

E.A. Graphics, Ethnic Artwork, Inc., 44002 Phoenix Dr., Sterling Heights, MI 48078: Free information ■ Baseball uniforms and caps. 313–726–1400.

Empire Sporting Goods Manufacturing Company, 443 Broadway, New York, NY 10013: Free information ■ Uniforms, undershirts, caps, and socks. 800–221–3455; 800–EMPIRE–6 (in NY).

F & C Sportswear, 20239 W. Warren, Dearborn Heights, MI 48127: Free information ■ Uniforms, caps, and socks. 800–521–0260; 800–482–5340 (in MI).

Fab Knit Manufacturing, Division Anderson Industries, 1415 N. 4th St., Waco, TX 76707: Free information ■ Caps, uniforms, and undershirts. 800–333–4111; 817–752–2511 (in TX).

Felco Athletic Wear Company, Inc., 900 Passaic Ave., Harrison, NJ 07029: Free information ■ Uniforms, caps, socka, and undershirts. 800–221–8240; 201–484–4200 (in NJ).

Foremost Athletic Apparel, 1307 E. Maple Rd., Troy, MI 48083: Free information ■ Socks, caps, and undershirts. 800–433–9486; 800–882–4333 (in MI).

General Shoelace Company, 642 Starks Building, Louisville, KY 40202: Free information ■ Shoes. 502–585–4191.

Just T-Shirts, Fashion Wear, Inc., 3615 Superior Ave., Cleveland, OH 44114: Free information ■ Uniforms, caps, and undershirts. 800–321–3710; 216–881–2922 (in OH).

Kajee, Inc., 101 E. Wayne St., Franklin, IN 46131: Free information ■ Uniforms, caps, and socks. 800–428–4314; 317–736–8032 (in IN).

Loco Athletics/YNot Jackets, 199–B Brook Ave., Deer Park, NY 11729: Free information ■ Uniforms, caps, and undershirts. 515–586–2225.

Majestic Athletic Wear, Ltd., 636 Pen Argyl St., Pen Argyl, PA 18072: Free information ■ Uniforms, caps, and undershirts. 215–863–6161.

Maple Manufacturing Company, 1309 Noble St., Philadelphia, PA 19123: Free information ■ Uniforms, caps, socks, and undershirts. 215–925–2313.

Markwort Sporting Goods Company, 4300 Forest Park Ave., St. Louis, MO 63108: Free catalog ■ Clothing and equipment. 314–652–3757.

New South Athletic Company, Inc., 1010 N. Maine St., P.O. Box 398, Lowell, NC 28098: Free information ■ Shoes, uniforms, caps, undershirts, and socks. 800–438–9934; 704–824–4678 (in NC).

Nike Footwear, Inc., One Bowerman Dr., Beaverton, OR 97005: Free information ■ Shoes. 800–344–6453.

Puma USA, Inc., 147 Centre St., Brockton, MA 02403: Free information ■ Shoes and other athletic clothing. 508–583–9100.

Ranger Athletic Manufacturing Company, P.O. Box 28405, Dallas, TX 75228: Free information ■ Uniforms, socks, and un-

dershirts. 800–433–5518; 800–492–9125 (in TX).

Saucony/Hyde, P.O. Box 6046, Centennial Industrial Park, Peabody, MA 01961: Free information ■ Shoes. 508–532–9000.

Sportsprint, Inc., 9305 Natural Bridge Rd., St. Louis, MO 63134: Free information ■ Uniforms, caps, and socks. 800–325–4858; 314–429–7979 (in MO).

T-Shirt Ink, Inc., 5624 Lincoln Dr., Edina, MN 55436: Free information ■ Uniforms, caps, socks, and undershirts. 612–938–1116.

Venus Knitting Mills, Inc., 140 Spring St., Murray Hill, NJ 07974: Free information ■ Uniforms, caps, socks, and undershirts. 800–955–4200; 201–464–2400 (in NJ).

Western Sales Group, KSG, Inc., 907 Hastings Dr., Concord, CA 94518: Free information ■ Caps and ready-made uniforms. Will custom make uniforms. 510–686–3106.

Wilson Sporting Goods, 2233 West St., River Grove, IL 60171: Free information ■ Caps and socks. 800–323–1552.

Equipment

Andia Progress Company, 47 Soundview Ave., White Plains, NY 10606: Free information ■ Baseballs and softballs, bats, catcher masks, chest protectors, mitts, and softballs. 800–431–2775; 914–948–2685 (in NY).

Apsco, Inc., 1st Ave. & 50th St., Building 57, Brooklyn, NY 11232: Free information ■ Uniform bags, baseballs and softballs, gloves and mitts, and bats. 718–965–9500.

ATEC, 115 Post St., Santa Cruz, CA 95060: Free information ■ Ball, bat, and uniform bags; baseballs and softballs; field equipment; and miscellaneous supplies and accessories; baseball and softball pitching machines; and training aids. 800–547–6273; 408–425–1484 (in CA).

Bolco Athletic Company, P.O. Box 489, Cooksville, TN 38501: Free information ■ Field equipment that includes bases and home plates and pitcher plates. 800–423–4321; 615–526–2109 (in TN).

Cannon Sports, P.O. Box 11179, Burbank, CA 91510: Free information ■ Bags for bats, balls, and uniforms; softballs and baseballs; bats; field equipment; mitts and gloves; protective gear; and miscellaneous equip-

ment and accessories. 800–223–0064; 818–503–9570 (in CA).

Champion Sports Products Company, P.O. Box 138, Sayreville, NJ 08872: Free information ■ Ball and bat bags, softballs and baseballs, bats, field equipment, mitts and gloves, protective gear, and miscellaneous equipment and accessories. 908–238–0330.

Creative Athletic Products & Services, Inc., Box 7731, Des Moines, IA 50322: Free information ■ Softballs, baseballs, and training equipment. 800–227–4579; 515–280–5352 (in IA).

Dalco Athletic, P.O. Box 550220, Dallas, TX 75355: Free information ■ Baseballs and softballs, bats, batting gloves, batting helmets, catcher masks, chest protectors, gloves, and mitts. 800–288–3252; 214–494–1455 (in TX).

Diamond Sports Company, P.O. Box 637, Los Alamitos, CA 90720: Free information ■ Baseballs and softballs, bats, gloves and mitts, and bags for balls, bats, and uniforms. 800–272–3186; 800–992–5758 (in CA).

Direct Trade International, Inc., P.O. Box 1396, Tacoma, WA 98401: Free information ■ Softballs and baseballs. 800–233–8840; 206–272–9764 (in WA).

Douglas Sport Nets & Equipment, 3441 S. 11th Ave., P.O. Box 393, Eldridge, IA 52748: Free information ■ Baseball equipment and supplies. 800–553–8907; 319–285–4162 (in IA).

Dudley Sports Company, 112 Maple Ave., Box 388, Dublin, PA 18917: Free information ■ Baseballs and softballs. 215–249–9000.

Easton Sports, 577 Airport Blvd., Ste. 810, Burlingame, CA 94010: Free information ■ Baseballs and softballs, bats, gloves, and mitts. 415–347–3900.

Faeth Outdoor Sales, R.J.F. Enterprises, Inc., 1151 S. 7th St., P.O. Box 118–A, St. Louis, MO 63166: Free information ■ Bat and ball bags, baseballs, bats, and gloves and mitts. 314–421–0030.

Hillerich & Bradsby Company, Inc., P.O. Box 35700, Louisville, KY 40232: Free information ■ Baseball and softball bats, gloves, and other equipment. 502–585–5226.

Jayfro Corporation, Inc., Unified Sports, Inc., 976 Hartford Tpk., P.O. Box 400, Waterford, CT 06385: Free catalog ■ Safety protectors for the field, batting tees, players benches, mats, baseball and softball practice cages, batting cubicles, and backstops. 203–447–3001.

Markwort Sporting Goods Company, 4300 Forest Park Ave., St. Louis, MO 63108: Free information ■ Baseballs and softballs, bats, batting gloves and helmets, catcher masks, chest protectors, gloves, and mitts. 314–652–3757.

Dick Martin Sports, Inc., 185 River Rd., P.O. Box 931, Clifton, NJ 07014: Free information ■ Bat bags, baseballs and softballs, gloves, protective gear, miscellaneous equipment, and supplies. 800–221–1993; 201–473–0757 (in NJ).

Pennsylvania Sporting Goods, 1360 Industrial Hwy., P.O. Box 451, Southhampton, PA 18966: Free information ■ Baseballs and softballs, aluminum bats; field equipment, batting gloves, protective gear, and bags for carrying balls, bats, and uniforms. 800–535–1122.

Premiere Sports Products, 4655 Stenton Ave., Philadelphia, PA 19144: Free information ■ Baseballs and softballs, bats, batting gloves and helmets, catcher masks, chest protectors, gloves, and mitts. 215–438–3400.

Rawlings Sporting Goods Company, P.O. Box 22000, St. Louis, MO 63126: Free information ■ Bags for carrying balls, bats and uniforms; baseballs; aluminum, graphite and wood bats; mitts, gloves, and batting gloves; and protective gear. 314–349–3500.

Sports Equipment, Inc., Curvemaster Division, P.O. Box 280777, Dallas, TX 75228: Free information ■ Baseball pitching machines. 800–727–2444; 214–412–4031 (in TX).

Steele's Sports Company, 1044 Vivian Dr., Grafton, OH 44044: Free information ■ Softball and baseball equipment. 800–321–3885.

BASKETBALL

Clothing

Above the Rim International, 620 C St., 6th Floor, San Diego, CA 92101: Free information ■ Ready-made and custom uniforms, warm-up jackets, and pants. 619–238–8540.

Active Knitting, Ltd., 89 Tycos Dr., Toronto, Ontario, Canada M6B 1W3: Free infor-

mation ■ Uniforms, warm-up jackets, and pants. 416–789–1101.

AVIA Athletic Footwear, 16160 SW Upper Boones Ferry Rd., Portland, OR 97224: Free information ■ Shoes. 503–684–0490.

Betlin Manufacturing, 1445 Marion Rd., Columbus, OH 43207: Free information ■ Uniforms, warm-up jackets, and pants. 614–443–0248.

Bristol Products Corporation, 700 Shelby St., P.O. Box 158, Bristol, TN 37621: Free information ■ Uniforms, socks, and wrist bands. 615–968–4140.

Brooks Shoe, Inc., Wolverine World Wide, 9341 Courtland Dr., Rockford, MI 49351: Free information ■ Shoes. 800–233–7531; 616–866–5500 (in MI).

Champion Products, Inc., 3141 Monroe Ave., Rochester, NY 14603: Free information ■ Uniforms, warm-up jackets, pants, socks, and shoes. 716–385–3200.

Direct Trade International, Inc., P.O. Box 1396, Tacoma, WA 98401: Free information ■ Warm-up jackets, pants, uniforms, basketballs, and other equipment. 800–233–8840; 206–272–9764 (in WA).

E.A. Graphics, Ethnic Artwork, Inc., 44002 Phoenix Dr., Sterling Heights, MI 48078: Free information ■ Custom uniforms, warm-up jackets, and pants. 313–726–1400.

Empire Sporting Goods Manufacturing Company, 443 Broadway, New York, NY 10013: Free information ■ Uniforms, warm-up jackets, pants, socks, and wristbands. 800–221–3455; 800–EMPIRE–6 (in NY).

Felco Athletic Wear Company, Inc., 900 Passaic Ave., Harrison, NJ 07029: Free information ■ Uniforms, warm-up jackets, pants, and socks. 800–221–8240; 201–484–4200 (in NJ).

GeorGI-Sports, Richmat, Inc., P.O. Box 1107, Lancaster, PA 17604: Free information ■ Uniforms, warm-up jackets, pants, and socks. 800–338–2527; 717–291–8924 (in PA).

Kaepa, Inc., 5410 Kaepa Ct., San Antonio, TX 78218: Free information ■ Shoes. 512–661–7463.

Landreth Manufacturing Company, Inc., 9631 Dayton Pike, Daisy, TN 37379: Free information ■ Uniforms. 615–332–9287.

Lotto Italia, Inc., 2301 McDaniel Dr., Carrollton, TX 75006: Free information ■ Shoes. 800–527–5126; 214–351–2537 (in TX).

Midwest Sales Group, 5055 Liberty Ave., P.O. Box 456, Vermillion, OH 43302: Free information ■ Ready-made and custom uniforms, warm-up jackets, and pants. 216–967–7355.

Midwest Sport Sales, Inc., 20239 W. Warren Ave., Dearborn Heights, MI 48127: Free information ■ Custom uniforms. 800–521–0260; 800–482–5340 (in MI).

Pedersons Unlimited, Inc., 201 Minnie St., Paynesville, MN 56362: Free information ■ Custom uniforms, warm-up jackets, and pants. 612–243–3404.

Pony Sports & Leisure, Inc., Meadows Office Complex, 7th Floor, 201 Rt. 17, Rutherford, NJ 07070: Free information ■ Shoes, socks, and wristbands. 800–654–7669; 201–896–0101 (in NJ).

Puma USA, Inc., 147 Centre St., Brockton, MA 02403: Free information ■ Warm-up jackets, pants, wristbands, shoes, and socks. 508–583–9100.

Wayne Saegert Company, Inc., P.O. Box 1584, Denton, TX 76202: Free information ■ Custom uniforms and warm-up jackets and pants. 817–566–3534.

Southland Athletic Manufacturing Company, P.O. Box 280, Terrell, TX 75160: Free information ■ Uniforms and warm-up jackets, and pants. 214–563–3321.

Spalding & Brothers, 425 Meadow St., P.O. Box 901, Chicopee, MA 01021: Free information ■ Uniforms, warm-up jackets, pants, wristbands, socks, shoes, and basketball equipment. 413–536–1200.

T-Shirt Ink, Inc., 5624 Lincoln Dr., Edina, MN 55436: Free information ■ Warm-up jackets, pants, socks, and wristbands. 612–938–1116.

Equipment

Alchester Mills Company, Inc., 314 S. 11th St., Camden, NJ 08103: Free information ■ Pads and guards, supporters, and knee braces. 609–964–9700.

Amko, Inc., 295 Dan Tibbs Rd., P.O. Box 5809, Huntsville, AL 35814: Free information ■ Leather-, rubber-, and synthetic-covered basketballs. 800–289–2656; 205–851–7080 (in AL).

Andia Progress Company, Inc., 47 Soundview Ave., White Plains, NY 10606: Free information ■ Leather-, rubber-, and synthetic-covered basketballs; ball carriers and nets; knee braces, supporters, knee pads, and guards; and miscellaneous equipment and accessories. 800–431–2775; 914–948–2685 (in NY).

B & G Wholesale, 47–09 30th St., Long Island City, NY 11101: Free information ■ Leather-, rubber-, and synthetic-covered basketballs. 718–706–0100.

Bike Athletic Company, Kazmaier Associates, Inc., 2801 Red Dog Dr., P.O. Box 666, Knoxville, TN 37901: Free information ■ Pads and guards, supporters, and knee braces. 800–251–9231; 615–546–4703 (in TN).

Cannon Sports, Inc., P.O. Box 11179, Burbank, CA 91510: Free information ■ Basketballs, ball carriers, goals, nets, knee braces, pads and guards, supporters, and whistles. 800–223–0064; 818–503–9570 (in CA).

Carron Net Company, P.O. Box 177, Two Rivers, WI 54241: Free information ■ Portable and stationary backboards, ball carriers, goals and nets, and whistles. 414–793–2217.

Cramer Products, Inc., 153 W. Warren St., P.O. Box 1001, Gardner, KS 66030: Free information ■ Knee braces, pads, and guards. 800–255–6621; 913–884–7511 (in KS).

Direct Trade International, Inc., P.O. Box 1396, Tacoma, WA 98401: Free information ■ Leather-, rubber-, and synthetic-covered basketballs; nets; knee braces, pads, guards, and supporters; and warm-up jackets and pants. 800–233–8840; 206–272–9764 (in WA).

Dreier Company, 375 Turnpike Rd., East Brunswick, NJ 08816: Free information ■ Basketballs, knee braces, and supporters. 908–257–0400.

John B. Flaherty Company, Inc., 120 Bruckner Blvd., Bronx, NY 10454: Free information ■ Pads and guards, knee braces, and supporters. 800–221–8742; 212–292–4030 (in NY).

Franklin Sports Industries, Inc., 17 Campanelli Pkwy., P.O. Box 508, Stoughton, MA 02072: Free information ■ Leather, rubber and synthetic basketballs, plus pads and

guards, and miscellaneous equipment. 617–344–1111.

GameMaster Athletic Company, 582 Goddard Ave., Chesterfield, MO 63107: Free information ■ Basketballs, portable and stationary backboards, goals and nets, whistles, score books, and other equipment. 800–325–4141; 314–532–4646 (in MO).

Grid, Inc., NDL Products, 2205 NW 30th Pl., Pompano Beach, FL 33069: Free information ■ Supporters, knee braces, pads, and guards. 800–543–1810; 800–843–3022 (in FL).

Holabird Sports Discounters, 9008 Yellow Brick Rd., Rossville Industrial Park, Baltimore, MD 21237: Free brochure ■ Save up to 40 percent on equipment and clothing for basketball, tennis, running and jogging, golf, exercising, and racquetball. 410–687–6400.

Huffy Sports, 2021 MacArthur Rd., P.O. Box 074931 Waukesha, WI 53188: Free information ■ Portable and stationary backboards, goals and nets, whistles, and other equipment. 800–558–5234; 414–548–0440 (in WI).

Jayfro Corporation, Inc., Unified Sports, Inc., 976 Hartford Tpk., P.O. Box 400, Waterford, CT 06385: Free catalog ■ Backboards, post standards, portable standards, and goals. 203–447–3001.

M.W. Kasch Company, 5401 W. Donges Bay Rd., Mequon, WI 53092: Free information ■ Balls, backboards, basketball sets, goals, and nets. 414–242–5000.

Pennsylvania Sporting Goods, 1360 Industrial Hwy., P.O. Box 451, Southampton, PA 18966: Free information ■ Balls, basketball sets, goals, nets, protective glasses, and score books. 800–535–1122.

Porter Athletic Equipment Company, 9555 W. Irving Park Rd., Schiller Park, IL 60176: Free information ■ Backboards, balls, goals, and nets. 708–671–0110.

Rawlings Sporting Goods Company, P.O. Box 22000, St. Louis, MO 63126: Free information ■ Balls, nets, and score books. 314–349–3500.

Spalding & Brothers, 425 Meadow St., P.O. Box 901, Chicopee, MA 01021: Free information ■ Basketballs, other equipment and accessories, uniforms, warm-up jackets and pants, wristbands, socks, and shoes. 413–536–1200.

Standard Merchandising Company, 1125 Wright Ave., Camden, NJ 08103: Free information ■ Supporters, knee braces, pads, and guards. 609–964–9700.

Star Specialty Knitting Company, Inc., 266 Union Ave., 2nd Floor, Laconia, NH 03246: Free information ■ Knee braces, supporters, pads, and guards. 603–528–STAR.

Toss Back, Inc., Old US 40, P.O. Box 189, Dorrance, KS 67634: Free information ■ Basketballs, backboards, rims, training equipment, and supports. 800–255–2990; 913–666–4242 (in KS).

Venus Knitting Mills, Inc., 140 Spring St., Murray Hill, NJ 07974: Free information ■ Balls, nets, and score books. 800–955–4200; 908–464–2400 (in NJ).

BASKETS

ACP Baskets, P.O. Box 1426, Salisbury, NC 28144: Catalog $1 ■ Basket-making materials, books, and kits. 704–636–3034.

Allens Basketworks, 8624 SE 13th, Portland, OR 97202: Free catalog with long SASE and two 1st class stamps ■ Basket-making supplies. 503–238–6384.

Alvin & Trevie Wood Baskets, 2415 E. Main St., Murfreesboro, TN 37130: Brochure $1 ■ Handmade and pounded traditional and original white oak Appalachia-style baskets. 615–895–0391.

Karen & Darryl Arawjo, P.O. Box 477, Bushkill, PA 18324: Free brochure with long SASE ■ White oak Shaker, Nantucket, and Appalachian baskets. 717–588–6957.

Ashwood Basket Corporation, Hadley Rd., Jaffrey, NH 03452: Catalog $1 ■ Handcrafted baskets. 603–532–4497.

Back Door Country Baskets, 10 Batchellor Dr., North Brookfield, MA 01535: Brochure 50¢ with long SASE ■ Basket-making kits, complete with materials and instructions. 508–867–3079.

Bamboo & Rattan Works, Inc., 470 Oberlin Ave. South, Lakewood, NJ 08701: Free catalog ■ Bamboo, flat and round reeds, rattan, cords, chair canes, and mattings. 908–370–0220.

Basket Hollow, Norbert & Barbara Hala, 1641 Etta Kable Dr., Beavercreek, OH 45432: Free brochure with long SASE ■ Handwoven round and flat reed baskets.

Available with a black walnut finish. 513–429–3937.

Basketry Studio, Rt. 1, P.O. Box 960, Eureka Springs, AR 72632: Catalog $1 ■ Flat and round reeds, smoked reed, cane, hoops, handles, raffia, dyes, and basket-weaving kits. 800–852–0025.

Baskets & Bears, 398 S. Main St., Geneva, NY 14456: Free brochure with long SASE ■ Black ash splint baskets in Shaker, Yankee, and Nantucket styles. 315–781–1251.

The Basket Works, 77 Mellor Ave., Baltimore, MD 21228: Price list $1 ■ Basket-making supplies. 410–448–0800.

Basquetrie, 8210 Rangeline, Columbia, MO 65201: Brochure $3 ■ Victorian picnic baskets and accessories, bed trays, and cameos and keepsakes for bridesmaids. 800–342–7278.

Berkshire Ash Baskets, P.O. Box 144, Lanesborough, MA 01237: Free information ■ Handwoven black ash baskets. 413–442–6354.

Berlin Fruit Box Company, Berlin Heights, OH 44814: Free information ■ Baskets for all uses. 419–588–2081.

Braid-Aid, 466 Washington St., Rt. 53, Pembroke, MA 02359: Catalog $4 ■ Braided rug kits and braiding accessories, wool by the pound or yard, and hooking, basket-making, shirret, and spinning and weaving supplies. 617–826–6091.

Butcher Block Shop, Etc., P.O. Box 146, Wrightsville, PA 17368: Brochure with 52¢ stamp ■ Basket-making and caning supplies. 717–252–2800.

Cane & Basket Supply Company, 1283 S. Cochran, Los Angeles, CA 90019: Catalog $1 ■ Caning and basket-making supplies. Includes flat, oval, and round reeds; fiber and genuine rush; Danish seat cord, raffia, rattan, and seagrass; and hoops and handles. 213–939–9644.

Caning Shop, 926 Gilman St., Berkeley, CA 94710: Catalog $1 (refundable) ■ Supplies and books for basket-making and chair-weaving. 510–527–5010.

Carol's Canery, Rt. 1, Box 48, Palmyra, VA 22963: Free catalog ■ Basket-making and caning supplies. 804–973–5645.

Connecticut Cane & Reed Company, 134 Pine St., Manchester, CT 06040: Catalog 50¢ ■ Caning and basket-making supplies. 203–646–6586.

Country Companions, 35 Chittenden Rd., Hebron, CT 06231: Brochure $2 ■ Handmade traditional Nantucket Lightship baskets. 203–228–3625.

Country Seat, RD 2, Box 24, Kempton, PA 19529: Send long SASE with 75¢ postage for price list ■ Supplies, equipment, and books for basket-making and chair-caning, 215–756–6124.

English Basketry Willows, RFD 1, Box 124A, South New Berlin, NY 13843: Brochures and samples $1 ■ Imported basket-making willows, tools, and books. 607–847–8264.

Frank's Cane & Rush Supply, 7252 Heil Ave., Huntington Beach, CA 92647: Free catalog ■ Cane, rush, and other basket-making and seat-weaving supplies, wood parts, tools, and accessories. 714–847–0707.

Jeffrey E. Gale, Basketmaker, RFD 1, Box 124A, South New Berlin, NY 13843: Brochure $1 with long SASE ■ Handmade white ash baskets. 607–847–8264.

Delana & Lorraine Geoghagan Baskets, P.O. Box 61, Holly Pond, AL 35083: Free information with long SASE ■ Handwoven white oak baskets in traditional and original styles. 205–586–1743.

GH Productions, 521 E. Walnut St., Scottsville, KY 42164: Catalog $1 (refundable) ■ Basket-making supplies.

Heirloom Baskets of Chatham, P.O. Box 1145, South Chatham, MA 02659: Brochure $1 ■ Nantucket Lightship and original coil-bound pine needle baskets. 508–432–8746.

Jack's Upholstery & Caning Supplies, 5498 Rt. 34, Oswego, IL 60543: Catalog $2 (refundable) ■ Upholstery, basket, and chair caning supplies and equipment. 312–554–1045.

Jonathan Kline Black Ash Baskets, 5066 Mott Evans Rd., Trumansburg, NY 14886: Brochure $2 ■ Traditional handmade black ash baskets. 607–387–5718.

Dave Lewis Basketry, RD 2, Box 684, Bedford, PA 15522: Free information with long SASE ■ Handwoven traditional splint baskets and antique basket restoration services. 814–623–2805.

John E. McGuire Basket Supplies, 398 S. Main St., Geneva, NY 14456: Free price list with long SASE ■ Basket-making supplies and tools. 315–781–1251.

Maine Island Baskets, 112 Euclid Ave., Portland, ME 04103: Brochure $1 ■ Reproduction lightship baskets in white oak. 207–797–7024.

Michigan Cane Supply, 5348 N. Riverview Dr., Kalamazoo, MI 49004: List $1 ■ Chair cane, rush, and basket-weaving supplies. 616–282–5461.

Susi Nuss, Basketmaker, 5 Steele Crossing Rd., Bolton, CT 06043: Brochure $2 ■ Handmade reproduction 19th-century baskets. 203–646–3876.

Gary O'Brien Baskets, Meadow Farm, Ruggles Hill Rd., Hardwick, MA 01037: Catalog $3.50 ■ Shaker, Yankee, and Indian-style baskets made from New England hardwoods. 413–477–8711.

Ozark Basketry Supply, P.O. Box 599, Fayettville, AR 72702: Catalog $1 ■ Books, basket-making kits, chair cane, dyes, hoops, and handles. 501–442–9292.

J. Page Basketry, 820 Albee Rd. West, Nokomis, FL 34275: Free catalog ■ Basket-making supplies, accessories, tools, books, wheat weaving and pine needle crafting supplies, and dried and preserved flowers and herbs. 813–485–6730.

Peerless Rattan & Reed, 222 Lake Ave., Yonkers, NY 10701: Catalog 50¢ ■ Basket-making and chair-caning supplies. 914–968–4046.

H.H. Perkins Company, 10 S. Bradley Rd., Woodbridge, CT 06525: Catalog $1 ■ Basket-making and seat-weaving supplies, macrame supplies, books, and how-to instructions. 203–389–9501.

Plymouth Reed & Cane, 1200 W. Ann Arbor Rd., Plymouth, MI 48170: Brochure $1 ■ Basket-making and chair-caning materials. Includes reed, cane, fiber rush, Shaker tape, handles, hoops, kits, dyes, tools, and books. 313–455–2150.

Royalwood, Ltd., 517 Woodville Rd., Mansfield, OH 44907: Catalog $1 (refundable) ■ Basket-weaving and caning supplies. Includes reeds, books, hops, handles, tools, and dyes. 419–526–1630.

Splintworks, P.O. Box 858, Cave Junction, OR 97523: Brochure $1 ■ Handwoven baskets. 503–592–2311.

Stannard Mountain Basketry, RD 1, Box 1385, East Hardwick, VT 05386: Brochure $1 with long SASE ■ Sweetgrass and Vermont brown ash traditional baskets. 802–533–7760.

Tint & Splint, 30100 Ford Rd., Sheridan Square, Garden City, MI 48135: Free catalog with long SASE and two 1st class stamps ■ Basket-making supplies. Includes reeds, chair cane, chair webbing, tools, and books. 318–522–7760.

Walnut Creek Baskets, Carol Nelson, P.O. Box 84, Illinois City, IL 61259: Catalog $2.50 ■ Handwoven traditional baskets. 309–791–0194.

Weaving Works, 4717 Brooklyn Ave. NE, Seattle, WA 98105: Catalog $1 ■ Basket-making supplies, looms, spinning wheels, yarns and fibers, hand- and machine-knitting supplies, dyes, and how-to books. 206–524–1221.

Martha Wetherbee Basket Shop, H.C.R. 69, Box 116, Sanbornton, NH 03269: Catalog $3 ■ Handwoven and pounded, brown ash Shaker basket reproductions. 603–286–8927.

White Oak Basketmakings, Alvin & Trevle Wood, 2415 E. Main St., Murfreesboro, TN 37130: Catalog $2 ■ Original and traditional Appalachian-style baskets in white oak. 615–895–0391.

Stephen Zeh Basketmaker, P.O. Box 381, Temple, ME 04984: Catalog $2 ■ Hand-split and woven traditional brown ash baskets in Indian, Shaker, and other styles. 207–778–2351.

BATHROOM FIXTURES & ACCESSORIES

A-Ball Plumbing Supply, 1703 W. Burnside St., Portland, OR 97209: Free catalog ■ Modern, European, and Victorian plumbing fixtures. 503–228–0026.

Alumax, Box 40, Magnolia, AR 71753: Free information ■ Bathroom fixtures and shower enclosures. 501–234–4260.

American Standard, Inc., P.O. Box 6820, Piscataway, NJ 08854: Free information ■ Whirlpool tubs with molded headrest and grab bars, toilets, and other fixtures and accessories. 800–821–7700.

Antique Baths & Kitchens, 2220 Carlton Way, Santa Barbara, CA 93109: Brochure $2 ■ Reproduction sinks, toilets, tank toilets, pedestal basins, marble vanity tops, faucets, medicine chests, and cast-iron tubs. 805–962–8598.

Antique Hardware Store, 9718 Easton Rd., Rt. 611, Kintnersville, PA 18930: Catalog $3 ■ Antique pedestal sinks, faucets, high-tank toilets, cabinet hardware, and accessories. 800–422–9982.

Baldwin Hardware Corporation, 841 E. Wyomissing Blvd., Box 15048, Reading, PA 19612: Bathroom accessories brochure 75¢; lighting fixtures brochure $3; door hardware brochure 75¢; decor hardware brochure 75¢ ■ Brass dead bolts and door hardware, bathroom accessories, and lighting fixtures. 215–777–7811.

Bathlines, 2054 N. Halsted, Chicago, IL 60614: Free information ■ Shower systems for addition to old-styled bathtubs; old-style bathroom fixtures and accessories. 312–472–0777.

BESCO Plumbing & Heating Sales, 729 Atlantic Ave., Boston, MA 02111: Catalog $5 ■ Classic bathroom fixtures and fittings, in complete bathroom assemblies, or as separate fixtures and fittings. 617–423–4535.

Bona Decorative Hardware, 3073 Madison Rd., Cincinnati, OH 45209: Catalog $2 ■ English and French-style bathroom fittings and accessories, cabinet and door hardware, fireplace tools, and other bathroom accessories. 513–321–7877.

Briggs Industries, 4350 W. Cypress, #800, Tampa, FL 33631: Free information ■ Acrylic one-piece tub-shower combination units and multi-jet whirlpool tubs. 813–878–0178.

Cheviot Products, Inc., 7622 Winston St., Burnaby, British Columbia, Canada V5A 2H4: Free brochure ■ Old-fashioned period pedestal lavatories. 604–420–8989.

Crane Plumbing, 1235 Hartley Ave., Evanston, IL 60202: Free information ■ Toilets and water closets. 708–864–9777.

D.E.A. Bathroom Machineries, 495 Main St., Box 1020, Murphys, CA 95247: Catalog $3 ■ Early American bathroom fixtures and accessories. Includes classic brass and hard-to-find parts. 209–728–2031.

Decorum, 235–237 Commercial St., Portland, ME 04101: Free information ■ Plumbing and bathroom fixtures in styles from yesterday. Includes pedestal sinks, faucets, and high-tank toilets. 207–775–3346.

DeWeese Woodworking Company, Hwy. 492, P.O. Box 576, Philadelphia, MS 39350: Free brochure ■ Oak commode seats, tissue roll holders, toothbrush and glass holders, and towel bars. 601–656–4951.

Eljer Plumbingware, P.O. Box 869037, Plano, TX 75086: Free information ■ Bathroom accessories in chrome and polished brass, frameless shower doors, and designer tubs with multi jets. 800–753–5537.

Buddy Fife & Company, 9 Main St., Northwood, NH 03261: Free catalog ■ Custom-made toilet seats in cherry, mahogany, and walnut. Other woods available upon request. 603–942–8777.

Granite Lake Pottery, Inc., Rt. 9, Munsonville, NH 03457: Free brochure ■ Hand-crafted stoneware sinks, bathroom accessories, and tile. 800–443–9908.

Heads Up/Sonoma Woodworks, Inc., 133 Copeland St., Petaluma, CA 94952: Brochure $1 ■ High tank pull-chain toilets, solid oak cabinets, and other accessories for bathrooms. Includes medicine and vanity cabinets. 707–762–5548.

Home Decorators Collection, 2025 Concourse Dr., St. Louis, MO 63146: Free catalog ■ Bathroom accessories in oak, high-glazed porcelain, chrome and brass, and wicker. 800–245–2217; 314–993–1516 (in MO).

Kemp & George, 2515 E. 43rd St., P.O. Box 182230, Chattanooga, TN 37422: Free catalog ■ Bathroom fixtures and accessories, decorative items for the home, and indoor and outdoor lighting fixtures. 800–562–1704.

Kohler Company, Kohler, WI 53044: Catalog $8 ■ Functional and decorative bathroom accessories and tubs and toilets in different shapes and sizes. 800–4–KOHLER.

MAC the Antique Plumber, 885 57th St., Sacramento, CA 95819: Catalog $6 (refundable) ■ Antique plumbing accessories and fixtures. 916–454–4507.

Masterworks, Inc., 450 S. Pickett St., Alexandria, VA 22034: Free brochure ■ Pedestal lavatories in vitreous china, classic or contemporary styling, and other bathroom fixtures, decorative hardware and fittings, and design components from England. 703–849–8384.

Olde Mill House Shoppe, 105 Strasburg Pike, Lancaster, PA 17602: Catalog $1 ■ Country-style bathroom accessories, hand-crafted furniture, braided rugs, homespun table linens, and dolls. 717–299–0678.

Ole Fashion Things, 402 SW Evangeline, Lafayette, LA 70501: Catalog $5 ■ Clawfoot bathtubs, pedestal lavatories, plumbing hardware, and accessories. 318–234–4800.

Plan-A-Flex, A Stanley Tools Company, 600 Myrtle St., New Britain, CT 06050: Free information ■ Bathroom, kitchen, landscape, and closet designer kits. 800–648–7654.

Reon Shower, 7486 La Jolla Blvd., Ste. 555, La Jolla, CA 92037: Free brochure ■ All-brass, directional shower arm. 800–776–REON.

Research Products, 2639 Andjon, Dallas, TX 75220: Free information ■ Self-contained INCINOLET electric non-polluting and waterless toilet that incinerates waste to clean ash. 214–358–4238.

Restoration Works, Inc., 810 Main St., Buffalo, NY 14205: Catalog $3 ■ Plumbing fixtures and bathroom accessories, ceiling medallions and trims, furniture, and hardware. 800–735–3535.

Roy Electric Company, Inc., 1054 Coney Island Ave., Brooklyn, NY 11230: Catalog $6 ■ Antique plumbing fixtures and accessories. 800–366–3347; 718–434–7002 (in NY).

Santile International Corporation, 1201 W. Loop North, Ste. 170, Houston, TX 77055: Free information ■ Decorator faucets in silver, chrome, nickel, or treated brass. 713–688–1862.

Showerlux, Chatahoochee Ave. NW, Box 20202, Atlanta, GA 30325: Free information ■ Shower enclosures and components. 800–333–8326.

Sink Factory, 2140 San Pablo Ave., Berkeley, CA 94702: Catalog $3 ■ Vanity basins and pedestal lavatories, and bathroom accessories and faucets with floral appliques and hand painting to match fabrics and wallcoverings. 510–540–8193.

Sonoma Woodworks, Inc., 133 Copeland St., Petaluma, CA 94952: Brochure $1 ■

Handcrafted solid oak bathroom accessories. 800–659–9003; 707–762–5548 (in CA).

Sterling Plumbing Group, 1375 Remington Rd., Schaumberg, IL 60173: Free information ■ Faucets in fired-on epoxy colors, chrome, and polished brass.

Sunrise Specialty Company, 5540 Doyle St., Emeryville, CA 94608: Catalog $2 ■ Victorian-style bathroom fixtures and accessories. 510–654–1794.

Swan Corporation, One City Centre, St. Louis, MO 63101: Free information ■ Shower enclosures and components. 314–231–8148.

Touch of Class, Huntingburg, IN 47542: Free catalog ■ Bathroom accessories, comforters, pillows and shams, window treatments, towels and rugs, and nightwear and robes for men, women, and children. 800–457–7456.

Buddy Fife & Company, 9 Main St., Northwood, NH 03261: Free catalog ■ Custom-made toilet seats in cherry, mahogany, and walnut. Other woods available upon request. 603–942–8777.

Granite Lake Pottery, Inc., Rt. 9, Munsonville, NH 03457: Free brochure ■ Handcrafted stoneware sinks, bathroom accessories, and tile. 800–443–9908.

Heads Up/Sonoma Woodworks, Inc., 133 Copeland St., Petaluma, CA 94952: Brochure $1 ■ High tank pull-chain toilets, solid oak cabinets, and other accessories for bathrooms. Includes medicine and vanity cabinets. 707–762–5548.

Home Decorators Collection, 2025 Concourse Dr., St. Louis, MO 63146: Free catalog ■ Bathroom accessories in oak, high-glazed porcelain, chrome and brass, and wicker. 800–245–2217; 314–993–1516 (in MO).

Kemp & George, 2515 E. 43rd St., P.O. Box 182230, Chattanooga, TN 37422: Free catalog ■ Bathroom fixtures and accessories, decorative items for the home, and indoor and outdoor lighting fixtures. 800–562–1704.

Kohler Company, Kohler, WI 53044: Catalog $8 ■ Functional and decorative bathroom accessories and tubs and toilets in different shapes and sizes. 800–4–KOHLER.

MAC the Antique Plumber, 885 57th St., Sacramento, CA 95819: Catalog $6 (refun-

dable) ■ Antique plumbing accessories and fixtures. 916–454–4507.

Masterworks, Inc., 450 S. Pickett St., Alexandria, VA 22034: Free brochure ■ Pedestal lavatories in vitreous china, classic or contemporary styling, and other bathroom fixtures, decorative hardware and fittings, and design components from England. 703–849–8384.

Olde Mill House Shoppe, 105 Strasburg Pike, Lancaster, PA 17602: Catalog $1 ■ Country-style bathroom accessories, hand-crafted furniture, braided rugs, homespun table linens, and dolls. 717–299–0678.

Ole Fashion Things, 402 SW Evangeline, Lafayette, LA 70501: Catalog $5 ■ Clawfoot bathtubs, pedestal lavatories, plumbing hardware, and accessories. 318–234–4800.

Plan-A-Flex, A Stanley Tools Company, 600 Myrtle St., New Britain, CT 06050: Free information ■ Bathroom, kitchen, landscape, and closet designer kits. 800–648–7654.

Reon Shower, 7486 La Jolla Blvd., Ste. 555, La Jolla, CA 92037: Free brochure ■ All-brass, directional shower arm. 800–776–REON.

Research Products, 2639 Andjon, Dallas, TX 75220: Free information ■ Self-contained INCINOLET electric non-polluting and waterless toilet that incinerates waste to clean ash. 214–358–4238.

Restoration Works, Inc., 810 Main St., Buffalo, NY 14205: Catalog $3 ■ Plumbing fixtures and bathroom accessories, ceiling medallions and trims, furniture, and hardware. 800–735–3535.

Roy Electric Company, Inc., 1054 Coney Island Ave., Brooklyn, NY 11230: Catalog $6 ■ Antique plumbing fixtures and accessories. 800–366–3347; 718–434–7002 (in NY).

Santile International Corporation, 1201 W. Loop North, Ste. 170, Houston, TX 77055: Free information ■ Decorator faucets in silver, chrome, nickel, or treated brass. 713–688–1862.

Showerlux, Chatahoochee Ave. NW, Box 20202, Atlanta, GA 30325: Free information ■ Shower enclosures and components. 800–333–8326.

Sink Factory, 2140 San Pablo Ave., Berkeley, CA 94702: Catalog $3 ■ Vanity basins and pedestal lavatories, and bathroom accessories and faucets with floral appliques and hand painting to match fabrics and wallcoverings. 510–540–8193.

Sonoma Woodworks, Inc., 133 Copeland St., Petaluma, CA 94952: Brochure $1 ■ Handcrafted solid oak bathroom accessories. 800–659–9003; 707–762–5548 (in CA).

Sterling Plumbing Group, 1375 Remington Rd., Schaumberg, IL 60173: Free information ■ Faucets in fired-on epoxy colors, chrome, and polished brass.

Sunrise Specialty Company, 5540 Doyle St., Emeryville, CA 94608: Catalog $2 ■ Victorian-style bathroom fixtures and accessories. 510–654–1794.

Swan Corporation, One City Centre, St. Louis, MO 63101: Free information ■ Shower enclosures and components. 314–231–8148.

Touch of Class, Huntingburg, IN 47542: Free catalog ■ Bathroom accessories, comforters, pillows and shams, window treatments, towels and rugs, and nightwear and robes for men, women, and children. 800–457–7456.

BEAD CRAFTING

Abeada Corporation, 1205 N. Main St., Royal Oak, MI 48067: Free catalog ■ Beads, bead-stringing kits, and findings. 800–521–6326; 313–399–6326 (in MI).

Alpha Supply, 1225 Hollis St., Box 2133, Bremerton, WA 98310: Catalog $1 (refundable with $15 order) ■ Beads, engraving and jewelry-making tools, and supplies. 206–373–2133.

ARA Imports, P.O. Box 41044, Brecksville, OH 44141: Catalog $1 ■ Semi-precious beads, fresh water pearls, precious metal beads, and findings. 216–838–1372.

Arizona Gems & Minerals, Inc., 6370 East Hwy. 69, Prescott Valley, AZ 86314: Catalog $4 ■ Chip beads, other beads and findings, geodes, silversmithing and lapidary tools, and jewelry-making supplies. 602–772–6443.

Art to Wear, 4202 Water Oaks Ln., Tampa, FL 33624: Catalog $1 ■ Beads, bead-stringing supplies, findings, and tools. 813–265–1681.

Artway Crafts, Box 699, Tom Bean, TX 75489: Catalog $1 (refundable) ■ Beads, bead-stringing and jewelry-making supplies, and findings. 903–546–6755.

B & J Rock Shop, 14744 Manchester Rd., Ballwin, MO 63011: Catalog $3 ■ Rock-hounding equipment and supplies, beads, bead-stringing supplies, quartz crystals, other imported and domestic gemstones, and jewelry-making and bead-stringing supplies. 314–394–4567.

Bally Bead Company, P.O. Box 934, Rockwall, TX 75087: Catalog $4.95 ■ Beads and findings. 214–771–2992.

Banasch, 426 E. 6th St., Cincinnati, OH 45202: Free catalog ■ Beads, pearls, sewing notions, and buttons. 800–543–0355; 800–582–0330 (in OH).

Baubanbea Enterprises, P.O. Box 1205, Smithtown, NY 31117 : Catalog $1 ■ Rhinestones, sequins, beads, semi-precious and precious gemstones, and other craft supplies that include lace, appliques, fringes, trims, feathers, imported and domestic fabrics, and silk flowers. 516–724–4661.

Beada Beada, 4262 N. Woodward Ave., Royal Oak, MI 48073: Free information ■ Beads, bead-stringing supplies, and findings. 313–549–1005.

Bead Broker, P.O. Box 3278, Austin, TX 78764: Catalog $3 (refundable) ■ Beads and bead-stringing supplies.

The Beadcomber, Penn's Station, Central Ave., Flemington, NJ 08822: Catalog $3 ■ Beads and findings. 908–806–8355.

The Bead Company, P.O. Box 12329, San Diego, CA 92112: Catalog $3 ■ Contemporary and ethnic styled beads. 619–239–6330.

Bead It, P.O. Box 3505, Prescott, AZ 86302: Catalog $3 ■ Czechoslovakian beads, gemstones, charms, bone, findings, supplies, and books. 602–445–9234.

Beads-By-The-Bay, P.O Box 5488, Novato, CA 94947: Catalog $4.25 ■ Czechoslovakian beads, other beads, findings, and jewelry-making supplies. 415–883–1093.

Beads Galore International, Inc., 2123 S. Priest, #202, Tempe, AZ 85282. Free information ■ Beads and bead-stringing supplies. 800–424–9577; 602–945–0063 (in AZ).

The Bead Shop, 177 Hamilton Ave., Palo Alto, CA 94301: Catalog $3 ■ Beads and bead-stringing supplies.

Bead Works, 105 N. Cortez St., Prescott, AZ 86301: Catalog $2.50 ■ Czechoslovakian beads. 602–771–0921.

Beadworks, 139 Washington St., South Norwalk, CT 06854: Catalog $10 (refundable) ■ Wood, metal, porcelain, ceramic, bone, plastic, mother of pearl, Swarovski crystal, glass, and other beads. 203–852–9194.

Bourget Bros., 1636 11th St., Santa Monica, CA 90404: Catalog $5 ■ Beads, bead-stringing supplies, and tools and supplies for jewelry-making. 800–828–3024; 310–450–6556 (in CA).

Brahm Limited, P.O. Box 1, Lake Charles, LA 70602: Catalog $2 ■ Precious and semi-precious costume, designer beads, findings, jewelry-making supplies, and rhinestones.

Bucks County Classic, 73 Coventry Lane, Langhorne, PA 19047: Price list $1 ■ Gemstone, Chinese cloisonne, Austrian crystal, stone accent, and metal beads; cabochons; fresh water pearls; and findings. 800–942–GEMS.

Charlie's Rock Shop, 620 J St., Penrose, CO 81240: Catalog $3 (refundable with $25 order) ■ Beads, bead-stringing and jewelry-making supplies, jewelry boxes, and faceted gemstones 800–336–6923.

Janet Coles Beads, P.O. Box 786, Indianola, PA 15051: Catalog $5 (refundable) ■ Beads, findings, jewelry kits, and exclusive beaded items. 412–767–9404.

Contempo Lapidary, 12273 Foothill Blvd., Sylmar, CA 91342: Catalog $3 ■ Beads, bead-stringing supplies, lapidary equipment and supplies, and tools. 800–356–2441; 818–899–1973 (in CA).

The Cracker Box, Solebury, PA 18963: Catalog $4.50 ■ Beading craft kits. 215–862–2100.

Petronella Daubin, P.O. Box 5, Hampton, CT 06247: Catalog $5 (refundable) ■ Handmade fimi beads.

East Wind Bead Supply, 129 S. Phelps Ave., Box 501, Rockford, IL 61108: Catalog $2 (refundable with $10 order) ■ Beads, rhinestones, sequins, pony beads, studs, other craft supplies, bead patterns, and books. 815–399–7687.

Ebersole Lapidary Supply, Inc., 11417 West Hwy. 54, Wichita, KS 67209: Catalog $2 ■ Beads, bead-stringing supplies, carving materials, tools, findings, mountings, cabochons and rocks, and jewelry kits. 316–722–4771.

Oso Famoso, Box 654, Ben Lomond, CA 95005: Price list with long SASE and $1 ■ Handmade beads, scrimshaw, and bulk fossilized ivory. 408–336–2343.

Firemountain Gems, 28195 Redwood Hwy., Cave Junction, OR 97523: Catalog $3 ■ Beads, findings, tools, and bead-stringing and jewelry-making supplies. 800–423–2319; 503–592–2222 (in OR).

Freed Company, 415 Central NW, P.O. Box 394, Albuquerque, NM 87103: Brochure $1 ■ Beads and hand-sewn beaded and sequined appliques. 505–247–9311.

Garden of Beadin', P.O. Box 1535, Redway, CA 95560: Catalog $2 ■ Seed beads, crystals, semi-precious gemstones, books, and bead-stringing supplies. 800–BEAD–LUV; 707–943–3829 (in CA).

Gem-O-Rama, Inc., 150 Recreation Park Dr., Hingham, MA 02043: Free catalog ■ Beads and bead-stringing supplies. 617–749–8250.

General Bead, 637 Minna St., San Francisco, CA 94103: Free information ■ Japanese seed beads, fashion accessory components, charms, and Swarovski of Austria items. 415–621–8187.

The Great Wall Trading Company, 196 Spring St., West Roxbury, MA 02132: Free price list ■ Imported cloisonne beads from China.

Hansa, 4315 Upton Ave. South, Minneapolis, MN 55410: Catalog $2 ■ Venetian glass beads. 800–325–2930.

International Bead & Jewelry Supply, 2368 Kettner St., San Diego, CA 92101: Catalog $2 ■ Exotic hand-fashioned beads from around the world. 619–233–6822.

International Manufacturing Company, P.O. Box 308, Lillian Springs, FL 32351: Catalog $1 ■ Beads, pine cones, potpourri

materials, other craft supplies, silk plants and trees, and flower arranging supplies. 904–875–2918.

Jackson Hole Lapidary, Box 2704, Jackson, WY 83001: Free catalog ■ Beads, bead-stringing supplies, gem trees, and gem tree kits. 307–733–7672.

Jeanne's Rock & Jewelry, 5420 Bissonet, Bellaire, TX 77401: Free information ■ Beads, bead-stringing supplies, seashells, petrified wood products, and lapidary supplies. 713–664–2988.

KUMA Beads, Box 2719, Glenville, NY 12325: Catalog $2 ■ Beads, bead-stringing supplies, semiprecious gemstones, tools, findings, and craft kits. 518–384–0110.

Victor H. Levy, Inc., 1355 S. Flower St., Los Angeles, CA 90015: Catalog $5 ■ Beads, seed beads, rocailles, bugles, fancy beads, and bone beads; shells; and jewelry-making supplies. 800–421–8021; 213–749–8247 (in CA).

Necklines, P.O. Box 1042, Paso Robles, CA 93447: Free catalog ■ Beads and bead-stringing supplies and kits. 805–239–3965.

Promenade Le Bead Shop, P.O. Box 2092, Boulder, CO 80306: Catalog $2.50 (refundable) ■ Beads, bead crafting kits, books, and supplies. 303–440–4807.

Quintessence, P.O. Box 723544, Atlanta, GA 30339: Catalog $3 ■ Beads, rhinestones, hand-carved shells, jewelry-making supplies, and beaded appliques. 404–264–1759.

Red & Green Minerals, Inc., 7595 W. Florida Ave., Lakewood, CO 80226: Free information ■ Beads, bead-stringing supplies, petrified wood products, clocks, clock movements and parts, and rock and mineral specimens. 303–985–5559.

Riviera Lapidary Supply, 30192 Mesquite, Riviera, TX 78379: Catalog $3 ■ Beads, bead-stringing supplies, bead-stringing kits, seashells, petrified wood products, cabochons, slabs, cabbing rough, gemstones, and crystals. 512–296–3958.

Shipwreck Beads, Inc., 5021 Mud Bay Rd., Olympia, WA 98502: Catalog $3 ■ Beads, bead-stringing supplies, and findings. 206–866–4061.

Westbrook Bead Company, P.O. Box 918, Anderson, CA 96007: Catalog $2 ■ Gemstone beads, faceted glass beads, cobalt

blue beads, old trade beads, other beads, and bead-stringing supplies. 916–357–3143.

BEAR MAKING

Animal Crackers Patterns, 5824 Isleta SW, Albuquerque, NM 87105: Catalog $2.50 ■ Bear-making supplies. Includes plastic joint sets, music boxes, growler voice boxes, and fur fabrics. 505–274–BEAR.

Bear Clawset, 27 Palermo Walk, Long Beach, CA 90803: Catalog $2 ■ Bear-making supplies. 310–434–8077.

Carver's Eye Company, P.O. Box 16692, Portland, OR 97216: Information $1 ■ Glass and plastic eyes, noses, joints, growlers, and eye glasses for bears and dolls. 503–666–5680.

CR's Crafts, Box 8, Leland, IA 50453: Catalog $2 ■ Doll- and bear-making supplies; new jointed bears, some with electronic melody units, or kits and patterns; and other crafts supplies. 515–567–3652.

Double D Productions, Inc., 4110 Willow Ridge Rd., Douglasville, GA 30135: Catalog $1 ■ Bear- and toy-making supplies that include kits, parts and accessories, patterns, music box movements, and fur. 404–949–3648.

Edinburgh Imports, Inc., P.O. Box 722, Woodland Hills, CA 91365: Free price list with two 1st class stamps ■ Bear-making supplies. 800–EDINBRG; 818–703–1122 (in CA).

The Fantasy Den, 25 Morehouse Ave., Stratford, CT 06497: Catalog $2 ■ Bear-making supplies, bearaphernalia, artwork, and collectible bears. 203–377–2968.

Gaillorraine Originals, P.O. Box 137, Tehachapi, CA 93561: Catalog $2 ■ Jointed bears, antique replica bear patterns, and bear-making supplies that include fur, joints, eyes, noses, and leather. 805–822–1857.

Grizzlies, 30497 Hixson Rd., Elberta, AL 36530: Free information ■ Bear-making supplies. Includes kits, jointed bears, patterns, and accessories. 205–962–2500.

North Star Bear Country Store, 1126 W. Jefferson St., Brooksville, FL 34601: Free catalog with long SASE ■ Collectible bears and bear-making supplies that include kits, patterns, music boxes, growlers, eyes, noses, joints, and stands. 904–796–8970.

Patterns by Diane, 1126 Ivon Ave., Endicott, NY 13760: Catalog $1 ■ Bear-making supplies. Includes glass eyes and noses, crown and plastic joints, growlers and music boxes, furs and mohair, suede, glasses, stands, patterns, and kits. 607–754–0391.

Spare Bear Parts, Box 56, Interlochen, MI 49643: Catalog $1 ■ Bear-making supplies, patterns, and kits. 616–275–6993.

Tailormaid Togs for Teddybears, 4037 161st St. SE, Bellevue, WA 98006: Catalog $3 ■ Clothing and accessories for bears. 206–644–4469.

Teddy Works, 46–50 54th Ave., Maspeth, NY 11378: Free catalog ■ Bear-making parts and accessories, patterns, books, parasols, and clothing. 718–361–1833.

Unicorn Studios, Box 370, Seymour, TN 37865: Catalog $1 ■ Wind-up and electronic music box movements, voices for talking dolls and bears, winking light units, and supplies. 615–984–0145.

BEARS

Animal Haus, Ltd., 7784 Montgomery Rd., Cincinnati, OH 45236: Free catalog with four 1st class stamps ■ Collectible bears. 513–984–9955.

Bear Emporium, 955 Ashley Blvd., New Bedford, MA 02740: Free information ■ Collectible bears. 508–995–2221.

Bear Hugs, 7 Cooper Ave., Marlton, NJ 08053: Free information ■ Collectible bears and bear clothes. 609–596–2050.

Bear-In-Mind, Inc., 54 Bradford St., Concord, MA 01742: Catalog $1 ■ Exclusive handcrafted bears and other collectibles. 508–369–1167.

Bear Kingdom, 350 S. Lake Ave., #106, Pasadena, CA 91101: Free information ■ Collectible bears and clown dolls. 818–792–2327.

Bearly Ours, P.O. Box 490, Flagstaff, AZ 86002: Catalog $2 ■ Collectible bears.

Bearly Yours, 12643 State Rd., North Royalton, OH 44133: Free price list ■ Collectible bears. 216–582–3254.

Bear Pawse, 502 S. Montezuma, Prescott, AZ 86303: Catalog $6 ■ Collectible bears. 602–445–3800.

Bears 'n Wares, 312 Bridge St., New Cumberland, PA 17070: Brochure $2 ■ Collectible bears. 717–774–1261.

The Bears of Bruton Street, 107 S. Bruton St., Wilson, NC 27893: Free information with long SASE ■ Collectible artist and manufacturer bears. 800–488–BEAR.

Bea's House of Dolls & Teddies, 9438 Magnolia Ave., Riverside, CA 92503: Free information with long SASE ■ Collectible and limited edition dolls and bears, books, patterns, and paper dolls. 714–359–6770.

Christy's Bears, Box 509, Buckingham, PA 18912: Free information with long SASE ■ Collectible bears. 215–794–3132.

Collector's Corner, 104 Hoffman St., P.O. Box 682, Saugatuck, MI 49453: Catalog $1 ■ New and retired collectible bears. 616–857–1739.

CR's Crafts, Box 8, Leland, IA 50453: Catalog $2 ■ Doll- and bear-making supplies; new jointed bears, some with electronic melody units, or kits and patterns; and other crafts supplies. 515–567–3652.

Suzanne De Pee, 2208 S. Valley Dr., Visalia, CA 93277: Catalog $2 ■ Original handcrafted bears and other collectibles. 408–479–8080.

Doll Den, 231 W. Douglas, El Cajon, CA 92020: Free information with long SASE ■ Dolls and stuffed animals for collectors. 619–444–2198.

The Doll House, 5022 N. May Ave., Oklahoma City, OK 73112: Free brochure ■ Collectible bears. Includes limited editions. 405–943–1498.

Dolls & Stuff, 928 S. Main St., Kokomo, IN 46901: Free information with long SASE ■ Collectible bears. 317–452–1211.

dolls 'n bearland, P.O. Box 14634, Scottsdale, AZ 85267: Free catalog ■ Collectible bears. 800–359–9541; 602–944–0265 (in AZ).

Enchanted Doll House, Rt. 7A, Manchester Center, VT 05255: Catalog subscription $2 ■ Collectible bears, toys, and dolls. 802–362–3031.

The Fantasy Den, 25 Morehouse Ave., Stratford, CT 06497: Catalog $2 ■ Bears, bear-making supplies, bearaphernalia, and art prints. 203–377–2968.

Galleria West, 18900 W. Bluemound, Waukesha, WI 53186: Free information ■ Collectible bears. 414–796–0450.

Gi Gi's Dolls & Sherry's Teddy Bears, Inc., 7550 N. Milwaukee Ave., Chicago, IL 60648: Free catalog with three 1st class stamps ■ Collectible bears, dolls, plush toys, and miniatures. 800–442–3655; 312–594–1540.

Groves Quality Collectibles, 349 S. Jameson Ave., Lima, OH 45805: Free catalog with four 1st class stamps ■ Bears from the United States and international sources. 419–229–7177.

House of Bears, P.O. Box 384, Hudson, MA 01749: Free brochure ■ New and retired Raikes collectible bears. Also special orders for current designs by selected bear artists. 508–562–4849.

K.C.'s Collectables-Dolls & Bears, Inc., 825 S, Waukegan Rd., Lake Forest, IL 60045: Free information ■ Collectible artist and manufacturer bears. 708–295–3535.

Imaginings, 2443 Fair Oaks Blvd., Suite 114, Sacramento, CA 95825: Free catalog ■ "Therapy Bear," designed to facilitate communication with abused children and "Teachin Bear," designed to faciliate learning.

Littlethings, 129 Main St., Irvington, NY 10533: Free list with long SASE ■ Bears, dollhouses, miniatures, furniture, miniature paintings, and other collectibles. 914–591–9150.

McB Bears, 380 N. Andreasen, Escondido, CA 92029: Free information with long SASE ■ Bears for collectors. 619–480–1936.

Marj's Doll Sanctuary, 5280 Northland Dr. NE, Grand Rapids, MI 49505: Free catalog with two 1st class stamps ■ Collectible bears and dolls. 616–361–0054.

Moore Bears, Rt. 896, P.O. Box 232, Strasburg, PA 17579: Free information ■ Custom bears and other collectibles. 717–687–6954.

Jean Nordquist's Collectible Doll & Bear Company, 1421 N. 34th St., Seattle, WA 98103: Free information with long SASE ■ Collectible bears. 800–468–3655.

North American Bear Company, 401 N. Wabash, Ste. 500, Chicago, IL 60610: Free information with long SASE ■ Bears for collectors. 800–682–3427; 312–329–0020 (in IL).

North Star Bear Country Store, 1126 W. Jefferson St., Brooksville, FL 34601: Free catalog with long SASE ■ Collectible bears and bear-making supplies that include kits, patterns, music boxes, growlers, eyes, noses, joints, and stands. 904–796–8970.

Old Friends Antiques, P.O. Box 754, Sparks, MD 21152: Annual subscription of monthly lists $10 ■ Steiff bears and other plush animals. 410–472–4632.

Romerhaus Creations, 951 S. Alvord Blvd., Evansville, IN 47714: Catalog $7.50 ■ Miniature bears and accessories. 812–473–7277.

Second Hand Rose Doll House Store, Inc., 5826 W. Bluemound, Milwaukee, WI 53213: Catalog $2.50 ■ Collectible bears and dolls and dollhouse accessories. 414–259–9965.

Shirley's Doll House, 20509 North Hwy. 21, P.O. Box 99A, Wheeling, IL 60090: Free information with long SASE ■ Bears and dolls for collectors, other collectibles, doll-making supplies, and dollhouse furniture. 708–537–1632.

Stuff'd 'N Stuff, 10001 Westheimer, Houston, TX 77042: Catalog $1 ■ Bears and other plush animals, from aardvarks to zebras. 713–266–4352.

The Teddy Bear Emporium LTD, 51 N. Broad St., Lititz, PA 17543: Free information with long SASE ■ Collectible artist and manufacturer bears. 717–626–TEDI.

Teddy Bear House, 349 S. Jameson Ave., Lima, OH 45805: Free catalog with four 1st class stamps ■ Collectible bears. 419–229–7177.

Teddy's Bears' & Moore, 510 E. Ben Franklin Hwy., Rt. 422 East, Douglassville, PA 19518: Brochure $1 ■ Collectible bears. 215–385–6251.

Teddytown U.S.A., 76 White Bridge Rd., Nashville, TN 37205: Free information ■ Collectible bears. 800–874–8648; 615–356–AHUG (in TN).

Ted E. Bear's Emporium, 21 N. 4th St., Harrisburg, PA 17101: Free information ■ Handcrafted bears, original bear art, bear clothing, books, accessories, miniatures, and novelties. 717–232–3401.

Tide-Rider, Inc., P.O. Box 429, Oakdale, CA 95361: Free information ■ Handmade bears and stuffed animals from Mer-

rythought Iron Bridge in Great Britain. 209–848–4420.

Timbears, 4776 Red Rock Dr., Larkspur, CO 80118: Catalog $4 ■ Original artist bears. 303–681–2019.

BEDDING

Comforters & Bed Coverings

Alden Comfort Mills, P.O. Box 55, Plano, TX 75086: Free folder and fabric swatches ■ Down-filled comforters. 800–822–5336; 214–423–4000 (in TX).

Antique Quilt Source, 385 Springview Rd., Carlisle, PA 17013: Catalog $6 ■ Antique quilts. 717–245–2054.

Arkansas Quilts, 2609 Shay Cove, Little Rock, AR 72204: Free price list ■ Hand and machine-made quilts. 501–227–9248.

Betsy Bourdon, Weaver, Scribner Hill, Wolcott, VT 05680: Brochure $3 ■ Hand-woven blankets, rugs, and linens. 802–472–6508.

Carter Canopies, Rt. 2, Box 270, Troutman, NC 28166: Free brochure ■ Hand-tied cotton fishnet canopies, dust ruffles, coverlets, and other country-style bedroom furnishings. 704–528–4071.

Chambers, Mail Order Department, P.O. Box 7841, San Francisco, CA 94120: Free catalog ■ Bed and bath furnishings. 800–334–9790.

Chrisalem by Malerich, 2158 Charlton Rd., Sunfish Lake, MN 55119: Catalog $1 ■ Comforters, pillows and sheets, tablecloths, and other linens. 612–451–6690.

Cindy's Corner, 585 Goode St., RD 2, Ballston Spa, NY 12020: Brochure $1 (refundable) ■ Twin, double/queen, and king-size country-style patchwork quilts with matching curtains, dust ruffles, pillows, and shams. 518–885–8182.

The Company Store, 500 Company Store Rd., LaCrosse, WI 54601: Free catalog ■ Down-filled pillows and comforters, linens, mattress pads, and down-filled outerwear. 800–323–8000.

Laura Copenhaver Industries, Inc., P.O. Box 149, Marion, VA 24354: Catalog $2 ■ Handmade quilts, coverlets, hand-tied canopies, and curtains. 800–227–6797; 703–783–4663 (in VA).

The Coverlet Company, 7135 SE 32nd Ave., Portland, OR 97202: Brochure $2.50 ■ Reproductions of historical coverlets for beds and tables. 503–771–5946.

Cuddledown of Maine, 42 N. Elm St., P.O. Box 667, Yarmouth, ME 04096: Free catalog ■ Down and feather/down comforters, sheets, sleepwear, mattress pads, throw pillows, flannel bedding, and nursery items. 800–323–6793; 207–846–9781 (in ME).

Domestications, P.O. Box 40, Hanover, PA 17333: Catalog $2 ■ Save up to 35 percent on comforters, sheet sets, pillows, blankets, bedspreads, throws, solid or lace tablecloths, mini blinds, shower curtains, and bathroom accessories. 717–633–3313.

Down-Home Comforters, P.O. Box 281, West Brattleboro, VT 05301: Catalog $1 ■ Down comforters and pillows. 802–348–7712.

Dutch Country Designs, 2404 Bellevue Rd., Harrisburg, PA 17104: Catalog $3 ■ Amish quilts, wall hangings, and pillows. 717–238–9043.

Falling Water Comforts, P.O. Box 360126, Strongsville, OH 44136: Free catalog ■ Cotton afghans. 216–572–0613.

Family Heir-Loom Weavers, RD 3, Box 59D, Red Lion, PA 17856: Brochure $3 ■ Coverlets woven in the tradition of Pennsylvania German weavers in the early 1800s. 717–246–2431.

Feathered Friends Mail Order, 2013 4th Ave., Seattle, WA 98121: Catalog $1 (refundable) ■ Down comforters and robes, slip covers, pillows, shams, dust ruffles, and flannel sheets. 206–443–9549.

Freedom Quilting Bee, Rt. 1, P.O. Box 72, Alberta, AL 36720: Free information ■ Handmade custom quilts. 205–573–2225.

Garnet Hill, 262 Main St., Franconia, NH 03580: Free catalog ■ Natural fiber bedding that includes linens and sheets, blankets, and comforters. 800–622–6216.

Gazebo of New York, 127 E. 57th St., New York, NY 10022: Catalog $6 ■ Patchwork quilts and hand-woven rag, hooked, and braided rugs. 212–832–7077.

The Horchow Collection, P.O. Box 620048, Dallas, TX 75262: Free catalog ■ Linens and bed coverings and home decorating accessories. 800–395–5397.

In Detail, 1633 Broadway, New York, NY 10019: Free catalog ■ Designer comforters and bed coverings, decor accessories, linens and sheets, and bathroom towels. 212–830–7484.

JANICE Corporation, 198 Rt. 46, Budd Lake, NJ 07828: Free catalog ■ Allergy-free, women's and men's clothing, exercise wear, sleepwear, and robes; towels and bath accessories; mattresses, pads, and quilts and covers; linens; personal grooming aids; hats, gloves, and scarves; underwear; and accessories. 800–JANICES.

Kelly & Company, 3080 Coolidge, Conklin, MI 49403: Free information ■ Machine-washable quilts for cribs up to king-size beds. 616–899–2694.

Lakota Collection, St. Joseph Lakota Development Council, St. Joseph Indian School, Chamberlain, SD 57326: Free catalog ■ Sioux Indian Star quilts and other Indian crafts and gifts. 605–734–6021.

Landau, 114 Nassau St., P.O. Box 671, Princeton, NJ 08542: Free catalog ■ Machine washable wool blankets. 800–932–0709.

Leron, 750 Madison Ave., New York, NY 10021: Free catalog ■ Linens, towels, pillows and covers, and imported handkerchiefs for men and women. Monogramming available. 212–753–6700.

Linen & Lace, 4 Lafayette, Washington, MO 63090: Catalog $2 ■ Custom bed ruffles, canopies, and curtains. 800–332–5223.

The Linen Source, 5401 Hangar Ct., P.O. Box 31151, Tampa, FL 33631: Free catalog ■ Bedroom ensembles, linens, pillows, curtains, and other items. 800–431–2620.

Deborah Mallow Designs, Inc., 1261 Broadway, New York, NY 10001: Free information with long SASE ■ Quilted bedspreads for Victorian and country-style beds, pillows, valances, curtains, and draperies. 212–779–0540.

Midwest Quilt Exchange, 495 S. 3rd St., Columbus, OH 43215: Free information ■ Antique quilts. 614–221–8400.

Missouri Breaks Industries, Inc., Quilt Brochure, P.O. Box 262, Timber Lake, SD 57656: Free brochure ■ Original Sioux Indian Star quilts. 605–865–3418.

Mother Hart's Natural Products, P.O. Box 4229, Boynton Beach, FL 33424: Free information ■ Natural fiber flannel sheets, blankets, water bed sheets, pillows, quilt covers, shams, down comforters, wool mattress pads, and cotton mattress pads and covers. 407–738–5866.

Ozark Weaving Studio, P.O. Box 286, Cane Hill, AR 72717: Brochure $2.50 ■ Handwoven wool and cotton coverlets and throws. 501–824–3920.

Quiltery, RD 4, Box 337, Boyerstown, PA 19512: Brochure $2 ■ Handmade quilts. 215–845–3129.

Quilts Unlimited, 440A Duke of Gloucester St., Williamsburg, VA 23185: Catalog $6 ■ Save up to 30 percent on antique quilts. 804–253–8700.

J. Schachter Corporation, 85 Ludlow St., New York, NY 10002: Catalog $1 ■ Shams, ruffles, table covers, and draperies. Will custom make using your materials. 800–INTO–BED; 212–533–1150 (in NY).

Upstairs/Downstairs, 3200 SE 14th Ave., Fort Lauderdale, FL 33316: Free catalog ■ Quilts and bed coverings, pillows, and other linens. 305–761–2350.

Warm Things, 180 Paul Dr., San Rafael, CA 94903: Free catalog ■ Down quilts, pillows, and quilt covers. 415–472–2154.

Western Trading Post, 32 Broadway, P.O. Box 9070, Denver, CO 80209: Catalog $3 ■ Blankets, Navajo wool rugs, and Eagle-design bed throws. 303–777–7750.

Yankee Pride, 29 Parkside Cir., Braintree, MA 02184: Catalog $3 (refundable) ■ Hand-crafted quilts, comforters, and bedspreads; hand-braided, hooked wool, and rag rugs. 617–848–7610.

Pillows & Sheets

Betsy Bourdon, Weaver, Scribner Hill, Wolcott, VT 05680: Brochure $3 ■ Linens, handwoven blankets, and rugs. 802–472–6508.

Chrisalem by Malerich, 2158 Charlton Rd., Sunfish Lake, MN 55119: Catalog $1 ■ Comforters, pillows and sheets, tablecloths, and other linens. 612–451–6690.

Cindy's Corner, RD 2, 585 Goode St., Ballston Spa, NY 12020: Brochure $1 (refundable) ■ Twin, double/queen, and king-size country-style patchwork quilts, with matching curtains, dust ruffles, pillows, and shams. 518–885–8182.

The Company Store, 500 Company Store Rd., LaCrosse, WI 54601: Free catalog ■ Down-filled pillows and comforters, linens, mattress pads, and down-filled outerwear. 800–323–8000.

Cuddledown of Maine, 42 N. Elm St., P.O. Box 667, Yarmouth, ME 04096: Free catalog ■ Down and feather/down comforters, sheets, sleepwear, mattress pads, throw pillows, flannel bedding, and nursery items. 800–323–6793; 207–846–9781 (in ME).

Domestications, P.O. Box 40, Hanover, PA 17333: Catalog $2 ■ Save up to 35 percent on comforters, sheet sets, pillows, blankets, bedspreads, throws, solid or lace tablecloths, mini blinds, shower curtains, and bathroom accessories. 717–633–3313.

Down-Home Comforters, P.O. Box 281, West Brattleboro, VT 05301: Catalog $1 ■ Down comforters and pillows. 802–348–7712.

Downtown Design Supply, 4860 Olive St., Commerce City, CO 80022: Free information ■ Down throw pillows, wicker and rattan furniture cushions, and comforters. 303–287–2863.

Feathered Friends Mail Order, 2013 4th Ave., Seattle, WA 98121: Catalog $1 (refundable) ■ Down comforters and robes, slip covers, pillows, shams, dust ruffles, and flannel sheets. 206–443–9549.

Garnet Hill, 262 Main St., Franconia, NH 03580: Free catalog ■ Natural fiber linens and sheets, blankets, and comforters. 800–622–6216.

The Horchow Collection, P.O. Box 620048, Dallas, TX 75262: Free catalog ■ Linens and bed coverings and home decorating accessories. 800–395–5397.

In Detail, 1633 Broadway, New York, NY 10019: Free catalog ■ Designer comforters and bed coverings, decor accessories, linens and sheets, and bathroom towels. 212–830–7484.

JANICE Corporation, 198 Rt. 46, Budd Lake, NJ 07828: Free catalog ■ Allergy-free, women's and men's clothing, exercise wear, sleepwear, and robes; towels and bath accessories; mattresses, pads, and quilts and covers; linens; personal grooming aids; hats, gloves, and scarves; underwear; and accessories. 800–JANICES.

Leron, 750 Madison Ave., New York, NY 10021: Free catalog ■ Linens, towels, pillows and covers, and imported handkerchiefs for men and women. Monogramming available. 212–753–6700.

Harris Levy, 278 Grand St., New York, NY 10002: Free information with long SASE ■ Save up to 40 percent on linens for tables, beds, and baths. Monogramming available. 800–221–7750; 212–226–3102 (in NY).

Linen Mart, 720 Anderson Ave., St. Cloud, MN 56395: Free catalog ■ Closeout and irregular linens, towels, and bedding ensembles. 800–541–1252.

The Linen Source, 5401 Hangar Ct., P.O. Box 31151, Tampa, FL 33631: Free catalog ■ Linens, pillows, curtains, and bedroom ensembles. 800–431–2620.

Deborah Mallow Designs, Inc., 1261 Broadway, New York, NY 10001: Free information with long SASE ■ Quilted bedspreads for Victorian and country-style beds, pillows, valances, curtains, and draperies. 212–779–0540.

Mother Hart's Natural Products, P.O. Box 4229, Boynton Beach, FL 33424: Free information ■ Natural fiber flannel sheets, blankets, water bed sheets, pillows, quilt covers, shams, down comforters, wool mattress pads, and cotton mattress pads and covers. 407–738–5866.

Olde Mill House Shoppe, 105 Strasburg Pike, Lancaster, PA 17602: Catalog $1 ■ Country-styled homespun table linens, handcrafted furniture, braided rugs, and bathroom accessories. 717–299–0678.

Palmetto Linen Company, Box 109, Hardeeville, SC 29927: Free information ■ Sheets and matching dust ruffles, bath towels, blankets, comforters, pillows, tablecloths, place mats, and shower curtains. 800–833–3506.

Rubin & Green, Inc., 290 Grand St., New York, NY 10002: Free information ■ Save from 30 to 40 percent on bed, bath, and table linens. 212–226–0313.

Rue de France, 78 Thames St., Newport, RI 02840: Catalog $3 ■ Pillows, tablecloths and runners, and lace curtains. 800–777–0998.

Shaxted of Beverly Hills, 350 N. Camden Dr., Beverly Hills, CA 90210: Free information ■ Linens for the table, bed, and bath. 310–273–4320.

Warm Things, 180 Paul Dr., San Rafael, CA 94903: Free catalog ■ Down quilts, pillows, and quilt covers. 415–472–2154.

BEEKEEPING

Archia's Seed Store, 106 E. Main St., Sedalia, MO 65301: Free catalog ■ Beekeeping equipment and supplies, vegetable and flower seeds, and gardening supplies. 816–826–1330.

B & B Honey Farm, Rt. 2, Box 245, Houston, MN 55943: Free catalog ■ Beekeeping and candle-making supplies and equipment. 507–896–3955.

Bee Bob's Apiaries, 7461 Porter Rd., Dixon, CA 95620: Free brochure ■ Queen bees. 916–678–2495.

Bee Happy Apiaries, 8307 Quail Canyon Rd., Vacaville, CA 95688: Free information ■ Italian and Carnolian queen bees. 916–795–2124.

Brushy Mountain Bee Farm, Rt. 1, P.O. Box 135, Moravian Falls, NC 28654: Free catalog ■ Beekeeping supplies. Includes gloves and protective clothing, equipment for processing honey, books, and video tapes. 800–233–7929.

Calvert Apiaries, P.O. Box 4, Calvert, AL 36513: Free information ■ Queen bees. 800–BEES–989; 205–829–6183 (in AL).

Cowen Manufacturing Company, Inc., P.O. Box 399, Parowan, UT 84761: Free information ■ Honey extracting equipment. 801–477–3338.

Elliott Curtis & Sons, P.O. Box 893, LaBelle, FL 33935: Free information ■ Italian queen bees. 813–675–1566.

Harold P. Curtis Honey Company, P.O. Box 1012, LaBelle, FL 33935: Free information ■ Italian queen bees. 813–675–2187.

Dadant & Sons, Inc., Hamilton, IL 62341: Free catalog ■ Honey extracting equipment, honey containers, beeswax foundation and plasticell, woodenware, and queen and package bees. 217–847–3324.

East Texas Bee Company, Rt. 3, Box 104, Buna, TX 77612: Free information ■ Italian queen bees and cells. 409–994–2612.

Floyd's Apiaries, 825 Williams Lake Rd., Pineville, LA 71360: Free information ■ Italian queen bees. 318–443–1982.

Forbes & Johnston, Box 535, Homerville, GA 31634: Catalog $1.25 ■ Beekeeping supplies. 912–487–5410.

John Foster Apiaries, P.O. Box 699, Esparto, CA 95627: Free information ■ Italian and Carnolian package bees and queens. 916–787–3044.

Glenn Apiaries, 40521 De Luz Rd., Fallbrook, CA 92028: Free information ■ Italian and Carnolian queen bees. 619–728–3731.

Glorybee Honey & Supplies, P.O. Box 2744, Eugene, OR 97402: Catalog 50¢ ■ Equipment and supplies for beekeeping and honey processing, honey, honey-prepared foods, and gift assortments. 800–456–7923; 503–689–0913 (in OR).

Gregg & Sons Honeybee Farm, Rt. 2, Box 92, Millry, AL 36558: Free information ■ Queen bees. 205–846–2366.

Hardeman Apiaries, P.O. Box 214, Mt. Vernon, GA 30445: Free information ■ Italian package bees and queens. 912–583–2710.

Heitkams' Honey Bees, Rt. 2, Box 2542, Orland, CA 95963: Free information ■ Queen bees. 916–865–9562.

Homan Honey Farm, P.O. Box 365, Shannon, MS 38868: Free information ■ Caucasian and Italian package bees and queens. 601–767–3960.

F.W. Jones & Son, Ltd., 44 Dutch St., Bedford, Quebec, Canada J0J 1A0: Free information ■ Wax, wooden, and metal beekeeping supplies. 514–248–3323.

K & K Honey Bee Farm, Rt. 21, Box 166A, Millry, AL 36558: Free information ■ Three-banded Italian package bees and queens. 205–846–2934.

Walter T. Kelley Company, Inc., Clarkson, KY 42726: Free catalog ■ Beekeeping supplies. 502–242–2012.

C.F. Koehnen & Sons, Inc., Rt. 1, Box 240, Glenn, CA 95943: Free information ■ Italian package bees and queens. 916–891–5216.

Kona Queen Company, P.O. Box 768, Captain Cook, HI 96704: Free information ■ Italian and Carnolian cross queen bees. 808–328–9016.

Lapp's Bee Supply Center, 500 S. Main St., Reeseville, WI 53579: Free information ■ Package bees, fructose, beeswax, glass accessories, honey, and woodenware. 414–927–3848.

Mann Lake Supply, County Rd. 40 & 1st St., Hackensack, MN 56452: Free information ■ Beekeeping and honey production equipment, protective clothing, accessories, and candle molds. 800–233–6663.

Maxant Industries, Inc., P.O. Box 454, Ayer, MA 01432: Catalog $5 ■ Honey processing equipment. 508–772–0576.

McCary Apiaries, P.O. Box 87, Buckatunna, MS 39322: Free information ■ Italian and Carnolian queen bees. 601–648–2747.

Mitchell's Apiaries, Bunkie, LA 71322: Free information ■ Italian queen bees. 318–346–2176.

Norman Bee Farms, P.O. Box 26, Ramer, AL 36069: Free information ■ Italian bees and queens. 205–562–3542.

Homer E. Park, P.O. Box 38, Palo Cedro, CA 96073: Free information ■ Italian queen bees. 916–547–3391.

Penner Apiaries, Inc., P.O. Box 567, Red Bluff, CA 96080: Free information ■ Italian and Carnolian package bees and queens. 800–525–5876; 916–527–4382.

Plantation Bee Company, P.O. Box 777, Baxley, GA 31513: Free information ■ Italian queen bees. 912–367–2984.

Powell Apiaries, Rt. 5, Box 5246, Orland, CA 95963: Free information ■ Italian package bees and queens, nucs, cell builders, hives, and other beekeeping supplies. 916–865–3346.

A.I. Root Company, P.O. Box 706, Medina, OH 44258: Free catalog ■ Beekeeping supplies and equipment. Includes hives, protective clothing and gloves, tools, honey-processing equipment, books, video tapes, and smokers. 800–289–7668.

Rossman Apiaries, Inc., P.O. Box 905, Moultrie, GA 31768: Free information ■ Italian queens and package bees, beekeeping supplies, pollination supplies, and honey. 800–333–7677; 912–985–7200 (in GA).

Ruhl Bee Supply, 12713 NE Whitaker Way, Portland, OR 97230: Free catalog ■ Bees and beekeeping supplies. 503–256–4231.

Jerry Shumans Apiaries, Rt. 4, Box 1710, Baxley, GA 31513: Free information ■

Italian queen bees. 800–368–7195; 912–367–2243 (in GA).

Strachan Apiaries, Inc., 2522 Tierra Buena Rd., Yuba City, CA 95991: Free information ■ Queen bees. 916–674–3881.

Sunstream Bee Supply Company, P.O. Box 225, Eighty Four, PA 15230: Catalog $1 (refundable) ■ Bees, beekeeping supplies, clothing and other protective gear, and honey. 412–222–3330.

Wenner Honey Farms, Inc., Rt. 1, Box 284, Glenn, CA 95943: Free information ■ Queens and package bees. 916–934–4944.

Wilbanks Apiaries, Box 12, Claxton, GA 30417: Free information ■ Three-banded Italian package bees and queens. 912–739–4820.

York Bee Company, P.O. Box 307, Jesup, GA 31545: Free information ■ Starlines, midnites, Italians, double hybrids, caucasians, and queen bees. 912–427–7311.

Cathy Zou Apiaries, 1936 Orchard Ln., La Canada, CA 91011: Free information ■ Italian queen bees and cells. 818–790–2064.

BEER CANS & STEINS

Carolina Collection, 1502 N. 23rd St., Wilmington, NC 28405: Free catalog ■ Collectible, limited edition steins from major breweries, National Football League, National Basketball Association, and organizations that support wildlife conservation. 919–251–1110.

Classic Cans, Maple Grove Rd., RD 2, Box 4755, Bennington, VT 05201: Free list with long SASE ■ Dumpers, cones, and current cans.

D & A Investments, Darrell Bowman, 2055–E Burnside Cir., Salt Lake City, UT 84109: Free price list ■ Mugs, steins, and other brewery collectibles. 800–336–2055.

Ron Fox Auctions, 416 Throop St., North Babylon, NY 11704: Free catalog ■ Collectible beer steins. 516–669–7232.

Gene's Can Shop, RD 1, Box 72, Martville, NY 13111: Free list with 1st class stamp ■ Hard-to-find collectible beer cans.

Glentiques, Ltd., P.O. Box 337, Glenford, NY 12433: Free information ■ Collectible beer steins. 914–657–6261.

Charlie Golden, Jr., 345 S. Sterley St., Shillington, PA 19607: United States list $1; foreign list $1 ■ Beer cans from over 40 countries. 215–777–7078.

Kansgalore, 505 Bosworth Rd., Knoxville, TN 37919: Free list with long SASE ■ Cans, labels, and coasters.

Chet Kilanowicz, 5446 Rockwood Rd., Columbus, OH 43229: List $1 ■ Beer cans. 614–888–0917.

Lager Sales, Box 612164, Dallas, TX 75261: Free information ■ Brewery collectibles. 817–354–0232.

Museum of Beverage Containers, 1055 Ridgecrest Dr., Goodlettsville, TN 37072: Free catalog ■ Beer and soda cans, signs, trays, caps, openers, and glasses.

Rogalski Brothers, 9404 NW 17th Pl., Ste. C, Gainesville, FL 32606: Free list ■ Beer cans. 904–332–3330.

Rolf's Steinwerke, 9420 Reseda Blvd., #800, Northridge, CA 91324: Catalog $10 (refundable) ■ Traditional, limited edition, and retired beer steins from Thewalt, Girmscheid, Sitzendorfer, Gertz, King, Unterweissbach, Mettlach, Ceramarte, and others. 818–368–2786.

Tony Steffen, 615 Chester, Ste. B, Elgin, IL 60120: Free catalog ■ Beer cans, mugs, and steins for collectors. 800–443–8712.

Steins-N-Stuff Unlimited, 2231 Sunset Ave., Wasco, CA 93280: Free price list ■ Beer mugs, steins, and other collectibles. 805–758–8210.

Union Jack Trading Company, P.O. Box 3680, Nashua, NH 03061: Free information ■ Authentic British pint and half pint beer mugs used in British pubs and taverns. Mugs bear the Crown stamp of authenticity. 603–888–9601.

BICYCLES & ACCESSORIES

Bicycles

Action Sports/Colian, 2126 E. Apache Blvd., Tempe, AZ 85281: Free information ■ Custom mountain, road, hybrid, and sport bicycles. 602–921–7990.

Aerosports, 2240 E. Cedar St., Ontario, CA 91761: Free information ■ Custom mountain bicycles. 714–841–1578.

Albe's Action Sports, 5759 E. 13 Mile Rd., Warren, MI 48092: Catalog $1 ■ Bicycles, parts, and accessories. 800–635–0845; 313–264–1150 (in MI).

Angle Lake Cyclery, 20840 Pacific Hwy. South, Seattle, WA 98188: Catalog $2 ■ Racing bicycles. 206–878–7457.

Aries International, 16443 San Pablo Ave., Berkeley, CA 94702: Free information ■ Racing bicycles. 510–528–6383.

Matthew Assenmacher Bikes, 8053 Miller Rd., Swartz Creek, MI 48473: Free information ■ Custom mountain and tandem bicycles. 313–635–7844.

Avon Seagull Marine, 1851 McGaw Ave., Irvine, CA 92714: Free information ■ Folding bicycles. 714–250–0880.

Bianchi USA, 270 Littlefield, Ste. C, South San Francisco, CA 94080: Free information ■ Racing, mountain, and city bicycles. 415–872–1414.

Bicycle Corporation of America, 2811 Brodhead Rd., Bethlehem, PA 18017: Free information ■ Mountain bicycles. 800–225–2453.

Bike Nashbar, 4111 Simon Rd., P.O. Box 3449, Youngstown OH 44512: Free catalog ■ Racing, sport touring, touring, and mountain bicycles. 800–345–BIKE; 216–542–3671 (in OH).

Bike Rack, Inc., 11 Constance Ct., Hauppauge, NY 11788: Free information ■ Racing and mountain bicycles. 516–348–6900.

Bridgestone Cycle USA, Inc., 15021 Wicks Blvd., San Leandro, CA 94577: Free information ■ Racing, sport touring, and mountain bicycles. 800–847–5913.

Burley Design Cooperative, 4080 Stewart Rd., Eugene, OR 97402: Free information ■ Tandem bicycles. 503–687–1644.

Cannondale Corporation, 9 Brookside Pl., Georgetown, CT 06829: Free information ■ Racing, sport touring, and touring bicycles. 800–BIKE–USA.

Clark-Kent Innovations, 2300 W. Alemeda, Denver, CO 80223: Free information ■ Custom mountain bicycles. 303–935–7550.

Columbia Manufacturing Company, P.O. Box 1230, Westfield, MA 01085: Free information ■ Racing bicycles. 413–562–3664.

Columbine Cycle Works, 6450 W. 10th St., Unit M, Greeley, CO 80634: Free information ■ Custom mountain, tandem, and track bicycles. 303–351–7710.

Corso Bicycle Distributors, 349 W. 14th St., New York, NY 10014: Free information ■ Racing, sport touring, and mountain bicycles. 212–675–2161.

Cycle Composites, 265 Westridge Dr., Watsonville, CA 95076: Free information ■ Racing and sport touring bicycles. 408–724–9079.

Cycles LaMoure, 416 1st St., Cheney, WA 99004: Free information ■ Custom mountain, track, and women's bicycles. 509–235–2297.

Cycles Peugeot, 555 Gotham Pkwy., Carlstadt, NJ 07072: Free information ■ Racing, sport touring, mountain, and city bicycles. 201–460–7000.

Cycles Plus, 101 Manorhaven Blvd., Port Washington, NY 11050: Free information with long SASE ■ Bicycles, accessories, clothing, and books. 516–944–8567.

Dahon California, 2949 Whipple Rd., Union City, CA 94587: Free information ■ Folding bicycles. 510–471–6330.

Davidson Cycles, 2116 Western Ave., Seattle, WA 98121: Free information ■ Custom mountain, tandem, and women's bicycles. 206–441–9998.

Erickson Cycles, 6119 Brooklyn NE, Seattle, WA 98115: Free information ■ Custom mountain, tandem, women's, track, and touring bicycles. 206–527–5259.

Expensive Toys, 1709 Marshall Ct., Annapolis, MD 21401: Free information ■ Folding bicycles and accessories. 800–869–8697.

Fat City Cycles, P.O. Box 218, Somerville, MA 02143: Free information ■ Custom mountain and racing bicycles. 617–625–4922.

1st Class B-M-X, P.O. Box 66290, Portland, OR 97266: Catalog $2 ■ Bicycle kits, parts, and accessories. 503–253–8688.

Fisher Mountainbikes, 140 Mitchell Blvd., San Rafael, CA 94901: Catalog $2 ■ Mountain and tandem bicycles. 415–479–1883.

Fuji of America, Box 60, Oakland, NJ 07436: Free information ■ Racing, sport touring, touring, mountain, and city bicycles. 201–337–1700.

Giant Bicycle Company, 475 Apra St., Rancho Dominguez, CA 90220: Free information ■ Racing, mountain, and city bicycles. 800–874–4268.

Gios of America, 450 W. 44th St., New York, NY 10036: Free information ■ Racing bicycles. 212–757–9433.

Gita Sporting Goods, 12600 Steele Creek Rd., Charlotte, NC 28273: Free information ■ Racing and track bicycles. 704–588–7550.

Gitane of America, 2 Union Dr., Olney, IL 62450: Free information ■ Racing and tandem bicycles. 618–392–3777.

Jack & Susan Goertz - Tandems Limited, Rt. 19, Box 248, Birmingham, AL 35244: Free information ■ American and English tandems, parts, and accessories. 205–991–5519.

GT Bicycles, 17800 Gothard St., Huntington Beach, CA 92647: Free information ■ Mountain bicycles. 714–841–1169.

Haro Designs, Inc., 2225 Faraday Ave., Ste. A, Carlsbad, CA 92009: Free information ■ Mountain bicycles. 619–438–4812.

Hensley Bicycles, P.O. Box 759, Colstrip, MT 59323: Free information ■ Racing and sport touring bicycles. 406–748–4225.

HH Racing Group, 1901 S. 13th St., Philadelphia, PA 19148: Free information ■ Racing, touring, tandem, and track bicycles. 215–334–8500.

Ibis Cycles, P.O. Box 275, Sebastopol, CA 95473: Free information ■ Mountain and tandem bicycles. 707–829–5615.

KHS Bicycles, 1264 E. Walnut St., Carson, CA 90746: Free information ■ Mountain and hybrid bicycles.

Klein Bicycle Corporation, 118 Klein Rd., Chehalis, WA 98532: Free information ■ Mountain, road, sport touring, and women's bicycles. 206–262–3305.

Lawee Cycles, Inc., 3030 Walnut Ave., Long Beach, CA 90807: Free information ■ Racing, sport touring, touring, mountain, and city bicycles. 310–426–0474.

Lighthouse Cycles, 3498 Willow St., Santa Ynez, CA 95060: Free information ■ Custom mountain, hybrid, women's, and track bicycles. 805–688–6385.

Lippy Bikes, 60265 Fuagarwee Cir., Bend, OR 97702: Free information ■ Tandem bicycles. 503–389–2503.

Maplewood Bicycle, 7534 Manchester, St. Louis, MO 63143: Free information ■ Bicycles and accessories. 314–781–9566.

Marin Mountain Bikes, 999 Andersen Dr., Ste. 140, San Rafael, CA 94901: Free information ■ Mountain bicycles.

Marinoni USA, Inc., P.O. Box 374, Montgomery Center, VT 05471: Free information ■ Racing bicycles. 802–326–4321.

Merlin Metalworks, Inc., 285 Washington St., Somerville, MA 02143: Free information ■ Custom road and mountain bicycles. 617–628–7855.

Miyata Bicycle of America, Inc., 2526 W. Pratt Blvd., Elk Grove, IL 60007: Free information ■ Racing, sport touring, touring, and mountain bicycles. 708–228–5450.

Mongoose Bicycles, 23879 Madison St., Torrance, CA 90505: Catalog $2 ■ Lightweight fitness bicycles. 800–645–5806.

Montague Folding Bicycle Company, P.O. Box 1118, Cambridge, MA 02238: Free information ■ Folding bicycles. 617–491–7200.

Mountain Bike Specialists, 340 S. Camino Del Rio, Durango, CO 81301: Catalog $3 ■ Mountain bicycles, parts, and accessories. 800–255–8377; 800–538–9500 (in CO).

Mountain Goat Cycles, Box 3923, Chico, CA 95927: Free information ■ Custom mountain, hybrid, and tandem bicycles. 916–342–4628.

MS Racing, 850 Marlborough, Riverside, CA 92507: Free information ■ Mountain bicycles. 714–686–1006.

Nobilette Cycles, 220 Felch, Ann Arbor, MI 48104: Free information ■ Racing, touring, sport touring, mountain, and tandem bicycles. 313–769–1115.

Norco Products USA, Inc., 18201 Olympic Ave. South, Tuckwila, WA 98188: Free information ■ Racing, sport touring, mountain, and city bicycles. 206–251–9370.

Ochsner International, 4341 W. Peterson Ave., Chicago, IL 60646: Free information ■ Racing, mountain, and trail bicycles. 312–286–3111.

Palo Alto Bicycles, 171 University Ave., Palo Alto, CA 94301: Free catalog ■ Bicycles, parts, and accessories. 800–227–8900.

Panasonic Bicycle Division, Panasonic Way, Secaucus, NJ 07094: Free information ■ Racing, sport touring, touring, and mountain bicycles. 201–348–5375.

R & A Cycles, Inc., 105 5th Ave., Brooklyn, NY 11217: Free information ■ Bicycles and frames. 718–636–5242.

Raleigh Cycle Company of America, 22710 72nd Ave. South, Kent, WA 98032: Free information ■ Racing, sport touring, and mountain bicycles. 206–395–1100.

Reflex Bikes, P.O. Box 535037, Salt Lake City, UT 84127: Free information ■ Mountain bicycles. 801–539–8001.

Ritchey USA, 1326 Hancock Ave., Redwood City, CA 94061: Free information ■ Mountain bicycles. 415–368–4018.

Rock Lobster Cycles, 219 Trescony St., Santa Cruz, CA 95060: Free information ■ Custom mountain, track, and hybrid bicycles. 408–429–1356.

Rocky Mountain Bicycle Company, 423 Telegraphy Rd., Bellingham, WA 98226: Free information ■ Mountain bicycles. 604–270–2710.

Romic Cycle Company, 4434 Steffani Ln., Houston, TX 77041: Free information ■ Racing, touring, and sport touring bicycles. 713–466–7806.

Ross Bicycles USA, 51 Executive Blvd., Farmingdale, NY 11735: Free information ■ Mountain and hybrid bicycles. 604–270–2710.

Richard Sachs Cycles, 1 Main St., Chester, CT 06412: Free information ■ Custom road and racing bicycles. 203–526–2059.

Santana Cycles, Inc., Box 1205, Claremont, CA 91711: Free information ■ Tandem bicycles and accessories. 714–621–6943.

Schwinn Bicycle Company, 217 N. Jefferson St., Chicago, IL 60606: Free information ■ Racing, mountain, tandem, and city bicycles. 312–454–7400.

Scott USA, P.O. Box 2030, Sun Valley, ID 83353: Free information ■ Mountain bicycles. 208–622–1000.

Seattle Bike Supply, 440 W. Colorado, Glendale, CA 91204: Free information ■ Racing, sport touring, touring, and mountain bicycles. 818–246–3228.

Security Bicycle, 32 Intersection St., Hempstead, NY 11551: Free information ■ Racing bicycles. 516–485–6100.

Service Cycle Bicycle Company, 23879 Madison Ave., Torrance, CA 90274: Free information ■ Racing and mountain bicycles. 310–378–5505.

Specialized Bicycle Components, 15130 Concord Cir., Morgan Hill, CA 95037: Free information ■ Racing and mountain bicycles. 408–779–6229.

Stuyvesant Bicycles, 349 W. 14th St., New York, NY 10014: Catalog $2.50 ■ Bicycles for children and adults. Includes domestic and imported models, lightweight folding bicycles, unicycles, and bicycles built for two. 212–254–5200.

Ten Speed Drive Imports, Inc., P.O. Box 9250, Melbourne, FL 32902: Free information ■ Racing and mountain bicycles. 407–777–5777.

Terry Precision Bicycles for Women, 1704 Wayneport Rd., Macedon, NY 14445: Free information ■ Racing, sport touring, touring, and mountain bicycles. 315–986–2103.

Torelli Imports, 409 Calle San Pablo, Ste. 109, Camarillo, CA 93010: Free information ■ Racing bicycles. 805–484–8705.

Trek Bicycle Corporation, 801 W. Madison St., Waterloo, WI 53594: Free information ■ Racing, sport touring, touring, mountain, and city bicycles. 414–478–2191.

Veloce Bikes, 3436 Lincoln Ave., Allentown, PA 18103: Free information ■ Custom road, hybrid, tandem, track, sport, and women's bicycles. 215–432–7254.

Veltec-Boyer, 801 California Ave., Sand City, CA 93955: Free information ■ Racing bicycles. 408–394–7114.

West Coast Cycle, 717 E. Artesia, Carson, CA 90746: Free information ■ Racing, sport touring, mountain, and city bicycles. 310–515–1514.

Western States Imports Company, 4030 Via Pescador, Camarillo, CA 93010: Free information ■ Racing, sport touring, mountain, and city bicycles. 805–484–9058.

Ted Wojcik, 23 Noel St., Amesbury, MA 01913: Free information ■ Custom mountain, road, sport, hybrid, tandem, and track bicycles. 508–388–4150.

Zinn Bicycles, 7437 S. Boulder Rd., Boulder, CO 80303: Free information ■ Racing, touring, sport touring, mountain, tandem, and track bicycles. 303–499–6008.

Parts & Accessories

All American Products, Inc., 2011 Swanson Ct., Gurnee, IL 60031: Free information ■ Car-mounted bicycle carriers and child carriers. 708–249–5656.

Antique Cycle Supply, RR 1, Cedar Springs, MI 49319: Catalog $5 ■ Antique, classic, and balloon tire bicycle parts and literature. 616–636–8200.

Avenir, 1837 De Haviland Dr., Newbury Park, CA 91320: Free information ■ Frame and saddle bags. 805–499–2603.

Avocet, Inc., P.O. Box 7615, Menlo Park, CA 94025: Free information with long SASE ■ Bike computer that computes speed, distance, and time. 800–428–6238; 415–321–8501 (in CA).

Beacon Associates, Inc., 10255 Pacific Ave., Franklin Park, IL 60131: Free information ■ Car-mounted bicycle carriers and child carriers, horns, lamps, locks, packs and bags, speedometers, and tubes. 708–671–7688.

Bell Helmets, 15301 Shoemaker Ave., Norwalk, CA 90650: Free information ■ Lightweight helmet in compliance with ANSI and Snell standards. 310–921–9451.

Beto USA, Inc., 19443 Laurel Park Rd., Ste. 112, Rancho Dominquez, CA 90220: Free information ■ Cycling accessories.

Bikecentennial, P.O. Box 8308, Missoula, MT 59807: Free catalog ■ Bike touring maps and books. 406–721–1776.

Bike Nashbar, 4111 Simon Rd., P.O. Box 3449, Youngstown OH 44512: Free catalog ■ Bicycles, bicycle components, saddlebags, and accessories. 800–345–BIKE; 216–542–3671 (in OH).

Bike Stuff, 12370 Merrick Dr., St. Louis, MO 63146: Catalog $1 ■ Bicycles, components and parts, and safety equipment. 314–878–7784.

Blackburn Designs, 1510 Dell Ave., Campbell, CA 95008: Free information with long SASE ■ Bike repair stand that folds up for storage. 408–370–1010.

Blue Sky Cycle Carts, P.O. Box 704, Redmond, OR 97756: Brochure $1 ■ Children's trailers/carts for attachment to adult bicycles, with seats and safety harnesses, and optional canopy. 503–548–7753.

Brite Lite Cycling Lights, P.O. Box 1386, Soquel, CA 95073: Free brochure ■ Rechargeable halogen cycling lights with a quick release mounting. 800–34–BRITE.

Burley Design Cooperative, 4080 Stewart Rd., Eugene, OR 97402: Free brochure ■ Bike trailers for children, with chest harness, seat belt, and roll bar. 503–687–1644.

Conrad's Bikeshop, 25 Tudor City Pl., New York, NY 10017: Free information ■ Bicycles, frames, parts and accessories, clothing, and safety gear. 212–697–6966.

Cosmopolitan Motors, Inc., 301 Jacksonville Rd., Hatboro, PA 19040: Free information ■ Bicycle locks, packs and bags, and tires. 800–523–2522; 215–672–9100 (in PA).

Custom Designed Imports, 3115 Garden Brook, Dallas, TX 75234: Free information ■ Bicycle lamps, locks, racks, tires, and tubes. 800–548–2453; 214–620–0124 (in TX).

Cycle Goods, 2801 Hennepin Ave. South, Minneapolis, MN 55408: Catalog $4 (refundable) ■ Parts and tools for repairing and building bicycles, clothing, books, transporting equipment, and safety gear. 612–872–7600.

CyclePro, 717 E. Artesia Blvd., Carson, CA 90746: Free information ■ Frame and saddle bags. 310–515–1514.

Cycle Products Company, 2900 Rightview Dr., Memphis, TN 38116: Free information ■ Car-mounted bicycle carriers and child carriers, horns, lamps, locks, packs and bags, reflectors, speedometers, tires and tubes, and helmets. 800–842–2472; 901–345–5090 (in TN).

Cycles Plus, 101 Manorhaven Blvd., Port Washington, NY 11050: Free information with long SASE ■ Bicycles and accessories, clothing, and books. 516–944–8567.

Cyclo Sport USA, 1540 Barclay Blvd., Buffalo Grove, IL 60089: Free information ■ Compact bicycle computer. 800–279–2820.

D & R Industries, 7111 Capitol Dr., Lincolnwood, IL 60645: Free information ■ Car-mounted bicycle carriers and child carriers, horns, lamps, locks, packs and bags, racks, reflectors and speedometers, tires and tubes, and helmets. 800–323–2852; 708–677–3200 (in IL).

Denver Spoke, 1715 E. Evans, Denver, CO 80210: Catalog $1 (refundable) ■ Bicycle parts and accessories. 800–327–8532; 800–327–8358 (in CO).

Eastpak, 50 Rogers Rd., Ward Hill, MA 01830: Free information ■ Frame and saddle bags. 508–373–1581.

Eldon Group America, Inc., 175 Clearbrook Rd., Elmsford, NY 10523: Free catalog ■ Car-mounted bicycle carriers. 914–592–4812.

Excel Sports International, 1855 38th St., Boulder, CO 80301: Free catalog ■ Bicycle computers, off-road equipment, bicycle frame sets, and tires and tubes. 800–627–6664.

Fairfield Processing Corporation, P.O. Box 1130, Danbury, CT 06813: Free information ■ Lightweight bicycle fairing that folds down out of the way. 800–442–2271; 203–371–1901 (in CT).

Frankford BMX, 964 N. State St., Girard, OH 44420: Free information ■ Bicycles, components and accessories, clothing, safety equipment, high tops, and T-shirts. 216–545–0392.

Giro Sport Designs, 2880 Research Park Dr., Soquel, CA 90573: Free information ■ Lightweight foam helmets. 800–969–4476.

Graber Products, Inc., 5253 Verona Rd., Madison, WI 53711: Free information ■ Roof-mounted, bumper, and trunk-mounted car carriers and racks for bicycles. 800–542–6644; 608–274–6550 (in WI).

Grant Helmets, Division Land Tool Company, 650 E. Gilbert, Wichita, KS 67211: Free information ■ Helmets. 800–835–LAND; 316–265–5665 (in KS).

Kangaroo, Division Alpenlite, 3891 N. Ventura Ave., Ventura, CA 93001: Free information ■ Frame and saddle bags. 805–653–0431.

Lone Peak, 3474 S. 2300 East, Salt Lake City, UT 84109: Free information ■ Frame and saddle bags. 800–777–7679.

Madden/USA, 2400 Central Ave., Boulder, CO 80301: Free information ■ Frame and saddle bags. 303–442–5828.

Night Sun, 1104 Mission St., South Pasadena, CA 91030: Free brochure ■ Halogen lights for helmet and bicycle mounting, flashing tail lights, and dual lamp systems with high and low beam settings. 818–790–7749.

Overland Equipment, 2145 Park Ave., Ste. 4, Chico, CA 95928: Free information ■ Frame and saddle bags. 916–894–5605.

Pasmir Engineering, Box 942, Boylston, MA 01505: Free information ■ Adjustable bicycle storage rack that can be stored in a closet, hallway, or garage. 508–869–2795.

Pedal Pusher Ski & Sport, 658 Easton Rd., Rt. 611, Horsham, PA 19044: Free catalog ■ Bicycles, frames, components, accessories, tools, clothing, and carry-all racks for cars. 215–672–0202.

Pedal Pusher - Top Gear, 1599 Cleveland Ave., Santa Rosa, CA 95401: Free information ■ Bicycles, frame sets, handlebars, brake levers, brakes, tires, grips, pedals, tubes, chains, seats, safety equipment, tools, locks, and pumps. 215–672–0202.

Performance Bicycle Shop, P.O. Box 2741, Chapel Hill, NC 27514: Free catalog ■ Clothing and accessories, frames, bicycles and parts, and frame and saddle bags. 800–727–2453.

REI Recreational Equipment Company, Sumner, WA 98352: Free information ■ Frame and saddle bags. 800–426–4840.

Schwinn Bicycle Company, 217 N. Jefferson, Chicago, IL 60601: Free information with long SASE ■ Bicycle computer that measures current and maximum speeds, trip distance, odometer readings, and cadence. 312–454–7400.

Malcom Smith Products, 850 Marlborough, Riverside, CA 94403: Free information ■ Ultralight bicycle helmet that meets ANSI standards. 800–854–4742; 714–686–1006 (in CA).

Specialized Bicycle Components, 15130 Concord Cir., Morgan Hill, CA 95037: Free information ■ Frame and saddle bags. 408–779–6229.

Spectrum Cycles, Inc., RD 2, Box 59, Dorney Rd., Breinigsville, PA 18031: Free brochure with long SASE ■ Bicycle frames. 215–398–1986.

Spoke A.R.T., 1715 E. Evans, Denver, CO 80210: Catalog $1 (refundable) ■ Bicycle parts and accessories. 800–327–8532; 800–327–8358 (in CO).

Sturmey-Archer of America, Inc., 1014 Carolina Ave., West Chicago, IL 60185: Free information with long SASE ■ Bicycle frame tube sets with design options. 312–231–5150.

Summit Mountain Bike Supply, 253 Albany Tpk., P.O. Box 85, Canton, CT 06019: Free information ■ Mountain bicycle parts and components. 203–658–6061.

Third Hand, P.O. Box 212, Mt. Shasta, CA 96067: Free catalog ■ Bicycle repair tools, repair stands, small parts, and how-to books. 916–926–2600.

Trend Bike Source, P.O. Box 201778, Austin, TX 78720: Catalog $1 ■ Mountain bicycles, components, parts and accessories, clothing, and safety gear. 512–338–4466.

U-locks, 11911 Hamden Pl., Santa Fe Springs, CA 90670: Free information ■ Bicycle security lock system. 310–948–3181.

United States Marketing Corporation, 266 E. Jericho Tpk., Huntington Station, NY 11746: Free information ■ Solar-charging bicycle light. 800–845–4509.

Vetta/Orleander USA, 14553 Delano St., Van Nuys, CA 91411: Free information with a long SASE ■ Bicycle computers. 818–780–8808.

Wild Side Designs, P.O. Box 621, Beaverton, OR 97075: Free brochure ■ Bicycle racks with holding security. 503–649–9085.

WSI, 1837 De Haviland Dr., Newbury Park, CA 91320: Free information ■ Lightweight foam helmet for bikers that meets ANSI standards. 805–499–2603.

ZZIP Designs, Box 14, Davenport, CA 95017: Catalog $1 ■ Bicycle fairings. 408–425–8650.

Clothing

Bolters, 1307 Gertrude Pl., Santa Ana, CA 92705: Free information ■ Winter apparel for bikers. 714–434–7010.

Canari, 8360 Clairmont Mesa Blvd., Ste. 105, San Diego, CA 92111: Free information ■ Winter apparel for bikers. 619–277–3377.

Cannondale Corporation, 9 Brookside Pl., Georgetown, CT 06821: Free information ■ Jackets and tights for women and frame and saddle bags. 800–BIKE–USA.

Chamberlain, CN 1041, South Plainfield, NJ 07080: Free catalog ■ Clothing and accessories for bikers, decorative accessories for the home, statuary, clocks, paperweights, porcelain, art, garden and greenhouse accessories, dolls, and other gifts. 908–906–0071.

Colorado Cyclist, 2455 Executive Dr., Colorado Springs, CO 80308: Free information ■ Dante sports apparel, Lycra cycling shorts and tights, and polypropylene liner tights. 719–442–4418.

Deluz California, 8360 Clairmont Mesa Blvd., Ste. 105, San Diego, CA 92111: Free information ■ Winter apparel for bikers. 619–277–3377.

The Finals, 21 Minisink Ave., Port Jervis, NY 12771: Free catalog ■ Bicycling, aerobic, swimming, running, and exercise clothing. 914–856–4456.

Frankford BMX, 964 N. State St., Girard, OH 44420: Free information ■ Bicycles, components and accessories, clothing, safety equipment, high tops, and T-shirts. 216–545–0392.

Lite Speed, 3918 W. 1st, Eugene, OR 97402: Catalog $1 ■ Bikewear and rainwear for men, women, and children. 503–342–4082.

Pearl Izumi, 2300 Central Ave., Boulder, CO 80301: Free information ■ Wind-resistant tights and jerseys with zippers for easy removal of the front panel. 303–938–1700.

Puma USA, Inc., 147 Centre St., Brockton, MA 02403: Free information ■ Clothing, shoes, and gloves. 508–583–9100.

Schnaubelt Shorts, Inc., 1128 4th Ave., Coraopolis, PA 15108: Free information ■ Clothing for bicyclists and custom silk-screening on clothing and T-shirts. 800–782–TEAM.

Vigorelli, 2200 Adeline St., Oakland, CA 94607: Free information ■ Men's and women's clothing with optional team logos. Includes fashions for racers, off-road riders, and recreational bikers. 800–327–4232; 800–332–4232 (in CA).

BILLIARDS

Adam Custom Cues, 25 Hutcheson Pl., Lynbrook, NY 11563: Free information ■ Pool cues. 800–645–2162; 516–593–5050 (in NY).

Amerola Sports, Inc., 4719 Hatfield St., Pittsburgh, PA 15201: Free information ■ Billiard balls, bridges, chalk, cues, cue cases, and racks. 800–426–3765.

Bensen Pool Cues, 516 E. 1st Ave., Kennewick, WA 99336: Free brochure ■ Pool cues. 509–586–7277.

Black Boar, 4908 Lehigh Rd., College Park, MD 20740: Free information ■ Handcrafted pool cues. 301–277–3236.

Cornhusker Billiard, 4825 S. 16th, Lincoln, NE 68512: Free catalog ■ Billiards and dart supplies. 800–627–8888.

Cue Stix, 742 Rocky Point Rd., Covington, GA 30209: Free brochure ■ Pool cues. 404–786–1189.

D & R Industries, 7111 Capitol Dr., Lincolnwood, IL 60645: Free information ■ Billiard balls, bridges, chalk, cues, cue cases, and racks. 800–323–2852; 708–677–3200 (in IL).

Designs for Leisure, Ltd., 41 Kensico Dr., Mount Kisco, NY 10549: Free information ■ Billiard balls, bridges, chalk, cue cases and racks, and slate tables. 914–241–4500.

Dufferin, Inc., 4240 Grove Ave., Gurnee, IL 60031: Free information ■ Pool cues. 708–244–4762.

Huebler Industries, Inc., P.O. Box 644, Linn, MO 65051: Free information ■ Pool cues. 314–897–3692.

International Billiards, Inc., 2311 Washington Ave., Houston, TX 77007: Free information ■ Billiard balls, bridges, chalk, cues, cue cases, and racks. 800–255–6386; 713–869–3237 (in TX).

It's George, 360 Gloria St., Shreveport, LA 71105: Free information ■ Pool cue cases. 318–868–1987.

Joss International, P.O. Box 6643, Santa Rosa, CA 95406: Free brochure ■ Pool cues. 707–545–JOSS.

JP Custom Cues, 1331 Cedar St., Green Bay, WI 54302: Free information ■ Handcrafted custom cues. 414–437–0020.

J-S Sales Company, Inc., 5 S. Fulton Ave., Mt. Vernon, NY 10550: Free information ■ Billiard balls, bridges, chalk, cues, cue cases, racks, and non-slate and slate tables. 800–431–2944; 914–668–8051 (in NY).

Mustad Corporation, 4212 Baldwin Ave., El Monte, CA 91731: Free catalog ■ Pool cues, billiards accessories, and mini pool tables. 818–401–0656.

National Billiards of Canada, 7650 20th St., Burnaby, British Columbia, Canada V3N 2Y8: Free brochure ■ Snooker and pool tables. 604–520–6381.

Olhaussen Pool Table Manufacturing, 12460 Kirkham Ct., Poway, CA 92064: Free information ■ Pool tables. 619–277–0450.

Palmer Billiard Corporation, 307 Morris Ave., Elizabeth, NJ 07208: Free information ■ Billiard balls, bridges, chalk, cues, cue cases, and racks. 909–289–4778.

Sauner-Wilhem Company, 3216 5th Ave., Pittsburgh, PA 15213: Free catalog ■ Billiards and bowling equipment and accessories. 412–621–4350.

Schmelke Manufacturing Company, 1879 28th Ave., Rice Lake, WI 54868: Free information ■ Pool cue cases. 715–234–6553.

Pat Sheehan Billiard Tables, 5231 SE McLoughlin Blvd., Portland, OR 97202: Free information ■ Restored antique billiards tables. 503–231–7566.

Sportsmen Accessories, Inc., 955 Connecticut Ave., Bridgeport, CT 06607: Free information ■ Metal, plastic, and wood cues. 203–579–0686.

Thumtectors, Inc., 18316 Hampshire Ln., San Diego, CA 92128: Free information ■ Billiard balls, bridges, chalk, cues, cue cases, racks, non-slate and slate tables. 619–451–8577.

Voit Sports, 1451 Pittstand-Victor Rd., 100 Willowbrook Office Park, Fairport, NY 14450: Free information ■ Billiard balls, bridges, chalk, cues, cue cases, and racks. 800–367–8648; 716–385–2390 (in NY).

Wa-Mac, Inc., Highskore Products, 178 Commerce Rd., P.O. Box 128, Carlstadt, NJ 07072: Free information ■ Billiard balls, bridges, chalk, cues, cue cases, and racks. 800–447–5673; 201–438–7200 (in NJ).

World of Leisure Manufacturing Company, 758 E. Edna Pl., Covina, CA 91723: Free information ■ Billiard balls, bridges, chalk, cues, cue cases, and racks. 818–322–5997.

BINOCULARS

Adorama, 42 W. 18th St., New York, NY 10011: Free information ■ Binoculars, telescope equipment, and accessories. 212–741–0052.

Airies Optics, Rt. 1, Box 143G, Palouse, WA 99161: Free information ■ Binoculars and accessories. 509–878–1713.

American Sailing Association, 13922 Marquesas Way, Marina Del Ray, CA 90292: Free information ■ Binoculars and accessories. 310–822–7171.

Armchair Sailor, 543 Thames St., Newport, RI 02840: Free information ■ Binoculars and accessories. 800–29–CHART; 401–847–4252 (in RI).

Astronomics, 2401 Tee Cir., Ste. 106, Norman, OK 73069: Information with long SASE and 75¢ ■ Binoculars and accessories. 405–364–0858.

Astro-Tech, 222 W. Main, P.O. Box 2001, Ardmore, OK 73402: Catalog $1 ■ Binoculars, telescopes and accessories, electro-optical equipment, filters, telescope mounts, other science equipment, and star maps and atlases. 405–226–3074.

Beckson Marine, 165 Holland Ave., Bridgeport, CT 06605: Free information ■ Binoculars and accessories. 203–333–1412.

Celestron International, 2835 Columbia St., Torrance, CA 90503: Catalog $2 ■ Binoculars and accessories. 310–328–9560.

Chinon America, Inc., 1065 Bristol Rd., Mountainside, NJ 07092: Free information ■ Binoculars and accessories. 908–654–0404.

Compass Industries, 104 E. 25th St., New York, NY 10010: Free information ■ Binoculars and accessories. 212–473–2614.

Danley's, P.O. Box 4401, Half Moon, NY 12065: Free catalog ■ Binoculars and cases. 518–664–2014.

W.H. Denouden, Inc., P.O. Box 8712, Baltimore, MD 21240: Free information ■ Binoculars and accessories. 410–796–4740.

Edmund Scientific Company, Edscorp Bldg., Barrington, NJ 08007: Free catalog ■ Binoculars, telescopes, and other educational and science equipment. 609–573–6260.

Europtik, Ltd., P.O. Box 319, Dunmore, PA 18509: Free information ■ Binoculars and accessories. 717–347–6049.

Fawcett Boat Supplies, Inc., 2017 Renard Ct., On the City Dock, Annapolis, MD 21401: Free information ■ Binoculars and accessories. 410–224–0920.

Fraser-Volpe, 1025 Thomas Dr., Warminster, PA 18974: Free information ■ Binoculars and accessories. 215–443–5240.

Fujinon, Inc., 10 High Point Dr., Wayne, NJ 07470: Free information ■ Binoculars and accessories. 201–633–5600.

Helix, 310 S. Racine, Chicago, IL 60607: Free information ■ Binoculars and accessories. 800–621–6471.

HP Marketing Group, 16 Chapin Rd., Pine Brook, NJ 07058: Free brochure: Free information ■ Binoculars and accessories. 201–808–9010.

A. Jaegers Optical Supply Company, 6915 Merrick Rd., Lynbrook, NY 11563: Catalog 25¢ ■ Surplus binoculars, telescopes, lenses, and prisms. 516–599–3167.

Jason Empire, 9200 Cody, Box 14930, Overland Park, KS 66214: Free information ■ Binoculars and accessories.

Jones of Boulder, 6367 Arapahoe Rd., P.O. Box 3096, Boulder, CO 80303: Free information ■ Binoculars and accessories. 800–321–8300; 303–447–8727 (in CO).

Kalimar, 622 Goddard Ave., Chesterfield, MO 63017: Free information ■ Binoculars and accessories. 800–525–4627.

Landfall Navigation, 354 W. Putnam Ave., Greenwich, CT 06830: Free information ■ Binoculars and accessories. 203–661–3176.

Leica USA, Inc., 156 Ludlow St., Northvale, NJ 07647: Free information ■ Binoculars, camera equipment, and accessories. 201–767–7500.

Leupold & Stevens, Inc., P.O. Box 688, Beaverton, OR 97075: Free information ■ Binoculars and accessories. 503–646–9171.

Mardiron Optics, 4 Spartan Cir., Stoneham, MA 02180: Send two 1st class stamps for brochure ■ Binoculars and astronomy equipment. 617–938–8339.

Meade Instruments Corporation, 1675 Toronto Way, Costa Mesa, CA 92626: Free information ■ Binoculars and accessories. 714–556–2291.

F.C. Meichsner Company, 182 Lincoln St., Boston, MA 02111: Free information with long SASE ■ Binoculars and accessories. 800–321–8439.

Minolta, 101 Williams Dr., Ramsey, NJ 07446: Free information ■ Binoculars and accessories. 201–825–4000.

Mirador Optical, 4051 Glencoe Ave., Marina Del Rey, CA 90292: Free information ■ Binoculars and accessories. 213–821–5587.

National Camera Exchange, 9300 Olson Memorial Hwy., Golden Valley, MN 55427: Free information ■ Binoculars and spotting scopes. 800–624–8107; 612–546–6831 (in MN).

New England Astro-Optics, Inc., P.O. Box 834, Simsbury, CT 06070: Catalog $2 ■ Binoculars and accessories. 203–658–0701.

Nikon, 1300 Walt Whitman Rd., Melville, NY 11747: Free information ■ Binoculars and accessories. 800–NIKON–US.

Optica b/c Company, 4100 MacArthur Blvd., Oakland, CA 94619: Catalog $5 ■ Binoculars and accessories, telescopes, telescope-making supplies, mounts, books, cameras, computers and software, eyepieces and filters, and planetariums. 510–530–1234.

Optical Advantage, Box 32791, Pikesville, MD 21208: Free catalog ■ Binoculars and accessories. 410–653–3306.

Parks Optical Company, 270 Easy St., Simi Valley, CA 93065: Free information ■ Binoculars and accessories. 805–522–6722.

Pauli's Wholesale Optics, 29 Kingswood Rd., Danbury, CT 06811: Catalog $10 ■ Binoculars and accessories. 203–748–3579.

Pentax Corporation, 35 Inverness Dr. East, Englewood, CO 80112: Free information ■ Binoculars, cameras, lenses, and other optical accessories. 303–799–8000.

Ranging Binoculars, Rt. 5 & 20, East Bloomfield, NY 14443: Free information ■

Binoculars and accessories. 800–828–1495; 716–657–6161 (in NY).

Redlich Optical, 711 W. Broad St., Falls Church, VA 22046: Free information ■ Binoculars, spotting scopes, telescopes, and accessories. 703–241–4077.

Ricoh Consumer Products Group, 180 Passaic Ave., Fairfield, NJ 07004: Free information ■ Binoculars and accessories. 201–882–7762.

Selsi Binoculars, 40 Veterans Blvd., Carlstadt, NJ 07072: Free information ■ Binoculars and accessories.

Simmons Outdoor Company, 14205 SW 119th St., Miami, FL 33186: Free information ■ Binoculars and accessories.

Steiner Binoculars, c/o Pioneer Marketing & Research, 216 Haddon Ave., Westmont, NJ 08108: Free information ■ Binoculars and accessories. 609–854–2424.

Swarovski Optik, One Wholesale Way, Cranston, RI 02920: Free information ■ Binoculars and accessories. 800–426–3089.

Swift Instruments, Inc., 952 Dorchester Ave., Boston, MA 02125: Free brochure ■ Binoculars and cases, and spotting scopes that can be used on cameras. 800–446–1115; 617–436–2960 (in MA).

Tamron Industries, Inc., P.O. Box 388, Port Washington, NY 11050: Free brochure ■ Binoculars and spotting scopes that can be adapted for camera use as an ultra-telescopic zoom lens. 516–484–8880.

Tasco Sales, Inc., P.O. Box 523735, Miami, FL 33122: Free information ■ Binoculars, other optical equipment, and accessories. 305–591–3670.

Tokina Optical Corporation, 1512 Kona Dr., Compton, CA 90220: Free information ■ Binoculars and accessories. 310–537–9380.

Trade-Wind Instruments, 1076 Loraine St., Enumclaw, WA 98022: Free information ■ Binoculars and accessories. 206–825–2294.

Unitron, Inc., 175 Express St., Plainview, NY 11803: Free information ■ Binoculars and accessories. 516–822–4601.

University Optics, P.O. Box 1205, Ann Arbor, MI 48106: Free information ■ Binoculars and accessories. 800–521–2828.

Vivitar Corporation, 9350 DeSoto Ave., P.O. Box 2193, Chatsworth, CA 91311: Free information ■ Binoculars and accessories. 818–700–9380.

Zeiss Optical, Inc., 1015 Commerce St., Petersburg, VA 23803: Free brochure ■ Zeiss binoculars and accessories. 804–861–0033.

BIRD FEEDERS AND HOUSES

American Pie Company, RD 1, Box 1431, Lake George, NY 12845: Free information ■ Weatherproof bird feeders. 518–668–3963.

Bird 'N Hand, 40 Pearl St., Framingham, MA 01701: Free information ■ Birdseed and feeders. 508–879–1552.

Bortner & Bortner, 368 Bluff City Blvd., Elgin, IL 60120: Free information ■ Bird houses. 708–741–3700.

Brushy Mountain Bee Farm, Inc., Rt. 1, P.O. Box 135, Moravian Falls, NC 28654: Free catalog ■ Birdhouses and feeders and beekeeping supplies. 800–233–7929.

C & S Products Company, Inc., Box 848, Fort Dodge, IA 50501: Free catalog ■ Wild bird suet products and feeders. 515–955–5605.

Cockerum Oregon Insects, Tillamook, OR 97141: Free information ■ Oregon insect and suet wild bird food. 800–63–FLIES.

Dakota Quality Bird Food, Box 3084, Fargo, ND 58108: Free catalog ■ Niger thistle, small black sunflower seeds, wild birdseed mixes, royal finch mix, and safflower seed. 800–356–9220.

John Deere & Company, 1400 3rd Ave., Moline, IL 61265: Free catalog ■ Birdhouses and feeders, planters, outdoor furniture,lawn care and garden aids, and mailboxes. 800–544–2122.

Droll Yankees, Inc., P.O. Box 98, Foster, RI 02825: Free catalog ■ Bird feeders. 401–647–2727.

Duncraft, Penacook, NH 03303: Catalog 50¢ ■ Wild bird supplies, squirrel-proof feeders, birdhouses, bird baths, and books. 603–224–0200.

Feed, Feather & Farm Supply, 4531–9 St. Augustine Rd., Jacksonville, FL 32207: Catalog $1 ■ Birdseed and supplies. 904–396–4273.

Forest Time Products, Inc., P.O. Box 1042, Litchfield, MN 55355: Free information ■ Bird houses. 612–693–7892.

Hyde Bird Feeder Company, 56 Felton St., P.O. Box 168, Waltham, MA 02254: Free catalog ■ Bird feeders and wild bird food. 617–893–6780.

Lady Slipper Designs, Inc., Rt. 3, Box 556, Bemidji, MN 56601: Free information ■ Bird houses. 800–950–5903.

Lazy Hill Farm Designs, Lazy Hill Rd., Colerain, NC 27924: Free information ■ Bird houses. 919–356–2828.

Mac Industries, 8125 South I–35, Oklahoma City, OK 73149: Brochure $1 ■ Traditional and colonial-style Martin houses, with galvanized steel telescoping pole, perch pole, stops, and weather vane. 800–654–4970.

Maine Manna, Inc., Box 248, Gorham, ME 04038: Free information ■ Ready-to-hang feeder bells filled with a preservative-free blend of prime beef and birdseed. 207–839–6013.

Mr. Birdhouse, 2307 Hwy. 2 West, Grand Rapids, MN 55744: Free information ■ Aluminum Martin houses and pole kits and other bird houses. 218–326–3044.

Old Elm Feed & Supplies, Box 57, Elm Grove, WI 53122: Free catalog ■ Bird feeders, houses, books, squirrel baffles, bird baths, and birdseed boxes. 414–786–3304.

Plow & Hearth, 301 Madison Rd., P.O. Box 830, Madison, VA 22960: Free catalog ■ Outdoor furniture and accessories, bird houses and feeders, bird baths, and gardening tools and supplies. 800–866–6072.

Wild Bird Supplies, 4815 Oak St., Crystal Lake, IL 60012: Free catalog ■ Feeders, bird houses, bird baths, birdseed mixes, and books on bird care. 815–455–4020.

Wildlife Nurseries, P.O. Box 2724, Oshkosh, WI 54903: Literature $1 ■ Special upland game birdseed combinations and gardening supplies. 414–231–3780.

Woodmark Products, 43 Kensington Dr., Chelmsford, MA 01824: Free catalog ■ Bird feeders and other accessories. 508–256–3543.

Dot Zero Birdhouses, 165 5th Ave., New York, NY 7 10010: Free information ■ Bird houses. 212–533–8322.

BIRTH ANNOUNCEMENTS

Babygram Service Center, 301 Commerce, Ste. 1010, Fort Worth, TX 76102: Free brochure ■ Photographic birth announcements. 817–334–0069.

Baby Name-A-Grams, P.O. Box 8465, St. Louis, MO 63132: Free brochure ■ Hand-drawn calligraphy designer birth announcements. 314–966–BABY.

Birth-O-Gram Company, P.O. Box 140398, Miami, FL 33114: Catalog 50¢ ■ Birth announcements with work-related, sport, and hobby themes. 305–267–1479.

BirthWrites, P.O. Box 684, Owings Mills, MD 21117: Free brochure ■ Birth announcements with formal, religious, humorous, ethnic, and artistic themes. Will custom print cards. 410–363–0872.

Blue Sky Baby Company, 3903 Bandini Ave., Riverside, CA 92506: Free brochure ■ Birth announcements. 800–726–9405.

Contemporary Statements, 9844 S. Hamlin, Evergreen Park, IL 60642: Free brochure ■ Personalized birth announcements. 708–422–3325.

Custom Cards, RD 2, Box 127, Montgomery, NY 12549: Catalog $3.50 ■ Custom and in-stock birth announcements, gift cards, and thank-you cards.

Family News Birth Announcements, 6381 Balmoral Dr., Huntington Beach, CA 92647: Free samples ■ Custom mini-newspaper birth announcements.

H & F Invitations, 3734 W. 95th, Leawood, KS 66206: Free information ■ Custom birth announcements and invitations. 800–338–4001.

Heart Thoughts, 6200 E. Central, Ste. 100, Wichita, KS 67208: Free brochure and samples ■ Birth announcements and thank you notes. 316–688–5781.

Joy Bee Designs, 3650 Greenfield Ave., Los Angeles, CA 90034: Catalog $3 ■ Birth announcements, thank you cards, invitations, birthday cards, with custom-lettered calligraphy. 310–473–8123.

New Moons, 530 Rhodora Heights Rd., Lake Stevens, WA 98258: Free information with long SASE ■ Birth announcements. 206–334–6403.

Pride & Joy Announcements, 7154 W. State St., Ste. 42217, Boise, ID 83703: Free catalog ■ Custom birth announcements. 800–657–6404.

Printed Personals, 138 Magnolia St., Westbury, NY 11590: Free brochure ■ Personalized birth announcements.

BLACKSMITHING

Centaur Forge, Ltd., 117 N. Spring St., P.O. Box 340, Burlington, WI 53105: Catalog $3 ■ Equipment and supplies for horseshoers. 414–763–9175.

Cumberland General Store, Rt. 3, Box 81, Crossville, TN 38555: Catalog $3 ■ Blacksmithing equipment, hand pumps, windmills, wood cooking ranges, gardening tools, cast-iron ware, farm bells, buggies, and harnesses. 800–334–4640.

Mankel Blacksmith Shop, P.O. Box 29, Cannonsburg, MI 49317: Catalog $1 (refundable) ■ Forging supplies and equipment. 616–874–6955.

NC Tool Company, 6568 Hunt Dr., Pleasant Garden, NC 27313: Free information ■ Equipment and supplies for blacksmiths and farriers. 800–446–6498.

BOATS & BOATING
Boat-Building Kits

Aladdin Products, RFD 2, Wiscasset, ME 04578: Free information ■ Canoe, kayak, and catamaran kits. 207–882–5504.

Benford Design Group, P.O. Box 447, St. Michaels, MD 21663: Catalog and information package $10 ■ Catboats, cruising yachts, and other boats. 410–745–3235.

Bridges Point Boat Yard, Box 342, Brooklin, ME 04616: Free information ■ Boat kits. 207–359–2713.

Britannia Boats, Ltd., P.O. Box 5033, Annapolis, MD 21403: Free information ■ Boat kits. 410–269–6617.

ClarkCraft Boat Company, 16 Aqualane, Tonawanda, NY 14150: Catalog $3 ■ Boat kits, plans for powerboats and sailboats, supplies, accessories, and hardware. 716–873–2640.

Cooper Boatbuilding & Design, P.O. Box 211, Falmouth, MA 02541: Information $3 ■ Easy-to-build epoxy-wood construction sail-

ing dinghy. Plans, kits, and assembly of boats available. 508–548–2297.

Country Ways, Inc., 15235 Minnetonka Blvd., Minnetonka, MN 55343: Free catalog ■ Kits for prams, kayaks, and canoes. Other items include duck decoys, outdoor clothing, and mandolin kits. 612–935–0022.

Crawford Boat Building, Box 430, Humarock, MA 02047: Information $1 ■ Fiberglass 16-foot hull. 617–837–3666.

Feather Canoes, Inc., 3080 N. Washington Blvd., Sarasota, FL 34234: Free information ■ Boat kits. 813–953–7660.

Glen-L Marine Designs, 9152 Rosecrans, Box 1084, Bellflower, CA 90706: Catalog boats & plans $4; marine hardware $2 ■ Kits for canoes, kayaks and dinghies, plywood and fiberglass boats, and power boats. Other items include marine hardware and boat-building supplies. 310–630–6258.

Great Lakes Boat Building Company, Rt. 5, Box 120, South Haven, MI 49090: Free information ■ Boat kits. 616–637–6805.

Hudson Canoe, 14 Hillside Ave., Croton, NY 10520: Free information ■ Boat kits. 914–271–5387.

Kurt Hughes Sailing Designs, 612–1/2 W. McGraw, Seattle, WA 98119: Design portfolio $10 ■ Power- and sail-operated multi-hulls. 206–284–6346.

Luger Boats, 424 S. 8th, P.O. Box 1398, St. Joseph, MO 64502: Free catalog ■ Boat kits with molded fiberglass hulls and factory-assembled decks. 816–233–5116.

Marine Concepts, 159 Oakwood St. East, Tarpon Springs, FL 34689: Free information ■ Boat kits. 813–937–0166.

Menger Boatworks, Inc., 121 Maple Ave., Bay Shore, NY 11706: Free information ■ Boat kits. 516–968–0300.

Monfort Associates, RR 2, Box 416, Wiscasset, ME 04878: List $2 ■ Boat plans. 207–882–5504.

New Hampshire Boat Builders, 10 Progress Ave., Nashua, NH 03062: Brochure $1 ■ Boat kits. 603–886–0300.

Old Wooden Boatworks, 106 8th St. East, Bradenton, FL 33508: Free information ■ Dinghy kit. 813–747–8898.

Rotocast Flotation Products, P.O. Box 1059, Brownwood, TX 76804: Free

brochure ■ Pontoon boat kits, from 17 to 24 feet. 800–351–1363.

Sara's Marine Enterprises, 415 29th St., Newport Beach, CA 92663: Brochure $1 (refundable) ■ Rowing and sailing dinghy kits, in 7– and 8–foot models, complete with a hand-laid fiberglass hull. 714–675–4684.

Shell Boats, RR 2, Box 289, St. Albans, VT 05478: Catalog $2 ■ Wooden sailing and rowing boats, in kits or assembled. 802–524–9645.

Sisu Boats, 91 Lafayette Rd., Portsmouth, NH 03801: Free information ■ Boat kits. 603–749–4452.

Thayer & Company, 2106 Atlee Rd., Mechanicsville, VA 23111: Information $3 ■ Sailing and pulling boats with fiberglass hulls and mahogany trim. Available assembled or as a kit. 804–746–0674.

WoodenBoat, P.O. Box 78, Brooklin, ME 04616: Free information ■ Wooden racing shell kit. 207–359–4651.

Canoes & Kayaks

Aire, P.O. Box 3412, Boise, ID 83703: Free information ■ Self-bailing, inflatable touring kayaks. 208–344–7506.

Ally Pakboats, P.O. Box 700, Enfield, NH 03748: Free information ■ Folding canoes. 603–632–7654.

Alumacraft, Inc., 315 W. St. Julien, St. Peter, MN 56082: Free information ■ Aluminum canoes. 507–931–1050.

American Traders Classic Canoes, 627 Barton Rd., Greenfield, MA 01301: Free information ■ Wooden canoes. 800–782–7816.

Aquaterra, 11190 Powdersville Rd., Easley, SC 29640: Free information ■ Kayaks. 803–859–7518.

Baer's River Workshop, Inc., P.O. Box 443, Yawgoo Valley Ski Area, Exeter, RI 02822: Free brochure ■ Canoes, kayaks, and other equipment. 401–295–0855.

Baidarka Boats, Box 6001, Sitka, AK 99835: Free catalog ■ Folding kayaks. 907–747–8996.

Baldwin Boat Company, RFD 2, Box 268, Orrington, ME 04474: Free information ■ Kayaks. 207–825–4439.

Barton Paddle Company, 931 Knollwood Dr., Grand Rapids, MI 55744: Free brochure

■ Lightweight carbon fiber canoe paddles. 218–326–8757.

L.L. Bean, Inc., Freeport, ME 04033: Free catalog ■ Canoes and boating accessories and equipment for outdoor sports and activities. 800–221–4221.

Bell Canoe Works, 28312 144th St., Zimmerman, MN 55398: Free information ■ Kevlar/glass composite solo cruising canoes. 612–856–2231.

Berkshire Outfitters, Rt. 8, Cheshire Harbor, Adams, MA 01220: Free information ■ Sea kayaks, whitewater kayaks, canoes, paddles, bag, clothing, gloves, canoe covers, and other equipment. 413–743–5900.

Blue Hole Canoe Company, 701 W. Front St., Burr Oak, MI 49030: Free information ■ ABS (acrylonitrile butadiene styrene) canoes for finessing rapids. 616–889–3684.

Caviness Woodworking Company, P.O. Box 710, Calhoun City, MS 38916: Free information ■ Paddles and oars. 601–628–5195.

Curtis Canoe, P.O. Box 188, Hemlock, NY 14466: Free information ■ Kevlar/glass solo and tandem canoes. 716–229–5022.

Dagger Canoe Company, P.O. Box 1500, Harriman, TN 37748: Free catalog ■ Canoes and kayaks. 615–882–0404.

Destiny Kayak Company, 111 S. Pine St., Tacoma, WA 98405: Free brochure ■ Touring kayaks. 206–847–7998.

Dirigo Boatworks, Ltd., 616 S. Wichita, Wichita, KS 67202: Free information ■ Sea kayaks. 316–262–6705.

Down River Equipment Company, 12100 W. 52nd Ave., Wheat Ridge, CO 80033: Free catalog ■ Canoes, inflatables, and accessories. 303–467–9489.

Easy Rider Canoe & Kayak Company, P.O. Box 88108, Seattle, WA 98138: Information package $5 ■ Single and double seater kayaks and canoes, rowing trainers, paddles, and whitewater and sea cruising paddles and accessories. 206–228–3633.

Ecomarine Ocean Kayak Center, 1668 Duranleau St., Vancouver, British Columbia, Canada V6H 3S4: Catalog $2 ■ Sea kayak equipment, folding kayaks, and kayak kits. 604–689–7575.

Eddyline Kayak Works, 1344 Ashten Rd., Burlington, WA 98223: Catalog $2 ■

Kayaks, paddles, and accessories. 206–757–2300.

Feathercraft Kayaks, 1244 Cartwright St., Granville Island, Vancouver, British Columbia, Canada V6H 3R8: Free brochure ■ Lightweight folding kayaks. 604–681–8437.

Four Corners River Sports, P.O. Box 379, Durango, CO 81302: Free catalog ■ Canoes, kayaks, rafts, catarafts, dories, and accessories. 800–426–7637.

Gillies Canoes & Kayaks, Margaretville, Nova Scotia, Canada B0S 1N0: Free information ■ Customized, high-performance canoes and kayaks. 902–825–3725.

Great Canadian Canoe Company, 240 Washington St., Auburn, MA 01501: Free catalog ■ Handmade Indian canoes. 800–98–CANOE.

Great River Outfitters, 3721 Shallow Brook, Bloomfield Hills, MI 48302: Catalog $1 ■ Sea kayaks and accessories. 313–644–6909.

Hydra Tuf-Lite Kayaks, 5061 S. National Dr., Knoxville, TN 37914: Free information ■ Touring kayaks for lakes, rivers, or the open sea. 800–537–8888; 615–522–9902 (in TN).

Jersey Paddler, Rt. 88 West, Brick, NJ 08724: Free information ■ Canoes and kayaks. 908–458–5777.

Keel Haulers Outfitters, 30940 Lorain Rd., North Olmsted, OH 44070: Free catalog ■ Canoes, kayaks, and accessories. 216–779–4545.

Ketter Canoeing, 101 79th Ave. North, Minneapolis, MN 55444: Free information ■ Canoes, paddles, yokes, and accessories. 612–561–2208.

Klepper America, 35 Union Square West, New York, NY 10003: Free information ■ Folding boats, kayaks, and accessories. 212–243–3428.

Lincoln Canoes, RR 2, Box 106, Freeport, ME 04032: Free information ■ Custom lightweight composite canoes. 207–865–0455.

Lotus Canoes, Inc., 7005 N. 40th St., Tampa, FL 33604: Free information ■ Lightweight easy-to-handle sport canoes. 813–985–9802.

Mad River Canoe, Inc., P.O. Box 610, Waitsfield, VT 05673: Free information ■

Handmade canoes for navigating rivers and rapids, or for pleasure boating. 802–496–3127.

Meyers Industries, Inc., P.O. Box 188, Tecumseh, MI 49286: Free brochure ■ Aluminum canoes for fishing and boating. 517–423–2151.

Mitchell Paddles, Inc., RD 2, P.O. Box 922, Canaan, NH 03741: Free information ■ Wooden canoe and kayak paddles, boats, and dry suits. 603–523–7004.

Mohawk Canoes, 963 North Hwy. 427, Longwood, FL 32750: Free information ■ Solo and tandem canoes in fiberglass, Kevlar/fiberglass, and Royalex. 407–834–3233.

Nautiraid USA, c/o Adventure Marketing, P.O. Box 1305, Ste. 238, Brunswick, ME 04011: Free information ■ Expedition-outfitted, folding kayaks that can be assembled in 20 minutes. 207–833–6606.

Navarro Canoe Company, 17901 Van Arsdale, Potter Valley, CA 95469: Free information ■ Lightweight fiberglass and wood canoes. 707–743–1255.

Necky Kayaks, Ltd., 1100 Riverside Rd., Abbotsford, British Columbia, Canada V25 4N2: Free information ■ Touring kayaks. 604–850–1206.

Northwest Kayaks, 15145 NE 90th, Redmond, WA 98052: Free information ■ Handcrafted kayaks. 800–648–8908; 206–869–1107 (in WA).

Nova Craft Canoe, 235 Exeter Rd., London, Ontario, Canada N6L 1A4: Free catalog ■ Whitewater kayaks in fiberglass, Kevlar/Cap, and Kevlar 49, with aluminum or ash gunwhales. 519–652–3649.

Ocean Kayak, Inc., 1920 Main St., Ferndale, WA 98248: Free information ■ Ocean kayaks, clothing, and accessories. 800–8–KAYAKS.

Old Town Canoe Company, 58 Middle St., Old Town, ME 04468: Free catalog ■ Over 30 models of canoes made with modern materials and traditional wood construction. 800–543–3673.

Onboard Products, 459 Main St., Amesbury, MA 01913: Free information ■ Sliding foot rower for sailboards, canoes, or skiffs. 508–388–0162.

Osagian Boats, Inc., Rt. 7, Box 506, Lebanon, MO 65536: Free information ■

Aluminum canoes and canoeing accessories. 417–532–7288.

Peconic Paddler, 89 Peconic Ave., Riverhead, NY 11901: Free information ■ Canoes and kayaks, equipment and accessories, paddles, life jackets, and dry suits. 516–727–9895.

Perception, 1110 Powdersville Rd., Easley, SC 29640: Free catalog ■ Kayaks for river running. 803–859–7518.

Piece Boat Watercraft, Inc., 71 Marsh Rd., Noank, CT 06340: Free information ■ Easy-to-assemble, lightweight folding kayak. Options include wheels for easy transporting and carrying bag/backpack. 203–572–7414.

Piragis Northwoods Company, 105 N. Central Ave., Ely, MN 55731: Free catalog ■ Canoes, boating gear and accessories, boats, videos and tapes, and trail foods. 800–223–6565.

Poseidon Kayak Imports, Box 120, Walpole, ME 04573: Free information ■ Kayaks. 207–644–8329.

Pro Advantage, Inc., 2030 N. Redwood Rd., Ste. 10, Salt Lake City, UT 84116: Free information ■ Inflatable boats, canoes, kayaks, dinghies, and oars and paddles. 801–532–4822.

Pygmy Boat Company, P.O. Box 1529, Port Townsend, WA 98368: Information $2 ■ Kayak and rowing skiff kits. 206–385–6143.

Raven Boats, 9 N. Yukon Dr., Ely, MN 55731: Information packet $1 ■ Custom solo and tandem canoes. 218–365–4322.

Sawyer Canoe Company, 234 S. State St., Oscoda, MI 48750: Free information ■ Kevlar/glass racing and cruising canoes. 517–739–9181.

Seda Products, P.O. Box 997, Chula Vista, CA 91912: Free catalog ■ Kayaks and canoes, life vests, paddles, and other accessories. 619–425–3222.

Sevylor USA, 6651 E. 26th St., Los Angeles, CA 90040: Free information ■ Inflatable boats, canoes, kayaks, dinghies, paddles, and oars. 213–727–6013.

Southern Exposure Sea Kayaks, P.O. Box 4530, Tequesta, FL 33469: Free information ■ Sea kayaks. 407–546–1261.

Stowe Canoe & Snowshoe Company, River Rd., Box 207, Stowe, VT 05672: Free

information ■ Lightweight fiberglass Allagash canoes. 802–253–7398.

Two Good Kayaks, 171 Hamakua Dr., Kailua, HI 96734: Free information ■ Custom surfing skis. 808–262–5656.

Wave Track, Ltd., 491 Madison St., Winnipeg, Manitoba, Canada R3J 1J2: Free information ■ Canoes, kayaks, accessories, and camping equipment. 204–832–1862.

We-No-Nah Canoes, Box 247, Winona, MN 55987: Free booklet ■ Canoes for whitewater and flatwater boating and racing. 507–454–5430.

Wilderness House, 1048 Commonwealth Ave., Boston, MA 02215: Free information ■ Small boats, sea kayaks, canoes, lightweight sleeping bags, tents, packs, shoes and boots, and clothing. 617–277–5858.

Wildwasser Sport USA, Inc., P.O. Box 4617, Boulder, CO 80306: Free information ■ Prijon racing and touring kayaks. 303–444–2336.

Wonder Boats, 465 Hamilton Rd., Bossier City, LA 71111: Free brochure ■ Easy-to-clean polyethylene canoes and dinghy-workboats. 318–742–1100.

Woodstrip Watercraft Company, 1818 Swamp Pike, Gilbertsville, PA 19525: Free information ■ Handcrafted wooden canoes, kayaks, and small sailing and rowing craft. 215–326–9282.

General Supplies & Equipment

Aamstrand Corporation, 629 Grove, Manteno, IL 60950: Free information ■ Anchor and winch ropes and general rigging ropes. 800–338–0557; 312–458–8550 (in IL).

Ace Flag & Pennant Factory, 224 Haddon Rd., Woodmere, Long Island, NY 11598: Free information ■ Boating flags and pennants, gifts, and supplies. 516–295–2358.

ACR Electronics, P.O. Box 5247, Fort Lauderdale, FL 33310: Free information ■ Marine safety, survival, and security equipment. 305–981–3333.

Adventure 16, Inc., 4620 Alvarado Canyon Rd., San Diego, CA 92120: Free information ■ Compasses, boat bags, water purifiers, rigging ropes, and other accessories. 800–854–2672; 800–854–0222 (in CA).

Armchair Sailor International, 543 Thames St., Newport, RI 02840: Free information ■ Navigation aids. 800–29–CHART; 401–847–4252 (in RI).

Avon Seagull Marine, 1851 McGaw Ave., Irvine, CA 92714: Free information ■ Anchors, barometers, bilge pumps, general purpose ropes and cordage, and other equipment. 714–250–0880.

Baker, Lyman & Company, 3220 South I–10 Service Rd., Metairie, LA 70001: Free information ■ Navigation aids. 800–535–6956.

Bending Branches Paddles, 1101 Stinson Blvd. NE, Minneapolis, MN 55413: Free information ■ Wood cruising paddles with resin-reinforced tips. 612–378–1825.

Berkley, Inc., One Berkley Dr., Spirit Lake, IA 51360: Free information ■ Bilge pumps, compasses, boating cables, cordage and rigging ropes, anchor ropes, winch ropes, and other marine ropes. 800–237–5539; 712–336–1520 (in IA).

Black Bart Paddles, 5830 US 45 South, Bruce Crossing, MI 49912: Free information ■ Ultralight graphite paddles for racing, cruising, and whitewater. 906–927–3405.

James Bliss Marine Company, 201 Meadow Rd., Edison, NJ 08818: Free catalog ■ Nautical accessories, supplies, and equipment for sail and power boats. 908–819–7400.

Boat Owners Association of the United States, Washington National Headquarters, 880 S. Pickett St., Alexandria, VA 22304: Free catalog ■ Boating equipment and accessories. 800–937–9307; 823–9550 (in DC).

Boulter Plywood Corporation, 24 Broadway, Somerville, MA 02145: Free catalog ■ Plywood and hardwood lumber for building boats. 617–666–1340.

L.S. Brown Company, Pawly Industries Corporation, 3610 Atlanta Industrial Dr. NW, Atlanta, GA 30331: Free information ■ Anchors, bumpers, cables, deck chairs, compasses, rigging and cordage ropes, general boating and convenience accessories, paddles, and ropes. 404–691–8200.

Carlisle Paddles, 4562 N. Downriver Rd., P.O. Box 488, Grayling, MI 49738: Free information ■ Kayak paddles. 517–348–9886.

Maurice L. Condon Company, 252 Ferris Ave., White Plains, NY 10603: Catalog $2 ■ Sitka spruce mast and spar grade; Philippine,

African, and Honduras mahogany; western red and white cedar; oak; teak; cypress; and Alaskan yellow cedar lumber for boat building and repairs. 914–946–4111.

Crook & Crook, 2795 SW 27th Ave., P.O. Box 109, Miami, FL 33133: Free catalog ■ Boating gear and equipment. 305–854–0005.

Cruise 'N Carry, P.O. Box 560, Long Beach, CA 90801: Free information ■ Lightweight portable outboards for canoes, inflatables, runabouts, and dinghies. 310–603–9888.

Cruising Equipment, 6315 Seaview Ave. NW, Seattle, WA 98107: Free catalog ■ Electrical systems for marine use. 206–782–8100.

Dan River Paddle, Rt. 2, Box 427, Madison, NC 27025: Free information ■ Handcrafted wood canoe paddles. 919–427–8536.

Datrex, 3795 NW 25th St., Miami, FL 33142: Free information ■ Safety and survival gear. 800–327–6451.

Discount Sailing Source, P.O. Box 20926, St. Petersburg, FL 33742: Free catalog ■ Sailboat equipment. 813–577–3220.

Durham Boat Company, RFD 2, Newmarket Rd., Durham, NH 03824: Free information ■ Rowing equipment and hardware, wood and composite shells, oars, clothes, books, and videos. 603–659–2548.

E & B Marine Supply, Inc., 201 Meadow Rd., P.O. Box 3138, Edison, NJ 08818: Free catalog ■ Marine accessories and supplies for sail and power boats. 800–533–5007.

Eastern Marine, 931 S. Chapel St., Newark, DE 19713: Free catalog ■ Trailer equipment and parts for boats, electronic parts, bimini tops, and boat covers. 800–622–2628.

Essex Industries, Pelfisher Rd., Mineville, NY 12956: Free information ■ Canoe accessories. Includes a portable, easy-to-store canoe seat backrest. 518–942–6671.

Faeth Outdoor Sales, R.J.F. Enterprises, Inc., 1151 S. 7th St., P.O. Box 118–A, St. Louis, MO 63166: Free information ■ Boating bags, inflators, bumpers, paddles, oars and oar locks, compasses, anchor and winch ropes, other marine ropes, toilets, and water purifiers. 314–421–0030.

Fawcett Boat Supplies, Inc., 2017 Renard Ct., On the City Dock, Annapolis, MD 21401: Free information ■ Safety and survival gear. 410–224–0920.

Fireboy Halon Systems, P.O. Box 152, Grand Rapids, MI 49501: Free information ■ Fire extinguishers for boats. 616–454–8337.

Flounder Bay Boatbuilding, 1019 3rd St., Anacortes, WA 98221: Free information ■ Imported hardwood, marine plywood, epoxies, fasteners, paint, and varnish for boat-building and repairs. 206–293–2369.

Bob Foote Products, 4606 E. 11th St., Tulsa, OK 74112: Free catalog ■ Whitewater paddles and other canoeing accessories. 918–836–FOOT.

Frabill, Inc., 536 Main St., Allentown, WI 53002: Free information ■ Anchors, bilge pumps, convenience and comfort accessories, lighting equipment, and marine and anchor ropes. 414–629–5506.

Freeport Marine Supply, 47 W Merrick Rd., Freeport, NY 11520: Free catalog ■ Save up to 40 percent on boating supplies and equipment.

Gander Mountain, Inc., P.O. Box 248, Gander Mountain, Wilmot, WI 53192: Free catalog ■ Boating equipment. 800–558–9418.

Givens Ocean Survival Systems, 1741 Main Rd., Tiverton, RI 02878: Free information ■ Safety and survival gear. 800–328–8050; 401–624–6697 (in RI).

Glenwood Marine, 1627 W. El Segundo Blvd., Gardena, CA 90249: Catalog $3 ■ Marine hardware. 213–757–3141.

Goldbergs' Marine, 201 Meadow Rd., Edison, NJ 08818: Free catalog ■ Equipment and accessories for power and sail boating and fishing. 800–523–2926.

Grey Owl Paddle Company, 62 Cowansview Rd., Cambridge, Ontario, Canada N1R 7N3: Free information ■ Paddles. 519–622–0001.

The Harbor Sales Company, Inc., 1401 Russell St., Baltimore, MD 21230: Free information ■ Teak, okoume, sapele, fir, lauan, and other boat-building lumber. 800–345–1712.

Hudson Marine Plywoods, P.O. Box 1184, Elkhart, IN 46515: Free information ■

Mahogany, gaboon, decora hardwood, flooring, decking boards, marine plywoods and other lumber for boat-building. 219–262–3666.

Imtra, 30 Barnet Blvd., New Bedford, MA 02745: Free information ■ Anchors. 508–990–2700.

Jamestown Distributors, 28 Narragansett Ave., P.O. Box 348, Jamestown, R.I. 02835: Free catalog ■ Boat-building supplies, marine fasteners, hand tools, resins, and other accessories. 800–423–0030; 401–423–2520 (in RI).

KT Anchors, Ltd., P.O. Box 2388, Niagara Falls, NY 14302: Free information ■ Lightweight, portable anchors for canoes and rubber boats. 416–682–7081.

M & E Marine Supply Company, P.O. Box 601, Camden, NJ 08101: Catalog $2 ■ Power and sail equipment, replacement parts, and accessories. 609–858–1010.

Maridyne Products Division, Parker St., Clinton, MA 01510: Free information ■ Marine hardware. 508–368–8761.

Marine Development & Research Corporation, 116 Church St., Freeport, NY 11520: Free catalog ■ Air conditioners for boats. 516–546–1162.

Maritime Lumber Supply, The Teak Connection, 2391 SE Dixie Hwy., Stuart, FL 34996: Free catalog ■ Teak accessories and furnishings, moldings, lumber, and plywood. 800–274–TEAK 404–287–0463 (in FL).

Marine Surplus, Inc., 14350 NE 19350 193rd Pl., Woodinville, WA 98072: Free information ■ New and used engines and parts. 800–869–7094.

Marinetics Corporation, P.O. Box 2676, Newport Beach, CA 92663: Catalog $3 ■ Electrical power systems and controls, instruments, distribution panels, alert and alarm systems, and other boating equipment. 800–754–4601; 714–646–8889 (in CA).

Mar-Quipt, Inc., 231 SW 5th St., Pompano Beach, FL 33060: Free brochure ■ Cranes and davits, gang planks, masts, other marine equipment, and accessories. 305–942–0440.

Matrix Desalination, Inc., 3295 SW 11th Ave., Fort Lauderdale, FL 33315: Free information ■ Desalinization equipment for making drinking water. 305–524–5120.

M.M.O.S. Marine Equipment, 15231 Michigan Ave., Dearborn, MI 48126: Free catalog ■ Marine equipment and accessories. 800–759–6667.

Mohawk Canoes, 963 North Hwy. 427, Longwood, FL 32750: Free information ■ Canoe and kayak paddles. 407–834–3233.

Nautica International, 6135 NW 167th St., Miami, FL 33015: Free information ■ Safety and survival gear. 305–556–5554.

Nauticus, 2662 S. Dixie Hwy., Miami, FL 33133: Free information ■ Safety and survival gear. 305–858–0474.

New Found Metals, Inc., 240 Airport Rd., Port Townsend, WA 98368: Catalog $3 ■ Silicon and manganese bronze marine hardware. 206–385–3315.

Northwest Design Works, Inc., 12414 Hwy. 99 South, Everett, WA 98204: Free information ■ Handcrafted kayak paddles for whitewater and touring. 206–743–3277.

Onboard Products, 459 Main St., Amesbury, MA 01913: Free information ■ Sliding foot rower for sailboards, canoes, or skiffs. 508–388–0162.

Peconic Paddler, 89 Peconic Ave., Riverhead, NY 11901: Free information ■ Canoes and kayaks, equipment and accessories, paddles, life jackets, and dry suits. 516–727–9895.

Piragis Northwoods Company, 105 N. Central Ave., Ely, MN 55731: Free catalog ■ Canoes, boating gear and accessories, boats, videos and tapes, and trail foods. 800–223–6565.

Pro Advantage, Inc., 2030 N. Redwood Rd., Ste. 10, Salt Lake City, UT 84116: Free information ■ Anchors and anchor ropes, other marine ropes, bilge pumps, deck chairs, bumpers, rigging ropes, marine gauges, inflators and ladders, oars and oar locks, and paddles. 801–532–4822.

R.G.P. Composites, 9628 153rd Ave. NE, Redmond, WA 98052: Free information ■ Custom composite paddles and oars. 206–869–7272.

The Rigging Company, 1 Maritime Dr., Portsmouth, RI 02871: Catalog $2 ■ Sailboat rigging supplies and tools. 800–322–1525; 401–683–1525 (in RI).

Rope Store, 615 Tarklin Hill Rd., New Bedford, MA 02745: Free information ■ Dock and anchor lines, sheets and guys in twisted nylon, spun dacron, and filament dacron, braided parallel filament dacron cordage, and hardware. 800–634–ROPE.

Rule Industries, Inc., 70 Blanchard Rd., Burlington, MA 01803: Free information ■ Compasses, anchors, pumps, and other marine equipment.

Safety Flag Company of America, P.O. Box 1005, Pawtucket, RI 02862: Free catalog ■ Safety equipment for boats. Includes flags, vests, and belts. 401–722–0900.

Sawyer Paddles & Oars, P.O. Box 624, Rogue River, OR 97537: Free information ■ Wooden paddles and oars with fiberglass tips. 503–535–3606.

Sea Spike Marine Supply Company, Inc., 994 Fulton St., Farmingdale, NY 11735: Free information ■ Anchors and anchor ropes, bumpers, bilge pumps, carriers and trailers, rigging ropes and cordage, compasses, boating cables, cordage and rigging ropes, and other marine ropes. 516–249–2241.

Sonic Technology Products, 120 Richardson St., Grass Valley, CA 95945: Free information ■ Diagnostic listening tool for pinpointing problems in engines, motors, compressors, and other mechanical equipment. 800–247–5548.

Sportac Industries, 3165 Irma St., Victoria, British Columbia, Canada V9A 1S9: Free information ■ Easy-to-install sails for canoes and kayaks. 604–361–4420.

Spring Creek Outfitters, Inc., 5714 Mineral Ave., Box 246, Mt. Iron, MN 55768: Free catalog ■ Canoe accessories. 218–735–8719.

SSI Boating Accessories, P.O. Box 99, Hollywood, MD 20636: Free catalog ■ Accessories and equipment for boating and sport fishing enthusiasts. 301–373–2372.

Survival Technologies Group, 101 16th Ave. South, St. Petersburg, FL 33701: Free information ■ Safety and survival gear. 813–822–4749.

Switlik Parachute, 1325 E. State St., Trenton, NJ 08607: Free information ■ Safety and survival gear. 609–587–3300.

Travaco Laboratories, 345 Eastern Ave., P.O. Box 297, Chelsea, MA 02150: Free catalog ■ Supplies and accessories for repairing boats. 617–884–7740.

12 Volt Products, Inc., P.O. Box 664, Holland, PA 18966: Free catalog ■ Twelve-volt operated accessories for boats, RVs, vans, trucks, and cars. 215–355–0525.

Value Carpets, Inc., Marine Division, 1802 Murray Ave., Dalton, GA 30721: Free information ■ Do-it-yourself replacement carpet kits for boats. 800–634–3702.

Voyageur's, P.O. Box 207, Waitsfield, VT 05673: Free catalog ■ Waterproof bags, packs, camera bags, and storage and flotation systems. 802–496–3127.

Wave Track, Ltd., 491 Madison St., Winnipeg, Manitoba, Canada R3J 1J2: Free information ■ Canoes and kayaks, paddlesport accessories, and camping equipment. 204–832–1862.

Werner Paddle Company, Division of Northwest Design Works, 12414 Hwy. 99 South, Everett, WA 98204: Free information ■ Handcrafted kayak and canoe paddles. 800–275–3311.

West Marine Products, 500 Westridge Rd., Watsonville, CA 95076: Free catalog ■ Power and sail boat accessories and supplies. 408–728–2700.

World Ski Lines, 25 Pamaron Way, Novato, CA 94947: Free information ■ Anchors and anchor ropes, bilge pumps, boating comfort and convenience accessories, ladders, inflators, cordage and rigging ropes, winch ropes, and other marine ropes. 415–883–3700.

Inflatable Boats

Academy Broadway Corporation, 5 Plant Ave., Vanderbilt Industrial Park, Smithtown, NY 11787: Free information ■ Inflatable boats and dinghies. 516–231–7000.

Achilles Inflatable Craft, 1407 80th St. SW, Everett, WA 98203: Free information ■ Inflatable boats. 206–353–7000.

Aire, P.O. Box 3412, Boise, ID 83703: Free information ■ Self-bailing inflatable touring kayaks. 208–344–7506.

Altco Trading International, 6 Macaulay St. East, Hamilton, Ontario, Canada L8L 8B1: Free information ■ Soft and rigid bottom inflatable dinghies. 416–521–1061.

Alvimar Manufacturing Company, Inc., 51–02 21st St., Long Island City, NY 11101: Free information ■ Inflatable boats. 718–937–0404.

A.R.C., P.O. Box 4488, Annapolis, MD 21403: Free information ■ Rigid hull inflatable dinghies. 410–268–6622.

Avon Seagull Marine, 1851 McGaw Ave., Irvine, CA 92714: Free information ■ Inflatable boats. 714–250–0880.

Bat Inflatable Boats, Inc., 2330 Shelter Island Dr., San Diego, CA 92106: Free information ■ Rigid inflatables, from 7 to 30 feet. 619–223–9792.

Berry Scuba Company, 6674 Northwest Hwy., Chicago, IL 60631: Free catalog ■ Inflatable boats, watches, clothing, skin diving and scuba equipment, diving lights, and underwater cameras. 800–621–6019; 312–763–1626 (in IL).

Coleman Outdoor Products, Inc., 250 N. Saint Francis, P.O. Box 2931, Wichita, KS 67201: Free information ■ Inflatable boats, canoes, and dinghies. 800–835–3278.

High Seas Foul Weather Gear, 880 Corporate Woods Pkwy., Vernon Hills, IL 60061: Free information ■ Inflatable dinghies. 708–913–1100.

Kirby Kraft, Box 582, Seachelt, British Colombia, Canada V0N 3A0: Free information ■ Folding fiberglass, 12–foot rigid bottom inflatable. 614–885–2695.

Legend Inflatables, 301 4th St., Annapolis, MD 21403: Free information ■ Inflatable dinghies. 410–268–6816.

Metzeler Inflatable Boats, c/o Zodiac Group, P.O. Box 400, Stevensville, MD 21666: Free information ■ Inflatable boats. 410–643–4141.

Nautica International, 6135 NW 167th St., Miami, FL 33015: Free information ■ Inflatable dinghies. 305–556–5554.

Nelson/Weather Rite Products, Inc., Fuqua Sports, 14760 Santa Fe Trail Dr., Lenexa, KS 66215: Free information ■ Inflatable boats and paddle boats. 800–255–6061; 913–452–3200 (in KS).

Northwest River Supplies, Inc., 2009 S. Maine, Moscow, ID 83843: Free catalog ■ Inflatable boats. 800–635–5202.

Novurania Inflatable Boats, 711 Gardena Blvd., Gardena, CA 90248: Free information ■ Inflatable boats. 310–323–1405.

Outdoor Sports Headquarters, Inc., 967 Watertower Ln., Dayton, OH 45449: Free information ■ Inflatable boats, canoes, and paddle boats. 513–865–5855.

Poolmaster, Inc, 1200 Hamilton Ct., P.O. Box 2288, Menlo Park, CA 94025: Free information ■ Inflatable boats. 800–227–8355; 800–982–5831 (in CA).

Pro Advantage, Inc., 2030 N. Redwood Rd., Ste. 10, Salt Lake City, UT 84116: Free information ■ Inflatable boats, canoes, kayaks, and dinghies, and paddles and oars. 801–532–4822.

Rex Marine Center, 144 Water St., South Norwalk, CT 06854: Catalog $5 ■ Inflatable boats, dinghies, and dive boats. 203–854–9955.

Sea Eagle, 200 Wilson St., Port Jefferson Station, NY 11776: Free catalog ■ Inflatable boats that can be used as fishing platforms, motor runabouts, or yacht tenders. Other items include paddles, safety gear, pumps, outboard engines, and marine accessories. 800–852–0925.

Sea Nymph, Inc., P.O. Box 337, Syracuse, IN 46567: Free information ■ Inflatable boats, cruisers and, dinghies, and paddles and oars. 219–457–3131.

Sevylor USA, 6651 E. 26th St., Los Angeles, CA 90040: Free information ■ Inflatable boats, canoes, kayaks, and dinghies, and paddles and oars. 213–727–6013.

Sillinger Inflatable Boats, 1851 McGaw Ave., Irvine, CA 92714: Free information ■ Inflatable boats. 714–250–1188.

Zodiac of North America Inflatable Boats, P.O. Box 400, Stevensville, MD 21666: Free information ■ Inflatable boats. 410–643–4141.

Instruments & Electronics

Alpha Marine Systems, 996 Hanson Ct., Milpitas, CA 95035: Free information ■ Autopilots. 800–ALPHA–25; 408–945–1155 (in CA).

Apelco Marine Electronics, 46 River Rd., Hudson, NH 03051: Free information ■ Loran, RDF and VHF equipment, depth sounders, ADF and EPIRB equipment, and other marine electronics. 603–881–9605.

Aqua Meter Instrument Corporation, Rule Industries, Cape Ann Industrial Park, Gloucester, MA 01930: Free catalog ■ Speed logs, depth finders, and other marine instruments. 508–281–0440.

Autohelm America, Box 308, New Whitfield St., Guilford, CT 06437: Free information ■ Boat speed indicators, water temperature and depth gauges, electronic compasses, autopilots, and video plotters. 203–453–8753.

Brookes & Gatehouse, 23 Broad Common Rd., Bristol, RI 02809: Free information ■ Depth sounders, knotmeters, wind instruments, autopilots, speed logs, electronic compasses, and other boating supplies. 401–253–6200.

Celestaire, 416 S. Pershing, Wichita, KS 67218: Free information ■ Navigation instruments and accessories. Includes sextants, books, and computers. 316–686–9785.

Coast Navigation, 116 Legion Ave., Annapolis, MD 21401: Free catalog ■ VHF equipment, Loran, compasses, autopilots, anchors, chains, and accessories. 410–268–3120.

Datamarine International, Inc., 53 Portside Dr., Pocasset, MA 02559: Free information ■ Depth sounders, knotmeters, speed logs, wind instruments, video charts, Loran, antennas, and other equipment. 617–563–7151.

Davis Instruments Corporation, 3465 Diablo Ave., Hayward, CA 94545: Free information ■ Compasses, depth finders, direction finders, range finders, speedometers, ladders, lighting equipment, paddles, and accessories. 800–678–3669.

Eagle Electronics, P.O. Box 669, Catoosa, OK 74015: Free information ■ Depth finders, depth sounders, depth gauges, speedometers, thermometers, and other marine electronics. 800–331–2301; 918–266–5373 (in OK).

Euro Marine Trading, Inc., 64 Halsey St., Building 27, Newport, RI 02840: Free information ■ Depth sounders, speed logs, wind instruments, electronic compass, water temperature instruments, and barometers. 401–849–0060.

Furuno USA, Box 2343, South San Francisco, CA 94083: Free information ■ Boat speed indicators, water temperature and depth gauges, electronic compasses, autopilots, alarm systems, Loran, radar, radio equipment, and video plotters. 415–873–9393.

Jay Stuart Haft, P.O. Box 11210, Bradenton, FL 34207: Free information ■ Depth sounders, speed logs, knotmeters, and electronic compasses. 813–746–7161.

ICOM America, 2380 116th Ave. NE, Bellevue, WA 98004: Free information ■ Boat speed indicators, water temperature and depth gauges, electronic compasses, autopilots, weather fax, radar, and video plotters. 800–999–9877.

International Marine Instruments, New Whitfield St., Guilford, CT 06437: Free information ■ Loran, wind and speed logs, depth sounders, autopilots, hand-bearing compasses, and other marine electronics. 203–453–4374.

Ray Jefferson, Main & Cotton, Philadelphia, PA 19127: Free information ■ Depth sounders, VHF equipment, water temperature instruments, radar, wind instruments, RDF equipment, speed logs, knotmeters, and antennas. 603–881–5200.

King Marine Electronics, Inc., 5320 140th Ave. North, Clearwater, FL 34620: Free information ■ Loran, VHF equipment, autopilots, RDF equipment, speed logs, depth sounders, and antennas. 813–530–3411.

Kleid Navigation, 443 Ruane St., Fairfield, CT 06430: Free information ■ Navigation equipment and electronics. 203–259–7161.

Lowrance Electronics, 12000 E. Skelly Dr., Tulsa, OK 74070: Free information ■ Boat speed indicators, water temperature and depth gauges, and Loran. 918–437–6881.

Marinetek, Abbott Ave., Milpitas, CA 95035: Free information ■ Boat speed indicators, water temperature and depth gauges, and VHF equipment. 408–262–2600.

Micrologic, 9610 DeSoto Ave., Chatsworth, CA 91311: Free information ■ Loran equipment. 818–998–1216.

Morad Electronics, 1125 NW 46th St., Seattle, WA 98107: Free information ■ Antennas for use on boats. 206–789–2525.

Navico, Inc., 7411 114th Ave. North, Ste. 310, Largo, FL 34643: Free information ■ Autopilots, VHF equipment, wind and speed logs, depth sounders, knotmeters, and accessories. 813–546–4300.

Ockam Instruments, 26 Higgins Dr., Milford, CT 06460: Free information ■ Wind and speed logs, depth sounders, knotmeters, and accessories. 203–877–7453.

Plastimo USA, Inc., 6605 Selnick Dr., Rt. 100, Business Park, Baltimore, MD 21227: Free information ■ Speed logs, depth sounders, autopilots, wind instruments, knotmeters, and other equipment. 410–796–0002.

C. Plath, 222 Severn Ave., Annapolis, MD 21403: Free information ■ Anemometers, barometers, direction finders, compasses, navigation equipment, range finders, thermometers, and other marine electronics equipment. 410–263–6700.

Radio-Holland Group, 8943 Gulf Freeway, Houston, TX 77017: Free information ■ Boat speed indicators, water temperature and depth gauges, electronic compasses, VHF and radio equipment, alarm systems, Loran, cellular phones, autopilots, and video plotters. 713–943–3325.

Raytheon Marine Company, 46 River Rd., Hudson, NH 03051: Free information ■ Boat speed indicators, water temperature and depth gauges, weather fax, alarm systems, and video plotters. 603–881–5200.

RH Trading, 19019 36th Ave. West, Building A, Ste. E, Seattle, WA 98036: Free information ■ Water temperature and depth gauges, electronic compasses, alarm systems, radar, autopilots, and video plotters. 206–672–6751.

Ritchie Compasses, 243 Oak St., Pembroke, MA 02359: Free catalog ■ Magnetic marine compasses. 617–826–5131.

Robertson-Shipmate, 400 Oser Ave., Hauppauge, NY 11788: Free information ■ Boat speed indicators, water temperature and depth gauges, electronic compasses, autopilots, and video plotters. 516–273–3737.

Signet Marine, 3401 Aerojet Ave., El Monte, CA 91734: Free information ■ Depth sounders, knotmeters and speed logs, and digital magnetic compasses. 818–571–2772.

Si-Tex Marine Electronics, Box 6700, Clearwater, FL 34618: Free information ■ Boat speed indicators, water temperature and depth gauges, electronic compasses, autopilots, alarm systems, and video plotters. 813–536–0898.

Skipper Marine Electronics, Inc., 3170 Commercial Ave., Northbrook, IL 60062: Free information ■ Electronics for boats. 800–621–2378.

Sperry Marine, 1070 Seminole Trail, Charlottesville, VA 22901: Free information ■

Boat speed indicators, water temperature and depth gauges, electronic compasses, autopilots, and video plotters. 804–974–2000.

Teiresias, Inc., Sag Harbor Tpk., Box 1980, Sag Harbor, NY 11963: Free information ■ Antennas for use on boats. 516–537–7400.

Trimble Navigation, Marine Division, P.O. Box 3642, Sunnyvale, CA 94088: Free information ■ Navigation systems for marine use. 800–TRIMBLE; 800–221–3001 (in CA).

W-H Autopilots, 655 NE Northlake Pl., Seattle, WA 98105: Free information ■ Autopilots. 206–633–1830.

Yazaki Instrumentation, Airport Rd., Rt.4, Princeton, MN 55371: Free information ■ Wind and speed instruments, depth sounders, knotmeters, and compasses. 612–389–2303.

Miscellaneous Boats

Acrylicraft Designs, Inc., P.O. Box 562123, Miami, FL 33256: Free information ■ Easy-to-transport glass bottom boats. 305–663–2422.

American Sail, 74350 Pepperdam Ave., Pepperdam Industrial Park, Charleston, SC 29418: Free information ■ Rigid dinghies. 803–552–8548.

The Anchorage, 65 Miller St., Warren, RI 02885: Free information ■ Rigid dinghies. 401–245–3300.

Atlas Boat Works, P.O. Box 2011, Cape Coral, FL 33910: Free information ■ Inboard diesel, lobster-style, weekender cruiser. 813–574–2628.

F.M. Barretta Rowing Boats, P.O. Box 57, Cold Spring Harbor, NY 11742: Free brochure ■ Long-cockpit, 19–foot open water rowing shell with extra storage space and rigged with oars. 516–421–1103.

Bauteck Marine, 2060 Dobbs Rd., St. Augustine, FL 32086: Free brochure ■ Traditionally crafted small boat. 904–824–8826.

Boston Whaler, 1149 Hingham St., Rockland, MA 02370: Free information ■ Rigid dinghies. 617–871–1400.

Brookins Boatworks, Ltd., 24 Sand Island Rd., Honolulu, HI 96819: Free information ■ Custom 17–, 19–, 21–, and 26–foot classic runabouts. 808–842–0032.

Brooklin Boat Yard, Brooklin, ME 04616: Free information ■ Custom built boats. 207–359–2236.

William Clements, Boat Builder, 18 Mt. Pleasant St., P.O. Box 87, North Billerica, MA 01862: Free information ■ Classic cruising boats, from 13 to 20 feet; double-paddle and decked sailing canoes; and canoe yawls. 508–663–3103.

Clubhouse Boatworks, 217 S. River Clubhouse Rd., Harwood, MD 20776: Free information ■ Custom wood skiffs, prams, lapstrakes, and rowing boats. 410–798–5356.

Custom Fiberglass Products of Florida, Inc., 8136 Leo Kidd Ave., Port Richey, FL 34668: Free information ■ Custom boats that include a 16–foot daysailer, 17–foot weekender, 18–foot pocket cruiser, 20–foot shoal keel, and a 24–foot cruiser. 813–847–5798.

Davard Marine, 21460 Encina Rd., Topanga, CA 90290: Free information ■ Four-section nesting dinghy. 310–455–3109.

Dayton Marine Products, 2101 N. Lapeer Rd., Lapeer, MI 48446: Free information ■ Rigid dinghies. 313–664–0850.

Edey & Duff, 128 Aucoot Rd., Mattapoisett, MA 02739: Free information ■ Rigid dinghies. 508–758–2743.

Ellis Boat Company, Inc., Manset, ME 04656: Free information ■ Custom fiberglass boats, from 20 feet to 32 feet, with a variety of interiors and other options. 207–244–9221.

Ensign Dinghies, 57 Maple Ave., Rye, NY 10508: Free information ■ Rigid dinghies, from 7– to 15–feet. 914–967–1656.

Folbot, Inc., P.O. Box 70877, Charleston, SC 29415: Free catalog ■ Sail, power, and paddle wheel boats, from 10– to 17–foot. Others include folding boats and boat kits. 800–533–5099.

Futura Surf Skis, 730 W. 19th St., National City, CA 92050: Free brochure ■ Surf skis, in 16– and 19–foot models. 619–474–8382.

Johannsen Boat Works, P.O. Box 570097, Miami, FL 33257: Free information ■ Rowing/sailing dinghies that can be used as cruising tenders, in 8–, 10–, and 12–feet. 305–445–7534.

Lowell's Boat Shop, 459 Main St., Amesbury, MA 01913: Brochure $2 ■ Shoal draft, beachable, trailerable wooden boat with epoxied bottom construction and other wooden boats. 508–388–0162.

North River Boatworks, 6 Elm St., Albany, NY 12202: Information $2 ■ River skiffs and other boats for sails, oars, or engines. 518–434–4414.

Norton Boat Works, 535 Commercial, P.O. Box 464, Green Lake, WI 54941: Free information ■ Ready-to-use ice boats, parts, kits, and plans. 414–294–6813.

Pakboats, P.O. Box 700, Enfield, NH 03748: Free information ■ Portable boats that fold and can be carried in one bag, and used for general boating and whitewater and expedition activities. 603–632–7654.

Porta-Bote International, 1074 Independence Ave., Mountain View, CA 94043: Free information ■ Folding 8–, 10–, and 12–foot dinghies. 800–227–8882; 415–961–5334 (in CA).

Ranger Fiberglass Boats, 25802 Pacific Hwy. South, Kent, WA 98031: Free information ■ Custom-built 2–person fiberglass, economical-to-operate cabin boats. 206–839–5213.

Rosborough Boats, Ltd., P.O. Box 188, Armdale, Nova Scotia, Canada B3L 4J9: Free information ■ Hand-laid, all-fiberglass boats in several lengths and styles. 902–477–3262.

Saroca, 27 Hedley St., Portsmouth, RI 02871: Free catalog ■ Convertible boat that can be used as a sailboat, row boat, motor boat, canoe, or scull. 401–683–9003.

Shoco, Inc., P.O. Box 1825, Shelby, NC 28150: Free information ■ Lightweight recreational pedal boats. 704–482–7329.

Sumner Boat, 334 S. Bayview Ave., Amityville, NY 11701: Free information ■ Sailing and rowing dinghies. 516–264–1830.

Whitehall Reproductions, 1908 Store St., Victoria, British Columbia, Canada V8T 4R4: Free brochure ■ Handcrafted classic rowing and sailing boats, from 7 to 14 feet. 604–384–6574.

Wonder Boats, 465 Hamilton Rd., Bossier City, LA 71111: Free brochure ■ Easy-to-clean polyethylene canoes and dinghy-workboats. 318–742–1100.

Nautical Books & Gifts

Bennett Marine Video, 550 NW 12th Ave., Deerfield Beach, FL 33442: Catalog $1 ■ Video cassettes about boating, navigation and electronics, boat maintenance, boat handling, buying a boat, yachting, sailboat racing, cruising, Jacques Cousteau, adventure stories, water sports, scuba diving, general fishing, and fresh water and saltwater sport fishing. 305–427–1400.

Winslow J. Furber Marine Sculptor, P.O. Box 1224, York Harbor, ME 03911: Free information ■ Custom bronze and steel nautical sculptures. 207–363–3867.

International Marine Publishing Company, Rt. 1, Box 220, Camden, ME 04843: Free information ■ Nautical books. 207–236–4837.

Moby Dick Marine Specialties, 27 William St., New Bedford, MA 02740: Catalog $5 ■ Nautical gifts, decorative accessories, and scrimshaw. 800–343–8044; 800–732–5700 (in WA).

Mystic Seaport Book & Print Shop, Seaport Museum Stores, 39 Greemanville Ave., Mystic, CT 06355: Free information ■ Gifts with a nautical and historical theme. 203–572–8551.

Nautical Antiques, P.O. Box 785, Kennebunkport, ME 04046: Catalog $3 ■ American paintings, scrimshaw, and nautical antiquities. 207–967–3218.

Preston's, Main Street Wharf, Greenport, NY 11944: Free catalog ■ Ship's wheels, clocks and bells, tavern signs, harpoons, binoculars, nautical lamps, caps and sweaters, antique maps, glassware, and marine paintings. 516–477–1990.

Ship's Hatch, 10376 Main St., Fairfax, VA 22030: Brochure $1 ■ Military patches, pins and insignia, official USN ship ball caps, ship's clocks, hatchcover tables, nautical and military gifts, jewelry, lamps, lanterns, ship's wheels, custom military tables, jewelry boxes, and plaques. 703–691–1670.

WoodenBoat, P.O. Box 78, Brooklin, ME 04616: Free catalog ■ Books about boats, building and repairing, woodworking and tools, and seamanship and sailing. 207–359–4651.

Rowing Boats & Shells

Advance USA, P.O. Box 452, East Haddam, CT 06423: Free information ■ Lightweight recreational rowing shells. 800–443–5797; 203–873–8643 (in CT).

F.M. Barretta Rowing Boats, P.O. Box 57, Cold Spring Harbor, NY 11742: Free brochure ■ Open water rowing shells rigged with oars. 516–421–1103.

Durham Boat Company, RFD 2, Newmarket Rd., Durham, NH 03824: Free information ■ Rowing equipment and hardware, wood and composite shells, oars, clothes, books, and videos. 603–659–2548.

Johannsen Boat Works, P.O. Box 570097, Miami, FL 33257: Free information ■ Rowing and sailing dinghy. 305–445–7534.

Little River Marine, P.O. Box 986, Gainesville, FL 32602: Free information ■ Rowing shells. 904–378–5025.

MAAS Rowing Shells, 1453 Harbour Way South, Richmond, CA 94804: Free brochure ■ Open water rowing shells. 510–232–1612.

Martin Marine Company, 141 Rt. 236, Eliot, ME 03903: Free brochure ■ Rowing boats, single hull ocean shells, and a sliding seat rowing skiff kit. 800–477–1507.

Sailboats & Supplies

Bacon & Associates, 112 West St., P.O. Box 3150, Annapolis, MD 21403: Free catalog ■ Hardware, equipment, and accessories for sailboats. 410–263–4880.

James Bliss Marine Company, 201 Meadow Rd., Edison, NJ 08818: Free catalog ■ Nautical accessories, supplies, and equipment for sail and power boats. 908–819–7400.

Dwyer Aluminum Mast Company, Inc., 21 Commerce Dr., North Branford, CT 06471: Free catalog ■ Sailboat masts, booms, rigging, and hardware. 203–484–0419.

E & B Marine Supply, Inc., 201 Meadow Rd., P.O. Box 3138, Edison, NJ 08818: Free catalog ■ Marine accessories and boating supplies for sail and power boats. 800–533–5007.

Goldbergs' Marine, 201 Meadow Rd., Edison, NJ 08818: Free catalog ■ Equipment and accessories for power and sail boating and fishing. 800–523–2926.

M & E Marine Supply Company, P.O. Box 601, Camden, NJ 08101: Catalog $2 (refundable) ■ Power and sail equipment and hard-to-find marine parts and accessories. 609–858–1010.

Sailrite Kits, 305 W. Van Buren, Box 987, Columbia City, IN 46725: Catalog $2 ■ Sailmaking supplies and tools, information on how to make sails, and sewing machines. 800–348–2769.

Thayer & Company, 2106 Atlee Rd., Mechanicsville, VA 23111: Information $3 ■ Traditional sailing and pulling boats with fiberglass hulls and mahogany trim. Available assembled, as a kit, or just the hull. 804–746–0674.

West Marine Products, 500 Westridge Rd., Watsonville, CA 95076: Free catalog ■ Power and sail boat accessories. 415–728–2700.

Uniforms & Boating Attire

Atlantis, 30 Barnet Blvd., New Bedford, MA 02745: Free catalog ■ Foul weather gear and clothing for yachtsmen and fishermen.

Colorado Kayak, P.O. Box 3059, Buena Vista. CO 81211: Free catalog ■ Boating fashions for men and women. 800–535–3565.

Fletcher-Barnhardt & White, 1211 S. Tyron St., Charlotte, NC 28203: Free catalog ■ Sportswear and accessories. 800–543–5453.

Patagonia Mail Order, P.O. Box 8900, Bozeman, MT 59715: Free catalog ■ Sportswear and foul weather clothing. 800–336–9090.

Rainbow Designs, P.O. Box 3155, Boulder, CO 80307: Free information ■ Water sports clothing and equipment. 303–444–8495.

Smallwoods Yachtwear, 1001 SE 17th St., Fort Lauderdale, FL 33316: Free catalog ■ Uniforms and casual boating attire. 800–771–2283; 305–523–2282 (in FL).

BOCCIE

Indian Industries, Inc., 817 Maxwell, P.O. Box 889, Evansville, IN 47711: Free information ■ Boccie balls and sets. 812–426–2281.

Pennsylvania Sporting Goods, 1360 Industrial Hwy., P.O. Box 451, Southampton, PA 18966: Free information ■ Boccie sets. 800–535–1122.

Regent Sports Corporation, 45 Ranick Rd., Hauppage, NY 11787: Free information ■ Boccie balls and sets. 516–234–2948.

Sport Fun, Inc., 4621 Sperry St., P.O. Box 39150, Los Angeles, CA 90039: Free information ■ Boccie sets. 800–423–2597; 818–240–6700 (in CA).

Venus Knitting Mills, Inc., 140 Spring St., Murray Hill, NJ 07974: Free information ■ Boccie sets. 800–955–4200; 908–464–2400 (in NJ).

BOOKKEEPING & ACCOUNTING SUPPLIES

Accountants' Supply House, 518 Rockaway Ave., P.O. Box 310, Valley Stream, NY 11582: Free catalog ■ Stationery, envelopes, forms, and labels, adding machines, shipping materials, disk storage cabinets, typewriter and data processing ribbons, furniture, attache cases, and portfolios. Custom printing available. 800–DIAL–ASH; 516–561–7700 (in NY).

HG Professional Forms Company, 2020 California St., Omaha, NE 68102: Free catalog ■ Pre-printed forms and supplies, accounting accessories, computer paper and forms, record-keeping systems, general use forms and pads, ruled writing pads, pad holders, binders, report covers, and envelopes 800–228–1493.

Medical Arts Press, 3440 Winnetka Ave. North, Minneapolis, MN 55427: Free catalog ■ Office forms and supplies for medical and dental professions. 800–328–2179.

BOOKPLATES & BOOKMARKS

Antioch Publishing Company, 888 Dayton St., Yellow Springs, OH 45387: Free catalog ■ Personalized bookplates, bookmarks, albums, diaries, scrapbooks, and memo boards. 513–767–7379.

Lixx Labelsz, 2619 14th St. S.W., P.O. Box 32055, Calgary, Alberta, Canada T2T 5X0: Free catalog ■ Labels and bookmarks that combine wildlife designs and calligraphy. 403–245–2331.

BOOK REPAIR & BINDING

Associated Bindery, Inc., 405 E. 70th St., New York, NY 10021: Free information ■ Book repair and binding services. 212–879–5080.

Colophon Book Arts Supply, 3046 Hogum Bay Rd. NE, Olympia, WA 98506: Catalog $2 ■ Bookbinding and marbling supplies and books. 206–459–2940.

Sky Meadow Bindery, 20 Sky Meadow Rd., Suffern, NY 10901: Free information ■ Document and book repair and binding services. 914–354–7101.

TALAS, 213 W. 35th St., New York, NY 10001: Catalog $5 ■ Bookbinding supplies and accessories. 212–736–7744.

BOOKS

Bargain Books

Barnes & Noble, 126 5th Ave., New York, NY 10011: Free catalog ■ Bargain books, records, and tapes. 800–242–6657.

Critics' Choice Video, P.O. Box 549, Elk Grove Village, IL 60009: Free catalog ■ Save up to 90 percent on books, records, and video cassettes. 800–544–9852.

Daedalus Books, Inc., 4601 Decatur St., Hyattsville, MD 20781: Free catalog ■ Save from 50 to 90 percent on publishers' overstocks and remainders. 301–779–4102.

Discount Books & Videos, Inc., P.O. Box 928, Vineland, NJ 08360: Free catalog ■ Save up to 90 percent on publishers' overstocks and remainders. 609–691–1620.

Edward R. Hamilton, Bookseller, Box 15, Falls Village, CT 06031: Free catalog ■ Bargain books selected from publishers overstocks.

Children's Books

Aims International Books, Inc., 7709 Hamilton, Ave., Cincinnati, OH 45231: Free information ■ Books for children and adults in foreign languages. 513–521–5590.

Aladdin/Collier Books, MacMillan Children's Book Group, 866 3rd Ave., New York, NY 10022: Free information ■ Board books, pop-ups, and paperbacks for children age 3 to 16. 212–702–2000.

Astor Books, 62 Cooper Square, New York, NY 10003: Free information ■ Sesame Street Musical Story books, Sesame Street All about Music series, music folios, and other books and cassettes for children. 212–777–3700.

The Bookworm, P.O. Box 186, Goessel, KS 67053: Free catalog ■ Mail-order books for children.

Boyds Mill Press, 2300 W. 5th Ave., P.O. Box 269, Columbus, OH 43230: Free information ■ Children's books. 614–487–2720.

Checkerboard Press, 30 Vesey St., New York, NY 10007: Free catalog ■ Books for children. 212–571–6300.

Cheshire Cat Children's Books, 5512 Connecticut Ave. NW, Washington, DC 20015: Free newsletter ■ Books, records, and tapes for children. 202–244–3956.

Children's Book & Music Center, 2500 Santa Monica Blvd., Santa Monica, CA 90406: Catalog $1 ■ Books, records, and other educational materials for children. 800–443–1856; 310–829–0215 (in CA).

Children's Press, 5440 N. Cumberland Ave., Chicago, IL 60656: Free catalog ■ Books for children. 312–693–0800.

Chinaberry Book Service, 2830 Via Orange Way, Ste. B, Spring Valley, CA 92078: Free catalog ■ Books and music for children and adults. 619–670–5200.

Collier/Macmillan Publishing Company, 866 3rd Ave., New York, NY 10022: Free information ■ Novelty books, board books, and pop-ups for children age 3 to 16. 212–702–9026.

Columbia Publishers, 709 Columbia Dr., Sacramento, CA 95864: free information ■ Series of books designed to get girls thinking about career choices.

Dover Publications, Inc., 31 East 2nd St., Mineola, NY 11501: Free catalog ■ Children's classics, cut-and-assemble books, coloring books, paper dolls and stickers, and other educational activity books. 516–294–7000.

EDC Publishing, 10302 E. 55th Pl., Tulsa, OK 74146: Free catalog ■ Children's activity books, travel games, art books, picture word books, picture bibles, and nature and geography books. 800–331–4418.

Free Spirit Publishing, Inc., 400 1st Ave. North, Ste. 616, Minneapolis, MN 55401: Free catalog ■ Nonfiction, psychology and self-help materials for and about gifted, talented, and creative young people and parents and teachers. 612–338–2068.

Holiday House, Inc., 425 Madison Ave., New York, NY 10017: Free catalog ■ Books for children, from kindergarten through grade three, grades four through six, and grades seven and up. 212–688–0085.

Ideals Publishing Corporation, 565 Marriott Dr., Ste. 890, Nashville, TN 37210: Free catalog ■ Nostalgic and family-oriented books, children's board books with cassettes, other children's books, inspirational books, and cookbooks. 615–885–8270.

Intervisual Books, Inc., 2850 Ocean Park Blvd., Santa Monica, CA 90405: Free catalog ■ Children's pop-up, novelty, three-dimensional, and puppet books. 310–396–8708.

Kar-Ben Copies, Inc., 6800 Tildenwood Ln., Rockville, MD 20852: Free catalog ■ Judaic books and cassettes for children. 800–452–7236.

Klutz Press, 2121 Staunton Ct., Palo Alto, CA 94306: Free information ■ How-to fun books and song books for children. 415–857–0888.

The Learning Works, 5720 Thornwood Dr., Goleta, CA 93117: Free information ■ Children's books for the home and school. 800–235–5767.

Metacom, Inc., 5353 Nathan Ln., Plymouth, MN 55442: Free catalog ■ Cassette of Golden Age Radio programs, comedy super stars of past years, famous radio plays, and foreign languages. Other items include read-along books and cassettes for teaching children to read and coloring books with stories. 800–328–0108.

Music for Little People, P.O. Box 1460, Redway, CA 95560: Free catalog ■ Music books, musical instruments, cassettes, and videos for children. 707–923–3991.

Picture Book Studio, 10 Central St., Saxonville, MA 01701: Free catalog ■ Children's books and book-cassettes that include classics, holiday favorites, and childhood tales. 508–788–0911.

School Zone Publishing Company, P.O. Box 777, Grand Haven, MI 49417: Free information ■ Educational workbooks, flashcards, games, audio and video items, and reading books. 616–846–5030.

Silver Burdett Press, Inc., Simon & Schuster Children's Book Division, 1230 Avenue of Americas, New York, NY 10020: Free information ■ Beginning-to-read books, and books about nature and animals, science, holiday fun, teen issues, and other subjects. 201–592–3424.

General Books

ABCDEF Bookshop, 726 N. Hanover St., Carlisle, PA 17013: Catalog $1 (refundable) ■ Civil War books. 717–243–5802.

Academic Press, Inc., 1250 6th Ave., San Diego, CA 92101: Free information ■ Scientific and technical books. 619–231–0926.

Acropolis Books, Ltd., 11741 Bowman Green Dr., Reston, VA 22090: Free information ■ How-to, parenting, business, cooking, education, social science, health, and self-improvement books. 703–709–0006.

ACS Publications, Inc., 408 Nutmeg St., San Diego, CA 92103: Free information ■ Books on astrology, Tarot reading, psychic understanding, nutrition, healing, and channeling. 619–297–9203.

Bob Adams, Inc., 260 Center St., Holbrook, MA 02343: Free information ■ Books on careers, parenting, self-help, job hunting, and business. 617–767–8100.

Addison-Wesley Publishing Company, Rt. 128, Reading, MA 01867: Free catalog ■ Books about computers and teacher resources, biographies, child care and health, children's activities, psychology, current affairs, and business. 617–944–3700.

Always Jukin', 221 Yesler Way, Seattle, WA 98104: Catalog $2 ■ Jukebox service manuals, books about jukeboxes, and books and manuals about old phonographs and radios. 206–233–9460.

American Fireworks News, Star Route Box 30, Dingmans Ferry, PA 18328: Free brochure ■ Books, manuals, and reports on fireworks and fireworks memorabilia. 717–828–8417.

American Geographic Publishers, P.O. Box 5630, Helena, MT 59604: Free information ■ Travel, exploration, and geography books. 406–443–2842.

The American Gourd Society, Inc., P.O. Box 274, Mt. Gilead, OH 43338: Free information with long SASE ■ Books on gourds.

The American Institute of Architects Press, 1735 New York Ave. NW, Washington DC 20006: Free information ■ Books, posters, note cards, and models on the history and practice of architecture. 202–626–7498.

American Map Corporation, Inc., 46–35 54th Rd., Maspeth, NY 11378: Free information ■ Bilingual dictionaries, travel guides and atlases, travel language products, maps, and other educational publications. 718–784–0055.

American Psychiatric Press, Inc., 1400 K St. NW, Washington, DC 20005: Free information ■ Books on psychiatry and mental illness. 202–682–6219.

American Showcase, Inc., 724 5th Ave., New York, NY 10019: Free information ■ Books on photography, illustrating, and graphic design. 212–245–0981.

Amie's Books for Bakers, 1083 Orchard Lane, P.O. Box 1478, Redway, CA 95560: Free catalog ■ Books on baking, cake decorating, candy making, and other treats. 707–923–9960.

The Anglers Art, P.O. Box 148, Plainfield, PA 17081: Free catalog ■ Books on fly-fishing. 800–848–1020.

Another Chicago Press, P.O. Box 11223, Chicago, IL 60611: Free information ■ Fiction and poetry books. 312–243–5111.

Antheil Booksellers, 2177 Isabelle Ct., North Bellmore, NY 11710: Catalog $4 ■ Books about the navy, maritime subjects, aviation, and the military. 516–826–2094.

Antique Collectors Club, Market Street Industrial Park, Wappingers Falls, NY 12590: Free information ■ Books on the fine and decorative arts, architecture, and gardening. 914–297–0003.

Aperture Foundation, 20 E. 23rd St., New York, NY 10010: Free information ■ Photography books for amateur and professional photographers. 212–505–5555.

Appalachian Mountain Club Books, 5 Joy Street, Boston, MA 02108: Free information ■ Hiking, river, and recreation guides and maps. 617–523–0636.

Applause Theatre & Cinema Books, Inc., 211 W. 71st St., New York, NY 10023: Free information ■ Musicals, acting, biography, anthologies, screenplays, and other books on the theater and cinema. 212–496–7511.

Audel Library, MacMillan General Books Division, 866 3rd Ave., New York, NY 10022: Free catalog ■ Books about vocational trades and crafts. 212–702–2000.

Audio-Forum, 96 Broad St., Guilford, CT 06437: Free information ■ Self-instructional foreign language courses. 800–551–6300.

August House, Inc., 201 E. Markham St., Plaza Level, Little Rock, AR 72203: Free information ■ Fiction, humor, and folklore books. 501–372–5450.

Aviation Book Company, 25133 Anza Dr., Unit E, Santa Clarita, CA 91355: Catalog $1 ■ Books about sport aircraft and flying, home built aircraft, and construction methods. 805–423–2708.

Backcountry Bookstore, Box 191, Snohomish, WA 98290: Catalog $1 (refundable) ■ Books, maps, videos on backpacking, skiing, biking, paddle sports, trekking, and climbing.

Bantam/Doubleday/Dell, 666 5th Ave., New York, NY 10103: Free catalog ■ Fiction and non-fiction books. 212–492–9624.

Bantam/Doubleday/Dell Electronic Publishing, 666 5th Ave., New York, NY 10103: Free information ■ Books about computers. 212–765–9624.

Bantam/Doubleday/Dell Travel Books, 666 5th Ave., New York, NY 10103: Free information ■ Travel guidebooks, atlases, and travel information books. 212–765–9624.

Barron's Educational Series, 250 Wireless Blvd., Hauppage, NY 11788: Free catalog ■ Test preparatory books, child care and pet books, crafts and cookbooks, and children's books. 516–434–3311.

Basic Books, Inc., 10 E. 53rd St., New York, NY 10022: Free information ■ Books on psychology, business, history, science, political science, women's studies, and other subjects. 212–207–7057.

Berkshire House Publishers, P.O. Box 297, Stockbridge, MA 01262: Free information ■ Travel, recreation, self-help, crafts, psychology, and cooking books. 413–298–3636.

Berlitz Guides, 866 3rd Ave., New York, NY 10022: Free information ■ Travel guides and self-instruction foreign language courses in French, Spanish, German, and Italian. 212–702–9630.

Best Bet Books, P.O. Box 2948, Fayetteville, AR 72702: Free catalog ■ Books, software, videos, and other items for horse racing enthusiasts. 800–782–3884; 501–521–0598 (in AR).

Better Homes & Gardens Books, 1716 Locust St., Des Moines, IA 50336: Free information with long SASE ■ Books on cooking, gardening, how-to, crafts, and other subjects. 515–284–3000.

Betterway Publications, Inc., P.O. Box 219, Crozet, VA 22932: Free catalog ■ Books on parenting, health, cooking and nutrition, small business and finance, home building and remodeling, resource guides and handbooks, and books for young readers. 804–823–5661.

Bicycle Books Publishing, Inc., 1282A 7th Ave., San Francisco, CA 94122: Free information ■ Books about mountain bicycles, racing, repairs, touring, commuting, fitness, biographies, and how-to subjects. 415–665–8214.

Warren Blake, Old Science Books, 308 Hadley Dr., Trumbull, CT 06611: Free catalog ■ Hard-to-find, old to early 20th-century astronomy books and prints. 203–459–0820.

Blue Sky Marketing, Inc., P.O. Box 21583, St. Paul, MN 55121: Free brochure ■ How-to books on cooking and dieting. 612–456–5602.

Boerum Street Press, 131 Boerum St., Brooklyn, NY 11206: Free information ■ Travel guides. 718–599–1393.

Bohemian Brigade Book Shop & Publishers, 8705 Vultee Ln., Knoxville, TN 37923: Catalog $1 ■ Civil War books and militaria. 615–694–8227.

Book Publishing Company, P.O. Box 99, Summertown, TN 38483: Free brochure ■ Books on cooking, pest control, natural birth control, midwifery, fertility, and spiritual teachings. 615–964–3571.

Book Sales, Inc., 110 Enterprise Ave., Secaucus, NJ 07094: Free catalog ■ Books on Americana, animals, nature and gardening, Civil War, fine arts, militaria, photography, religion and Judaica, travel, humor, health, cooking, food and drinks, art instruction, crafts, and for children. 201–864–6341.

Books By Mail, 1750 California Ave., Ste. 114, Corona, CA 91719: Free book list with two 1st class stamps ■ Books on clowning. 909–273–0900.

Books By Wire, BBW International, Inc., 4950 N. Dixie Hwy., Fort Lauderdale, FL 33334: Free catalog ■ Cookbooks, gift books, fiction, humor, and books on hobbies and sports. 800–52–BOOKS.

Boonton Bookshop, 121 Hawkins Pl., Boonton, NJ 07005: Free catalog ■ Civil War books. 800–234–1862.

Brielle Maritime Bookstore, 428 Euclid Ave., Brielle, NJ 08730: Free catalog ■ Books about travel, boat maintenance, ocean liner history, commercial diving, search and rescue, rowing, and sailing. 908–528–8444.

Bowling's Bookstore, Tech-Ed Publishing Company, P.O. Box 4, Deerfield, IL 60015: Free information ■ Books and VHS and Beta videos on bowling. 708–945–3169.

Broadfoot Publishing Company, 1907 Buena Vista Cir., Wilmington, NC 28405: Free catalog ■ Books about the Civil War. 919–686–4816.

Butterworth/Heinemann, 80 Montvale Ave., Stoneham, MA 02180: Free information ■ Scientific, technical, medical, and legal books. 617–438–8464.

C & T Publishing, 502 Blum Rd., Martinez, CA 94553: Free information ■ Books on hobbies and crafts. 510–370–9600.

Calibre Press, Inc., 666 Dundee Rd., Ste. 1607, Northbrook, IL 60062: Free catalog ■ Law enforcement videos, books, and survival products. 800–323–0037; 708–498–5680 (in IL).

Cambridge University Press, 40 W. 20th St., New York, NY 10011: Free information ■ General reference books, textbooks, bibles, dictionaries, encyclopedias, and reference books. 212–924–3900.

Capability's Books, 2379 Hwy. 46, Deer Park, WI 54007: Free catalog ■ Books for gardeners. 800–247–8154.

Capra Press, P.O. Box 2068, Santa Barbara, CA 93120: Free information ■ Books on cat and bird watching. 805–966–4590.

Capri Arts & Crafts, 864 S. McGlincey Ln., Campbell, CA 95008: Free book list with long SASE ■ Books on decorative and fabric painting. 408–377–3833.

S. Carwin & Sons, Ltd., P.O. Box 147, Canoga Park, CA 91304: Free information ■ Books on aircraft, ships, armor and the military, and adventure. 800–562–9182.

Challenge Publications, 7950 Deering Ave., Canoga Park, CA 91304: Free information ■ Books on military aviation.

Chicago Review Press, Inc., 814 N. Franklin St., Chicago, IL 60610: Free information ■ How-to, adventure, nature, cooking, and travel books. 312–337–0747.

Chilton Book Company, One Chilton Way, Radnor, PA 19089: Free catalog ■ Books about automotive mechanics and repair. 215–964–4000.

The China Decorator Library, P.O. Box 575, Shingle Springs, CA 95682: Free catalog ■ Books for china painters. 916–677–1455.

Chronicle Books, 275 5th St., San Francisco, CA 94103: Free catalog ■ Books about cooking and food, art and photography, architecture, nature, travel, and history. 415–777–7240.

Chronimed Publishing, 13911 Ridgedale Dr., Ste. 250, Minneapolis, MN 55343: Free information ■ Health, nutrition, wellness, fitness, psychology, and cooking books. 612–541–0239.

Cinebooks, Inc., 990 Grove St., Evanston, IL 60201: Free information ■ Books on motion pictures. 708–475–8400.

Classics on Tape, P.O. Box 969, Ashland, OR 97520: Free catalog ■ Unabridged recordings on tape that include biography, history, politics, economics, philosophy, religion, social issues, and timeless literature. 800–729–2665.

Cliffs Notes, Inc., P.O. Box 80728, Lincoln, NE 68501: Free information ■ Study aids, test preparation guides, and complete study editions. 402–423–5050.

Collector Books, P.O. Box 3009, Paducah, KY 42002: Free catalog ■ Books on antiques, glass and pottery, depression glassware, pottery, toys, dolls, teddy bears, thimbles, and books by the American Quilters Society. 502–898–6211.

The College Board, 45 Columbus Ave., New York, NY 10023: Free information ■ Books that assist students and their families in the transition from high school to college and college to work. 212–713–8166.

Columbia University Press, 562 W. 113th St., New York, NY 10025: Free information ■ Scholarly books on the humanities, social sciences, and literary translations. 212–316–7131.

Compass American Guides, 6051 Margarido Dr., Oakland, CA 94618: Free information ■ United States and Canada travel guides. 510–547–7233.

Complete Traveler Bookstore, 199 Madison Ave., New York, NY 10016: Catalog $1 ■ Travel guides and books, accessories, and maps. 212–685–9007.

Computer Publishing Enterprises, 3655 Ruffin Rd., Ste. 110, San Diego, CA 92123: Free information ■ Easy-to-read books for the novice and intermediate computer user. 619–576–0353.

Conflict Book Store, 213 Steinwehr Ave., Gettysburg, PA 17325: Free information ■ Books about the Civil War, World War II, Korean, and Vietnam Wars. 717–334–8003.

Congressional Quarterly, Inc., 1414 22nd St. NW, Washington, DC 20037: Free information ■ Books on government, political science, and current affairs. 202–887–8500.

Consumer Guide Books, 7373 N. Cicero Ave., Lincolnwood, IL 60646: Free catalog ■ Books about automobiles, fitness and exercise, health and medicine, entertainment, and other consumer issues. 708–676–3470.

Consumer Information Center, Pueblo, CO 81009: Free catalog ■ United States Government books and pamphlets for consumers. New publications added almost daily. Written inquiries only.

Consumer Reports Books, 101 Truman Ave., Yonkers, NY 10703: Free catalog ■ Books on consumer information. 914–378–2627.

The Cookbook Store, 850 Yonge St., Toronto, Ontario, Canada M4W 2H1: Free catalog ■ Cookbooks from around the world. 416–920–2665.

John S. Craig, 111 Edward Ave., P.O. Box 1637, Torrington, CT 06790: Free information ■ Instruction manuals for photography equipment. Includes many hard-to-find, older publications. 203–496–9791.

Creative Homeowner Press, 24 Park Way, Upper Saddle River, NJ 07458: Free information ■ Do-it-yourself books on home improvement and repair. 800–631–7795.

Crown Publishers, Inc., 201 E. 50th St., New York, NY 10022: Free information ■ Fiction and nonfiction books. Include natural history, military, art, and the Living Language cassette and book language courses. 212–254–1600.

Dance Mart, P.O Box 48, Homecrest Station, Brooklyn, NY 11229: Free catalog with long SASE ■ Books, prints, music, autographs, and collectibles on dancing. 718–627–0477.

Daw Books, Inc., 375 Hudson St., 3rd Floor, New York, NY 10014: Free information ■ Science fiction, fantasy, and horror books. 212–366–2096.

DBI Books, Inc., 4092 Commercial Ave., Northbrook, IL 60062: Free information ■ Sport, recreational, and general titles. 708–272–6310.

Cy Decosse Incorporated, 5900 Green Oak Dr., Minnetonka, MN 55343: Free information ■ How-to books on cooking, sewing, hunting, and fishing. 612–936–4700.

Delta Group, P.O. Box 1625, 215 S. Washington St., El Dorado, AR 71731: Free catalog ■ A mail order source for military, police, survival, adventure books, other publications, posters, and military insignias. 501–862–4984.

Delta Systems, 1400 Miller Pkwy., McHenry, IL 60050: Free catalogs ■ English and foreign language books. 815–363–3582.

Dover Publications, Inc., 31 E. 2nd St., Mineola, NY 11501: Free catalog ■ Books on arts and crafts, business, hobbies, architecture, chemistry, juvenile interests, health, fiction, and other subjects. 516–294–7000.

Drama Book Publishers, 260 5th Ave., New York, NY 10001: Free catalog ■ Books on television, films, theater, and other performing arts. 212–725–5377.

Duncan Mail-Order Bookstore, 5695 E. Shields Ave., Fresno, CA 93727: Free information ■ Books and videos about ceramics. 800–237–2642.

Durham's Antiques, 909 26th St. NW, Washington, DC 20037 Free list ■ Jukebox service manuals and other books on coin-operated machines. 202–338–1342.

Eastman Kodak Company, Information Center, 343 State St., Rochester, NY 14650: Free brochure ■ Photography books and publications. 800–462–6495.

Empire Publishing Service, P.O. Box 1344, Studio City, CA 91614: Free catalog ■ Books about the entertainment industry and performing arts, plays and musicals, musical scores, film and theatrical personalities, and music. 818–784–8918.

Farnsworth Military Gallery, 401 Baltimore St., Gettysburg, PA 17325: Free information ■ New, used, and rare Civil War books and art prints. 717–334–8838.

The Feminist Press, The City University of New York, 311 E. 94th St., New York, NY 10128: Free information ■ Books by and about women. 212–360–5790.

50 Plus Guidebook, P.O. Box 1945, Marion, OH 43305: Free information ■ Books for people over 50 on planning for retirement, money management, leisure, health, housing, working in retirement, living alone, and Social Security. 212–715–2787.

Fodor's, 201 E. 50th St., New York, NY 10022: Free information ■ Travel books. 212–872–8255.

Forsythe Travel Library, Inc., 9154 W. 57th St., P.O. Box 2975, Shawnee Mission, KS 66201: Free brochure ■ Books, maps, and other publications for worldwide travelers. 800–367–7984; 913–384–3440 (in KS).

Samuel French Catalog, 45 W. 25th St., New York, NY 10010: Catalog and supplement $2.75 ■ Scripts for plays and other theatrical productions. 800–PLAY–PUB; 212–206–8990 (in NY).

Samuel French Trade, 7623 Sunset Blvd., Hollywood, CA 90046: Free catalog ■ Books about everything and everyone connected with the film industry. 213–876–0570.

Fun Publishing Company, 2121 Alpine Pl., Cincinnati, OH 45206: Free information ■ Teach-yourself books for the portable keyboard, piano, and xylophone, and the How to Coach Soccer books. 513–533–3636.

Gallaudet University Press, 800 Florida Ave. NE, Washington, DC 20002: Free information ■ Books about deafness and hard-of-hearing persons. Other subjects include travel, parenting, sign language, and children's books. 202–651–5488.

Gambler's Book Club, 630 S. 11th St., Las Vegas, NV 89101: Free catalog ■ Books and computer software on gambling. 800–634–6243.

Gemstone Press, Rt. 4, Sunset Farm Offices, P.O. Box 237, Woodstock, VT 05091: Free information ■ Books for the consumer, hobbyist, investor, and retail trade on buying, identifying, selling, and enjoying jewelry and gems. 802–457–4000.

Genealogical Publishing Company, 1001 N. Calvert St., Baltimore, MD 21202: Free catalog ■ Books on genealogy. 800–727–6687.

Gingerbread Bookstore, P.O. Box 909, Idaho Springs, CO 80452: Catalog $2 (refundable) ■ How-to books on restoration and renovation, history and architecture, decorating, and remodeling houses. 303–567–2003.

Globe Pequot Press, 138 W. Main St., Box Q, Chester, CT 06412: Free catalog ■ Travel guides, cookbooks, and journalism, outdoor recreation, and nautical books. 800–962–0973.

Graywolf Press, 2402 University Ave., Ste. 203, St. Paul, MN 55114: Free information ■ New books and reprints of poetry, fiction, and nonfiction. 612–641–0077.

Grey Castle Press, Pocket Knife Square, Lakeville, CT 06039: Free catalog ■ Large print literary classics and other books about wildlife, the Civil War, world literature, for children, American biographies, citizenship, sports, and foreign countries. 203–435–2518.

Gryphon House Books, P.O. Box 275, Mt. Rainier, MD 20712: Free catalog ■ Books for parents, children, and teachers. 301–779–6200.

Hammond Incorporated, 515 Valley St., Maplewood, NJ 07040: Free catalog ■ Atlases, maps and prints, travel guides and road atlases, adult and juvenile reference books, and business references. 201–763–6000.

Ham Radio's Bookstore, Greenville, NH 03048: Free information ■ Books for ham radio operators. 603–878–1441.

Harmonica Music Publishing, P.O. Box 671, Hermosa Beach, CA 90254: Free information ■ Books and video, audio, and instructional tapes on the harmonica. 310–320–0599.

HarperCollins Publishers, 10 E. 53rd St., New York, NY 10022: Free information ■ Books for preschool children through young adult, fiction and nonfiction for children and adults, cookbooks, business titles, religion, and other subjects. 212–207–7137.

Harrowsmith, Ferry Rd., Charlotte, VT 05445: Free information ■ Books and magazines on country living and skills, gardening, food, health, crafts, building, and the environment. 802–425–3961.

Harsand Financial Press, 206 S. Pine Ave., Arlington Heights, IL 60005: Free catalog ■ Books on personal and financial management; kids: futures and finances; life stages and transitions; job/career search and survival; personal financial investment; and small business organization. 800–451–0643.

The Harvard Common Press, 535 Albany St., Boston, MA 02118: Free catalog ■ Books on cooking, family issues, and travel. 617–423–5803.

Haynes Publications, Inc., 861 Lawrence Dr., Newbury Park, CA 91320: Free catalog ■ Automotive and motorcycle repair manuals, and history, travel, and adventure books. 818–889–5400.

Hazelden Publishing, 15251 Pleasant Valley Rd., Center City, MN 55012: Free catalog ■ Books and audio cassettes for people in Twelve Step programs. 612–257–4010.

Health Communications, Inc., 3201 SW 15th St., Deerfield Beach, FL 33442: Free information ■ Self-help recovery books on drug addiction. 305–360–0909.

Heimburger House Publishing Company, 7236 W. Madison St., Forest Park, IL 60130: Free information ■ Books on model and prototype railroads, cooking, history, humor, and Walt Disney. 708–366–1973.

Himalayan Publishers, RR 1, Box 405, Honesdale, PA 18431: Free information ■ Holistic health, yoga, preventive medicine, meditation, diet and health, and self-development books. 717–253–5551.

Hippocrene Books, Inc., 171 Madison Ave., New York, NY 10016: Free information ■ Books on travel and history, dictionaries and maps, and Polish-interest subjects. 212–685–4371.

Historic Aviation, 1401 Kings Wood Rd., Eagan, MN 55122: Free information ■ History, biography, classic, humor, and aviation books and videos. 800–225–55? 2493 (in MN).

Hobby House Press, Inc., 900 Frederick St., Cumberland, MD 21502: Free information ■ Books on dolls and teddy bears, postcards, costumes, and crafts. 301–759–3770.

Home Planners, Inc., 3275 W. Ina Rd., Ste. 110, Tucson, AZ 85741: Free information ■ Books and blueprints on home planning, architectural design, landscaping, and remodeling. 602–297–8200.

Howell Book House, Inc., MacMillan Publishing Company, 866 3rd Ave., 21st Floor, New York, NY 10022: Free information ■ Books about dogs, cats, birds, horses, and other animals. 212–702–9633.

Hudson Hills Press, 230 5th Ave., Ste. 1308, New York, NY 10001: Free information ■ Books on photography and fine art. 212–889–3090.

Humanities Press, 165 1st Ave., Atlantic Highlands, NJ 07716: Free catalog ■ Books on philosophy and religion, political science, economics, literature, history, art theory and criticism, women's studies, archeology, and current affairs. 908–872–1441.

Hunter Publishing, Inc., 239 S. Beach Rd., Hobe Sound, FL 33455: Free information ■ Travel guides, language cassette courses, and maps. 407–546–7986.

Ideals Publishing Corporation, 565 Marriott Dr., Ste. 890, Nashville, TN 37210: Free catalog ■ Nostalgic and family-oriented books, children's board books with cassettes, other children's books, inspirational books, and cookbooks. 615–885–8270.

IDG Books Worldwide, 155 Bovet Rd., San Mateo, CA 94402: Free information ■ Computer books and magazines. 714–821–8380.

Intel Corporation, 3065 Bowers Ave., Mail Stop GR 1–68, Santa Clara, CA 95051: Free catalog ■ Computer books. 408–765–1709.

International Marine Publishing Company, Rt. 1, Box 220, Camden, ME 04843: Free catalog ■ Nautical books. 207–236–4837.

Interweave Press, 306 N. Washington Ave., Loveland, CO 80537: Free catalog ■ Books on basket-making, weaving and spinning, sweater designing, hand and machine knitting, rug weaving, tapestry-making, fabric designing and sewing, and spinning wheels. 303–669–7672.

Israel Book Export Institute, 3 Station Plaza, Woodmere, NY 11598: Free information ■ History, political, and religion books for adults and children, in Hebrew and English. 516–569–0324.

Jameson Books/Frontier Library, 722 Columbus St., Ottawa, IL 61350: Free information ■ General fiction titles and books on American history. 815–434–7905.

Japan Publications, 114 5th Ave., New York, NY 10011: Free information ■ Books on health and macrobiotics, needle- and papercrafts, and other books in English and Japanese. 212–727–6460.

Jessica's Biscuit, The Cookbook People, Box 301, Newtonville, MA 02160: Free catalog ■ Cookbooks. 800–225–4264; 800–322–4027 (in MA).

Johns Hopkins University Press, 701 W. 40th St., Ste. 275, Baltimore, MD 21211: Free catalog ■ Books on a variety of subjects. 410–516–6936.

Johnson Publishing Company, Inc., 820 S. Michigan Ave., Chicago, IL 60605: Free information ■ Books by and about Afro-American people. 312–322–9200.

JTG of Nashville, 1024 18th Ave. South, Nashville, TN 37212: Free information ■ Professional and educational books and music products. 615–329–3036.

Keepsake Quilting, Dover Street, P.O. Box 1459, Meredith, NH 03253: Catalog $1 ■ Quilting books, patterns, notions, fabric medlets, quilting aids, scrap bags, cotton fabrics, and batting.

KiteLines, P.O. Box 466, Randallstown, MD 21133: Free catalog ■ Domestic and foreign books about kites. 410–922–1212.

Klutz Press, 2121 Staunton Ct., Palo Alto, CA 94306: Free information ■ How-to, fun, and song books for children. 415–857–0888.

Krause Publications, 700 E. State St., Iola, WI 54990: Free information ■ Books on hobbies, collectibles, and the outdoors. 715–445–2214.

La Rock's Fun & Magic Outlet, 2123 Central Ave., Charlotte, NC 28205: Free information ■ Clown and balloon sculpture how-to books. 704–333–3434.

Hal Leonard Publishing, P.O. Box 13819, Milwaukee, WI 53213: Free information ■ Music and music-related books for music lovers and musicians. 612–332–3344.

Alan Levine Movie & Book Collectibles, P.O. Box 1577, Bloomfield, NJ 07003: Catalog $2 with long SASE ■ Books on collecting; old-time movie posters and lobby cards; and old radio, television, and movie magazines. 201–743–5288.

Lewis Books, P.O. Box 41137, Cincinnati, OH 45241: Free information ■ Bird books. 513–733–0617.

Liberty Belle Books, 4250 S. Virginia St., Reno, NV 89502: Catalog $2 ■ Books on slot and coin-operated machines. 702–826–2607.

Light Impressions, 439 Monroe Ave., Rochester, NY 14607: Free catalog ■ Books on photography. 800–828–6216.

Lindsay's Electrical Books, P.O. Box 583, Manteno, IL 60950: Catalog $1 ■ Electrical books.

Lonely Planet Publications, 112 Linden St., Oakland, CA 94607: Free information ■ Guidebooks and phrasebooks for travelers. 510–893–8555.

Louisiana State University Press, LSU Press, 102 Frenc House, Baton Rouge, LA 70893: Free catalog ■ Books about the Civil War and scholarly subjects. 504–388–6666.

Herbert A. Luft, 46 Woodcrest Dr., Scotia, NY 12302: Free list ■ Rare and current astronomy books.

MacMillan Publishing Company, 866 3rd Ave., New York, NY 10022: Free information ■ Fiction and non-fiction books for children and adults. 212–702–2000.

Merriam-Webster, Inc., 47 Federal St., P.O. Box 281, Springfield, MA 01102: Free brochure ■ Dictionaries and reference books. 413–734–3134.

David Meyer Magic Books, Box 427, Glenwood, IL 60425: Catalog $1 ■ New and old books on magic.

Micro Publishing Press, 21150 Hawthorne Blvd., Torrance, CA 90503: Free information ■ Computer books. 310–371–5787.

Microsoft Press, One Microsoft Way, Redmond, WA 98052: Free information ■ Books on computer programming. 206–882–8080.

The Mind's Eye, 4 Commercial Blvd., Novato, CA 94949: Free catalog ■ Audio cassettes, compact disks, and books. Includes children's favorites and classics, military intrigue, mystery, horror, science fiction, adventure, drama, history, comedy, poetry, and self-improvement. 415–883–7701.

The MIT Press, 55 Hayward St., Cambridge, MA 02142: Free catalog ■ Books about many areas of interest. 617–253–5641.

William Morrow & Company, 1350 Avenue of Americas, New York, NY 10019: Free information ■ Fiction and non-fiction for adults and children. 212–261–6500.

John Muir Publications, Railroad Yards, P.O. Box 613, Santa Fe, NM 87504: Free catalog ■ Books on travel, cultural and environmental topics, and automotive repair. 505–982–4078.

Mystic Seaport Book & Print Shop, Seaport Museum Stores, 39 Greemanville Ave., Mystic, CT 06355: Free information ■ Books about American maritime history and Mystic Seaport Museum collections. 203–572–8551.

National Geographic Society, P.O. Box 2806, Washington, DC 20013: Free price list ■ Books on geography, history, archeology, science, and industry. 301–869–3485.

Naval Institute Press, United States Naval Institute, Preble Hall, Annapolis, MD 21402: Free catalog ■ Books on navigation, seamanship, naval history and literature, ships, and aircraft. 410–268–6110.

Needham Book Finders, P.O. Box 3067, Santa Monica, CA 90408: Free catalog ■ Cookbooks and other books on cooking, wine, herbs, and household management. 310–395–0538.

The New Careers Center, Inc., 1515 23rd St., P.O. Box 297, Boulder, CO 80306: Free catalog ■ Books on alternative careers, new work options, self-employment and working, for college graduates and returning students, and travel-related subjects. 303–447–1087.

New Catalog, P.O. Box 37000, Washington, DC 20013: Free catalog ■ Best-selling Federal government publications.

New Harbinger Publications, 5674 Shattuck Ave., Oakland, CA 94609: Free catalog

■ Self-help books on psychology. 510–652–0215.

NightinGale Resources, P.O. Box 322, Cold Spring, NY 10516: Catalog $3 ■ Cookbooks and a search service for out-of-print and rare titles.

Nolo Press, 950 Parker St., Berkeley, CA 94710: Free catalog ■ Self-help law books and computer software. 510–549–1976.

O'Hara Publications, Inc., 1813 Victory Pl., P.O. Box 7728, Burbank, CA 91510: Free information ■ Books about the martial arts. 818–843–4444.

Olde Soldier Books, Inc., 18779 N. Frederick Ave., Gaithersburg, MD 20879: Free information ■ Civil War books, documents, autographs, prints, and Americana. 301–963–2929.

Olsson's Books & Records, 1239 Wisconsin Ave. NW, Washington, DC 20007: Free information ■ Books on fiction, poetry, history, biography, the classics, philosophy, children's books, humor, travel, mystery, art, photography, cooking, interior design, antiques, and collecting. Other items include compact disks and cassettes. 202–338–9544.

Ortho Information Services, 6001 Bollinger Canyon Rd., Bldg. T, Room 1334, San Ramon, CA 94583: Free information ■ Books about gardening, cooking, and home improvement. 510–842–1969.

The Overlook Connection, P.O. Box 526, Woodstock, GA 30188: Catalog $2 ■ Books, audio cassettes, and magazines on horror, science fiction, fantasy, and mystery. 404–926–1762.

Owens Civil War Books, P.O. Box 13622, Richmond, VA 23225: Free catalog and search service ■ New, used, and rare books about the Civil War era. 804–272–8888.

Peri Lithon Books, Box 9996, San Diego, CA 92169: Catalog $2 ■ Books about gemstones, minerals, fossils, jewelry, and geology. 619–488–6904.

Pet Bookshop, P.O. Box 507, Oyster Bay, NY 11771: Catalog $2.95 ■ Over a thousand titles about pets. Includes birds, dogs, cats, fish, reptiles and other pets. 800–676–0067.

Bud Plant Comic Art, P.O. Box 1689, Grass Valley, CA 95945: Free catalog ■ Comic book-related material that includes graphic novels, comic strip collections, history of comics and comic creators, limited editions books, and prints. 916–273–2166.

Pruett Publishing Company, 2928 Pearl St., Boulder, CO 80301: Free catalog ■ Books about the history and people of the American West, outdoor adventures, railroads, cooking, and horticulture. 303–449–4919.

Random House, 201 E. 50th St., New York, NY 10022: Free catalog ■ Books for adults and children. Includes fiction, travel guides, hobbies, references, and other subjects. Other items include calendars, puzzles, and video cassettes. 212–872–8244.

Reader's Digest, Pleasantville, NY 10570: Free catalog ■ Books on gardening, crafts and hobbies, do-it-yourself, travel, science and nature, cooking and health, history and geography, religion and archeology, and song books. 914–241–7445.

San Francisco Museum of Modern Art, Museum Books Mail Order, P.O. Box 182203, Chattanooga, TN 37422: Free catalog ■ Art books, children's books, adult and children's toys, handmade crafts, cards, and gifts. 800–447–1454.

Scott Publications, 30595 W. 8 Mile Rd., Livonia, MI 48152: Free catalog ■ Books for the ceramist, china painter, and doll maker. 313–477–6650.

Self-Counsel Press, Inc., 1704 N. State St., Bellingham, WA 98225: Free catalog ■ Law, business, and other reference books. 206–676–4530.

Show-Biz Services, 1735 E. 26th St., Brooklyn, NY 11229: Free list ■ Books for magicians. 718–336–0605.

Sierra Club Books, 100 Bush St., 13th Floor, San Francisco, CA 94104: Free information ■ Books about ecology, natural history, environment, wildlife, outdoor activities, and nature photography. 415–291–1600.

Sifriyon B'nai B'rith, Box 410, Beech Creek, PA 16822: Free catalog ■ Judaica books. 717–962–3985.

Small Press Distribution, Inc., 1814 San Pablo Ave., Berkeley, CA 94702: Free catalog ■ Contemporary literature and books from publishers in the United States, Canada, and Great Britain. 415–549–3336.

Smithsonian Institution Press, 470 L'-Enfant Plaza, Ste. 7100, Washington, DC 20560: Free catalog ■ Books on art, aviation, anthropology and archeology, and museum studies. 202–287–3738.

Soldier Shop, Inc., 1222 Madison Ave., New York, NY 10128: Free information ■ Military books, prints, and memorabilia. 212–535–6788.

Springhouse Publishing Company, 1111 Bethlehem Pike, P.O. Box 908, Springhouse, PA 19477: Free catalog ■ Books on nursing and consumer health. 215–646–8700.

Squadron/Signal Publications, Inc., 1115 Crowley Dr., Carrollton, TX 75011: Free catalog ■ Books on aviation, armor, ships, and military history. 800–527–7427.

Sterling Publishing Company, Inc., 387 Park Ave. South, New York, NY 10016: Free catalog ■ Body building, hobbies, crafts, occult, herbs and gardening, science, cooking, health, sports, music and the theater, self-defense, and children's books. 212–532–7160.

Storey Communications, Schoolhouse Rd., Pownal, VT 05261: Free catalog ■ Books on gardening, woodworking and building, cooking, country skills, crafts, nature, home improvement, animals, and the outdoors. 802–823–5811.

Strand Bookstore, 828 Broadway, New York, NY 10003: Free information ■ Books on photography for beginners, amateurs, and professionals. Includes out-of-print books. 212–473–1452.

Sybex Computer Books, 2021 Challenger Dr., Alameda, CA 94501: Free catalog ■ Computer books, video-based programs, and tutorial/quick reference/template kits. 510–523–8233.

Tab Books, Inc., 13311 Monterey Ave., Blue Ridge Summit, PA 17294: Free catalog ■ How-to books on electronics, computers, aviation, science, hobbies, automobiles, crafts, and other subjects. 717–794–2191.

Tartan Book Sales, 500 Arch St., Williamsport, PA 17705: Free catalog ■ Nonfiction and fiction hardbound editions at discount prices. 800–233–8467.

Theatre Communications Group, 355 Lexington Ave., New York, NY 10017: Free catalog ■ Books about the theater and performing arts. 212–697–5230.

Maps, 17731 Cowan St., … Free catalog ■ Atlases, … maps. 714–863–1984.

The Tool Chest, 45 Emerson Plaza East, Emerson, NJ 07630: Catalog $2 (refundable) ■ Books on home remodeling and maintenance, tools, contracting, and projects for home and recreation.

Travelers Bookstore, 113 Corporation Rd., Hyannis, MA 02601: Free catalog ■ Maps and books on travel, student opportunities, adventure, trekking, hiking, biking, kayaking, and mountaineering.

Travel Keys Books, P.O. Box 160691, Sacramento, CA 95816: Free information ■ Travel guides to Europe. 916–452–5200.

Unicorn Books, 1304 Scott St., Petaluma, CA 94954: Catalog $1 ■ New, old, and unusual books on weaving, spinning, dyeing, and knitting. 707–762–3362.

University Press of Kansas, 2501 W. 15th St., Lawrence, KS 66049: Free information ■ Books on American and military history, presidential studies, Western Americana, and the Great Plains and Midwest. 913–864–4154.

Vestal Press, Ltd., P.O. Box 97, Vestal, NY 13851: Catalog $2 (refundable) ■ Posters, recordings, and books on carrousels, music boxes, player pianos and other music machines, antique radios and phonographs, early movie stars, and radio personalities. 607–797–4872.

Vintage '45 Press, P.O. Box 266, Orinda, CA 94563: Free brochure ■ Books for midlife problems and older women.

Barbara Weindling Cookbook Catalog, 69 Ball Pond Rd., Danbury, CT 06811: Free catalog ■ Hundreds of cookbooks.

Western Horseman Books, P.O. Box 7980, Colorado Springs, CO 80933: Free information ■ Books on western horsemanship and training, barrel racing, team and calf roping, reining, cutting, health problems, games, horse breaking, and horseshoeing. 800–874–6774.

Western Publishing Company, Inc., 1220 Mound Ave., Racine, WI 53404: Free catalog ■ Golden Field Guides on birds, reptiles, rocks and minerals, seashells, astronomy, trees, insects, fishes, fossils, and weather. 414–633–2431.

Woodbine House, 5615 Fishers Lane, Rockville, MD 20852: Free catalog ■ Consumer reference and regional books, and The Special Needs Collection, a series of books on disabilities for parents, educators, and medical professionals. 800–843–7323; 301–468–8800 (in MD).

WoodenBoat, P.O. Box 78, Brooklin, ME 04616: Free catalog ■ Books about wooden boats, and calendars, posters, and prints. 207–359–4651.

Workman Publishing Company, Inc., 708 Broadway, New York, NY 10003: Free catalog ■ Cooking, food and wine, travel, homes and gardens, space, humor, exercise and health, pregnancy and babies, sports and television, games, hobbies and handicrafts, computer, and children's books. 212–254–5900.

Writer's Digest Books, 1507 Dana Ave., Cincinnati, OH 45207: Free catalog ■ Self-help and how-to books for writers, fine and graphic artists, songwriters, musicians, photographers, homemakers, and children. 513–531–2222.

Zenith Books, P.O. Box 1, Osceola, WI 54020: Free catalog ■ Over 3,000 titles on ragwings to supersonic spy planes, and video tapes on military aircraft, plastic and radio control modeling, warplanes, and aviation history, and calendars. 800–826–6600.

Large Print Books

American Printing House for the Blind, 1839 Frankfort Ave., P.O. Box 6085, Louisville, KY 40206: Free catalog ■ Books in Braille for the visually impaired. 502–895–2405.

Grey Castle Press, Pocket Knife Square, Lakeville, CT 06039: Free catalog ■ Large print books on literary classics, and books about wildlife, the Civil War, world literature, for children, American biographies, citizenship, sports, and foreign countries. 203–435–2518.

G.K. Hall, 70 Lincoln St., Boston, MA 02111: Free catalog ■ Bestsellers in large print format. 617–423–3990.

Thorndike Press, P.O. Box 159, Thorndike, ME 04986: Free catalog ■ Books in large print format. 207–948–2962.

Religious Books

Abingdon Press, 201 8th Ave. South, Nashville, TN 37202: Free information ■ Religious books. 615–749–6452.

Augsburg Fortress Publishers, 426 S. 5th St., P.O. Box 1209, Minneapolis, MN 55440: Free information ■ Religious, inspirational, and academic/theological books. 800–328–4648.

Baker Book House, P.O. Box 6287, Grand Rapids, MI 49516: Free information ■ Religious books for the home, church, and school. 616–676–9185.

Behrman House Publishers, Inc., 235 Watchung Ave., West Orange, NJ 07052: Free information ■ Books on Jewish subjects for children and adults. 201–669–0447.

God's World Publications, Box 2330, Asheville, NC 28802: Free catalog ■ Selected books from Christian and secular publishers. 704–253–8063.

Immaculata Bookstore, St. Mary's Campus, P.O. Drawer 159, St. Mary's, KS 66536: Free catalog ■ Catholic publications. Includes education, inspiration, and music tapes, compact disks, and full score music books of great composers. 913–437–2471.

Israel Book Export Institute, 3 Station Plaza, Woodmere, NY 11598: Free information ■ History, political, and religion books for adults and children, in Hebrew and English. 516–569–0324.

Jewish Publication Society, 1930 Chestnut St., Philadelphia, PA 19103: Free information ■ Books about Judaica. 215–564–5925.

Lion Publishing Corporation, 1705 Hubbard Ave., Batavia, IL 60510: Free information ■ Christian books for children and adults. 708–879–0707.

Thomas Nelson Publishers, Nelson Place at Elm Hill Pike, P.O. Box 141000, Nashville, TN 37214: Free catalog ■ Bibles and religious books. 615–889–9000.

1–800–Judaism, America's Jewish Bookstore, 2028 Murray Ave., Pittsburgh, PA 15217: Free catalog ■ Current and classic Jewish books for adults and children. 1–800–JUDAISM.

Orbis Books, Walsh Building, Box 308, Maryknoll, NY 10545: Free catalog ■ Religious books. 914–941–7636.

Fleming H. Revell Company, 120 White Plains Rd., Tarrytown, NY 10591: Free catalog ■ Religious and inspirational books. 914–332–8500.

Riverside Book & Bible House, 1500 Riverside Dr., Iowa Falls, IA 50126: Free catalog ■ Bibles and religious books. 515–648–4271.

Zondervan, 5300 Patterson Ave. SE, Grand Rapids, MI 49530: Free catalog ■ Bibles and religious books. 616–698–6900.

Used Books

The American Botanist, 1103 W. Truitt Ave., Chillicothe, IL 61523: Catalog $1 ■ Used, out-of-print, and rare books on gardening. 309–274–5254.

Anchor & Dolphin Books, P.O. Box 823, 30 Franklin St., Newport, RI 02840: Catalog $1 (refundable) ■ Used, out-of-print books, and rare books on gardening, landscaping, horticulture, and related areas. 401–946–6890.

Benedikt & Salmon Record Rarities, 3020 Meade Ave., San Diego, CA 92116: Free catalogs, indicate choice of (1) rare books and autographs; (2) classical; (3) jazz, big bands, and blues, and (4) personalities, soundtracks, and country music ■ Autographed memorabilia and rare books on music and the performing arts, antique phonographs and cylinders for collectors, and rare recordings from the 1890s to date. 619–281–3345.

Boston Book Annex, 705 Centre St., Jamaica Plain, MA 02130: Free catalog ■ First edition books in their original bindings. 617–522–2100.

Michael Campbell Fine Art, 7824 E. Lewis Ave., Scottsdale, AZ 85251: Free information ■ Out-of-print art books, contemporary and Latin American paintings, sculptures, graphics, pre-Columbian art, and Spanish paintings. 602–947–5399.

Michael Dennis Cohan Bookseller, 502 W. Alder St., Missoula, MT 59802: Free list ■ Out-of-print and rare books on geology, mining, and related subjects. 406–721–7379.

David E. Doremus Books, 100 Hillside Ave., Arlington, MA 02174: Information $2 ■ Civil War books that include biographies, battle reports, Union and Confederate subjects, and other topics. 617–646–0892.

Editions, Boiceville, NY 12412: Catalog $2 ■ Used books.

Heartland Books, P.O. Box 1094, Woodstock, IL 60098: Free catalog ■ Out-of-print and rare books on cowboys and the cattle range, outlaws and lawmen, Custer and the military, the frontier, Indians, and explorers and settlers. 815–338–5272.

Historical Technology, Inc., 6 Mugford St., Marblehead, MA 01945: Annual catalog subscription $12 ■ Rare books and antique scientific instruments. 617–631–2275.

Imperial Fine Books, 790 Madison Ave., Room 200, New York, NY 10021: Catalog $3 ■ Antique leatherbound books in full sets or singles. 212–861–6620.

Kenneth Karmlole Bookseller, 1225 3rd St. Promenade, Santa Monica, CA 90069: Free information with long SASE ■ Old and rare books. 310–451–4342.

Herbert A Luft, 46 Woodcrest Dr., Scotia, NY 12302: Free list ■ Rare and current astronomy books.

McGowan Book Company, P.O. Box 222, Chapel Hill, NC 27514: Free information ■ Rare, out-of-print books and collectible Southern Americana, black Americana, and American Revolution; and Civil War artifacts. 919–968–1121.

David Meyer Magic Books, Box 427, Glenwood, IL 60425: Catalog $1 ■ New and old books on magic.

Military Bookman, 29 E. 93rd St., New York, NY 10128: Free information with long SASE ■ Rare and out-of-print books on military, aviation, and naval history. 212–348–1280.

Old Hickory Bookshop, Ltd., 20225 New Hampshire Ave., Brinklow, MD 20862: Free catalog ■ Used medical books. 301–924–2225.

Owens Civil War Books, P.O. Box 13622, Richmond, VA 23225: Free catalog and search service ■ New, used, and rare Civil War books. 804–272–8888.

Bud Plant Illustrated Books, P.O. Box 1689, Grass Valley, CA 95945: Catalog $2 ■ Rare and out-of-print children's books, art monographs and history of book illustration, and books about comic books, comic strips, and their creators. 916–273–2166.

Wallace D. Pratt, Bookseller, 1801 Gough St., San Francisco, CA 94109: Free catalog ■ Out-of-print and rare books about the Civil War, Indian Wars, and naval history. 415–673–0178.

Red Lancer, P.O. Box 8056, Mesa, AZ 85214: Catalog $6 ■ Rare books, Victorian era campaign medals and helmets, old toy soldiers, and original 19th-century military art. 602–964–9667.

The M.T. Sterling Rebel, P.O. Box 481, Mt. Sterling, KY 40353: Free catalog ■ Out-of-print, used, and rare Civil War books. 606–498–5821.

Tattered Cover, 2023 Boston Pike, Richmond, IN 47374: Free information with long SASE ■ Rare and used hardback books and paper collectibles. 317–935–6293.

Teaneck Book Store, 838 Palisade Ave., Teaneck, NJ 07666: Free information with long SASE ■ Vintage books and magazines. 201–217–9675.

Unicorn Books, 1304 Scott St., Petaluma, CA 94954: Catalog $1 ■ New, old, and unusual books on weaving, spinning, dyeing, and knitting. 707–762–3362.

Wooden Porch Books, Box 262, Middlebourne, WV 26149: Catalog $3 ■ Out-of-print books on fiber arts.

BOOK SEARCH SERVICES

American Indian Books & Relics, P.O. Box 683, Athens, AL 35611: Free catalog ■ Book search services for books about American Indians. 205–423–4586.

Attic Owl Books, William Reid, New Sharon, ME 04955: Free information ■ Search services for hard-to-find and out-of-print books. 207–778–2006.

Avonlea Books, P.O. Box 74, White Plains, NY 10602: Free information ■ Search services for hard-to-find and out-of-print books. 914–946–5923.

Book Associates, Bob Snell, P.O. Box 687, Orange, CT 06477: Free information ■ Searches for hard-to-find and out-of-print books. 203–795–3107.

Book Hunters, P.O. Box 7519, North Bergen, NJ 07047: Free information ■ Book search services for hard-to-find and out-of-print books.

Bookservice, P.O. Box 3253, San Clemente, CA 92672: Free information ■ Search services for hard-to-find and out-of-print books. 714–492–2976.

Booksource, Russ Stockman, 15 Roxbury St., Keene, NH 03431: Free information ■ Search services for hard-to-find and out-of-print books. 603–352–3202.

Michael Dennis Cohan Bookseller, 502 W. Alder St., Missoula, MT 59802: Free information ■ Book search services for books on geology, mining, and related subjects. 406–721–7379.

Donan Book Shop, 220 E. 82nd St., New York, NY 10028: Free information ■ Search services for hard-to-find and out-of-print books. 212–734–0707.

Goodspeed's, 7 Beacon St., Boston, MA 02108: Catalog $5 ■ Search services for hard-to-find and out-of-print books. 617–523–5970.

Harvard Cooperative, 1400 Massachusetts Ave., Cambridge, MA 02238: Free information ■ Search services for hard-to-find and out-of-print books. 617–499–2000.

Hooked on History Antiques Center, 100 West, NW Highway, Mt. Prospect, IL 60056: Free information ■ Book search services for hard-to-find and out-of-print Civil War books.

Rose Lasley Estate Books, 5827 Burr Oak, Berkeley, IL 60163: Free information ■ Book search services for hard-to-find and out-of-print books.

NightinGale Resources, P.O. Box 322, Cold Spring, NY 10516: Catalog $3 ■ Search service for out-of-print and rare cookbooks.

Out of State Book Service, Box 3253, San Clemente, CA 92672: Free information ■ Search services for hard-to-find and out-of-print books. 714–492–2976.

Owens Civil War Books, P.O. Box 13622, Richmond, VA 23225: Free information ■ Search services for books about the Civil War era. 804–272–8888.

Pro Libris, Gertrude Toll, 88 Ossipee St., Somerville, MA 02144: Free information ■ Searche services for hard-to-find and out-of-print books. 617–628–7487.

Ellen Roth, 47 Truman Dr., Marlboro, NJ 07746: Free information ■ Book search ser-

vices for hard-to-find and out-of-print books. 908–536–0850.

Significant Books, P.O. Box 9248, Cincinnati, OH 45209: Free information ■ Book search services for hard-to-find and out-of-print books.

George Tramp Books, 709 2nd St., Jackson, MI 49203: Free information ■ Book search services for hard-to-find and out-of-print books.

BOOKS ON TAPE

Audio Diversions, 306 Commerce St., Occoquan, VA 22125: Free catalog ■ Best selling books on tape for sale or rent. 800–628–6145.

Audio Editions, Books on Cassette, 1133 High St., Auburn, CA 95603: Free catalog ■ Books on cassette. Includes best sellers, business and management titles, classics, drama and poetry, all-time favorites, books for young people, personal growth subjects, and languages. 916–888–7803.

Book of the Road, 7175 SW 47th St., Ste. 202, Miami, FL 33155: Free information ■ Audio cassette recordings of books. 305–667–5762.

Books on Tape, Inc., P.O. Box 7900, Newport Beach, CA 92658: Free catalog ■ Books recorded on cassettes. 800–626–3333.

Brilliance Corporation, 1810 Industrial, Grand Haven, MI 49417: Free catalog ■ Cassette recordings of books. 616–846–5256.

Dercum Audio, 910 Waltz Rd., P.O. Box 1425, West Chester, PA 19380: Free information ■ Books on cassettes. Includes mysteries, science fiction, and classics for adults and children. 215–430–8889.

Dove Books on Tape, Inc., 12711 Ventura Blvd., Studio City, CA 91604: Free catalog ■ Tape recordings of books. 800–762–6662.

A Gentle Wind, P.O. Box 3103, Albany, NY 12203: Free information ■ Music and story cassettes for children ages 1 to 12. Includes winners from the American Library Association's Notable Children's Recording Program. 518–436–0391.

Recorded Books, Inc., 270 Skipjack Rd., Prince Frederick, MD 20678: Free catalog ■ Unabridged books on cassettes. 800–638–1304.

BOOMERANGS

Boomerang Man, 1806 N. 3rd St., Monroe, LA 71201: Free catalog ■ Boomerangs from the United States, England, France, Germany, and Australia. 318–325–8157.

Colonel Gerrish Boomerangs, 4885 SW 78th Ave., Portland, OR 97225: Free information ■ Boomerangs. 503–292–5697.

Into the Wind/Kites, 1408 Pearl St., Boulder, CO 80302: Catalog $1 ■ Boomerangs, kites, and accessories for kites. 800–541–0314.

What's Up, 4500 Chagrin River Rd., Chagrin Falls, Ohio 44022: Free information ■ Boomerangs, kites and accessories, air toys, and books. 216–247–4222.

BOWLING

Clothing

Cal Pacific Racing Apparel, 16629 Valley View, Cerritos, CA 90701: Free information ■ Shirts, blouses, and jackets. 213–926–2512.

Converse, Inc., One Fordham Rd., North Reading, MA 01864: Free information ■ Shoes. 800–554–2667; 508–657–5500 (in MA).

Dexter Shoe Company, 1230 Washington St., West Newton, MA 02165: Free information ■ Shoes. 617–332–4300.

E.A. Graphics, Ethnic Artwork, Inc., 44002 Phoenix Dr., Sterling Heights, MI 48078: Free information ■ Shirts and blouses. 313–726–1400.

Eastern Bowling/Hy-Line, Inc., 4717 Stenton Ave., Philadelphia, PA 19144: Free information ■ Shoes. 800–523–0140; 215–438–9000 (in PA).

Four Seasons Garment Company, 1111 Western Row Rd., Mason, OH 45040: Free Information ■ Jackets, shirts, and blouses. 513–793–4105.

General Shoelace Company, 642 Starks Building, Louisville, KY 40202: Free information ■ Shoes. 502–585–4191.

King Louie International, 13500 15th St,. Grandview, MO 64030: Free information ■ Jackets, shirts, and blouses. 800–521–5212; 816–765–5212 (in MO).

National Sporting Goods Corporation, 25 Brighton Ave., Passaic, NJ 07055: Free information ■ Shoes. 201–779–2323.

Nike Footwear, Inc., One Bowerman Dr., Beaverton, OR 97005: Free information ■ Shoes, shirts, blouses, and bowling ball bags. 800–344–6453.

Saucony/Hyde, P.O. Box 6046, Centennial Industrial Park, Peabody, MA 01961: Free information ■ Shoes. 508–532–9000.

Sports Dynamics Corporation, 89 Leuning, Unit B–2, South Hackensack, NJ 07606: Free information ■ Shoes, gloves, and bowling ball and shoe bags. 800–322– DYNA; 201–342–0500 (in NJ).

Thumtectors, 18316 Hampshire Ln., San Diego, CA 92128: Free information ■ Shoes, gloves, jackets, shirts, and blouses. 619–451– 8577.

Universal Bowling & Golf Corporation, 619 S. Wabash, Chicago, IL 60605: Free catalog ■ Bowling supplies and shoes. 312– 922–5255.

Wa-Mac, Inc., Highskore Products, 178 Commerce Rd., P.O. Box 128, Carlstadt, NJ 07072: Free information ■ Shoes and gloves, bowling ball and shoe bags, grips, novelties, and towels. 800–447–5673; 201–438–7200 (in NJ).

Wolverine Boots & Shoes, 9341 Courtland Dr., Rockford, MI 49351: Free information ■ Shoes. 616–866–5500.

Equipment

The Bag Company, 3508 De La Cruz Blvd., Santa Clara, CA 95050: Free information ■ Bags. 800–531–0700; 800–556–8008 (CA).

Bowling's Bookstore, Tech-Ed Publishing Company, P.O. Box 4, Deerfield, IL 60015: Free information ■ Books and VHS and Beta videos on bowling. 708–945–3169.

Columbia 300, 5005 West Ave., San Antonio, TX 78213: Free information ■ Bowling balls. 512–344–9211.

Cosom Sporting Goods, Grandview Ave., P.O. Box 10, Woodbury Heights, NJ 08097: Free information ■ Bowling balls. 609–853– 0300.

Hilco, Inc., Hilsport Division, 2102 Fair Park Blvd., Harlingen, TX 78550: Free infor-

mation ■ Bowling ball and shoe bags. 512– 423–1885.

J-S Sales Company, Inc., 5 S. Fulton Ave., Mt. Vernon, NY 10550: Free information ■ Bowling ball bags, grips, towels, and novelties. 800–431–2944; 914–668–8051 (in NY).

Kansas Industries for the Blind, 425 S. MacVicar, Topeka, KS 66606: Free information ■ Bags. 913–296–3211.

Master Industry, Inc., 17222 Von Karman Ave., Irvine, CA 92713: Free information ■ Bags, balls, grips, novelties, and towels. 714–660–0644.

Nike Footwear, Inc., One Bowerman Dr., Beaverton, OR 97005: Free information ■ Bowling ball bags, shoes, shirts, and blouses. 800–344–6453.

Pantos Corporation, 74 Rumford Ave., P.O. Box 585, Waltham, MA 02254: Free information ■ Bowling ball and shoe bags. 617–891–4930.

Sauner-Wilhem Company, 3216 5th Ave., Pittsburgh, PA 15213: Free catalog ■ Bowling and billiards equipment and accessories. 412–621–4350.

Sports Calc Division, Cygnus of South Florida, Inc., 1290 Weston Rd., Ste. 300, Fort Lauderdale, FL 33326: Free information ■ Easy-to-use, pocket-size personal bowling computer to record of league bowling scores. 800–624–6022; 305–384–1281 (in FL).

Sports Dynamics Corporation, 89 Leuning, Unit B–2, South Hackensack, NJ 07606: Free information ■ Bowling ball and shoe bags, shoes, and gloves. 800–322– DYNA; 201–342–0500 (in NJ).

Universal Bowling & Golf Corporation, 619 S. Wabash, Chicago, IL 60605: Free catalog ■ Bowling supplies and shoes. 312– 922–5255.

Universal Trav-Ler, 359 Wales Ave., Bronx, NY 10454: Free information ■ Bowling ball and shoe bags. 800–833–3026; 212– 993–7100 (in NY).

Wa-Mac, Inc., Highskore Products, 178 Commerce Rd., P.O. Box 128, Carlstadt, NJ 07072: Free information ■ Bowling ball and shoe bags, grips, novelties, towels, shoes, and gloves. 800–447–5673; 201–438–7200 (in NJ).

BOXING

Equipment

Ameri-Fit Corporation, 1237 The Plaza, Charlotte, NC 28205: Free information ■ Punching bags and skip ropes. 704–372– 3294.

B & G Wholesale, 47–09 30th St., Long Island City, NY 11101: Free information ■ Punching bags and skip ropes. 718–706– 0100.

Betlin Manufacturing, 1445 Marion Rd., Columbus OH 43207: Free information ■ Robes and trunks. 614–443–0248.

Cannon Sports, Inc. P.O. Box 11179, Burbank, CA 91510: Free information ■ Punching bags and skip ropes. 800–223–0064; 818–503–9570 (in CA).

Everlast Sporting Goods Manufacturing Company, Inc., 750 E. 132nd St., Bronx, NY 10454: Free information ■ Punching bags, boxing rings, skip ropes, gloves, head guards, helmets, and tooth and mouth protectors. 800–221–8746; 212–993–0100 (in NY).

Faber Brothers, 4141 S. Pulaski Rd., Chicago, IL 60632: Free information ■ Clothing for boxers. 312–376–9300.

G & S Sporting Goods, Inc., 43 Essex St., New York, NY 10002: Free brochure ■ Leather foul-proof cups, clothing, shoes, ropes, heavy bags, striking bags, mouthpieces, and exercise equipment. 212–777– 7590.

Genesport Industries, Ltd., Hokkaido Karate Equipment Manufacturing Company, 150 King St., Montreal, Quebec, Canada H3C 2P3: Free information ■ Punching bags, skip ropes, boxing rings, robes, shoes, trunks, gloves, head guards, helmets, and tooth and mouth protectors. 514–861–1856.

Ivanko Barbell Company, P.O. Box 1470, San Pedro, CA 90733: Free information ■ Punching bags and skip ropes. 213–514– 1155.

Macho Products, Inc., 2550 Kirby Ave. NE, Palm Bay, FL 32905: Free information ■ Tooth and mouth protectors and head guards. 800–327–6812; 407–729–6137 (in FL).

NDL Products, Inc., 2313 NW 30th Pl., Pompano Beach, FL 33069: Free information ■ Punching bags and skip ropes. 800–843–3021; 800–843–3022 (in FL).

G. Pacillo Company, Inc., P.O. Box 1643, Buffalo, NY 14216: Free information ■ Clothing, mouth guards, head guards, gloves, hand weights, hand wraps, and training equipment. 716–873–4333.

Tuf-Wear USA, P.O. Box 239, Sidney, NE 69162: Free information ■ Punching bags, skip ropes, boxing rings, robes, shoes, trunks, gloves, head guards, helmets, and tooth and mouth protectors. 308–254–4011.

Uniquity, 215 4th St., P.O. Box 6, Galt, CA 95632: Free information ■ Punching bags. 800–521–7771; 209–745–2111 (in CA).

Winston Sports Corporation, 200 5th Ave., New York, NY 10010: Free information ■ Punching bags and gloves. 212–255–6870.

Clothing

Adidas USA, 15 Independence Blvd., Warren, NJ 07060: Free information ■ Shoes. 908–580–0700.

Alpha Sportswear, Inc., 2525 16th St., San Francisco, CA 94103: Free information ■ Trunks. 800–227–4266.

Butwin Sportswear Company, 3401 Spring St. NE, Minneapolis, MN 55413: Free information ■ Robes. 800–328–1445; 800–238–0303 (in MN).

Converse, Inc., One Fordham Rd., North Reading, MA 01864: Free information ■ Shoes. 800–554–2667; 508–664–1100 (in MA).

Faber Brothers, 4141 S. Pulaski Rd., Chicago, IL 60632: Free information ■ Bags, gloves, and head guards. 312–376–9300.

Franklin Sports Industries, Inc., 17 Campanelli Parkway, P.O. Box 508, Stoughton, MA 02072: Free information ■ Bags and gloves. 617–344–1111.

General Shoelace Company, 642 Starks Building, Louisville, KY 40202: Free information ■ Shoes. 502–585–4191.

Genesport Industries, Ltd., Hokkaido Karate Equipment Manufacturing Company, 150 King St., Montreal, Quebec, Canada H3C 2P3: Free information ■ Robes, shoes,

trunks, punching bags, skip ropes, and boxing rings. 514–861–1856.

Gould Athletic Supply Company, 3156 N. 96th St., Milwaukee, WI 53222: Free information ■ Bags and gloves. 414–871–3943.

Markwort Sporting Goods Company, 4300 Forest Park Ave., St. Louis, MO 63108: Free information ■ Bags, gloves, and headguards. 314–652–3757.

Pony Sports & Leisure, Inc., Meadows Office Complex, 7th Floor, 201 Rt. 17 North, Rutherford, NJ 07070: Free information ■ Shoes. 800–654–669; 201–896–0101 (in NJ).

Tuf-Wear USA, P.O. Box 239, Sidney, NE 69162: Free information ■ Robes, shoes, and trunks. 308–254–4011.

BREAD MAKING

Dough Kneader, AA1 Manufacturing, 1457 Bassett Ave., Bronx, NY 10461: Free information ■ Easy-to-use kneaders for making bread at home. 212–828–4510.

BRIDGE

Baron Barclay Bridge Supplies, 3600 Chamberlain Ln., Ste. 230, Louisville, KY 40201: Free catalog ■ Bridge supplies and books. 800–274–2221.

Timeless Expectations, P.O. Box 1180, Fairfield, IA 52556: Free information ■ Electronic games that include Scrabble, chess, bridge, backgammon, gin, and cribbage. Other items include regular board games, books, and gifts. 800–622–1558.

BRUSHES

Fuller Brush Mail Order, P.O. Box 34309, Omaha, NE 68134: Free catalog ■ Brooms and brushes that help keep everything from grills to silver clean, kitchen tools, space-saving organizers, and other home accessories. 800–522–0499.

BUMPER STICKERS

Carswell's Creations, 3476 Alward Rd., Pataskala, OH 43062: Catalog $1 ■ Automobile-related bumper stickers, buttons, magnets, mirrors, rubber stamps, note cards, and award certificates. 614–927–5224.

Lancer Label, 301 S. 74th St., Omaha, NE 68114: Free catalog ■ Custom-printed

bumper stickers and labels in rolls, sheets, and pinfeed for computers. 800–228–7074.

Magic Systems, Inc., P.O. Box 23888, Tampa, FL 33623: Free details ■ Easy-to-use, portable bumper sticker printing machine, supplies, and accessories. 813–886–5495.

Royal Graphics, Inc., 3117 N. Front St., Philadelphia, PA 19133: Free brochure ■ Bumper stickers, posters, and show cards. 215–739–8282.

N.G. Slater Corporation, 220 W. 19th St., New York, NY 10011: Free catalog ■ Equipment and supplies for making all kinds of buttons. Other items include custom advertising novelties, T-shirts, clips and pins, I.D. cards, and bumper stickers. 212–924–3133.

Stik-R-Kits, 1402 E. Las Olas, Fort Lauderdale, FL 33301: Sample and information $3 ■ Do-it-yourself bumper sticker kits.

BUSINESS CARDS, ID CARDS & CARD CASES

Advanced Products, 11201 Hindry Ave., Los Angeles, CA 90045: Free catalog ■ Plastic ID cards, calendars, and Rolodex cards. 800–421–2858; 213–410–9965 (in CA).

Amity Hallmark, Ltd., P.O. Box 929, Linden Hill Station, Flushing, NY 11354: Free catalog ■ Business cards, custom stationery, and special occasion cards. 718–939–2323.

Artistic Greetings, Inc., 409 William St., P.O. Box 1623, Elmira, NY 14902: Free catalog ■ Business cards, personalized stationery, and memo and informal note cards. 607–733–6313.

Arthur Blank & Company, Inc., 225 Rivermoor St., Boston, MA 02132: Free information ■ Plastic credit, ID, membership, and other cards. 800–776–7333; 617–325–9600 (in MA).

The Business Book, One E. 8th Ave., Oshkosh, WI 54906: Free catalog ■ Pressure sensitive labels, mailing labels, stampers, personalized business envelopes, custom stationery, speed letters, memo pads, business cards and forms, greeting cards, books, and office accessories and other supplies. 800–558–0220.

Business Cards Plus, 939 S. Kirkwood Rd., Kirkwood, MO 63122: Free information ■ Color photo business cards. 800–966–2545.

Business Envelope Manufacturers, Inc., 900 Grand Blvd., Deer Park, NY 11729: Free catalog ■ Business cards, imprinted envelopes, forms, stationery, and labels. 516–667–8500.

Cards by Lowell, 25346 Via Telino, Valencia, CA 91355: Plastic, 3–D, paper, opaque, and hot foil stamped business cards. 805–259–8047.

Century Thermographers, P.O. Box 1417, New Britain, CT 06050: Catalog $10 (refundable) ■ Thermographed business cards. 203–827–1018.

Color Cards, Drawer 113, Coldwater, OH 45828: Free information ■ Color business cards. 800–248–6665.

Comprehensive Identification Products, Inc., 1043 Commonwealth Ave., Boston, MA 02215: Free catalog ■ Instant photo ID system cameras and equipment, accessories and supplies for making photo ID cards and badges, badge holders, and luggage tags. 617–783–4666.

Day-Timers, Allentown, PA 18001: Free catalog ■ Business cards, stationery, forms, and office supplies. 215–395–5884.

Enfield Stationers, 215 Moody Rd., Enfield, CT 06082: Free catalog ■ Business cards, calendars, and gifts. 203–763–3980.

Fantastic Impressions, P.O. Box 2432, North Babylon, NY 11704: Free catalog ■ Business cards, letterheads, and envelopes. 516–242–9199.

Grayarc, P.O. Box 2944, Hartford, CT 06104: Free catalog ■ Stationery, business cards, forms, labels, and envelopes. 203–379–9941.

Hodgins Engraving, P.O. Box 597, Batavia, NY 14021: Free catalog ■ Thermographed business cards. 800–666–8950.

Jackson Marketing Products, Brownsville Rd., Mt. Vernon, IL 62864: Free information ■ Custom business cards and supplies and equipment for making rubber stamps. 618–242–1334.

L & D Press, 78 Randall St., Box 641, Rockville Centre, NY 11570: Free price list ■ Custom business cards, stationery, envelopes, planning boards, calendars, and work organizers. 516–593–5058.

Lance Sales, P.O. Box 29285, St. Louis, MO 63126: Free information ■ Business cards. 314–832–1137.

Lee's Company, Inc., 121–22 Dupont St., Plainview, NY 11803: Free information ■ Photo business cards. 800–LEES–023.

Mid-South Business Cards, Cavehouse Rd., Rt. 4, Jackson, TN 38305: Free catalog ■ Thermographed business cards.

The Penn Press, Inc., 325 Hendrickson Ave., Lynbrook, NY 11563: Free information ■ Thermographed letterheads, envelopes, announcements, and business cards. 516–887–7800.

Photo Images, 554 Park Dr., Jackson, MS 39208: Free information ■ Photo business cards. 800–637–1440.

Plasti-Card Corporation, Box 630146, Miami, FL 33163: Free catalog ■ Plastic and 3–dimensional business cards. 305–944–2726.

Prolitho, Inc., 630 New Ludlow Rd., South Hadley, MA 01075: Free catalog ■ Thermographed business cards and stationery and envelopes with flat and raised printing. 413–532–9473.

Pronto Business Cards, Box 548, Safety Harbor, FL 34695: Free catalog ■ Raised business cards.

Shelby Business Cards, P.O. Box 2344, Shelby, NC 28150: Free catalog ■ Business cards. 704–481–8341.

Showcase Press, Inc., P.O. Box 387, Commack, NY 11725: Free catalog ■ Business cards. 516–499–1010.

Supreme Cards, Inc., P.O. Box 5578, Clearwater, FL 34618: Free catalog ■ Business cards. 800–771–5273.

Unique Reproductions, 18720 Oxnard St., Unit 115, Tarzana, CA 91356: Free information ■ Plastic, 3–D, paper, opaque, and hot foil stamped business cards. 818–343–4434.

V.I.P. Print Shoppe, Inc., P.O. Box 2026, Indianapolis, IN 46206: Free information ■ Thermo-engraved business cards, plastic cards, fold-overs, and Rolodex cards. 317–632–5466.

BUTTERFLIES

American Butterfly Company, 3609 Glen Ave., Baltimore, MD 21215: Free information ■ Imported and domestic butterfly specimens.

Butterfly Company, 51–17 Rockaway Beach Blvd., Far Rockaway, NY 11691: Free brochure ■ Butterflies, moths, other insects. kits and supplies, boards, mounting pins, display cases, books, and chemicals. 212–945–5400.

Scientific, P.O. Box 307, Round Lake, IL 60073: Catalog $1 ■ Exotic moths, butterflies, and other insects. 708–546–3350.

CABINETS

Bathroom Cabinets

Brammer Manufacturing, Box 3547, Davenport, IA 52808: Free information ■ Custom bathroom cabinets. 319–326–2585.

Decora, P.O. Box 420, Jasper, IN 47546: Free information ■ Custom bathroom cabinets, knobs, and pulls. 812–482–2537.

Heads Up/Sonoma Woodworks, Inc., 133 Copeland St., Petaluma, CA 94952: Brochure $1 ■ Solid oak cabinets and other furniture for bathrooms. Includes medicine and vanity cabinets and high-tank pull chain toilets. 707–762–5548.

NuTone, Inc., Madison & Red Bank Rds., Cincinnati, OH 45227: Free information ■ Bathroom cabinets, other fixtures, and decorative accessories for the home. 513–527–5100.

General Purpose Cabinets

Campbell Cabinets, 39 Wall St., Bethlehem, PA 18018: Brochure 50¢. 215–835–7775.

John Congdon Cabinetmaker, RFD 1, P.O. Box 1765, Moretown, VT 05660: Catalog $3. 802–496–4767.

Hutton Cabinetry, 706 W. State St., St. Johns, MI 48879: Free information. 517–224–9457.

Iberia Millwork, 500 Jane St., New Iberia, LA 70560: Free brochure. 318–365–5644.

LaPointe Cabinetmaker, 41 Gulf Rd., Pelham, MA 01002: Free information. 413–256–1558.

E.T. Moore Company, 3100 N. Hopkins Rd., Richmond, VA 23224: Free information. 804–231–1823.

Kitchen Cabinets

Alno Kitchen Cabinets, 196 Quigley Blvd., New Castle, DE 19720: Free information. 302–323–0421.

Aristokraft, 1 Aristokraft Square, P.O. Box 420, Jasper, IN 47547: Free information. 812–482–2527.

Boro Wood Products Company, Inc., P.O. Box 636, Bennettsville, SC 29512: Free information. 803–479–2811.

Brammer Manufacturing, 1701 Rockingham Rd., Davenport, IA 52808: Free information. 319–326–2585.

Capri Custom Cabinets, Armstrong Rd., Plymouth, MA 02360: Free information. 617–746–4912.

Crystal Cabinet Works, Inc., 1100 Crystal Dr., Princeton, MN 55371: Free information. 612–389–4223.

Decora, P.O. Box 420, Jasper, IN 47546: Free information. 812–482–2537.

Dutch Built Kitchens, 1494 N. Charlotte St., Pottsdown, PA 19464: Free information. 215–323–4400.

Excel Wood Products Company, Inc., One Excel Plaza, Lakewood, NJ 08701: Free information. 908–364–2000.

Ferretti USA, 200 N. Robertson Blvd., Beverly Hills, CA 90211: Free information. 213–271–4545.

Fieldstone Cabinetry, Inc., P.O. Box 109, Northwood, IA 50459: Free information. 515–324–2114.

Haas Cabinet Company, Inc., 625 W. Utica St., Sellersburg, IN 47172: Free information. 800–457–6458.

Hirsh Company, 8051 Central Ave., Skokie, IL 60076: Free information. 708–673–6610.

HomeCrest Corporation, P.O. Box 595, Goshen, IN 46526: Free information. 219–533–9571.

Imperia Cabinet Corporation, P.O. Box 718, Hanson, MA 02341: Free information. 617–293–4010.

Kitchen Kompact, Inc., P.O. Box 868, Jeffersonville, IN 47130: Free information. 812–282–6681.

KraftMaid Cabinetry, Inc., 16052 Industrial Pkwy., P.O. Box 1055, Middlefield, OH 44062: Free information. 800–654–3008.

Merillat Industries, Inc., Kitchen Design & Planning Kit, P.O. Box 1946, Adrian, MI 49221: Free information. 800–624–1250.

Plain 'n Fancy Kitchens, P.O. Box 519, Schaefferstown, PA 17088: Free information. 717–949–6571.

Plan-A-Flex, A Stanley Tools Company, 600 Myrtle St., New Britain, CT 06050: Free information ■ Kitchen, bathroom, closet, and landscape designer kits. 800–648–7654.

Poggenpohl U.S.A. Corporation, 5905 Johns Rd., Tampa, FL 33634: Free information. 813–882–9292.

Quaker Maid, Rt. 61, Leesport, PA 19533: Free information. 215–926–7218.

Riviera Cabinets, Inc., 2707 Gateway Dr., Pompano Beach, FL 33069: Free information. 800–735–4433.

Rutt Custom Kitchens, P.O. Box 129, Goodville, PA 17528: Information guide $3. 215–445–6751.

Triangle Pacific Corporation, 16803 Dallas Pkwy., Dallas, TX 75266: Free information. 214–931–3000.

WCI Cabinet Group, P.O. Box 1567, Richmond, IN 47374: Free information. 317–935–2211.

Wilsonart, 600 General Bruce Dr., Temple, TX 76504: Free information. 817–778–2711.

Wood-Hu Kitchens, Inc., 343 Manly St., West Bridgewater, MA 02379: Free information. 800–343–7919; 800–344–8777 (in MA).

Wood-Metal Industries, Inc., One 2nd St., Kreamer, PA 17833: Free information. 717–374–2711.

CALENDARS

Abingdon Press, 201 8th Ave. South, Nashville, TN 37202: Free information ■ Calendars. 615–749–6452.

Antioch Publishing Company, 888 Dayton St., Yellow Springs, OH 45387: Free information ■ Calendars. 513–767–7379.

Cedco Publishing Company, 2955 Kerner Blvd., San Rafael, CA 94901: Free catalog ■ Calendars, datebooks, and soft-cover books. 415–457–3893.

Consumer Guide Books, 7373 N. Cicero Ave., Lincolnwood, IL 60646: Free information ■ Calendars. 708–676–3470.

Down East Books, Rt. One Roxmont, Rockport, ME 04856: Free information ■ Calendars. 207–594–9544.

Enfield Stationers, 215 Moody Rd., Enfield, CT 06082: Free catalog ■ Business cards, calendars, and gifts. 203–763–3980.

Georgi Publishers, P.O. Box 6059, Chelsea, MA 02150: Free catalog ■ Fine art and photo art calendars. 617–387–7300.

Hobby House Press, Inc., 900 Frederick St., Cumberland, MD 21502: Free information ■ Calendars. 301–759–3770.

Kar-Ben Copies, Inc., 6800 Tildenwood Lane, Rockville, MD 20852: Free information ■ Calendars. 800–452–7236.

Naval Institute Press, United States Naval Institute, Preble Hall, Annapolis, MD 21402: Free information ■ Calendars. 410–268–6110.

Sormani Calendars, Inc., P.O. Box 6059, Chelsea, MA 02150: Free catalog ■ Calendars with pictures of wildlife, famous art, sports, mountains, museums, fishing, cities and states, churches and religion, trains, automobiles, planes, and foreign countries. 617–387–7300.

Starwood Publishing, 5230 MacArthur Blvd. NW, Washington, DC 20016: Free catalog ■ Calendars with pictures of famous cities, dinosaurs, and garden scenes. 202–362–7404.

Thoroughbred Racing Calendar, Warsaw, VA 22572: Free catalog ■ Calendars with pictures of winners of major thoroughbred horse races from the previous year, handcrafted fiberglass mailboxes, doormats, sweat shirts and T-shirts, mugs, glasses, jewelry, wall clocks, and limited edition prints of famous horse racing events. 800–777–RACE.

Tide-Mark Press, Ltd., P.O. Box 280311, East Hartford, CT 06108: Free catalog ■ Calendars. 203–289–0363.

Zenith Books, P.O. Box 1, Osceola, WI 54020: Free catalog ■ Calendars, books, and video tapes about aviation. 800–826–6600.

CALLIGRAPHY

Ken Brown Studio, P.O. Box 637, Hugo, OK 74743: Free information with long SASE ■ Birthday card-making kit, complete with three prints, calligraphy marker, and instructions.

Calpen, 176 Jaxine Dr., Altadena, CA 91001: Free information ■ Calligraphy pens, prepared gesso for gilding, quill knives, goose quills, quill and reed pens, felt pens, and pen holders.

Coit Pen System, Coit Calligraphics, Inc., P.O. Box 239, Georgetown, CT 06829: Free brochure ■ Single line and multiple line pens for calligraphy, instruction books, and pen cleaner. 203–938–9081.

Ebersole Arts & Crafts Supply, 11417 W. Hwy. 54, Wichita, KS 67209: Free information ■ Calligraphy and other art supplies. 316–722–4771.

Hunt Manufacturing Company, 230 S. Broad St., Philadelphia, PA 19102: Free information ■ Fountain pens, pen sets, nibs, inks, calligraphy papers and markers, calligraphy kits, acrylics, oil paints, water colors, modeling knives and blades, and modeling tools. 215–732–7700.

Pendragon, P.O. Box 25036, 1890 Wooddale Dr., Ste, 700, Woodbury, MN 55125: Catalog $2 ■ Calligraphy supplies.

Pyramid of Urbana, 2107 N. High Cross Rd., Urbana, IL 61801: Free catalog ■ Calligraphy and lettering supplies, other crafts supplies, office accessories and supplies, art supplies, and school equipment. 217–328–3099.

CAMCORDERS

Retailers

Camera Express, 724 7th Ave., New York, NY 10019: Free information ■ Camcorders and accessories. 800–448–3738; 212–397–1081 (in NY).

Camera World, 4619 W. Market St., Greensboro, NC 27407: Free information ■ Video equipment, camcorders, and accessories, and photography equipment. 800–634–0556.

Camera World of Oregon, Camera World Building, 500 SW 5th Ave., Portland, OR 97204: Free information ■ Camcorders,

video tapes, and video accessories. 503–227–6008.

Cam-O-Lap, 97 Broadway, Hicksville, NY 11801: Free information ■ Camcorders, lenses, tripods, television sets, cases, batteries, video lights, microphones, title makers, and other accessories. 800–688–3098.

Electronic Wholesalers, 1160 Hamburg Tpk., Wayne, NJ 07470: Free information ■ Camcorders and accessories, television sets, cassette players/recorders, 8-mm and Beta home decks, audio/hi-fi receivers, audio cassette decks, compact disk players, laser disk equipment, and telephones. 201–696–6531.

Haven Electronics, 16 Nassau Ave., Rockville Centre, NY 11570: Free information ■ Video equipment, camcorders, and accessories. 800–231–0031.

Highvoltage, 39 W. 32nd St., New York, NY 10001: Free information ■ Camcorder equipment and accessories, disk players, lighting equipment, video tape stabilizers, tripods, hi-fi components, car stereos, tape maintenance systems, video recorders, and tapes. 212–564–4410.

Just Camcorders, 39 White St., Ste. 106, New York, NY 10013: Free information ■ Camcorders, video tapes, and video accessories. 800–777–9148.

Lewis & Clark, 136 W. 32nd St., Ste. 504, New York, NY 10001: Free information ■ Video equipment and accessories and camcorders. 800–331–4516; 212–714–2732 (in NY).

Mibro Cameras, Inc., 64 W. 36th St., New York, NY 10018: Free information ■ Camcorders and accessories, video lights, battery packs, wireless microphones, and photography equipment. 800–223–0322; 212–967–2353 (in NY).

Not-Just-Video, Inc., 58 Walker St., New York, NY 10013: Catalog $2.75 ■ Video equipment, television sets and monitors, audio equipment, camcorders, and other electronic equipment. 800–856–9890.

PowerVideo, 4413 Blue Bonnett, Stafford, TX 77477: Free information ■ Camcorders, television sets, cassette players/recorders, and video equipment. 713–240–3202.

6th Ave. Electronics City, 331 Rt. 4W, Paramus, NJ 07652: Free information ■ Video equipment, television sets and monitors, audio equipment, camcorders,

laser players, and other electronic equipment. 201–489–1792.

Super Video, Inc., 93 1st St., Hackensack, NJ 07601: Free information ■ Cassette players/recorders, video cameras, television sets, monitors, and accessories. 800–524–1596.

Tri-State Camera, 160 Broadway, New York, NY 10038: Free information ■ Audio and video equipment and accessories, camcorders, video tape cassettes, fax machines, and other equipment. 212–349–2555.

Video Depot, 1500 N. State St., Bellingham, WA 98225: Free information ■ Video and telephone equipment and accessories. 206–671–2500.

Video Direct Distributors, 116 Production Dr., Yorktown, VA 23693: Free catalog ■ Video equipment, television sets and monitors, audio equipment, camcorders, microphones, carrying cases, and other electronic equipment. 800–368–5020.

Video Wholesaler, 1600 Broadway, New York, NY 10019: Free information ■ Camcorders, video tapes, and video accessories. 800–331–5423; 212–245–3152 (in NY).

Vidicomp Distributors, Inc., 16219 North Freeway, Houston, TX 77090: Free information ■ Video equipment and accessories. 713–440–0040.

Manufacturers

Allsop, 4201 Meridian, Box 23, Bellingham, WA 98227: Free information ■ Camcorders and accessories. 206–734–9090.

Ambico, 50 Maple St., Norwood, NJ 07648: Free information ■ Loudspeakers, camcorders and accessories, video processors/enhancers, character/effects generators, decoders, audio controllers/processor, and headphones. 201–767–4100.

Azden Corporation, 147 New Hyde Park Rd., Franklin Square, NY 11010: Free information ■ Camcorders and accessories and headphones. 516–328–7500.

BASF, Crosby Dr., Bedford, MA 01730: Free information ■ Camcorders and accessories. 617–271–4000.

Bib, P.O. Box 27682, Denver, CO 80227: Free information ■ Camcorders and accessories. 303–972–0410.

Canon, One Canon Plaza, Lake Success, NY 11042: Free information ■ Cassette players/recorders, camcorders and accessories, surround sound processors, character/effects generators, and decoders. 516–488–6700.

Casio, 570 Mount Pleasant Ave., P.O. Box 7000, Dover, NJ 07801: Free information ■ Camcorders and accessories. 201–361–5400.

Chinon America, Inc., 1065 Bristol Rd., Mountainside, NJ 07092: Free information ■ Camcorders and accessories. 908–654–0404.

Curtis-Mathes, 1141 Greenway Dr., Irving, TX 75062: Free information ■ Loudspeakers, camcorders and accessories, cassette players/recorders, and television sets. 214–550–8050.

Discwasher, 46–233 Crane St., Long Island City, NY 11101: Free information ■ Camcorders and accessories. 800–223–6009.

Eastman Kodak Company, Kodak Information Center, 343 State St., Rochester, NY 14650: Free information ■ Camcorders and accessories. 800–462–6495.

Emerson Radio Corporation, 1 Emerson Ln., North Bergen, NJ 07047: Free information ■ Camcorders and accessories, monitors-receivers, cassette players/recorders, compact disk players, and television sets. 800–922–0738.

Fisher, 21350 Lassen St., Chatsworth, CA 91311: Free information ■ Loudspeakers, cassette players/recorders, compact disk players, surround sound processors, audio/video receivers-amplifiers, camcorders and accessories, monitors-receivers, television sets, and universal remotes. 818–998–7322.

Geneva, 7255 Flying Cloud Dr., Eden Prairie, MN 55344: Free information ■ Camcorders and accessories, decoders, and audio controllers. 612–829–1724.

Hitachi Sales Corporation, 401 W. Artesia Blvd., Compton, CA 90220: Free information ■ Cassette players/recorders, camcorders and accessories, monitors-receivers, compact disk players, audio/video receivers-amplifiers, and television sets. 310–537–8383.

Instant Replay, 2601 S. Bayshore Dr., Miami, FL 33133: Free information ■ Camcorders and accessories, and cassette players/recorders. 305–854–6777.

JVC, 41 Slater Dr., Elmwood Park, NJ 07407: Free information ■ Cassette players/recorders, camcorders and accessories, compact disk players, audio/video receivers-amplifiers, television sets, and headphones. 201–794–3900.

Maxell, 22–08 Rt. 208 South, Fair Lawn, NJ 07410: Free information ■ Camcorders and accessories. 201–794–5900.

Memorex, 1600 II Tandy Center, Fort Worth, TX 76102: Free information ■ Camcorders and accessories. 800–548–8308.

Minolta, 101 Williams Dr., Ramsey, NJ 07446: Free information ■ Cassette players/recorders, camcorders, and accessories. 201–825–4000.

Mitsubishi Electronics, 5757 Plaza Dr., Cypress, CA 90630: Free information ■ Audio/video systems, cassette players/recorders, camcorders and accessories, compact disk players, and television sets. 714–220–2500.

NAP Consumer Electronics, 1 Phillips Dr., Knoxville, TN 37914: Free information ■ Camcorders and accessories. stereo television sets, cassette players/recorders, and compact disk players. 615–521–4391.

NEC Home Electronics, 1400 Estes Ave., Elk Grove Village, IL 60007: Free information ■ Camcorders, cassette players/recorders, compact disk players, audio/video receivers-amplifiers, and television sets. 708–228–5900.

Olympus Corporation, 145 Crossways Park, Woodbury, NY 11797: Free information ■ Camcorders and accessories. 800–221–3000.

Panasonic, Panasonic Way, Secaucus, NJ 07094: Free information ■ Audio/video systems, cassette players/recorders, compact disk players, television sets, camcorders and accessories, monitors-receivers, stereo television sets, decoders, and headphones. 201–348–7000.

Pentax Corporation, 35 Inverness Dr. East, Englewood, CO 80112: Free information ■ Cassette players/recorders, camcorders and accessories, and stereo cassette players/recorders. 303–799–8000.

Quasar, 1707 N. Randall Rd., Elgin, IL 60123: Free information ■ Audio/video systems, cassette players/recorders, compact disk players, camcorders and accessories, monitors-receivers, and television sets. 708–468–5600.

Radio Shack, Division Tandy Corporation, 1500 One Tandy Center, Fort Worth, TX 76102: Free information ■ Cassette players/recorders, compact disk players, camcorders and accessories, and universal remotes. 817–390–3700.

RCA Sales Corporation, 600 N. Sherman Dr., Indianapolis, IN 46201: Free information ■ Audio/video systems, cassette players/recorders, compact disk players, stereo television sets, camcorders and accessories, monitors-receivers, surround sound processors, character/effects generators, decoders, and audio controllers. 317–267–5000.

Ricoh Consumer Products Group, 180 Passaic Ave., Fairfield, NJ 07004: Free information ■ Camcorders and accessories. 201–882–7762.

Sanyo Electronics, 1200 W. Artesia Blvd., Compton, CA 90220: Free information ■ Cassette players/recorders, compact disk players, camcorders and accessories, television sets, surround sound processors, decoders, and universal remotes. 310–537–5830.

Sears, Roebuck & Company, Catalog Division, 925 S. Homan Ave., Chicago, IL 60607: Free information ■ Cassette players/recorders, camcorders and accessories, and television sets. (Catalog also available from local stores.) 312–875–2500.

Sharp Electronics, Sharp Plaza, Mawah, NJ 07430: Free information ■ Cassette players/recorders, compact disk players, camcorders and accessories, stereo television sets, audio/video receivers-amplifiers, and decoders. 800–BE–SHARP.

Sony Consumer Products, Sony Dr., Park Ridge, NJ 07656: Free information ■ Camcorders and accessories, loudspeakers, cassette players/recorders, compact disk players, audio/video receivers-amplifiers, surround sound processors, character/effects generators, decoders, universal remotes, and headphones. 201–930–1000.

TDK, 12 Harbor Park Dr., Port Washington, NY 11050: Free information ■ Camcorders and accessories. 516–625–0100.

Vidicraft, SW Bancroft St., Portland, OR 97201: Free information ■ Camcorders and accessories, character/effects generators, and video processors/enhancers. 503–223–4884.

Zenith, 1000 Milwaukee Ave., Glenview, IL 60025: Free information ■ Cassette players/recorders, camcorders and accessories, monitors-receivers, television sets, decoders, and universal remotes. 708–391–7000.

CAMPING & BACKPACKING

Clothing

Academy Broadway Corporation, 5 Plant Ave., Vanderbilt Industrial Park, Smithtown, NY 11787: Free information ■ Clothing and rainwear. 516–231–7000.

Adidas USA, 15 Independence Blvd, Warren, NJ 07060: Free information ■ Hiking and climbing shoes. 908–580–0700.

Adventure International Corporation, Adventure Gear, 8039 Deering Ave., Canoga Park, CA 91304: Free information ■ Clothing and rainwear. 818–594–0380.

Amsec International Ammo Depot, 1849–B Candy Ln. SW, Marietta, GA 30060: Catalog $10 (refundable) ■ Camping, hunting, archery, and ammunition supplies. 800–622–1121.

Asolo Boots, 8141 W. I–70 Frontage Rd. North., Arvada, CO 80002: Free information ■ Outdoor footwear. 303–425–1200.

Eddie Bauer, P.O. Box 3700, Seattle, WA 98124: Free catalog ■ Men's and women's active and casual clothes, footwear, and goose down outerwear. 800–426–8020.

L.L. Bean, Inc., Freeport, ME 04033: Free catalog ■ Clothing for hiking, camping fishing, sports, and other activities. 800–221–4221.

Bowhunter Supply, Inc., 1158 46th St., P.O. Box 5010, Vienna, WV 26105: Free information ■ Rainwear and hiking shoes. 800–624–1923; 800–642–2638 (in WV).

Brenco Enterprises, Inc., 77 S. 180th St., Kent, WA 98032: Free information ■ Climbing and hiking shoes. 206–251–5020.

Brigade Quartermasters, Inc., 1025 Cobb International Blvd., Kenesaw, GA 30144: Free information ■ Clothing and rainwear. 404–428–1234.

Browning Company, Dept. C006, Morgan, UT 84050: Catalog $2 ■ Clothing,-rainwear, and hiking shoes. 800–333–3288.

Campmor, P.O. Box 998, Paramus, NJ 07653: Free catalog ■ Outdoor clothing and climbing, camping, hiking, backpacking, and biking equipment. 201–445–5000.

Coleman Outdoor Products, Inc., 250 N. Saint Francis, P.O. Box 2931, Wichita, KS 67201: Free information ■ Clothing, hiking shoes, and climbing shoes. 800–835–3278.

Crescent Down Works, 500 15th Ave. East, Seattle, WA 98112: Catalog $1 ■ Custom outdoor clothing. Includes parkas with white polish goose down and weather-resistant Gore-Tex. 206–328–3696.

Damart Thermawear, 1811 Woodbury Ave., Portsmouth, NH 03801: Free information ■ Thermal underwear. 800–258–7300; 603–431–4700 (in NH).

Dorman-Pacific Company, Inc., 7900 Edgewater Dr., Oakland, CA 94621: Free information ■ Clothing and rainwear. 800–DORFMAN; 800–4DP–HATS (in CA).

Enka America, 1 N. Pack Square, P.O. Box 2659, Asheville, NC 28802: Free information ■ Clothing, rainwear, and hiking and climbing shoes. 704–258–5015.

Fabiano Shoe Company, 850 Summer St., South Boston, MA 02127: Free information ■ Insulated hiking and climbing shoes. 617–268–5625.

Faeth Outdoor Sales, R.J.F. Enterprises, Inc., 1151 S. 7th St., P.O. Box 118–A, St. Louis, MO 63166: Free information ■ Clothing, rainwear, and hiking and climbing shoes. 314–421–0030.

Five-Tennie Footwear, P.O. Box 1185, Redlands, CA 92373: Free information ■ Outdoor footwear. 714–798–4222.

Hiker's Hut, 126 Main St., Box 542, Littleton, NH 03561: Free information ■ Boots and outdoor footwear. 603–444–5532.

Holubar Mountaineering, Ltd., Box 7, Boulder, CO 80306: Free information ■ Outdoor clothing, equipment, tents, and sleeping bags. 303–499–1731.

Kirkham's Outdoor Sports Products, 3125 S. State St., Salt Lake City, UT 84115: Free information ■ Outdoor clothing and accessories. 801–486–4161.

Leisure Unlimited, P.O. Box 308, Cedarburg, WI 53012: Free information ■ Clothing and rainwear. 800–323–5118; 414–377–7454 (in WI).

Lowe Alpine Systems, P.O. Box 1449, Broomfield, CO 80038: Free catalog ■ Outdoor clothing and mountaineering fleecewear.

Marathon Rubber Products Company, Inc., 510 Sherman St., Wausau, WI 54401: Free information ■ Rainwear. 715–845–6255.

Martin Archery, Inc., Rt. 5, Box 127, Walla Walla, WA 99362: Free information ■ Hiking shoes. 509–529–2554.

Merrell Footwear, P.O. Box 4249, South Burlington, VT 05406: Free information ■ Outdoor footwear. 800–869–3348.

O.H. Mullen Sales, Inc., RR 2, Oakwood, OH 45873: Free information ■ Clothing and rainwear. 800–258–6625; 800–248–6625 (in OH).

Nelson/Weather-Rite Products, Inc., Fuqua Sports, 14760 Santa Fe Trail Dr., Lenexa, KS 66215: Free information ■ Clothing, rainwear, and hiking and climbing shoes. 800–255–6061; 913–492–3200 (in KS).

New Balance Athletic Shoe, Inc., 38 Everett St., Boston, MA 02134: Free information ■ Hiking shoes. 800–253–SHOE.

Nike Footwear, Inc., 800 Bowerman Dr., Beaverton, OR 97005: Free information ■ Climbing shoes. 800–344–6453.

North by Northeast, 181 Conant St., Pawtucket, RI 02862: Free information ■ Clothing and rainwear. 800–556–7262.

North Face, 999 Harrison St., Berkeley, CA 94710: Free information ■ Clothing and rainwear. 800–654–1751.

One Sport Outdoor Footwear, 7877 S. 180th St., Kent, WA 98032: Free information ■ Outdoor footwear. 800–826–1598.

Orvis, Historic Rt. 7A, Manchester, VT 05254: Free catalog ■ Outdoor clothing, equipment, and accessories. 800–548–9548.

Pachmayr, Ltd., 1875 S. Mountain Ave., Monrovia, CA 91016: Free catalog ■ Shooting and hunting accessories, clothing, camping and other equipment, books, and video tapes. 800–423–9704.

Patagonia Mail Order, Inc., P.O. Box 8900, Bozeman, MT 59715: Free catalog ■ Outdoor clothing. 800–336–9090.

Pro Advantage, Inc., 2030 N. Redwood Rd., Ste. 10, Salt Lake City, UT 84116: Free information ■ Rainwear and hiking shoes. 801–532–4822.

Rainshed Outdoor Fabrics, 707 NW 11th, Corvallis, OR 97330: Catalog $1 ■ Bion II, Cordura, Lycra, Thinsulate, Polypropylene, Polarfleece, Nylons, Packcloth, and Polarplus outdoor fabrics. Other supplies include hardware, webbing, patterns, and accessories. 503–753–8900.

Ramsey Outdoor Store, 226 Rt. 17, P.O. Box 1689, Paramus, NJ 07652: Free catalog ■ Outdoor apparel and equipment. 201–261–5000.

REI Recreational Equipment Company, Sumner, WA 98352: Free catalog ■ Outdoor equipment and clothing, exercise and walking shoes, Gore-Tex rain equipment, day packs that convert to tents, clothing, shoes, ski equipment, knives and utensils, sunglasses, and camping foods. 800–426–4840.

Rettinger Importing Company, 125 Enterprise, Secaucus, NJ 07094: Free information ■ Clothing, rainwear, and hiking shoes. 800–526–3142; 201–432–7400 (in NJ).

Schnee's Boot Works, 411 W. Mendenhall, Bozeman, MT 59715: Free catalog ■ Outdoor and casual footwear for men and women. 406–587–0981.

Sierra Trading Post, 105 N. Sparks Blvd., Ste. 115, Sparks, NV 89434: Free catalog ■ Outdoor clothing and equipment. 702–355–3377.

Sportif USA, Inc., 445 E. Glendale Ave., Sparks, NV 89431: Free information ■ Clothing. 702–359–6400.

Tecnica USA, 19 Technology Dr., West Lebanon, NH 03784: Free information ■ Outdoor footwear. 603–298–8032.

Vasque Boots, Red Wing Shoe Company, Red Wing, MN 55066: Free brochure ■ Hiking boots. 801–972–5220.

Jack Wolfskin, P.O. Box 2487, Binghamton, NY 13902: Free catalog ■ Functional outerwear, packs, sleeping bags, tents, travel luggage, and accessories.

Wyoming River Raiders, 601 Wyoming Blvd., Casper, WY 82609: Free catalog ■ Clothing for outdoors, books, and equipment for camping, river expeditions, fishing, and hiking. 800–247–6068; 307–235–8624 (in WY).

Wyoming Woolens, P.O. Box 3127, Jackson Hole, WY 83001: Free information ■ Clothing and rainwear. 307–733–2889.

Equipment

Academy Broadway Corporation, 5 Plant Ave., Vanderbilt Industrial Park, Smithtown, NY 11787: Free information ■ Backpacks and equipment, dining equipment and supplies, knives, axes and camping tools, and sleeping bags. 516–231–7000.

All Outdoors Mountain Equipment, Inc., 196 Elm St., Manchester, NH 03101: Free catalog ■ Gear and equipment for climbing, hiking, kayaking, canoeing, skiing, and camping. 800–624–1468.

B & G Wholesale, 47–09 30th St., Long Island City, NY 11101: Free information ■ Backpacks, camping equipment, and sleeping bags. 718–706–0100.

Bass Pro Shops, 1935 S. Campbell, Springfield, MO 65807: Catalog $3 ■ Camping and backpacking equipment for sportsmen, hunters, campers, boating enthusiasts, and fishermen. 800–BASS–PRO.

Bay Archery Sales, 1001 N. Johnson St., Bay City, MI 48708: Free catalog ■ Camping and backpacking equipment and survival supplies. 517–894–0777.

L.L. Bean, Inc., Freeport, ME 04033: Free catalog ■ Tents, backpacks, bicycles, boats, and other equipment for the outdoors. 800–221–4221.

Bear Archery Company, 4600 SW 41st Blvd., Gainesville, FL 32601: Free information ■ Backpacks, eating utensils, knives, axes and camping tools, lanterns and flashlights, and other equipment. 800–874–4603; 800–342–4751 (in FL).

Bianchi International, 100 Calle Cortez, Temecula, CA 92390: Free information ■ Backpacks, knives, axes and camping tools, and sleeping bags. 714–676–5621.

Bibler Tents, 5441 Western, Boulder, CO 80301: Free catalog ■ Light, easy-to-set up tents. 303–449–7351.

Bowhunter Supply, Inc., 1158 46th St., P.O. Box 5010, Vienna, WV 26105: Free information ■ Backpacks and equipment. 800–624–1923; 800–642–2638 (in WV).

Brunton U.S.A., 620 E. Monroe, Riverton, WY 82501: Free brochure ■ Pocket transits, accessories, and cases; compasses; binoculars; and knives. 307–856–6559.

Brush Hunter Sportswear, Inc., 3 NE 21st St., Washington, IN 47501: Free information ■ Hunting and camping equipment and clothing. 812–254–4962.

Buck Knives, P.O. Box 1267, El Cajon, CA 92022: Free information ■ All-purpose knives for campers. 800–326–2825; 619–449–1100 (in CA).

Cabela's, 812 13th Ave., Sidney, ME 69160: Free catalog ■ Tents, sleeping bags, outdoor clothing, footwear, and hunting equipment. 800–237–4444.

Camping World, Three Springs Rd., Bowling Green, KY 42102: Free catalog ■ Camping equipment and supplies. 800–626–5944.

Campmor, P.O. Box 998, Paramus, NJ 07653: Free catalog ■ Clothing and climbing, camping, hiking, backpacking, and biking equipment. 800–626–5944.

Camp Trails, P.O. Box 966, Binghamton, NY 13902: Free information ■ Backpacks, eating utensils, sleeping bags, and other equipment. 607–779–2200.

Caribou Mountaineering, Inc., 46 Loren Ave., Chico, CA 95928: Free information ■ Backpacks, sleeping bags, tents, shoulder bags, travel packs, and soft luggage. 800–824–4153.

Casco USA, 80 Common Rd., Dresden, ME 04342: Free catalog ■ Sleeping bags, clothing, moccasins, and other camping equipment. 800–327–9285; 207–737–8516 (in ME).

Coghlan's, The Outdoor Accessory People, 121 Irene St., Winnipeg, Manitoba, Canada R3T 4C7: Free information ■ Camping, fishing, hunting, backpacking, trailering, and boating equipment. 204–284–9550.

Coleman Outdoor Products, Inc., 250 N. Saint Francis, P.O. Box 2931, Wichita, KS 67201: Free information ■ Backpacks, dining utensils, knives, axes and camping tools, lanterns and flashlights, sleeping bags, and other equipment. 800–835–3278.

Colorado Tent Company, 2228 Blake St., Denver, CO 80205: Free catalog ■ Tents and sleeping bags. 303–294–0924.

Dana Designs, 109 Commercial Dr., Bozeman, MT 59715: Free information ■ Custom backpacks and external frames for men and women. 406–587–4188.

Diamond Branch Canvas Products, Hwy. 25, Naples, NC 28760: Free information ■ Backpacks for men, women, and children, and two- and four-person tents. 800–258–9811.

Duluth Tent & Awning, 1610 W. Superior St., P.O. Box 16024, Duluth, MN 55816: Free information ■ Handmade packs, bags, and luggage for outdoor buffs. 218–722–3898.

Early Winters, Ltd., P.O. Box 4333, Portland, OR 97208: Catalog $1 ■ Clothing and equipment for campers and backpackers. 800–821–1286.

Eastern Mountain Sports, Inc., One Vose Farm Rd., Peterborough, NH 03458: Free catalog ■ Camping equipment and outdoor clothing. 603–924–9571.

Eastpak, 50 Rogers Rd., Ward Hill, MA 01830: Free information ■ Backpacks that convert to a suitcase. 508–373–1581.

Eureka Tents, P.O. Box 968, Binghamton, NY 13902: Catalog $1 ■ Self-supporting tents with shock-corded frames. 800–848–3673.

Faeth Outdoor Sales, R.J.F. Enterprises, Inc., 1151 S. 7th St., P.O. Box 118–A, St. Louis, MO 63166: Free information ■ Backpacks, eating utensils, knives, axes and camping tools, lanterns and flashlights, sleeping bags, and other equipment. 314–421–0030.

Famous Trails, Inc., 3804 Main St., Ste. 1, Chula Vista, CA 92011: Free information ■ Backpacks, eating utensils, knives, axes and

camping tools, sleeping bags, and other equipment. 619–422–8810.

Feathered Friends Mail Order, 2013 4th Ave., Seattle, WA 98121: Free catalog ■ Sleeping bags in short, regular, and long sizes, with Gore-Tex, down collar, overfill, or underfill options. 206–443–9549.

Feline Archery, Inc., 229 Rt. 30 West, Ligonier, PA 15658: Free information ■ Backpacks and outdoor equipment. 412–238–3673.

Flaghouse Camping Equipment, 150 Macquesten Pkwy., Mt. Vernon, NY 10550: Free catalog ■ Outdoor equipment and accessories. 800–221–5185.

Gander Mountain, Inc., P.O. Box 248, Gander Mountain, Wilmot, WI 53192: Free catalog ■ Outdoor equipment, boats, archery supplies, knives, rifle reloading equipment, rifle scopes, camping equipment, and videos on hunting and fishing. 800–558–9418.

Gold-Eck of Austria, 6313 Seaview Ave. NW, Seattle, WA 98107: Free information ■ Sleeping bags. 206–781–0886.

Grade VI, P.O. Box 8, Urbana, IL 61801: Free information ■ Anatomically shaped backpacks. 217–328–6666.

Gregory Mountain Products, 100 Calle Cortez, Temecula, CA 92390: Free information ■ External-frame backpacks. 800–477–8545.

Heliopower, Inc., One Centennial Plaza, Piscataway, NJ 08854: Free information ■ Solar rechargeable lantern with up to 5 hours of fluorescent light per charge. 800–344–3546.

Henderson Camp Products, Inc., 414 N. Orleans St., Chicago, IL 60601: Free information ■ Tents and sleeping bags. 312–226–6400.

High Sierra, 880 Corporate Woods Pkwy., Vernon Hills, IL 60061: Free information ■ Backpacks, dining utensils, sleeping bags, and other equipment. 800–323–9590.

Bob Hinman Outfitters, 1217 W. Glen, Peoria, IL 61614: Free information ■ Outdoor equipment and supplies. 309–691–8132.

Holubar Mountaineering, Ltd., Box 7, Boulder, CO 80306: Free information ■ Out-

door clothing, equipment, tents, and sleeping bags. 303–499–1731.

Igloo Products Corporation, P.O. Box 19322, Houston, TX 77024: Free catalog ■ Cookers and ice chests for outdoor use. 713–465–2571.

Indiana Camp Supply, P.O. Box 211, Hobart, IN 46342: Free information ■ Medical and camping gear, freeze-dried foods, and books on camping.

JanSport, Inc., 10931 32nd Place West, Everett, WA 98204: Free information ■ Backpacks and sleeping bags. 800–552–6776.

Kelty Packs, Inc., P.O. Box 7048–A, St. Louis, MO 63141: Free catalog ■ Sleeping bags and cordura nylon backpacks that convert to luggage.

Kieser Manufacturing Company, 555 Stuyvesant Ave., Irvington, NJ 07111: Free information ■ Backpacks and equipment. 201–372–3038.

Koolatron Industries, Ltd., 2 Treadeasy Ave., Batavia, NY 14020: Free information ■ Portable refrigerators and coolers for campers. 716–343–6695.

Lafuma USA, Inc., P.O. Box 812, Farmington, GA 30638: Free information ■ Backpacks, sleeping bags, and two-, three-, and four-person tents. 404–769–6627.

Lowe Alpine Systems, P.O. Box 1449, Broomfield, CO 80038: Free information ■ Backpacks and equipment. 303–465–3706.

Madden/USA, 2400 Central Ave., Boulder, CO 80301: Free information ■ Backpacks and other equipment. 303–442–5828.

Mark One Distributors, 515 W. 16th St., Bloomington, IN 47404: Free catalog ■ Camping equipment, sporting goods, hardware and outdoor maintenance products, and safety items. 812–333–8496.

Marmot Mountain Works, Ltd., 2321 Circadian Way, Santa Rosa, CA 95407: Free information ■ Sleeping bags. 707–544–4590.

Michale & Company, 29 Dravus St., Seattle, WA 98109: Free information ■ Backpacks for women and men. 206–281–7861.

Midwest Company, 9043 S. Western Ave., Chicago, IL 60620: Free information ■ Leather backpacks with roomy cargo sections and expandable outside pockets. 312–445–6166.

Miller Ski Company, Inc., N. 1200 West, Orem, UT 84057: Free information ■ Backpacks, dining utensils, knives, axes and camping tools, sleeping bags, and other equipment. 801–225–1100.

Moonstone Mountaineering, 5350 Ericson Way, Arcata, CA 95521: Free information ■ Sleeping bags. 707–822–2985.

Moss Tents, Inc., P.O. Box 309, Camden, ME 04843: Free information ■ One-, two-, three-, and four-person tents. 207–236–8368.

Mountain Equipment, Inc., 4776 E. Jensen, Fresno, CA 93725: Free information ■ Adjustable backpacks for a custom fit. 800–344–7422.

Mountainsmith, 15866 W. 7th Ave., Unit A, Golden, CO 80401: Free information ■ Packs and external frames and two-, four-, and eight-person tents. 800–426–4075.

O.H. Mullen Sales, Inc., RR 2, Oakwood, OH 45873: Free information ■ Backpacks, dining utensils, knives, axes and camping tools, sleeping bags, and other equipment. 800–258–6625; 800–248–6625 (in OH).

Nalge Company, P.O. Box 20365, Rochester, NY 14624: Free catalog ■ Outdoor equipment and supplies. 716–586–8800.

Nelson/Weather-Rite Products, Inc., Fuqua Sports, 14760 Santa Fe Trail Dr., Lenexa, KS 66215: Free information ■ Backpacks, eating utensils, knives, axes and camping tools, lanterns and flashlights, sleeping bags, and other equipment. 800–255–6061; 913–492–3200 (in KS).

North Face, 999 Harrison St., Berkeley, CA 94710: Free information ■ Backpacks, camping equipment, and sleeping bags. 800–654–1751.

Northwest River Supplies, Inc., 2009 S. Main, Moscow, ID 83843: Free information ■ Backpacks and equipment. 800–635–5202.

Optimus, Inc., 1100 Boston Ave., P.O. Box 1950, Bridgeport, CT 06601: Free information ■ Compasses. 203–333–0499.

Osprey Packs, P.O. Box 539, Dolores, CO 81323: Free information ■ External-frame backpacks. 303–882–2221.

Outbound, 1580 Zephyr, Haywood, CA 94545: Free information ■ Backpacks, sleeping bags, and two-, three-, and four-person tents. 800–866–9880.

Pachmayr, Ltd., 1875 S. Mountain Ave., Monrovia, CA 91016: Free catalog ■ Shooting and hunting accessories, clothing, camping and outdoor equipment, books, and video tapes. 800–423–9704.

Pro Advantage, Inc., 2030 N. Redwood Rd., Ste. 10, Salt Lake City, UT 84116: Free information ■ Backpacks, dining utensils, knives, axes and camping tools, sleeping bags, and other equipment. 801–532–4822.

Ramsey Outdoor Store, 226 Rt. 17, P.O. Box 1689, Paramus, NJ 07652: Free information ■ Equipment for camping and backpacking. 201–261–5000.

Ranger Manufacturing Company, Inc., 1536 Crescent Dr., P.O. Box 14069, Augusta, GA 30919: Free information ■ Camouflage clothing. 404–738–2023.

REI Recreational Equipment Company, Sumner, WA 98352: Free catalog ■ Exercise and walking shoes, Gore-Tex rain gear, day packs that convert to tents, shoes, ski equipment, gifts, knives and other utensils, sunglasses, and camping foods. 800–426–4840.

Remington Outdoor Products, 14760 Santa Fe Trail Dr., Lenexa, KS 66215: Free information ■ Backpacks, sleeping bags, and two-, three-, and four-person tents. 913–492–3202.

Rettinger Importing Company, 125 Enterprise, Secaucus, NJ 07096: Free information ■ Backpacks, sleeping bags, and other equipment. 800–526–3142; 201–432–7400 (in NJ).

A.G. Russell Company, 1705 Hwy. 471 North, Springdale, AR 72764: Catalog $2 ■ Knives and cutlery. 800–255–9034.

Sierra Trading Post, 105 N. Sparks Blvd, Ste. 115, Sparks, NV 89434: Free catalog ■ Outdoor clothing and equipment. 702–355–3377.

Sims Stoves, P.O. Box 21405, Billings, MT 59104: Free information ■ Folding camp stoves, tents, packsaddles, books, and other equipment. 800–736–5259.

Slumberjack, Inc., P.O. Box 31405, Los Angeles, CA 90031: Free brochure ■ Insulated sleeping bags. 213–225–5905.

Suunto USA, 2151 Las Palmas Dr., Carlsbad, CA 92009: Free information ■ Precision engineered compasses. 619–931–6788.

Taymor/Outbound, Outdoors Division, 1580 Zephyr St., Hayward, CA 94545: Free information ■ Backpacks, dining utensils, knives, axes and camping tools, sleeping bags, and other equipment. 800–338–8143; 510–783–0412 (in CA).

Texsport, P.O. Box 55326, Houston, TX 77255: Free information ■ Backpacks, dining utensils, knives, axes and camping tools, lanterns and flashlights, sleeping bags, and other equipment. 800–231–1402; 800–392–9800 (in TX).

U.S. Cavalry, 2855 Centennial Ave., Radcliff, KY 40160: Catalog $3 ■ Camping equipment. 800–777–7732.

Vaude USA, P.O. Box 12353, Boulder, CO 80303: Free information ■ Backpacks, tents, and other equipment for camping, outdoor activities, and mountaineering. 303–440–0822.

Walrus, Inc., 929 Camelia St., Berkeley, CA 94710: Free information ■ One-, two-, three-, and four-person tents. 510–526–8961.

Wiggy's, Inc., P.O. Box 2124, Grand Junction, CO 81502: Free information ■ Sleeping bags. 303–241–6465.

Wild Country USA, 27 Whitelaw Dr., Center Conway, NH 03813: Free catalog ■ Tents. 603–356–9316.

Wilderness Experience, 20721 Dearborn St., Chatsworth, CA 91311: Free information ■ External-frame backpacks. 818–341–5774.

Jack Wolfskin, P.O. Box 2487, Binghamton, NY 13902: Free catalog ■ Functional outerwear, packs, sleeping bags, tents, travel luggage, and accessories.

Wyoming River Raiders, 601 Wyoming Blvd., Casper, WY 82609: Free catalog ■ Clothing, camping, and river expedition equipment. 800–247–6068; 307–235–8624 (in WY).

Food

Adventure Foods, Rt. 2, Whittier, NC 28789: Free brochure ■ Camping foods and stoves. 704–497–4113.

AlpineAire, P.O. Box 1600, Nevada City, CA 95959: Free information ■ Freeze-dried and concentrated foods. 800–322–MEAL.

Cobi Foods, Inc., Freeze-Dry Division, 579 Speers Rd., Oakville, Ontario, Canada L6K 2G4: Free information ■ Freeze-dried and concentrated foods. 416–844–1471.

Faeth Outdoor Sales, R.J.F. Enterprises, Inc., 1151 S. 7th St., P.O. Box 118–A, St. Louis, MO 63166: Free information ■ Freeze-dried and concentrated foods. 314–421–0030.

Indiana Camp Supply, P.O. Box 211, Hobart, IN 46342: Free information ■ Medical and camping gear, books, and freeze-dried foods.

Myers Meats, Rt. 1, Box 132, Parshall, ND 58770: Free brochure ■ Original or peppered beef jerky and beef stick. 800–ND–JERKY; 701–743–4451 (in ND).

Oregon Freeze Dry Foods, Inc., 525 25th Ave. SW, P.O. Box 1048, Albany, OR 97321: Free information ■ Freeze-dried and concentrated foods. 503–967–6001.

Outdoor Kitchen, Box 1600, Nevada City, CA 95959: Free catalog ■ Additive-free freeze-dried foods in bulk. 800–322–MEAL.

Richmoor Corporation, P.O. Box 8092, Van Nuys, CA 91409: Free information ■ Freeze-dried and concentrated foods. 800–423–3170; 818–787–2510 (in CA).

Survival Supply, Box 1745, Shingle Springs, CA 95682: Free catalog ■ Freeze-dried and storage foods. 916–621–3836.

Trail Foods Company, P.O. Box 9309, North Hollywood, CA 91609: Free information ■ Two- and four-person meal pouches. 818–897–4370.

CANDLES & CANDLE MAKING

ADA Village Candle, 3572 Roger B. Chaffee, Grand Rapids, MI 49508: Catalog 50¢ ■ Candle-making supplies and books, macrame supplies, dough art mediums, and other craft supplies. 616–247–8353.

Barker Enterprises, Inc., 15106 10th Ave. SW, Seattle, WA 98166: Catalog $2 ■ Candle-making supplies and molds. 800–543–0601.

Candlechem Products, P.O. Box 705, Randolph, MA 02368: Catalog $1 ■ Oils, perfume oils, dyes, and other scenting materials for making candles and perfumery items. 617–986–7541.

Candle Mill, Old Mill Rd., P.O. Box 248, East Arlington, VT 05252: Catalog 25¢ ■ Candle-making supplies. 802–375–6068.

Candles by Anita, Main St., Helen, GA 30545: Free catalog ■ Handmade candles for Christmas and other occasions. 404–878–3214.

Candlewic Company, 35 Beulah Rd., New Britain, PA 18901: Catalog $2 (refundable) ■ Candle-making supplies and equipment. 215–348–9285.

Hawthorne Products Company, P.O. Box 3683, Bloomington, IL 61701: Free brochure ■ Candle-making supplies and molds. 309–828–9656.

Jack-Be-Nimble Candleworks, Box 3965, RD 3, Reading, PA 19606: Free price list ■ Hand-dipped candles. 800–462–2031.

Mann Lake Supply, County Rd. 40 & 1st St., Hackensack, MN 56452: Free information ■ Beekeeping and honey production equipment, protective clothing and accessories, and candle molds. 800–233–6663.

Pourette Manufacturing, 6910 Roosevelt Way NE, Seattle, WA 98115: Catalog $2 (refundable) ■ Candles and candle- and soap-making supplies and equipment. 206–525–4488.

Pyramid of Urbana, 2107 N. High Cross Rd., Urbana, IL 61801: Free catalog ■ Candle-making and other craft, office, art, and school supplies and equipment. 217–328–3099.

Traditional Country Crafts, Box 111, Landisville, PA 17538: Brochure $1 ■ Hand-dipped candles in standard and mini sizes. 717–653–5969.

CANDY MAKING

Assouline & Tung, Inc., 314 Brown St., Philadelphia, PA 19123: Free information ■ Cocoa powder and chocolate couverture.

Cooking Craft, Inc., 300 W. Main St., St. Charles, IL 60174: Free catalog ■ Chocolate and candy-making supplies. 708–377–1730.

Holcraft Collection, 211 El Cajon Ave., P.O. Box 792, Davis, CA 95616: Free brochure with long SASE ■ Animal, decorative, and other molds for making chocolate candy. 916–756–3023.

Lorann Oils, 4518 Aurelius Rd., P.O. Box 22009, Lansing, MI 48910: Free information ■ Supplies and equipment for making suckers and other hard candies. 800–248–1302; 517–882–0215 (in MI).

Maid of Scandinavia, 3244 Raleigh Ave., Minneapolis, MN 55416: Catalog $2 ■ Utensils and kitchen tools, cake molds, candy-making molds, and candy-making ingredients. 800–328–6722; 800–851–1121 (in MN).

Meadow's Chocolate & Cake Supplies, P.O. Box 448, Richmond Hill, NY 11419: Catalog $2 ■ Candy-making and cake-decorating supplies and equipment. 718–835–3600.

Paradigm Chocolate Company, 5775 SW Jean Rd., Lake Oswego, OR 97034: Catalog $1 (refundable) ■ Chocolate products for bakers and candy makers. 503–636–4880.

Albert Uster Imports, Inc., 9211 Gaither Rd., Gaithersburg, MD 20877: Free information ■ Chocolate couverture, cocoa powder, disposable pastry bags, and candy boxes. 301–258–7350.

Wilton Enterprise, Inc., 2240 W. 75th St., Woodbridge, IL 60517: Catalog $6 ■ Equipment and supplies for making candies, cookies, and cakes. 708–963–7100.

CANES & WALKERS

Able Walker, Inc., 1122 Fir Ave., Blaine, WA 98230: Free information ■ Adjustable walker, with a shopping basket and convertible seat, that folds for storage. 800–663–1305.

Albee American Arts, P.O. Box 2861, Riverside, CA 92516: Free information ■ Handcarved red cedar hiking staffs and walking sticks. 714–780–7892.

AliMed, Inc., 297 High St., Dedham, MA 02026: Free catalog ■ Readers; dressing aids; adapted eating utensils; cuffs; plate guards and adapted dinner plates; adapted cups, mugs, and straws; home and kitchen accessories; bathing and personal care items; toilet seats and commodes; and walkers, walking, and communication aids. 617–329–2900.

American Foundation for the Blind, Inc., Product Center, 100 Enterprise Pl., P.O. Box

7044, Dover, DE 19903: Free catalog ■ Canes, watches and clocks, household and personal care supplies, and calculators for visually impaired persons. 800–829–0500.

American Walker, Inc., 742 Market St., Oregon, WI 53575: Free information ■ Walkers and walk-a-cycles for rough terrains. 800–765–3452.

DutchGuard, P.O. Box 411687, Kansas City, MO 64141: Free catalog ■ Canes with standard heads or custom heads in silver, brass, gold, and wood; gadget canes; flask canes; and secrecy sticks, in lustrous hardwoods, blackthorns, and costly exotics. 800–821–5157.

ETAC USA, 2325 Parklawn Dr., Ste. P, Waukesha, WI 53186: Free brochure ■ Walking aids, bath safety equipment, wheelchairs, and other aids to make daily living easier. 800–678–ETAC; 414–796–4600 (in WI).

Guardian Products, Inc., 12800 Wentworth St., Arieta, CA 91331: Free catalog ■ Walkers and accessories; crutches, canes, and accessories; home activity aids; beds, lifters, and ramps; and lifters and transport products. 800–255–5022; 818–504–2820 (in CA).

Health Supplies of America, P.O. Box 1059, Burlington, NC 27834: Free catalog ■ Canes, walkers, crutches, wheelchairs, wheelchair parts and accessories, other health care accessories, and supplies. 800–334–1187.

House of Canes & Walking Sticks, 767 Old Onion, Wilderville, OR 97543: Brochure $1 (refundable) ■ Walking sticks and staffs in wrist, elbow, and shoulder lengths.

Miles Kimball Company, 41 W. 8th Ave., Oshkosh, WI 54901: Free catalog ■ Canes and other accessories for people with physical disabilities. 414–231–3800.

Poestenkill Hiking Staff Manufacturing Company, P.O. Box 300, Poestenkill, NY 12140: Brochure $1 ■ Victorian-style cane replicas. 518–279–3011.

Tracks Walking Staffs, 4000 1st Ave. South, Seattle, WA 98134: Free information ■ Telescoping sectioned walking staffs. 800–527–1527.

Uncle Sam Umbrella Shop, 161 W. 57th St., New York, NY 10019: Free information

■ Umbrellas, canes, and walking sticks. 212–247–7163.

Whistle Creek, 5050 Quorum, Dallas, TX 75240: Free information ■ Handcrafted hardwood hiking and walking sticks. 214–239–0220.

CANNING & PRESERVING

Berry-Hill Limited, 75 Burwell Rd., St. Thomas, Ontario, Canada N5P 3R5: Free catalog ■ Canning equipment and supplies, weather vanes, cider press, and garden tools and equipment. 519–631–0480.

Farmer Seed & Nursery Company, 818 NW 4th St., Faribault, MN 55021: Free catalog ■ Canning equipment, accessories, and supplies. 507–334–1623.

Glashaus/Weck Home Canning, 415 W. Golf Rd., Ste, 13, Arlington Heights, IL 60005: Free catalog ■ Canning supplies and equipment.

Gurney Seed & Nursery Company, 110 Capitol St., Yankton, SD 57079: Free catalog ■ Canning equipment, supplies, and accessories. 605–665–1930.

Earl May Seeds & Nursery Company, N. Elm St., Shenandoah, IA 51603: Free catalog ■ Canning equipment, supplies, and accessories. 712–246–1020.

Mellinger's, Inc., 2328 W. South Range Rd., North Lima, OH 44452: Free catalog ■ Canning equipment and supplies. 216–549–9861.

Modern Homesteader, 1825 Big Horn Ave., Cody, WY 82414: Free catalog ■ Canning equipment and supplies. 800–443–4934; 307–587–5946 (in WY).

CARNIVAL SUPPLIES

N & D Novelty Company, 13 Hamden Park Dr., Hamden, CT 06517: Free information ■ Balloons, inflatable toys, stuffed plush toys, carnival supplies, and plastic toys. 203–287–9990.

Oriental Trading Company, Inc., P.O. Box 3407, Omaha, NE 68103: Free catalog ■ Carnival supplies, toys, giftwares, novelties, fund raisers, and holiday and seasonal items. 800–228–0475.

U.S. Toys, 2008 W. 103rd Terrace, Leawood, KS 66206: Free catalog ■ Car-

nival supplies, prizes, games, and equipment. 913–642–8244.

CAROUSEL FIGURES & ART

Americana Antiques, Rusty & Emmy Donohue, P.O. Box 650, Oxford, MD 21654: Free brochure with long SASE ■ Antique wooden carousel horses and menagerie figures. 410–226–5677.

Amusement Arts, Bruce Zubee, P.O. Box 1158, Burlington, CT 06013: Free information with long SASE ■ Antique carousel figures. 203–675–7653.

Antiques & Collectables, Dave Boyle, 36 Andrews Trace, New Castle, PA 16102: Free information with long SASE ■ Carousel figures and memorabilia. 412–656–8181.

Jim Aten, 14938 S. Burkstrom Rd., Oregon City, OR 97045: Free information ■ Antique horses and other carousel figures. 503–655–3164.

Brass Ring Graphics, Phil & Molly Rader, 2277 Ogden Rd., Wilmington OH 45177: Free information with long SASE ■ Carousel T-shirts, sweatshirts, and prints. 513–382–3266.

Carousel Antiques, P.O. Box 47, Millwood, NY 10546: Free list with long SASE ■ Genuine antique carousel animals.

Carousel Corner, Jon Abbott, P.O. Box 420, Clarkston, MI 48016: Information $3 ■ Authentic carousel horses. 313–625–1233.

Carousel Fantasies, The Village Green at Smithville, 615 E. Moss Mill Rd., Smithville, NJ 08201: Free information with long SASE ■ Carousel art from brass rings to full-size figures. 609–748–0011.

The Carousel Man, P.O. Box 455, Rexburg, ID 83440: Price list $1 with long SASE ■ Carousel do-it-yourself horse kits, from one-third scale to full size.

Carousel Memories, Inc., Karin Osborne, 7400 SW 112th St., Miami, FL 33156: Free information with long SASE ■ European carousel animals and art. 305–252–2416.

Carousel Shopper, P.O. Box 47, Millwood, NY 10546: Catalog $2.50 ■ Carousel collectibles. 914–245–2926.

Dreamtex Collectibles, 8835 Shirley Ave., Northridge, CA 91324: Catalog $2.50 (refundable) ■ Authentic miniature replicas of carousel horses and menagerie animals. 800–733–8464.

Manny Frank, 6428 Coral Lake Ave., San Diego, CA 92119: Free information ■ In-stock and custom carousel horses. 619–463–3711.

Guyot Arts, 2945 SE 140th St., Portland, OR 87236: Free price list with long SASE ■ Handcarved carousel figures in miniature. 503–761–9519.

A Horse of a Different Color Showroom, 22829 NE 54th St., Redmond, WA 98053: Free list with long SASE ■ American antique carousel figures bought, sold, and restored. 206–868–9344.

Layton's Studio, RD 4, P.O. Box 163, New Castle, PA 16101: Free information ■ Replica carousel figures, art paintings, and prints. 412–924–2916.

Joseph Leonard Custom Woodcarving, P.O. Box 510, Burton, OH 44021: Free information ■ Life-size handcarved carousel reproductions. 216–834–4343.

A Magical Carousel Shop, The Carousel at Casino Pier, Seaside Heights, NJ 08751: Free information with long SASE ■ Carousel reproductions, music boxes, books, miniatures, and jewelry. 908–830–4183.

Merry-Go-Round Antiques, Al Rappaport, 29541 Roan Dr., Warren, MI 48093: Free information with long SASE ■ Buys, sells, and trades antique carousel figures. 313–751–8078.

Raymarie Carousels, 8485 Sunshine Grove Rd., Brooksville, FL 34613: Catalog $3 with long SASE ■ Ready-to-paint fiberglass carousel reproductions, custom cut wooden horses, and decorative pieces. 904–596–4137.

Shriver's Carving Kits, 502 Barclay, Dewey, OK 74029: Free catalog with long SASE ■ Kits for carving carousel miniatures. Complete with base and hardware for mounting. 918–534–2730.

The Spirited Steeds, 837 W. Tyson St., Chandler, AZ 85224 ■ Free list with long SASE ■ Buys, sells, and restores carousel art. 602–899–7092.

Total Restorations, Ken Gross, 311–315 E. McGaffey, Roswell, NM 88201: Free information ■ Custom handcarved original and

reproduction carousel horses, band organ figures, and circus wagons. 505–623–9091.

Vestal Press, Ltd., P.O. Box 97, Vestal, NY 13851: Catalog $2 (refundable) ■ Posters, recordings, and books about carousels. 607–797–4872.

The Wooden Horse, Marianne Stevens, 920 W. Mescalero Rd., Roswell, NM 88201: Free information ■ Carousel art. 505–622–7397.

CERAMICS

Aardvark Clay & Supplies, 1400 E. Pomoma St., Santa Ana, CA 92705: Price list $1 ■ Ceramic supplies. 714–541–4157.

Aegean Sponge Company, Inc., 4722 Memphis Ave., Cleveland, OH 44144: Free catalog ■ Ceramic supplies. 216–749–1927.

Africana Colors, Batavia, OH 45103: Free information ■ Textured stains for ceramics. 513–625–9486.

Aim Kilns, 369 Main St., Ramona, CA 92065: Free literature ■ Electric kilns. 800–647–1624; 800–222–KILN (in CA).

Alberta-Meitin Ceramic Decals, 323 N. Roscoe Blvd., Ponte Vedra Beach, FL 32082: Free information ■ Ceramic decals. 407–732–2071.

Alberta's Molds, Inc., P.O. Box 2018, Atascadero, CA 93423: Catalog $6 ■ Ceramic molds. 805–466–9255.

Judy Alexander, P.O. Box 5, Glen Rock, NJ 07452: Free information ■ Custom ceramic and glass decals. 201–447–1955.

AMACO, 4717 W. 16th St., Indianapolis, IN 46222: Free information ■ Underglaze colors for brush application on bisque or greenware. 317–244–6871.

American Art Clay Company, Inc., 4717 W. 16th St., Indianapolis, IN 46222: Free catalog ■ Clays, kilns, pottery-making equipment, glazes, tools, coloring materials, and metal enameling supplies. 800–428–3239.

Art Decal Company, 1145 Loma Ave., Long Beach, CA 90804: Free information ■ Custom ceramic decals. 310–434–2711.

Artfare, 469 Country Club Dr., Longwood, FL 32750: Free information with long SASE ■ Ceramic decals with a country motif. 407–834–1184.

A.R.T. Studio Clay Co. Ave., Elk Grove Village, $4 ■ Ceramic supplies and 323–0212; 708–593–6060 (in

Astro Artcraft Supply, 1026 W. Norfolk, VA 23508: Free informat. Ceramic supplies. 800–872–2678.

Atlantic Mold Corporation, 55 Main Trenton, NJ 08620: Catalog $6 ■ Ceramic molds. 609–581–0880.

Badger Air-Brush Company, 9128 W. Belmont Ave., Franklin Park, IL 60131: Brochure $1 ■ Air brushes. 708–678–3104.

Bailey Ceramic Supply, Box 1577, Kingston, NY 12401: Free catalog ■ Ceramic supplies. 800–431–6067.

Bee Doll Molds, 11925 Las Vegas Blvd., South Las Vegas, NV 89123: Catalog $3.50 ■ Ceramic molds. 702–361–5422.

Bennett's Pottery & Ceramic Supplies, 420 S. Norton Ave., Orlando, FL 32805: Free information ■ Pottery and ceramic supplies and equipment. Includes kilns, glazes, wheels, clay, slip, and tools. 407–849–0414.

B.J. Mold Company, P.O. Box 20361, Albuquerque, NM 87154: Catalog $3 ■ Ceramic molds. 505–294–1951.

Black Magic Cleaners, 1139 Hwy. DD, Burlington, WI 53105: Free information ■ Easy-to-use greenware cleaner. 414–763–4270.

Bleu-J-Suede, P.O. Box 160156, St. Louis, MO 63116: Color chart $2.50 ■ Over 30 colors of velvet and 19 colors of gloss paints. 314–942–2191.

Bluebird Manufacturing, Inc., P.O. Box 2307, Fort Collins, CO 80522: Free information ■ Potter's wheels. 303–484–3243.

Blue Diamond Kiln Company, P.O. Box 172, Metarie, LA 70004: Free information ■ Automatic kilns. 800–USA–KILN; 504–835–2035 (in LA).

Boothe Mold Company, 767 Mark Sharon Ind. Ct., St. Louis, MO 63125: Free information ■ Ceramic molds. 314–631–3535.

Brent Potter's Equipment, 4717 W. 16th St., Indianapolis, IN 46222: Free information ■ Potter wheels and equipment, ware carts, slab rollers, and hand extruders. 800–358–8252; 317–244–6871 (in IN).

ckyard House of Ceramics, 4721 W.
th St., Speedway, IN 46222: Free informa-
n ■ Glazes, stains, underglazes, brushes,
ools, molds, kilns, and kiln and wheel repair
arts. 800–523–3289.

Brush Country Molds, Catalog Department, 4218 Callicoatte, Corpus Christi, TX
78410: Catalog $3.50 ■ Ceramic molds. 512–
241–7586.

Byrne Ceramics, 95 Bartley Rd., Flanders,
NJ 07836: Free literature ■ Supplies for pottery-making. Includes wheels, kilns, tools,
brushes, colors, oxides, porcelains, and
glazes. 201–584–7492.

C & F Wholesale Ceramics, 3241 E. 11th
Ave., Hialeah, FL 33013: Catalog $4 ■
Ceramic supplies, stains and glazes, brushes,
tools, music boxes, clockworks, Paasche air
brushes, and accessories. 305–835–8200.

Cedar Heights Clay Company, Inc., 50
Portsmouth Rd., Oak Hill, OH 45656: Free
information ■ Foundry and ceramic grades
of clay. 614–682–7794.

Central Penn Ceramic Center, 125 Enola
Dr., Enola, PA 17025: Catalog $5.95 ■
Ceramic molds. 717–732–0762.

Ceramic/Art Distributors, 7576
Clairemont Mesa Blvd., San Diego, CA
92111: Catalog $4.50 ■ Ceramic projects,
supplies, and equipment. 619–279–4437.

Ceramichrome, P.O. Box 327, Stanford,
KY 40484: Free information ■ Ceramic
molds, colors, and supplies. 606–365–3193.

Cerami Corner, 342 Bolt View Rd., Grants
Pass, OR 97527: Catalog $5 ■ Ceramic
molds, decals, china paints, decals, and
brushes. 800–423–8543.

Ceramic Supply of New Jersey, 10 Dell
Glen Ave., Lodi, NJ 07644: Catalog $4 ■
Electric and gas kilns, clays, colors, slip casting accessories and equipment, potters
wheels, sculpting equipment and tools, and
glazes. 201–340–3005.

Ceramic Supply of New York, 534 La
Guardia Pl., New York, NY 10012: Catalog
$4 ■ Electric and gas kilns, clays, colors, slip
casting accessories and equipment, potters
wheels, sculpting equipment and tools, and
glazes. 212–475–7236.

Cer Cal Decals, Inc., 626 N. San Gabriel
Ave., Azusa, CA 91702: Free brochure ■
Custom decals. 818–969–1456.

Chaselle, Inc., 9645 Gerwig Ln., Columbia,
MD 21046: Catalog $4 ■ Art software and
books, brushes and paints, tempera colors,
acrylics and sets, pastels, ceramic molds and
kilns, sculpture equipment, silk-screen painting supplies, and other arts and crafts supplies. 800–242–7355.

Clay Magic Ceramic Products, Inc.,
21201 Russell Dr., P.O. Box 148, Rockwood, MI 48173: Catalog $3.50 ■ Ceramic
molds. 313–379–3400.

Cohol's Sponges & Decals, 445 Park Ave.,
Poland, OH 44514: Catalog $3.50 ■ Decals
and sponges. 216–758–1167.

Continental Clay Company, 1101 Stinson
Blvd., Minneapolis, MN 55413: Free information ■ Ceramics supplies and equipment.
800–432–CLAY; 612–331–9332 (in MN).

Creative Hobbies, 900 Creek Rd.,
Bellmawr, NJ 08031: Free catalog ■
Ceramic supplies, accessories, and equip-
ment. 800–THE–KILN; 609–933–2540 (in
NJ).

Creek-Turn, Inc., Rt. 38, Hainesport, NJ
08036: Free information ■ Porcelain slip for
casting, making jewelry and tiles, and modeling. Other supplies include stoneware and
porcelain glazes. 800–634–2297; 609–267–
1170 (in NJ).

Cress Manufacturing Company, Inc.,
1718 Floradale Ave., South El Monte, CA
91733: Free catalog ■ Automatic and
manual operated kilns for ceramics, porcelain crafts, stoneware, china painting, and
lost wax process. 800–423–4584; 818–443–
3081 (in CA).

Cricket Mold Company, 3715 W. Alexis
Rd., Toledo, OH 43623: Ceramic mold
catalog $11.80; jewelry mold catalog $7.30
■ Ceramic molds. 313–856–4649.

Cridge, Inc., Box 210, Morrisville, PA
19067: Free catalog ■ Jewelry supplies for
decorating ceramics. 215–295–3667.

Crusader Kilns, 4717 W. 16th St., Indianapolis, IN 46222: Free information with
long SASE ■ Energy-saving kilns. 800–358–
8252; 317–244–6871 (in IN).

Cutter Ceramics, Inc., 47 Athletic Field
Rd., Waltham, MA 02154: Free catalog ■
Ceramic supplies that include clay, glazes
and raw materials; brushes; tools, and accessories; handbuilding equipment and wheels;
kilns; miscellaneous studio equipment; and
books. 617–893–1200.

Daisy Books, 3824 Smith St., Everett, WA
98201: Free catalog ■ Books on ceramics.
206–252–1648.

Dakota Specialties, P.O. Box 307, Mandan,
ND 58554: Free information ■ Kits for two-
piece molds. 701–663–5047.

Lou Davis Wholesale, 1490 Elkhorn Rd.,
Lake Geneva, WI 53147: Free catalog ■
Ceramic-making supplies and accessories.
414–248–2000.

Doc Holliday Molds, Inc., 773 E. Westland
Dr., Lexington, KY 40504: Catalog $6.50 ■
Ceramic molds. 800–354–9237; 606–252–
0446 (in KY).

Dona's Molds, Inc., P.O. Box 145, West
Milton, OH 45383: Catalog $6 ■ Ceramic
molds and coloring materials. 513–947–
1333.

Dove Products, 280 Terrace Rd., Tarpon
Springs, FL 34689: Catalog $2.50 ■
Brushes. 800–334–3683.

Duncan Mail Order Bookstore, 5695 E.
Shields Ave., Fresno, CA 93727: Free information ■ Books, videos, and other information materials about ceramics.
800–237–2642.

Emboss Art/Suncrest Manufacturing,
P.O. Box 97, Hooper, UT 84315: Free
catalog ■ Ceramic molds. 801–825–4933.

Evenheat Kiln, Inc., 6949 Legion Rd.,
Caseville, MI 48725: Free catalog ■ Kilns
and accessories. 517–856–2281.

Ex-Cel, Inc., 1011 N. Hollywood, Memphis, TN 38108: Free information ■ Slip for
ceramic casting. 901–324–3851; 800–228–
6675 (in TN).

Fash-en-Hues, 118 Bridge St., Piqua, OH
45356: Free information ■ Translucent
colors for staining ceramic and porcelain
crafts. 513–778–8500.

Gare Molds, 165 Rosemont St., Haverhill,
MA 01830: Catalog $6 ■ Ceramic molds,
fired colors, stains, stonewashed glazes,
brushes, tools, and kilns. 508–373–9131.

Georgie Mold & Clay Manufacturer, 756
NE Lombard, Portland, OR 97211: Mold
catalog $5; supply catalog $5.75 ■ Ceramic
supplies, equipment, and molds. 503–283–
1353.

Frank Gleason Ceramic Molds, Inc., 1219
N. Jesse James Rd., Excelsior Springs, MO

64024: Free information ■ Ceramic molds. 816–637–3800.

Highlands Ceramic Supply, 4605 Oak Circle, Sebring, FL 33872: Free information ■ Ceramic molds, kilns and kiln parts, pouring equipment, slips and clay, and greenware. 813–385–6656.

Hill Decal Company, 5746 Schutz St., Houston, TX 77032: Catalog $2 ■ In-stock and custom floral decals for ceramics and glass. 713–449–1942.

Holland Mold, Inc., 1040 Pennsylvania Ave., P.O. Box 5021, Trenton, NJ 08638: Catalog $6 ■ Custom and in-stock ceramic molds. 609–392–7032.

House of Ceramics, Inc., 1011 N. Hollywood, Memphis, TN 38108: Free catalog ■ Molds for ceramics and chinaware crafting. 901–324–3851.

Jay-Kay Molds, P.O. Box 2307, Quinlan, TX 75474: Catalog $5 ■ Ceramic molds. 903–356–3416.

Jones Mold Company, 416 Harding Industrial Dr., Nashville, TN 37211: Catalog $4.75 ■ Ceramic molds. 615–333–0683.

K-Ceramic Imports, 732 Ballough Rd., Daytona Beach, FL 32114: Catalog $10 ■ European decals, sponges, and brushes. 904–252–6530.

Kelly's Ceramics, Inc., 3016 Union Ave., Pennsauken, NJ 08109: Free information ■ Ceramic supplies and molds. 609–665–4181.

Kemper Tools, Kemper Manufacturing, Inc., P.O. Box 696, Chino, CA 91710: Free catalog ■ Tools for pottery-crafting. 800–388–5367; 714–627–6191 (in CA).

Kerry Specialties, P.O. Box 5129, Deltona, FL 32728: Free information ■ Brushes and cleaning tools. 407–574–6209.

Kimple Mold Corporation, 415 Industrial, Goddard, KS 67052: Catalog $9 ■ Ceramic molds. 316–794–8621.

L & L Manufacturing Company, 142 Conchester Rd., Chester P.O. Box 938, Twin Oaks, PA 19016: Free information ■ Kilns.

Laguna Clay Company, 14400 Lomitas Ave., City of Industry, CA 91746: Free catalog ■ Clays, glazes, tools, equipment, and other ceramic supplies. 800–4–LAGUNA.

Lamp Specialties, Inc., 688 S. 21st St., Irvington, NJ 07111: Catalog $4 (refundable) ■ Electrical parts and supplies for ceramic crafting. Other supplies include ceramic decals (catalog $3.50). 800–666–LAMP.

Lee's Ceramic Supply, 103 Honeysuckle Dr., West Monroe, LA 71291: Catalog $1.50 (refundable) ■ Ceramic supplies, molds, decals, and kits. 800–424–LEES.

Lehman Manufacturing Company, Inc., P.O. Box 46, Kentland, IN 47951: Free catalog ■ Casting machines, mixing machines, custom equipment, parts, slip and formulation. 219–474–6011.

Lotties Molds, P.O. Box 189, St. Thomas, PA 17252: Free information ■ Ceramic molds. 717–369–4941.

Macky Ceramic Products, Inc., 30893 Ehlen Dr., P.O. Box 1118, Albany, OR 97321: Catalog $6.50 ■ Ceramic molds. 503–967–4055.

Marjon Ceramics, Inc., 3434 W. Earll Dr., Phoenix, AZ 85017: Free information ■ Ceramic supplies, accessories, and tools. 602–272–6585.

Marx Brush Manufacturing Company, Inc., 400 Commercial Ave., Palisades Park, NJ 07650: Catalog $2 ■ Ceramic adhesive for mending greenware, bisque, or for fastening greenware to bisque, adding pieces, mending hairline cracks, and repairing broken stilts and hard spots. 800–654–6279.

Maryland China Company, 54 Main St., Reisterstown, MD 21136: Free catalog ■ Ready-to-paint chinaware and other tableware. 800–638–3880.

Mayco Molds, 4077 Weaver Ct. South, Hilliard, OH 43026: Free information with long SASE ■ Ceramic molds.

Miami Clay Company, 270 NE 183rd St., Miami, FL 33179: Catalog $2 ■ Pottery supplies. 305–651–4695.

Mike's Ceramic Molds, Inc., 5217 8th Ave. South, St. Petersburg, FL 33707: Catalog $4 ■ Ceramic molds. 813–321–3725.

Mile Hi Ceramics, Inc., 77 Lipan, Denver, CO 80223: Free catalog ■ Clays and other ceramic supplies. 303–825–4570.

Minnesota Ceramic Supply, 962 Arcade St., St. Paul, MN 55106: Free information ■ Ceramic molds and supplies. 800–652–9724.

National Artcraft Company, 23456 Mercantile Rd., Beachwood, OH 44122: Catalog $4 (refundable) ■ Ceramic supplies and equipment. 216–292–4944.

Nowell's Molds, 1532 Pointer Ridge Rd., Bowie, MD 20716: Free information ■ Ceramic molds. 301–249–0846.

Ohio Ceramic Supply, Inc., 2861 State Rt. 59, P.O. Box 630, Kent, OH 44240: Free information ■ Supplies and equipment for ceramics. 800–899–4627.

Olympic Enterprises, P.O. Box 321, Campbell, OH 44405: Catalog $2.50 ■ Ceramic supplies, decals, chinaware, and brushes. 216–755–2726.

Paragon Industries, 2011 S. Town East Blvd., Mesquite, TX 75149: Free catalog ■ Kilns. 800–876–4328; 214–288–7557 (in TX).

PCM Molds, P.O. Box 2167, Riverview, MI 48192: Catalog $2.50 ■ Ceramic molds. 313–283–0722.

Pekin Ceramic Supply, 515 Charlotte, Pekin, IL 61554: Free price list with long SASE ■ Porcelain slip. 309–346–7916.

Pierce Tools, 1610 Parkdale Dr., Grants Pass, OR 97527: Free catalog ■ Tools for the ceramist, potter, dollmaker, and sculptor. 503–476–1778.

Poly Crafts, 1839 61st St., Sarasota, FL 34243: Free information ■ Ceramic molds and Dona's Hues, Mayco colors, and Duncan products. 813–355–9755.

Provincial Ceramic Products, 4821 E. 345th St., Willoughby, OH 44094: Catalog $7 ■ Ceramic supplies and molds. 216–942–1843.

Pyramid of Urbana, 2107 N. High Cross Rd., Urbana, IL 61801: Free catalog ■ Ceramic supplies and tools. 217–328–3099.

Red Barn Ceramics, Inc., Rt. 13 South, Cortland, NY 13045: Catalog $3 (refundable) ■ Ceramic supplies. 607–756–2039.

Carol Reinert Ceramics, 1100 Grosser Rd., Gilbertsville, PA 19525: Free information ■ Molds and ceramic supplies. 215–367–4373.

Riverview Molds, Inc., 1660 W. Post Rd. SW, Cedar Rapids, IA 52404: Catalog $6 ■ Ceramic molds. 319–396–5555.

R-Molds, 18711 St. Clair Ave., Cleveland, OH 44110: Catalog $6.75 ■ Ceramic molds. 216–531–9185.

Heinz Scharff Brushes, P.O. Box 746, Fayetteville, GA 30214: Free catalog ■ Brushes for ceramic and tole painting, china and decorative painting, and general art work. 404–461–2200.

Scioto Ceramic Products, Inc., 2455 Harrisburg Pike, Grove City, OH 43123: Catalog $5.95 ■ Ceramic molds. 614–871–0090.

Scott Publications, 30595 W. 8 Mile Rd., Livonia, MI 48152: Free catalog ■ Books for the ceramist, china painter, and doll maker. 313–477–6650.

Seeley-Olevia, 9 River St., Oneonta, NY 13820: Free price list and color chart ■ Ceramic colors that can be applied by brushing, spraying, dipping, or splashing. 607–432–1240.

Skutt Ceramic Products, 2618 SE Steele St., Portland, OR 97202: Free information ■ Electric kilns. 503–231–7726.

Southern Oregon Pottery & Supply, 111 Talent Ave., Box 158, Talent, OR 97540: Free brochure ■ Kilns and accessories. Includes 110–and 240–volt, manual, automatic, and electronic models. 503–535–6700.

Spectrum Manufacturing Company, 960 S. Bellevue Blvd., Memphis, TN 38106: Free information ■ Kilns, slip and ceramic molds, and casting equipment. 901–942–5242.

Sponge Imports, 6949 Kennedy Ave., Hammond, IN 46325: Free catalog ■ Brushes, tools, and knives. 219–845–5666.

Stewart's of California, Inc., 16055 Heron Ave., La Mirada, CA 90638: Catalog $2 ■ Ceramic supplies and equipment. 714–523–2603.

Sugar Creek Industries, Inc., P.O. Box 354, Linden, IN 47955: Free brochure ■ Ceramic equipment. 317–339–4641.

Tampa Bay Mold Company, 1320 20th St. North, St. Petersburg, FL 33713: Catalog $2 ■ Ceramic molds. 813–823–3784.

Thompson Enamel, Division of Ceramics Coating Company, P.O. Box 310, Newport, KY 41072: Free information ■ Ceramics supplies. 606–291–3800.

A Touch of Class, 12496 SW 128th St., Bay 109, Miami, FL 33186: Free information ■ Glazes, stains, overglazes, sprays, chalks, china paints, decals, underglazes, and specialty products. Includes the Africana line of over 970 colors. 800–368–9468; 305–378–5695 (in FL).

Transworld Supplies, Inc., 246 S. Cleveland Ave., Loveland, CO 80537: Free brochure ■ Jayne Houston French brushes, mediums, paints, books, and miscellaneous supplies. 303–663–3009.

Trenton Mold Boutique, 329 Whitehead Rd., Trenton, NJ 08619: Catalog $4 ■ Ceramic molds. 609–890–0606.

Truebite, Inc., 2590 Glenwood Rd., Vestal, NY 13850: Free catalog ■ Cutting, drilling, and cleaning tools.

VIP Molds, Inc., 1819 German St., Erie, PA 16503: Catalog $6.75 ■ Ceramic molds. 814–455–3396.

Vitrex Ceramics, Ltd., 5365 Munro Ct., Burlington, Ontario, Canada L7L 5M7: Catalog $5 ■ Ceramic molds. 416–637–8137.

WC Molds, 3160 Campus View Rd., Grants Pass, OR 97527: Catalog $5 ($3.50 refundable on $30 order) ■ Ceramic molds.

Weidlich Ceramics, Inc., 2230 W. Camplain Rd., Somerville, NJ 08876: Free information ■ Greenware, kilns, and fire and non-fire colors. 908–725–8554.

Werner's Mold Company, Rt. 1, Box 52, Brumley, MO 65017: Free information ■ Molds for the porcelain and ceramic artist. 314–369–2480.

Westwood Ceramic Supply Company, 14400 Lomitas Ave., City of Industry, CA 91746: Catalog $3 ■ Ceramic tools and supplies. 818–330–0631.

Wise Screenprint, Inc., 1015 Valley St., Dayton, OH 45404: Free information ■ Custom decals for ceramics and glass made from rough sketches, photographs, or artwork. 513–223–1573.

The Wishing Well, 221 W. 8th, Box 226, Cozad, NE 69130: Free information ■ Water soluble, non-toxic ceramic paints and liquid suede kits. 308–784–3100.

Yozie Molds, Inc., RD 1, Box 415, Dunbar, PA 15431: Catalog $5.50 ■ Ceramic molds. 412–628–3693.

Zembillas Sponge Company, Inc., P.O. Box 24, Campbell, OH 44405: Catalog $3.50 ■ Decals, brushes, and tools. 216–755–1644.

CHAIR CANING

Barap Specialties, 835 Bellows Ave., Frankfort, MI 49635: Catalog $1 ■ Caning supplies and tools, lamp parts, turned wood parts, and other craft supplies. 616–352–9863.

Cane & Basket Supply Company, 1283 S. Cochran, Los Angeles, CA 90019: Catalog $1 ■ Caning and basket-making supplies. Includes flat, oval and round reeds; fiber and genuine rush; Danish seat cord; raffia; and rattan and seagrass. 213–939–9644.

Caning Shop, 926 Gilman St., Berkeley, CA 94710: Catalog $1 (refundable) ■ Caning and basket-making supplies, accessories, and tools. 510–527–5010.

Carol's Canery, Rt. 1, Box 48, Palmyra, VA 22963: Catalog $1 ■ Basket-making and caning supplies. 804–973–5645.

Connecticut Cane & Reed Company, 134 Pine St., Manchester, CT 06040: Catalog 50¢ ■ Caning and basket-making supplies. 203–646–6586.

Country Seat, Rt. 2, Box 24, Kempton, PA 19529: Send long SASE with 75¢ postage for price list ■ Caning and basket-making supplies and how-to books. 215–756–6124.

Frank's Cane & Rush Supply, 7252 Heil Ave., Huntington Beach, CA 92647: Free catalog ■ Cane, rush, other basket-making supplies, and wood parts. 714–847–0707.

Go-Cart Shop, 168 Main St., Fairhaven, MA 02719: Catalog 25¢ ■ Chair cane, ready woven cane, flat and oval reeds, basket-making reeds, imitation rush, caning pegs, and instruction books. 508–992–5811.

Jack's Upholstery & Caning Supplies, 5498 Rt. 34, Oswego, IL 60543: Catalog $2 (refundable) ■ Upholstery, basket-making, and chair caning supplies and equipment. 312–554–1045.

Michigan Cane Supply, 5348 N. Riverview Dr., Kalamazoo, MI 49004: List $1 ■ Chair cane, rush, and basket weaving supplies. 616–282–5461.

Newell Workshop, 19 Blaine Ave., Hinsdale, IL 60521: Free catalog ■ Caning kits and restoration materials. 708–323–7367.

Peerless Rattan & Reed, 222 Lake Ave., Yonkers, NY 10701: Free catalog ■ Caning supplies and equipment. 914–968–4046.

H.H. Perkins Company, 10 S. Bradley Rd., Woodbridge, CT 06525: Catalog $1 ■ Seat weaving and basket-making supplies, macrame supplies, and how-to books. 203–389–9501.

Plymouth Reed & Cane, 1200 W. Ann Arbor Rd., Plymouth, MI 48170: Brochure $1 ■ Basket-making and caning materials. Includes reed, cane, fiber rush, Shaker tape, handles, hoops, kits, dyes, tools, and books. 313–455–2150.

Royalwood, Ltd., 517 Woodville Rd., Mansfield, OH 44907: Catalog $1 ■ Caning and basket-making supplies, tools, kits, and dyes. 419–526–1630.

Tint & Splint, 30100 Ford Rd., Sheridan Square, Garden City, MI 48135: Free catalog with long SASE and two 1st class stamps ■ Reeds, chair cane, chair webbing, basket-making supplies, books, and tools. 318–522–7760.

Veterans Caning Shop, 550 W. 35th St., New York, NY 10001: Free information ■ Caning supplies and accessories. 212–868–3244.

CHEERLEADING

Active Knitting, Ltd., 89 Tycos Dr., Toronto, Ontario, Canada M6B 1W3: Free information ■ Sweaters and uniforms. 416–789–1101.

Air Design Limited, 8809 148th Ave NE, Redmond, WA 98053: Free information ■ Pom poms. 800–247–0800; 206–867–9227 (in WA).

Apsco, Inc., 1st Ave. & 50th St., Building 57, Brooklyn, NY 11232: Free information ■ Caps and hats, pennants and banners, and sweaters. 718–965–9500.

Asics Tiger Corporation, 10540 Talbert Ave., Fountain Valley, CA 92708: Free information ■ Shoes. 714–962–7654.

Boyko USA, Inc., 3304 Barton Creek Blvd., Austin, TX 78735: Free information ■ Caps, hats, and megaphones. 512–327–6156.

Cran Barry, Inc., 2 Lincoln Ave., Marblehead, MA 01945: Free information ■

Caps and hats, megaphones, pom poms, and sweaters. 617–631–8510.

Danskin, 111 W. 40th St., New York, NY 10018: Free information ■ Uniforms. 212–764–4630.

Dodger Manufacturing Company, 1702 21st St., Eldora, IA 50627: Free information ■ Sweaters. 800–247–7879; 800–542–7972 (in IA).

Fisher Athletic Equipment, Inc., Rt. 8, Box 602, Salisbury, NC 28144: Free information ■ Megaphones. 704–636–5713.

Flocking Equipment Manufacturing Company, 337 1st St., P.O. Box 2119, Calexico, CA 92231: Free information ■ Pom poms and sweaters.

Wm. Getz Corporation, 1024 S. Linwood Ave., Santa Ana, CA 92705: Free information ■ Pom poms and megaphones. 800–854–7447; 800–221–7447 (in CA).

Hamilton Electronics Corporation, 2003 W. Fulton St., Chicago, IL 60612: Free information ■ Megaphones. 312–421–5442.

Hatchers Manufacturing, Inc., 31 Green St., Box 1088, Marblehead, MA 01945: Free information ■ Megaphones, pom poms, and sweaters. 617–631–9373.

Just T-Shirts, Fashion Wear, Inc., 3615 Superior Ave., Cleveland, OH 44114: Free information ■ Uniforms. 800–321–3710; 216–881–2922 (in OH).

Keezer Manufacturing Company, Chadwick St., Plainstow, NH 03865: Free information ■ Pennants and banners. 603–382–8500.

Dick Martin Sports, Inc., 201 River Rd., P.O. Box 931, Clifton, NJ 07014: Free information ■ Megaphones. 800–221–1993; 201–473–0757 (in NJ).

J. Miller Industries, 3334 W. Castor St., Santa Ana, CA 92704: Free information ■ Pennants and banners. 714–754–6851.

Mohr's International, 10624 Weaver Ave., South El Monte, CA 91733: Free information ■ Caps, hats, and pom poms. 818–401–0074.

Pedersohn's Unlimited, Inc., 201 Minnie St., Paynesville, MN 56362: Free information ■ Uniforms. 612–243–3404.

Pepco Poms, Hwy. 60, P.O. Box 950, Wharton, TX 77488: Free information ■

Megaphones and pom poms. 800–527–1150; 800–992–1048 (in TX).

Perma Power Electronics, Inc., 5601 W. Howard Ave., Chicago, IL 60648: Free information ■ Megaphones. 312–647–9414.

Plastimayd Corporation, 14450 SE 98th Ct., P.O. Box 1550, Clackamas, OR 97015: Free information ■ Uniforms. 503–654–8502.

Recreonics Corporation, 7696 Zionsville Rd., Indianapolis, IN 46268: Free information ■ Megaphones. 800–428–3254; 800–792–3489 (in IN).

Valley Decorating Company, Cheerleader Division, P.O. Box 9470, Fresno, CA 93792: Free information ■ Pom poms, batons, and megaphones. 209–275–2500.

Wear-Ever Lace & Braid, 90 Cherry St., Hudson, MA 01749: Free information ■ Pom poms. 508–562–4155.

CHEESE MAKING

New England Cheesemaking Supply Company, P.O. Box 85, Ashfield, MA 01330: Catalog $1 (refundable) ■ Supplies and equipment for making cheese, butter, yogurt, and buttermilk. 413–628–3808.

CHESS

Institutional Computer Development Corp., 21 Walt Whitman Rd., Huntington Station, NY 11746: Free information ■ Computer chess sets. 512–424–3300.

U.S. Chess Federation, 186 Rt. 9W, Newburgh, NY 12550: Free catalog ■ Conventional chess sets, computer chess sets, books, accessories, and competition supplies. 914–562–8350.

CHINA PAINTING & METAL ENAMELING

Allcraft Tool & Supply Company, 666 Pacific St., Brooklyn, NY 11207: Catalog $2.50 ■ Metal enameling tools and supplies. 800–645–7124.

American Metalcraft, Inc., 4545 Homer Street, Chicago, IL 60639: Free information ■ Copper projects for enameling and aluminum bowls and trays for mosaic tile application. 312–342–9133.

Barb's Porcelain Studio, 5418 Woodmont Dr., Portage, MI 49001: Catalog $3 ■ Porcelain bisque for china painting. 616–342–1494.

Cerami Corner, 342 Bolt View Rd., Grants Pass, OR 97527: Price list $1 ■ China paints, brushes, and ceramic decals. 800–423–8543.

Charlie's Rock Shop, 620 J St., Penrose, CO 81240: Catalog $3 (refundable) ■ Metal enameling tools and supplies. 800–336–6923.

Chaselle, Inc., 9645 Gerwig Ln., Columbia, MD 21046: Catalog $4 ■ Art software and books, brushes and paints, tempera colors, acrylics and sets, pastels, ceramic molds and kilns, sculpture equipment, and screen painting supplies. 800–242–7355.

The China Decorator Library, P.O. Box 575, Shingle Springs, CA 95682: Free catalog ■ Books for china painters. 916–677–1455.

Cridge, Inc., Box 210, Morrisville, PA 19067: Free catalog ■ Supplies and equipment for china painting on porcelain. Includes gold and silver settings, bisque and glazed porcelain insets, and exclusive porcelain gifts. 215–295–3667.

DEEliteful Designs, Inc., 5042 Linda St., Venice, FL 34293: Free information ■ Plates, platters, and tiles. 813–493–1340.

Dee's Creations, Rt. 2, Box 1114, Kendrick, ID 83537: Free information with long SASE ■ Porcelain ornaments.

Enamelwork Supply Company, 1022 NE 68th, Seattle, WA 98115: Catalog $2 ■ Metal enameling tools and supplies.

Evenheat Kiln, Inc., 6949 Legion Rd., Caseville, MI 48725: Free information ■ Kilns and accessories. 517–856–2281.

Firemountain Gems, 28195 Redwood Highway, Cave Junction, OR 97523: Catalog $3 ■ Metal enameling tools and supplies. 800–423–2319; 503–592–2222 (in OR).

T.B. Hagstoz & Son, Inc., 709 Sansom St., Philadelphia, PA 19106: Catalog $5 (refundable with $25 order) ■ Metal enameling tools and supplies. 800–922–1006; 215–922–1627 (in PA).

House of Clay, Inc., 1100 NW 30th, Oklahoma City, OK 73118: Catalog $3 (refundable) ■ China, kilns, and other supplies. 405–524–5610.

Jayne Houston Products, 246 S. Cleveland, Loveland, CO 80537: Free brochure ■ French brushes, paints, mediums, and books. 303–663–3009.

Kit 'N Kaboodle, 3189 Westcliff Rd., Fort Worth, TX 76109: Free catalog ■ Paints, brushes, motorized banding wheels, other supplies, and books. 817–924–5374.

Maryland China Company, 54 Main St., Reisterstown, MD 21136: Free catalog ■ Supplies for china painters and decorators. 800–638–3880.

Meyer's Porcelain Art Studio, 9330 S. 191st East Ave., Broken Arrow, OK 74012: Free brochure ■ China paints and supplies. 918–455–6023.

National Artcraft Company, 23456 Mercantile Rd., Beachwood, OH 44122: Free catalog ■ Tiles, china, paints and other coloring preparations, mediums, and brushes for china painting. 216–292–4944.

Paragon Industries, 2011 S. Town East Blvd., Mesquite, TX 75149: Free catalog ■ Kilns. 800–876–4328; 214–288–7557 (in TX).

Rynne China Company, 222 W. 8 Mile Rd., Hazel Park, MI 48030: Free information ■ China painting supplies and equipment. Includes decals, books, china and glass paints, overglaze, kilns, and brushes. 800–468–1987.

Southern Oregon Pottery & Supply, 111 Talent Ave., Box 158, Talent, OR 97540: Free brochure ■ Skutt, Cress, AIM, and Paragon kilns and accessories, 110– and 240–volt, manual, automatic, and electronic models. 503–535–6700.

Thompson Enamel, Division of Ceramics Coating Company, P.O. Box 310, Newport, KY 41072: Free information ■ Metal enameling supplies. 606–291–3800.

Transworld Supplies, Inc., 246 S. Cleveland Ave., Loveland, CO 80537: Free brochure ■ French brushes, paints, books, china, and other supplies. 303–663–3009.

CHINA, POTTERY & STONEWARE

William Ashley, 50 Boor St. West, Toronto, Ontario, Canada M4W 3L8: Free information ■ Save up to 50 percent on china, crystal, and silver. 800–268–1122.

Barrons, P.O. Box 994, Novi, MI 48376: Free information ■ Save up to 65 percent on china, crystal, and silver. 800–538–6340.

Bastine Pottery, RR 3, Box 111, Noblesville, IN 46060: Price list $1.50 ■ Hand-turned stoneware and pottery in traditional designs and tole patterns in cobalt blue and iron red colors. 317–776–0210.

Mildred Brumback, P.O. Box 132, Middletown, VA 22645: Free information ■ Discontinued china and crystal. 703–869–1261.

China & Crystal Marketing, Box 25602, Philadelphia, PA 19111: Free information ■ China, earthenware, and crystal. Includes discontinued patterns. 215–342–7919.

The China Cabinet, P.O. Box 266, Clearwater, SC 29822: Free information with long SASE ■ China and crystal. 803–593–9655.

The China Connection, Box 972, Pineville, NC 28134: Free information ■ Inactive fine and everyday china. 800–421–9719.

The China Hutch, 6453 Shoreline Dr., Charlotte, NC 28214: Free information ■ Discontinued china. 800–524–4397.

China Replacements, 2263 Williams Creek Rd., High Ridge, MO 63049: Free information with long SASE ■ Discontinued china and crystal. 800–562–2655; 677–5577 (in St. Louis).

Clintsman International, 327 W. Main, Waukesha, WI 53186: Free information with long SASE ■ Discontinued china and crystal. 414–547–7327.

Crafted Keepsakes, 9221 Wildwood Dr., Highland, IN 46322: Brochure $1 ■ Soup tureens, casseroles, crock and cider jugs, and other country-style ceramics. 219–923–8422.

Crystal Match, 72 Longacre Rd., Rochester, NY 14621: Free information ■ Replacement crystal and china. 716–338–3781.

Dining Elegance, Ltd., Box 4203, St. Louis, MO 63163: Pattern list 75¢ ■ Fine china and crystal. 314–865–1408.

East Knoll Pottery, 46 Albrecht Rd., Torrington, CT 06790: Brochure $1 ■ Hand-thrown and decorated reproduction yellowware.

Eastside Gifts & Dinnerware, Inc., 351 Grand St., New York, NY 10002: Free information ■ China, crystal, flatware, and other gifts. 212–982–7200.

Eldreth Pottery, 902 Hart Rd., Oxnard, PA 19363: Catalog $1 ■ Hand-turned and salt-glazed stoneware and molded sculptures. 717–529–6241.

Michael C. Fina, 580 5th Ave., New York, NY 10036: Free catalog ■ Sterling serving pieces, tea sets, crystal stem ware, bone china, and pewter. 212–869–5050.

Fortunoff Fine Jewelry, P.O. Box 1550, Westbury, NY 11590: Catalog $2 ■ China, sterling flatware, silverplate and stainless steel serving pieces, and accessories. 800–937–4376.

Gailin Collection, P.O. Box 53921, Fayettesville, NC 28305: Catalog $3 ■ Save from 35 to 55 percent on European china and crystal. 919–864–7372.

Greater New York Trading, 81 Canal St., New York, NY 10002: Free information with long SASE ■ Silver, china, and glassware. 800–336–4012.

Jacquelyn Hall, 10629 Baxter, Los Altos, CA 94022: Free information ■ Lenox china and crystal. 408–739–4876.

Kelley Haney Art Gallery, P.O. Box 103, Seminole, OK 74868: Free brochure with long SASE ■ Original Indian paintings, sculpture, jewelry, baskets, and pottery. 405–382–3915.

Hockridge Dinnerware & Giftwares, 638 Yonge St., Toronto, Ontario, Canada M4Y 1Z8: Free information ■ China and other gifts. 416–922–1668.

House of 1776, P.O. Box 472927, Garland, TX 75047: Free information ■ China place settings and open stock, tableware, and gifts. 800–989–1776.

Hutschenreuther Corporation, 41 Madison Ave., New York, NY 10010: Free information ■ Crystal and 19th-century style porcelain serving pieces and dinnerware. 212–685–1198.

Jacquelynn's China, 219 N. Milwaukee St., Milwaukee, WI 53202: Free information with long SASE ■ China matching service for discontinued patterns. 414–272–8880.

Jepson Studios, Inc., P.O. Box 36, Harveyville, KS 66431: Brochure $2 (refundable) ■ Country ceramics. 913–589–2481.

James Kaplan Jewelers, 40 Freeway Dr., Cranston, RI 02920: Free catalog ■ Sterling and china. 800–343–0712.

Karlin Pottery, 1443 Ryan St., Flint, MI 48532: Brochure $1 ■ Country pottery and stoneware. 800–933–7096.

Kingston Pottery, 1505 Geyers Church Rd., Middletown, PA 17057: Catalog $3 ■ Hand-thrown and painted 17th- and 18th-century English-style delftware. 717–944–5445.

Lanac Sales, 73 Canal St., New York, NY 10002: Free information ■ China, crystal, sterling, and gifts. 212–925–6422.

Lenox Collections Gifts, P.O. Box 3020, Langhorne, PA 19047: Free catalog ■ China, crystal, and porcelain sculptures. 800–233–1885.

Locators, Inc., 908 Rock St., Little Rock, AR 72202: Free information ■ Discontinued china, crystal, and silver. 800–367–9690.

Meengs, P.O. Box 6066, Thousand Oaks, CA 91359: Free information ■ Buys and sells discontinued china. 805–495–4378.

Midas China & Silver, 4315 Walney Rd., Chantilly, VA 22021: Free catalog ■ Save up to 60 percent on silverware, table settings, gifts, and china. 800–368–3153.

Teresita Naranjo, Santa Clara Pueblo, Rt. 1, Box 455, Espanola, NM 87532: Free information with long SASE ■ Traditional Santa Clara black and red pottery. Includes ceremonial and melon bowls, wedding vases, and other gifts. 505–753–9655.

Noritake Service Center, P.O. Box 3240, Chicago, IL 60654: Free information ■ Noritake china replacements. 800–562–1991.

Past & Presents, 65–07 Fitchett St., Rego Park, NY 11374: Free information ■ Replacement china, crystal, and flatware. 718–897–5515.

Pfaltzgraff Consumer Services, P.O. Box 2048, York, PA 17405: Catalog $1 ■ Stoneware irregulars. Includes dinnerware, baking and serving accessories, and decorative pieces. 717–757–2200.

Replacements, Ltd., 1089 Knox Rd., P.O. Box 26029, Greensboro, NC 27420: Free information ■ Discontinued china, earthenware, and crystal. 919–697–3000.

Robin Importers, 510 Madison Ave., New York, NY 10022: Brochure $1 with long SASE ■ China, crystal, and stainless steel flatware. 800–223–3373; 212–753–6475 (in NY).

Rogers & Rosenthal, 22 W. 48th St., Room 1102, New York, NY 10036: Free information with long SASE ■ China, crystal, and stainless steel. 212–827–0115.

Ross-Simons Jewelers, 9 Ross Simons Dr., Cranston, RI 02920: Free information ■ Sterling and china. 800–556–7376.

Rowantrees Pottery, 9 Union St., Blue Hill, ME 04614: Free catalog ■ Stoneware and pottery. 207–374–5535.

Rowe Pottery Works, 404 England St., Cambridge, WI 53523: Catalog $2 ■ Salt-glazed stoneware in early authentic folk designs. 800–356–5003.

Rudi's Pottery, Silver & China, State Hwy 17, Paramus, NJ 07652: Free information with long SASE ■ Glass stemware, china, and gifts. 201–265–6096.

Nat Schwartz & Company, 549 Broadway, Bayonne, NJ 07002: Free catalog ■ Crystal, sterling, and china. 800–526–1440.

Smith & Smith Potters, 12 School St., Bath, ME 04530: Free catalog ■ Hand-cast stoneware. 207–443–8153.

Sophia's China, 141 Segewick Rd., Syracuse, NY 13203: Free information ■ Discontinued china and crystal. 315–472–6834.

Table Treasures, 319 E. Weber Ave., Stockton, CA 95202: Free information with long SASE ■ Discontinued china, earthenware, crystal, and silver. 209–463–3607.

Thurber's, 14 Minnesota Ave., Warwick, RI 02888: Free information ■ China and sterling. 800–848–7237.

Unity Stoneware, Box 685, Newport, VT 05855: Free brochure ■ Stoneware serving dishes and accessories. 802–334–6516.

Van Ness China Company, 1124 Fairway Dr., Waynesboro, VA 22980: Free information ■ Discontinued bone china. 703–942–2827.

Carol Vigil, P.O. Box 443, Jemez Pueblo, NM 87024: Free information with long SASE ■ Carved and painted Jemez pottery.

Walker's Haviland China Matchers, Box 357, Athens, OH 45701: Free information ■ Buys and sells French and American pieces and sets of Haviland china. 614–593–5631.

Wesson Trading Company, 1316 Willow Street Dr., Woodstock, GA 30188: Catalog

$2 ■ Handcrafted pottery, textiles, and folk art. 404–928–6145.

Marilyn White, Box 4246, Shreveport, LA 71134: Free information with long SASE ■ Discontinued china and crystal. 318–861–1543.

Wisconsin Pottery, W3199 Hwy. 16, Columbus, WI 53925: Free catalog ■ Handcrafted and hand-decorated salt-glazed stoneware and redware pottery. 800–669–5196.

Workshops of David T. Smith, 3600 Shawhan Rd., Morrow, OH 45152: Catalog $5 ■ Reproduction furniture, pottery, lamps, and chandeliers. 513–932–2472.

Yankee Redware Pottery, Steve Nutt, 25 Ellicott Pl., Staten Island, NY 10301: Free information ■ Handcrafted dishwasher- and oven-safe redware pottery. 718–273–6815.

CHOIR GOWNS

Lyric Choir Gown Company, P.O. Box 16954, Jacksonville, FL 32245: Free catalog and fabric samples ■ Professionally tailored choir gowns. 904–725–7977.

CHRISTMAS DECORA-TIONS & ORNAMENTS

Borse, Inc., Hurst, TX 76053: Catalog $2 ■ Ornaments and gifts from Kathe Wohlfahrt's Old-World Gifts, in Rothenburg, Germany, one of Europe's largest year-round Christmas stores. 800–227–3515.

Candles by Anita, Main St., Helen, GA 30545: Free catalog ■ Handmade candles for Christmas and other occasions and festivities. 404–878–3214.

Christmas Branch, 511 Highland Ave., Oak Park, IL 60304: Free catalog ■ Wooden Christmas ornaments. 708–383–7462.

The Cracker Box, Solebury, PA 18963: Catalog $4.50 ■ Christmas ornament kits. 215–862–2100.

The Faith Mountain Company, P.O. Box 199, Sperryville, VA 22740: Catalog 50¢ ■ Kitchen utensils and accessories, country style gifts, folk art reproductions, toys and dolls, handmade Appalachian baskets, and Christmas decorations. 800–822–7238.

Seams Sew Easy, P.O. Box 2189, Manassas, VA 22110: Free information ■ Patterns

and instructions for sewing Christmas ornaments and decorations. 703–330–1727.

Wooden Soldier, Kearsage St., North Conway, NH 03860: Free catalog ■ Christmas decorations and ornaments and designer clothes for children. 603–356–6343.

CLOCKS & CLOCK MAKING

Alpha Supply, 1225 Hollis St., Box 2133, Bremerton, WA 98310: Catalog $1 (refundable with $15 order) ■ Clocks, clock movements and parts, engraving tools, and supplies. 206–377–5629.

Armor Products, P.O. Box 445, East Northport, NY 11731: Catalog $1 ■ Replacement clock movements for mantel, banjo, and grandfather clocks. 800–292–8296.

B & J Rock Shop, 14744 Manchester Rd., Ballwin, MO 63011: Catalog $3 (refundable with $15 order) ■ Quartz clock movements and kits. 314–394–4567.

Beemans Clock Manufacturing, 109 W. Van Buren, Centerville, IA 52544: Catalog $2 ■ Quartz clock movements, faces, hands, and numbers, and other parts.

Bradco Enterprises, 2424 22nd St. North, St. Petersburg, FL 33713: Free catalog ■ Mini quartz clock movements. 813–894–7176.

Cas-Ker Company, Box 2347, Cincinnati, OH 45201: Catalog $1 ■ Clock movements, dials, accessories, hands, and tools. 513–241–7073.

Charlie's Rock Shop, 620 J St., Penrose, CO 81240: Catalog $3 ■ Clocks, clock movements and parts, beads, jewelry-making supplies, jewelry display boxes, and faceted gemstones. 800–336–6923.

Chelsea Clock Company, 284 Everett Ave., Chelsea, MA 02150: Brochure $2 ■ Clocks and accessories. 617–884–0250.

Clock Repair Center, 33 Boyd Dr., Westbury, NY 11590: Catalog $4.50 ■ Clock movements, parts, accessories, and tools. 516–997–4810.

Clocks, Etc., 3401 Mt. Diablo Blvd., Lafayette, CA 94549: Brochure $1 ■ Old and new clocks, antique furniture, and other gifts. 510–284–4720.

Craft Products Company, P.O. Box 326, Clintonville, WI 54929: Catalog $2.50 ■

Parts and accessories for building clocks. 715–823–5101.

Ebersole Lapidary Supply, Inc., 11417 West Hwy. 54, Wichita, KS 67209: Catalog $2 ■ Clocks, clock-making supplies and parts, tools, findings, mountings, cabochons and rocks, and jewelry kits. 316–722–4771.

Ed's House of Gems, 7712 NE Sandy Blvd., Portland, OR 97211: Free information with long SASE ■ Clocks, clock-making parts and supplies, crystals, minerals, gemstones, and lapidary equipment and tools. 503–284–8990.

Eloxite Corporation, 806 10th St., Wheatland, WY 82201: Catalog 75¢ ■ Clock-making supplies, tools and equipment, cut gemstones, belt buckles, and mountings and equipment for rock hounds and jewelry do-it-yourself crafters. 307–322–3050.

Emperor Clock Company, Emperor Industrial Park, P.O. Box 1089, Fairhope, AL 36533: Catalog $1 ■ Grandfather clock kits, assembled clocks, and parts. 800–642–0011; 205–928–2316 (in AL).

Haskell's Handcraft, 40 College Ave., Waterville, ME 04901: Catalog $3 (refundable) ■ Quartz clock movements, dials, pendulums, digitals, electric supplies, kits, and assembled clocks. 205–928–2316.

It's About Time, 7151 Ortonville Rd., Clarkston, MI 48016: Catalog $5 ■ Save up to 50 percent on grandfather clocks. 800–423–4225.

Heinz Jauch, Inc., P.O. Box 405, Fairhope, AL 36532: List $1 ■ Grandfather clock kits. 205–928–0467.

King Clock Company, 509 E. Section Ave., Foley, AL 36535: Catalog $1 ■ Grandfather, mantel, wall, and cuckoo clocks.

Klockit, P.O. Box 636, Lake Geneva, WI 53147: Free catalog ■ Grandfather clock kits, other clock kits, quartz and mechanical movements and components, music box movements and kits, wood-finishing supplies, and woodworking tools. 800–556–2548.

Kraftkit, P.O. Box 636, Lake Geneva, WI 53147: Free catalog ■ Clocks and other craft and needlework supplies. 414–248–1150.

Kuempel Chime, 21195 Minnetonka Blvd., Excelsior, MN 55331: Catalog $3 ■ Kits and plans for grandfather clocks with bells or chimes, hand-painted moon wheels, West German movements, and handcrafted pendulums. 800–328–6445.

Mason & Sullivan, 586 Higgins Crowell Rd., West Yarmouth, Cape Cod, MA 02673: Catalog $1 ■ Clock kits, dials, movements, tools, hardware, books, and accessories. 800–933–3010.

Merritt's Antiques, Inc., RD 2, P.O. Box 277, Douglassville, PA 19518: Clock supplies catalog $2; clock catalog $1 ■ Clock repair supplies and accessories, antique reproduction grandfather clocks, and wall and shelf clocks. 215–689–9541.

Howard Miller Clock Company, 860 E. Main St., Zeeland, MI 49464: Catalog $2 ■ Parts and accessories for building and repairing clocks. 616–772–9131.

Modern Technical Tool & Supply Company, 211 Nevada St., Hicksville, NY 11801: Catalog $3.50 ■ Clock-making parts and accessories. 516–931–7875.

Newport Enterprises, Inc., 2313 W. Burbank Blvd., Burbank, CA 91506: Catalog $1 ■ Clock components and accessories. 213–845–0555.

Olmsted Wood Products, 8153 Orchard St., Olmsted Falls, OH 44138: Catalog $1 ■ Clock movements, epoxy resin, hands, numerals, dials, and music boxes. 216–235–4020.

Precision Movements, P.O. Box 689, Emmaus, PA 18049: Free catalog ■ Clock kits, quartz movements and accessories, hands, dials, and bezels. 800–533–2024; 215–967–3156 (in PA).

Primex, P.O. Box 194, Lake Geneva, WI 53147: Free catalog ■ Clock movements and components. 800–5440–0909.

Red & Green Minerals, Inc., 7595 W. Florida Ave., Lakewood, CO 80226: Free information ■ Clocks, movements, parts, jewelry-making supplies, mineral specimens, and petrified wood products. 303–985–5559.

Richardson's Recreational Ranch, Ltd., Gateway Route, Box 440, Madras, OR 97741: Free information ■ Clocks, movements, and parts, and rock specimens from worldwide sources. 503–475–2680.

Simply Country Furniture, HC 69, Box 147, Rover, AR 72860: Brochure $2 ■ Grandfather clocks. 501–272–4794.

Steebar, P.O. Box 463, Andover, NJ 07821: Catalog $3 ■ Clock kits, quartz movements, music box movements, components, plans, and epoxies.

Time Gallery, 3121 Battleground Ave., Greensboro, NC 28603: Free information ■ Grandfather clocks at discount prices. 800–683–TIME.

Turncraft Clock Imports Company, P.O. Box 27288, Golden Valley, MN 55427: Catalog $3.50 ■ Clock kits and parts. 612–544–1711.

Westwood Clocks 'N Kits, 3210 Airport Way, Long Beach, CA 90806: Catalog $2 ■ Clock kits and movements, and hardware and accessories for grandfather, wall, and mantel clocks. 310–595–4981.

CLOSETS & STORAGE SYSTEMS

California Closet Company, 6409 Independence Ave., Woodland Hills, CA 91367: Free information ■ Custom shelves, drawers, and cubbyholes for remodeling closets. 818–888–5888.

Clairson International, 720 SW 17th St., Ocala, FL 32674: Free information ■ Modular shelving for organizing family rooms, offices, closets, and other storage areas. 800–221–0641.

Closetmaid, 720 SW 17th St., Ocala, FL 32674: Free information ■ Wire basket caddies. 800–227–8319.

Crawford Products, Inc., 301 Winter St., West Hanover, MA 02339: Free information ■ Storage systems. 800–225–5832; 617–826–8141 (in MA).

Elfa Closet Storage Accessories, Princeton Professional Park, 601 Ewing St., Princeton, NJ 08540: Free information ■ Epoxy-covered steel shelves, bins, and rods for storage rooms and closets. 609–683–0660.

Feeny Manufacturing, 6625 N. Old State Rd. 3, Box 191, Muncie, IN 47308: Free information ■ Under-the-counter and in-the-cabinet storage racks, with right- or left-installation design options. 317–288–8730.

Giles & Kendall, Inc., P.O. Box 188, Huntsville, AL 35804: Free information ■ Easy-to-install cedar paneling for closets. 205–776–2978.

Heller Designs, Inc., 41 Madison Ave., New York, NY 10010: Free information ■ Wall hooks, baskets, and shelves for storage design. 212–685–4200.

Hirsh Company, 8051 Central Park Ave., Skokie, IL 60076: Free information ■ Easy-to-install closet organizers and shelf units. 708–673–6610.

Kemp & George, 2515 E. 43rd St., P.O. Box 182230, Chattanooga, TN 37422: Free catalog ■ Bath accessories, decor hardware, closet organizers, and lighting fixtures. 800–562–1704.

Laminations, Inc., 3311 Laminations Dr., Holland, MI 49424: Free information ■ Easy-to-install storage units, shelves, and rods. 616–399–3311.

Plan-A-Flex, A Stanley Tools Company, 600 Myrtle St., New Britain, CT 06050: Free information ■ Closet, kitchen, bath, and landscape designer kits. 800–648–7654.

Rubbermaid, 1147 Akron Rd., Wooster, OH 44691: Free information ■ Storage accessories that include easy-to-install plastic bins, wall-mounted holders, and storage containers.

Rutt Custom Kitchens, 1564 Main St., P.O. Box 129, Goodville, PA 17528: Free information ■ Custom cabinets for storage room and closet design. 215–445–6751.

Schulte Corporation, 11450 Grooms Rd., Cincinnati, OH 45242: Free information ■ Closet and room storage organizers and accessories. 800–669–3225.

White Home Products, 2401 Lake Park Dr., Atlanta, GA 30080: Free information ■ Automatic revolving carousels for closets. 404–431–0900.

CLOTHING

Bridal Fashions

After Six Bridal Collection, 1385 Broadway, New York, NY 10018: Brochure $2 ■ Bridal clothing for women and formal clothing for men. 212–921–0368.

Angelair Bridals, 1001 W. Van Buren St., Chicago, IL 60607: Free information ■ Designer wedding gowns, headpieces, and veils. 312–243–5900.

Badhir Trading, Inc., 8429 Sisson Hwy., Eden, NY 14057: Catalog $2.50 (refundable) ■ Beaded, sequined, and jeweled appliques and trims for dresses, costumes, and bridal clothing. 800–654–9418.

Christos, Inc., 575 8th Ave., New York, NY 10018: Free information ■ Designer bridal clothing and accessories. 212–714–2496.

I Do I Do Bridal Salon, 1963 86th St., Brooklyn, NY 11214: Free information ■ Save from 30 to 50 percent on clothing for the bride, bride's mother, and attendants. 718–946–0011.

Impression Bridal, 10850 Wilcrest, Houston, TX 77099: Free information ■ Designer wedding gowns, headpieces, and veils. 800–274–3251; 713–530–6695 (in TX).

La Sposa Veils, Division of Sposabella, 252 W. 40th St., New York, NY 10018: Catalog $3 (refundable) ■ Bridal headpieces. 212–354–4729.

J.C. Penney Company, Inc., Catalog Division, Milwaukee, WI 53263: Free catalog ■ Petite, misses, and selected clothing in regular and tall sizes for brides and attendants. 800–222–6161.

Romantic Bridals, 1920 Buffalo Ave., P.O. Box 1742, Niagara Falls, NY 14302: Free information ■ Bridal gowns and accessories. 716–835–7163.

San-Martin Bridals, 3353 Verdugo Rd., Los Angeles, CA 90065: Free information ■ Designer bridal clothing. 213–257–5333.

Children's Clothing

Aberdeen & Dunbar, 25 Independence Ct., Box 4, Folcroft, PA 19032: Free catalog ■ Children's casual clothing. 215–237–7363

After the Stork, 1501 12th St. NW, Albuquerque, NM 87104: Free catalog ■ Natural fiber clothing for infants and children up to age 7. 800–333–5437.

The Alice Dress Company, P.O. Box 1664, Orleans, MA 02653: Catalog $2 ■ Children's clothing. 617–240–0401.

Alice in Wholesale Land, 140 Linden St., Oakland, CA 94607: Catalog $2 ■ Children's clothing, for newborns up to size 14. 510–452–0507.

American Widgeon, 376 Brannan St., San Francisco, CA 94107: Free information ■ Outerwear for newborns through size 14. 415–974–6803.

Hanna Anderson, 1010 NW Flanders, Portland, OR 97209: Free catalog ■ Children's clothing made in Sweden. 800–222–0544.

Annabetta, P.O. Box 1590, Cathedral Station, New York, NY 10025: Free brochure ■ Cardigan and pull-over sweaters with matching hats and mittens. 212–666–7871.

Biobottoms, P.O. Box 6009, Petaluma, CA 94953: Free catalog ■ Cotton outerwear and dress-up clothing for infants, toddlers, and older children. 800–766–1254; 707–778–7152 (in CA).

Blue Balloon, 8228 Starland Dr., El Cajon, CA 92021: Catalog $1 ■ Clothing for infants and children, up to size 7. 619–561–0868.

Brights Creek, Bay Point Pl., Hampton, VA 23653: Free catalog ■ Clothing and accessories for infants and children up to 12 years old. 804–827–1850.

Cherry Tree Clothing, 166 Valley St., Providence, RI 02909: Free information ■ Children's outerwear. 800–869–7742.

Childcraft, P.O. Box 29137, Overland Park, KS 66201: Free catalog ■ Children's play clothes for infants; toddlers; boys, in sizes 4 to 16; and girls, sizes 4 to 6X and 7 to 14. 800–222–7725.

Children's Collection, 1717 Post Oak Blvd., Houston, TX 77056: Free catalog ■ Clothing for infants and young boys and girls. 713–622–4415.

Children's Shop, P.O. Box 625, Chatham, MA 02633: Free catalog ■ Clothing for infants and toddlers. 800–433–1895.

Children's Wear, 2515 E. 43rd St., P.O. Box 22728, Chattanooga, TN 37422: Free catalog ■ Clothing for school, playtime, dressing up, and keeping warm. 800–433–1895.

F.R.A.N.N.E.S. Kids, 8306 Wilshire Blvd., Ste. 7065, Beverly Hills, CA 90211: Free catalog ■ Mix-and-match clothes. 800–526–5437.

Garnet Hill, 262 Main St., Franconia, NH 03580: Free catalog ■ Natural fiber underwear, sleepwear, and outerwear for children; adult sleepwear; and maternity clothing. 800–622–6216.

Gerber Childrenswear, Inc., Customer Relations Department, 531 S. Main St., Greenville, SC 29602: Free information ■

Baby's sleepwear in small, medium, and large. 803–240–2840.

Happy Endings, 12391 SE Indian River Dr., Hobe Sound, FL 33455: Free catalog ■ Children's clothing. 407–283–1042.

Helly-Hansen, Box 97031, Redmond, WA 98073: Free information ■ Waterproof outerwear for children and adults. 206–883–8823.

Just for Kids, P.O. Box 29141, Shawnee, KS 66201: Free catalog ■ Clothing, toys, and gifts for infants and children. 800–443–5827.

Karin & John, 525 S. Raymond Ave., Pasadena, CA 91105: Free catalog ■ Boys' and girls' clothing in 100 percent cotton, for newborns through size 6. 800–626–9600.

Kids at Large, Bldg. 32, Endicott St., Norwood, MA 02062: Free catalog ■ Children's clothing in large sizes. 800–KID–SFIT; 617–769–8575 (in MA).

Land's End, Inc., 1 Land's End Ln., Dodgeville, WI 53595: Free catalog ■ School and playtime clothing for children. 800–356–4444.

La Petite Etoile, 725 5th Ave., Trump Tower, 4th Level, New York, NY 10022: Free information ■ Trend-setting clothes for boys and girls, from infant to pre-teen sizes. 212–371–0388.

Les Petits, Response Service Center, Independence Court, Folcroft, PA 19032: Free catalog ■ Clothing for children, from birth to age 14. Includes dressing-up clothing, playtime clothes, shoes and slippers, sweaters, sleepwear, school clothes, and outerwear. 215–492–6328.

Livonia Baby Shoes, 10 Main St., P.O. Box 495, Chester, NY 10918: Free catalog ■ Baby shoes, cotton terry bibs and bathrobes, suede slippers, and rattles. 914–469–2449.

Maggie Moore, Inc., 170 Ludlow St., Yonkers, NY 10705: Catalog $2 ■ Children's clothing, for infants to size 14. 914–968–0799.

Patagonia Mail Order, P.O. Box 8900, Bozeman, MT 59715: Free catalog ■ Rugged, everyday clothing for children. 800–336–9090.

J.C. Penney Company, Inc., Catalog Division, Milwaukee, WI 53263: Free catalog ■ Children's clothing in large sizes, from girl's 8-1/2 to 18-1/2, and boy's 8 through 20. 800–222–6161.

Pleasant Company, Box 998, Middleton, WI 53562: Free catalog ■ Classic clothing for little girls. 800–845–0005.

Premiewear, 6475 Ridge Pl., Rt. 3, Twin Falls, ID 83301: Free catalog ■ Clothing for premature and low birthweight babies. 800–992–8469.

Red Flannel Factory, 157 W. Beach St., P.O. Box 370, Cedar Springs, MI 49319: Free catalog ■ Clothing for children and adults. 800–533–9276; 616–696–9240 (in MI).

Rubens & Marble, Inc., P.O. Box 14900, Chicago, IL 60614: Free brochure with long SASE ■ Clothing and bedding for infants. 312–348–6200.

The Schwab Company, 112 W. 34th St., New York, NY 10120: Free information ■ Small, medium, and large 100 percent cotton sleepwear for babies.

Sears, Roebuck & Company, Catalog Division, 925 S. Homan Ave., Chicago, IL 60607: Free catalog ■ Clothing for infants and children, nursery room furniture, toys and games, tricycles, nursery room accessories, cribs, swings, playpens, and strollers. (Catalog also available from local stores.) 312–875–2500.

Soft as a Cloud Children's Clothing, 1355 Meadowbrook Ave., Los Angeles, CA 90019: Catalog $1 (refundable) ■ Cotton clothing and other natural fiber items for babies up to toddlers. 213–933–4417.

Spiegel, P.O. Box 6340, Chicago, IL 60680: Catalog $2 ■ School clothes, shoes, and toys. 800–345–4500.

Storybook Heirlooms, 1215 O'Brien Drive, Menlo Park, CA 94025: Free catalog ■ Clothing and gifts for children. 800–899–7666.

SUZO Clothing, P.O. Box 186, Grafton, VT 05146: Free catalog ■ Playsuits and one-piece velour jumpsuits, and other clothing that can be used as costumes. 802–843–2555.

Talbots Kids, 175 Beal St., Hingham, MA 02043: Free catalog ■ Clothing and accessories, sizes 4 to 12 for boys; sizes 4 to 14 for girls. 800–225–8200.

Toad'ly Kids, 2428 Patterson Ave., Roanoke, VA 24016: Free catalog ■ Outer-wear, playtime clothes, underwear, sleep-wear, and clothes for school and dressing-up. 703–981–0233.

Tortellini, P.O. Box 2515, Sag Harbor, NY 11963: Free catalog ■ Dressing-up and fun-to-wear clothing for the younger set. 800–527–8725.

Wear It Now, 1501 12th St. NW, Albuquerque, NM 87104: Free catalog ■ Cotton clothing for children, age 7 to 14. 505–243–8022.

Wooden Soldier, Kearsage St., North Conway, NH 03860: Free catalog ■ Children's designer clothing. 603–356–6343.

Exercise Clothing

Adidas USA, Inc., 15 Independence Blvd., Warren, NJ 07060: Free information ■ Men's and women's shorts and singlets, aerobic and workout shoes, socks, and warm-up suits. 908–580–0700.

Advantage Uniforms, Inc., 115 W. Main, P.O. Box 186, Manchester, MI 48158: Free information ■ Men's and women's shorts, singlets, and warm-up suits. 313–428–8522.

Aerobic Wear, Inc., 25 Depot St., Huntington Station, NY 11746: Free information ■ Leotards and leg warmers. 516–673–1830.

Athletic Supply, 156 Front St. West, Toronto, Ontario, Canada M5J 2L6: Free catalog ■ Everything for the sports fan from pins and caps to jerseys, jackets, and other clothing. 416–971–5222.

Austad's, 4500 E. 10th St., P.O. Box 1428, Sioux Falls, SD 57196: Free catalog ■ Equipment, accessories, and clothing for most major sports. 800–444–1234.

Body Wrappers, Attitudes in Dressing, Inc., 1350 Broadway, Ste. 304, New York, NY 10018: Free information ■ Exercise suits, leotards, headbands, leg warmers, women's shorts and warm-up suits. 800–323–0786; 212–279–3492 (in NY).

California Best, 970 Broadway, Ste. 104, Chula Vista, CA 91911: Free catalog ■ Men's and women's exercise and fitness clothing. 800–438–9327.

Champion Products, Inc., 3141 Monroe Ave., Rochester, NY 14618: Free information ■ Exercise clothing, leotards, and shorts and singlets for men and women. 716–385–3200.

Danmar Products, Inc., 221 Jackson Industrial Dr., Ann Arbor, MI 48103: Free catalog ■ Hydrofitness products for water aerobic workouts. Includes soft swim boots for sensitive feet. 313–761–1990.

Danskin, 111 W. 40th St., New York, NY 10018: Free information ■ Exercise suits, headbands, leg warmers, leotards, singlets for women, warm-up suits, and wrist bands. 212–764–4630.

Ellesse USA, Inc., 1430 Broadway, New York, NY 10018: Free information ■ Exercise suits, headbands, leotards, aerobic and workout shoes, shorts and singlets for men and women, socks, warm-up suits, and wrist bands. 212–840–6111.

Fox Racing, 909 Dell Ave., Campbell, CA 95008: Catalog $1 ■ Men's and women's clothing for jet skiing and other watercraft activities.

Freed of London, Inc., 922 S. 7th Ave., New York, NY 10019: Free price list ■ Gym shoes, exercise clothing, and custom-made footwear for women and men. 212–489–1055.

Gold's Gym, 360 Hampton Dr., Venice, CA 90291: Free information ■ Gloves, headbands, leotards, aerobic and workout shoes, shorts, singlets, and warm-up suits. 800–457–5375; 213–392–3005 (in CA).

Hind Sportswear, 3765 S. Higuera St., San Luis Obispo, CA 93401: Free information ■ Exercise suits, gloves, leotards, shorts and singlets for men and women, and socks. 800–426–4463; 800–544–8555 (in CA).

Jazzertogs, 1050 Joshua Way, Vista, CA 92083: Catalog $1 ■ Exercise clothing and accessories. 800–FIT–ISIT.

Jet Trends, P.O. Box 110937, Miami, FL 33011: Free catalog ■ Men's and women's clothing for jet skiing and other watercraft activities. 800–231–9279; 305–635–2411 (in FL).

Johnstown Knitting Mill Company, Inc., 309 W. Montgomery St., Johnston, NY 12095: Free information ■ Exercise suits, workout shoes, shorts, singlets, and warm-up suits. 518–762–3156.

Leo's Dancewear, Inc., 1900 N. Narragansett Ave., Chicago, IL 60639: Free information ■ Leg warmers, leotards, workout shoes, and headbands. 312–889–7700.

Gilda Marx Industries, 11755 Exposition Blvd., Los Angeles, CA 90064: Free information ■ Exercise suits, headbands, leg warmers, leotards, shorts, and warm-up suits. 800–876–6279; 310–473–0872 (in CA).

Merry Fitness Apparel, 104 Foster St., Lewisburg, WV 24901: Catalog $2 ■ Fitness clothing, walking socks, and exercise bras. 304–645–2093.

New Balance Athletic Shoe, Inc., 38 Everett St., Boston, MA 02134: Free information ■ Exercise suits, leotards, workout shoes, shorts and singlets for men and women, socks, and warm-up suits. 800–253–SHOE.

Pony Sports & Leisure, Inc., Meadows Office Complex, 7th Floor, 201 Rt. 17, Rutherford, NJ 07070: Free information ■ Exercise suits, headbands, leotards, leg warmers, aerobic and workout shoes, shorts, singlets, and warm-up suits. 800–654–7669; 201–896–0101 (in NJ).

The Potomac Company, 29908 S. Stockton, Farmington Hills, MI 48024: Free catalog ■ Specially designed clothing and equipment for competitive and recreational rowers. 313–471–4448.

Puma USA, Inc., 147 Centre St., Brockton, MA 02403: Free information ■ Exercise suits, head bands, leotards, leg warmers, aerobic and workout shoes, shorts, singlets, socks, and warm-up suits. 508–583–9100.

Royal Textile Mills, Inc., Firetower Rd., P.O. Box 250, Yanceyville, NC 27379: Free information ■ Leotards, leg warmers, exercise suits, headbands, and wrist bands. 800–334–9361; 919–694–4121 (in NC).

S & S Hosiery, 135 W. 50th St., New York, NY 10020: Free information ■ Exercise clothing, dancewear, hosiery, and lingerie. 212–586–3288.

Sampson & Delilah, 7324 Reseda Blvd., Ste. 208, Reseda, CA 91335: Free catalog ■ Original fitness clothing and swimwear for men and women. 800–451–2981; 818–998–7094 (in CA).

Softouch Company, Inc., 1167 NW 159th Dr., Miami, FL 33169: Free information ■ Leotards, leg warmers, headbands, shorts for women, socks, and wrist bands. 800–327–1539; 305–624–5581 (in FL).

Spalding & Brothers, 425 Meadow St., P.O. Box 901, Chicopee, MA 01021: Free information ■ Exercise suits, headbands, leotards, aerobic and workout shoes, warm-up suits, and shorts and singlets for men and women. 413–536–1200.

Sport Club, 615 W. Johnson Ave., Cheshire, CT 06410: Catalog $2 ■ Fitness clothing for men and women in regular and large sizes. 800–345–3610; 203–272–3384 (in CT).

Sport World Distributors, 3060 Clermont Rd., P.O. Box 27131, Columbus, OH 44327: Free information ■ Leotards and leg warmers. 614–838–8511.

Teri Sleeper, Inc., Westview Ln., Norwalk, CT 06854: Free information ■ Leotards, leg warmers, exercise suits, warm-up suits, and shorts and singlets for men and women. 203–854–5561.

Full-Figured Women's Clothing

August Max Woman, Marketing Department, 100 Phoenix Ave., Enfield, CT 06082: Free catalog ■ Women's clothing, sizes 14 to 24.

Brownstone Studio, Inc., 685 3rd Ave., New York, NY 10017: Free catalog ■ Clothing and accessories for full-figured women, sizes 12W to 26W. 800–221–2468.

Lane Bryant, P.O. Box 8303, Indianapolis, IN 46209: Free catalog ■ Misses clothing in size 14 to 20, half sizes 12½ to 34½, and size 36 to 60; shoes, size 6 to 12, AA to EEE. 800–477–1188.

Just Right Clothing, 30 Tozer Rd., Beverly, MA 01915: Free information ■ Clothing for full-figured women, size 14 and up. 800–767–6666.

Lerner Woman, 2300 Southeastern Ave., Indianapolis, IN 46206: Free catalog ■ Clothing in large and misses sizes. Includes half sizes, 12½ to 34½; women's sizes 34 to 54; misses sizes 12 to 24; and shoes, size 6 to 12, AA to EEE. 800–288–7004.

Making It Big, 9595 Main St., P.O. Box 806, Penngrove, CA 94951: Free catalog ■ Natural fiber clothing for full-figured women. 707–795–2324.

Old Pueblo Traders, Palo Verde at 34th, P.O. Box 27800, Tucson, AZ 85726: Catalog $2 ■ Clothing for women in misses, full-figured, and half sizes. 602–748–8600.

J.C. Penney Company, Inc., Catalog Division, Milwaukee, WI 53263: Free catalog ■ Clothing for full-figured and tall women, in sizes up to 32W. 800–222–6161.

Premiere Editions, Hanover, PA 17333–0012: Free catalog ■ Sportswear and casual clothing for women in fashion fabrics, for misses and petites. 717–633–3311.

Jeanne Rafal, 435 5th Ave., New York, NY 10016: Free catalog ■ Fashions for women, from size 16 to 26. 212–685–8545.

Regalia, Palo Verde at 34th, P.O. Box 27800, Tucson, AZ 85726: Catalog $1 ■ Fashions in large and half sizes for full-figured women and shoes in hard-to-fit sizes. 602–747–5000.

Roaman's, P.O. Box 8360, Indianapolis, IN 46283: Free catalog ■ Clothing for full-figured women, in sizes 12–26 for misses, 34 to 56 for full-figured women, half sizes, and shoes and boots in hard-to-fit sizes and widths. 800–274–7240.

Sears, Roebuck & Company, Catalog Division, 925 S. Homan Ave., Chicago, IL 60607: Free catalog ■ Women's clothing in half sizes, lingerie, and shoes. (Catalog also available from local stores.) 312–875–2500.

Showcase of Savings, P.O. Box 748, Rural Hall, NC 27098: Free information ■ Large-size lingerie for full-figured women. 919–744–1790.

Silhouettes, 340 Poplar St., Hanover, PA 17333: Free information ■ Sportswear and casual clothing in large sizes. 800–621–5800.

Spiegel, P.O. Box 6350, Chicago, IL 60680: Catalog $2 ■ Sportswear and casual clothing in large sizes. 800–345–4500.

Nicole Summers, Winterbrook Way, P.O. 3003, Meredith, NH 03253: Free catalog ■ All-occasion clothing for women, sizes 10 to 20. 800–448–4988.

Lingerie & Underwear

Avon Fashions, Avon Ln., Newport News, VA 23630: Free catalog ■ Daytime and nighttime intimate clothing. 804–827–9000.

Lauren Bogen, 1044 Lexington Ave., New York, NY 10021: Free brochure ■ Women's lingerie. 212–570–9529.

Lane Bryant, P.O. Box 8303, Indianapolis, IN 46209: Free catalog ■ Intimate clothing, outerwear, dresses, coordinates, blouses, sweaters, and footwear. 800–477–1188.

Chock Catalog Corporation, 74 Orchard St., New York, NY 10002: Catalog $1 ■ Lingerie, hosiery, and underwear for women, men, and children. 800–222–0020; 212–473–1929 (in NY).

D & A Merchandise Company, Inc., 22 Orchard St., New York, NY 10002: Catalog $1.50 ■ Underclothing, hosiery and socks, and lingerie. 212–925–4766.

Damart Thermawear, 1811 Woodbury Ave., Portsmouth, NH 03801: Free catalog ■ Thermal underwear for men and women. 800–258–7300; 603–431–4700 (in NH).

Frederick's of Hollywood, P.O. Box 229, Hollywood, CA 90099: Free catalog ■ Intimate clothing and lingerie, summer and casual clothing, bathing suits, jewelry, and shoes. 310–637–7770.

Green Pond Company, 3060 Peachtree Rd., Atlanta, GA 30305: Free brochure ■ Boxer shorts for men. 800–827–POND.

Intimate Appeal, Palo Verde at 34th, P.O. Box 27800, Tucson, AZ 85726: Free catalog ■ Intimate clothing and clothing for women who have had mastectomies. 602–748–8600.

Jeffries Socks Outlet, P.O. Box 1680, Burlington, NC 27216: Free catalog ■ Hosiery and socks for men, women, and children. 800–637–SOCK.

Mellow Mail, P.O. Box 8000, San Rafael, CA 94912: Free catalog ■ Intimate clothing and lingerie, career clothing, and other casual clothing for women. 415–456–1800.

National Wholesale, 400 National Blvd., Lexington, NC 27294: Free catalog ■ Hosiery and lingerie. 704–249–0211.

Night 'n Day Intimates, Hanover, PA 17333–0022: Catalog $2 ■ Intimate clothing and women's clothing for vacation and casual wearing. 717–633–3311.

No Nonsense Direct, 2515 E. 43rd St., P.O. Box 23368, Chattanooga, TN 37422: Free catalog ■ Panty hose. 615–867–1302.

Petticoat Express, 318 W. 39th St., New York, NY 10018: Free catalog ■ Lingerie. 212–594–1276.

Primary Layer, P.O. Box 6697, Portland, OR 97228: Free catalog ■ Undergarments for men and women, in sizes to fit almost everyone. 800–282–8206.

Roby's Intimates, 1905 Sansom St., Philadelphia, PA 19103: Catalog $1 (refundable) ■ Save up to 25 percent on bras, lingerie, hosiery, and other intimate clothing. 800–8788–BRA; 215–751–1730 (in PA).

Romantic Images, 25 McLeland Rd., St. Cloud, MN 56395: Free catalog ■ Intimate clothing and lingerie, casual clothing, outerwear, and accessories. 800–255–3356.

Sambar Hosiery, 55 Orchard St., New York, NY 10002: Free information ■ Hosiery. 212–925–9650.

Secret Passions, P.O. Box 8870, Chapel Hill, NC 27515: Free catalog ■ Intimate clothing, lingerie, and hosiery. 800–334–5474.

Shapely Figures, 2515 E. 43rd St., P.O. Box 182216, Chattanooga, TN 37422: Free catalog ■ Designer lingerie and hosiery for women. 615–867–9977.

Showcase of Savings, P.O. Box 748, Rural Hall, NC 27098: Free information ■ Lingerie for full-figured women. 919–744–1790.

Socks Galore, 220 2nd Ave. South, Franklin, TN 37064: Free catalog ■ Socks for men, women, and children, and hosiery for women. 800–626–7625; 615–790–7625 (in TN).

Sport Club, 615 W. Johnson Ave., Cheshire, CT 06410: Free catalog ■ Jogging bras. 800–345–3610; 203–272–3384 (in CT).

Undergear, 101 Kindig Pl., Hanover, PA 17333: Free catalog ■ Men's active clothing and underwear. 717–633–3300.

Victoria's Secret, North American Office, P.O. Box 16589, Columbus, OH 43216: Free catalog ■ Pajamas and other nighttime clothing, robes, silks, bras, panties, panty hose, slippers, outerwear, and formal and casual clothing. 800–888–1500.

Mendell Weiss, Inc., 91 Orchard St., New York, NY 10002: Free brochure ■ Women's lingerie, underwear, and lounging clothing. 212–925–6814.

Maternity Clothing

Bosom Buddies, P.O. Box 6138, Kingston, NY 12401: Free catalog ■ Maternity clothing for fashion-conscious women. 914–338–2038.

5th Avenue Maternity, P.O. Box 21826, Seattle, WA 98111: Catalog $2 ■ Stylish clothing for pregnant women. 800–426–3569; 206–343–9470 (in WA).

Garnet Hill, 262 Main St., Franconia, NH 03580: Free catalog ■ Natural fiber maternity clothing, sleepwear, underwear, and outerwear. 800–622–6216.

Mother's Place, 6836 Engle Rd., P.O. Box 94512, Cleveland, OH 44101: Free catalog ■ Dresses and jumpers, shirts and blouses, jackets, sweaters, active clothing, lingerie, and bedtime clothing for mothers-to-be. 800–444–6864.

Mothers Work, 1309 Noble St., 5th Floor, Philadelphia, PA 19123: Catalog $3 ■ Maternity business suits and dresses. 215–625–0151.

Holly Nicolas, P.O. Box 7121, Orange, CA 92613: Free brochure with long SASE and two 1st class stamps ■ Clothing for mothers-to-be. 714–639–5933.

J.C. Penney Company, Inc., Catalog Division, Milwaukee, WI 53263: Free catalog ■ Career and casual maternity clothing in petite, misses, tall, and regular sizes. 800–222–6161.

Reborn Maternity, 564 Columbus Ave., New York, NY 10024: Catalog $2 ■ Sophisticated clothing for mothers-to-be. 212–362–6965.

ReCreations Maternity, P.O. Box 191038, Columbus, OH 43209: Catalog $3 ■ Maternity clothing for casual and weekend clothing. 800–621–2547; 614–236–1109 (in OH).

Men's & Women's Clothing

Aberdeen & Dunbar, 25 Independence Ct., Box 4, Folcroft, PA 19032: Free catalog ■ Women's casual clothing. 215–237–7363.

Allegra & Coe, P.O. Box CN 1043, South Plainfield, NJ 07080: Free catalog ■ Women's casual clothing, swimwear, accessories, and gifts. 908–906–0498.

Allen Allen, USA, 2358 Perimeter Park Dr., Ste. 310, Atlanta, GA 30341, Attn: Catalog Order: Free catalog ■ Women's sportswear, casual clothing, and swim wear. 800–422–0466.

American Eagle Outfitters, Direct Mail Division, 150 Thorn Hill Dr., P.O. Box 788, Warrendale, PA 15095: Free catalog ■ Sweaters, sportswear, bedtime, and outdoor clothing for men and women. 800–777–1910.

American View, 741 F St., Box 129027, San Diego, CA 92112: Free catalog ■ Men's and women's casual clothing and accessories. 717–633–3300.

Anartex Sheepskins, P.O. Box 1, New Lebanon, NY 12125: Catalog $1 ■ Sheepskin coats, jackets, and accessories. 518–794–7997.

Andover Shop, 127 Main St., P.O. Box 5127, Andover, MA 01810: Free catalog ■ Handmade silk ties. 508–475–2252.

Anne's Collection, 530 Lakeview Plaza Blvd., Ste. D, Worthington, OH 43085: Free catalog ■ Clothing and accessories for women. 614–842–4400.

Johnny Appleseed, 30 Tozer Rd., P.O. Box 1020, Beverly, MA 01915: Free catalog ■ Clothing and accessories for women, sizes 4 to 18. 800–767–6666.

Armoir, 408 Pasadena Ave., Ste. 1, Pasadena, CA 91105: Free catalog ■ Women's casual clothing and accessories. 800–528–3131.

Array, 33 Hill St., P.O. Box 1025, Beverly, MA 01915: Free catalog ■ Women's formal and casual clothing, separates, and accessories. 800–767–6776.

Laura Ashley, Inc., 1300 MacArthur Blvd., Mahwah, NJ 07430: Free catalog ■ Women's clothing. 800–223–6917.

Athletic Supply of Dallas, Inc., 10812 Alder Cir., Dallas, TX 75238: Free catalog ■ Men's and women's swimwear, casual clothing, and accessories. 214–348–3600.

Jennifer Austin, P.O. Box CN 1045, South Plainfield, NJ 07080: Free catalog ■ Women's clothing, costume jewelry and accessories, and gifts. 908–906–0498.

Adrian Avery for Brownstone Studio, P.O. Box 3666, New York, NY 10163: Free catalog ■ Women's clothing for daytime and nighttime. 800–322–2991.

Avon Fashions, Avon Ln., Newport News, VA 23630: Free catalog ■ Women's swimwear, casual coordinates, shoes, lingerie, sweaters, and sportswear. 804–827–9000.

Bachrach, P.O. Box 8740, Decatur, IL 62524: Free catalog ■ Men's clothing and accessories. 800–637–5840.

Jos. A. Bank Clothiers, 25 Crossroads Dr., P.O. Box 567, Owings Mills, MD 21117: Catalog $1 ■ Classic and traditional clothing and accessories for men and women. 410–837–8838.

G.H. Bass by Mail, 301 US Rt. 1, Scarborough, ME 04074: Free catalog ■ Career and casual clothing and shoes for men and women. 800–333–0386.

Eddie Bauer, P.O. Box 3700, Seattle, WA 98124: Free catalog ■ Active clothing and casual clothing for men and women. Includes goosedown outerwear and footwear. 800–426–8020.

L.L. Bean, Inc., Freeport, ME 04033: Free catalog ■ Outdoor clothing, footwear, and sporting accessories for men and women. 800–221–4221.

Bedford Fair, 421 Landmark Dr., Wilmington, NC 28410: Free catalog ■ Women's casual, career, and beach attire. 919–763–7300.

Bila of California, 324 W. Venice Blvd., Los Angeles, CA 90015: Free catalog ■ Women's casual clothing and jewelry. 800–824–3541; 213–746–4190 (in CA).

Britches of Georgetown, 1321 Leslie Ave., Alexandria, VA 22301: Free catalog ■ Men's and women's clothing, gifts, and accessories. 703–548–0200.

Brooks Brothers, 350 Campus Plaza, P.O. Box 4016, Edison, NJ 08818: Free catalog ■ Men's sweaters, shirts, ties, suits, sport jackets, sportswear, belts, casual clothing, outerwear, shoes, and accessories; women's casual and career clothing and sleepwear. 800–274–1816.

Brownstone Studio, Inc., P.O. Box 3666, New York, NY 10163: Free catalog ■ Women's sportswear, lounging attire, party clothing, sleepwear, and career clothing. 800–322–2991.

Lane Bryant, P.O. Box 8303, Indianapolis, IN 46209: Free catalog ■ Women's outerwear, dresses, blouses, sweaters, intimate clothing, and footwear. 800–477–1188.

Bullock & Jones, P.O. Box 883124, San Francisco, CA 94188: Free catalog ■ Clothing and accessories for men and women. 800–227–3050.

Cable Car Clothiers, 1 Grant Ave., San Francisco, CA 94108: Free catalog ■ Men's clothing and accessories. 415–397–7733.

Camp Beverly Hills, 9640 Santa Monica Blvd., Beverly Hills, CA 90210: Catalog 50¢ ■ Sportswear and accessories for men and women. 310–858–3925.

Carabella Collection, 2168 A South Hathaway, Santa Ana, CA 92705: Free catalog ■ Women's swimwear and casual clothing. 714–434–1482.

Career Guild, McSherrystown, PA 17344: Free catalog ■ Women's career clothing, coordinates, knits, and casual clothing. 717–633–3317.

Cashmeres of Scotland, Trump Tower, 725 5th Ave., New York, NY 10022: Free information ■ Cashmere clothing from Scotland for men and women. Includes sweaters, dresses, robes, coats, jackets, blankets, hats, ties, and scarves. 212–758–7621.

Chadwick's of Boston, One Chadwick Pl., Box 1600, Brockton, MA 02403: Free catalog ■ Women's casual and career clothing. 508–583–7200.

Chantille, P.O. Box CN 1038, South Plainfield, NJ 07080: Free catalog ■ Women's swimwear, casual attire, sportswear, jewelry, handbags, and accessories. 908–906–0494.

Chelsea Collection, P.O. Box 56, Hanover, PA 17333: Free catalog ■ Casual, career, and formal clothing for women. Includes lingerie and clothing for petites. 717–633–3314.

Claudia Christy, 8 Olsen Ave., Edison, NJ 08820: Free catalog ■ Women's clothing, accessories, gifts, and specialty merchandise. 908–906–6622.

City Spirit, 1226 Ambassador Blvd., St. Louis, MO 63132: Free catalog ■ Women's sportswear and casual clothing. 800–445–6811; 314–993–0502 (in MO).

Clifford & Wills, One Clifford Way, Asheville, NC 28810: Free catalog ■ Career and casual clothing for women. 800–922–1035.

Collections, P.O. Box 882883, San Francisco, CA 94188: Free catalog ■ Men's shirts, ties, sweaters, slacks, jackets, cardigans, pajamas and robes, nightshirts, shoes, and outerwear. 800–762–7036.

Joan Cook, 3200 SE 14th Ave., Fort Lauderdale, FL 33350: Free catalog ■ Classic clothing for women. 305–761–2350.

Cotton Company, 2515 E. 43rd St., P.O. Box 23667, Chattanooga, TN 37422: Free catalog ■ Women's casual clothing, bedtime clothing, lingerie, and outerwear in cotton. 800–421–4548.

J. Crew Outfitters, One Ivy Crescent, Lynchburg, VA 24513: Free catalog ■ Casual clothing for men and women in traditional styles. Includes shirts, shoes, ties, jackets, hats, outerwear, belts, gloves, scarves, shoes and boots, and sweaters. 800–932–0043.

Mark Cross, 670 George Washington Hwy., Lincoln, RI 02865: Free catalog ■ Clothing for men and women. 800–223–1678.

Custom Coat Company, Inc., P.O. Box 69, Berlin, WI 54923: Free catalog ■ Deerskin clothing and accessories. Will custom make. 414–361–0900.

Damart Thermawear, 1811 Woodbury Ave., Portsmouth, NH 03801: Free catalog ■ Thermal underwear for men and women. 800–258–7300; 603–431–4700 (in NH).

Deerskin Place, 283 Akron Rd., Ephrata, PA 17522: Free brochure ■ Save up to 50 percent on cowhide, sheepskin, and deerskin clothing and accessories. 717–733–7624.

Deerskin Trading Post, 119 Foster St., Box 6008, Peabody, MA 01961: Free catalog ■ Leather shoes and slippers, gloves, shoulder bags, and boots. 508–532–4040.

Designer Direct, Designer Circle, Salem, VA 24156: Free catalog ■ Women's designer clothes. 800–848–2929.

DEVA Cotton Clothing, 303 E. Main St., Burkittsville, MD 21718: Catalog $1 (refundable) ■ Cotton pants, tops, skirts, and dresses. 800–222–8024.

Early Winters, Inc., P.O. Box 4333, Portland, OR 97208: Free catalog ■ Outdoor clothing and accessories for men and women. Includes ski clothing and accessories and leisure separates. 800–821–1286.

Elegant Outlet, P.O. Box CN 1039, South Plainfield, NJ 07080: Free catalog ■ Women's casual clothing, sportswear, evening and formal clothing, bedroom attire, and accessories. 908–906–0496.

Esplanade, 8 Olsen Ave., Edison, NJ 08820: Free catalog ■ Formal, casual, and leisure clothing and accessories for women. 908–906–0496.

Essence by Mail, P.O. Box 62, Hanover, PA 17333: Free catalog ■ Women's clothing and accessories. 717–633–3333.

Exclusively Chipp by Mail, 222 Grace Church St., Port Chester, NY 10573: Free information ■ Neckwear. 914–937–0110.

Fashion Galaxy, P.O. Box 26, Hanover, PA 17333: Free catalog ■ Women's career and casual clothing, lingerie, swimwear, tops, and shoes and sandals. 713–633–3311.

FBS, P.O. Box 10, Hanover, PA 17333: Free catalog ■ Casual clothes for the entire family. 717–633–3300.

John Fields Bow Ties, P.O. Box 406, Kenwood, CA 95452: Free brochure ■ All-silk designer bow ties. 707–833–1112.

The Finals, 21 Minisink Ave., Port Jervis, NY 12771: Free catalog ■ Bicycling, aerobic, swimming, running, sweats, and exercise clothing. 914–856–4456.

Florian Design, 16212 Bothell & Everett Hwy., Millcreek, WA 98012: Free information ■ Outerwear for climbing, skiing, backpacking, mountaineering, biking, and other activities. 206–742–7212.

Frederick's of Hollywood, P.O. Box 229, Hollywood, CA 90099: Free catalog ■ Women's intimate and casual clothing, lingerie, bathing suits, jewelry, accessories, and shoes. 310–637–7770.

French Creek Sheep & Wool Company, Elverson, PA 19520: Free catalog ■ Wool, silk, cashmere, and cotton sweaters and outerwear for men and women. 215–286–5700.

Fun Wear Brands, Inc., 141 E. Elkhorn Ave., Box 2800, Estes Park, CO 80517: Free catalog ■ Men's and women's sportswear, boots, moccasins, hats, jackets and vests, Levi's, jeans, shirts, T-shirts and tank tops, socks, belts, coats, and skirts. 303–586–3361.

Gantos, Catalog Center, P.O. Box 280, Grand Rapids, MI 49502: Free catalog ■ Women's formal, casual, and denim and leather fashions. 800–458–3796.

Garnet Hill, 262 Main St., Franconia, NH 03580: Free catalog ■ Natural fiber adult sleepwear, underwear and outerwear, maternity clothing, and babies and children clothing. 800–622–6216.

Charles S. Gelles & Son Neckwear, 662 Cross St., P.O. Box 100, Malden, MA 02148: Free information ■ Ties. 617–828–1866.

Barbara George Collection, P.O. Box CN 1041, South Plainfield, NJ 07080: Free catalog ■ Women's formal and casual clothing, sportswear, swimsuits, lounging clothes, accessories, and gifts. 908–906–0494.

Georgetown Leather Design, Catalog Center, 10710 Tucker St., Beltsville, MD 20705: Free catalog ■ Leather clothing, bags, boots, attache cases, and accessories, for men, women, and children. 301–937–5111.

Gerry Sportswear, 1051 1st Ave. South, Seattle, WA 98134: Free information ■ Men's and women's outerwear. 206–623–4194.

Golden Fleece, 998 Airport Rd., Minden, NV 89423: Free catalog ■ Sheepskin clothing. 702–782–2842.

GORE-TEX Outerwear, Style Catalog, 100 Enterprise Pl., P.O. Box 7035, Dover, DE 19903: Free catalog ■ Waterproof outerwear and rainwear for men and women. 800–843–6330.

Gray-Walsh Capes International, P.O. Box 1912, Amarillo, TX 79105: Catalog $1 ■ Denim, taffeta, fine meltons, and wool cashmere capes. 800–999–2212.

Hall of Hanover, P.O. Box 56, Hanover, PA 17333: Free catalog ■ Women's fashions for lounging, casual entertaining, everyday dress, evening clothing, and travel. 717–633–3333.

Harvest Almanac, 100 Enterprise Pl., Box 7037, Dover, DE 19903: Free catalog ■ Sportswear and casual fashions for men and women. 800–441–6681.

Helly-Hansen, Box 97031, Redmond, WA 98073: Free information ■ Waterproof outerwear for adults and children. 206–883–8823.

Hermes of Paris, Inc., Manager of Direct Marketing, 745 5th Ave., Ste. 800, New York, NY 10151: Free catalog ■ Hermes scarves from France. 800–441–4488.

Hill's Court, Winterbrook Corporation, Winterbrook Way, Merideth, NH 03253: Free catalog ■ Tennis and other sportswear. 603–279–7051.

His Favorite Tie, 27 Glenn Way, P.O. Box 758, Holmdel, NJ 07733: Free information ■ Hand-sewn ties. 800–552–TIES.

Joyce Holder Just Bikinis, Inc., P.O. Box 40, Balboa Island, CA 92662: Free catalog ■ Beach fashions for women. 800–245–4647.

Honeybee, 1840 County Line Rd., Huntingdon Valley, PA 19006: Free catalog ■ Sport, leisure, and casual fashions; swimwear; evening clothing; sweaters and outerwear; and shoes. 215–357–6200.

The Horchow Collection, P.O. Box 620048, Dallas, TX 75262: Free catalog ■ Women's casual clothing. 800–395–5397.

Hot Zone, P.O. Box 7211, 1400 N. Shoreline Blvd., Mountain View, CA 94039: Free catalog ■ Swimsuits and other beach fashions for women. 800–424–9969.

H.T.C., Inc., P.O. Box 217, Pittsford, MI 49271: Free brochure ■ Insulated outerwear for men, women, and children. 517–523–2167.

H2O Zone, 1041 W. 18th St., Ste. 108, Costa Mesa, CA 92627: Free catalog ■ Men's and women's swimwear, shorts and tank shirts, print separates, jackets, and T-shirts. 714–681–8393.

Huntington Clothiers, 1285 Alum Creek Dr., Columbus, OH 43209: Free catalog ■ Traditional fashions for men and women. 800–848–6203.

Images, 317 St. Paul Ave., Jersey City, NJ 07306: Free catalog ■ Women's fashions for daytime and evening. 201–653–6599.

International Male, Hanover, PA 17333–0075: Free catalog ■ Men's clothing and accessories. 717–633–3300.

Intime for Brownstone Studio, P.O. Box 3666, New York, NY 10163: Free catalog ■ Women's casual and nighttime attire. 800–322–2991.

James River Traders, James River Landing, Hampton, VA 23631: Free catalog ■ Indoor and outdoor casual clothing for men and women. Includes beach attire, shirts, shoes, ties, robes, sweaters, and socks 804–827–6000.

J. Jill, Ltd., Winterbrook Way, P.O. Box 3004, Meredith, NH 03253: Free catalog ■ Fashions for women. Includes cotton flannel nightgowns. 800–448–4988.

Charles Keath, Ltd., P.O. Box 48800, Atlanta, GA 30362: Free catalog ■ Women's casual clothing and jewelry. 800–388–6565; 404–449–3103 (in GA).

Knights, Ltd. Catalog, 2025 Concourse Dr., St. Louis, MO 63146: Free catalog ■ Women's casual and formal fashions, shoes, and accessories. 800–445–6811; 314–993–1516 (in MO).

Joseph Kraso, Inc., P.O. Box 784, Printers Court, Waterbury, CT 06720: Free information ■ Work clothes, sportswear, hosiery, and underwear. 203–574–0667.

La Costa Products International, 2875 Laker Ave. East, Carlsbad, CA 92009: Free catalog ■ Men's and women's clothing, accessories, and spa essentials. 800–LA–COSTA.

A.B. Lambdin, US Hwy. 19 North, Americus, GA 31710: Free catalog ■ Women's sportswear, casual and beach attire, and career clothing. 912–928–0626.

Landau, 114 Nassau St., P.O. Box 671, Princeton, NJ 08542: Free catalog ■ Men's and women's hand-knit sweaters, Icelandic light wool coats and jackets, blanket throws, coats from Austria, sportswear, cotton knits, sleeping attire, and shirts. 800–932–0709.

Land's End, Inc., 1 Land's End Ln., Dodgeville, WI 53595: Free catalog ■ Men's and women's flannel shirts, sweaters, slacks, sport shorts, sport pants, ladies' knee knockers, Rugby shirts, sweatshirts, knit shirts, sweats, swimwear, shoes and slippers, nighttime clothing, socks, skirts, and dresses. Other items include luggage, belts, and children's clothing. 800–356–4444.

Leather City, 54 W. 39th St., New York, NY 10018: Free information ■ Leather clothing. 212–997–1152.

Lee-McClain Company, Inc., Rt. 6, Box 381A, Shelbyville, KY 40065: Free brochure ■ Men's suits, jackets, coats, and blazers. 502–633–3823.

Lerner New York, Midwest Distribution Center, P.O. Box 8380, Indianapolis, IN 46283: Free catalog ■ Women's sportswear, casual clothing, sweaters, accessories, lingerie, jewelry, shoes and boots, and outerwear. 800–288–7004.

Lerner Woman, 2300 Southeastern Ave., Indianapolis, IN 46206: Free catalog ■ Women's sportswear. 800–288–7004.

Lewis Creek Company, 3 Webster Rd., Shelburne, VT 05482: Free information ■ Outerwear. 800–336–4884.

Loft, 499 7th Ave., South Tower, 19th Floor, New York, NY 10018: Free information ■ Save up to 50 percent on American and European designer fashions. 212–736–3358.

Madeline Fashions, Inc., 1112 7th Ave., Monroe, WI 53566: Free catalog ■ Sweaters, skirts, pants, blouses, coats, jackets, and shoes. 800–344–1994.

Lew Magram, Ltd., 516 W. 54th St., New York, NY 10001: Free catalog ■ Casual, career, coordinates, and formal fashions for women. 212–695–8148.

Mary Orvis Marbury, 1711 Blue Hills Dr., P.O. Box 12000, Roanoke, VA 24022: Free catalog ■ Women's career, casual, evening clothes, and gifts. 800–541–3541.

Philippe Marcel, 6800 Engle Rd., P.O. Box 94610, Cleveland, OH 44101: Free catalog ■ Women's designer fashions and accessories. 800–869–9901.

Mark, Fore & Strike, 6500 Park of Commerce Blvd. NW, P.O. Box 5056, Boca Raton, FL 33431: Free catalog ■ Classic, casual, and sports fashions for men and women. 800–327–3627.

Men America, 2800 Midway Dr., P.O. Box 85043, San Diego, CA 92110: Free catalog ■ Tailored clothes for men. 717–633–3300.

Monarch, One Monarch Pl., Lexington, NC 27294: Free catalog ■ Sportswear and casual clothing for women in leather, suedes, classic silks, and other fabrics. 800–367–6002.

Montege, P.O. Box CN 1040, South Plainfield, NJ 07080: Free catalog ■ Women's formal and casual attire, coordinates, and sleepwear. 908–906–0495.

David Morgan, 11812 Northcreek Pkwy., Ste. 103, Bothell, WA 98011: Free catalog ■ Hand-braided belts, fur hats, and wool and sheepskin clothing. 206–485–2132.

National Wholesale, 400 National Blvd., Lexington, NC 27294: Free catalog ■ Women's hosiery and panty hose, lingerie, pajamas, and gowns. 704–249–0211.

North Beach Leather, Catalog Division, P.O. Box 99682, San Francisco, CA 94109: Free catalog ■ Leather fashions and accessories for men and women.

Thos. Oak & Sons, 901 Main St., Salem, VA 24156: Free catalog ■ Fashions, shoes, gifts, and accessories for older persons. 703–375–3420.

Olsen's Mill Direct, 1641 S. Main St., Oshkosh, WI 54901: Free catalog ■ Clothing for the entire family. 414–233–7799.

Oomingmak Musk Ox Producers' Cooperative, 604 H St., Anchorage, AK 99501: Free brochure ■ Hand-knitted garments in traditional patterns, made from rare wools from the domestic Arctic Musk Ox. 907–272–9225.

Orvis Manchester, Historic Rt. 7A, Manchester, VT 05254: Free catalog ■ Casual fashions, sportswear, skirts, shirts, coats, lingerie, shoes, slacks, sweaters, and accessories for outdoor activities. 800–548–9548.

Barrie Pace, Ltd., 921 Eastwind Dr., Ste. 114, Westerville, OH 43081: Free catalog ■ Tailored separates and dresses. 800–441–6011.

Pagano Gloves, Inc., 5 Church St., Johnston, NY 12095: Catalog $3 (refundable) ■ Deerskin clothing, footwear, and gloves. Will custom make. 518–762–8425.

Palette by Gumps, 250 Post St., San Francisco, CA 94108: Free catalog ■ Coordinated women's fashions and accessories for the home. 800–284–8677.

Pendleton Woolen Mill, SW Columbia & 2nd Sts., P.O. Box 800, Portland, OR 97207: Free catalog ■ Men's and women's sweaters and sportswear, throws, robes, blankets, and shirts. 800–826–9665.

J.C. Penney Company, Inc., Catalog Division, Milwaukee, WI 53263: Free catalog ■ Women's work clothes in all sizes. Includes full-figured and extra-tall sizes. Also casual and career fashions. 800–222–6161.

Claudette Penot Collection, 145 W. 86th St., New York, NY 10024: Free catalog ■ Clothing, leather accessories, jewelry, craft items, and gifts. 212–580–2956.

Penthouse Gallery, Inc., 116 E. 16th St., New York, NY 10003: Free catalog ■ Women's sportswear, casual, and playtime clothing. 212–673–7070.

J. Peterman Company, 2444 Palumbo Dr., Lexington, KY 40509: Free information ■ Clothing and accessories for men. 800–874–4616.

Premiere Editions, Hanover, PA 17333–0012: Free catalog ■ Sportswear and casual clothing for women in fashion fabrics, for misses and petites. 717–633–3311.

Prime Time Fashions, 117 Chestnut Rd., P.O. Box 9950, Chapel Hill, NC 27515: Free catalog ■ Stylish fashions for women in their prime, many with velcro fasteners instead of buttons. 800–654–7878.

Railriders, Ltd., 55 Appleton St., Cambridge, MA 02138: Free information ■ Outerwear. 617–864–5969.

Red Flannel Factory, 157 W. Beach St., P.O. Box 370, Cedar Springs, MI 49319: Free catalog ■ Classic clothing for the entire family. 800–533–9276; 616–696–9240 (in MI).

Carroll Reed, 1777 Sentry Pkwy. West, Dublin Hall, Ste. 300, Blue Bell, PA 19422: Free catalog ■ Women's sportswear, casual fashions, and playtime clothing. 800–343–5770.

Anthony Richards, 6836 Engle Rd., P.O. Box 94503, Cleveland, OH 44101: Free catalog ■ Save up to 70 percent on fashions for women. 216–826–1712.

Roaman's, P.O. Box 8360, Indianapolis, IN 46283: Free catalog ■ Women's casual coats, career fashions, dress-up clothes, knits, boots and shoes, intimate clothing and lingerie, bedtime clothing, coordinates, pants, and suits. Includes fashions for full-figured women in misses sizes 12–26, women's sizes 34 to 56, and half sizes, and shoes and boots in hard-to-fit sizes and widths. 800–274–7240.

Royal Silk, Ltd., Rt. 1, Box 33, Fairfield, IA 52556: Free catalog ■ Silk and silk-blended clothing and accessories. 515–472–3795.

A. Rubinstein & Son, 63 E. Broadway, New York, NY 10002: Free brochure ■ Men's clothing, shirts and ties, sportswear, rain wear, and outerwear. 212–226–9696.

Saint Laurie, Ltd., 897 Broadway, New York, NY 10003: Catalog $2 ■ Save from 33 to 50 percent on hand-tailored clothing. 800–221–8660; 212–473–0100 (in NY).

Sarah Glove Company, Inc., P.O. Box 1940, Waterbury, CT 06722: Catalog $1 ■ Lee jeans and other work clothes, shoes and boots, shirts, jackets, and gloves. 203–574–4090.

Serendipity, Palo Verde at 34th, P.O. Box 27800, Tucson, AZ 85726: Catalog $2 ■ Formal and casual fashions, coordinates, sweaters, and shoes for women. 602–748–8600.

Shopping International, Palo Verde at 34th, P.O. Box 27800, Tucson, AZ 85726: Free catalog ■ Women's coordinates that include mix-and-match blouses, skirts, and pants. 602–748–8600.

Showcase of Savings, P.O. Box 748, Rural Hall, NC 27098: Free catalog ■ Machine-washable, cotton-velour warm-up suits, other fashions, jewelry, gifts, and home accessories. 919–744–1790.

Sickafus Sheepskins, Rt. 78, Exit 7, Strausstown, PA 19559: Free catalog ■ Sheepskin clothing. 215–488–1782.

Sidney's, 5568 Airport Rd., Roanoke, VA 24012: Free catalog ■ Casual and contemporary fashions for women. 800–835–7514.

Ben Silver, 149 King St., Charleston, SC 29401: Free catalog ■ Blazer buttons with college and prep school motifs and monograms, cuff links, suspenders, breast patches, blazers, cotton sweats, neckties, dress shirts and trousers, and English leather goods. 800–221–4671.

Simply Tops, P.O. Box 12, Hanover, PA 17333: Free catalog ■ Designer tops. 717–633–3311.

Sketches, P.O. Box 48350, Atlanta, GA 30362: Free catalog ■ Women's swimwear, sportswear, accessories, gifts, and housewares. 800–388–6565; 449–3100 (in Atlanta).

Smith & Hawken, 25 Corte Madera, Mill Valley, CA 94941: Free catalog ■ Men's and women's casual clothing. 415–383–6399.

Sport Club, 615 W. Johnson Ave., Cheshire, CT 06410: Free catalog ■ Men's and women's workout and fitness clothing, swim wear, clothing for bicycle riders, exercise equipment, and weights and body shaping equipment. 800–345–3610; 203–272–3384 (in CT).

Sporting Life, 5302 Eisenhower Ave., P.O. Box 9136, Alexandria, VA 22304: Free catalog ■ Tennis attire and other athletic and active clothing. Includes shorts, socks, headbands, wristbands, hats, tennis shoes, boat shoes, beach sandals, sweatshirts, and sweatsuits. 800–336–0222.

Sportspages, 3373 Towerwood Dr., Dallas, TX 75234: Free catalog ■ Men's and women's clothing, jewelry, and shoes. 214–247–3101.

George Stafford & Sons, 808 Smith Ave., P.O. Box 2055, Thomasville, GA 31799: Free catalog ■ Men's and women's sportswear, casual fashions, clothing for relaxation wearing, accessories, jewelry, luggage, shoes, books, and gifts. 912–226–4306.

Christina Stuart, 5302 Eisenhower Ave., Alexandria, VA 22304: Free catalog ■ Casual and formal fashions for women. 800–554–1162.

Paul Stuart, Madison Ave. at 45th St., New York, NY 10017: Catalog $2 ■ Women's casual, career, and dressing-up fashions. 212–682–0320.

Sussex Clothes, Ltd., 302 5th Ave., New York, NY 10001: Catalog $5 ■ Clothing and accessories for men. 212–279–4610.

Talbots, 175 Beal St., Hingham, MA 02043: Free catalog ■ Women's clothing and coordinates for workdays, relaxation wearing, and outdoor activities. 800–992–9010.

Ann Taylor, P.O. Box 805, New Haven, CT 06503: Free catalog ■ Women's career, weekend, and dress-up fashions and accessories. 203–777–4200.

The Territory Ahead, 27 E. Mason St., Santa Barbara, CA 93101: Free catalog ■ Men's clothing and accessories. 805–962–5333.

Thai Silks, 252 State St., Los Altos, CA 94022: Free brochure ■ Save up to 30 percent on imported silk and crepe blouses, ties, lingerie, dresses, and scarves. 800–722–SILK; 800–221–SILK (in CA).

Norm Thompson, P.O. Box 3999, Portland, OR 97208: Free catalog ■ Men's and women's contemporary clothing, shoes and boots, and other items for the bath, baby, health, automotive maintenance, and storage and closet organizing. 800–547–1160.

Title 9 Sports, 1054 Heinz Ave., Berkeley, CA 94702: Free catalog ■ Clothing and accessories for athletic women. 510–549–2592.

Todd Work Apparel, 12970 Maurer Industrial Dr., St. Louis, MO 63127: Free catalog ■ Save up to 30 percent on work clothing and uniforms. 800–458–3402.

Tog Shop, Lester Square, Americus, GA 31710: Free catalog ■ Women's jump suits, classic styled shirts, outerwear, skirts and blouses, sleepwear, swim fashions, and shoes and sandals. 912–924–4800.

Touch of Class, Huntingburg, IN 47542: Free catalog ■ Sleepwear and robes for men, women, and children; bathroom accessories; and comforters, pillows and shams, window treatments, towels, and rugs. 800–457–7456.

Trifles, P.O. Box 620048, Dallas, TX 75262: Free catalog ■ Clothing, accessories, and jewelry for men, women, and children. 214–556–6055.

Tweeds, One Avery Row, Roanoke, VA 24012: Free catalog ■ Men's and women's casual fashions in linen, washed silk, cotton, and rayon. 800–444–9449.

The Ujena Company, 1400 N. Shoreline Blvd., P.O. Box 7211, Mountain View, CA 04039: Free catalog ■ Women's swimsuits and sportswear. 800–227–8318.

Ultimate Outlet, P.O. Box 88251, Chicago, IL 60680: Free catalog ■ Men's and women's clothing for swimming, work, or relaxing in. 312–954–2772.

Undergear, 101 Kindig Pl., Hanover, PA 17333: Free catalog ■ Men's active clothing and underwear. 717–633–3300.

Underwear, International Male, Hanover, PA 17333–0075: Free catalog ■ Men's exercise and running clothing, underwear, outdoor clothing, and sleepwear. 717–633–3300.

The Very Thing, Winterbrook Way, P.O. Box 3005, Meredith, NH 03253: Free catalog ■ Women's clothing and accessories. 800–448–4988.

Victoria's Secret, North American Office, P.O. Box 16589, Columbus, OH 43216: Free catalog ■ Women's dress-up, casual, outer, career clothing, lingerie, pajamas and other bedtime clothing, robes, silks, bras and panties, panty hose, and slippers. 800–888–1500.

Wallach's, 32–36 47th Ave., Long Island City, NY 11101: Free catalog ■ Clothing and accessories for men and women. 718–361–7500.

Walrus, Inc., 929 Camelia St., Berkeley, CA 94710: Free information ■ Outerwear. 510–526–8961.

WearGuard Corporation, Box 400, Hingham, MA 02043: Free catalog ■ Clothing for the working man and woman. 800–343–4406.

Eileen West, 33 Grant Ave., San Francisco, CA 94108: Free catalog ■ Women's casual clothing and bedtime attire. 415–982–2275.

Willow Ridge, 421 Landmark Dr., Wilmington, NC 28410: Free catalog ■ Women's career, dress-up, and casual clothing. 919–763–7500.

WinterSilks, 2700 Laura Ln., P.O. Box 130, Middleton, WI 53562: Free catalog ■ Silk turtlenecks, socks and glove liners, longjohns, and ski clothing. 800–621–3229.

Wissota Trader, 1313 1st Ave., Chippewa Falls, WI 54729: Free catalog ■ Men's and women's clothing and shoes in regular and hard-to-fit sizes. 800–833–6421.

Workmen's Garment Company, 15205 Wyoming, Detroit, MI 48238: Catalog $2 (refundable) ■ Work clothes in small, big, and tall sizes. 313–834–7236.

Laura Wright Alaskan Parkas, 223 E. 5th Ave., Anchorage, AK 99501: Free information ■ Eskimo-style summer and winter parkas. 907–274–4215.

Natural Fiber Clothing

Garnet Hill, 262 Main St., Franconia, NH 03580: Free information ■ Natural fiber clothing, bed linens, comforters, blankets, pillows and pillow shams, and towels. 800–622–6216.

JANICE Corporation, 198 Rt. 46, Budd Lake, NJ 07828: Free catalog ■ Allergy-free, women's and men's clothing, exercise wear, sleepwear, and robes; towels and bath accessories; mattresses, pads, and quilts and covers; linens; personal grooming aids; hats, gloves, and scarves; underwear; and accessories. 800–JANICES.

Making It Big, 9595 Main St., P.O. Box 806, Penngrove, CA 94951: Free catalog ■ Natural fiber clothing for full-figured women. 707–795–2324.

Mother Hart's Natural Products, P.O. Box 4229, Boynton Beach, FL 33424: Free information ■ Natural fiber bedding and clothing that includes cotton sweaters, dresses, blouses, shirts, tank tops, socks for men, leotards, leg warmers, tights, body suits, camisoles, and underwear. 407–738–5866.

Vermont Country Store, Mail Order Office, P.O. Box 3000, Manchester Center, VT 05255: Free catalog ■ Natural fiber clothing and household items. 802–362–2400.

Petite Fashions

A.R.I.E.L.L.E, 3131 Randall Pkwy., Wilmington, NC 28410: Free catalog ■ Contemporary clothes for misses and petites. 919–251–8555.

Jos. A. Bank Clothiers, 25 Crossroads Dr., P.O. Box 567, Owings Mills, MD 21117: Free information ■ Sportswear and casual fashions. 800–999–7472.

Chelsea Collection, P.O. Box 56, Hanover, PA 17333: Free information ■ Sportswear and casual fashions. 717–633–3314.

The Horchow Collection, P.O. Box 620048, Dallas, TX 75262: Free catalog ■ Petite women's clothing, in sizes 10 to 24. 800–395–5397.

Old Pueblo Traders, Palo Verde at 34th, P.O. Box 27800, Tucson, AZ 85726: Catalog $2 ■ Dresses and casual fashions, coordinates, outerwear, shoes, lingerie, skirts, pants, and sweaters for women, 5'4" and under. 602–748–8600.

J.C. Penney Company, Inc., Catalog Division, Milwaukee, WI 53263: Free information ■ Sportswear and casual fashions. 800–222–6161.

Petite Ms, 555 Perkins, Memphis, TN 38117: Catalog $2 ■ Clothing in sizes 2 to 14, for women 5'4" and under. 901–366–5191.

Petite Sophisticate, 25 Sand Creek Rd., Albany, NY 12205: Free catalog ■ Exclusive fashions for petites, sizes 2 to 12.

Premiere Editions, Hanover, PA 17333–0012: Free catalog ■ Sportswear and casual clothing for petites. 717–633–3311.

Sears, Roebuck & Company, Catalog Division, 925 S. Homan Ave., Chicago, IL 60607: Free catalog ■ Fashions for petites, accessories, jewelry, outerwear, shoes, and lingerie. (Catalog also available from local stores.) 312–875–2500.

Shopping International, Palo Verde at 34th, P.O. Box 27800, Tucson, AZ 85726: Free catalog ■ Mix-and-match blouses, skirts, pants, and accessories for petites. 602–748–8600.

Spiegel, P.O. Box 640, Chicago, IL 60680: Catalog $2 ■ Career and weekend fashions for women under 5'4" tall. 800–345–4500.

Sporting Life, 5302 Eisenhower Ave., Alexandria, VA 22304: Free information ■ Sportswear and casual fashions. 800–554–1162.

Christina Stuart, 5302 Eisenhower Ave., Alexandria, VA 22304: Free information ■ Sportswear and casual fashions. 800–554–1162.

Talbots, 175 Beal St., Hingham, Mass 02043: Free catalog ■ Clothing for petites. 800–992–9010.

Unique Petite, Palo Verde at 34th, P.O. Box 27800, Tucson, AZ 85726: Catalog $2 ■ Sweaters, jeans, swim wear, and other attire, for women 5'4" and under, sizes 2 to 16. Includes shoes in hard-to-fit sizes, starting with size 2. 602–747–5000.

Shirts

Burberrys Limited, 9 E. 57th St., New York, NY 10022: Free catalog ■ Burberrys' English sporting classics in cotton shirts. Includes Registered Check Shirts, Heather Plaids, Black Fill Oxfords, Soft Touch Plaids, Sportsman Stripes, and others. 212–371–5010.

Paul Frederick Shirt Company, 140 W. Main St., Fleetwood, PA 19522: Free catalog ■ Men's shirts, with French cut, buttondown, tab, or straight collars, and button or French cuffs. 800–247–1417.

Huntington Clothiers, 1285 Alum Creek Dr., Columbus, OH 43209: Free catalog ■ Men's shirts with optional monograms. 800–848–6203.

James River Traders, James River Landing, Hampton, VA 23631: Free catalog ■ Men's and women's casual clothes, beach attire, shirts, shoes, ties, robes, sweaters, and socks. 804–827–6000.

Land's End, Inc., 1 Land's End Ln., Dodgeville, WI 53595: Free catalog ■ Casual and career wear for men and women. Includes shirts and blouses, outerwear, sweaters, and nighttime wear. 800–356–4444.

Reggie's, Shore Rd., Ogunquit, ME 03907: Free information ■ Change-of-season shirts in 60 percent cotton/40 percent polyester, with front yoke and 4–button placket. 207–646–5050.

A. Rubinstein & Son, 63 E. Broadway, New York, NY 10002: Free brochure ■ Men's shirts, ties, sportswear, rain wear, and outerwear. 212–226–9696.

Special-Needs Clothing

Avenues Unlimited, 1199 Avenida Acaso, Ste. K, Camarillo, CA 93012: Free catalog ■ Exercise equipment and easy-to-wear clothing, footwear, and accessories for men and women in wheelchairs. 800–848–2837.

Buck & Buck, Inc., 3111 27th Ave. South, Seattle, WA 98144: Free catalog ■ Clothing for nursing home residents. 206–722–4196.

Danmar Products, Inc., 221 Jackson Industrial Dr., Ann Arbor, MI 48103: Free catalog ■ Special-needs clothing for alternative wear in special medical conditions. 313–761–1990.

Everest & Jennings Avenues, 3233 E. Mission Oaks Blvd., Camarillo, CA 93012: Free catalog ■ Clothing and accessories for people with various physical problems. 800–848–2837.

FashionAble for Better Living, 99 West St., Medfield, MA 02052: Free catalog ■ Special-needs assistive items that include clothing and leg wear; daily living aids; visual, reading, writing, and phone aids; foot care supplies; comfort products; personal hygiene aids; beauty and health aids; eating, and kitchen and bathroom aids. 609–921–2563.

Fashion Ease, Division M & M Health Care, 1541 60th St., Brooklyn, NY 11219: Free catalog ■ Special-needs clothing and accessories for people with disabilities. 800–221–8929.

Hen's Nest, P.O. Box 531, Colby, KS 67701: Free catalog ■ Easy to put on men's, women's, and children's clothing in washable, woven cotton or cotton blended fabrics, with pressure tape closures. 913–462–3104.

Indepth Sock Company, 92 Candy Lane, Syosset, NY 11791: Free information ■ Extra-wide socks for diabetics and people who wear casts. Available in large and extra-large size, and 100 percent cotton. 516–921–4248.

Laurel Designs, 5 Laurel Ave., Belvedere, CA 94920: Free catalog ■ Special-needs clothing and other items for people with physical disabilities. 415–435–1891.

Special Clothes, P.O. Box 4220, Alexandria, VA 22303: Free catalog (specify adults' or children's) ■ Special-needs clothing. 703–683–7343.

Support Plus, Box 500, Medfield, MA 02052: Free catalog ■ Medically acceptable support hosiery, personal hygiene aids, home health care aids, bath safety products and accessories, and walking shoes. 508–359–2910.

Wardrobe Wagon, 555 Valley Rd., West Orange, NJ 07052: Free catalog ■ Special-needs clothing. 800–992–2737.

Wheelmates, 611 E. Washington, Pittsfield, IL 62363: Free brochure ■ Special-needs ponchos, in small, medium, large, and extra-large. Other items include a nose and face cover, bib, and mitmuff/leg warmer. 217–285–6520.

Worldwide Home Health Center, Inc., 926 E. Tallmadge Ave., Akron, OH 44310: Free catalog ■ Ostomy appliances and supplies, incontinence supplies, mastectomy breast forms, special-needs clothing, skin care products, and supplies for treating and preventing pressure sores. 800–223–5938; 800–621–5938 (in OH).

Suspenders

Bernardo, 2400 Westheimer, Houston, TX 77098: Free brochure ■ Suspenders. 713–526–2686.

Sweaters

Henri Bendel, Attn: Catalog Department, P.O. Box 1926, New York, NY 10116: Free catalog ■ Casual, outdoor, and dress sweaters for women. 800–H–BENDEL.

J. Crew Outfitters, One Ivy Crescent, Lynchburg, VA 24513: Free catalog ■ Mock turtlenecks, cardigans, button down styles, jeans sweaters, Oxfords, and Gansy sweaters for men and women. 800–932–0043.

Fall River Knitting Mills, Inc., 69 Alden St., Fall River, MA 02723: Free catalog ■ Sweaters for the entire family. 800–446–1089; 508–679–5227 (in MA).

Christine Foley Knitwear, 430 9th St., San Francisco, CA 94103: Free catalog ■ Designer knitwear for men, women, and children. 415–621–6157.

French Creek Sheep & Wool Company, Elverson, PA 19520: Catalog $2 ■ Wool,

silk, cashmere, cotton, and flax sweaters and outerwear. 215–286–5700.

James River Traders, James River Landing, Hampton, VA 23631: Free catalog ■ Men's and women's sweaters. 804–827–6000.

Landau, 114 Nassau St., P.O. Box 671, Princeton, NJ 08542: Free catalog ■ Men's and women's hand knit wool sweaters, Icelandic light wool coats and jackets, blanket throws, wool sportswear and shirts, and cotton knits. 800–932–0709.

Pendleton Woolen Mill, SW Columbia & 2nd Streets, P.O. Box 800, Portland, OR 97207: Free catalog ■ Sweaters and sportswear for men and women, and throws, robes, and blankets. 800–826–9665.

Peruvian Connection, Canaan Farm, Box 58, Tonganoxie, KS 66086: Free catalog ■ Handmade sweaters in Pima cotton and Alpaca wool, imported from Peru. 913–845–2450.

Rose Cottage, 2401 N. Forest Rd., Amherst, NY 14068: Free catalog ■ Cashmere sweaters and other knitted fashions for men and women. 800–695–6950.

Winona Knitting Mills, 910 E. 2nd St., Winona, MN 55987: Free catalog ■ Wool sweaters and other knitwear. 507–454–4381.

WinterSilks, 2700 Laura Ln., P.O. Box 130, Middleton, WI 53562: Free catalog ■ Turtlenecks, sweaters, silk long johns, accessories, and other fashions. 800–621–3229.

Tall & Big Men's Clothing

Botany 500, 135 W. 50th St., New York, NY 10020: Free information ■ Fashions for men in big and tall sizes. 212–307–8040.

Danbury Belts, Madison, NC 27025: Free information ■ Belts for big and tall men. 919–548–9624.

Harris Casuals, 110 W. 11th St., Los Angeles, CA 90015: Free information ■ Casual clothing for big and tall men. 800–533–5066; 213–749–5066 (in CA).

Imperial Wear, 48 W. 48th St., New York, NY 10036: Free catalog ■ Clothing for tall and big men. 212–719–2590.

King Size Company, P.O. Box 9115, Hingham, MA 02043: Free catalog ■ Clothes for tall and big men. Includes dress shirts to 24 neck, casual shirts to 6XL, jackets and outer-

wear to 6XL, slacks and jeans to 72 waist, and shoes to 16EEE. 800–846–1600.

London Majesty, 1211 Avenue of Americas, New York, NY 10036: Free information ■ British tweeds, knitwear, suits, and casual jackets, for big and tall men. 212–221–1860.

J.C. Penney Company, Inc., Catalog Division, Milwaukee, WI 53263: Free catalog ■ Shirts, pants, and other fashions for big and tall men. 800–222–6161.

Sears, Roebuck & Company, Catalog Division, 925 S. Homan Ave., Chicago, IL 60607: Free catalog ■ Fashions for big and tall men. (Catalog also available from local stores.) 312–875–2500.

I. Spiewak & Sons, Inc., 505 8th Ave., New York, NY 10018: Free brochure ■ Outerwear for men, sizes 6X to XXXXLT. 800–223–6850; 212–695–1620 (in NY).

Tall Women's Clothing

Jos. A. Bank Clothiers, 25 Crossroads Dr., P.O. Box 567, Owings Mills, MD 21117: Free information ■ Sportswear and casual fashions for tall women. 800–999–7472.

J.C. Penney Company, Inc., Catalog Division, Milwaukee, WI 53263: Free catalog ■ Sportswear and casual fashions for tall women. 800–222–6161.

Old Pueblo Traders, Palo Verde at 34th, P.O. Box 27800, Tucson, AZ 85726: Catalog $2 ■ Fashions for women 5'7" and taller. 602–748–8600.

Tall Girl/Tallcrest, 380 Brunet Rd., Mississauga, Ontario, Canada L4Z 2C2: Free brochure: Tall women fashions and footwear in sizes 0 to 13. 416–890–2430.

Tall Tempting Fashions, 3535 East Coast Hwy., Ste. 325, Corona Del Mar, CA 92625: Free catalog ■ Clothing for tall women in small, medium, and large. Includes turtlenecks, tunics, pants, tops, and skirts. 800–248–8255.

T-Shirts & Sweatshirts

Aerie Design, 141 Blackberry Inn, Weaverville, NC 28787: Catalog $1 ■ T-shirts with contemporary wildlife graphics. 800–233–0229.

American Photographer, P.O. Box 740, Holmes, PA 19043: Free information ■

Rugby jerseys and sweatshirts for photographers. 800–345–8112.

Beer Gear, P.O. Box 90318, San Diego, CA 92109: Free information ■ T-shirts in 100 percent cotton. 800–323–9440.

Bommer's T-Shirts, P.O. Box 929, Folly Beach, SC 029439: Catalog $1 (refundable) ■ T-shirts with environmental graphics. 803–588–9585.

Caledonian Graphics, P.O. Box 875, Zephyrhills, FL 34283: Free catalog ■ Astronomy designs on heavyweight T-shirts, long sleeve T-shirts, and sweatshirts. 800–223–4607.

California Cheap Skates, 4035 S. Higuera St., San Luis Obispo, CA 93401: Free catalog ■ T-shirts, shoes, stickers, skateboards and parts, and safety gear. 805–541–6911.

Cali4nia Skate Express, 4629 N. Blythe, Fresno, CA 93722: Free information ■ T-shirts, stickers, shoes, and skateboards. 800–426–9177.

Computer Portraits, P.O. Box 66, Macungie, PA 18062: Free information ■ T-shirts and sweatshirts in children's and adult sizes with computerized photo reproductions. 215–966–2585.

Crazy Shirt, 99–969 Iwaena St., Aiea, HI 96701: Free catalog ■ T-shirts and jackets in adult and junior sizes, and adult box tops in small, medium, large, and extra-large. 808–367–7044.

Dallas Alice, 8001 Cessna Ave., Ste. 203, Gaithersburg, MD 20879: Free catalog ■ Custom silk-screened T-shirts. 301–948–0400.

Stanley DeSantis, Inc., 4250 Wilshire Blvd., Los Angeles, CA 90010: Catalog $1 ■ Silk-screened T-shirts and sweatshirts in 100 percent cotton. 213–933–8205.

Dolan's Sports, Inc., 26 Hwy. 547, P.O. Box 26, Farmingdale, NJ 07727: Free catalog ■ T-shirts with martial arts designs, training equipment, uniforms, safety equipment, shoes, Samurai swords, bags, and books. 908–938–6656.

Eastern Emblem, Box 828, Union City, NJ 07087: Free catalog ■ T-shirts and jackets, patches, cloisonne pins, decals, and stickers. 800–344–5112.

Habitat Wildlife T-Shirts, 924 Spring Creek Blvd., Montrose, CO 81401: Free catalog ■ T-shirts with nature and wildlife graphics. 303–249–3333.

Historical Products, P.O. Box 403, East Longmeadow, MA 01025: Brochure 75¢ ■ T-shirts and sweatshirts with pictures of famous persons from history. 800–747–2747; 413–525–2250 (in MA).

Howard Graphics, P.O. Box 7208, Loveland, CO 80537: Free catalog ■ T-shirts and sweatshirts with native American graphics. 303–667–8477.

Just for Kids, P.O. Box 29141, Shawnee, KS 66201: Free catalog ■ Children's T-shirts and tops, toys and games, dolls, arts and crafts, musical instruments, school bags, and videos. 800–443–5827.

Kasumi-mono, 1594 Rydalmount, Cleveland, OH 44118: Free catalog with long SASE ■ Kasumi T-shirts with designs based on traditional woodblock prints by Japanese artists. Includes renditions from the satire, the Urban Samurai, and modern Japanese culture. 216–932–9475.

J. Miller & Sons Outdoor Outfitters, P.O. Drawer 50668, Albany, GA 31705: Free catalog ■ Nature and environmental T-shirts in 100 percent cotton. 800–344–3323.

Jim Morris T-Shirts, P.O. Box 831, Boulder, CO 80306: Free catalog ■ Environmental and wildlife T-shirts and sweatshirts. 303–444–6430.

The Nature Company, Home Office, 750 Hearst Ave., Berkeley, CA 94710: Free catalog ■ T-shirts with pictures of African animals on the front and back. 800–227–1114.

Pedigrees Pet Catalog, P.O. Box 905, Brockport, NY 14120: Free catalog ■ T-shirts with pictures of pets, pet clothing, collars, carriers, toys, and books. 716–637–1434.

Ridge Runner Naturals, 1033–1/3 Balsam Rd., Waynesville, NC 28786: Free catalog ■ T-shirts and sweatshirts with nature graphics, for adults and children. 704–456–3003.

Schnaubelt Shorts, 1128 4th Ave., Coraopolis, PA 15108: Free information ■ Custom silk-screening on bike clothing and T-shirts. 800–782–TEAM.

Searchlight Designs, P.O. Box 431, Jonestown, PA 17038: Free brochure ■ T-shirts with aquarist and scuba diver designs. 717–865–6227.

Shoosh Designs, 476 Arbutus Ave., Morro Bay, CA 93442: Free information ■ Yoga T-shirts and sweatshirts. 805–772–9253.

Skate Ware-House, 4035 S. Higuera St., San Luis Obispo, CA 93401: Free information ■ Canvas and suede hi-tops and T-shirts, and skateboards and parts. 800–666–7723.

Stookey's, P.O. Box 1635, High Point, NC 27261: Free information ■ Bike-oriented T-shirts for adults, in 100 percent cotton. 919–886–4063.

USA SportWear, 4901 W. Van Buren, Ste. 1, Phoenix, AZ 85043: Catalog $2 ■ Motorcycle theme T-shirts. 800–323–7734.

Vantage Communications, Inc., Box 546, Nyack, NY 10960: Free information ■ T-shirts in adult sizes. 800–872–0068; 914–358–0147 (in NY).

Warner Brothers Catalog, 4000 Warner Blvd., Burbank, CA 91522: Catalog $3 ■ Bugs Bunny and Looney Tunes T-shirts and sweatshirts, for adults and children. 800–223–6524.

Whirlwind T-Shirt Designs, 65 Inman St., Cambridge, MA 02139: Free information ■ Astronomy and weather-related pictures silk-screened on 100 percent cotton T-shirts. 617–868–0946.

Wild Basin, P.O. Box 13455, Austin, TX 78711: Free information ■ "Wild things" T-shirts. 512–476–4120.

Wireless, P.O. Box 64422, St. Paul, MN 55164: Catalog $1 ■ T-shirts, sweatshirts, boxer shorts, toy banks, coffee mugs, and other items. 800–669–9999.

Wonderwear, 2441 Rincon Villa Dr., Escondido, CA 92027: Catalog $1 (refundable) ■ Buddhist, Hindu, Zen, and Taoist T-shirts and sweatshirts. 619–738–1243.

Uniforms

Barco, 350 W. Rosecrans Ave., Gardena, CA 90248: Catalog $1 ■ Uniforms and career wear. 213–766–1230.

Dornan Uniforms, 653 11th Ave., New York, NY 10036: Free catalog ■ Uniforms. 212–247–0937.

Industrial Uniforms, 906 E. Waterman, Wichita, KS 67202: Free information ■ Uniforms and work clothing. 316–264–2871.

J.C. Penney Company, Inc., Catalog Division, Milwaukee, WI 53263: Free catalog ■ Women's uniforms for health care personnel, in petite, misses, tall, and regular sizes. 800–222–6161.

Sears, Roebuck & Company, Catalog Division, 925 S. Homan Ave., Chicago, IL 60607: Free catalog ■ Uniforms in petite, misses, tall, full-figured women, and half sizes. (Catalog also available from local stores.) 312–875–2500.

Western Clothing

J.M. Capriolla Company, 500 Commercial St., Elko, NV 89801: Catalog $4.50 ■ Western-style apparel and custom gear for men and women. 702–738–5816.

Cheyenne Outfitters, P.O. Box 29, Cheyenne, WY 82003: Free catalog ■ Authentic western wear, accessories, jewelry, and gifts. 307–775–7550.

Jackson Originals, Box 1049, Mission, SD 57555: Free price list with long SASE ■ Men's, women's, and children's leather vests and jackets with bead work designs; denim shirts, vests and jackets with applique or embroidered designs; and western traditional style Sioux ribbon shirts and dresses. 605–856–2541.

Luskey's Western Stores, Inc., 101 N. Houston St., Fort Worth, TX 76102: Free catalog ■ Western fashions, boots, and hats for the entire family. 817–335–5833.

The Old Frontier Clothing Company, P.O. Box 691836, Los Angeles, CA 90069: Free catalog ■ Men's and women's western clothing and accessories. 800–422–9257; 310–657–9257 (in CA).

Old West Outfitters, 7213 E. 1st Ave., Scottsdale, AZ 85251: Catalog $3 ■ Authentic men's and women's western wear, from the 1800s and later. Other items include old-time cowboy dry goods and accouterments. 800–447–5277.

Roemers, 1920 N. Broadway, Santa Maria, CA 93455: Free catalog ■ Western styles and gifts for men and women. 800–242–1890; 800–232–1890 (in CA).

Romie's S/D & Western Wear, 3827 El Cajon Blvd., San Diego, CA 91304: Free in-formation ■ Square dance clothing and western-style fashions. 619–280–2150.

Ryon's Western Wear, 2601 N. Main, Fort Worth, TX 76106: Free catalog ■ Western-style clothing for men and women. 817–625–2391.

Sheplers, Box 7702, Wichita, KS 67277: Free catalog ■ Western clothing for men and women and country-style gifts and accessories. 800–835–4004.

Soda Creek Industries, Box 4343, Steamboat Springs, CO 80477: Free catalog ■ Western clothing, hats, and dusters for men and women. 800–824–8426; 303–879–3146 (in CO).

CLOWN SUPPLIES

Abracadabra Magic Shop, P.O. Box 714, Middlesex, NJ 08846: Catalog $3.95 ■ Magician's supplies, juggling equipment, balloons, clown accessories, costumes, and make-up. 908–805–0200.

Artistic Clowns, Clown Paraphernalia, P.O. Box 811, Mt. Clemens, MI 48046: Catalog $1 (refundable with $5 order) ■ Clown stickers.

Ashland Rubber Products, Sherman at 7th St., Ashland, OH 44805: Free catalog ■ Balloons and accessories for party decorations and clowns. 800–323–0405.

Balloon Box, 2416 Ravendale Ct., Kissimmee, FL 32758: Free information ■ Balloons and accessories. 407–933–8888.

Bigfoot Stilt Company, 7111 Gardner St., Winter Park, FL 32792: Free information ■ Custom made stilts. 407–677–5900.

Books by Mail, 1750 California Ave., Ste. 114, Corona, CA 91719: Free book list with two 1st class stamps ■ Books on clowning. 909–273–0900.

Chazpro Magic Company, 603 E. 13th, Eugene, OR 97401: Catalog $3 ■ Clown supplies, books, juggling accessories, jokes, and novelties. 503–345–0032.

Circus Clowns, 3556 Nicollet Ave., Minneapolis, MN 55408: Catalog $3 ■ Clown costumes, gimmicks, and props. 612–822–4243.

Circus Wagon Balloons, 3424 Belle Terrace, Bakersfield, CA 93309: Free information ■ Balloons, magic, comedy props and gags, and other clown supplies. 805–837–0252.

Clown Heaven, 4792 Old State Rd. 37 South, Martinsville, IN 46152: Free information ■ Clown props and supplies that include balloons, make-up, puppets, wigs, ministry and gospel items, books, novelties, and magic. 800–3–CLOWNS; 317–342–6888 (in IN).

Clowns by the Bunch, P.O. Box 103, Columbia, MD 21045: Catalog $1 ■ Costumes and accessories that include collars, cuffs, vests, bow ties, hats, props, and make-up. 410–964–1976.

Comanche Clown Shoes, Comanche Shoe Mfg., Ltd., HC 32, Box 10, Lawton, OK 73501: Free information ■ Clown shoes. 405–529–2220.

A Complete Clown Shop, 1104 Richmond Dr., Nashville, TN 37216: Free information ■ Costumes, wigs, shoes, and make-up. 800–624–9517; 615–227–6511 (in TN).

Steve Dawson's Magic Touch, 144 N. Milpitas Blvd., Milpitas, CA 95035: Catalog $3 ■ Magic, props, and accessories for magicians and clowns. 408–263–9404.

The Entertainers Supermarket, 21 Carol Pl., Staten Island, NY 10303: Free brochure ■ Supplies and props for clowns, magicians, balloon sculpturists, jugglers, face painters, stilt wakers, and other entertainers. 718–494–6232.

Freckles Clown Supplies, 4231 Timuquana Rd., Jacksonville, FL 32210: Catalog $5 ■ Costumes, make-up, clown supplies, puppets, how-to books on clowning and ballooning, and other theatrical supplies. 904–778–3977.

Bob Gibbon's Fun Technicians, Inc., 4782 Streets Dr., P.O. Box 160, Syracuse, NY 13215: Free information ■ Clown props and supplies. 315–492–4523.

Holly Sales, 9926 Beach Blvd., Ste. 114, Jacksonville, FL 32216: Free information ■ Custom clown stickers. 904–223–5828.

Indianapolis Costume Company, Inc., 615–619 Virginia Ave., Indianapolis, IN 46203: Free information ■ Magic, make-up, balloons, books, wigs, costumes, and accessories. 317–634–2229.

John the Clown Shoemaker, 9417 Bay Colony, Des Plaines, IL 60016: Free catalog with long SASE ■ Custom shoes for clowns. 708–824–9635.

Ken's Illusionarium, 3288 Main St., Vancouver, British Colombia, Canada V5V 3M5: Free newsletter ■ Books, magic equipment, and supplies and accessories for magicians, mentalists, clowns, jugglers, ventriloquists, and puppeteers. 604–875–9712.

Kidshow Creations, 101 Dorchester Dr., Baltimore, OH 43105: Free information ■ Books, tapes, comedy props, and other supplies for children's shows.

La Rock's Fun & Magic Outlet, 2123 Central Ave., Charlotte, NC 28205: Free information ■ Clown and balloon how-to books, balloons, balloon sculpture kits, and magic supplies. 704–333–3434.

Lynch's Clown Supplies, 939 Howard, Dearborn, MI 48124: Catalog $5 (refundable) ■ Clown wigs, shoes, noses, novelty items, make-up, and costume accessories and trims. 313–565–3425.

Mecca Magic, Inc., 49 Dodd St., Bloomfield, NJ 07003: Free brochure ■ Clown equipment, theatrical make-up, balloons, magic, costumes and wigs, puppets, ventriloquism accessories, props, and juggling supplies. 201–429–7597.

Priscilla Mooseburger Originals, P.O. Box 529, Maple Lake, MN 55358: Catalog $1 ■ Clown hats, tuxedos, coats, pants, dresses, skirts, and shirts. 612–963–6277.

Morris Costumes, 3108 Monroe Rd., Charlotte, NC 28205: Catalog $15 + $1.98 (postage) ■ Costumes, clown props, masks, joke items, magic tricks and special effects, novelties, balloons, and books. 704–333–4653.

Novelties Unlimited, 410 W. 21st St., Norfolk, VA 23517: Free list ■ Clown supplies, props, and gags; magic; balloons; make-up; party decorations; and other supplies. 804–622–0344.

Ben Nye Makeup, 5935 Bowcroft St., Los Angeles, CA 90016: Free catalog ■ Clown make-up. 310–839–1984.

Patsy & Blimpo, P.O. Box 2075, Huntington Beach, CA 92647: Free catalog ■ Clown make-up, wigs, and supplies. 714–897–0749.

M.E. Persson, 1 Thornton Ln., Lee/Durham, NH 03824: Catalog $1 ■ Clown supplies. 603–659–8148.

Spear Specialty Shoe Company, 12 Orlando St., Springfield, MA 01108: Brochure $2 ■ Clown shoes.

Under the Big Top, P.O. Box 807, Placentia, CA 92670: Catalog $4 ■ Clown props, costumes, make-up, juggling supplies, balloon accessories and supplies, and party supplies. 714–579–1144.

Up, Up & Away, P.O. Box 147, Beallsville, PA 15313: Free price information ■ Clown make-up and props. 412–769–5447.

Alan Zerobnick, Tenderfoot Trading Company, P.O. Box 1349, Port Townsend, WA 98368: Catalog $3 ■ Clown shoes in original designs. 206–385–6164.

COFFEE & ESPRESSO MAKERS

Georgetown Coffee, Tea & Spice, 1330 Wisconsin Ave. NW, Georgetown, DC 20007: Free catalog ■ Imported and domestic coffees, specialty blends, unroasted green beans, sampler assortments, decaffeinated teas, brewing equipment, coffee filters, replacement beakers, and gifts. 202–338–3801.

Mazzoli Coffee, Inc., 236 Ave. U, Brooklyn, NY 11223: Catalog 50¢ ■ Coffee brewers, grinders, and accessories. 718–449–0909.

Zabar's & Company, 2245 Broadway, New York, NY 10024: Free catalog ■ Cookware, food processors, microwave ovens, kitchen tools, coffee makers, gourmet foods, and gift baskets. 800–221–3347; 212–787–2000 (in NY).

COIN-OPERATED MACHINES

Ancient Slots & Antiques, 3127 Industrial Rd., Las Vegas, NV 89109: Free information ■ Buys, sells, and trades old slot machines. Before sending, will advise on status of legality for shipping to a specific state. 800–228–SLOT; 702–796–7779 (in NV).

The Antique Emporium, 1119 Industrial, San Carlos, CA 94070: Free information ■ Jukeboxes, slot machines, pinball machines, candy and gumball machines, cash registers,

and other coin-operated devices. 510–886–1727.

Antique Slot Machine Part Company, 140 N. Western Ave., Carpentersville, IL 60110: Free catalog ■ Parts for slot machines, jukeboxes, pinball machines, books and manuals, slot stands, and slot pads. 708–428–8476.

Balls & Slots, 174 Main St., Acton, MA 01720: Free information ■ Vintage pinball and slot machines. 508–263–6480.

Bernie Berten, 9420 S. Trumbull Ave., Evergreen Park, IL 60642: Free catalog with two 1st class stamps ■ Slot machines and parts. 708–499–0688.

City-Slicker Antiques, Leo & Denise Zawilla, 2009 Parkview Cir., Hoffman Estates, IL 60195: Free information ■ Buys and sells slot machines, barber poles, coin-operated machines, gum ball machines, and gambling paraphernalia. 708–490–9818.

Classic Coin-Ops, 7038 Hoke Rd., Clayton, OH 45315: Free information with long SASE ■ Jukeboxes, slot machines, and coke machines. 513–833–5143.

Coin-Op Amusements Company, Steve Gronowski, RR 2, Bateman Cir., Barrington Hills, IL 60010: Free information ■ Buys, sells, and trades antique penny arcade and slot machines. 708–381–1234.

CSSK Amusements, Box 6214, York, PA 17406: Free list with long SASE ■ Pinball machines, jukeboxes, other coin-operated collectibles, and jukebox and pinball parts. 800–PINBALL.

Durham's Antiques, 909 26th St. NW, Washington, DC 20037: List $2 ■ Antique coin-operated vending and arcade machines, pinballs, counter top games, and books. 202–338–1342.

Gumballs Galore, Randy and Sue Razzoog, 716 Fairfield NE, Grand Rapids, MI 49504: Free information ■ Buys, sells, and trades coin-operated gumball, stamp, peanut, and other coin-operated machines. 616–453–8044.

Tom Gustwiller, 116 W. Main St., Ottawa, OH 45875: Free information ■ Antique coin-operated machines. 419–523–6395.

Home Arcade Corporation, 1108 Front St., Lisle, IL 60532: Free catalog ■ Restored Coca-Cola machines and parts for coke machines and jukeboxes. 708–964–2555.

Illinois Antique Slot Machine Company, Frank Zygmunt, P.O. Box 542, Westmont, IL 60559: Free information ■ Buys and sells slot machines, Wurlitzer jukeboxes, nickelodeons, music boxes, and other coin-operated machines. 708–985–2742.

J & R Saloon Novelties, 920 Meadow Dr., Elgin, IL 60123: Free information ■ Slot machines, coke machines, and saloon items. 708–464–5661.

Jian Worldwide Group, Ltd., 1033 Franklin Rd., Marietta, GA 30067: Free information ■ Antique and reproduction music and gaming machines, billiard and snooker tables, coke machines, and other nostalgic items. 404–578–4482.

Norm & Mary Johnson, County Home Rd., Bowling Green, OH 43402: Free information with long SASE ■ Buys, sells, trades, and repairs slot machines, old arcade games, peanut and gumball machines, mechanical and still banks, and others. 419–352–3041.

Jukebox Classics & Vintage Slot Machines, Inc., 6742 5th Ave., Brooklyn, NY 11220: Free information ■ Antique coin-operated machines and jukeboxes. 718–833–8455.

Lloyd's Jukeboxes, 22900 Shaw Rd., Sterling, VA 22170: Free information ■ Jukeboxes, pinballs, Coke and Pepsi machines, video games, slots, tin toys, advertising signs, and other items from the 1950s. Also parts and restoration and repair services. 703–834–6699.

Marvelous Music Machines, 203 Central St., Hudson, NH 03051: Free information with long SASE ■ Vintage jukeboxes, slot machines, pinball machines, and other collectibles. 603–880–1882.

National Jukebox Exchange, Box 460, Mayfield, NY 12117: Free information ■ Antique slot machines, jukeboxes, other arcade items, and parts. 518–661–5639.

Bob Nelson's Gameroom Warehouse, Bob Nelson, 826 W. Douglas, Wichita, KS 67203: Free information ■ Buys, sells, trades, restores, and reproduces antique coin-operated machines and parts. 316–263–1848.

North Penn Amusement & Vending, 105 N. Main, Souderton, PA 18924: Free information ■ Buys, sells, and trades pinball machines, shuffle alleys, jukeboxes, vending machines, video games, and pool tables. 215–723–7459.

Orange Trading Company, 57 S. Main St., Orange, MA 01364: Free list with long SASE ■ Antique and collectible jukeboxes, pinballs, coke machines, and other coin-operated machines. 508–544–6683.

Tom Patch, 4320 Farmington Ln., Racine, WI 53403: Free information ■ Juke boxes, slots, brass cash registers, peep show machines, music boxes, 78 rpm picture record machines, and others. Includes many rare machines. 414–552–7701.

Royal Bell, Ltd., 5776 Lamar St., Arvada, CO 80002: Catalog $5 ■ Collectible slot machines and other mechanical memorabilia. 303–431–9266.

St. Louis Slot Machine Company, 2111 S. Brentwood Blvd., St. Louis, MO 63144: Catalog $3 ■ Buys, sells, and repairs very common to rare Coca Cola and other coin-operated machines. 314–961–4612.

Alan Sax Slot Machines, 3239 RFD, Long Grove, IL 60047: Free information ■ Slot machines. 708–438–5900.

Slot-Box Collector, Dick Bueschel, 414 N. Prospect Manor Ave., Mt. Prospect, IL 60056: Free list with long SASE and four 1st class stamps ■ Old saloon artifacts, coin-operated machines, advertising collectibles, and other memorabilia.

Larry Zeidman, 744 Kohler St., Los Angeles, CA 90021: Free information ■ Buys, sells, and repairs slot machines. Ships only to states in which slot machines are legal. 310–558–1578.

COMIC BOOKS

Abacus Hobbies, Coin, Comic & Baseball World, 2088 Edgewood Dr., Lakeland, FL 33328: Free information with long SASE ■ Comic books for collectors. 813–665–8586.

Avalon Comics, P.O. Box 821, Medford, MA 02155: Free catalog ■ Comic books, from 1935 to 1968. 617–391–5614.

Bags Unlimited, Inc., 7 Canal St., Rochester, NY 14608: Free information ■ Comic book storage and protection poly bags, cardboard backings, storage and display boxes, card savers, and other archival supplies. 800–767–BAGS.

Cliffs Comic World, 5050 State Hwy 303 SW, Ste. 107, East Bremerton, WA 98310: Free information with long SASE ■ Silver and Golden Age comic books, collectible

art, sports cards, Disney items, and games. 206–377–0196.

Bill Cole Enterprises, Inc., P.O. Box 60, Randolph, MA 02368: Free information ■ Comic book protection and storage plastic bags, acid-free boxes, and other archival supplies. 617–986–2653.

Collectors World, Elysian Fields Krogers, 5751 Notensville Rd., Nashville, TN 37211: Free information ■ Comics, posters, baseball cards, models, miniatures, and other collectibles. 615–333–9458.

College of Comic Book Knowledge, 3151 Hennepin Ave. South, Minneapolis, MN 55408: Free list with two 1st class stamps ■ Comic books for collectors. 612–822–2309.

Comic Classics, 365 Main St., Laurel, MD 20707: Free information with long SASE ■ Comic books, sports cards, and archival supplies. 301–490–9811.

Comic Relief, 2138 University Ave., Berkeley, CA 94704: Free information with long SASE ■ Gold and Silver Age comic books. 510–843–5002.

Comics for Heroes, 1702 W. Foster, Chicago, IL 60640: Catalog $1 ■ Back issue comic books.

Gart Dolgoff Comics, Brooklyn Navy Yard, Building 280, Ste. 608/609, Brooklyn, NY 11205: Free information with long SASE ■ Comic books for collectors. 718–596–5719.

Fantasy Factory Comics, Harbortowne Plaza, Tilton Rd. & Blackhorse Pike, Cardiff, NJ 08232: Free information ■ Collectible comic books. 609–641–0025.

Fantasy Illustrated, P.O. Box 3340, Anaheim, CA 92803: Catalog $1 ■ Vintage comic books. 714–537–0087.

Geppi's Comic World, Inc., 8317 Fenton St., Silver Springs, MD 20910: Free information ■ Comic books, Japanese toys and books, and science fiction magazines. 301–588–2545.

BT & WD Giles, P.O. Box 271, Keithville, LA 71047: Free price list with long SASE ■ Comic books for collectors. 318–925–6654.

Kingpin Comics & Collectibles, 943 S. 48th St., Ste. 124, Tempe, AZ 85281: Free information with long SASE ■ Back issue comic books, hardcovers, graphic novels, trade paperbacks, and other magazines. 602–921–7670.

Joseph Koch, 206 41st St., Brooklyn, NY 11232: Free information with long SASE ■ Old and new comic books for collectors. 718–768–8571.

Mint Condition Comic Books & Baseball Cards, Inc., 143 Main St., Port Washington, NY 11050: Free information with long SASE ■ Current and back issue comic books and sports cards. 516–883–0631.

Moondog's Comicland, 1201 Oakton St., Ste. 1, Elk Grove Village, IL 60007: Free information ■ Comic book covers, Mylar sleeves and snugs, and backer boards. 800–344–6060; 708–806–6060 (in IL).

Motor City Comics, 19785 W. 12 Mile Rd., Ste. 231, Southfield, MI 48076: Free catalog ■ Collectible comic books. Includes many rare issues. 313–350–2633.

New England Comics, P.O. Box 310, Quincy, MA 02169: Catalog $1 ■ Collectible comic books. 617–770–1848.

Bud Plant Comic Art, P.O. Box 1689, Grass Valley, CA 95945: Catalog $1 ■ Comic book-related materials that include graphic novels, comic strip collections, books about the history of comics and comic creators, limited editions books, and prints. 916–273–2166.

St. Mark's Comics, 11 St. Mark's Pl., New York, NY 10003: Free information with long SASE ■ Comic books. 212–598–9439.

Sparkle City Comics, P.O. Box 67, Sewell, NJ 08080: Free catalog ■ Old comic books. Includes golden and silver age issues.

Lee Tennant Enterprises, Inc., 6963 W. 111th St., P.O. Box 296, Worth, IL 60482: Free information ■ New issues and collector comic books, and preservation products. 800–356–6401; 708–532–1771 (in IL).

Tomorrow is Yesterday, 5600 N. 2nd St., Rockford, IL 61111: Free information with long SASE ■ New and back issue comic books, games, books, and other collectibles. 815–633–0330.

COMPUTERS
Computer Manufacturers

Acer American Corporation, 401 Charcot Ave., San Jose, CA 95131: Free information ■ IBM compatible computers and laptops. 800–733–2237; 408–922–0333 (in CA).

Advanced Logic Research, Inc., 9401 Jeronimo, Irvine, CA 92718: Free information ■ IBM compatible computers and portable computers. 800–444–4257; 714–581–6770 (in CA).

AEG Olympia, Inc., 3140 Rt. 22, Box 22, Somerville, NJ 08876: Free information ■ IBM compatible portable computers. 201–231–8300.

Airis Computer Corporation, 1824 N. Besly Ct., Chicago, IL 60622: Free information ■ IBM compatible portable computers. 312–384–5608.

Altima Systems, Inc., 1390 Willow Pass Rd., Ste. 1050, Concord, CA 94520: Free information ■ IBM compatible portable computers. 510–356–5600.

American Microtech Corporation, 4801 Keller Springs Rd., Dallas, TX 75248: Free information ■ IBM compatible portable computers. 800–332–7462; 214–248–0644 (in TX).

American Mitac Corporation, 410 E. Plumeria Dr., San Jose, CA 95134: Free information ■ IBM compatible computers and portables. 800–648–2287; 408–432–1160 (in CA).

American Research Corporation, 1101 Monterey Pass Rd., Monterey Park, CA 91754: Free information ■ IBM compatible portable computers. 800–346–3272; 213–265–0835 (in CA).

Apple Compatible Laser Computers, Laser Computer, Inc., 800 N. Church St., Lake Zurich, IL 60047: Free information ■ Apple compatible computers, monitors, and laser and dot matrix printers. 708–540–8086.

Apple Computer, Inc., 20525 Mariani Ave., Cupertino, CA 95014: Free information ■ Macintosh computers and portable

computers, printers, and other peripherals. 408–996–1010.

Aquiline Computers, Inc., 449 Main St., Bennington, VT 05201: Free information ■ IBM compatible portable computers. 800–221–1119; 802–442–1526 (in VT).

Associated Mega Sub System, Inc., 4801 Little John St., Unit A, Baldwin Park, CA 91706: Free information ■ IBM compatible portable computers. 818–814–8851.

AST Research, Inc., 16215 Alton Pkwy., Irvine, CA 92713: Free information ■ IBM compatible computers and portable computers. 800–876–4AST.

Atari Computer, 1196 Borregas Ave., Sunnyvale, CA 94088: Free information ■ Atari computers and portable computers. 408–745–2000.

AT & T Computers, 1 Speedwell Ave., Morristown, NJ 07960: Free information ■ IBM compatible computers and portable computers. 800–247–1212; 908–302–5800.

Austin Computer Systems, 10300 Metric Blvd., Austin, TX 78758: Free information ■ IBM compatible computers and portable computers. 800–752–4121; 512–339–3500 (in TX).

Autotech/Viktron Group, 343 St. Paul Blvd., Carol Stream, IL 60188: Free information ■ IBM compatible portable computers. 800–527–2841; 708–668–3355 (in IL).

Auva Computer, Inc., 16851 Knott Ave., La Mirada, CA 90638: Free information ■ IBM compatible portable computers. 714–562–6999.

Blue Star Computer, Inc., 2312 Central Ave. NE, Minneapolis, MN 55418: Free information ■ IBM compatible portable computers. 800–950–8854; 612–788–1092 (in MN).

Bona International Systems, Inc., 10 Corporate Place South, Corporate Park 287, Piscataway, NJ 08854: Free information ■ IBM compatible portable computers. 800–999–2662; 908–981–0118 (in NJ).

Chaplet Systems, 252 N. Wolfe Rd., Sunnyvale, CA 94086: Free information ■ IBM compatible portable computers. 408–732–7950.

Commax Technologies, 2031 Concourse Dr., San Jose, CA 95131: Free information ■ IBM compatible portable computers. 800–526–6629; 408–435–5000 (in CA).

Commodore Business Machines, Inc., 1200 Wilson Dr., West Chester, PA 19380: Free information ■ Commodore computers and portable computers. 800–448–9987; 215–431–9100 (in PA).

Compaq Computer Corporation, 20555 FM 149, P.O. Box 692000, Houston, TX 77269: Free information ■ IBM compatible computers and portable computers. 713–370–0670.

CompuAdd Corporation, 12303 Technology Blvd., Austin, TX 78727: Free information ■ IBM compatible computers, portable computers, and monitors. 800–999–9901; 512–250–1489 (in TX).

Computers First, Inc., 27 W. 20th St., New York, NY 10011: Free information ■ IBM compatible portable computers. 800–875–7580; 212–366–6673 (in NY).

Comtrade Electronics USA, Inc., 1016–B Lawson St., City of Industry, CA 91748: Free information ■ IBM compatible portable computers. 800–969–2123; 818–964–6688 (in CA).

Cordata/DaeWoo, Inc., 1055 W. Victoria St., Compton, CA 90220: Free information ■ IBM compatible portable computers. 800–233–3602; 310–603–2901 (in CA).

Core Pacific USA, Inc., 197 Meister Ave., Branchburg, NJ 08876: Free information ■ IBM compatible portable computers. 201–704–8383.

Data General Corporation, 3400 Computer Dr., Westborough, MA 01580: Free information ■ IBM compatible portable computers and dot matrix printers. 800–328–2436; 508–366–8911 (in MA).

Dataworld, Inc., 3733 San Gabriel River Pkwy., Pico Rivera, CA 90660: Free information ■ IBM compatible portable computers. 800–722–7702; 310–695–3777 (in CA).

Dauphin Technology, Inc., 1125 E, St. Charles Rd., Lombard, IL 60148: Free information ■ IBM compatible portable com-

puters. 800–782–7922; 708–627–4004 (in IL).

Dell Computer Corporation, 9505 Arboretum Blvd., Austin, TX 78759: Free information ■ IBM compatible computers and portable computers. 512–338–4400.

Dolch Computer Systems, 372 Turquoise St., Milpitas, CA 95305: Free information ■ IBM compatible portable computers. 800–538–7506; 408–957–6575 (in CA).

Dynamac Computer Products, Inc., 555 17th St., Ste. 1450, Denver, CO 80202: Free information ■ IBM compatible portable computers. 800–234–2349; 303–296–0606 (in CO).

Engineering Systems, Inc., 601 E. Williams St., Ann Arbor, MI 48104: Free information ■ IBM compatible portable computers. 800–282–5747; 313–668–8154 (in MI).

Epson America, Inc., 20770 Madrona Ave., Torrance, CA 90503: Free information ■ IBM compatible computers, portable computers, and dot matrix and laser printers. 800–289–3776; 310–782–0770 (in CA).

Ergo Computing, One Intercontinental Way, Peabody, MA 01960: Free information ■ IBM compatible portable computers. 800–633–1925; 508–535–7510 (in MA).

Everex Systems, Inc., 48431 Milmont Dr., Fremont, CA 94538: Free information ■ IBM compatible computers. 800–821–0806; 510–498–1111 (in CA).

Fora Computers, Inc., 308 N. 1st St., San Jose, CA 95134: Free information ■ IBM compatible portable computers. 408–944–0393.

Fornet Corporation, 46718 Fremont Blvd., Fremont, CA 94538: Free information ■ IBM compatible portable computers. 800–232–4638; 510–623–7800 (in CA).

Goldstar Technology, Inc., 3003 N. 1st St., San Jose, CA 95134: Free information ■ IBM compatible computers. 408–432–1331.

Grid Systems, 47211 Lakeview Blvd., Fremont, CA 94537: Free information ■ IBM compatible computers and portable computers. 800–222–4743; 510–656–4700 (in CA).

The Hewlett-Packard Company, 100 NE Circle Blvd., Corvalis, OR 97330: Free infor-

mation ■ IBM compatible portable computers and laser printers. 800–443–1254; 503–752–7736 (in OR).

Hyundai Electronics America, 166 Baypointe Pkwy., San Jose, CA 95134: Free information ■ IBM compatible computers and portable computers. 800–727–6972; 408–473–9200 (in CA).

The IBM Corporation, Armonk, NY 10504: Free information ■ IBM computers, portable computers, dot matrix and laser printers, and other accessories and peripherals. 800–426–2468.

Insight Computers, 1912 W. 4th St., Tempe, AZ 85281: Free information ■ IBM compatible portable computers. 800–776–7600; 602–350–1176 (in AZ).

Intelligence Technology Corporation, 16526 Westgrove Dr., Dallas, TX 75248: Free information ■ IBM compatible portable computers. 800–356–3493; 214–250–4277 (in TX).

Kontron Elektronik US, 66 Cherry Hill Dr., Ste. 200, Beverly, MA 01915: Free information ■ IBM compatible portable computers. 800–227–8834; 508–927–6575 (in MA).

Kris Technologies, Inc., 260 E. Grand Ave., South San Francisco, CA 94080: Free information ■ IBM compatible portable computers. 800–282–5747; 415–875–6729 (in CA).

Leading Edge Products, Inc., 117 Flanders Rd., Westborough, MA 01581: Free information ■ IBM compatible computers and portable computers. 508–836–4800.

Leading Technology, Inc., 10430 SW 5th St., Beaverton, OR 97005: Free information ■ IBM compatible portable computers. 800–999–5323; 503–646–3424 (in OR).

The Librex Corporation, 1731 Technology Dr., Ste. 700, San Jose, CA 95110: Free information ■ IBM compatible portable computers. 408–441–8500.

Maxtron Corporation, 1825A Durfee Ave., South El Monte, CA 91733: Free information ■ IBM compatible portable computers. 800–266–5706; 818–350–5706 (in CA).

Mectel International, Inc., 3385 Viso Ct., Santa Clara, CA 95054: Free information ■ IBM compatible portable computers. 800–248–0255; 408–980–4709 (in CA).

Micro Express, 1801 Carnegie Ave., Santa Ana, CA 92705: Free information ■ IBM compatible computers and portable computers. 800–642–7621; 714–852–1400 (in CA).

Micro Generation Computers, 300 McGaw Dr., Edison, NJ 08837: Free information ■ IBM compatible computers and portable computers. 800–872–2841; 201–225–8899 (in NJ).

Micronics Computers, Inc., 232 E. Warren Ave., Fremont, CA 94539: Free information ■ IBM compatible portable computers. 800–659–5901; 510–651–2300 (in CA).

Midern Computer, Inc., 18005 Courtney Ct., City of Industry, CA 91748: Free information ■ IBM compatible portable computers. 800–669–1624; 818–964–8682.

Mitsuba Computers, 1925 Wright Ave., La Verne, CA 91750: Free information ■ IBM compatible portable computers. 800–648–7822; 714–392–2000 (in CA).

Modern Computer Corporation, 1 World Trade Center, Ste. 7967, New York, NY 10048: Free information ■ IBM compatible portable computers. 212–488–5916.

Morse Technology, Inc., 17531 Railroad St., Unit 1, City of Industry, CA 91748: Free information ■ IBM compatible portable computers. 800–356–8688; 818–854–8688 (in CA).

NCR Corporation, 1700 S. Patterson Blvd., Dayton, OH 45479: Free information ■ IBM compatible portable computers. 513–445–1184.

NEC Technologies, Inc., 1414 Massachusetts Ave., Boxborough, MA 01719: Free information ■ IBM compatible computers, portable computers, and printers. 800–FONENEC; 508–264–8000 (in MA).

Northgate Computer Systems, Inc., P.O. Box 59080, Minneapolis, MN 55459: Free information ■ IBM compatible computers and portable computers. 800–549–1993; 612–943–8181 (in MN).

Olivetti USA, Office Products Division, 765 U.S. Hwy. 202 South, Somerville, NJ 08876: Free information ■ IBM compatible computers and portable computers. 800–243–4821; 201–526–8200 (in NJ).

Panasonic, Panasonic Way, Secaucus, NJ 07094: Free information ■ IBM compatible portable computers. 201–348–7000.

Philips Consumer Electronics Company, One Philips Dr., Knoxville, TN 37914: Free information ■ IBM compatible portable computers. 615–521–4316.

Psion Computers, 118 Echo Lake Rd., Watertown, CT 06795: Free information ■ IBM compatible portable computers. 203–274–7521.

Radio Shack, Division Tandy Corporation, 1500 One Tandy Center, Fort Worth, TX 76102: Free catalog ■ IBM compatible computers, portable computers, monitors, dot matrix and laser printers, and other accessories. 817–390–3700.

SAI Systems Laboratories, Inc., 911 Bridgeport Ave., Shelton, CT 06484: Free information ■ IBM compatible portable computers. 800–331–0488; 203–926–0374 (in CT).

The Sampo Corporation of America, Industrial Products Division, 5550 Peachtree Industrial Blvd., Norcross, GA 30342: Free information ■ IBM compatible portable computers. 404–449–6220.

Sharp Electronics, Sharp Plaza, Mahwah, NJ 07430: Free information ■ IBM compatible computers and portable computers. 800–BE–SHARP.

Tangent Computer, Inc., 197 Airport Blvd., Burlingame, CA 94010: Free information ■ IBM compatible computers and portable computers. 800–223–6677; 415–342–9388 (in CA).

Texas Instruments, Inc., P.O. Box 202230, Austin, TX 78720: Free information ■ IBM compatible portable computers. 800–527–3500.

Toshiba America, 9740 Irvine Blvd., Irvine, CA 92718: Free information ■ IBM compatible portable computers. 800–334–3445; 714–583–3000 (in CA).

Zenith Data Systems, 2150 E. Lake Cook Rd., Buffalo Grove, IL 60089: Free information ■ IBM compatible computers, portable computers, and monitors. 800–553–0331; 708–808–5000 (in IL).

Zeos International, Ltd., 530 5th Ave., St. Paul, MN 55112: Free information ■ IBM compatible computers and portable computers. 800–423–5891; 612–633–4591 (in MN).

Computer Retailers

Alltech Electronics Company, Inc., 602 Garrison St., Oceanside, CA 92054: Free information ■ Apple disk drives, RAM chips, diskettes, monitors, RAM disks and expansion cards, power supplies, accessories and cables, hard drives, and other peripherals. 619–721–7733.

CDA Computer Sales, 1 CDA Plaza, P.O. Box 533, Califon, NJ 07830: Free catalog ■ Apple and Macintosh computers, hard drives, modems, printers, peripheral boards, accessories, software, image scanners, printer ribbons, cables, dust covers, and paper. 201–832–9007.

Roger Coats, 20200 Nine Mile Rd., St. Clair Shores, MI 48080: Free information ■ Apple accessories and peripherals, Laser 128 computers and printers, Applied Engineering cards, chips, drives, scanners, modems, system savers, peripheral cards, other hardware, and software. 800–438–2883; 313–774–8240 (in MI).

Computer Direct, Inc., 22292 N.Pepper Rd., Barrington, IL 60010: Free catalog ■ Apple compatible computers, accessories, and software. 800–BUY–WISE.

Computer Works, 4544 Memorial Dr., Ste. 302, Decatur, GA 30032: Free information ■ Laser computers, disk drives, cards, RAM, monitors, printers, modems, cables, and other accessories. 800–969–6757.

Digital Vision, Inc., 270 Bridge St., Dedham, MA 02026: Free information ■ Color video digitizer for the Apple IIgs and IIe. 617–329–5400.

Fas-Track Computer Products, 7030 Huntley Rd., Columbus, OH 43229: Free information ■ Apple accessories and peripherals. Includes Applied Engineering cards, chips by Zip Technologies, drives, modems, scanners, joysticks, and software. 800–421–4698; 614–847–4050 (in OH).

Golem Computers, P.O. Box 6698, Westlake Village, CA 91360: Free information ■ Disk drives, hard drives, monitors, printers, modems, utility accessories, hardware, peripheral boards, RAM cards, and software. 800–248–0363; 805–499–7689 (in CA).

Montgomery Grant Mail Order Department, P.O. Box 58, Brooklyn, NY 11230: Free information ■ Equipment and accessories for Commodore and Amiga computers. 718–692–1148.

Jameco Electronics, 1355 Shoreway Rd., Belmont, CA 94002: Free information ■ Accessories and equipment for Apple, Apple IIgs, Macintosh, and IBM computers. 800–831–4242.

Kenosha Computer Center, 2133 91st St., Kenosha, WI 53140: Free information ■ Computers and accessories, cards and peripherals, and software. 414–697–9595.

LRO Computer Sales, 665 W. Jackson St., Woodstock, IL 60098: Free information ■ Apple and Macintosh computers and accessories, memory cards, software, digitizers and scanners, printers, hard drives, modems, and accelerator cards. 800–869–9152; 815–338–8685 (in IL).

Memory Plus Distributors, Inc., 505 S. 48th St., Ste. 104, Tempe, AZ 85281: Free information ■ Accessories and peripherals for Apple computers. 602–820–8819.

Preferred Computing, P.O. Box 815828, Dallas, TX 75381: Free information ■ Software, disk drives and controllers, modems, peripheral boards, transporter cards, audio animator boards, joysticks, mouse devices, and hardware. 800–327–7234.

Q Labs, 15102 Charlevoix, Grosse Pointe, MI 48230: Free catalog ■ Apple IIgs computers, hard drives, Applied Engineering cards, Laser hardware, other peripherals and accessories, and software. 800–443–6697; 313–331–0700 (in MI).

Quality Computers, P.O. Box 665, St. Clair Shores, MI 48080: Free information ■ Macintosh, Apple, and IBM computers software, and Apple accessories. 800–777–3642.

Scottsdale Systems, 1555 W. University Dr., Tempe, AZ 85281: Free information ■ IBM compatible computers, peripherals, accessories, and cards. 602–966–8609.

Sunnytech, 17 Smith St., Englewood, NJ 07631: Free information ■ IBM compatible computers, hard and floppy disk controllers, hard drives, system boards, disk drives, video cards, power supplies, keyboards, and monitors. 201–569–7773.

USA Micro, 2888 Bluff St., Ste. 257, Boulder, CO 80301: Free information ■ Apple and IBM compatible computers and

accessories. 800–537–8596; 303–938–9089 (in CO).

ZIMCO International, Inc., 85–39 213th St., Queens Village, NY 11427: Free information ■ Software, disk drives and controllers, modems, peripheral boards, hardware, monitors, Apple compatible computers and equipment, and other accessories. 718–479–7888.

Dust Covers & Cases

Co-Du-Co Computer Dust Covers, 4802 W. Wisconsin Ave., Milwaukee, WI 53208: Free information ■ Dust covers for computer protection. 800–735–1584.

Computer Covers Unlimited, 3578 Mt. Acadia, San Diego, CA 92111: Free catalog ■ Covers, protectors, and carrying cases for computers and peripherals. 619–277–0622.

Printers, Peripherals & Accessories

APLUS Computer, Inc., 10016 Pioneer Blvd., Santa Fe Springs, CA 90670: Free information ■ I/O cards, disk drives, key boards, system boards, video boards, chassis, power supplies, controllers, hard dives, and monitors for the IBM. 310–949–9345.

Applied Engineering, 3210 Beltline, Dallas, TX 75234: Free information ■ Apple peripherals, cards, and accessories. 214–241–6060.

Buffalo Products, Inc., 2805 19th St. SE, Salem, OR 97302: Free information ■ Printer-sharing control units. 800–345–2356.

Bulldog Computer Products, 3241 Washington Rd., Martinez, GA 30907: Free information ■ Cards and peripherals, disk drives, monitors, cards, mouse devices, modems, software, laptops, and other accessories for the IBM. 800–438–6039.

Canon, One Canon Plaza, Lake Success, NY 11042: Free information ■ Portable printers. 516–488–6700.

Roger Coats, 20200 Nine Mile Rd., St. Clair Shores, MI 48080: Free information ■ Software, Apple accessories and peripherals, Laser 128 computers and printers, Applied Engineering cards, chips, disk drives, scanners, modems, system savers, peripheral cards, and other hardware. 800–438–2883; 313–774–8240 (in MI).

CompUSA, Inc., 15160 Marsh Ln., Dallas, TX 75234: Free catalog ■ Software, DOS, windows, and CD-ROM software; desktop and portable PCs; portable accessories; cards; networking and communications accessories; furniture; books; videogame cartridges; office products and supplies; chips, disk drives, scanners, modems, system savers, peripheral cards, and other equipment. 800–451–7638.

CompuServe, P.O. Box 20212, Columbus, OH 43220: Free information ■ PC/AT emulator for the Amiga. 800–848–8990; 614–457–8650 (in OH).

Computer Covers Unlimited, 3578 Mt. Acadia, San Diego, CA 92111: Free catalog ■ Monitor filters, anti-theft devices, mouse pads, hand/arm rests, foot rests. 619–277–0622.

Computer Discount Warehouse, 2840 Maria, Northbrook, IL 60062: Free information ■ Hardware, software, and peripherals. 800–233–4426; 708–498–1426 (in IL).

Computer Friends, Inc., 14250 NW Science Park Dr., Portland, OR 97229: Free information ■ Ribbon re-inkers, inks, and cartridges. 503–626–2291.

Educational Resources, 1550 Executive Dr., Elgin, IL 60123: Free catalog ■ Computer software, diskettes, accessories and supplies, peripherals and cards, and computers. 800–624–2926; 708–888–8300 (in IL).

Fas-Track Computer Products, 7030 Huntley Rd., Columbus, OH 43229: Free information ■ Software, Apple accessories and peripherals, Applied Engineering cards, chips by Zip Technologies, disk drives, modems, scanners, joysticks, and other hardware. 800–421–4698; 614–847–4050 (in OH).

Gems Computers, Inc., 2115 Old Oakland Rd., San Jose, CA 95131: Free information ■ Accessories for IBM computers and compatibles. Includes controllers, power supplies, floppy disk drives, hard drives, memory cards and chips, video display cards, monitors, modems, back up tapes, mouse devices, trackballs, scanners, math co-processors, keyboards, cases, and cables. 408–432–7557.

Golem Computers, P.O. Box 6698, Westlake Village, CA 91360: Free information ■ Software, disk drives, hard drives, monitors, printers, modems, utility accessories, hardware, peripheral cards, and other accessories. 800–248–0363; 805–499–7689 (in CA).

Great Valley Products, 600 Clark Ave., King of Prussia, PA 19406: Free information ■ Amiga peripheral cards and accessories and hard drives. 215–337–8770.

Harmony Computers, 1801 Flatbush Ave., Brooklyn, NY 11210: Free information ■ IBM cards, peripherals, computers, software, and portable computers. 718–692–2828.

Ingenuity, Inc., 14922 Ramona Blvd., Baldwin Park, CA 91706: Free information ■ Hard drives. 800–346–0811; 818–960–1485 (in CA).

Kinson Products Corporation, 482–484 Sunrise Hwy., Rockville Centre, NY 11570: Free information ■ Transporter cards, disk drives, and hard drives for Apple computers. 516–763–0906.

K–12 MicroMedia Publishing, 6 Arrow Rd., Ramsey, NJ 07446: Free catalog ■ Teaching aids, software, and accessories for Apple, IBM, Macintosh, and Tandy computers. 800–292–1997; 201–825–8888 (in NJ).

Memory Plus Distributors, Inc., 505 S. 48th St., Ste. 104, Tempe, AZ 85281: Free information ■ Apple, Franklin Ace, and Laser 128 computers, peripherals, and accessories. 602–820–8819.

Nisca, Inc., 1919 Old Denton Rd., Ste. 104, Carrollton, TX 75006: Free information ■ Hand-held scanner for IBM computers. 800–245–7226.

Olivetti USA, Office Products Division, 765 US Hwy. 202, Somerville, NJ 08876: Free information ■ Image scanners and dot matrix printers. 800–243–4821; 201–526–8200 (in NJ).

Panasonic, Panasonic Way, Seacaucus, NJ 07094: Free information ■ Monitors and printers. 201–348–7000.

Para Systems, Inc., 1455 LeMay Dr., Carrollton, TX 75007: Free information ■ Uninterruptible power supplies. 800–238–7272.

Rose Electronics, P.O. Box 742571, Houston, TX 77274: Free information ■ Printer-sharing control units. 800–333–9343.

Seiko Instruments USA, Inc., Graphic Devices and Systems Division, 1130

Ringwood Ct., San Jose, CA 95131: Free information ■ Thermal-transfer printer. 408–922–5800.

Silicon Express, 50 E. Mill, Pataskala, OH 43062: Free catalog ■ Software for most computers, printers, disk drive controllers, peripheral cards, mouse devices, joysticks, Apple II compatible hardware and accessories. 800–927–9555; 614–927–0052 (in OH).

Spirit Technology Corporation, 220 W. 2950 South, Salt Lake City, UT 84115: Free information ■ Amiga accessories, peripheral cards, hard drives, and disk drives. 800–433–7572.

Standard Peripherals, P.O. Box 65187, West Des Moines, IA 50265: Free catalog ■ Computer accessories and peripherals for Apple, Laser 128, and Macintosh computers. 800–535–1707; 515–225–7033 (in IA).

Street Electronics Corporation, 6420 Via Real, Carpinteria, CA 93013: Free information ■ Speech processor for Apple computers. 805–684–4593.

Supra Corporation, 1133 Commercial Way, Albany, OR 97321: Free information ■ Hayes-compatible modem, disk drives, hard drives, RAM expansion cards, and other accessories for Amiga computers. 800–727–8772.

Tatung Company of America, Inc., 2850 El Presidio St., Long Beach, CA 90801: Free information ■ Monitors. 310–637–2105.

Tenex Computer Express, P.O. Box 6578, South Bend, IN 46660: Free catalog ■ Amiga and Commodore computers, accessories, tools, software, and supplies. 219–259–7051.

Thunderware, 21 Orinda Way, Orinda, CA 94563: Free information ■ Image scanner for use with the ImageWriter printer. 510–254–6581.

Tic-La-Dex, 3443 Camino Del Rio South, Ste. 326, San Diego, CA 92108: Free catalog ■ Disk keepers, lap top computer case, wrist rests to fit under keyboards as a prevention for carpal tunnel syndrome. 800–827–9467; 619–281–7242.

Tripp-Lite, 500 N. Orleans, Chicago, IL 60610: Free information ■ Power control center. 312–329–1777.

Vitesse, Inc., 13909 Amar Rd., Ste. 2A, La Puente, CA 91746: Free information ■ Image scanner. 818–813–1270.

Software (Public Domain)

Alternative Personal Software, 269 Springside Dr., Ste. C, Hamilton, Ontario, Canada L9B 1P8: Free information ■ Public domain software and shareware for IBM computers. 416–577–4068.

Best Bits & Bytes, P.O. Box 8225, Van Nuys, CA 91409: Free catalog ■ Software for IBM and Macintosh computers. 800–245–2983.

Best Byte Software, P.O. Box 5614, Ste. C, Montreal, Quebec, Canada H2K 1E7: Free catalog ■ Software for the IBM. 514–523–5488.

Big Red Computer Club, 423 Norfolk Ave., Norfolk, NE 68701: Free information ■ Software for Apple II and Apple IIgs computers. 402–379–4680.

Caloke Industries, P.O. Box 18477, Raytown, MO 64133: Free catalog ■ Apple public domain software. 816–478–6185.

Christella Enterprise, P.O. Box 82205, Rochester, MI 48307: Catalog and demonstration disk $2 ■ Public domain software for Apple II and IIgs computers.

CompuServe, P.O. Box 20212, Columbus, OH 43220: Free information ■ Public domain software and shareware for IBM computers. 800–848–8990; 614–457–8650 (in OH).

Computer Analysts, 12904 Buccaneer Rd., Silver Spring, MD 20904: Free information ■ Public domain software and shareware for the IBM. 301–384–1998.

Computer Budget Shopper, 2203 Park Ave., Cheyenne, WY 82007: Catalog $3 ■ Apple II public domain and shareware software.

Computer Supply, 100 Seneca Ave., Rochester, NY 14621: Free information ■ Public domain software and shareware for IBM computers. 716–342–8140.

Diskette Gazette Library, International Datawares, 2278 Trade Zone Blvd., San Jose, CA 95131: Free information ■ Apple II public domain software. 408–262–6660.

Educomp Computer Services, 7434 Trade St., San Diego, CA 92121: Free information

■ Public domain software for Macintosh and IBM computers. 800–843–9497; 619–536–9999 (in CA).

Florida Computer Resources, Inc., 3950 Confederate Point Rd., Jacksonville, FL 32210: Free information ■ Public domain software and shareware for IBM computers. 904–771–7422.

Gemini Marketing, Inc., P.O. Box 640, Duvall, WA 98019: Free catalog ■ Public domain software and shareware for the IBM. 800–346–0139.

High Tech Systems, 138 Main St., Kensington, CT 06037: Free information ■ Public domain software and shareware for IBM computers. 203–828–9938.

Interface Software & Systems, P.O. Box 329, Cookstown, Ontario, Canada L0L 1L0: Free catalog ■ Software for the IBM. 416–229–2381.

International Software Library, 511–104 Encinitas Blvd., Encinitas, CA 92024: Free information ■ Apple software. 619–942–9998.

Krantz Komputer Systems, 1512 Anthony Dr., West Columbia, SC 29172: Free information ■ Public domain software and shareware for the IBM. 803–755–0793.

Micro Star, 1945 Camino Vida Roble, Carlsbad, CA 92008: Free information ■ Public domain software for the IBM. 800–444–1343.

Moonlight Software, P.O. Box 179144, San Diego, CA 92177: Free catalog ■ Software for Apple II and IIgs computers.

PC-Link Hawaii, 1154 Fort Street Mall, Ste. 401, Honolulu, HI 96813: Free information ■ Public domain software and shareware for IBM computers. 808–537–3073.

PC-SIG, 1030D E. Duane Ave., Sunnyvale, CA 94086: Free information ■ Public domain software for the IBM. 800–245–6717.

P.D.E. Software, 2078 Walsh Ave., Santa Clara, CA 95050: Free information ■ Software for Apple II, Apple IIgs, and Macintosh computers. 800–331–8125; 408–496–0624 (in CA).

People's Choice Public Domain Software & Shareware, 235 Germantown Bend Cove, Cordova, TN 38018: Free information

■ Public domain software for the IBM. 800–999–0471.

Public Brand Software, P.O. Box 51315, Indianapolis, IN 46251: Free catalog ■ Public domain software for the IBM. 800–426–3475.

Public Domain Exchange, 2078C Walsh Ave., Santa Clara, CA 95050: Free information ■ Public domain software for Apple II, Apple IIgs, and IBM computers. 800–331–8125; 408–496–0624 (in CA).

Public Domain Software Resource, P.O. Box 7175, Loma Linda, CA 92354: Free information ■ Public domain software for Amiga computers.

Public Software Library, P.O. Box 35705, Houston, TX 77235: Free information ■ Public domain software and shareware for IBM computers. 713–524–6394.

Raymark Enterprises, P.O. Box 70443, Oakland, CA 94612: Free catalog ■ Public domain software and shareware for Apple II and Apple IIgs computers. 800–2APPLE2.

Reasonable Solutions, 2101 W. Main St., Medford, OR 97501: Free information ■ User-supported software for the IBM. 800–876–3475; 503–776–5777 (in OR).

Software Excitement, 6476 Crater Lake Hwy., P.O. Box 3789, Central Point, OR 97502: Free catalog ■ User-supported software and accessories for Apple, Macintosh, Commodore, Amiga, and IBM computers. 800–444–5457.

The Software Labs, 3767 Overland Ave., Los Angeles, CA 90034: Free catalog ■ Public domain software and shareware for IBM computers and compatibles. 800–359–9998.

Trans-Canada Software, 5334 Yonge St., Ste. 2123, Toronto, Canada H2K 1E7: Free list ■ Software for the IBM. 514–523–5488.

Wayzata Technology, 16221 Main Ave., P.O. Box 87, Prior Lake, MN 55372: Free information ■ Apple II public domain software. 612–447–7321.

Software Publishers

Aadvark Development Labs, Inc., Red Bud Cove, Ste. 4, Austin, TX 78746: Free information ■ Graphics and business management software for the Macintosh. 800–336–8002; 512–327–2255 (in TX).

Aatrix Software, P.O. Box 5359, Grand Forks, ND 58200: Free information ■ Business management and personal/home management software for the Macintosh. 800–426–0854.

Abacus, Inc., 547 Frederick St., San Francisco, CA 94117: Free information ■ Software for Amiga, Commodore, IBM, and Macintosh computers. 415–759–9508.

Abacus Software, 5370 52nd St. SE, Grand Rapids, MI 49508: Free information ■ Word processing software for the Commodore. Home/business applications and utilities software for the IBM. 616–698–0325.

Abracadata, P.O. Box 2440, Eugene, OR 97402: Free catalog ■ Graphics software for Apple II, Apple IIgs, IBM, and Macintosh computers. Education, home/business applications, and utilities for the Apple II. 800–451–4871.

Accolade, Inc., 550 S. Winchester Blvd., San Jose, CA 95128: Free information ■ Software for Amiga, Apple II, Apple IIgs, Atari, Commodore, IBM, and Macintosh computers. 408–296–8400.

Acius Software, Inc., 10351 Bubb Rd., Cupertino, CA 95014: Free information ■ Database software for the Macintosh. 408–252–4444.

ACTAsoft, 19700 Wells Dr., Woodland Hills, CA 91364: Free information ■ Home/business applications and education software for Apple computers. 818–996–6731.

Activision, 3885 Bohannon Dr., Menlo Park, CA 94025: Free information ■ Software for Amiga, Apple II, Apple IIgs, Atari, Commodore, IBM, and Macintosh computers. 415–329–0500.

Addison-Wesley Publishing Company, Rt. 128, Reading, MA 01867: Free information ■ Software for Amiga, Apple II, Apple IIgs, Commodore, IBM, and Macintosh computers. 617–944–3700.

Adobe Systems, Inc., 1585 Charleston Rd., P.O. Box 7900, Mountain View, CA 94039: Free information ■ Desktop publishing and graphics software for the IBM. Desktop publishing, graphics, home/business applications, and productivity software for the Macintosh. 415–961–4400.

Advanced Data Systems, Inc., P.O. Box 5717, Winter Park, FL 32793: Free information ■ Education, home/business applications, programming tools, and productivity software for the Macintosh. 407–657–4805.

After-Hours Software, 5636 Van Nuys Blvd., Ste. B, Van Nuys, CA 91401: Free information ■ Database, general and miscellaneous management, programming tools, and business management software for the Macintosh. 818–780–2220.

Aldus Corporation, 411 1st Ave., Seattle, WA 98104: Free information ■ Desktop publishing software for the IBM. Desktop publishing, education, graphics, home/business applications, and utilities software for the Macintosh. 206–622–5500.

Alsoft Software, Inc., P.O. Box 927, Spring, TX 77383: Free information ■ Macintosh communications, programming tools, utilities, and health management software. 713–353–4090.

AM Software, P.O. Box 25010, Kansas City, MO 64119: Free information ■ Home/business applications software for the IBM. 813–452–2127.

Anco Software USA, Inc., P.O. Box 292, Burgettston, PA 15021: Free information ■ Amiga word processing and entertainment/games software. 412–947–4246.

Aperture Technologies, Inc., 84 W. Park Pl., Stamford, CT 06901: Free information ■ Productivity software for the Macintosh. 203–975–7587.

Apple Computer, Inc., 2025 Mariani Ave., Cupertino, CA 95014: Free information ■ Database, spreadsheet, and word processing software for Apple II, Apple IIgs, and Macintosh computers. 408–996–1010.

Artworx Software Company, Inc., 1844 Penfield Rd., Penfield, NY 14526: Free information ■ Education and entertainment/games software for Amiga, Apple II, Commodore, IBM, and Macintosh computers. Home/business applications for the Macintosh. 800–828–6573.

Ashton-Tate, 20101 Hamilton Ave., Torrance, CA 90509: Free information ■ Word processing, education, and database software for IBM and Macintosh computers. 310–329–8000.

Baudville, Inc., 5380 52nd St. SE, Grand Rapids, MI 49512: Free information ■ Software for Amiga, Apple II, Apple IIgs, Commodore, IBM, and Macintosh computers. 616–698–0888.

Beagle Brothers, 6215 Ferris Square, Ste. 100, San Diego, CA 92121: Free information ■ Software for Apple II, Apple IIgs, Commodore, IBM, and Macintosh computers. 619–452–5500.

Bede Tech, Inc., 8327 Clinton Rd., Cleveland, OH 44144: Free information ■ Macintosh graphics software. 216–631–4214.

Bemak Enterprises, 728 Royal St., Alton, IL 62002: Free information ■ Entertainment/games software for Apple computers.

Berkeley Systems, 1700 Shattuck Ave., Berkeley, CA 94709: Free information ■ Software for Apple II, Commodore, IBM, and Macintosh computers. 510–540–5535.

Best Choice, 129 Wheeler Ave., Los Gatos, GA 95032: Free information ■ Macintosh graphics software. 800–358–2984; 800–553–2188 (in CA).

Bible Research Systems, 2013 Wells Branch Pkwy., #304, Austin, TX 78728: Free brochure ■ Bible education software for Apple II, IBM, and Macintosh computers. 800–423–1228; 512–251–7541 (in TX).

Big Red Computer Club, 423 Norfolk Ave., Norfolk, NE 68701: Free catalog ■ Utilities, education, productivity, entertainment/games, graphics, and programming tools for Apple II and Apple IIgs computers. 402–379–4680.

Bloc Publishing Group, 800 SW 37th Ave., Ste. 765, Coral Gables, FL 33134: Free information ■ Productivity software for the IBM. 305–445–0903.

Blue Ribbon Bakery, Inc., 1248 Clairmont Rd., Ste. 3D, Atlanta, GA 30030: Free information ■ Education and business/home applications software for the Amiga. 404–377–1514.

Blyth Software, 1065 E. Hillsdale Blvd., Ste. 300, Foster City, CA 94404: Free information ■ Database and productivity software for the Macintosh. 415–571–0222.

Bootware Software Company, Inc., 28024 Dorothy Dr., Agoura Hills, CA 91301: Free information ■ Graphics software for the Macintosh. 818–706–3887.

Borland International, 1800 Green Hills Rd., Scotts Valley, CA 95066: Free information ■ Debugger and assembly software for IBM computers. Database, desktop publishing, education, programming tools, and

utilities software for the Macintosh. 800–331–0877.

William K. Bradford Publishing Company, P.O. Box 1355, Concord, MA 01742: Free information ■ Educational software for Apple, IBM, and Tandy computers. 800–421–2009.

BrainPower, Inc., 30497 Canwood St., Ste. 201, Agoura Hills, CA 91301: Free information ■ Database, education, home/business applications, programming tools, and word processing software for the Macintosh. 818–707–1712.

Robert A. Brent Software, Station B, P.O. Box 26183, San Francisco, CA 94126: Free information ■ Productivity and entertainment/games software for Apple computers. 415–397–5759.

Britannica Software, Inc., 545 4th St., San Francisco, CA 94107: Free information ■ Education and entertainment/games software for the Amiga and Apple IIgs. 415–597–5555.

Broderbund Software, Inc., P.O. Box 6125, Novato, CA 94948: Free information ■ Software for Amiga, Apple, Apple IIgs, Atari, Commodore, IBM, and Macintosh computers. 800–521–6263; 415–492–3200 (in CA).

The Byte Works, Inc., 4700 Irving Blvd. NW, Ste. 207, Albuquerque, NM 87114: Free information ■ Education, programming tools, and utilities software for the Apple IIgs. 505–898–8183.

Centaur Software, Inc., P.O. Box 4400, Redondo Beach, CA 90278: Free information ■ Utilities, entertainment/games, and education software for the Amiga. 310–542–2226.

Central Point Software, Inc., 15220 NW Greenbrier Pkwy., Beaverton, OR 97006: Free information ■ Utilities software for Apple II, Apple IIgs, IBM, and Macintosh computers. 503–690–8090.

CE Software, Inc., P.O. Box 65580, West Des Moines, IA 50265: Free information ■ Macintosh communications, graphics, home/business applications, and utilities software. 515–224–1995.

Champion Swiftware, 6617 Gettysburg Dr., Madison, WI 53705: Free information ■ Word processing software for the Macintosh. 608–833–1777.

Chariot Software Group, 3659 India St., Ste. 100, San Diego, CA 92103: Free information ■ Education and personal/home management Macintosh software. 619–298–0202.

CheckMark Software, Inc., 1520 E. Mulberry, Ste. 200, Fort Collins, CO 80524: Free information ■ Home/business applications software for the Macintosh. 303–484–3541.

Checkmate Technology, Inc., 509 S. Rockford Dr., Tempe, AZ 85281: Free information ■ Apple II communications software. 602–966–5802.

ChipSoft, Inc., 5045 Shoreham Pl., Ste. 100, San Diego, CA 92122: Free information ■ Home/business applications software for the IBM. 619–453–8722.

Cinnemaware Corporation, 4165 Thousand Oaks Blvd., Westlake Village, CA 91362: Free information ■ Entertainment/games and education software for the Amiga and Apple IIgs. 805–495–6515.

Claris Corporation, 5201 Patrick Henry Dr., P.O. Box 58168, Santa Clara, CA 95052: Free information ■ Word processing software for Apple II, Apple IIgs, IBM, and Macintosh computers. 408–727–8227.

Classic Concepts Futureware, P.O. Box 786, Bellingham, WA 98227: Free information ■ Graphics and word processing software for the Amiga. 206–733–8342.

CompServCo, 1921 Corporate Square, Ste. 1, Slidell, LA 70458: Free information ■ Macintosh graphics software. 504–649–0484.

Compu-Arch, 9348 Civic Center Dr., Ste. 101, Beverly Hills, CA 90210: Free information ■ Macintosh graphics software. 310–312–6632.

Compu-Teach, Inc., 78 Olive St., New Haven, CT 06511: Free information ■ Education and entertainment/games software for Apple computers. 800–44–TEACH; 203–777–7738 (in CT).

Computerware, P.O. Box 668, Encinitas, CA 92024: Free information ■ Home/business applications software for the Amiga. 619–436–3512.

Conduit, The University of Iowa, Oakdale Campus, Iowa City, IA 52242: Free information ■ Education software for Apple II,

Apple IIgs, and IBM computers. 319–335–4100.

Cougar Mountain Software, 2609 Kootenai, Box 6886, Boise, ID 83707: Free information ■ Accounting software for IBM computers. 800–344–2540; 208–344–2540 (in ID).

Cyma, 1400 E. Southern Ave., Tempe, AZ 85282: Free information ■ Accounting software for IBM computers. 602–831–2607.

Data East USA, 1850 Little Orchard St., San Jose, CA 95125: Free information ■ Entertainment/games software for Amiga, Apple II, Apple IIgs, and Commodore computers. 408–286–7080.

Davidson & Associates, Inc., 3135 Kashiwa St., Torrance, CA 90505: Free information ■ Education software for Amiga, Apple II, Apple IIgs, Commodore, IBM, and Macintosh computers. Communications software for Apple computers. 800–556–8141; 310–534–4070 (in CA).

Davka Corporation, 7074 N. Western Ave., Chicago, IL 60645: Free information ■ Education, graphics, entertainment/games, desktop publishing, word processing, graphics, personal/home management, and other software for Apple, IBM, and Macintosh computers. 800–621–8227; 312–465–4070 (in IL).

Dayna Communications, 50 S. Main St., 5th Floor, Salt Lake City, UT 84144: Free information ■ Communications software for the Macintosh. 801–531–0203.

Delta Point, 200 Heritage Harbor, Ste. G, Monterey, CA 93940: Free information ■ Word processing software for the IBM. 408–648–4000.

Deneba Software, 3305 NW 74th Ave., Miami, FL 33122: Free information ■ Macintosh productivity, utilities, and graphics software. 305–594–6965.

Designing Minds, Inc., 3006 N. Main St., Logan, UT 84321: Free information ■ Education, graphics, and entertainment/games software for the Amiga. 801–752–2501.

Desktop Graphics, 7208 Franciscan Dr., Fort Worth, TX 76133: Free information ■ Graphics, home/business applications, and productivity software for the Macintosh. 817–346–0556.

Digital Creations, 2865 Sunrise Blvd., Ste. 103, Rancho Cordova, CA 95742: Free infor-

mation ■ Amiga graphics and productivity software. 916–344–4825.

DigiTech Systems, 34684 Ricard O. Dr., Sterling Heights, MI 48310: Free information ■ Macintosh graphics software. 313–264–3039.

Walt Disney Computer Software, 500 S. Buena Vista St., Burbank, CA 91521: Free information ■ Entertainment/games software for Apple computers. 818–560–1111.

Dow Jones & Company, Inc., P.O. Box 300, Princeton, NJ 08543: Free information ■ Communications, home/business applications, and productivity software for the Macintosh. 609–452–7040.

Dream Maker Software, 7217 Foothill Blvd., Tujunga, CA 91042: Free information ■ Clip art software for the Macintosh and IBM computers. Includes business images, sports, and world flags. 800–876–5665.

Dubl-Click Software, Inc., 9316 Deering Ave., Chatsworth, CA 91311: Free information ■ Macintosh graphics and utilities software. 818–700–9525.

Dynamic Graphics, Inc., 6000 N. Forest Park Dr., Peoria, IL 61614: Free information ■ Macintosh graphics software. 309–688–8800.

Educational Activities, 1937 Grand Ave., Baldwin, NY 11510: Free information ■ Education software for Apple computers. 800–645–3739; 516–223–4666 (in NY).

Electronic Arts, 1450 Fashion Island Blvd., San Mateo, CA 94404: Free information ■ Software for Amiga, Apple II, Apple IIgs, Commodore, IBM, and Macintosh computers. 800–245–4525.

Eliot Software Company, P.O. Box 337, Eliot, ME 03903: Free information ■ Macintosh communications and home/business applications software. 800–755–9887.

EZWare Corporation, 29 Bala Ave., Ste. 206, Bala Cynwyd, PA 19004: Free information ■ Macintosh home/business applications software. 215–667–4064.

FantasyWorks Software, 2333 Don Dodson Dr., Ste. 258, Bedford, TX 76021: Free information ■ Entertainment/games software for Apple computers. 817–283–7440.

First Byte, 3100 S. Harbor Blvd., Ste. 150, Santa Ana, CA 92704: Free information ■ Education software for Amiga, Apple IIgs, and Macintosh computers. Desktop publishing software for the Apple and entertainment/games for the Macintosh. 800–523–8070; 714–432–1740 (in CA).

1st Desk Systems, Inc., 7 Industrial Park Rd., Medway, MA 02053: Free information ■ Database software for the Macintosh. 800–522–2286.

Flexware, 15404 E. Valley Blvd., City of Industry, CA 91746: Free information ■ Macintosh home/business applications and productivity software. 818–961–0237.

Fox Software, Inc., 134 W. South Broadway, Perrysburg, OH 43551: Free information ■ Database management software for IBM computers. 419–874–0162.

Frame Technology Corporation, 1010 Rincon Cir., San Jose, CA 95131: Free information ■ Desktop publishing software for IBM computers. 408–433–3311.

D.V. Franks, 3721 Sue Ellen Dr., Raleigh, NC 27604: Free information ■ Graphics software for the Macintosh. 919–872–5379.

Freemyers Design, 575 Nelson Ave., Oroville, CA 95965: Free information ■ Macintosh graphics and productivity software. 916–533–9365.

The FreeSoft Company, 105 McKinley Rd., Beaver Falls, PA 15010: Free information ■ Communications software for the Macintosh. 412–846–2700.

Free Spirit Software, Inc., 58 Noble St., P.O. Box 128, Kutztown, PA 19530: Free information ■ Education, entertainment/games, and other software for Amiga computers. 215–683–5609.

Gamco Industries, Box 1911, Big Spring, TX 79721: Free information ■ Education, entertainment/games software for Apple computers. 800–351–1404; 915–267–6327 (in TX).

Gamestar, Mediagenic, 3885 Bohannon Dr., Menlo Park, CA 94025: Free information ■ Entertainment/games for Amiga, Apple, Commodore, and IBM computers. 415–329–0800.

Gessler Publishing Company, Inc., 55 W. 13th St., Ste. 34, New York, NY 10011: Free information ■ Education/games software for Apple, Apple IIgs, Commodore, and IBM computers. 212–627–0099.

Gold Disk, Inc., 5155 Spectrum Way, Unit 5, Mississauga, Ontario, Canada L4W 5A1: Free information ■ Desktop publishing, entertainment/games, home/business applications, and graphics software for Amiga computers. 416–602–4000.

Graham Software Company, 8609 Ingalls Cir., Arvada, CO 80003: Free information ■ Utilities and word processing software for the Macintosh. 303–422–0757.

Great Wave Software, 5353 Scotts Valley Dr., Scotts Valley, CA 95066: Free information ■ Education software for Apple IIgs and Macintosh computers. 408–438–1990.

Harvard Associates, Inc., 10 Holworthy St., Cambridge, MA 02138: Free information ■ Home/business applications, graphics, and utilities software for IBM and Macintosh computers. 617–492–0660.

Hayes Microcomputer Products, Inc., P.O. Box 105203, Atlanta, GA 30348: Free information ■ Communications software for IBM and Macintosh computers. 404–449–8791.

Heizer Software, P.O. Box 232019, Pleasant Hill, CA 94523: Free information ■ Business management, graphics, communications, computer management, programming tools, spreadsheets, utilities, education, word processing, and personal/home management software for the Macintosh. 800–888–7667.

HindSight, P.O. Box 4242, Highlands Ranch, CO 80126: Free information ■ Home/business applications software for the Macintosh. 303–791–3770.

Hi Tech Expressions, 584 Broadway, Ste. 509, New York, NY 10012: Free information ■ Software for Amiga, Apple, Apple IIgs, Atari, Commodore, and IBM computers. Includes graphics, desktop publishing, education, word processing, entertainment/games, and utilities. 212–941–1224.

Holosoft Technologies, 701 Paul St., Escondido, CA 92027: Free information ■ Graphics software for the Amiga. 619–743–0089.

HowardSoft, 1224 Prospect St., Ste. 150, La Jolla, CA 92037: Free information ■ Home/business applications and productivity software for the Apple IIgs and IBM. 800–822–4TAX.

Image Club Graphics, 1902 11th St. SE, Ste. 5, Calgary, Alberta, Canada T2G 3G2: Free information ■ Clip art, desktop publishing, and fonts software for the Macintosh. 403–262–8008.

Impulse, Inc., 6870 Shingle Creek Pkwy., Ste. 112, Minneapolis, MN 55430: Free information ■ Graphics software for the Amiga. 612–566–0221.

inCider/A+ Special Products, 80 Elm St., Peterborough, NH 03458: Free information ■ Productivity, graphics, desktop publishing, education, and home/business applications software for Apple computers. 800–343–0728; 924–0100 (in NH).

Incognito Software, 26717 Plymouth, Redford, MI 48239: Free information ■ Entertainment/games and graphics software for Amiga computers. 313–937–1850.

Infocom, Inc., 3885 Bohannon Dr., Menlo Park, CA 94025: Free information ■ Entertainment/games software for Amiga, Apple, Apple IIgs, Commodore, IBM, and Macintosh computers. 415–329–0800.

Informix Software, Inc., 4100 Bohannon Dr., Menlo Park, CA 94025: Free information ■ Spreadsheet software for the Macintosh. 415–322–4100.

Innovation Advertising & Design, 41 Mansfield Ave., Essex Junction, VT 05452: Free information ■ Clip art software for advertising copy design graphics for IBM and Macintosh computers. Includes logos, trademarks, international symbols, icons, and world flags. 802–879–1164.

Insight Development Corporation, 2200 Powell St., Ste. 500, Emeryville, CA 94608: Free information ■ Utilities software for the Macintosh. 510–652–4115.

Interleaf, Inc., Ten Canal Pk., Cambridge, MA 02141: Free information ■ Desktop publishing software for IBM computers. 617–577–9800.

Interstel Corporation, c/o Electronic Arts, 1450 Fashion Island Blvd., San Mateo, CA 94404: Free information ■ Entertainment/games software for the Amiga and IBM. 800–245–4525.

Intracorp, Inc., 14540 SW 136th St., Miami, FL 33186: Free information ■ Desktop publishing, education, entertainment/games, graphics, and home/business applications software for the Amiga and

IBM. Entertainment/games software for Apple and Commodore. 800–468–7226.

Intuit, 66 Willow Pl., Menlo Park, CA 94025: Free information ■ Home/business applications software for the IBM and Macintosh. 800–624–8742.

Island Computer Services, 3501 E. Yacht Dr., Long Beach, NC 28461: Free information ■ Education/games software for Apple, Commodore, and IBM computers. 919–278–7444.

Jam Technologies, 685 Market St, Ste. 860, San Francisco, CA 94105: Free information ■ Home/business applications and programming tools software for the Macintosh. 415–442–0795.

JPL Associates, 18 Sequoia Way, San Francisco, CA 94127: Free information ■ Macintosh utilities software. 415–469–8862.

Kabbalah Software, 8 Price Dr., Edison, NJ 08817: Free price list ■ Hebrew and Jewish software for the IBM. Includes word processing software, professional clip art, Hebrew fonts for laser printers, fonts and graphics for the Print Shop, and Jewish calendar conversion software. 908–572–0891.

Keypunch Software, 1221 Pioneer Building, St. Paul, MN 55101: Free information ■ Entertainment/games software for the Amiga and IBM. 612–292–1490.

Krell Software Corporation, Flowerfield Bldg. #7, Ste. 1D, St. James, NY 11780: Free information ■ Education software for Apple computers. 800–245–7355; 516–584–7900 (in NY).

K–12 MicroMedia Publishing, 6 Arrow Rd., Ramsey, NJ 07446: Free catalog ■ Teaching aids, software, and accessories for Apple, IBM, Macintosh, and Tandy computers. 800–292–1997; 201–825–8888 (in NJ).

Lake Forest Logic, Inc., 28101 Ballard Rd., Unit E, Lake Forest, IL 60045: Free information ■ Programming and utilities software for the Amiga. 708–816–6666.

Lattice, Inc., 2500 S. Highland Ave., Lombard, IL 60148: Free information ■ Productivity and home/business applications software for Amiga computers. 800–444–4309; 708–916–1600 (in IL).

Lawrence Productions, 1800 S. 35th St., Galesburg, MI 49053: Free information ■

Entertainment/games software for Amiga and Apple IIgs computers. 800–421–4157; 616–665–7075 (in MI).

The Learning Company, 6493 Kaiser Dr., Fremont, CA 94555: Free information ■ Education/games software for Apple, Apple IIgs, Commodore, IBM, and Macintosh computers. Word processing software for the Apple. 800–852–2255; 510–792–2101 (in CA).

Letraset USA, 40 Eisenhower Dr., Paramus, NJ 07653: Free information ■ Graphics software for the Macintosh. 201–845–6100.

Lionheart Press, Inc., P.O. Box 379, Alburg, VT 05440: Free information ■ Amiga home/business applications and productivity software. 514–933–4918.

Live Studios, 30151 Branding Iron Rd., San Juan Capistrano, CA 92675: Free information ■ Entertainment/games software for the Amiga. 714–661–8337.

Lotus Development Corporation, 55 Cambridge Pkwy., Cambridge, MA 02142: Free information ■ Communications; desktop publishing; education; graphics; home/business applications; productivity; utilities; and word processing software for the IBM. 617–577–8500.

Magnum Software, 21115 Devonshire St., Ste. 337, Chatsworth, CA 91311: Free information ■ Entertainment/games, graphics, and productivity software for Macintosh computers. 818–700–0510.

Mastertronic International, 18001 Cowan Ct., Ste. A, Irvine, CA 92714: Free information ■ Entertainment/games software for the Amiga, Commodore, and IBM. 714–833–8710.

Meca Software, P.O. Box 907, Westport, CT 06881: Free information ■ Home/business applications software for Apple, Apple IIgs, IBM, and Macintosh computers. 800–223–7200.

MECC Software, 6160 Summit Dr. North, Minneapolis, MN 55430: Free information ■ Education software for Apple computers. 800–685–MECC; 612–569–1500 (in MN).

Metro Imagebase, Inc., 18623 Ventura Blvd., Ste. 210, Tarzana, CA 91356: Free information ■ Clip art software for the Macintosh or IBM. 800–525–1552.

MicroGram Systems, P.O. Box 252, La Honda, CA 94020: Free information ■

Programming tools and productivity and education software for Apple computers. 415–747–0811.

MicroIllusions, 17408 Chatsworth St., Grenada Hills, CA 91344: Free information ■ Entertainment/games and education software for the Amiga, Apple IIgs, Commodore, and IBM. Home/business applications and graphics software for the Amiga. 818–360–3715.

Microlytics, Inc., 2 Tobey Village Office Park, Pittsford, NY 14534: Free information ■ Macintosh Word processing software. 716–248–9150.

MicroMaps Software, P.O. Box 757, Lamberville, NJ 08530: Free brochure ■ Maps in clip art software for desktop publishing for the Macintosh and IBM. 800–334–4291.

MicroProse Software, Inc., 180 Lakefront Dr., Hunt Valley, MD 21030: Free information ■ Entertainment/games software for the Amiga, Apple, Apple IIgs, Atari, Commodore, and IBM. 410–771–1151.

MicroSearch, Inc., 9896 Southwest Freeway, Houston, TX 77074: Free information ■ Desktop publishing, graphics and word processing software for Amiga computers. 713–988–2818.

Microserve, 4412 Spicewood Springs, Ste. 1000–F, Austin, TX 78759: Free information ■ Macintosh desktop publishing, home/business applications, and productivity software. 512–343–0180.

Microsoft Press, One Microsoft Way, Redmond, WA 98052: Free catalog ■ Productivity software for the Amiga and Macintosh. Educational software for the Apple. Database, entertainment/games, graphics, home/business applications, productivity and programming tools, and spreadsheet software for the Macintosh. 206–882–8080.

MicroSPARC/Nibble Publications, 52 Domino Dr., Concord, MA 01742: Free information ■ Software for Apple, Apple IIgs, and Macintosh computers. 800–888–1660.

Milliken Publishing, 1100 Research Blvd., P.O. Box 21579, St. Louis, MO 63132: Free information ■ Desktop publishing and entertainment/games software for the Apple and Apple IIgs. 800–643–0008; 314–991–4220 (in MO).

Mindplay Software, 3130 N. Dodge Blvd., Tucson, AZ 85716: Free information ■

Education software for Apple computers. 800–221–7911.

Mindscape, Inc., 3444 Dundee Rd., Northbrook, IL 60062: Free information ■ Education and entertainment/games software for Amiga, Apple, Apple IIgs, Atari, Commodore, IBM, and Macintosh. Home/business applications software for the IBM, and graphics software for the Macintosh. 708–480–1948.

New Horizons Software, Inc., 206 Wild Basin Rd., Ste. 109, Austin, TX 78746: Free information ■ Graphics and word processing software for the Amiga. 512–328–6650.

Nolo Press, 950 Parker St., Berkeley, CA 94710: Free information ■ Home/business and productivity software for Apple, Apple IIgs, IBM, and Macintosh computers. 510–549–1976.

Nordic Software, 917 Carlos Dr., Lincoln, NE 68505: Free information ■ Education, productivity, and utilities software for the Macintosh. 402–488–5086.

Peter Norton Company, 100 Wilshire Blvd., 9th Floor, Santa Monica, CA 90401: Free information ■ Utilities software for IBM computers. 310–319–2000.

Nuvo Labs, 10264 E. Estates Dr., Cupertino, CA 95014: Free information ■ Utilities software for the Macintosh. 408–253–5766.

On Technology, Inc., One Cambridge Center, Cambridge, MA 02142: Free information ■ Desktop publishing software for the IBM. 617–225–2545.

On Three, Inc., 123 Groveland Ave., Riverside, IL 60546: Free information ■ Apple IIgs programming tools and utilities software. 708–447–3924.

Opcode Systems, 3641 Haven Dr., Ste. A, Menlo Park, CA 94025: Free information ■ Macintosh education software. 415–369–8131.

Orange Cherry Software, P.O. Box 390, Pound Ridge, NY 10576: Free catalog ■ Education software for Macintosh, Apple IIgs, and IBM computers. 800–672–6002.

Orange Micro, Inc., 1400 N. Lakeview Ave., Anaheim, CA 92807: Free information ■ Communications and education software for Apple and Apple IIgs computers. 800–832–3201.

Origin Systems, Inc., 136 Harvey Rd., Building B, Londonberry, NH 03053: Free information ■ Entertainment/games software for the Amiga and IBM. 603–644–3360.

Oxxi, Inc., 1339 E. 28th St., Long Beach, CA 90806: Free information ■ Amiga entertainment/games, graphics, and home/business applications software. 310–427–1227.

Paracomp, Inc., 1725 Montgomery St., 2nd Floor, San Francisco, CA 94111: Free information ■ Graphics software for the Macintosh. 415–956–4091.

Paragon Concepts, Inc., 990 Highland Dr., Ste. 312, Solana Beach, CA 92075: Free information ■ Word processing software for the Macintosh. 619–481–1477.

PC Globe, Inc., 4700 S. McClintock Dr., Tempe, AZ 85282: Free information ■ Educational and entertainment/games software for Apple computers. 800–255–2789.

Personal Bibliographic Software, Inc., P.O. Box 4250, Ann Arbor, MI 48106: Free information ■ Communications and word processing software for the Macintosh. 313–996–1580.

Personal Financial Services, P.O. Box 1401, Melville, NY 11747: Free information ■ Tax preparation software for Apple IIgs computers. 516–757–3201.

Pixel Perfect, P.O. Box 2470, Escondido, CA 92033: Free information ■ Business and animal clip art software for the Macintosh and IBM.

Polarware, Inc., 1055 Paramount Pkwy., Ste. A, Batavia, IL 60510: Free information ■ Amiga, Commodore, and Macintosh education and entertainment/games software. Entertainment/games and graphics software for the Apple, Apple IIgs, and IBM. 708–232–1984.

Power Industries LP, 37 Walnut St., Wellesley Hills, MA 02181: Free information ■ Graphics and productivity software for Apple computers. 800–395–5008; 617–235–7733 (in MA).

Power-Up Software, P.O. Box 7600, San Mateo, CA 94403: Free information ■ Communications, database, desktop publishing, education, graphics, home/business applications, productivity, programming tools, spreadsheets, word processing, and utilities software for the IBM. 800–851–2917; 800–223–1479 (in CA).

Pre-Engineering Software, 1266 Kimbro Dr., Baton Rouge, LA 70808: Free information ■ Education software for Apple computers. 504–769–3728.

Prelude Software, P.O. Box 1317, Costa Mesa, CA 92628: Free information ■ Productivity software for Apple computers. 714–751–5736.

Print Shop Users Club, P.O. Box 150, Renton, WA 98057: Free information ■ Graphics clip art software for Apple and Apple IIgs computers. 206–251–6570.

Prodigy Services Company, 445 Hamilton Ave., White Plains, NY 10601: Free information ■ Utilities software for Macintosh and IBM computers. 800–222–6922.

Programmed Intelligence Corporation, 3295 River Exchange Dr., Ste. 550, Norcross, GA 30092: Free information ■ Report writing software for the IBM. 800–458–0386; 404–446–8880 (in GA).

Pro Plus Software, 919 N. Stapley, Ste. N, Mesa, AZ 85203: Free information ■ Home/business applications and productivity software for the Macintosh. 602–461–3296.

Psygnosis, 29 Saint Marys Ct., Brookline, MA 02146: Free information ■ Entertainment/games software for the Amiga computer. 617–731–3553.

P3 Software, Inc., 246 Nottingham Ave., Glenview, IL 60025: Free information ■ Home/business applications and productivity software for the Macintosh. 708–729–2555.

Qualitas Trading Company, 6907 Norfolk Rd., Berkeley, CA 94705: Free information ■ Graphics/drawing, word processing, business management, and education software for the Macintosh. 510–848–8080.

Quality Computers, P.O. Box 665, St. Clair Shores, MI 48080: Free information ■ Education and productivity software for Apple computers. 800–777–3642.

Quark, Inc., 300 S. Jackson, Denver, CO 80209: Free information ■ Desktop publishing software for Macintosh and IBM computers. Macintosh education and productivity software. 303–934–2211.

Quinsept, Inc., P.O. Box 216, Lexington, MA 02173: Free information ■ Home/business applications software for Apple, IBM, and Macintosh computers. 800–637–7668; 617–641–2930 (in MA).

Radio Shack, Division Tandy Corporation, 1500 One Tandy Center, Fort Worth, TX 76102: Free information ■ Software for Tandy computers. 817–390–3700.

RainBird Software, P.O. Box 2227, Menlo Park, CA 94026: Free information ■ Entertainment/games software for Amiga computers. 415–322–3995.

Random House Software, Inc., 400 Hahn Rd., Westminster, MD 21157: Free information ■ Software in all categories for the Apple, Apple IIgs, Commodore, and IBM. 800–638–6460.

RealData, Inc., 78 N. Main St., South Norwalk, CT 06854: Free information ■ Macintosh home/business applications and productivity software. 203–857–4310.

Resource-Central, P.O. Box 11250, Overland Park, KS 66207: Free information ■ Education and utilities software for Apple computers. 913–469–6502.

Santis Systems, Inc., 900 South US Highway One, Jupiter, FL 33477: Free brochure ■ Business management software for the IBM. 407–575–1030.

SBT Corporation, One Harbor Dr., Sausalito, CA 94965: Free information ■ Home/business applications software for the Macintosh. 415–331–9900.

Scandinavian PC Systems, 51 Monroe St., #1101, Rockville, MD 20850: Free information ■ Word processing and education software for the IBM. 301–294–7453.

Scholastic Software, 2931 E. McCarty St., P.O. Box 7502, Jefferson City, MO 651012: Free information ■ Education, utilities, programming tools, and word processing software for Apple, Apple IIgs, and IBM. 800–541–5513.

Semaphore Corporation, 207 Granada Dr., Aptos, CA 95003: Free information ■ Macintosh communications software. 408–688–9200.

Sensible Software, Inc., 335 E. Big Beaver, Ste. 207, Troy, MI 48083: Free information ■ Software for Apple, Apple IIgs, IBM, and Macintosh computers. 313–528–1950.

Seven Hills Software Corporation, 2310 Oxford Rd., Tallahassee, FL 32304: Free information ■ Education, graphics, and

desktop publishing software for Apple computers. 904–575–0566.

Sierra On-Line, Inc., P.O. Box 485, Coarsegold, CA 93614: Free information ■ Software for Amiga, Apple, Apple IIgs, Atari, IBM, and Macintosh computers. 209–683–8989.

Silicon Beach Software, 9770 Carroll Center Rd., Ste. J, San Diego, CA 92126: Free information ■ Education, entertainment/games, information management, desktop publishing, graphics, and utilities software for the Macintosh. 619–695–6956.

Smith Micro Software, Inc., P.O. Box 7137, Huntington Beach, CA 92615: Free information ■ Communications and home/business applications software for the Macintosh. 714–964–0412.

Tom Snyder Productions, 90 Sherman St., Cambridge, MA 02140: Free information ■ Education software for the Apple II, Apple IIgs, IBM, and Macintosh. 800–342–0236.

Softdisk Publishing, P.O. Box 30008, Shreveport, LA 71130: Free information ■ Software for the Apple, Apple IIgs, Commodore, IBM, and Macintosh. 800–831–2694.

Soft Logik Corporation, 11131 S. Towne Square, Ste. F, St. Louis, MO 63123: Free information ■ Desktop publishing software for the Amiga. 314–894–8608.

SoftSpoken, P.O. Box 18343, Raleigh, NC 27619: Free information ■ Software for exchanging Appleworks data files with most popular MS-DOS software. Converts word processing, database, and spreadsheet files. 919–870–5694.

Softsync, Inc., 162 Madison Ave., New York, NY 10016: Free information ■ Software for Apple, Apple IIgs, Commodore, IBM, and Macintosh computers. 212–685–2080.

Softview, 1721 Pacific Ave., Ste. 100, Oxnard, CA 93033: Free information ■ Home/business applications, programming tools, and utilities software for IBM and Macintosh computers. 805–388–5000.

Software Advantage Consulting Corporation, 37346 Charter Oaks Blvd., Mt. Clemens, MI 48043: Free information ■ Amiga home/business applications software. 313–463–4995.

Software Discoveries, Inc., 137 Krawski Dr., South Windsor, CT 06074: Free information ■ Database, home/business applications, and productivity software for the Macintosh. 203–644–9225.

The Software Toolworks, 60 Leveroni Ct., Novato, CA 94949: Free information ■ Education and entertainment/games software for the Amiga, IBM, and Macintosh. 415–883–3000.

Spectrum Holobyte, 2061 Challenger Dr., Alameda, CA 94501: Free information ■ Software for Amiga, Apple, Apple IIgs, Commodore, IBM, and Macintosh computers. 510–522–1164.

Spinnaker Software Corporation, 201 Broadway, 6th Floor, Cambridge, MA 02139: Free information ■ Software for Amiga, Apple II, Apple IIgs, Commodore, IBM, and Macintosh computers. 617–494–1200.

Sports Software Associates, P.O. Box 458, Hingham, MA 02403: Free information ■ Sports scheduling software for Apple, Apple IIgs, and IBM computers. 617–749–7880.

Spreadware, P.O. Box 4552, Palm Desert, CA 92261: Free information ■ Home/business applications, productivity, and spreadsheet software for the Macintosh. 510–794–4388.

Springboard Software, 7808 Creekridge Cir., Minneapolis, MN 55435: Free information ■ Software for Apple II, Apple IIgs, Commodore, IBM, and Macintosh computers. 612–944–3915.

Strategic Simulations, Inc., 675 Almanor Ave., Sunnyvale, CA 94086: Free information ■ Entertainment/games software for Amiga, Apple, Apple IIgs, Commodore, and IBM computers. 408–737–6800.

Strategic Studies Group, 1747 Orleans Ct., Walnut Creek, CA 94548: Free information ■ Entertainment/games software for the Apple IIgs computer. 510–932–3019.

SubLOGIC Corporation, 713 Edgebrook Dr., Champaign, IL 61820: Free information ■ Entertainment/games software for Amiga, Apple, Commodore, IBM, and Macintosh computers. 800–637–4983.

Sunburst Communications, 39 Washington Ave., Pleasantville, NY 10570: Free information ■ Entertainment/games software for the Apple IIgs computer. 800–628–8897; 914–747–3310 (in NY).

SuperMac Technology, 485 Potrero Ave., Sunnyvale, CA 94086: Free information ■ Graphics software for the Macintosh. 408–245–2202.

Survivor Software, Ltd., 11222 La Cienega Blvd., Ste. 450, Inglewood, CA 90304: Free information ■ Macintosh home/business applications software. 310–410–9527.

Symantec Corporation, 10201 Torre Ave., Cupertino, CA 95014: Free information ■ Graphics, productivity, communications, and utilities software for the Macintosh. 800–441–7234; 800–626–8847 (in CA).

Synergistic Systems, 442 3rd St., Neptune Beach, FL 32266: Free information ■ Business management software for the IBM. 904–249–0201.

Teachers Idea & Information Exchange, P.O. Box 6229, Lincoln, NE 68506: Free information ■ Productivity software for Apple computers. 402–483–6987.

Teach Yourself by Computer Software, Inc., 349 W. Commercial St., Ste. 1000, East Rochester, NY 14445: Free information ■ Macintosh education software. 716–381–5450.

TechPool Studios, 1463 Warrensville Rd., Cleveland, OH 44121: Free catalog ■ Anatomy, dental, and emergency medical clip art software for Macintosh and IBM computers. 800–777–8930.

Techware Corporation, P.O. Box 151085, Altamonte Springs, FL 32715: Free information ■ Education software for Apple computers. 206–823–8198.

3G Graphics, 11410 NE 124th St., Ste. 6155, Kirkland, WA 98034: Free information ■ Clip art software for the Macintosh and IBM. Includes accents and borders, business graphics, symbols, and other graphics. 800–456–0234.

Timeworks, Inc., 625 Academy Dr., Northbrook, IL 60062: Free information ■ Software for Apple, Apple IIgs, Atari, Commodore, IBM, and Macintosh computers. 708–559–1300.

T/Maker Company, 1390 Villa St., Mountain View, CA 94041: Free information ■ IBM word processing software. Education, graphics, productivity, and word processing software for the Macintosh. 415–962–0195.

TML Systems, Inc., 8837–B Goodbys Executive Dr., Jacksonville, FL 32217: Free in-

formation ■ Education, programming tools, utilities, and communications software for the Apple and Apple IIgs. 904–636–8592.

Totem Graphics, Inc., 519 Capitol Blvd., Tumwater, WA 98501: Free catalog ■ Macintosh and IBM full-color clip art software in 13 subject areas. Includes wild and domestic animals, birds, fish, business, holidays, food, flowers, nautical, tools, sports, insects, and women. 206–352–1851.

Tronsoft, Inc., 133 W. De La Guerra St., Santa Barbara, CA 93101: Free information ■ Graphics, clip art, and business management software for the Macintosh. 805–564–3386.

True BASIC, Inc., 12 Commerce Ave., West Lebanon, NH 03784: Free information ■ Communications, desktop publishing, education, graphics, programming tools, and productivity software for the Macintosh. Education and programming tools software for the Amiga. 800–872–2742.

Unicorn Software Company, 6000 S. Eastern Ave., Bldg. 610, Ste. I, Las Vegas, NV 89119: Free information ■ Education software for the Amiga, Apple, Apple IIgs, Commodore, IBM, and Macintosh. Entertainment/games software for the Apple IIgs and Macintosh. 702–597–0818.

Unison World, 1321 Harbor Bay Pkwy., Alameda, CA 94501: Free information ■ Software for the Amiga, Apple, Commodore, and IBM. 510–748–6670.

United Software, 22231 Mulholland Hwy., Ste. 212A, Woodland Hills, CA 91364: Free information ■ Communications software for the Apple and Apple IIgs. 818–887–5800.

Ventura Publishing Company, 15175 Innovation Dr., San Diego, CA 92128: Free information ■ Desktop publishing software for IBM computers. 800–822–8221.

Vitesse, Inc., 13909 Amar Rd., Ste. 2, La Puente, CA 91746: Free information ■ Apple IIgs utilities software. 818–813–1270.

Virginia Systems Software Services, 5509 W. Bay Ct., Midlothian, VA 23112: Free information ■ Macintosh word processing software. 804–739–3200.

The Voyager Company, 1351 Pacific Coast Hwy., Santa Monica, CA 90401: Free information ■ Programming tools, utilities, and education software for the Macintosh. 800–446–2001; 800–443–2001 (in CA).

Roger Wagner Publishing, Inc., 1050 Pioneer Way, Ste. P, El Cajon, CA 92020: Free information ■ Software for the Apple and Apple IIgs. 800–421–6526; 619–442–0522 (in CA).

Wayzata Technology, Inc., 16221 Main Ave., P.O. Box 87, Prior Lake, MN 55372: Free information ■ Graphics, clip art, business management, programming tools, education, and personal/home management software for the Macintosh. 612–447–7321.

Weekly Reader Software, Division Optimum Resource, Inc., 10 Station Pl., Norfolk, CT 06058: Free information ■ Software for the Apple, Apple IIgs, Commodore, and IBM. 203–542–5553.

Williams AG Products, 9191 Towne Centre Dr., Ste. 175, San Diego, CA 92122: Free information ■ Graphics and productivity software for the Macintosh. 619–558–9193.

WordPerfect Corporation, 1555 N. Technology Way, Orem, UT 84057: Free information ■ Word processing software for Amiga, Apple II, Apple IIgs, Commodore, IBM, and Macintosh computers. 801–225–5000.

Software Retailers

The AAMIGA Center, 5920 Roswell Rd., Atlanta, GA 30328: Free information ■ Software for the Amiga computer. 800–388–2700.

Briwall, 58 Noble St., P.O. 129, Kutztown, PA 19530: Free information ■ Software for Commodore and Amiga computers. 215–683–5433.

Coast to Coast Technologies, Inc., 1855 S.R. 434, Ste. 208, Longwood, FL 32750: Free information ■ United Kingdom and European software for Amiga computers. 407–767–0938.

Roger Coats, 20200 Nine Mile Rd., St. Clair Shores, MI 48080: Free information ■ Software, Apple accessories and peripherals, Laser 128 computers and printers, Applied Engineering cards, chips, disk drives, scanners, modems, system savers, peripheral cards, and other hardware. 800–438–2883; 313–774–8240 (in MI).

CompUSA, Inc., 15160 Marsh Ln., Dallas, TX 75234: Free catalog ■ Software, DOS, windows, and CD-ROM software; desktop and portable PCs; portable accessories;

cards; networking and communications accessories; furniture; books; videogame cartridges; office products and supplies; chips, disk drives, scanners, modems, system savers, peripheral cards, and other equipment. 800–451–7638.

Computer Basics, 1490 N. Hermitage Rd., Hermitage, PA 16148: Free information ■ Software, accessories, and peripherals for Amiga computers. 412–962–0533.

Creative Computers, 4453 Redondo Beach Blvd., Lawndale, CA 90260: Free information ■ Software, accessories, and peripherals for Amiga computers. 310–214–0000.

Direct Link Software, P.O. Box 2302, Muncie, IN 47307: Free information ■ User-supported software for the IBM. 800–999–6883.

Dustin Discount Software, 20969 Ventura Blvd., Woodland Hills, CA 91364: Free price list ■ Software for the IBM. 800–274–6611.

Educational Resources, 1550 Executive Dr., Elgin, IL 60123: Free catalog ■ Software, diskettes, accessories and supplies, peripheral and cards, and computers. 800–624–2926; 708–888–8300 (IN IL).

Fas-Track Computer Products, 7030 Huntley Rd., Columbus, OH 43229: Free information ■ Software, Apple accessories and peripherals, Applied Engineering cards, chips by Zip Technologies, disk drives, modems, scanners, joysticks, and other hardware. 800–421–4698; 614–847–4050 (in OH).

Go Amiga, 2682 Middlefield Rd., Redwood City, CA 94063: Free information ■ Amiga software, hardware, and accessories. 415–364–9714.

Gold Hill Software, P.O. Box 663, Gold Hill, OR 97525: Free catalog ■ User-supported software for the IBM. 800–234–6467.

Golem Computers, P.O. Box 6698, Westlake Village, CA 91360: Free information ■ Software, disk drives, hard drives, monitors, printers, modems, peripheral boards, and other accessories. 800–248–0363; 805–499–7689 (in CA).

Interface Software and Systems, P.O. Box 329, Cookstown, Ontario, Canada L0L 1L0: Free catalog ■ Software for the IBM. 416–229–2381.

MacWarehouse, 1690 Oak St., P.O. Box 3013, Lakewood, NJ 08701: Free catalog ■ Macintosh software. 800–255–6227.

Media Magic, P.O. Box 507, Nicasio, CA 94946: Free catalog ■ Educational and entertainment software, computer books, and videotapes. 415–662–2426.

PC Connection, 6 Mill St., Marlow, NH 03456: Free information ■ Software for IBM computers. 800–776–7777.

Programmer's Paradise, 1163 Shrewsbury Ave., Shrewsbury, NJ 07702: Free catalog: Software for IBM computers. 201–389–9229.

The Programmer's Shop, 5 Pond Park Rd., Hingham, MA 02043: Free information ■ Software for the IBM. 800–421–8006; 617–740–2510 (in MA).

Programs Plus, 55 Heritage Ave., Portsmouth, NH 03801: Free information ■ Software, hardware, backup utilities and boards, printer interface cards, disk drives, peripheral boards, printers, diskettes, and other accessories. 603–433–6531.

Q Labs, 15102 Charlevoix, Grosse Pointe, MI 48230: Free catalog ■ Apple business, entertainment/games, education, graphics, utilities and language, word processing, and programming tools software, and accessories that include hard disks, Applied Engineering cards, Laser hardware and accessories, and peripherals. 800–443–6697; 313–331–0700 (in MI).

Silicon Express, 50 E. Mill, Pataskala, OH 43062: Free catalog ■ Software for most computers, printers, disk drive controllers, peripheral cards, mouse devices, joysticks, and Apple II compatible hardware and accessories. 800–927–9555; 614–927–0052 (in OH).

Software Discounters International, 5607 Baum Blvd., Pittsburgh, PA 15206: Free information ■ Software for most computers. 800–225–7638.

Supplies

Dayton Computer Supply, 1220 Wayne Ave., Dayton, OH 45410: Free information ■ Over 350 different black and color ribbons. 800–331–6841; 513–252–1247 (in OH).

Inmac, 2465 Augustine Dr., P.O. Box 58031, Santa Clara, CA 95052: Free catalog ■ Computer supplies, furniture, cables and

accessories, desktop accessories, disks and tapes, networking products, data communications equipment, and other accessories. 800–547–5444.

Island Computer Supply, 305 Grand Blvd., Massapequa Park, NY 11762: Free information ■ Black and color printer ribbons and diskettes. 516–798–6500.

MEI/Micro Center, 1100 Steelwood Rd., Columbus, OH 43212: Free catalog ■ Disks, disk cases, ribbons, printer accessories, surge protectors, and other accessories. 800–634–3478.

National Computer Ribbons, 9566 Deereco Rd., Timonium, MD 21093: Free information ■ Printer ribbons. 800–292–6272; 410–561–0200 (in MD).

PaperDirect, Inc., 57 Romanelli Ave., South Hackensack, NJ 07606: Free information ■ Paper and envelopes in hundreds of styles, colors, weights, and finishes. 800–272–7377; 201–342–6432 (in NJ).

RAMCO Computer Supplies, P.O. Box 475, Manteno, IL 60950: Free information ■ Black and color printer ribbons, heat transfer ribbons, computer paper, and other supplies. 800–522–6922.

Ribbon Land, P.O. Box 506, Exton, PA 19341: Free catalog ■ Film and nylon ribbons, laser cartridges, auto-inkers, computer stationery, specialty and parchment paper, continuous forms printer paper, cleaning products, T-shirt iron-ons and printing software, and disks. 215–524–9760.

COOKIE CUTTERS

Brown Bag Cookie Art, Hill Design, Inc., 7 Eagle Square, Concord, NH 03301: Free information ■ Cookie molds. 800–228–4488.

D.D. Dillon, 850 Meadow Ln., Camp Hill, PA 17011: Free information ■ Springerle cookie molding boards and molds, and other cookie molds. 717–761–6895.

Hartstone, Inc., 1719 Dearborne St., P.O. Box 2626, Zanesville, OH 43702: Free information ■ Stoneware molds for making cookies and edible ornaments. 614–452–9992.

The Little Fox Factory, 931 Marion Rd., Bucyrus, OH 44820: Catalog 25¢ ■ Handcrafted cookie cutters in different shapes. 419–562–5420.

The Lyphon & Gryphon, 2000 Pereira Rd., Martinez, CA 94553: Catalog $4 (refundable) ■ Cookie cutters in different shapes and patterns. 510–372–0151.

Maid of Scandinavia, 3244 Raleigh A ., Minneapolis, MN 55416: Catalog $2 ■ Utensils and kitchen tools, cake molds and cookie cutters, candy-making molds, ingredients, and other supplies. 800–328–6722; 800–851–1121 (in MN).

Sur La Table, Pike Place Farmers Market, Seattle, WA 98101: Free information ■ Handcarved, thistle-pattern wood shortbread molds. 206–448–2244.

Wilton Enterprise, Inc., 2240 W. 75th St., Woodridge, IL 60517: Catalog $6 ■ Equipment and supplies for making cookies, candies, and cakes. 708–963–7100.

COPIERS & FAX MACHINES

AV Distributor, 16451 Space Center Blvd., Houston, TX 77058: Free information ■ Fax machines and audio, video, stereo, and television electronics and accessories. 800–843–3697.

Computability Consumer Electronics, P.O. Box 17882, Milwaukee, WI 53217: Free information ■ Fax machines and copiers. 800–558–0003; 414–357–8181 (in WI).

Computerlane, 22107 Roscoe Blvd., Canoga Park, CA 91304: Free information ■ Fax machines, computers and accessories, and software. 800–526–3482; 818–884–8644 (in CA).

Crutchfield, 1 Crutchfield Park, Charlottesville, VA 22906: Free catalog ■ Fax machines, telephones and answering machines, word processors, personal copiers, and computer systems and software. 800–336–5566.

Factory Direct, 131 W. 35th St., New York, NY 10001: Free information ■ Fax machines, and audio, video, stereo, and television equipment. 800–428–4567.

Olden Video, 1265 Broadway, New York, NY 10001: Free information ■ Telephones, copiers, photographic equipment, and supplies. 212–725–1234.

Reliable Home Office, P.O. Box 804117, Chicago, IL 60607: Free catalog ■ Computer accessories and furniture, fax machines, and filing and storage systems. 800–326–6230.

Staples, Inc., P.O. Box 160, Newton, MA 2195: Free catalog ■ Fax machines, typewriters, office supplies, computer supplies and paper, office furniture, and drafting equipment. 617–965–7030.

Tri-State Camera, 160 Broadway, New York, NY 10038: Free information ■ Fax machines, copiers, audio and video equipment, camcorders, and other equipment. 212–349–2555.

COSMETICS & SKIN CARE

Amica Cosmetics, 80 39th St., Brooklyn, NY 11232: Free catalog ■ Skin care products, lipsticks, shampoos, perfumes and other fragrances, and nail care items. 718–856–4499.

Barth Vitamins, 865 Merrick Ave., Westbury, NY 11590: Free catalog ■ Natural vitamin and mineral supplements, cosmetics, health foods, and home health aids. 800–645–2328; 800–553–0353 (in NY).

Baudelaire Fine Imported Cosmetics, Inc., Forest Rd., Marlow, NH 03456: Free information ■ Imported European therapeutic bath oils rich in herbal extracts and essential oils. 800–327–2324.

Beautiful Visions, 810 S. Hicksville Rd., C.S. 4001, Hicksville, NY 11855: Free catalog ■ Cosmetics, brushes, personal care items, Hoffritz scissors, nail care items, and jewelry.

Beauty Boutique, 6836 Engle Rd., P.O. Box 94520, Cleveland, OH 44101: Free catalog ■ Cosmetics and toiletries, skin care items, costume jewelry, and women's fashions. 216–826–3008.

The Body Shop, Inc., Attention: Catalog Department, 45 Horsehill Rd., Hanover Technical Center, Cedar Knolls, NJ 07927: Catalog $2 ■ Toiletries and cosmetics. 800–541–2535.

Borlin Industries, 11960 Wilshire Blvd., Los Angeles, CA 90025: Free catalog ■ Non-ecotoxic and biodegradable household cleaners and detergents, baby care products, and natural body care products. 800–825–4540.

Caswell-Massey Company, Ltd., Catalog Division, 100 Enterprise Place, Dover, DE 19901: Free catalog ■ Toiletries, cosmetics, bath items, and personal care products. 800–326–0500.

Chica Bella, Inc., 6505 E. Central, Wichita, KS 67206: Free catalog ■ All-natural soaps, hair and skin moisturizers, shampoos, rinse conditioners, facial lotions, and masks. 316–682–2686.

Crabtree & Evelyn Limited, P.O. Box 167, Woodstock Hill, CT 06281: Catalog $3.50 ■ Cosmetics and toiletries from England, Switzerland, and France. Includes soaps and shampoos, bath gels and oils, colognes and toilet waters, creams, lotions, talcum powders, sponges, and brushes and combs. 203–928–2766.

Essential Products Company, Inc., 90 Water St., New York, NY 10005: Free price list ■ Copies of fragrances for men and women, for a fraction of the price of the originals. 212–344–4288.

Esse Salon & Spa, Altid Park, P.O. Box 6529, Chelmsford, MA 01824: Free catalog ■ Professional salon cosmetic and skin care products. 800–879–3773.

The Florist Shop, 703 Madison Ave., New York, NY 10021: Free catalog ■ Hand-milled soaps, bath oils, body milk, talc, room fragrances, and potpourris. 800–J–FLORIS.

Fredericksburg Herb Farm, 310 E. Main St., Fredericksburg, TX 78624: Catalog $1 (does not include herb plants) ■ Herb plants, seeds, flowers, toiletries, oils, and seasonings. 512–997–8615.

General Nutrition Catalog, Puritan's Pride, 105 Orville Dr., Bohemia, NY 11716: Free catalog ■ Vitamins, health foods, natural cosmetics, books, and gifts. 800–645–1030.

Gentle Cosmetics, 110–49 62nd Dr., Forest Hills, NY 11375: Free information with long SASE ■ Kits to make cosmetics for persons with sensitive dry skin, allergies, or dandruff. Includes shower gels, creams, bath oils, and shampoos.

Gold Medal Hair Products, Inc., 1 Bennington Ave., Freeport, NY 11520: Free catalog ■ Wigs for black men and women, hair and beauty preparations, hair styling equipment and accessories, eye glasses, and jewelry. 516–378–6900.

Gale Hayman Beverly Hills, 1888 Century Pk. East, Ste. 1010, Century City, CA

90067: Free catalog ■ Cosmetics and jewelry. 800–FOR–GALE.

Health Savings Center, 1590 Privado Rd., Westbury, NY 11590: Free catalog ■ Vitamins, natural supplements, cosmetics and beauty aids, and household medicine chest supplies. 800–645–2978; 800–682–2286 (in NY).

Heaven's Herbal Creations, 8202 West M.L. Ave., Kalamazoo, MI 49009: Catalog $2 ■ Herbal body care products, potpourris, exclusive scents, and essential oils. 616–375–2934.

Herb Hollow, Safford Rd., East Otto, NY 14729: Catalog $1 (refundable) ■ Original herbal teas, seasonings, potpourris, handmade soaps, toiletries, and other herbal products. 716–257–5105.

Herb & Spice Collection, P.O. Box 118, Norway, IA 52318: Free catalog ■ Natural herbal body care products, potpourris, culinary herbs and spices, other herbs, and teas. 800–365–4372.

Holbrook, Inc., 1205 Broadway, Ste. 204, New York, NY 10001: Free catalog ■ Save up to 50 percent on designer fragrances, and up to 20 percent on the Lancome treatment line. 800–347–3738.

Holzman & Stephanie Perfumes, Inc., P.O. Box 921, Lake Forest, IL 60045: Catalog $1 ■ Copies of world-famous perfumes for men and women, for a fraction of the price of the originals. 708–234–7667.

Indiana Botanic Gardens, P.O. Box 5, Hammond, IN 46325: Catalog $1 ■ Vitamins, herbs, spices, and personal care products. 800–348–6434; 219–931–2480 (in IN).

Victoria Jackson Cosmetics, Inc., National Distribution Center, 16 Paoli Corporate Center, Paoli, PA 19301: Free catalog ■ Body, bath, hair care, and other cosmetic and skin care items. 800–392–9250.

Key West Aloe, Inc., 524 Front St., P.O. Box 1079, Key West, FL 33041: Free catalog ■ Cosmetics and skin care products, hair and bath products for women, and men's toiletries and personal care products. 800–445–2563.

Kneipp Corporation of America, Valmont Industrial Park, 675 Jaycee Dr., West Hazleton, PA 18201: Free information ■ Herbal baths and shower gels.

La Costa Products International, 2875 Laker Ave. East, Carlsbad, CA 92009: Free catalog ■ Hair, skin, and body care products for men and women. 800–LA–COSTA.

Le Parfumier, P.O. Box 40412, Philadelphia, PA 19106: Free catalog ■ Designer fragrances that include many imported, hard-to-find, and discontinued items. 800–544–0575.

Lucky Heart Cosmetics, 390 Mulberry St., Memphis, TN 38101: Free catalog ■ Cosmetics and skin care cosmetics. 800–526–5825.

Natural Lifestyle Supplies, 16 Lookout Dr., Asheville, NC 28804: Free catalog ■ Natural body care and baby care products, cereals and grains, prepared foods, nuts and seeds, seasonings, condiments, oils, and other natural food products. 800–752–2775.

Nature Food Centres, One Nature's Way, Wilmington, MA 01887: Free catalog ■ Vitamins, natural food products, and cosmetics for total skin care. 800–225–0857; 617–657–5000 (in MA).

New York Cosmetics & Fragrances, 318 Brannan St., San Francisco, CA 94107: Free catalog ■ Save from 10 to 70 percent on men's and women's fragrances, cosmetics, and skin, nail, hair, and bath care items. 415–543–3880.

The Old House, 294 Head of the Bay Rd., Buzzards Bay, MA 02532: Catalog 50¢ ■ Bayberry, cranberry, blueberry, herbal, lavender, strawberry, lilac, and pine scented soaps.

Parodon, P.O. Box 1863, Pollock Pines, CA 95726: Free brochure ■ Scented handmade soap with olive oil for delicate or dry skin. 916–644–5709.

Perfume Concepts, Inc., 11 Giffard Way, Melville, NY 11747: Free information ■ Reproductions of men's and women's fragrances. 516–367–8279.

Planta Dei Medicinal Herb Farm, Millville, New Brunswick, Canada E0H 1M0: Catalog $2 (refundable) ■ Biologically grown teas, medicinal herbs, healing tea mixtures, cosmetics, natural ointments, and massage oils. 506–463–8169.

A Second Look, 8502 Chapel View Rd., Ellicott City, MD 21043: Free catalog with long SASE ■ Skin care products. 410–465–6653.

Syd Simons Cosmetics, 2 E. Oak St., Chicago, IL 60611: Free price list ■ Skin care cosmetics and make-up for total body care. 312–943–2333.

Soap Opera, 319 State St., Madison, WI 55703: Free price list ■ Scented glycerin soaps, body lotions and creams, eye care cream, lip balms, suntan lotions, conditioners, bubble baths, bath oils, essential perfume oils, rare oils, designer fragrances, herbs, and perfume bases. 800–251–SOAP.

Jean Sorelle Bath Essentials, 50 Tice Blvd., Woodcliff Lake, NJ 07675: Free information with long SASE ■ Facial wash, foaming bath lotion, moisturizing lotion, shampoo, floral soaps, bath sponges, and other bath essentials imported from England. 201–391–0099.

Star Pharmaceuticals, Inc., 1500 New Horizons Blvd., Amityville, NY 11701: Free catalog ■ Save up to 60 percent on vitamin products. Other products include nutritional supplements, toiletries, health care products, and pet supplies. 800–274–6400.

Sunburst Biorganics, 838 Merrick Rd., Baldwin, NY 11510: Free catalog ■ Save from 25 to 70 percent on nutritional supplements and toiletries. 516–623–8478.

Tropical Botanicals, P.O. Box 1354, Rancho, Santa Fe, CA 92067: Free information ■ Natural shampoos and other skin care products. 800–777–1428; 619–756–1265 (in CA).

Tuli-Latus Perfumes, Ltd., 146–36 13th Ave., P.O. Box 422, Whitestone, NY 11357: Free brochure ■ Reproductions of famous perfumes for women and colognes for men. Features its own line of cosmetics and simulated pearl necklaces. 718–746–9337.

Union Express, 525 Kapahulu Ave., Honolulu, HI 96815: Free information ■ Tanning, after sun, and other skin care products for men and women. 808–734–8703.

Wynnewood Pharmacy, Wynnewood Shopping Center, Wynnewood, PA 19096: Free catalog ■ Save up to 50 percent on perfumes and colognes. 800–966–5999; 215–878–4999 (in PA).

COSTUMES

Abracadabra Magic Shop, P.O. Box 714, Middlesex, NJ 08846: Catalog $3.95 ■ Magician's supplies, close-up and stage magic, juggling equipment, balloons, clown accessories, costumes, and theatrical supplies. 908–805–0200.

Allstar Costumes, 125 Lincoln Blvd., Middlesex, NJ 08846: Catalog $1 ■ Costumes and accessories for adults and children. 908–805–0200.

Badhir Trading, Inc., 8429 Sisson Hwy., Eden, NY 14057: Catalog $2.50 (refundable) ■ Beaded, sequined, and jeweled appliques, trims and fringes for dresses, costumes, and bridal fashions. 800–654–9418.

Circus Clowns, 3556 Nicollet Ave., Minneapolis, MN 55408: Catalog $3 ■ Clown costumes, gimmicks, and props. 612–822–4243.

Dazian's, Inc., 2014 Commerce St., Dallas, TX 75201: Free catalog ■ Costume fabrics and trims, leotards, tights, and other dance wear. 214–748–3450.

Deborah's Attic, 719 S. Limestone St., Springfield, OH 45505: Free list with long SASE ■ Vintage clothing and accessories, from the 1900s to 1960s.

Eastern Costume Company, 510 N. Elm St., Greensboro, NC 27401: Free information ■ Costumes, make-up, and accessories. 919–379–1026.

Facemakers, Inc., 140 5th St., Savanna, IL 61074: Catalog $5 ■ Animal costumes.

Folkwear, Customer Service Dept., P.O. Box 5506, Newtown, CT 06470: Catalog $2 ■ Original folkwear patterns.

Freckles Clown Supplies, 4231 Timuquana Rd., Jacksonville, FL 32210: Catalog $5 ■ Costumes, make-up, clown supplies, puppets, how-to books on clowning and ballooning, and other theatrical supplies. 904–778–3977.

A.J. Fulks, P.O. Box 92, Whitestown, IN 46075: Catalog $2 ■ Authentic mid 19th-century clothing and uniforms. 317–769–5355.

Gladstone Fabrics, 16 W. 56th St., 2nd Floor, New York, NY 10019: Catalog and swatches $15 ■ Costume fabrics, trims, and beading. 212–765–0760.

Grand Illusions, 90 E. Main St., Newark, DE 19711: Catalog $2 ■ Reproduction Civil War uniforms and civilian clothing for men, women, and children. 302–366–0300.

Heidi's Pages & Petticoats, Heidi M. Marsh, 810 El Caminito, Livermore, CA

94550: Catalog $3 ■ Civil War clothing patterns for adults and children.

House of Costumes, 166 Jericho Tpk., Mineola, NY 11501: Free information ■ Costumes, make-up, wigs, and novelties. 516–294–0170.

Lacey Costume Wig, 249 W. 34th St., Ste. 707, New York, NY 10001: Free catalog ■ Wigs, mustaches, beards, and other supplies. 800–562–9911; 212–695–1996 (in NY).

Laidlacker Historical Garments, RD 2, Box 313A, Watsontown, PA 17777: Catalog $3 ■ Reproductions of 18th-, 19th-, and 20th-century clothing for men, women, and children. 717–546–5401.

Lynch's Clown Supplies, 939 Howard, Dearborn, MI 48124: Catalog $5 (refundable) ■ Clown wigs, shoes, noses, novelties, make-up, and costume accessories. 313–565–3425.

Judith A. Martin, 4566 Oakhurst, Sylvania, OH 43560: Catalog $2.50 ■ Authentic, custom clothing for women, from 1850 to 1865. 419–474–2093.

Mary Ellen & Company, 29400 Rankert Rd., North Liberty, IN 46554: Catalog $3 (refundable) ■ Victorian-style clothing, lace-up shoes, hats, fans, parasols, books, and patterns. 800–669–1860.

Masquerade, P.O. Box 1057, Maple Plain, MN 55348: Free catalog ■ Costumes and make-up for children and adults. 800–DRACULA.

Mecca Magic, Inc., 49 Dodd St., Bloomfield, NJ 07003: Free brochure ■ Costumes, wigs, and make-up. 201–429–7597.

Mediaeval Miscellanea, 6530 Spring Valley Dr., Alexandria, VA 22312: Catalog $2 ■ Historical clothing patterns. 703–354–7711.

Morris Costumes, 3108 Monroe Rd., Charlotte, NC 28205: Catalog $15 + $1.98 (postage) ■ Costumes, clown props, masks, joke items, magic tricks and special effects, novelties, and books. 704–333–4653.

New Columbia, P.O. Box 524, Charleston, IL 61920: Catalog $4.50 ■ Reproduction military uniforms and caps, from 1845 to 1945.

Quartermaster Shop, 5565 Griswold, Port Huron, MI 48060: Catalog $3 (refundable) ■ Authentic reproduction Union and Con-

federate Civil War era uniforms and civilian clothing. 313–367–6702.

Rubie's Costume Company, 120–08 Jamaica Ave., Richmond Hill, Queens, NY 11418: Free information ■ Costumes, make-up, hair goods, and special effects. 718–846–1008.

Salt Lake Costume Company, 1701 S. 1100 East, Salt Lake City, UT 84105: Free catalog ■ Historical costumes, make-up, and accessories. 801–467–7494.

Alan Sloane & Company, Inc., 80 Kean St., West Babylon, NY 11704: Free catalog ■ Costume gloves, clown and tuxedo suspenders, red union suits, cummerbunds, bow ties, fishnet hosiery, bandannas, St. Patrick Day items, and other theatrical items. 800–252–6266; 516–643–2262 (in NY).

Under the Big Top, P.O. Box 807, Placentia, CA 92670: Catalog $4 ■ Costumes, clown props, make-up, juggling supplies, and party supplies. 714–579–1144.

Victorian Dainties, Box 492162, Redding, CA 96049: Catalog $2 (refundable) ■ Victorian-style clothing in 100 percent cotton. 916–221–5230.

COUNTRY CRAFTS

Adirondack Store & Gallery, 109 Saranac Ave., Lake Placid, NY 12946: Free catalog ■ Country-style twig furniture, stoneware and pottery, rugs, fireboards, lawn furniture, solid wood furniture, baskets, and pillows. 518–523–2646.

American Country Crafts, Inc., P.O. Box 5399, Decatur, AL 35601: Catalog $3 ■ Rag baskets and other baskets, folk art silhouette shelves, rugs, dolls, wreaths, wooden bowls, and other country crafts. 800–654–2511.

Amish Country Collection, Sunset Valley Rd., RD 5, New Castle, PA 16105: Catalog $5 (refundable) ■ Amish-style pillows, quilts, wall hangings, rugs, other household items, and cribs and beds. 800–232–6474.

Anger Manufacturing Company, Hwy. 62 West, P.O. Box 1075, Pocahontas, AR 72455: Brochure $1 (refundable) ■ Bar stools, children's glider chair, oak swings, clocks, frames, plant stands, and other items. 501–892–4419.

Arts-Nic & Old Lace, P.O. Box 587215, Alsip, IL 60658: Free information ■ Signed and dated Early American-style mantel clocks with folk art designs. 708–424–0937.

Baskets & Things, 2408 Somersworth, Shreveport, LA 71118: Brochure $1 ■ Handwoven baskets. 318–688–3508.

Bayou Country Store, 823 E. Jackson St., Pensacola, FL 32501: Free catalog ■ Country crafts and decorative accessories. 800–262–5403; 904–432–5697 (in FL).

Berea College Crafts, CPO 2347, Berea, KY 40404: Catalog $2 ■ Handmade woodwork, weaving, iron, pottery, and brooms. 606–986–9341.

C.J. Brown Studios, 3618 N. Nelso Rd., DeKalb, IL 60115: Brochure $1 ■ Matted and framed limited edition prints. 815–758–8327.

Brush Strokes, Box 8045, South Bend, IN 46637: Brochure $3 ■ Signed and numbered limited edition prints reproduced from original oil paintings, with a choice of mats and custom frames. 219–277–5414.

R.B. Buckwalter Company, 516 Scotland Rd., Quarryville, PA 17566: Catalog $2 ■ Handmade, darkened tinware home accessories. 717–786–1131.

The Calico Cat, P.O. Box 123, Bath, OH 44210: Free catalog ■ Amish quilts, wooden toys, rugs, quilted Xmas wall hangings, dolls, and furniture. 216–659–4219.

Calico Corner, 513 E. Bowman St., South Bend, IN 46613: Catalog $1 ■ Punched copper candle holders, reproduction 18th-century furnishings, and other historical reproductions and decorative accessories. 219–234–1605.

Carpenter's General Store, 6347 Fair Ridge Rd., Hillsboro, OH 45133: Brochure $3 ■ Country-style wood decorative accessories. 800–345–5615.

Chriswill Forge, 2255 Manchester Rd., North Lawrence, OH 44666: Catalog $2 ■ Country-style floor lamps with a heavy-duty steel plate base and over 55 iron designs for the top. 216–832–9136.

Cinnamon & Spice by the Sea, Broadway at 7th St., Barnegat Light, NJ 08006: Brochure $1 ■ Handcrafted Victorian country-style gifts and accessories. 609–494–5413.

Colonial Casting Company, Inc., 443 S. Colony St., Meriden, CT 06450: Price list

50¢ ■ Handcrafted, lead-free pewter items. 203–235–5189.

Colonial Collections of New England, Inc., 202 Idlewood Dr., Stamford, CT 06905: Catalog $1 ■ Weather vanes, cupolas, sundials, mailboxes, door knockers, personalized and date plaques, lanterns, and other home and garden decorative items. 203–322–0078.

Conewago Junction, 1255 Oxford Rd., New Oxford, PA 17350: Catalog $2 ■ Handcrafted reproductions and accessories that include Colonial chests, cupboards, wooden buckets, tools, afghans, and tinware. 717–624–4786.

Cottage Country Baskets, 64346 Arrowhead Rd., Cambridge, OH 43725: Brochure $1 ■ Handcrafted baskets and rush seats. 614–439–4610.

The Cotton Gin, Inc., Deep Creek Farm, P.O. Box 24, Jarvisburg, NC 27947: Free catalog ■ Country collectibles, southern clothing, and fine antiques. 800–637–2446.

Cotton Patch Crafts, Rt. 3, Box 790, Mansfield, LA 71052: Brochures $2 ■ Country-style switch plates, decorative items, rag dolls, and other craft items. 318–697–5745.

Country Accents, P.O. Box 437, Montoursville, PA 17754: Catalog $5 ■ Museum tin replicas and accent pieces. 717–478–4127.

Country Blacksmith, P.O. Box 2097, McKinleyville, CA 95521: Catalog $2 ■ Antique Shaker reproductions, country folk art, and country cows. 707–839–0048.

Country Bouquet, P.O. Box 233, Kellogg, MN 55945: Brochure $2 ■ Candle holders and sconces; Raggedy Ann and Andy dolls; shelves, pegboards, and wall cupboards; folk items; stenciled aprons; and decorations and ornaments. 800–328–5598; 507–767–2230 (in MN).

Country Cupboard, 143 E. Main St., Zeeland, MI 49464: Catalog $2 ■ Country crafts, decorative items, and gifts. 616–772–1523.

Country Expressions, RR 1, Box 399, Perham, MN 56573: Information $3 ■ Oven-, microwave-, dishwasher-safe, and lead-free, hand-painted earthenware pottery. 218–346–2720.

Country Frames, Box 284, Rochert, MN 56578: Free flyer ■ Country-style frames. 800–289–8883.

Country Lane Stenciling, P.O. Box 517, West Chester, OH 45069: Brochure $2 ■ Hand-stenciled rolling kitchen furniture, cotton valances, tie backs, and table runners. 513–777–7027.

Country Loft, Mail Order Dept., S. Shore Park, Hingham, MA 02043: Free catalog ■ Lamps and chandeliers, cupboards, cabinets, crocks and carriers, Shaker reproductions, whimsical folk art, whirligigs, baskets, buckets, pillows, and braided rugs. 800–225–5408.

Country Manor, Mail Order Dept., Rt. 211, P.O. Box 520, Sperryville, VA 22740: Catalog $2 ■ Handwoven cotton rugs, kitchen utensils and accessories, other craft items, and decorative accessories. 800–344–8354.

Country Punchin', 14757 Glenn Dr., Whittier, CA 90604: Brochure $1 ■ Hand-punched, tarnish-proof name signs and plaques in solid copper or pewter-look metal. 310–944–1038.

Country Store, 28 James St., Geneva, IL 60134: Catalog $2 ■ Punched tin and turned wood chandeliers, ceiling lights, outlet covers, country-style decor accessories, braided rugs, and stoneware. 708–879–0098.

Country Tin Shop, Farrell Hill Rd., Deering, NH 03244: Portfolio $2 (refundable) ■ Handcrafted country gift items and decor accessories in copper, brass, and country colors. 603–529–7477.

The Country Touch, 8 Bonnywick Dr., Harrisburg, PA 17111: Information $1 ■ Handcrafted wooden country crafts and gifts. 717–566–6711.

Country Wicker, 2238D Bluemound Rd., Waukesha, WI 53186: Catalog $2 ■ Handcrafted country-style crafts. 414–782–6600.

Country Woods, P.O. Box 349, Auburn, NH 03032: Catalog $1 (refundable) ■ Unfinished, solid wood country-style furniture and accessories. 603–483–5566.

Craft Peddler, 28 Arbor Ridge Ln., South Setauket, NY 11720: Free catalog information ■ Homemade country crafts. 800–955–2707.

Creative Crafts, 308 S. Todd, McComb, OH 45858: Brochure $2 ■ Handcrafted earthenware pottery. 419–293–3838.

Darowood Farms, Rt. 1, Box 234, Cedar Grove, WI 53013: Brochure $1.50 ■ Handcrafted country wood items in pine. 414–564–3260.

The Faith Mountain Company, P.O. Box 199, Sperryville, VA 22740: Catalog 50¢ ■ Kitchen utensils and accessories, country-style gifts, folk art reproductions, toys and dolls, handmade Appalachian baskets, and Christmas decorations. 800–822–7238.

Grunewald Folk Art, P.O. Box 721, Wauconda, IL 60084: Catalog $2 ■ Signed and numbered limited edition lithographs of pen and ink drawings in color, of scenes of animals and people in rural American settings. 708–526–1417.

Heart of the Woods, Inc., P.O. Box 185, Ely, MN 55731: Catalog $1 (refundable) ■ Wooden country-style decor accessories. 800–852–2075.

Heartwood Crafts, Rt. 1, Box 2, Callands, VA 24530: Brochure $1 ■ Handcrafted country-style cabinets in pine. 804–724–7736.

Herndon & Merry, Inc., 519 W. Thompson Ln., Nashville, TN 37211: Free catalog ■ Mailbox stands, weather vanes, sundials, garden furniture, urns, and accessories. 615–254–8771.

Hickety Pickety, 120 Cherry Ave., Ames, IA 50010: Catalog $2 ■ Handcrafted crafts with a country decor look. 515–232–5394.

Holst, Inc., Box 370, Tawas City, MI 48764: Catalog $2 (refundable) ■ Country items, decor accessories, sundials and weather vanes, housewares, figurines, and holiday decorations. 517–362–5664.

Home Hearts, 1610 Saratoga Dr., Rio Rancho, NM 87124: Free brochure with long SASE ■ Country-style decorative accessories for the kitchen. 505–892–3319.

Homeplace Country Crafts, 416 Hall Rd., Anderson, SC 29624: Brochure $2 ■ Country-style decorative items, traditional pieces, and gifts. 800–753–2546.

Homestead Plaques, 9389 N. Oak Rd., Otisville, MI 48463: Free information ■ Personalized signs for homes, weddings, anniversaries, birthdays, and other occasions. 313–631–4092.

Home Sweet Home, 262 S.Main, P.O. Box 710, Walworth, WI 53184: Free information ■ Traditional country handmade and hand-decorated glazed stoneware. 414–275–8070.

House of Threads & Wood, 10 Brooks Dr., Rogers, AR 72756: Brochure $2 ■ Handcrafted household and gift items. 501–631–1438.

Independence Forge, Rt. 1, Box 1, Whitakers, NC 27891: Brochure $1 ■ Traditional, country-style, handcrafted iron pieces. Includes furniture, chandeliers, floor lamps, table lamps, and wall lamps. 919–437–2931.

International Treasury of Collectibles, Box 346, Swiss Carriage Square, Berne, IN 45711: Catalog $2 ■ Amish handmade crafts for the home.

Jepson Studios, Inc., P.O. Box 36, Harveyville, KS 66431: Brochure $2 (refundable) ■ Country ceramics. 913–589–2481.

Jori Handcast Pewter, 12681 Metro Pkwy., Fort Myers, FL 33912: Free catalog ■ Handcast pewter reproductions of 17th- and 18th-century tankards, sconces, candlesticks, lamps, and other items. 800–451–6743.

Karlin Pottery, 1443 Ryan St., Flint, MI 48532: Brochure $1 ■ Country pottery and stoneware. 800–933–7096.

Kingdom Enterprises, 1823 Willoughby, Holt, MI 48842: Brochure $2 ■ Country crafts and machine-washable window quilts with tiebacks. 517–694–5322.

Knot Shop, 5321 Spring Arbor Rd., Jackson, MI 49201: Free information ■ Hanging macrame decor pieces decorated with beads. 517–750–9216.

The Lamb's Loft, 225 Amistad Rd., San Angelo, TX 76901: Brochure $1 ■ Signed and dated, handcarved overboards for doors, windows, cabinets, mantles, and shelves. 915–944–2847.

Liberty Green, Box 5035, Station 1, Wilmington, NC 28403: Catalog $3 (refundable) ■ Handcrafted pine furniture reproductions and original folk crafts. 800–255–9704.

Loblolly Treasures, Box 273, Woodside, DE 19980: Free information ■ Hand-quilted Amish wall hangings, quilts, and other weavings. 800–562–8124; 302–284–9343 (in DE).

McVay's Old Wood Creations, P.O. Box 553, Leslie, MI 49251: Brochure $2 ■ Wall accent pieces, weather vanes, and other handcrafted household and gift items. 517–589–5312.

Mallard Pond Creations, P.O. Box 722, Cherryville, NC 28021: Free information ■ Country-style VCR tape cabinet, in two sizes. Available finished or unfinished. 704–732–4708.

Mapleleaf Workshop, P.O. Box 218, Stanford, IL 61774: Free catalog ■ Country-style wood crafts, tin ware accessories, kitchen accent pieces, placemats, hot pads, decor items, and sweatshirts. 309–379–5501.

Mathews Wire, 654 W. Morrison St., Frankfort, IN 46041: Free information ■ Country-style wire and wood decor accessories. 317–659–3542.

Michelle's Clothespin Dolls, P.O. Box 201954, Austin, TX 78720: Brochure $2 ■ Signed and numbered, handpainted clothespin dolls. Over 30 characters that include nursery rhyme and specialty dolls. 512–258–7023.

Moonlight Tiffanies, 2724 LaSalle Gardens, Lansing, MI 48912: Free information ■ Stained glass Tiffany-style lamps with brass-coated bases. 517–372–2795.

Mystic Wood Shop, RD 3, Box 83, New Berlin, NY 13411: Free information ■ Early American country-style furniture in solid cherry or oak. 607–847–8487.

Orleans Carpenters, Box 217, Orleans, MA 02653: Catalog $3 ■ Shaker-style oval bentwood boxes and other small wooden crafts. 508–255–2646.

The Owl's Nest, 112 SCT Dr., White House, TN 37188: Catalog $1 ■ Traditional country crafts. 615–672–9383.

Party House Pottery, 633 Maple, Carrollton, IL 62016: Free price list ■ Handmade, decorated pottery that is freezer, oven, dishwasher, and microwave safe. 217–942–3437.

Pesta's Country Store, 300 Standard Ave., Mingo Junction, OH 43938: Price list $1 ■ Country crafts for decorating and gift giving. 614–535–1873.

Prairie Glass Accents, P.O. Box 12272, Columbus, OH 43212: Brochure $2 ■ Stained glass accent pieces. 614–486–0592.

Raindrops on Roses Rubber Stamp Company, 4808 Winterwood Dr., Raleigh, NC 27613: Catalog $2 ■ Country stamp sets with brush markers. 919–846–8617.

RareFinds, 14631 Beach Ave., Box 18020, Irvine, CA 92714: Free catalog ■ International folk art, crafts, and collectibles. 714–552–7273.

Redwood Unlimited, P.O. Box 8326, Calabasa, CA 91372: Brochure $2 ■ Wall-mounted and post-mounted mailboxes with ornamental scrolls, posts, and weather vanes. 800–283–1717.

Rocking Horse Crafts, 529 Plymouth St., Bridgewater, MA 02324: Free catalog ■ Shadow boxes, decor pieces, toys, doll clothes, furniture, stuffed animals, and personalized signs. 508–697–7046.

The Scranberry Coop, Hwy. 206, RD 4, Box 681, Andover, NJ 07821: Brochure $1 ■ Handmade wood crafts. 800–344–6414.

Shaker Shops West, 5 Inverness Way, Inverness, CA 94937: Catalog $3 ■ Reproductions of traditional music boxes, country-style furniture, candles, accessories for the home, teas and herbs, and books on the lifestyles, traditions, and history of the Shakers. 415–669–7256.

Sharecropper's Handicrafts, 409 College St., Booneville, MS 38829: Catalog $2 ■ Stained glass, etched glass, bevelled glass, Tiffany lamps, fan lamps, quilts, woodwork, and clocks. 601–728–3120.

Simply Country Furniture, HC 69, Box 147, Rover, AR 72860: Brochure $2 ■ Grandfather clocks. 501–272–4794.

Simply Country Wholesale, Inc., P.O. Drawer 656, Wytheville, VA 24832: Brochure $2 (refundable) ■ Wallhangings, tablespreads, sofa covers, afghans, and cotton pillows. 703–228–6853.

A Special Blend of Country, RD 1, Box 56, Fabius, NY 13063: Catalog $2 ■ Country crafts, gifts, decor items, rugs, toys, and decoys. 315–683–5329.

Stoney Brook Manufacturing Company, Box 921, Blountsville, AL 35031: Free information ■ Country-style wine rack with stained glass-like panels. 205–429–2888.

The Strawberry Tree, Inc., One Merrimac St., Newburyport, MA 01950: Catalog $1 ■ Unfinished country woodenware. 508–465–5053.

Sutter Creek Antiques, 28 Main St., Box 699, Sutter Creek, CA 95685: Free brochure with long SASE ■ Antique country-style lamps, pottery, and carved wood items. 209–267–0230.

Eve Tenny, Santons De France, P.O. Box 536, Wiscasset, ME 04578: Catalog $1.50 ■ Handcrafted, terra cotta, peasants, craftsmen and creche figures made in Provence from antique molds. 207–882–7010.

The Texas Collection, P.O. Box 842, Manchaca, TX 78652: Catalog $3 ■ Country folk art that includes Texas Black Jack clay pottery. 512–295–6907.

Three Rivers Pottery Productions, Inc., 125 N. 2nd St., P.O. Box 462, Coshocton, OH 43812: Free information ■ Handmade pottery that is microwave, oven, and dishwasher safe. 614–622–4154.

Tin Bin, 20 Valley Rd., Neffsville, PA 17601: Catalog $2 ■ Handcrafted antiqued copper and brass country-style chandeliers. 717–569–6210.

A Touch of Country, RR 2, Box 147, Lexington, IL 61753: Brochure $2 ■ Country-style, handpainted wood ceiling fan/light pulls. 309–365–5041.

Touch of Dutch Mail Order, 112 S. Main St., P.O. Box 1374, Middlebury, IN 46540: Brochure $1 ■ Amish quilts and wall hangings, dolls, country-style shelving, and furniture. 800–669–2510.

Tradecraft, 2114 Church St., P.O. Box 709, East Troy, WI 53120: Brochure $1.50 ■ Wood decor accessories. 414–642–3201.

Traditions of Hendersonville, Inc., P.O. Box 3122, Hendersonville, NC 28793: Free information ■ Traditional country-style furniture. 800–456–1747.

Vaillancourt Folk Art, 145 Armsby Rd., Sutton, MA 01590: Catalog $3 ■ Reproductions of antique American grandfather clocks. 508–865–9183.

Walter's Wood Works, 506 N. Gammon Rd., Madison, WI 53717: Brochure $2 ■ Decorative country crafts. 608–833–9587.

Welcome Home, 4415 Richfield Rd., Flint, MI 48506: Brochure $2 ■ Signs, plaques, bird feeders, seed boxes, furniture, decor pieces, shadow boxes, and other wooden items. 313–736–7611.

Wesson Trading Company, 1316 Willow Street Dr., Woodstock, GA 30188: Catalog $2 ■ Pottery, textiles, and folk art. 404–928–6145.

Westwinds, 3540 76th, Caledonias, MI 49316: Free brochure ■ Weather vanes, signs, sundials, birdbaths, and other crafts. 800–635–5262.

Will Woodworking, 23376 Rd. R, Fort Jennings, OH 45844: Catalog $2 ■ Country-style wood crafts and decorative accessories. 419–286–2298.

Wind-Spirals by BB, P.O. Box 12044, Peoria, IL 61614: Free information ■ Weatherproof redwood wind spirals. 309–691–6020.

Woodcarvings by Ted Nichols, P.O. Box 1050, Salisbury, MD 21802: Catalog $1 ■ Original designs in handcarved and painted whimsical wood carvings. 410–546–9522.

Worthy Works, 1220 Rock St., Rockford, IL 61101: Brochure $1 ■ Decorative ceramic knobs for cabinets. 815–968–5858.

Zimmerman Handcrafts, 254 E. Main St., Leola, PA 17540: Brochure $1 ■ Country-style decorative items, traditional pieces, and gifts. 717–656–8290.

CRAFT SUPPLIES

Arrow Fastener Company, Inc., 271 Mayhill St., Saddle Brook, NJ 07662: Free information ■ Hot melt glue guns.

Artway Crafts, Box 699, Tom Bean, TX 75489: Catalog $1 (refundable) ■ Leather crafting, beading, wood crafting, and other arts and crafts supplies. 903–546–6755.

Baubanbea Enterprises, P.O. Box 1205, Smithtown, NY 11787: Catalog $4 ■ Imported rhinestones, sequins, beads, jewels, lace, appliques, fringe, trim, feathers, imported and domestic fabrics, and silk flowers. 516–724–4661.

Bersted's Hobby Craft, Box 40, Monmouth, IL 61462: Free catalog ■ Hobby and craft supplies. 309–734–7011.

Bolek's Craft Supplies, 330 N. Tuscarawas Ave., P.O. Box 465, Dover, OH 44622: Catalog $1.50 ■ Craft supplies and accessories, tools and equipment, and kits. 216–364–8878.

Brian's Crafts Unlimited, 1421 S. Dixie Freeway., New Smyrna, FL 32168: Catalog

$1 (refundable) ■ Craft supplies. 904–672–2726.

Carolan Craft Supplies, 4181 Rocky River Dr., Cleveland, OH 44135: Catalog $2 ($1 refundable) ■ Darice beads, plastic canvas, craft books, stencils, basket-making supplies, jewelry, quilts and needle crafts, pom poms, teddy bears, dolls, and wire crafts. 216–252–5255.

Chaselle, Inc., 9645 Gerwig Ln., Columbia, MD 21046: Catalog $4 ■ Art supplies, crayons for children, equipment for ceramists and pottery crafters, and supplies for sculpting, stained glass, weaving, leather crafting, etching, and other crafts. 800–242–7355.

Circle Craft Supply, P.O. Box 3000, Dover, FL 33527: Catalog $1 (refundable) ■ Arts and crafts supplies. 813–659–0992.

Classics, 586 Higgins Crowell Rd., West Yarmouth, MA 02673: Catalog $2 ■ Ready-to-assemble kits for ship models, steam engines, scaled reproductions, clocks, weather instruments, music boxes, and other items. 800–227–7418.

Coastal Shells & Crafts, 7424 W. 104th St., Bloomington, MN 55438: Catalog $2 ■ Supplies for making baskets, dolls, and jewelry; shell, candle, and silk flower crafting; and needle crafting. 612–941–2374.

The Corn Crib, RR 2, Box 164, Madison, MO 65263: Free information with long SASE ■ Natural and colored corn husks for crafting and how-to instruction books.

Craft Catalog, 6095 McNaughten Centre, Columbus, OH 43232: Catalog $2 ■ Supplies and accessories for arts and crafts. 800–777–1442.

Crafters Gallery, P.O. Box 4238, Huntington Station, New York, NY 11750: Catalog $1 ■ Craft supplies for needlepoint, crewel, cross stitch, and latch hook kits. 800–323–1800.

Craft King Mail Order Dept., P.O. Box 90637, Lakeland, FL 33804: Catalog $2 ■ Crafts, needlework, and macrame supplies. 813–686–9600.

Craft Resources, Inc., Box 828, Fairfield, CT 06430: Catalog $1 ■ Needlework kits for latch hooking, needlepoint, cross-stitching, and crewel; supplies for string art, basket making, metal and wood crafts, stained glass, and other crafts. 800–243–2874.

Craftsman's Touch, 812 Beltrami Ave., Bemidji, MN 56601: Catalog $2 ■ Supplies for fabric crafting, needle crafts, paper sculpting and quilling, fabric painting and dyeing, sewing, doll-making, egg crafting, basket-making and chair caning, spinning and weaving, stenciling, and quilting. 218–751–3435.

Craft Time Catalog, 211 S. State College Blvd., Anaheim, CA 92806: Catalog $2 (refundable) ■ Ready-to-paint plastercraft figurines.

Crafty's Featherworks, Manitowish Waters, WI 54545: Free information ■ Feathers for floral arrangements, Indian crafts, millinery, fly-tying, making accent pieces, and other crafts.

Creative Craft House, P.O. Box 2567, Bullhead City, AZ 86430: Catalog $2 (refundable) ■ Natural pine pods and cones, sea shells, florist materials, miniatures, jewelry findings, doll supplies, party and wedding favors, and holiday supplies.

Lou Davis, 1490 Elkhorn Rd., Lake Geneva, WI 53147: Free catalog ■ Craft supplies and accessories. 414–248–2000.

Design Originals, 2425 Cullen St., Fort Worth, TX 76107: Catalog $5 ■ Supplies and accessories for making rag rugs, baskets, wood crafts, belts, fabric crafts, cross stitching, and other crafts. 817–877–0067.

Earth Guild, 33 Haywood St., Asheville, NC 28801: Catalog $2 (refundable) ■ Basket-making, weaving, spinning, dyeing, pottery, woodcarving, hand and machine knitting, rug-making, netting, and chair caning supplies and accessories. 800–327–8448.

Eastern Craft Supply, P.O. Box 341, Wyckoff, NJ 07481: Catalog $2 ■ Stained glass kits, glass-etching supplies, glass coloring materials, mirror-removing supplies, wood-burning supplies, and how-to videos. 800–872–3458.

Enterprise Art, P.O. Box 2918, Largo, FL 34649: Free catalog $1 ■ Arts and crafts supplies. 813–536–1492.

Fairfield Processing Corporation, P.O. Box 1157, Danbury, CT 06813: Free information ■ Fiberfill and batting products. 800–442–2271; 203–371–1901 (in CT).

The Gourd Factory, P.O. Box 55311, Stockton, CA 95205: Free information with long SASE ■ Dry gourds. 209–943–5852.

Grey Owl Indian Craft Company, 113–15 Springfield Blvd., Queens Village, NY 11429: Catalog $1 ■ Supplies and kits for making American Indian crafts. 212–464–9300.

Guildcraft Company, 3158 Main St., Buffalo, NY 14214: Catalog $1 ■ Supplies for crafting with foil, chair caning, basket-making, plaster crafts, candle and wood crafting, leather and egg crafting, and fabric dyeing. 716–837–9346.

Fred & Clarita Hayes Gourds, Rt. 8, Box 828, Gilmer, TX 75644: Free information with long SASE ■ Gourds for crafting. 903–734–5204.

Heartland Craft Discounters, P.O. Box 65, Geneseo, IL 61254: Catalog $2 ■ Craft supplies, wood cutouts, ribbons, books, needle craft kits and accessories, doll parts, glues, and paints. 309–944–6411.

House of Crafts & Stuff, 5157 Gall Blvd., Zephyrhills, FL 33541: Catalog $2 ($1 refundable) ■ Supplies for needlework, bead-crafting, doll-making, and other crafts.

Kathy's Discount Craft Supply, P.O. Box 18025, Fountain Hills, AZ 85269: Free catalog ■ Craft, floral, wicker, and wedding supplies.

Kirchen Brothers, Box 1016, Skokie, IL 60076: Catalog $2 (refundable) ■ Supplies and accessories for arts and crafts. 708–676–2692.

Lamrite's Floral & Craft Supply, 565 Broadway, Bedford, OH 44146: Catalog $2 ■ Silk flowers and supplies for making floral arrangements; and supplies for making candles, painting, wood crafting, pom poms, and wicker items. 216–232–9300.

LHL Enterprises, Box 241, Solebury, PA 18963: Catalog $3 (refundable) ■ Arts and crafts supplies and needlework. 215–348–3611.

Luv'n Stuff, P.O. Box 85, Poway, CA 92064: Catalog $2 (refundable) ■ Rubber stamps for making craft and gift tags, stationery, and note paper; patterns for dolls, stuffed animals, holiday decorations and ornaments; and sewing supplies. 619–748–8060.

Nasco, 901 Janesville Ave., Fort Atkinson, WI 53538: Free catalog ■ Arts and crafts supplies for art projects, calligraphy, leather crafting, metal enameling, ceramics, photography, and needle crafts. 800–558–9595.

National Artcraft Company, 23456 Mercantile Rd., Beachwood, OH 44122: Catalog $4 (refundable) ■ Supplies and tools for clock, lamp, doll, magnets, decorations, and flowers, candle-making and jewelry-making crafts. 216–292–4944.

Prints Charming, 55 Mountain Blvd., Warren, NJ 07060: Catalog $3 ■ Patterns for arts and crafts projects. 908–668–1961.

The Pumpkin Farm & Gourd Place, 101 Creston Rd., Paso Robles, CA 93446: Free information with long SASE ■ Gourds for crafting. 805–238–0624.

Pyramid of Urbana, 2107 N. High Cross Rd., Urbana, IL 61801: Free catalog ■ Craft supplies, office accessories and supplies, art supplies, and school equipment. 217–328–3099.

Redhill Corporation, Box 81, Biglerville, PA 17307: Free information with long SASE ■ Hot melt glue sticks, glue guns, and sandpaper belts, sheets, and discs. 800–822–4003.

Sax Arts & Crafts, P.O. Box 51710, New Berlin, WI 51710: Catalog $4 (refundable) ■ Supplies and accessories for arts and crafts. 414–784–6880.

Schrock's Crafts & Hobby World, 1527 E. Amherst Rd., P.O. Box 1136, Massillon, OH 44648: Catalog $3 ■ Arts and craft and needlework supplies. 216–837–8845.

Skil-Crafts Division, 309 Virginia, Joplin, MO 64801: Catalog $5 ■ Arts and crafts supplies and accessories. 417–624–4038.

James Stephens Gourds, 501 Lee St., Attalia, AL 35954: Free information with long SASE ■ Gourds for crafting. 205–538–7030.

Suncoast Discount Arts & Crafts Warehouse, 9015 US 19 North, Pinellas Park, FL 34666: Catalog $2 ■ Arts and craft supplies and accessories. 813–577–6331.

Sunflower & Sunshine Company, 127 W. 30th St., Hutchinson, KS 67502: Free brochure ■ Wheat-weaving supplies, tools, books, kits, sewing pattern packets, painting and applique pattern packets, and folk art necklace kits. 316–665–6256.

Supplies 4 Less, 13001 Las Vegas Blvd., Las Vegas, NV 89124: Catalog $3.50 ■ Laces, appliques, ribbons, silk painting supplies, flowers, how-to books, and other craft accessories.

Warscokins, 17930 Magnolia, Fountain Valley, CA 92708: Catalog $3.50 ■ Arts and crafts supplies. 800–225–6356; 714–962–8991 (in CA).

Weaving Works, 4717 Brooklyn Ave. NE, Seattle, WA 98105: Catalog $1 ■ Supplies and accessories for making baskets, dyeing, weaving, spinning, and knitting. 206–524–1221.

Ziegler Art & Craft Supply, Inc., P.O. Box 50037, Tulsa, OK 74150: Catalog $2 (refundable) ■ Arts and crafts supplies and equipment. 918–584–2217.

Zim's, Inc., Box 7620, Salt Lake City, UT 84107: Catalog $5 ■ Arts and crafts and painting supplies. 801–268–2505.

Zimmerman's Discount Craft Supplies, 2884 34th St. North, St. Petersburg, FL 33713: Catalog $2 (refundable) ■ Arts and crafts supplies. 813–526–4880.

CRICKET

American Sports, Inc., 22 Longview Dr., Thornton, PA 19373: Free information ■ Bats, balls, and gloves. 215–459–8534.

General Sportcraft Company, Ltd., 140 Woodbine St., Bergenfield, NJ 07621: Free information ■ Bats, balls, and gloves. 201–384–4242.

Genesport Industries, Ltd., Hokkaido Karate Equipment Manufacturing Company, 150 King St., Montreal, Quebec, Canada H3C 2P3: Free information ■ Bats, balls, and gloves. 514–861–1856.

Don Jagoda Associates, Inc., 1 Underhill Blvd., Syosset, NY 11791: Free information ■ Bats, balls, and gloves. 516–496–7300.

CROQUET

Cannon Sports, P.O. Box 11179, Burbank, CA 91510: Free information ■ Croquet sets. 800–223–0064; 818–503–9570 (in CA).

Clarkpoint Croquet Company, P.O. Box 457, Southwest Harbor, ME 04679: Free information with long SASE ■ Croquet sets. 207–244–9284.

Forster Manufacturing Company, P.O. Box 657, Wilton, ME 04294: Free information ■ Croquet sets. 800–341–7574; 207–645–2574 (in ME).

Olympia Sports, School Tech, Inc., 745 State Cir., Ann Arbor, MI 48108: Free information ■ Croquet sets. 313–761–5135.

Porter Athletic Equipment Company, 9555 Irving Park Rd., Schiller Park, IL 60176: Free information ■ Croquet sets. 708–671–0110.

Regent Sports Corporation, 45 Ranick Rd., Hauppage, NY 11787: Free information ■ Croquet sets. 516–234–2948.

Russell Athletic, Division Russell Corporation, P.O. Box 272, Alexander City, AL 35010: Free information ■ Croquet sets. 205–329–5310.

CRYSTAL & GLASSWARE

Adler's Crystal, 722 Canal St., New Orleans, LA 70130: Free brochure ■ Waterford crystal stemware and other glassware. 504–523–5292.

Alberene Crystal, 221 W. Main, Charlottesville, VA 22901: Free information ■ Edinburgh and Thomas Webb crystal, and Perthshire paperweights. Includes discontinued items. 800–843–9078.

Barrons, P.O. Box 994, Novi, MI 48376: Free information ■ Save up to 65 percent on china, crystal, and silver. 800–538–6340.

Mildred Brumback, P.O. Box 132, Middletown, VA 22645: Free information ■ Discontinued china and crystal patterns. 703–869–1261.

The China Cabinet, P.O. Box 266, Clearwater, SC 29822: Free information with long SASE ■ China and crystal. 803–593–9655.

China & Crystal Marketing, Box 25602, Philadelphia, PA 19111: Free information ■ China, earthenware, and crystal. Includes discontinued patterns. 215–342–7919.

China Replacements, 2263 Williams Creek Rd., High Ridge, MO 63049: Free information with long SASE ■ Discontinued china and crystal. 800–562–2655; 677–5577 (in St. Louis).

Clintsman International, 327 W. Main, Waukesha, WI 53186: Free information with long SASE ■ Discontinued china and crystal patterns. 414–547–7327.

Cristalleries de Baccarat, 55 E. 57th St., New York, NY 10022: Free information ■ Will advise where Baccarat crystal can be purchased in the United States. 212–826–4100.

Crystal Lalique, 680 Madison Ave., New York, NY 10021: Free information ■ Will advise where Crystal Lalique can be purchased in the United States. 212–355–6550.

Crystal Match, 72 Longacre Rd., Rochester, NY 14621: Free information ■ Replacement crystal and china patterns. 716–338–3781.

Dining Elegance, Ltd., Box 4203, St. Louis, MO 63163: Pattern list 75¢ ■ China and crystal. 314–865–1408.

Gallery Nilsson, 138 Wooster St., New York, NY 10012: Free information ■ Will advise where Nilsson crystal can be purchased in the United States. 212–982–8509.

Greater New York Trading, 81 Canal St., New York, NY 10002: Free information with long SASE ■ Silver, china, and glassware. 800–336–4012.

Jacquelyn Hall, 10629 Baxter, Los Altos, CA 94022: Free information ■ Lenox china and crystal replacements. 408–739–4876.

Heirloom Completions, 1620 Venice, Granite, IL 62040: Free information ■ Matching china and silverplate replacement pieces. 618–931–4333.

Hoya Crystal Gallery, 450 Park Ave., New York, NY 10022: Catalog $6 ■ Exclusive art sculptures, vases, bowls, glass stemware, ornamental pieces, and crystal clocks. 212–223–6335.

Iittala Crystal, Rt. 6, Mahopac, NY 10541: Free information ■ Will advise where Iittala glass from Finland can be purchased in the United States. 800–678–2667.

Kosta Boda, 225 5th Ave., New York, NY 10010: Free information ■ Will advise where Kosta Boda crystal from Sweden can be purchased in the United States. 212–679–2280.

Lalique the Gallery, 680 Madison Ave., New York, NY 10021: Free information ■ Lalique crystal. 212–355–6550.

Lanac Sales, 73 Canal St., New York, NY 10002: Free information ■ Crystal, china, and sterling. 212–925–6422.

Lenox Collections Gifts, One Lenox Center, P.O. Box 3029, Langhorne, PA 19092: Free catalog ■ China, crystal, and porcelain sculptures. 800–233–1885.

Locators, Inc., 908 Rock St., Little Rock, AR 72202: Free information ■ Discontinued china, crystal, and silver. 800–367–9690.

Luigi Crystal, 7332 Frankford Ave., Philadelphia, PA 19136: Catalog $1 ■ Crystal accessories and decorative pieces. Includes table lamps, cut crystal chandeliers, hurricane lamps, and sconces. 215–338–2978.

Miki's Crystal Registry, Box 22506, Robbinsdale, MN 55422: Free information ■ Fostoria crystal matching service. 800–628–9394.

Orrefors, 58 E. 57th St., New York, NY 10022: Free information ■ Will advise where Orrefors crystal can be purchased in the United States. 800–351–9842; 212–753–3442 (in NY).

Past & Presents, 65–07 Fitchett St., Rego Park, NY 11374: Free information ■ Matches crystal, china, and flatware. 718–897–5515.

Replacements, Ltd., 1089 Knox Rd., P.O. Box 26029, Greensboro, NC 27029: Free information with long SASE ■ Discontinued bone china, earthenware, and crystal. 919–697–3000.

Robin Importers, 510 Madison Ave., New York, NY 10022: Brochure $1 with long SASE ■ China, crystal, and stainless steel flatware. 800–223–3373; 212–753–6475 (in NY).

Rogers & Rosenthal, 22 W. 48th St., Room 1102, New York, NY 10036: Free information with long SASE ■ Crystal, china, silver, silver plate, and stainless steel. 212–827–0115.

Rudi's Pottery, Silver & China, 178 State Hwy. 17, Paramus, NJ 07652: Free information with long SASE ■ Glass stemware, china, and gifts. 201–265–6096.

Steuben Glass, Customer Relations, Corning Glass Center, Corning, NY 14831: Catalog $8 ■ Steuben crystal and other items.

CURTAINS, DRAPES & BLINDS

Blinds & Window Shades

Advanced Consumer Products, P.O. Box 95, Garden City, MI 48135: Free information ■ Save up to 75 percent custom vertical blinds. 800–677–9090.

American Blind & Wallpaper Factory, 28237 Orchard Lake Rd., Farmington Hills, MI 48018: Free information ■ Save up to 75 percent on wooden blinds, vertical blinds, custom roller shades, pleated shades, and micro and mini blinds. 800–735–5300.

Blind Center USA, 30242 Littlecroft, Houston, TX 77286: Free information ■ Save up to 80 percent on vertical, pleated mini, micro, duettes, and wood blinds. 800–676–5029.

Blinds 'N Things, 516 Jefferson Blvd., Birmingham, AL 35217: Free information ■ Save from 50 to 60 percent on micro and mini blinds. 800–662–5894; 800–824–0632 (in AL).

Blinds Today, P.O. Box 218, Normal, IL 61761: Free information ■ Save up to 75 percent on window blinds and shades. 800–336–1611.

Bradd & Hall Blinds, 7234 New Market Ct. Manassas, VA 22110: Free information ■ Save up to 80 percent on window blinds. 800–542–7502.

Colorel Blinds, 8200 E. Park Meadows Dr., Littleton, CO 80124: Free information ■ Save up to 70 percent on custom window coverings. 800–877–4800.

Custom Windows & Walls, 32525 Stephenson Hwy., Madison Heights, MI 48071: Free information ■ Mini blinds. 800–772–1947.

Devenco Products, Inc., Box 700, Decatur, GA 30031: Free brochure ■ Authentic period reproductions of wooden blinds, movable shutters, and plantation and traditional shutters. 404–378–4597.

Factory Paint Store, 505 Pond St., South Weymouth, MA 02190: Free information ■ Window shades, lighting fixtures, wallpaper, and paint. 617–331–1200.

Headquarters Windows & Walls, 8 Clinton Pl., Morristown, NJ 07960: Free information ■ Save up to 65 percent on micro, mini, verticals, and pleated blinds, and up to 50 percent on wall coverings. 800–338–4882.

Hunter Douglas Window Fashions, 2 Duette Way, Broomfield, CO 80020: Free catalog ■ Window coverings. 800–32–STYLE.

National Blind Factory, 400 Galleria, Southfield, MI 48034: Free information ■ Save up to 75 percent on window blinds. 800–477–8000.

Post Wallcovering Distributors, Inc., 2065 Franklin, Bloomfield Hills, MI 48013: Free information ■ Save up to 75 percent on window blinds and up to 70 percent on wall coverings. 800–521–0650.

Premier Blind Company, 317 E. Hempstead, Giddings, TX 78492: Free information ■ Mini blinds, micros, pleated shades, verticals, and drapes. 800–441–1288.

3 Day Blinds, Attn: Mail Order, 2220 East Cerritos Ave., Anaheim, CA 92806: Free information ■ Vertical blinds, mini blinds, Riviera blinds, Monaco mini blinds, wooden, and pleated shades. 800–966–3DAY.

USA Blind Factory, 1312 Live Oak, Houston, TX 77003: Free information ■ Save up to 80 percent on vertical, pleated, mini, micro, and wood blinds. 800–275–3219.

Wells Interiors, 7171 Amador Valley Plaza Rd., Dublin, CA 95468: Free catalog ■ Kits for making energy-efficient Roman shades, or for adding fabric to existing decors; or save up to 60 percent on mini blinds, wooden blinds, verticals, pleated blinds, and woven woods. 800–547–8982.

The Wholesale Blind Company, P.O. Box 2005, Laurel, MS 39442: Free information ■ Custom 1– and 2–inch wood blinds, verticals, softlight shades, and 1– and 1/2–inch mini blinds. 800–523–6276.

Window Scapes, 11211 Sorrento Valley Rd., San Diego, CA 92121: Free information ■ Save up to 80 percent on vertical, pleated, mini, micro, and wood blinds. 800–786–3021.

Curtains & Drapes

Caroline's Country Ruffles, 420 W. Franklin Blvd., Gastona, NC 28052: Catalog $2 ■ Curtains and accessories, with a choice of fabrics. 800–426–1039.

Colonial Country Originals, Inc., P.O. Box 2010, Hanover, MA 02339: Catalog $3 ■ Reproduction Colonial and Early American and hand-stenciled curtains, with a choice of over 120 fabrics. 800–627–2878.

Country Curtains, Red Lion Inn, Stockbridge, MA 01262: Free catalog ■ Country-style curtains in cotton muslin or permanent press fabrics. 800–876–6123.

Designer Secrets, Box 529, Fremont, NE 68025: Catalog $2 (refundable) ■ Save up to 50 percent on window treatments and accessories, wall coverings and fabrics, bedspreads, and furniture. 800–955–2559.

Dianthus, Ltd., P.O. Box 870, Plymouth, MA 02362: Catalog $4 ■ Curtains and accessories with a country look. 508–747–4179.

Dorothy's Ruffled Originals, Inc., 6721 Market St., Wilmington, NC 28405: Catalog $4 ■ Custom ruffled curtains and accessories. 800–367–6849.

Especially Lace, 202 5th St., West Des Moines, IA 50265: Catalog $3.50 ■ European lace curtains and ready-to-hang valances. 515–277–8778.

Fabrics by Phone, P.O. Box 309, Walnut Bottom, PA 17266: Brochure and samples $3 ■ Custom draperies and accessories. 800–233–7012; 800–692–7345 (in PA).

Fabric Shop, 120 N. Seneca St., Shippensburg, PA 17257: Free information with long SASE ■ Custom draperies and accessories; antique satins; decorative draperies; and slipcover and upholstery fabrics. 800–233–7012; 800–692–7345 (in PA).

Faith's Lacery, 89 W. Main St., Dundee, IL 60118: Catalog $2 ■ Valances, cafes, swags, door panels, country lace curtains, Victorian curtains, runners, and table overlays.

Virginia Goodwin, Rt. 2, Box 770, Boone, NC 28607: Information $1 ■ Window valances, hand-tied fishnet bed canopies, custom dust ruffles, and bed spreads. 800–735–5191.

Linen & Lace, 4 Lafayette, Washington, MO 63090: Catalog $2 ■ Linen and imported Bavarian lace curtains, runners, and accent pillows. 800–332–5223.

London Lace, 167 Newbury St., Boston, MA 02116: Catalog $2.50 ■ Lace window coverings. 617–267–3506.

Mather's Department Store, 31 E. Main St., Westminster, MD 21157: Free catalog ■ Country-style curtains. Includes tabs, ruffles, fringes, calico prints, and French country-style prints. 410–848–6410.

Anne Roche Interiors, 255 Park Ave., Worcester, MA 01609: Free brochure ■ Handcrafted, custom window treatments. 508–757–4657.

Rue de France, 78 Thames St., Newport, RI 02840: Catalog $3 ■ Lace curtains, tablecloths, runners, and pillows. 800–777–0998.

Seraph, 5606 State Route 37, Delaware, OH 43015: Catalog $3 ■ Bed hangings and window treatments, with coordinating rugs and accessories. 614–369–1817.

South Bound Millworks, P.O. Box 349, Sandwich, MA 02563: Catalog $1 (refundable) ■ Wooden curtain rods and brackets, and wrought-iron and wooden accessories. 508–477–9355.

Vintage Valances, P.O. Box 43326, Cincinnati, OH 45243: Catalog and samples $12 ■ Ready-to-hang Victorian and Greek revival-style valances. 513–561–8665.

Window Quilt, P.O. Box 975, Brattleboro, VT 05301: Information $1 ■ Decorative insulating window shades. 800–257–4501.

DANCING

Ballet Barres

Alvas Barres, 1417 W. 8th St., San Pedro, CA 90732: Free brochure ■ Wall-mounted and free-standing ballet barres. 213–519–1314.

Ballet Barres, Inc., P.O. Box 261206, Tampa, FL 33685: Free catalog ■ Professional studio barres, portable barres, mirrors, record players, professional wall brackets, and floor stanchions. 800–767–1199.

Ballet Conservatory Products, 1812 7th St. NW, Winter Haven, FL 33881: Free information ■ Ballet barres. 813–293–0529.

Victoria's Dance-Theatrical Supply, 1331 Lincoln Ave., San Jose, CA 95125: Free brochure ■ Portable wall-mounted ballet barres. 408–295–9316.

Clothing & Costumes

American Harlequin Corporation, 3111 W. Burbank Blvd., Burbank, CA 91505: Free information ■ Dancewear and costumes for ballet, jazz, and modern dance. 800–642–6440.

Apparel Warehouse, 6010 Yolanda St., Tarzana, CA 91356: Free catalog ■ Briefs, leotards, dance belts, cotton tights, shiny tights, spandex tights, and leg warmer socks. 800–245–8434; 818–344–3224 (in CA).

Artistic Dance Fashions, 4915 Cordell Ave., Bethesda, MD 20814: Catalog $4 ■ Dancewear and costumes. 301–652–2324.

Baum's, Inc., 106 S. 11th St., Philadelphia, PA 19107: Free catalog ■ Costumes, leotards, shoes, fabrics, and majorette items. 215–923–2244.

Capezio Dance Shop, 126 Post St., San Francisco, CA 94108: Catalog $3 ■ Shoes, dancewear, and costumes. 415–421–5657.

Carushka, Inc., 15414 Cabrito Rd., Van Nuys, CA 91406: Catalog $2 ■ Women's bodywear, leotards, tank tops, trunks, bike tights, and turtleneck leotards. 818–904–0574.

Chatila Dance & Gymnastic Fashions, P.O. Box 508, Staten Island, NY 10304: Free catalog ■ Basic bodywear, matching leg and footwear, creative mood fashions, and leotards; tap, ballet, and jazz shoes; skating and belly dancer outfits; gymnastic leotards; and aerobic wear. 718–720–3632.

Curtain Call Costumes, 333 E. 7th Ave., P.O. Box 709, York, PA 17405: Free information ■ Dancing attire. 717–852–6910.

Dance Design, Rams Plaza, Chapel Hill, NC 27514: Free catalog ■ Dancewear, shoes, and accessories. 919–942–2131.

Dance Shop, 2603 8th Ave., Fort Worth, TX 76110: Free information ■ Shoes, bodywear, and accessories for dancers. 817–923–0017.

Dansant Boutique, P.O. Box 221999, Carmel, CA 93922: Free brochure ■ Dancewear, leotards, tights, shoes, and accessories. 408–625–0791.

Danskin, 111 W. 40th St., New York, NY 10018: Free information ■ Leotards, tights, costumes, ballet shoes, swimsuits, lingerie, and hosiery. 212–764–4630.

Dazian's, Inc., 2014 Commerce St., Dallas, TX 75201: Free catalog ■ Leotards, tights, and other dancewear, and costume fabrics, supplies, trimmings, and novelties. 214–748–3450.

Freed of London, Inc., 922 S. 7th Ave., New York, NY 10019: Free price list ■ Pointe shoes, soft ballet slippers, ballet accessories, leotards and ballroom attire, jazz and character shoes, gym shoes, and exercise wear. 212–489–1055.

Grace Costumes, Inc., 250 W. 54th St., New York, NY 10019: Free information ■ Custom costumes. 212–JU6–0260.

Herbet Dancewear, 129 W. 29th St., New York, NY 10001: Free information ■ Leotards, tights, costumes, records, and tap, toe, and ballet shoes. 212–695–2699.

Hoctor Products, P.O. Box 38, Waldwick, NJ 07463: Free catalog ■ Costumes and accessories, records, dance routines, videos, cassettes, phonographs and cassette players, and video recorders. 201–652–7767.

K.Ddids, 321 Rider Ave., 4th Floor, Bronx, NY 10451: Free catalog ■ Dancewear. 212–402–2012.

Kling's Theatrical Shoe Company, 218 S. Wabash Ave., Chicago, IL 60604: Free catalog ■ Shoes, dancewear, and accessories. 312–427–2028.

Marcea Lane Dancewear, P.O. Box 5306, Diamond Bar, CA 91765: Catalog $1 ■ Dancewear. 714–860–1588.

Lebo's of Charlotte, Inc., 4118 E. Independence Blvd., Charlotte, NC 28205: Free catalog ■ Costumes, footwear, leotards, tights, fabrics, record players, tapes, and records. 704–535–5000.

Loshin's Dancewear, 260 W. Mitchell Ave., Cincinnati, OH 45232: Free information ■ Costumes, leotards, tights, sequin trimmings, tiaras, hats, and shoes. 513–541–5400.

Lynch's Clown Supplies, Inc., 939 Howard, Dearborn, MI 48124: Catalog $5 ■ Dancewear, shoes, super tone taps, sequin appliques and trim, sequin fabrics, rhinestones, hats, and make-up. 313–565–3425.

Physical Fashions, 289 Allwood Rd., Clifton, NJ 07012: Free information ■ Dancewear for children and adults. 800–24–DANCE; 201–773–3887 (in NJ).

S & S Hosiery, 135 W. 50th St., New York, NY 10020: Free information ■ Exercise clothing, dancewear, hosiery, and lingerie. 212–586–3288.

H.W. Shaw, Inc., P.O. Box 4034, Hollywood, FL 33083: Free catalog ■ Dancewear. 800–327–9548; 305–989–1300 (in FL).

Showboat Dancewear & Gifts, 12408 Hesperia Rd., Victorville, CA 92392: Free information ■ Dancewear and shoes, gifts, and jewelry. 619–243–2363.

Star Styled Dancewear, P.O. Box 1805, Hialeah, FL 33011: Free information ■ Bodywear for dancers. 800–634–4628.

Art Stone Dancewear, 1795 Express Dr. North, Smithtown, NY 11787: Free catalog ■ Bodywear and footwear for dancers. 516–582–9500.

Taffy's-by-Mail, 701 Beta Dr., Cleveland, OH 44143: Catalog $3 ■ Dancewear, accessories, shoes, videos, and books. 216–461–3360.

Victoria's Dance-Theatrical Supply, 1331 Lincoln Ave., San Jose, CA 95125: Catalog $1 ■ Bodywear, leg and footwear, portable and adjustable ballet barres, hats, and fabrics and trims. 408–295–9316.

Weissman's Designs for Dance, 1600 Macklind Ave., St. Louis, MO 63110: Free catalog ■ Costumes for dancers. 314–773–9000.

R.B. Williams Company, Inc., 157 6th Ave. NE, St. Petersburg, FL 33701: Free information ■ Dance sweatpants in small, medium, and large. 800–843–7346; 813–822–1602 (in FL).

Wolff-Fording & Company, 2220 E. Main St., Richmond, VA 23223: Free catalog ■ Leotards, costumes, footwear, fabrics, and accessories. 804–643–2600.

Music

Dansounds, P.O. Box 27618, Philadelphia, PA 19118: Free information ■ Music for ballet dance classes.

Hoctor Products, P.O. Box 38, Waldwick, NJ 07463: Free information ■ Records, cassettes, dance routines, cassette players, video recorders, phonographs, and books. 201–652–7767.

Jay Distributors, Box 191332, Dallas, TX 75219: Free information ■ Records and tapes.

Lebo's of Charlotte, Inc., 4118 E. Independence Blvd., Charlotte, NC 28205: Free catalog ■ Costumes, dancewear, footwear, leotards and tights, fabrics, accessories, record players, tapes, and records. 704–535–5000.

Roper Records, P.O. Box 4386, Long Island City, NY 11104: Free catalog ■ Ballet and ballroom dance music.

Supreme Audio, P.O. Box 687, Ridgewood, NJ 07450: Free catalog ■ Professional audio equipment. 800–445–7398; 201–445–7398 (in NJ).

Shoes

American Dance, Inc., 185 N. Fraser, Kankakee, IL 60901: Free information ■ Jazz boots that combine flexibility and style, and with rubber or leather soles. 815–933–9551.

A Pied Manufacturing Company, 129 E. Center St., Milwaukee, WI 53212: Free catalog ■ Ballet shoes. 800–762–3138.

Bloch's Australia, 1031 S. Broadway, 9th Floor, Los Angeles, CA 90014: Free information ■ Dance shoes for men and women. 213–623–4227.

Chatila Dance & Gymnastic Fashions, P.O. Box 508, Staten Island, NY 10304: Free catalog ■ Tap, ballet, and jazz shoes, and dance and aerobic clothing. 718–720–3532.

Coast Shoes, Inc., P.O. Box 290, Cathedral City, CA 92234: Free brochure ■ Tap, jazz, ballet, and character dance shoes. 800–262–7851.

Dance Design, Rams Plaza, Chapel Hill, NC 27514: Free catalog ■ Dance shoes, dancewear, and accessories. 919–942–2131.

Danskin, 111 W. 40th St., New York, NY 10018: Free information ■ Ballet shoes, costumes, leotards, tights, swimsuits, lingerie, and hosiery. 212–764–4630.

Freed of London, Inc., 922 7th Ave., New York, NY 10019: Free price list ■ Pointe shoes, soft ballet slippers, jazz and character shoes, ballet accessories, and leotards. 212–489–1055.

Herbet Dancewear, 129 W. 29th St., New York, NY 10001: Free information ■ Tap, toe, and ballet shoes; leotards, tights and costumes; and records. 212–695–2699.

Kling's Theatrical Shoe Company, 218 S. Wabash Ave., Chicago, IL 60604: Free catalog ■ Shoes, dancewear, and accessories. 312–427–2028.

La Ray, 633 Alacci Way, River Vale, NJ 07675: Free information ■ Toe shoes and ballet slippers. 201–664–5882.

Miquelitos Dancing Shoes & Supplies, 7315 San Pedro Ave., San Antonio, TX

78216: Free information ■ Ballet, flamenco, gymnastic, jazz, folk, and tap shoes. 512–349–2573.

Repetto Dance Shoes, 30 Lincoln Plaza, New York, NY 10023: Free information ■ Classical ballet and contemporary dancewear and shoes. 212–582–3900.

Showboat Dancewear & Gifts, 12408 Hesperia Rd., Victorville, CA 92392: Free information ■ Shoes, dancewear, gifts, and jewelry. 619–243–2363.

Taffy's-by-Mail, 701 Beta Dr., Cleveland, OH 44143: Catalog $3 ■ Tap, jazz, pointed, and ballet shoes, and jazz boots, dancewear, and accessories. 216–461–3360.

DARTS

Accudart, 160 E. Union Ave., East Rutherford, NJ 07073: Free catalog ■ Darts, dart boards, and accessories. 201–438–9000.

Amerola Sports, Inc., 4719 Hatfield St., Pittsburgh, PA 15201: Free information ■ Dart boards and cabinets, dart-making supplies, and sets. 800–426–3765.

Bottelsen Dart Company, Inc., 942 W. McCoy Ln., Santa Maria, CA 93455: Free information ■ Dart boards and cabinets, dart-making supplies, and sets. 805–922–4510.

Cornhusker Billiard, 4825 S. 16th, Lincoln, NE 68512: Free catalog ■ Billiards and dart supplies. 800–627–8888.

Dart Mart, Inc., 19 W. 36th St., New York, NY 10018: Free information ■ Dart boards, cabinets, dart-making supplies, and sets. 800–423–3220; 212–643–DART (in NY).

Darts Unlimited, 282 N. Henry St., Brooklyn, NY 11222: Free information ■ Dart boards, cabinets, dart-making supplies, and sets. 718–389–7755.

Dart World, Inc., 65 Monroe St., P.O. Box 845, Lynn, MA 01903: Free information ■ Dart boards, cabinets, dart-making supplies, and sets. 800–225–2558; 617–581–6035 (in MA).

Franklin Sports Industries, Inc., 17 Campanelli Pkwy., P.O. Box 508, Stoughton, MA 02072: Free information ■ Dart boards, cabinets, and sets. 617–344–1111.

General Sportcraft Company, Ltd., 140 Woodbine St., Bergenfield, NJ 07621: Free information ■ Dart boards, cabinets, dart-making supplies, and sets. 201–384–4242.

Indian Industries, Inc., 817 Maxwell, P.O. Box 889, Evansville, IN 47711: Free information ■ Dart boards, cabinets, dart-making supplies, and sets. 800–426–2281.

Don Jagoda Associates, Inc., 1 Underhill Blvd., Syosset, NY 11791: Free information ■ Boards, cases, darts, and dart-making supplies. 516–496–7300.

Marksman Products, 5622 Engineer Dr., Huntington Beach, CA 92649: Free information ■ Dart boards, cabinets, dart-making supplies, and sets. 800–822–8005; 714–898–7535 (in CA).

Pennsylvania Sporting Goods, 1360 Industrial Hwy., P.O. Box 451, Southampton, PA 18966: Free information ■ Dart boards, cabinets, dart-making supplies, and sets. 800–535–1122.

Spalding & Brothers, 425 Meadow St., P.O. Box 901, Chicopee, MA 01021: Free information ■ Dart boards, cabinets, dart-making supplies, and sets. 413–536–1200.

Tide-Rider, Inc., P.O. Box 429, Oakdale, CA 95361: Free information ■ Dart boards, cabinets, dart-making supplies, and sets. 209–848–4420.

Valley Recreation Products, Inc., Box 656, Bay City, MI 48707: Free information ■ Dart boards, cabinets, dart-making supplies, and sets. 800–248–2837; 517–892–4536 (in MI).

DECALS, EMBLEMS & PATCHES

Conrad Industries, P.O. Box 695, Weaverville, NC 28787: Free catalog ■ Embroidered emblems. 704–064–3015.

Eastern Emblem, Box 828, Union City, NJ 07087: Free catalog ■ Patches, cloisonne pins, decals, stickers, T-shirts, caps, and jackets. 800–344–5112.

Goldsmith's Sporting Goods & Clothes Shop, 464 Main St., Rockland, ME 04841: Free brochure ■ Custom-embroidered jackets, caps, and jerseys. 207–594–8636.

Hoover's Manufacturing Company, 4015 Progress Blvd., Peru, IL 61354: Free catalog ■ Vietnam, Korea, and World War II hat pins; dog tag key rings, beer and coffee mugs, Zippo lighters, belt buckles, patches, and flags. 815–223–1159.

HSU Patches, P.O. Box 710187, San Jose, CA 95171: Free information ■ Custom-embroidered patches. 408–996–8989.

Namark Cap & Emblem Company, 6325 Harrison Dr., Las Vegas, NV 89120: Free information ■ Custom screen-printed emblems, caps, T-shirts, and jackets. 800–634–6271.

Recco Maid Embroidery Company, 4626 W. Cornelia Ave., Chicago, IL 60641: Free catalog ■ Embroidered emblems. 800–345–3458; 312–286–6333 (in IL).

W.N. Rich, 137 Old Long Ridge Rd., Stamford, CT 06903: Catalog $2 ■ Over 350 cloth-embroidered railroad emblems. 203–322–2256.

C. Sanders Emblems, 12965 Arroyo St., San Fernando, CA 91340: Free information ■ Cloisonne pins, custom-embroidered patches, stock pins, and custom pins for bowlers. 818–361–5999.

Southern Emblem, P.O. Box 8, Toast, NC 27049: Free information ■ Embroidered emblems. 919–789–3348.

Stadri Emblems, 57 Leroy, New York, NY 10014: Free catalog ■ Custom-embroidered emblems, pins, and decals. 212–929–2293.

DECORATIVE ITEMS

AD LIB, 1401 W. Paces Ferry Rd., Atlanta, GA 30327: Free information ■ Decor accessories for homes. 404–266–2425.

An Affair of the Hearth, P.O. Box 95174, Oklahoma City, OK 73143: Free catalog ■ Fireplace and decor accessories. 800–755–5488.

Amish Country Collection, Sunset Valley Rd., RD 5, New Castle, PA 16105: Catalog $5 (refundable) ■ Amish-style pillows, quilts, wall hangings, rugs, beds and cribs, and other crafts. 800–232–6474.

Baldwin Hardware Corporation, 841 E. Wyomissing Blvd., Box 15048, Reading, PA 19612: Bathroom accessories brochure 75¢; lighting fixtures brochure $3; door hardware brochure 75¢; decor hardware brochure 75¢ ■ Forged brass dead bolts and door hardware, bathroom accessories, lighting fixtures, and decorative hardware. 215–777–7811.

Ballard Designs, 1670 DeFoor Ave. NW, Atlanta, GA 30318: Catalog $3 ■ Furniture, pillows, prints, and decorative accessories and castings for indoor room arrangements and outdoor landscaping. 404–351–5099.

Basketville, Inc., Main St., P.O. Box 710, Putney, VT 05364: Catalog $2 ■ Woven baskets for home decor arrangements. 802–387–5509.

Betsy's Place, 323 Arch St., Philadelphia, PA 19106: Brochure $1 ■ Sundials and stands, brass reproductions of door knockers, trivets, and other ornaments. 215–922–3536.

Country Manor, Mail Order Dept., Rt. 211, P.O. Box 520, Sperryville, VA 22740: Catalog $2 ■ Kitchen utensils and accessories, rugs, and carpets. 800–344–8354.

The Country Mouse, Box 176, Harwinton, CT 06791: Free catalog ■ Antique custom decorator items for homes and gardens. 203–485–1419.

Crafts Manufacturing Company, 72 Massachusetts Ave., Lunenburg, MA 01462: Catalog 50¢ ■ Early American handmade tinware, lamps, candle holders, trays, and sconces. 508–342–1717.

Farmer's Daughter, P.O. Box 1071, Nags Head, NC 27959: Catalog $2 ■ Country accessories, pottery potpourri burners, potpourri candles, and electric candle lamps. 800–423–2196.

Historic Housefitters Company, Farm to Market Rd., Brewster, NY 10509: Catalog $3 ■ Hand-forged ironwork for 18th-century decors. 914–278–2427.

Home Decorators Collection, 2025 Concourse Dr., St. Louis, MO 63146: Free catalog ■ Decorative hardware, switch plates, mail boxes, weather vanes, custom upholstery, plant stands, furniture, clocks, lighting fixtures, chandeliers, bathroom accessories, and wicker items. 800–245–2217.

Hoya Crystal Gallery, 450 Park Ave., New York, NY 10022: Catalog $6 ■ Exclusive art sculptures, vases, bowls, glasses, ornamental pieces, and crystal clocks. 212–223–6335.

Kimric Decor, 162 Eastern Ave., Lynn, MA 01902: Catalog $1 (refundable) ■ Decorative accessories with Early American, nautical, western, English Pub, Italian, nostalgia, and railroad themes. 617–598–1400.

Mathews Wire, 654 W. Morrison St., Frankfort, IN 46041: Free information ■ Country-style wire and wood decorative accessories. 317–659–3542.

Museum of Modern Art New York, Mail Order Department, P.O. Box 2534, West Chester, PA 19380: Catalog $3 ■ Contemporary design items for homes and offices, or gifts. 212–708–9888.

Prairie Town Products, Inc., P.O. Box 1426, Sedalia, MO 65301: Brochure $1 ■ Solid wood switch plates with hand-painted ornaments and walnut finish. 816–826–4208.

The Renovator's Supply, Renovator's Old Mill, Miller Falls, MA 01349: Catalog $3 ■ Reproductions of antique hardware, lighting and plumbing fixtures, curtains, and decorative accessories. 413–659–2211.

Rose & Gerard, 55 Sunnyside, Mill Valley, CA 94941: Free catalog ■ Dinnerware and glasses, plant stands, pottery, serving pieces, place mats and napkins, lanterns, Dhurrie rugs, baskets, and candles. 415–383–6399.

Samplers by Virginia Colby, 205 Richmond Ave., Amityville, NY 11701: Free brochure with long SASE ■ Miniature counted-thread samplers, with optional framing. 516–264–5529.

Touch of Class, Huntingburg, IN 47542: Free catalog ■ Bedroom furnishings, decorative accessories, draperies, bathroom accessories, and women's clothing. 800–457–7456.

Allan Walker, Ltd., 3800 Ivy Rd. NE, Atlanta, GA 30305: Free information ■ Imported tapestries. 404–233–1926.

Wild Wings, South Hwy. 61, Lake City, MN 55041: Free catalog ■ Home furnishings and decorative accessories with a wildlife theme. 800–445–4833.

Wild Wood Gallery, 502 Factory Ave., Box 300, Syracuse, NY 13205: Catalog $1 ■ Pictures, mirrors, wall plaques, and groupings for the home. 315–454–8098.

Yield House, P.O. Box 5000, North Conway, NH 03860: Free catalog ■ Furniture and decorative accessories finished in a Shaker tradition. 800–258–4720.

DECOUPAGE

Adventure in Crafts, P.O. Box 6058, Yorkville Station, New York, NY 10128: Catalog $2.50 ■ Decoupage supplies and projects. 212–628–8081.

American Art Associates, 4701 Sangamore Rd., Washington, DC 20016: Catalog $1 ■ Decoupage supplies and tools. 301–229–5522.

Harrower House, P.O. Box 274, Hope, NJ 07844: Catalog $2 ■ Decoupage supplies, tools, and accessories. 908–459–5765.

Starkey's Artprints, Box 686, Mt. Clemens, MI 48046: Catalog $2 ■ Art prints for decoupage projects. 313–463–8253.

DECOYS

Beaver Dam Decoys, 1662 Beaver Dam Rd., Point Pleasant, NJ 08742: Free information ■ Wooden decoys, birds, and fish. 908–892–2542.

Decoys Unlimited, 518 N. 9th St., Clinton, IA 52732: Catalog $1 ■ Decoy kits. 319–243–3948.

Hieber's Decoys, 6147 Oak Glade Ln., Galion, OH 44833: Free brochure ■ Hand-carved decoys. 419–462–5834.

Will Kirkpatrick Shorebird Decoys, Inc., 124 Forest Ave., Hudson, MA 01749: Brochure $2 (refundable) ■ Hand-carved and hand-painted shorebird decoy reproductions. 508–562–7841.

Penn's Woods Products, Inc., 19 W. Pittsburgh St., Delmont, PA 15626: Free information ■ Decoys. 412–468–8311.

DEPARTMENT STORES

Each of the department stores listed below publishes at least one general merchandise catalog a year. Some stores also publish seasonal or special edition catalogs. There is often a nominal charge for these catalogs, although the price may be waived or refunded if you satisfy minimum purchase requirements. For information on how to obtain these catalogs, write or call the stores directly.

Bennett Brothers, Inc., 30 E. Adams St., Chicago, IL 60603. 312–263–4800.

Bergdorf Goodman, 754 5th Ave., New York, NY 10019. 800–662–5455.

Best Products Company, Inc., P.O. Box 26303, Richmond, VA 23260. 800–950–2378.

Bloomingdales's by Mail, Ltd., Federated Department Stores, 475 Knotter Dr., Cheshire, CT 06410. 800–777–0000.

Bonwit Teller, 1112 Ave. of Americas, New York, NY 10036. 718–784–2988.

Burdines Florida, P.O. Box 5060, Miami, FL 33101. 305–835–5151.

Carson Pirie Scott & Company, 1 S. State St., Chicago, IL 60603. 312–372–6800.

Cassidy Cosgrove, 127 E. Saint Paul St., Spring Valley, IL 61362. 815–663–2251.

Filene's, 426 Washington St., Boston, MA 02101. 800–345–3637.

Gucci, CSB 3168, Dept. 846, Melville, NY 11747. 800–221–2590.

Gump's, P.O. Box 890910, Dallas, TX 75389. 800–284–8677.

Hecht's, 685 N. Glebe Rd., Arlington, VA 22203. 703–524–5100.

I. Magnin, P.O. Box 2096, Oakland, CA 94604. 800–227–1125.

Jordan Marsh, 450 Washington St., Boston, MA 02107. 617–357–3000.

Jordan Marsh-Maas Brothers, P.O. Box 311, Tampa, FL 33601. 813–223–7525.

Lord & Taylor, 424 5th Ave., New York, NY 10018. 212–391–3300.

Macy's, Herald Square, New York, NY 10001. 212–971–6000.

Marshall Field, 111 N. State St., Chicago, IL 60601. 800–323–1717.

Neiman-Marcus, P.O. Box 2968, Dallas, TX 75221. 800–825–8000.

Nordstrom, 1501 5th Ave., Seattle, WA 98101. 206–628–2111.

J.C. Penney Company, Inc., Catalog Division, Milwaukee, WI 53263. 800–222–6161.

Rich's, P.O. Box 4236, Atlanta, GA 30302. 404–586–2322.

Saks Fifth Ave., Folio Collections, Inc., 557 Tuckahoe Rd., Yonkers, NY 10710. 800–345–3454.

Sears, Roebuck & Company, Catalog Division, 925 S. Homan Ave., Chicago, IL 60607. (Catalog also available from local stores.) 312–875–2500.

Service Merchandise Catalog Showroom, Mail Order Department, P.O. Box 24600, Nashville, TN 37202. 615–251–6666.

Spiegel, P.O. Box 6340, Chicago, IL 60680. 800–345–4500.

Whole Earth Access, 822 Anthony St., Berkeley, CA 94710. 800–829–6300.

Woodward & Lothrop, 1025 F St. NW, Washington, DC 20013. 800–333–0170.

DIABETIC SUPPLIES

Atwater-Carey, Ltd., 218 Gold Run Rd., Boulder, CO 80302: Free information ■ Purse-size and belt-pack carry-all cases for diabetic supplies. 800–359–1646.

Bischoff's Diabetic, 220C Airport Blvd., Freedom, CA 95019: Free information ■ Insulins, blood glucose monitoring equipment and accessories, test strips, and other supplies. 800–537–0404; 408–761–1441 (in CA).

Bruce Medical Supply, 411 Waverly Oaks Rd., P.O. Box 9166, Waltham, MA 02154: Free catalog ■ Health supplies and equipment for diabetics, ostomy patients, sick rooms, and first aid. 800–225–8446.

DERATA Corporation, 6701 Parkway Cir., Ste. 100, Minneapolis, MN 55430: Free information ■ Medi-Jector EZ needle-free insulin injection system. 800–328–3074; 612–566–1202 (in MN).

Diabetes Supplies, 8181 N. Stadium Dr., Houston, TX 77054: Free information ■ Insulins, blood glucose monitoring equipment and accessories, test strips, and other supplies. 800–622–5587.

Diabetic Express, P.O. Box 80037, Canton, OH 44708: Free information ■ Insulins, blood glucose monitoring equipment and accessories, test strips, and other supplies. 800–338–4656; 800–338–4657 (in OH).

The Diabetic & Nutrition Health Center, 122 University Ave., San Diego, CA 92103: Free information ■ Blood glucose monitoring systems. 619–491–0106.

Diabetic Promotions, P.O. Box 5400, Willowick, OH 44095: Free information ■ Insulins, blood glucose monitoring equipment and accessories, test strips, and other supplies. 800–433–1477; 800–334–1377 (in OH).

Dolby Scientific, P.O. Box 7316, Philadelphia, PA 19101: Free information ■ Blood glucose monitors, blood test strips, urine test strips, and other supplies. 800–622–7300; 800–662–2418 (in PA).

E & P Associates, 6 Birch Dr., Freehold, NJ 07728: Free information ■ Blood glucose meters and accessories, test strips, and other supplies for diabetics. 800–284–6294; 908–462–7297 (in NJ).

Gainor Medical U.S.A., Inc., P.O. Box 92077, Long Beach, CA 90809: Free information ■ Easy-to-use lancets that provide protection from accidental puncture and risks associated with cross-infection of blood-borne illnesses. 800–825–8282.

Health-o-meter, Division Continental Scale Corporation, 7400 W. 100th Pl., Bridgeview, IL 60455: Free information ■ Automated method of converting ounces and grams to diabetic food exchanges. 800–323–8363; 708–598–9100 (in IL).

Hospital Center Pharmacy, 433 Brookline Ave., Boston, MA 02215: Free information ■ Insulins, blood glucose monitoring equipment and accessories, test strips, and other supplies. 800–824–2401; 800–462–1122 (in MA).

H-S Medical Supplies, P.O. Box 42, Whitehall, PA 18052: Free information ■ Blood glucose meters, test strips, and other supplies for diabetics. 800–344–7633.

Indepth Sock Company, 92 Candy Lane, Syosset, NY 11791: Free information ■ Extra-wide 100 percent cotton socks for diabetics and persons who wear casts, in large and extra-large sizes. 516–921–4248.

Liberty Medical Supply, P.O. Box 1966, Palm City, FL 34990: Free information ■ Blood glucose meters, test strips, lancets, monolets, and other diabetic supplies. 800–762–8026.

Lifescan, Inc., A Johnson & Johnson Company, Mountain View, CA 94043: Free information ■ Glucosan blood glucose meter and foil wrapped test strips for blood glucose testing. 800–227–8862.

Mada Medical, 60 Commerce Rd., Carlstadt, NJ 07072: Free information ■ Vitajet Needleless Injector for dosage accuracy and ease of insulin administration. 201–460–0454.

Medicool, Inc., 23761 Madison St., Torrance, CA 90505: Free information ■ Insulin

protector for use while traveling. 800–433–2469; 800–654–1565 (in CA).

MediSense, Inc., 128 Sidney St., Cambridge, MA 02139: Free information ■ Blood glucose monitoring systems. 617–492–2373.

Miles, Inc., Diagnostics Division, P.O. Box 2001, Mishawaka, IN 46544: Free information ■ Glucometer blood glucose monitoring system. 800–445–5901.

MiniMed Technologies, 12744 San Fernando Rd., Sylmar, CA 91342: Free information ■ MiniMed pumps for insulin therapy control. 800–843–6687; 800–826–2099 (in CA).

Penny Saver Medical Supply, 1851 W. 52nd Ave., Denver, CO 80221: Free information ■ Blood glucose monitors and test strips, syringes, lancets and lancet devices, insulins, accessories, and other supplies. 800–748–1909.

Thrif-Tee Home Diabetic Center, 937 Apperson Dr., Salem, VA 24153: Free information ■ Diabetic supplies. 800–847–4383; 703–389–4195 (in VA).

Ulster Scientific, Inc., P.O. Box 819, New Paltz, NY 12561: Free information ■ Autojector which inserts the needle and injects insulin automatically and almost without pain. 800–431–8233; 800–522–2257 (in NY).

DISPLAY FIXTURES & PORTABLE EXHIBITS

Add-Sales Company, Inc., P.O. Box 1776, Manitowoc, WI 54220: Free information ■ Display fixtures and accessories. 414–682–6188.

Art-Phyl Creations, 16250 NW 48th Ave., Miami, FL 33024: Free information ■ Hooks for displaying merchandise on fixtures. 305–624–2333.

Childs Store Fixtures, 901 Killarney Dr., Pittsburgh, PA 15234: Free information ■ Display fixtures and accessories. 412–885–7300.

Columbus Show Case Company, 560 Goodrich Rd., Bellevue, OH 44811: Free information ■ Display fixtures and accessories. 800–848–3573; 419–483–2641 (in OH).

Creative Display Fixtures, One Ferry St., Easthampton, MA 01027: Free information

■ Display fixtures and accessories. 413–527–0300.

Display Fixtures Company, P.O. Box 7245, Charlotte, NC 28241: Free catalog ■ Display fixtures and accessories. 704–588–0880.

Equipto, 225 S. Highland Ave., Aurora, IL 60506: Free information ■ Display fixtures and accessories. 708–859–1000.

ESV Lighting, Inc., 525 Court St., Pekin, IL 61554: Free information ■ Lighting systems for display lighting needs. 800–225–5378.

The Fixture Factory, 835 N.E. 8th St., Gresham, OR 97030: Free information ■ Display fixtures and accessories. 503–661–6525.

Franklin Fixtures, Inc., Freeman's Way, Commerce Park, Brewster, MA 02631: Free catalog ■ Display fixtures and accessories. 508–896–3713.

Global Fixtures, Inc., 4121 Rushton St., Florence, AL 35631: Free catalog ■ Display fixtures and accessories. 205–767–5200.

Graphic Display Systems, 1243 Lafayette St., Lebanon, PA 17042: Free information ■ Lightweight, easy-to-set-up display system, complete with base, leg adjusters, and clips. 800–848–3020; 717–274–3954 (in PA).

Handy Store Fixtures, 337 Sherman Ave., Newark, NJ 07114: Free catalog ■ Display fixtures and accessories. 800–631–4280; 908–218–9800 (in NJ).

Hirsh Display Fixtures, Inc., P.O. Box 43, Deerfield, IL 60015: Free information ■ Display fixtures and accessories. 708–272–8080.

Ideation, Inc., Deco Projekt Store Fixturing, 222 S. State St., Ann Arbor, MI 48104: Free information ■ Display fixtures and accessories. 313–761–4360.

Model Display & Fixture Company, Inc., 1405 E. McDowell Rd., Phoenix, AZ 85006: Free information ■ Display fixtures and accessories. 800–528–5306; 800–876–6335 (in AZ).

Multiplex Display Fixture Company, 1555 Larkin Williams Rd., Fenton, MO 63026: Free information ■ Display fixtures and accessories. 314–343–5700.

Omnicraft, Inc., 512 W. Ireland Rd., South Bend, IN 46614: Free information ■ Display fixtures and accessories. 219–291–7222.

Randal Wood Displays, 305 Laura Dr., Addison, IL 60101: Free catalog ■ Display fixtures and accessories. 708–543–8030.

Reeve Company, P.O. Box 276, Pico Rivera, CA 90660: Free information ■ Display fixtures and accessories. 213–723–4791.

Reflector Hardware Corporation, 1400 N. 25th Ave., Melrose Park, IL 60160: Free information ■ Display fixtures and accessories. 708–345–2500.

Melvin S. Roos & Company, Inc., 4465 Commerce Dr. SW, Atlanta, GA 30336: Free information ■ Display fixtures and accessories. 800–241–6897; 800–282–9110 (in GA).

Showbest Fixture Corporation, 38–56 Long Ave., Hillside, NJ 07205: Free catalog ■ Display fixtures and accessories. 908–289–1400.

Siegel Display Products, P.O. Box 95, Minneapolis, MN 55440: Free information ■ Wire display units, product merchandisers, metal displays, and molded holders. 612–340–1493.

Sitka Store Fixtures, Inc., 3107 Gillham Rd., P.O. Box 410247, Kansas City, MO 64109: Free information ■ Display fixtures and accessories. 816–531–8290.

Streator Store Fixtures, 411 S. 1st Ave., Albert Lee, MN 56007: Free information ■ Display fixtures and accessories. 507–373–0611.

Universal Sales, Inc., P.O. Box 22, Lyons, IL 60534: Free information ■ Display fixtures and accessories. 708–788–3831.

Westwood Display Fixtures, 3342 Adobe Ct., Colorado Springs, CO 80907: Free catalog ■ Display fixtures and accessories. 719–471–4027.

DOLLHOUSES & MINIATURES

A-Cs' Emporium of Miniatures, 1580 McLaughkin Run Rd., Pittsburgh, PA 15241: Catalog $2.50 (refundable) ■ Collectible miniatures. 412–257–0340.

Andy's Little Houses, P.O. Box 363, Clarcona, FL 32710: Free information ■ Custom-built miniature houses, house kits, and house plans and drawings. 407–295–1258.

Angela's Miniature World, 2237 Ventura Blvd., Camarillo, CA 93010: Free information with long SASE ■ Miniatures, dollhouses, building materials and supplies, and other collectibles. 805–482–2219.

Bauder-Pine, Ltd., P.O. Box 518, Langhorne, PA 19047: Catalog $4 ■ Miniature furniture and furniture kits in ½–inch scale. 215–355–2033.

Beauvais Castle, 141 Union St., P.O. Box 4060, Manchester, NH 03108: Catalog $3 ■ Collectible miniatures. 800–282–8944.

Betty's Mini Creations, 596 Knollwood Rd., Severna Park, MD 21146: Catalog $6 ■ Miniatures and other collectibles. 410–544–6388.

B.H. Miniatures, 20805 N. 19th Ave., Ste. 5, Phoenix, AZ 85027: Catalog $3 ■ Prepasted wallpaper, coordinated print and solid color fabrics, velvet carpeting, and miniature furniture in kits or assembled. 602–582–3385.

Bob's Doll House Shop, 2822 NW 63rd St., French Market Mall, Oklahoma City, OK 73116: Free information with long SASE ■ Dollhouses and miniatures. 405–843–1094.

Carlisle Miniatures, 703 N. Elm, Creston, IA 50801: Free catalog with long SASE ■ Handcrafted miniature furniture, from the 1930s and 1940s.

Chan's Hobbies, 2450 Van Ness Ave., San Francisco, CA 94109: Free information with long SASE ■ Miniatures and accessories. 415–885–2899.

Chez Riche, 1616 Grinstead Dr., Louisville, KY 40204: Free catalog ■ Miniatures, dollhouses, accessories, lumber, lighting, and other collectibles. 502–587–6338.

Cindy's Workshop, 1609 Stanford Dr., Columbia, MO 65203: Price list $3 (refundable) ■ Miniature reproductions of European styled furniture. 314–445–2446.

Cir-Kit Concepts, Inc., 407 NW 14th St., Rochester, MN 55901: Catalog $4 ■ Electrical miniatures and wiring kits for dollhouses. 507–288–0860.

CJ Originals, P.O. Box 538, Bridgeville, PA 15017: Catalog $4 ■ Miniature rug kits.

The Company Mouse, 4932 Elm St., Bethesda, MD 20814: Free information ■ Miniatures, accessories, and supplies for dollhouses. 301–654–1222.

Concord Miniatures, 400 Markley St., P.O. Box 99, Port Reading, NJ 07064: Catalog $5 ■ Victorian furniture miniatures.

Country Cottage, 5628 W. Broadway, Richmond, IL 60071: Free information with long SASE ■ Country-style collectible miniatures. 815–678–4428.

Craft Creative Kits, 2200 Dean St., St. Charles, IL 60174: Catalog $1.50 ■ Dollhouse kits, accessories and miniatures, wallpaper patterns, and books. 708–584–9600.

CraftSmyths, 546 Foxwood Ln., Paoli, PA 19301: Price list $1 with long SASE ■ Handcrafted floral arrangements in miniature. 215–647–7289.

Create Your Own, 932 East Blvd., Alpha, NJ 08865: Free brochure ■ Miniature cross stitch and needlepoint rug kits. 908–454–3044.

Creative Crafts Dollhouse Centre, 425 Haddon Ave., Haddonfield, NJ 08033: Catalog $5.95 ■ Building supplies, lighting accessories, lumber, pewter, brass, wallpaper, dollhouses, furniture and furniture kits, and accessories. 609–428–1355.

Dawn's Artistic Treasures, 2801 Willow Creek Rd., Prescott, AZ 86301: Price $3 (refundable) ■ Collectible miniature musical instruments. 602–778–5707.

DD's Dollhouse, 931 Fennell Ave. East, Hamilton, Ontario, Canada L8V 1W9: Catalog $10 ($5 refundable) ■ Dollhouses and accessories. 416–574–2942.

Diminutive Specialties, 10337 Ellsworth Dr., Roscoe, IL 61073: Catalog $5 ■ Miniature photos. 815–623–2011.

The Dollhouse, Hilton Village, 6107 N. Scottsdale Rd., Scottsdale, AZ 85253: Free information with long SASE ■ Miniatures, accessories, and dollhouses. 602–948–4630.

Dollhouse Delights, 11 Starboard Dr., Taney Town, MD 21787: Catalog $1 (refundable) ■ Miniatures for dollhouse gardens. 410–756–2062.

The Dollhouse Factory, 157 Main St., Lebanon, NJ 08833: Catalog $5.50 ■ Dollhouses and accessories, miniatures, tools, books, and plans. 908–236–6404.

Dollhouse Shoppe, 20 Dawn Dr., Centereach, NY 11720: Catalog $15 plus $2 postage ■ Dollhouses, miniatures, and accessories. 516–737–0660.

Dollhouses & Miniatures of Myrtle Beach, 10127 North Hwy. 17, Myrtle Beach, SC 29572: Free information with long SASE ■ Dollhouses, accessories, furnishings, and miniatures. 803–272–0478.

Dwyer's Doll House, 1944 Warwick Ave., Warwick, RI 02889: Catalog $5 ■ Dollhouses, accessories, miniatures, and decorating and building supplies. 800–248–3655.

Elect-a-Lite, 742 E. Arctic Ave., Santa Maria, CA 93454: Free information with long SASE ■ Miniature electric lighting kits and components. 800–EAL–KITS.

Enchanted Doll House, Rt. 7A, Manchester Center, VT 05255: Catalog $3 ■ Dollhouses, dollhouse kits, miniature furniture, collector dolls, stuffed animals, and other toys. 802–362–3031.

Fantasy Fabrications, P.O. Box 164, Turner, OR 97392: Brochure $2.50 ■ Victorian, Art Deco, and original miniatures.

Fantasy in Miniature, 15070 Appleton Ave., Menomonee Falls, WI 53051: Catalog $5.95 ■ Dollhouses, building supplies, miniatures, decorating accessories, and electrical wiring. 414–251–5505.

Favorites from the Past, P.O. Box 739, Newan, GA 30264: Catalog $3 ■ Miniature furniture, accessories, lumber, tools, patterns, and electrical wiring for dollhouses. 404–427–3921.

Favorite Things, York & Monton Rds., Hereford, MD 21111: Free information with long SASE ■ Dollhouse furnishings and accessories, dollhouses, and English, Scottish, and American miniatures. 410–343–0400.

Freda's Fancy, 295 Fairview Ave., Bayport, NY 11705: Brochure $3 with long SASE ■ Dollhouse miniatures. 516–472–0078.

Fred's Dollhouse & Miniature Center, Rt. 7, Pittsford, VT 05763: Catalog $4 ■ Dollhouses and dollhouse kits, building supplies, furniture. and accessories. 802–483–6362.

Garden Path, 174 Blair Ln., Palatine, IL 60067: Price list $1 with long SASE ■ Miniature flowers, Christmas ornaments, English imports, and original watercolors from England. 708–358–3030.

G.E.L. Products, Inc., 19 Grove St., Vernon, CT 06066: Free information ■ Dollhouse kits. 203–872–6539.

Glass with Class, 1336 Lincoln Ave., San Jose, CA 95125: Free information with long SASE ■ Handcrafted miniatures and dollhouses. 408–286–8098.

Greenhouse Miniature Shop, 6616 Monroe St., Sylvania, OH 43560: Catalog $3 ■ Miniatures and other accessories. 419–882–8259.

Happy House Miniatures, 135 N. Main St., Mocksville, NC 27028: Catalog $5 (refundable) ■ Dollhouses and accessories. 704–634–1424.

Haslam's Doll Houses, 7208 S. Tamiami Trail, Sarasota, FL 34231: Free information with long SASE ■ Dollhouses, miniatures, accessories, and building supplies. 813–922–8337.

Hearth Song, P.O. Box B, Sebastopol, CA 95473: Free catalog ■ Dollhouse miniatures, books for children, toiletries for babies, cuddly dolls, party decorations, art supplies, and games. 800–533–4397.

J. Hermes, P.O. Box 4023, El Monte. CA 91734: Catalog $3 ■ Dollhouse kits.

His & Her Hobbys, 15 W. Busse Ave., Mt. Prospect, IL 60056: Free information with long SASE ■ Dollhouses, assembled or in kits; furniture, assembled or in kits; wallpaper and fabrics; building supplies; lighting accessories; staircases; roofing; and landscaping supplies. 708–392–2668.

The Hobby Gallery Miniature Loft, 1810 Meriden Rd., Wolcott, CT 06716: Free information with long SASE ■ Dollhouses, supplies and accessories, miniatures, plush animals, and dolls. 203–879–2316.

The Hobby Suite, P.O. Box 613, McComb, MS 39648: Catalog $18.50 ■ Kits and assembled miniatures, dollhouses and accessories, tools, rugs, wallpaper, and electrical supplies.

Hobby World Miniatures, 5450 Sherbrooke St. West, Montreal, Quebec, Canada H4A 1V9: Free catalog ■ Dollhouses and miniature. 514–481–5434.

House of Miniatures, 652–1/2 Main St. East, Aurora, NY 14052: Video catalog (specify beta or VHS) $12.50 ■ Miniatures and accessories. 716–652–5888.

In a Nutshell Miniatures, 305 Lakeshore Rd. East, Oakville, Ontario, Canada L6J 1J3: Catalog $6 ■ Miniatures and collectibles. 416–338–9631.

Jan's Dollhouse, 6600 Dixie Hwy., Rt. 4, Fairfield, OH 45014: Free information with long SASE ■ Miniatures, collectible dolls, bears, and dollhouses. 513–860–0595.

JM & J Miniatures, 1101 Fremont St., Carson City, NV 89701: Free information with long SASE ■ Miniatures and other collectibles. 702–883–1951.

Karen's Miniatures, 710 N. Mesa, Ste. 188, El Paso, TX 79912: Catalog $6 ■ Architectural moldings and cast metal miniature kits in 1/12 scale, from the United Kingdom.

Karin's Mini Garden, 6128 McLeod NE, Apt. 15, Albuquerque, NM 87109: Catalog $1.50 (refundable) ■ Indoor and outdoor miniature plants, cacti, succulents, and floral arrangements. 505–883–4561.

Keshishian Carpets, Box 3002, San Clemente, CA 92674: Brochure $3 ■ Carpets for dollhouses.

Kimberly House Miniatures, 3867 S. Valley View, Las Vegas, NV 89103: Catalog $7 ■ Landscaping miniatures. 702–253–9790.

The Lawbre Company, 888 Tower Rd., Mundelein, IL 60060: Catalog $4 ■ Custom and reproduction period-designed dollhouses and miniatures. 800–253–0491.

Lilliput Land, 89 Lisa Dr., Northport, NY 11768: Brochure $4 ■ English, French, and American handcrafted miniatures. 517–754–5511.

Little Goodies, P.O. Box 1004, Lewisville, TX 75067: Catalog $2 ■ Miniature pre-cut paper flowers in kits.

Little House of Miniatures on Chelsea Lane, 621½ Sycamore St., Waterloo, IA 50703: Catalog $15 ■ Dollhouses, furniture, dolls, wallpaper, carpets, electric wiring, and building supplies. 319–233–6585.

Little Lincoln's, County Rd. 550, Box 262, Marquette, MI 49855: Brochure $1 ■ Log cabin dollhouses in the style of homes circa 1850 to 1880. 527–366–5263.

Littlethings, 129 Main St., Irvington, NY 10533: Free list with long SASE ■ Miniature paintings, dollhouses, miniatures, furniture, bears, and other collectibles. 914–591–9150.

Littletown USA, 94th St. Ocean Plaza Mall, Ocean City, MD 21842: Free information ■ Dollhouse supplies, building materials, and miniatures. 410–524–5450.

Lolly's, 1054 Dundee Ave., Elgin, IL 60120: Catalog $13 (refundable with first $50 order) ■ Dollhouses and collectible miniatures. 708–697–4040.

Lookingglass Miniatures, P.O. Box 830, Winchester, OR 97495: Catalog $4 ■ Miniatures in kits. 503–673–5445.

Loscar Miniatures, Ernie Loscar, 746 W. Upjohn Rd., Ridgecrest, CA 93555: Catalog $2 ■ Reproduction antiques in miniature.

Lucille's Little House, 1504 Hancock St., Quincy, MA 02169: Free newsletter ■ Building materials for dollhouses, accessories, miniature furniture, accessories, other miniatures, and dolls. 617–479–1141.

Maison des Maisons, 23 Sedgwick Dr., Englewood, CO 80110: Free price list with long SASE ■ Southwest Indian furniture and other miniatures. 303–761–3355.

Marion's Doll & Miniature Center, 563 Titus Ave., Rochester, NY 14617: Free information with long SASE ■ Miniatures and supplies for dollhouses. 716–342–6770.

Mary Elizabeth Miniatures, 49–04 39th Ave., Woodside, NY 11377: Free brochure with long SASE ■ Handcrafted miniature ice cream parlor furnishings. 718–429–4114.

Mel's Miniz, 115 1st Ave., Highland Park, NJ 08904: Free information ■ Dollhouses and dollhouse kits, furniture, other furnishings, building supplies, tools, and electrical supplies. 201–545–0706.

Miniature Estates, 1451 S. Robertson Blvd., Los Angeles, CA 94510: Free information with long SASE ■ Custom-assembled dollhouses and miniatures. 310–552–2200.

Miniature Grand Pianos, Ralph E. Partelow, P.O. Box 3314, Littleton, CO 80161: Catalog $2 ■ Miniature keyboard instruments. 303–798–5014.

The Miniature Kingdom of River Row, 182 Front St., P.O. Box 39, Owego, NY 13827: Catalog $2 ■ Dollhouses in $1/12$ scale, handcrafted miniatures, pewter, and accessories. 607–687–5601.

Miniature Makers' Workshop, 4515 N. Woodward Ave., Royal Oak, MI 48073:

Catalog $10 ■ Furniture, accessories, dolls, and dollhouses and accessories, in $1/2$– and 1–inch scale. 313–549–0633.

Miniatures & Collectibles, 8330 Gulf Freeway, Houston, TX 77017: Catalog $15 (refundable with $100 order) ■ Miniatures and collectibles. 713–645–0855.

The Miniature Shop, 1115 4th Ave., Huntington, WV 25701: Catalog $10 ■ Dollhouses, accessories, furniture kits, and electrical and decorating supplies. 304–523–2418.

Miniatures In-Your-Mailbox, P.O. Box 32496, Cleveland, OH 44132: Free price list with long SASE ■ Dollhouses, accessories, furniture, electrical supplies, wall and floor coverings, tools, and finishing supplies. 800–283–8191.

Miniature Village, 1725 50th St., Kenosha, WI 53140: Catalog $7.50 ■ Dollhouses, furniture, electrical accessories, and supplies. 800–383–0188.

Mini-Facets, 7707 Indian Springs Dr., Nashville, TN 37221: Catalog $3 ■ Handcrafted and commercial miniatures and accessories in $1/4$– and 1–inch scale. 615–646–0695.

Mini Splendid Things, 626 Main St., Covington, KY 41011: Catalog $18.95 ■ Dollhouses, supplies, and miniatures. 606–261–5500.

Mini Temptations, 3633 W. 95th, Overland Park, KS 66206: Catalog $7.50 ■ Dollhouse accessories, miniatures, and other collectibles. 913–648–2050.

The Mini Tool Shop, P.O. Box 14451, Phoenix, AZ 85063: Free catalog with $2 and five 1st class stamps (refundable) ■ Tools, supplies, and accessories for dollhouses, dioramas, and other settings. 602–936–6529.

Miss Elaineous, 2904 Selwyn Ave., Charlotte, NC 28209: Free information with long SASE ■ Custom-assembled dollhouses, upholstered furniture, designer draperies, and other accessories. 704–375–8774.

Mosaic Press, 358 Oliver Rd., Cincinnati, OH 45215: Catalog $3 ■ Hand-bound miniature books made with traditional binding methods. 513–761–5977.

Mott Miniatures, 7700 Orangethorpe Ave., Ste. 8, Buena Park, CA 90621: Catalog $25 (refundable) ■ Dollhouse furniture and accessories, dolls, dollhouse kits and pre-as-

sembled dollhouses, building materials, and other supplies. 714–994–5979.

The Mountain Valley Miniature Shop, 199 Union St., P.O. Box 94, Occoquan, VA 22125: Free information ■ Dollhouses, finishing and decorating supplies, furniture, kits, and books. 703–690–1144.

Muskoka Miniatures, 510 Muskoka Rd. North, Box 218, Gravenhurst, Ontario, Canada P0C 1G0: Free information with long SASE ■ Custom miniatures. 705–687–3351.

My Dollhouse, 7 S. Broadway, Nyack, NY 10960: Free information with long SASE ■ Dolls, dollhouses, miniatures, and supplies. 914–358–4185.

My Sister's Shoppe, Inc., 1671 Penfield Rd., Rochester, NY 14625: Catalog $3 ■ Victorian furniture miniatures. 800–821–0097.

Nana's Attic, P.O. Box 56, Medicine Park, OK 73557: Catalog $15 (refundable with $100 order) ■ Dollhouse building supplies, furniture, accessories, and miniatures. 405–529–2225.

New Hampshire Woodworkers, 515 Winnacunnet Rd., Hampton, NH 03842: Free information with long SASE ■ Miniature fences for landscape settings.

Ni-Glo Lamps by Nicole, 5684 Sterling Rd., Hamburg, NY 14075: Catalog $4 ■ Hand-painted china lamps in miniature with replaceable bulbs. 716–627–4644.

Northeastern Scale Models, Inc., P.O. Box 727, Methuen, MA 01844: Catalog $1 ■ Materials and accessories for constructing dollhouses. 508–688–6019.

The Oakridge Corporation, P.O. Box 247, Lemont, IL 60439: Catalog $3 (refundable) ■ Dollhouse kits, building supplies, furniture, and accessories. 800–594–5115.

Laurie O'Halloran, 6978 S. Sills Rd., Clinton, WA 98236: Brochure $3 with long SASE and two 1st class stamps ■ Wheel-thrown and hand-formed porcelain miniatures. 206–321–6981.

Old World Craftsmen Dollhouses, Inc., 643 Industrial Dr., Hartland, WI 53029: Brochure $2 ■ In-stock and custom dollhouses. 800–234–4748; 414–367–2753 (in WI).

Patti's Miniature World, 4114 Hwy. 70 SW, Hickory, NC 28602: Free information with long SASE ■ Miniatures and accessories. 704–328–5088.

Peg's Dollhouse, 4019 Sebastopol Rd., Santa Rosa, CA 95407: Information $1 (refundable) ■ Miniatures and dollhouses. 707–546–6137.

Petite Innovations, 243 High St., Burlington, NJ 08016: Free information with long SASE ■ Dollhouses and furnishings, accessories, lighting supplies, building materials, and miniatures. 609–386–7476.

Pinocchio's Miniatures, 465 S. Main St., Frankenmuth, MI 48734: Catalog $18.50 ■ Handmade miniatures by local craft people. 517–652–2751.

P.J.'s Miniatures, 5818 Hwy. 74 West, Monroe, NC 28110: Catalog $14.95 ■ Miniatures and accessories. 704–821–9144.

Precious Little Things, The Fieldwood Company, P.O. Box 6, Chester, VT 05143: Catalog $3.50 ■ Handcrafted furnishings and accessories in ½– and 1–inch scales. 802–875–4127.

R & N Miniatures, 458 Wythe Creek Rd., Poquoson, VA 23662: Price list $2 ■ Everything to finish and furnish dollhouses. 804–868–7103.

Rondel Wood Products, 2679 Washington Rd., Waldoboro, ME 04572: Brochure $2 ■ Wagon and carriage kits in 1/12 scale. 207–832–6837.

Scientific Models, Inc., 340 Snyder Ave., Berkeley Heights, NJ 07922: Catalog $1 ■ Easy-to-assemble, museum-quality dollhouse furniture.

Second Childhood, Rt. 1, Box 180, Willis, VA 24380: Catalog $10 ■ Save 10 to 25 percent on miniatures and supplies. 703–789–4262.

Second Hand Rose Doll House Store, Inc., 5826 W. Bluemound, Milwaukee, WI 53213: Catalog $2.50 ■ Miniatures and accessories for dollhouses, and collector dolls and bears. 414–259–9965.

Shaker Workshops, P.O. Box 1028, Concord, MA 01742: Catalog $1 ■ Miniature furniture and dolls; Shaker furniture in kits or custom-assembled. 617–646–8985.

Shoda's Miniature Wonderland, 3504 Wells St., Fort Wayne, IN 46808: Free information with long SASE ■ Miniatures, music boxes, dolls, and figurines. 219–484–7167.

Sierra Miniatures, 912 Loyola St., Carson City, NV 89705: Catalog $15 plus $1.50 postage ■ Miniatures and collectibles. 702–883–6830.

Simms Miniatures, Ltd., P.O. Box 291, Williamsburg, VA 23187: Catalog $3 ■ Miniature furniture, silver and gold accessories, and tools. 804–220–3319.

Sir Thomas Thumb, 1398 Oregon Rd., Leola, PA 17540: Catalog $1 with long SASE ■ Handcrafted miniatures and accessories. 717–656–8838.

Small Ideas, 35 Keofferam, Old Greenwich, CT 06870: Catalog $5 ■ Museum-quality, 18th-century miniatures. 203–637–4264.

The Squirrel's Nest Miniatures, 401 Buckingham Rd., Pittsburgh, PA 15125: Free information with long SASE ■ Sterling silver, scale wrought iron hinges and fittings, Early American accessories, and dollhouse building supplies. 800–852–3156.

Sundance Potters, 6479 Dodge Rd., White City, OR 97503: Catalog $2 (refundable) ■ Handcrafted pottery miniatures. 503–826–8641.

T & T Creative Enterprise, 1932 Palisades Dr., Pacific Palisades, CA 90272: Free information with long SASE ■ Handcrafted English pewter miniatures, jointed dolls, toys, and animals. 213–573–1114.

Tanglewald Miniatures, P.O. Box 449, Dallas, OR 97338: Brochure $2 with long SASE (refundable) ■ Dollhouses, furniture, wall racks, and miniature porcelains.

Teri's Mini Workshop, P.O. Box 387, Goldenrod, FL 32733: Catalog $1 with long SASE ■ Miniature accessories for dollhouses and other settings.

This Old House, 5½ S. 8th St., Fargo, ND 58103: Catalog $2.50 ■ Miniature willow furniture and country styled accessories.

Thistle Seed Collection, 101 Leland Hill Rd., Sutton, MA 01527: Free brochure ■ Stained glass miniature windows and assembled post and beam dollhouses or kits. 508–865–4387.

Thomaston Miniature Works, Ginger Graham, 111 Main St., P.O. Box 272, Thomaston, ME 04861: Price list $1.50 with long SASE ■ Food, clothing, tools, and other miniatures. 207–354–0211.

The Thumbeline Touch, 8009 Parks Ln., Baltimore, MD 21207: Catalog $7 ■ Miniature accessories for dollhouses and other settings. 410–964–9217.

Tiny Dollhouse, 1146 Lexington Ave., New York, NY 10021: Free information ■ Miniatures, building supplies, lighting accessories, pewter, brass, silver, furniture and furniture kits, wallpaper, and dollhouses. 212–744–3719.

Marie Toner Lighting Designs, Inc., 725 Inverness Dr., Horsham, PA 19044: Catalog $1 with long SASE ■ Easy-to-install miniature ceiling and wall light fixtures.

The Toy Box, 4623 South US 1, Rockledge, FL 32955: Catalog $3 ■ Dollhouses and dollhouse kits, building supplies, dollhouse kits, electrical supplies and kits, furniture, accessories, and books. 407–632–2411.

Treasures by Paula K, Inc., RR 4, Lakewoods Dr., Katonah, NY 10536: Catalog $12 (refundable) ■ Dollhouse kits and supplies. 914–232–4291.

Treasure Shop, 858 Main St., Clifton Park, NY 12065: Catalog $4.50 ■ Miniatures, dollhouses, building materials, electrical supplies, and wallpaper. 518–877–5510.

Val-Le of the Dolls, 840 Hamilton Ave., Waterbury, CT 06706: Catalog $12 ■ Dollhouses, miniatures, furnishings, and building supplies. 203–754–1622.

Vernon Pottery, 441 Bethune Dr., Virginia Beach, VA 23452: Catalog $2 ■ Reproduction 19th century salt-glazed stoneware miniatures.

Vicki's Miniatures, P.O. Box 142407, Anchorage, AK 99514: Free brochure ■ Handcrafted gym equipment in miniature. 907–333–5470.

Village Emporium, 828 Professional Pl., West Chesapeake, VA 23320: Free quarterly newsletter ■ Dollhouses and dollhouse kits, furniture and furniture kits, building materials, and electrical supplies. 804–547–5814.

Village Miniatures, Box 142, Queenston, Ontario, Canada L0S 1L0: Catalog $5 ■ Miniatures, dollhouses and dollhouse kits, tools, landscaping materials, wallpaper and floor coverings, and building materials. 416–262–4779.

W & D Mini Homes, P.O. Box 1654, Bloomington, IN 47402: Brochure $1 with long SASE and two 1st class stamps ■ American Indian miniatures. 812–332–2499.

The Ward Warehouse, 1050 Ala Moana Blvd., Honolulu, HI 96814: VHS video catalog $10 ■ Handcrafted miniatures. 808–521–8803.

Warling Miniatures, 22453 Covello St., West Hills, CA 91307: Brochure $1 with long SASE and 45¢ postage ■ Victorian to modern wicker furniture kits, in ½– and 1–inch scale. 818–340–9855.

Wood Shoppe, 2908 Simmons Rd., Edmond, OK 73034: Free information with long SASE ■ Country classics in miniature. 405–341–2991.

DOLL MAKING & DOLL CLOTHING

Lyn Alexander Designs, P.O. Box 8341, Denver, CO 80201: Catalog $2.50 ■ Doll clothing patterns for antique, reproduction, modern, and cloth dolls.

BB Doll Supplies, 4216 Grandview Rd., Kansas City, MO 64137: Free information ■ Supplies to start, finish, and dress a doll. 800–227–3655.

Broadview Ceramics, 5323 Broadview Rd., Parma, OH 44134: Catalog $4 ■ Doll-making supplies. Includes doll bisque kits. 216–661–4856.

Brown House Dolls, 3200 N. Sand Lake Rd., Allen, MI 49227: Catalog $2 ■ Easy-to-sew patterns for doll clothing. 517–849–2833.

Calico Horse, 461 Tennessee, Redlands, CA 92373: Catalog $2 ■ Doll dress patterns, pleaters, smocking supplies, Swiss batiste, Swiss lawn, French laces, and Swiss embroideries. 714–793–1868.

Carolee Creations, 787 Industrial Dr., Elmhurst, IL 60126: Catalog $1 ■ Easy-to-sew doll kits that include country, folk, babies, and dress-me dolls. 708–530–7175.

Carver's Eye Company, P.O. Box 16692, Portland, OR 97216: Information $1 ■ Glass and plastic eyes, noses, joints, growlers, and eye glasses for dolls and bears. 503–666–5680.

Collectible Doll Company, 1421 N. 34th, Seattle, WA 98103: Catalog $5 ■ Doll clothes, molds, and supplies for making dolls. 800–468–DOLL; 206–634–3131 (in WA).

Create-A-Doll, 146 E. Chubbuck Rd., Chubbuck, ID 83202: Catalog $1.50 ■ Doll-making kits and patterns. 208–238–0433.

CR's Crafts, Box 8, Leland, IA 50453: Catalog $2 ■ Doll- and bear-making supplies; kits or patterns for making new jointed bears, some with electronic melody units. 515–567–3652.

Dee's Place of Dolls, 140 E. College St., Covina, CA 91723: Catalog $4 ■ Doll-making supplies and collectible dolls. 818–915–1005.

D'eja' Vu Originals, P.O. Box 55375, Riverside, CA 92517: Catalog $1 ■ Custom doll clothes. 714–780–7405.

Doll Boutique, Kathryn L. White, 2730 Denmark Rd., Columbus, OH 43232: Catalog $4 ■ Doll-making supplies. Includes over 200 antique and modern dolls in soft-fired greenware, bisque, and ready-to-paint kits. 614–861–2120.

The Doll Connection, P.O. Box 7661, Mesa, AZ 85216: Catalog $3.75 ■ Porcelain doll kits for antique and modern dolls. 602–641–9825.

Doll Creations, 1987 Santa Rita Rd., Pleasanton, CA 94566: Catalog $6 ■ Greenware, doll-making supplies, doll clothes, furniture, puzzles, posters, and paper dolls. 510–846–6120.

The Doll Depot, 4159 Crestdale, West Bloomfield, MI 48323: Free information with long SASE ■ Doll-making supplies. 313–363–7241.

The Doll Dress, 16018 Splitlog Dr., Tampa, FL 33618: Brochure $2 ■ Doll patterns and fabric kits for doll clothing. 813–963–1417.

Doll Gallery/Hospital, 1137 Susan St., Columbia, SC 29210: Free information with long SASE ■ Doll-making supplies and accessories. 803–798–7044.

A Dollmakers Marketplace, P.O. Box 110280, Campbell, CA 95011: Free information with long SASE ■ Doll-making supplies and accessories. 408–249–8318.

Doll Repair Parts, Inc., 9918 Lorain Ave., Cleveland, OH 44102: Catalog $1 ■ Wigs, crowns, glass eyes, doll shoes, socks, dress patterns, books, doll stands, reproduction bodies, and hands and feet. 216–961–3545.

Dolls by Maurice, 5741 Elizabeth Lake Rd., Pontiac, MI 48054: Free information ■ Doll-making supplies. 313–681–8907.

Dollspart Supply Company, 46–50 54th Ave., Maspeth, NY 11378: Catalog $3 ■ Wigs, glass eyes, doll stands, shoes, doll parts and bodies, ceramic supplies, clothing and accessories, patterns, and books. 718–361–1883.

Elaine's Doll House, 1645 E. Roosevelt St., Stockton, CA 95205: Free catalog with long SASE ■ Doll-making supplies. 209–948–1193.

Enchanted Dolls, 3674 E. Hastings St., Vancouver, British Columbia, Canada V5K 2A9: Free information with long SASE ■ Doll-making supplies and collectible dolls. 604–298–1079.

Eva Mae Doll Company, 1931 15th St., San Pablo, CA 94806: Catalog 50¢ ■ Dressed and undressed dolls, kits for making dolls, and parts. 510–235–3056.

Fabric Chalet, P.O. Box 25332, Colorado Springs, CO 80936: Samples $5 ■ Doll clothes patterns, sewing supplies, and fabrics that include China silks, cotton velveteens, Swiss lawns, Swiss organdy, English cottons, silk taffeta, Swiss batiste, and silk organza. 719–632–8862.

Formfit Shoe Fashions, P.O. Box 468, Livermore, CA 94550: Brochure $1 with long SASE ■ Handcrafted shoes for dolls in suede and combined braid and sequins. 510–449–6997.

Paule Fox Pattern Company, P.O. Box 387, Richmond, IL 60071: Catalog $1 with long SASE ■ Victorian clothing patterns for dolls.

Happy Apple Doll Company, 70 W. Highland Ave., Atlantic Highlands, NJ 07716: Free information with long SASE ■ Doll-making supplies, assembled dolls, and doll clothing. 908–291–5363.

Haskell's Handcraft, 40 College Ave., Waterville, ME 04901: Catalog $4 ■ Doll-making and clock-building supplies. 205–928–2316.

Herb's Porcelain Doll Studio, 1208 E. 15th St., Plano, TX 75074: Price list $2 (refundable) ■ Bisque kits for making dolls. 800–628–4696; 214–578–1128 (in TX).

Hey-IQ's Doll Shoppe, 88 W. Elm St., Pembroke, MA 02359: Free information with long SASE ■ Doll-making supplies and clothing. 617–826–0226.

Jayne Houston Products, 246 S. Cleveland, Loveland, CO 80537: Free brochure ■ French brushes, paints, mediums, and books for doll-making and porcelain crafts. 303–663–3009.

International Manufacturing Company, P.O. Box 405, Lillian Springs, FL 32351: Catalog $1 ■ Doll-making supplies, other craft supplies, pine cones, and potpourri materials. 904–875–2918.

Jomac Dolls & Uniques, 702 Crenshaw, Pasadena, TX 77504: Free information with long SASE ■ Greenware, bisque and wax kits, and other doll-making supplies. 713–944–8221.

Janna Joseph, P.O. Box 12367, Palm Desert, CA 92255: Catalog $3.75 ■ Miniature doll molds. 619–568–5788.

Joyce's Doll House of Parts, 20188 Williamson, Mt. Clemens, MI 48403: Catalog $1 ■ Doll parts, wigs, natural straw hats, eyes, sewing needs, and other supplies. 313–791–0469.

Judi's Dolls, P.O. Box 607, Port Orchard, WA 98366: Free information with long SASE and two 1st class stamps ■ Patterns and supplies for cloth dolls. 206–895–2779.

Karen Kay Porcelain Arts, P.O. Box 4028, El Paso, TX 79914: Free information with long SASE ■ Doll-making kits. 915–751–0966.

Kari & Judy's Creations, 5014 Argus Dr., Los Angeles, CA 90041: Free price list with long SASE ■ Finished and unfinished composition doll bodies. 213–257–8219.

Kay Jay's Doll Emporium & Hospital, 18 E. 9th St., NJ Plaza, Ocean City, NJ 08226: Free information ■ Antique and collectible designer dolls, doll parts, and doll-making supplies. 609–399–5632.

Kemper Doll Supplies, Inc., P.O. Box 696, Chino, CA 91710: Free catalog ■ Wigs, eyes, shoes, doll-making supplies, and tools. 800–388–5367; 714–627–6191 (in CA).

Kirchen Brothers, Box 1016, Skokie, IL 60076: Catalog $2 (refundable) ■ Doll-making supplies and kits, ready-to-wear and ready-to-sew clothing, shoes and socks, and other craft supplies and kits. 708–676–2692.

Land of Oz Dolls, 1723 Portland Ave., Savanna, IL 61074: Catalog $5 ■ Doll-making supplies that include greenware and bisque kits. 815–273–3964.

Ledgewood Studio, 6000 Ledgewood Dr., Forest Park, GA 30050: Catalog $2 with long SASE and two 1st class stamps ■ Dress patterns, period clothing, and supplies for antique dolls. Other items include braids, French laces, silk ribbons, silk taffeta, China silk, and Swiss, and notions and sewing supplies.

Victor H. Levy, Inc., 1355 S. Flower St., Los Angeles, CA 90015: Catalog $5 ■ Doll-making and jewelry-making supplies and accessories. 800–421–8021; 213–749–8247 (in CA).

Little Lotus, Box 105, Cambridge, WI 53523: Catalog $2 with long SASE ■ Ethnic dolls and patterns for clothes.

Magic Cabin Dolls, Box 64, Viroqua, WI 54665: Free catalog ■ Natural fiber doll-making supplies. Includes kits and patterns, skin-tone cotton knits, yarns, and handmade custom dolls. 608–637–2735.

Ma's Body Shop, 1628 Eifert Rd., Holt, MI 48842: Catalog $1 ■ Lightweight, unbreakable composition bodies for dolls. 517–694–9022.

Maybelle's Doll Works, 138 Space Park Dr., Nashville, TN 37211: Free information ■ Doll-making supplies and molds. 615–831–0661.

Mimi's Books & Supplies, P.O. Box 662, Point Pleasant, NJ 08742: Free price list ■ Dollmaking tools, supplies, and hard-to-find books.

Mini World, 9919 E. 63rd St., Raytown, MO 64133: Catalog $3 ■ Doll-making supplies. 800–762–3318; 816–353–6999 (in MO).

NMR Designs, P.O. Box 127, Rollins, MT 59931: Free catalog with long SASE ■ Soft fired greenware doll kits, and blank and painted bisque kits. 406–844–3962.

Opal Doll Fashions, 5375 Five Forks Trickum Rd., Lilburn, GA 30247: Catalog $4 ■ Doll-making supplies and accessories, wax for making dolls, and custom dresses for antique dolls. 404–381–6613.

Pekin Ceramic Supply, 515 Charlotte, Pekin, IL 61554: Free price list with long SASE ■ Porcelain slip. 309–346–7916.

Pierce Tools, 1610 Parkdale Dr., Grants Pass, OR 97527: Free catalog ■ Tools for the dollmaker, ceramist, potter, and sculptor. 503–476–1778.

Plum Creek Ceramics, Plum Creek Rd., Box 409, RD 3, Bernville, PA 19506: Catalog $3.50 ■ Doll-making supplies. 215–488–6568.

Rivendell, Inc., 8209 Proctor Rd., Painesville, OH 44077: Catalog $3 ■ Supplies for porcelain dolls. 216–254–4088.

Robin Hood Molds, 15224 Arrow Hwy., Baldwin Park, CA 91706: Catalog $6 ■ Doll molds. 818–962–0216.

Roman's, 9733 Palmetto Ave., Fontana, CA 92335: Catalog $2.50 ■ Doll molds. 714–823–1100.

Shoppe Full of Dolls, 39 N. Main St., New Hope, PA 18938: Catalog $2 ■ Dolls, accessories, and clothing. 215–862–5524.

Standard Doll Company, 23–83 31st St., Long Island City, NY 11105: Catalog $3 (refundable) ■ Supplies for making and repairing dolls, clothing, doll stands, shoes and socks, buttons, wigs, books, and sewing and other craft supplies. 718–721–7787.

Tallina's Doll Supplies, Inc., 15790 Southeast Hwy. 224, Clackamas, OR 97015: Catalog $1 ■ Doll-making supplies. 503–658–6148.

TM Ceramic Service, Division of T.M. Porcelain, 108 N. Henry, Bay City, MI 48706: Catalog $2.50 ■ Slip, molds, doll bodies, arms, legs, reproduction and character heads, and other supplies. 517–893–3526.

Touch of Country, 22388 Cortez Blvd., Brooksville, FL 34601: Free catalog with long SASE ■ Dolls and doll-making supplies. 904–799–0729.

Unicorn Studios, Box 370, Seymour, TN 37865: Catalog $1 ■ Easy-to-install windup and electronic music box movements, winking light units, accessories, and voices for talking dolls and bears. 615–984–0145.

Valley of the Dolls, 831 19th St., Bakersfield, CA 93301: Free information ■ Wigs, eyes, shoes, clothing, porcelain, tools, composition bodies, and greenware. 805–328–9554.

DOLLS

Ashton-Drake Galleries, 212 W. Superior, Chicago, IL 60610: Free information ■ Collectible dolls. 708–966–2770.

Aurelia's World of Dolls, Inc., 202 Merrick Rd., Merrick, NY 11566: Free newsletter and price list ■ Original dolls by local, national, and international artists. 516–378–3556.

Baby Me, 730 Boston Rd., Rt. 3A, Billerica, MA 01821: Free information ■ Collectible dolls. 508–667–1187.

Bear Kingdom, 350 S. Lake Ave., #106, Pasadena, CA 91101: Free information ■ Collectible dolls and bears. 818–792–2327.

Bea's House of Dolls & Teddies, 9438 Magnolia Ave., Riverside, CA 92503: Free information with long SASE ■ Collectible and limited edition dolls and bears, books, patterns, and paper dolls. 714–359–6770.

Bebe House of Dolls, 247 3rd Ave., Chula Vista, CA 91910: Free information with long SASE ■ Collectible dolls. 619–476–0680.

Best of Everything, 8301 5th Ave., Brooklyn, NY 11209: Free information ■ Felt dolls and other collectibles. 718–238–9626.

Biggs Limited Editions, 5517 Lakeside Ave., Richmond, VA 23228: Free information with long SASE ■ Limited edition artist designer and collector dolls. 800–637–0704.

Cabbages & Kings, 953 N. Hairston Rd., Atlanta, GA 30083: Free information with long SASE ■ Dolls for collectors. 404–469–0055.

Calico Corner, 3082 Niagara Falls Blvd., North Tonawanda, NY 14120: Free information with long SASE ■ Collectible dolls. 800–75–DOLLS.

Career Pals, 709 Columbia Dr., Ste. M, Sacramento, CA 95864: Free information ■ The Career Pals collection includes 26 dolls representing traditional and non-traditional jobs from A to Z. 916–978–2328.

Carol's World of Dolls, 9041 Miller Rd., Swartz Creek, MI 48433: Free information with long SASE ■ Dolls for collectors. 313–635–7212.

Celia's Dolls & Collectibles, 800 E. Hallandale Beach Blvd., Hallandale, FL 33009: Free information about catalogs available ■

Collectible dolls. 800–762–7994; 305–458–0661 (in FL).

Collectibly Yours, 43 East Rt. 59, Spring Valley, NY 10977: Free information ■ Dolls, Hummels, Rockwells, figurines, plates, and gifts. 914–425–9244.

Corbett's Collectable Dolls, 123 Creek Rd., Mount Laurel, NJ 08054: Free information ■ Doll artist and manufacturer dolls. 609–866–9787.

The Countess Madeleine Galleries, 20 E. 63rd St., New York, NY 10021: Free information with long SASE ■ Collectible dolls. Includes limited edition antique reproductions. 212–758–7606.

Country House, 424 Broad St., Elmer, NJ 08318: Free information with long SASE ■ Dolls and bears for collectors. 609–358–2048.

Doll Centre, P.O. Box 2188, Placerville, CA 95667: Free information ■ Collectible dolls. Includes limited editions. 800–231–5111.

Doll City USA, 2040 N. Tustin Ave., Orange, CA 92665: Catalog $2 ■ Dolls and accessories. 800–525–3655; 800–356–3655 (in CA).

Doll Cottage, 427 Meeting St., West Columbia, SC 29169: Free list with two 1st class stamps ■ Dolls and accessories. 803–794–2119.

Doll Den, 231 W. Douglas, El Cajon, CA 92020: Free information with long SASE ■ Dolls and stuffed animals. 619–444–2198.

Doll Emporium, P.O. Box 1000, Studio City, CA 91604: Free information with long SASE ■ Collectible antique dolls. 818–763–5937.

Doll Gallery, Old Academy Square, 7835 Remington Rd., Cincinnati, OH 45242: Free information ■ Collectible dolls. 800–648–3035; 513–791–6606 (in OH).

The Doll House, 5022 N. May Ave., Oklahoma City, OK 73112: Free Brochure ■ Collectible dolls. 405–943–1498.

Dollmakers Originals International, Ludwigs Corner Center, 5200 Pottsdown Pike, Glenmoore, PA 19343: Free information with long SASE ■ Handmade porcelain dolls by Angelika Mannersdorfer.

The Doll Palace, 51 George St., Pataskala, OH 43062: Free information ■ Doll artist and manufacturer dolls. 800–999–9680.

Doll Parlor, 7 Church Street, Allentown, NJ 08501: Free information with long SASE ■ Collectible dolls and accessories. 609–259–8118.

Doll Showcase, 104 Front St., Marietta, OH 45750: Free price list with long SASE ■ Doll artist and manufacturer dolls. 800–93–DOLLS.

Dollsville Dolls & Bearsville Bears, 461 N. Palm Canyon Dr., Palm Springs, CA 92262: Catalog $1 ■ Dolls and accessories. 619–325–3655.

Downeast Doll House, 295 Main St., Biddeford, ME 04005: Free information with long SASE ■ Dolls, dollhouses, miniatures and accessories, and other toys. 207–282–0316.

Dwyer's Doll House, 1944 Warwick Ave., Warwick, RI 02889: Catalog $5 ■ Collectible dolls, dollhouses, accessories, miniatures, and decorating and building supplies. 800–248–3655.

Enchanted Doll House, Rt. 7A, Manchester Center, VT 05255: Catalog subscription $2 ■ Collectible dolls, miniatures, bears and stuffed animals, and other toys. 802–362–3031.

Gi Gi's Dolls & Sherry's Teddy Bears, Inc., 7550 N. Milwaukee Ave., Chicago, IL 60648: Free catalog with three 1st class stamps ■ Collectible bears, dolls, plush toys, and miniatures. 800–442–3655; 312–594–1540 (in IL).

Hanon Company, P.O. Box 574, Elm Grove, WI 53122: Free brochure ■ Signed and dated replicas of collectible antique wooden dolls. 800–527–4710; 414–786–6721 (in WI).

The Hobby Gallery Miniature Loft, 1810 Meriden Rd., Wolcott, CT 06716: Free information with long SASE ■ Dolls, dollhouses, miniatures, and plush animals. 203–879–2316.

House of Caron, 10111 Larrylyn Dr., Whittier, CA 90603: Catalog $2 ■ Miniature doll molds in 1/2– and 1–inch scale, with a choice of faces. 213–947–6753.

Iron Horse Gifts, Rt. 9, Latham, NY 12110: Free information ■ Collectible designer dolls. 518–785–3735.

J & L Collectibles, 111 Bullard Pkwy., Tampa, FL 33617: Free information with long SASE ■ Dolls for collectors. 813–985–0483.

Kay Jay's Doll Emporium & Hospital, 18 E. 9th St., NJ Plaza, Ocean City, NJ 08226: Free information ■ Antique and collectible designer dolls, doll parts, and doll-making supplies. 609–399–5632.

Lee's Collectibles, P.O. Box 19133, Sacramento, CA 95819: Free information with long SASE ■ Contemporary artist dolls for collectors. Includes wooden and cloth dolls. 916–457–4308.

Seymour Mann, 230 5th Ave., Room 2005, New York, NY 10010: Catalog $2 ■ Collectible dolls. 212–683–7262.

Marj's Doll Sanctuary, 5280 Northland Dr. NE, Grand Rapids, MI 49505: Free list and newsletter with two 1st class stamps ■ Dolls and bears for collectors. 616–361–0054.

Mary D's Dolls & Bears & Such, 8407 W. Broadway, Brooklyn Park, MN 55445: Catalog $2 (refundable) ■ Collectible dolls. 612–424–4375.

Merry Christmas Shoppe, 785 Bedford St., Rt. 18, Whitman, MA 02382: Free information with long SASE ■ Collectible German dolls. Includes dolls from Rotraut Schrott, the American Heartland Collection by Annette Himstedt, and Hildegard Gunzel. 617–447–6677.

Michelle's Clothespin Dolls, P.O. Box 201954, Austin, TX 78720: Brochure $2 ■ Signed and numbered, handpainted clothespin dolls. Includes nursery rhyme figures. 512–258–7023.

Monarch Collectibles, 2121 NW Military Hwy., San Antonio, TX 78213: Free information ■ Collectible dolls. 512–341–DOLL.

My Doll Boutique, 905 W. Main St., Brightleaf Square, Durham, NC 27701: Free information with long SASE ■ Dolls and accessories. 919–682–5400.

My Doll Shoppe, Inc., 55 W. Queens Way, Hampton, VA 23669: Free information with long SASE ■ Dolls and accessories for collectors. 804–723–0000.

Not Just Dolls, 2447 Gus Thomasson Rd., Dallas, TX 75228: Price list $2 ■ Doll artist and manufacturer dolls. 214–321–0412.

Original Appalachian Artworks, Inc., P.O. Box 714, Cleveland, GA 30528: Free information ■ Cabbage Patch dolls. 706–865–2171.

Pewter Classics, 3635 28th St. SE, Eastbrook Mall, Grand Rapids, MI 49512: Free information with long SASE ■ Dolls, bears, and other collectibles. 800–833–DOLL.

Pleasant Company, Box 998, Middleton, WI 53562: Free catalog ■ Dolls and accessories. 800–845–0005.

Poppets, Inc., Annapolis Harbor Center, Annapolis, MD 21403: Free information with long SASE ■ Dolls for collectors. Includes out-of-production specials. 410–266–7713.

Rainbow Factory, 131 W. Vienna St., Clio, MI 48420: Free information with long SASE ■ Dolls, carrousels and music boxes, clowns, and bears. 313–687–1351.

Samurai Antiques, 229 Santa Ynez Ct., Santa Barbara, CA 93103: Price list $1 with long SASE ■ Japanese antique dolls by Samurai, Emperor, and Empress. 805–965–9688.

Sandy's Dolls & Collectables, Inc., 11224 SW Hwy., Palos Hills, IL 60465: List $1 ■ Artist and limited edition dolls. 800–423–DOLL.

Second Hand Rose Doll House Store, Inc., 5826 W. Bluemound, Milwaukee, WI 53213: Catalog $2.50 ■ Collectible dolls, bears, miniatures, and accessories for dollhouses. 414–259–9965.

Shirley's Doll House, 20509 North Hwy. 21, P.O. Box 99A, Wheeling, IL 60090: Free information with long SASE ■ Dolls, bears, antiques, doll house furniture, wigs, clothing, and shoes and socks. 708–537–1632.

Shoda's Miniature Wonderland, 3504 Wells St., Fort Wayne, IN 46808: Free information with long SASE ■ Dolls, miniatures, music boxes, and figurines. 219–484–7167.

Shoppe Full of Dolls, 39 N. Main St., New Hope, PA 18938: Catalog $2 ■ Dolls, accessories, and clothing. 215–862–5524.

Simply Lovely Gift Shoppe, 566A New Brunswick Ave., Fords, NJ 08863: Free list with long SASE ■ Dolls for collectors. 908–738–4181.

Bea Skydell Dolls & Toys, 476 Union Ave., Middlesex, NJ 08846: Catalog $3 ■ Dolls for collectors. 908–356–5400.

Kate Smalley's Antique Dolls, P.O. Box 945, Branford, CT 06405: Free information with long SASE ■ Antique dolls. 203–481–8163.

Cathy Smith Designs, 360 Higginsville Rd., Neshanic Station, NJ 08853: Catalog $1 ■ Rag dolls made from antique textiles. 908–782–6938.

Society's Child, 28686 W. Northwest Hwy., Barrington, IL 60010: Free information with long SASE ■ Artist and limited edition dolls. 800–232–DOLL.

Sutter Street Emporium, 731 Sutter St., Folsom, CA 95630: Free information with long SASE ■ Limited edition, original artist dolls, and other dolls. 916–985–4647.

Judi Tasch Original Dolls, 3208 Clearview, Austin, TX 78703: Catalog $4 ■ Original and reproduction 19th-century fabric dolls. 512–476–5021.

Theriault's, P.O. Box 151, Annapolis, MD 21404: Free newsletter ■ Antique and collectible dolls. 410–224–3655.

Tide-Rider, Inc., P.O. Box 429, Oakdale, CA 95361: Free information ■ American Beauty dolls. Includes handcrafted felt dolls with detailed facial features and costuming. 209–848–4420.

Toy Shoppe, 1003 Sycamore Square, P.O. Box 28, Midlothian, VA 23113: Free information ■ Collectible portrait dolls by English doll makers, Philip and Christine Heath. 800–447–7995.

Ryan Twist Gallery, 430 Teaneck Rd., Ridgefield Park, NJ 07660: Free information with long SASE ■ Collectible dolls. 800–421–0171.

The Ultimate Collection, Inc., 12773 W. Forest Hills Blvd., Ste. 1208, West Palm Beach, FL 33414: Free information with long SASE ■ Vinyl collectible dolls. Includes limited editions. 407–790–0137.

Richard Wright Antiques, Flowing Springs & Hollow Roads, Birchrunville, PA 19421: Free information with long SASE ■ Antique dolls. 215–827–7442.

DRAFTING SUPPLIES

Alvin Drafting, Engineering & Graphic Arts Supplies, P.O. Box 188, Windsor, CT 06095: Free catalog ■ Professional drafting, engineering, and graphic arts equipment and supplies. 800–444–ALVIN; 203–243–8991 (in CT).

Co-Op Artists' Materials, P.O. Box 53097, Atlanta, GA 30355: Catalog $2 (refundable) ■ Art supplies and accessories for painting, drafting, drawing, airbrushing, and graphic arts. 800–877–3242.

Fairgate Rule Company, Inc., 22 Adams Ave., P.O. Box 278, Cold Spring, NY 10516: Free catalog ■ Rulers, other measuring devices, stencils, and drawing aids. 800–431–2180; 914–265–3677 (in NY).

Foster-Trent, Inc., 29 Beechwood Ave., New Rochelle, NY 10801: Free information ■ Projector that enlarges pictures, patterns, and drawings up to 25 times and projects an image on to almost any surface.

Hearlihy & Company, 714 W. Columbia St., Springfield, OH 45504: Free catalog ■ Drafting equipment and supplies, computer software for computer-aided designing, other computer drawing and drafting instructional aids, graphics equipment, videos, teacher utilities, robotics software, plotters, and furniture. 800–622–1000.

Koh-I-Noor Rapidograph, Inc., 100 North St., Bloomsbury, NJ 08804: Free catalog ■ Drawing equipment and art supplies. 800–631–7646.

Norton Products, Box 2012, New Rochelle, NY 10802: Free information ■ Craft projector that projects an image onto most surfaces.

Professional Graphics of Maine, 220 Danville Corner Rd., P.O. Box 1327, Auburn, ME 04211: Free information ■ Drafting equipment, supplies, and accessories. 207–783–9132; 800–225–1900 (in ME).

Pyramid of Urbana, 2107 N. High Cross Rd., Urbana, IL 61801: Free catalog ■ Drawing and drafting supplies, crafts supplies, office accessories and supplies, art supplies, and school equipment. 217–328–3099.

EGG CRAFTING

Dennis Brand Handcrafted Eggs, 13236 Crenshaw Blvd., Gardena, CA 90249: Free information ■ Handcrafted eggs in different sizes from over 400 different polished stones. 800–553–6855; 310–327–2323 (in CA).

John J. Hejna Painted Eggs, 4529 289th St., Toledo, OH 43611: Free information with long SASE ■ Decorated and painted eggs. 419–726–8387.

Hoffman Goose Hatchery, Gratz, PA 17030: Free information ■ Blown goose, duck, turkey, and guinea hen eggs. 717–365–3407.

Olesky Enterprises, Rt. 1, Box 165, Wallace, MI 49893: Free information ■ Decorated chicken and geese eggs for Christmas, Easter, other holiday occasions, birthdays, and anniversaries. 906–863–9030.

Our Nest Egg, 205 S. 5th St., Mapleton, IA 51034: Catalog $4 ■ Eggshells, stands, findings, braids, miniatures, rhinestones, and egg decorating materials. 712–882–1940.

Schiltz Goose Farm, 7 W. Oak St., P.O. Box 267, Sisseton, SD 57262: Free information ■ Blown goose, duck, quail, and turkey eggs in jumbo, X-large, large, and regular sizes. Decorating supplies include stands, rhinestones, round and fused pearls, and tools. 605–698–7651.

Zimonick's Studio, Box 149, DePere, WI 54115: Catalog $2 ■ Jeweled Christmas egg kits.

ELECTRICAL SUPPLIES

Coghlin Electric & Electronics, 155 Summer St., P.O. Box 150858, Worcester, MA 01615: Free catalog ■ Electronics and electrical supplies, test equipment, and tools. 508–791–7861.

Marlin P. Jones & Associates, P.O. Box 12685, Lake Park, FL 33403: Free catalog ■ Electrical and electronics components. 407–848–8236.

Wiremold Company, 60 Woodlawn St., West Hartford, CT 06110: Free literature ■ Fixtures, switches, controls, and grounding outlets for installation without having to break into walls or ceilings. 800–621–0049.

ELECTRIC GENERATORS & ENGINES

Bangor Generator Company, Ammo Industrial Park, Bangor, ME 04401: Free information ■ Diesel-powered generators for standby power. 207–947–2440.

China Diesel Imports, 15749 Lyons Valley Rd., Jamul, CA 92035: Free information ■ Diesel-powered generators and parts for a dependable, economical power source. 619–699–1995.

Inland Harbors, Inc., P.O. Box 41368, Plymouth, MN 55441: Free catalog ■ Generators for electric power, recreational products, trailer parts, and boating accessories. 800–544–2525.

Leionic Energy Company, 163800 Everetts Way, Riverside, CA 92504: Free information ■ Heavy-duty diesel generator for an independent power source. 714–688–9478.

Small Engine City, 2612 Lyndale South, Minneapolis, MN 55408: Free catalog ■ Small engines, generators, and accessories. 612–872–4288.

ELECTRONICS EQUIPMENT

Components

A & S International Marketing Company, Inc., P.O. Box 672, Brentwood, NY 11717: Free catalog ■ Fiber optics components, instrumentation accessories and equipment, and microwave components and assemblies. 516–435–2999.

Ace Communications Monitor Division, 10707 E. 106th St., Fishers, IN 46038: Free information ■ Electronics components, accessories, and supplies. 800–445–7717.

Ace Electronics, 3210 Antoine, Houston, TX 77092: Free information ■ Surplus electronics components, parts, and accessories. 713–688–8114.

ACP Components, 1317 E. Edinger, Santa Ana, CA 92705: Free information ■ Surplus electronics components, parts, and accessories. 714–558–8822.

All Components, 5999 Summerside Pl., #208, Dallas, TX 75252: Free information ■ Surplus electronics components, parts, and accessories. 800–367–7312.

All Electronics Corporation, P.O. Box 567, Van Nuys, CA 91408: Catalog $2 ■ New and used electronics components, parts, and supplies. 800–826–5432.

Allied Electronics, 401 E. 8th St., Fort Worth, TX 76102: Catalog $1 ■ Electronics parts and components, tools, supplies, and books. 817–336–5401.

Alltronics, 2300 Zanker Rd., San Jose, CA 95131: Free catalog ■ Electronics components and test equipment. 408–943–9773.

American Design Components, Box 220, Fairview, NJ 07022: Free information ■ New, reconditioned, and used electro-mechanical and electronics equipment and components. 800–776–3800.

ARS Electronics, 7110 De Celis Pl., P.O. Box 7323, Van Nuys, CA 91406: Free information ■ Electronics tubes. 818–997–6279.

Battery-Tech, Inc., 28–25 215 Pl., Bayside, NY 11360: Free catalog ■ Replacement batteries. 800–442–4275; 718–631–4275 (in NY).

Braniff Industries, 91 S. Ottawa, Dixon, IL 61021: Free information ■ Surplus electronics components, parts, and accessories. 815–288–4500.

Calcera, P.O. Box 489, Belmont, CA 94002: Free information ■ Surplus electronics components, parts, and accessories. 800–257–5549.

Coghlin Electric & Electronics, 155 Summer St., P.O. Box 150858, Worcester, MA 01615: Free catalog ■ Electronics and electrical supplies, test equipment, and tools. 508–791–7861.

Consolidated Electronics, Inc., 705 Watervliet Ave., Dayton, OH 45420: Catalog $5 ■ Electronics parts and equipment. 800–543–3568.

Contact East, 335 Willow St. South, North Andover, MA 01845: Free catalog ■ Equipment and accessories for testing, repairing, and assembling electronics equipment. 800–225–5370; 508–682–2000 (in MA).

Crystek Corporation, 2351 Crystal Dr., Fort Myers, FL 33907: Free catalog ■ Crystals for radio amateurs, citizen band operators, and experimenters. 813–936–2109.

Dalbani Electronics, 2733 Carrier Ave., Los Angeles, CA 90040: Free catalog ■ Electronic components and accessories. 800–325–2264; 213–727–0054 (in CA).

Datak Corporation, 55 Freeport Blvd., Unit 23, Sparks, NV 89431: Free catalog ■ Printed circuit products, dry transfer letters, and electronics title sets for control panels. 702–359–7474.

Derf Electronics, 1 Biehn St., New Rochelle, NY 1080: Free information ■ Surplus electronics components, parts, and accessories. 800–431–2912.

Digi-Key Corporation, P.O. Box 677, Thief River, MN 56701: Free catalog ■ Electronics components and accessories. 800–344–5144.

Electronic Specialty Products, 3M Company, Attention: Electronics Dept., P.O. Box 2963, Austin, TX 78769: Free information ■ Solderless breadboards for electronics circuits. 800–321–9668.

Fair Radio Sales Company, Inc., P.O. Box 1105, Lima, OH 45802: Free information ■ Surplus electronics parts. 419–227–6573.

H & R Corporation, 401 E. Erie Ave., Philadelphia, PA 19134: Free catalog ■ Electronic components, tools, computer equipment, power supplies, test equipment, and meters. 215–426–1700.

H & R Enterprises, 21521 Blythe St., Canoga Park, CA 91304: Free information ■ Surplus electronics components, parts, and accessories. 818–703–8892.

Hosfelt Electronics, Inc., 2700 Sunset Blvd., Steubenville, OH 43952: Free catalog ■ Electronics components, accessories, and supplies. 800–524–6464.

J & C Electronics, Box 630, Salem, MA 01970: Free information ■ Surplus electronics components, parts, and accessories. 800–447–7014.

Jameco Electronics, 1355 Shoreway Rd., Belmont, CA 94002: Free catalog ■ Electronic components, kits, test equipment, and computer equipment. 800–831–4242.

Jan Crystals, P.O. Box 06017, Fort Myers, FL 33906: Free catalog ■ Crystals for radio amateurs, citizen band operators, and experimenters. 800–526–9825; 813–936–2397 (in FL).

Japan Electronics, 15138 Valley Blvd., City of Industry, CA 91744: Free information ■ Surplus electronics components, parts, and accessories. 818–369–5000.

JDR Microdevices, 2233 Branham Ln., San Jose, CA 95124: Free catalog ■ Electronic components, micro-devices, tools, chips, and computer equipment. 408–559–1200.

Jerome Industries, 8737 Shirley Ave., Northridge, CA 91324: Free information ■

Surplus electronics components, parts, and accessories. 818–993–1393.

Marlin P. Jones & Associates, P.O. Box 12685, Lake Park, FL 33403: Free catalog ■ Electrical and electronics components. 407–848–8236.

Joseph Electronics, 8830 N. Milwaukee Ave., Niles, IL 60648: Free catalog ■ Electronics components and accessories, test instruments, tools, chemicals, and soldering equipment. 800–323–5925; 708–297–4200 (in IL).

K & F Electronics, Inc., 33041 Groesbeck, Fraser, MI 48026: Free information ■ Custom-etched and drilled printed circuit boards. 313–294–8720.

Kelvin Electronics, 10 Hub Dr., Melville, NY 11747: Free catalog ■ Electronics components, test equipment, accessories, and other supplies. 800–645–9212; 516–756–1750 (in NY).

McGee's Electronics, 1901 McGee St., Kansas City, MO 64108: Free catalog ■ Speakers and electronics parts. 800–842–5092.

MCM Electronics, 650 Congress Park Dr., Centerville, OH 45459: Free catalog ■ Test equipment, computer accessories, telephone accessories, speakers, television components and parts, and electronics components. 800–543–4330.

Mendelson Electronics Company, Inc., 340 E 1st St., Dayton, OH 45402: Free catalog ■ Electronics components, accessories, and supplies. 800–422–3525; 513–461–3525 (in OH).

MFJ Enterprises, Inc., P.O. Box 494, Mississippi State, MS 39762: Free catalog ■ Equipment for electronics experimenters and HAM operators. 800–647–1800.

Micro-C, 11085 Sorrento Valley Ct., San Diego, CA 92121: Free information ■ Surplus electronics components, parts, and accessories. 619–552–1213.

Micro-Mart, 508 Central Ave., Westfield, NJ 07090: Free price list ■ Electronic components and accessories. 908–654–6008.

Microprocessors Unlimited, 24000 S. Peoria Ave., Beggs, OK 74421: Free information ■ Surplus electronics components, parts, accessories, and microprocessors. 918–267–4962.

Mouser Electronics, 2401 Hwy. 287 North, Mansfield, TX 76063: Free catalog ■ Electronics components and accessories. Includes computers and accessories. 800–992–9943.

New England Circuit Sales, 292 Cabot St., Beverly, MA 01915: Free information ■ Surplus electronics components, parts, and accessories. 800–922–NECS.

Ocean State Electronics, P.O. Box 1458, Westerly, RI 02891: Free catalog ■ Electronics equipment and accessories and educational kits. 401–596–3080.

Oracle Electronics, 1355 Adams Ct., Menlo Park, CA 94025: Free information ■ Surplus electronics components, parts, and accessories. 415–326–2660.

Parts Express, 340 E. 1st St., Dayton, OH 45042: Free catalog ■ Parts for electronics projects, repair, experimentation, and research. 800–338–0531; 513–222–0173 (in OH).

Pasternack Enterprises, P.O. Box 16759, Irvine, CA 92713: Free catalog ■ Over 2900 coaxial products. 714–261–1920.

Radio Shack, Division Tandy Corporation, 1500 One Tandy Center, Fort Worth, TX 76102: Free catalog ■ Electronics components, parts and accessories, science kits, computers, stereo equipment, toys and games, and other equipment. 817–390–3700.

RF Parts, Box 700, San Marcos, CA 92069: Free information ■ RF power transistors, and Motorola and Toshiba parts for amateurs, marine use, and commercial radio servicing. 619–744–0700.

Search Electronics, 228 E. Atara, Monrovia, CA 91016: Free information ■ Surplus electronics components, parts, and accessories. 818–359–3360.

Soft Light Manufacturing, 501 Simpson Chapel Rd., Bloomington, IN 47404: Free information ■ Solder-free breadboards. 800–365–2575.

Tucker Surplus Store, 1717 Reserve St., Garland, TX 75042: Free information ■ Surplus electronics equipment, accessories, and other supplies. 800–527–4642.

The Ultimate Saving Source, 2733 Carrier Ave., Los Angeles, CA 90040: Free catalog ■ Electronics components, and parts. 800–325–2264; 213–727–0054 (in CA).

Unicorn Electronics, 10010 Canoga Ave., Unit B–8, Chatsworth, CA 91311: Free information ■ Integrated circuits, other equipment, and accessories. 800–824–3432.

W & W Associates, 29–11 Parsons Blvd., Flushing, NY 11354: Free information ■ Communication batteries. 800–221–0732; 718–961–2103 (in NY).

Kits & Plans

Amazing Concepts, Box 716, Amherst, NH 03031: Catalog $1 ■ Easy-to-assemble subminiature FM transmitters for telephones and long-range voice transmission. 603–673–4730.

Consumertronics, 2011 Crescent Dr., P.O. Drawer 537, Alamogordo, NM 88310: Free information ■ Electronics kits, parts, and accessories. 505–434–0234.

Edlie Electronics, 2700 Hempstead Tpk., Levittown, NY 11756: Free catalog ■ Electronic kits, parts, supplies, and test equipment. 516–735–3330.

Eico Electronics Instrument Company, 363 Merrick Rd., Lynbrook, NY 11563: Free catalog ■ Do-it-yourself kits and factory-assembled electronics equipment. Includes test equipment, home security and fire alarms, multimeters, accessory probes, and electronics components and accessories. 516–599–5744.

The Electronic Goldmine, P.O. Box 5408, Scottsdale, AZ 85261: Free catalog ■ Easy-to-assemble kits. 602–451–7454.

Electronic Rainbow, 6254 LaPas Trail, Indianapolis, IN 46268: Free information ■ Easy-to-assemble kits. 317–291–7262.

Heath Company, P.O. Box 8589, Benton Harbor, MI 49023: Free catalog ■ Computers, robots, television sets, home convenience gadgets, test instruments, security devices, educational projects, and other kits. 800–44–HEATH.

Information Unlimited, Inc., Box 716, Amherst, NH 03031: Catalog $1 ■ Electronics projects. Includes lasers, communication equipment, electronic experiments, mini radios, rocketry equipment, flying saucers, and others. 603–673–4730.

Jameco Electronics, 1355 Shoreway Rd., Belmont, CA 94002: Free catalog ■ Electronics kits, test equipment, and computer equipment. 800–831–4242.

Krystal Kits, P.O. Box 445, Bentonville, AR 72712: Free catalog ■ Electronics kits and plans for amateur science experimenters. 501–273–5340.

Mark V Electronics, Inc., 8019 E. Slauson Ave., Montebello, CA 90640: Free catalog ■ Electronic kits for beginning, intermediate, and advanced hobbyists. 213–888–8988.

Ocean State Electronics, P.O. Box 1458, Westerly, RI 02891: Free catalog ■ Educational kits and electronics equipment and accessories. 401–596–3080.

PAIA Electronics, Inc., 3200 Teakwood Ln., Edmond, OK 73013: Free catalog ■ Electronics kits and books. 405–340–6300.

Radio Shack, Division Tandy Corporation, 1500 One Tandy Center, Fort Worth, TX 76102: Free catalog ■ Electronics components and accessories, science kits, computers, stereo equipment, toys and games, and other equipment. 817–390–3700.

Ramsey Electronics, Inc., 793 Canning Pkwy., Victor, NY 14564: Free information ■ Test equipment and electronics kits. Includes pre-amps, communications monitors, transmitters, aircraft receiver kits, personal speed radar equipment, and easy-to-assemble mini kits. 716–924–4560.

Xandi Electronics, Box 25647, Tempe, AZ 85282: Catalog $1 (refundable) ■ Build your own satellite TV receiver, voice disguisers, FM bugs, telephone transmitters, and phone snoops. 800–336–7389; 602–829–8152 (in AZ).

Test Equipment

Alfa Electronics, P.O. Box 8089, Princeton, NJ 08543: Free catalog ■ Multipurpose test equipment. 800–526–ALFA; 609–275–0220 (in NJ).

Wm. B. Allen Supply Company, Allen Square, 300 Block N. Rampart St., New Orleans, LA 70112: Free information ■ Multipurpose test equipment, replacement probes, and electronics components. 800–535–9593; 800–462–9520 (in LA).

Alltronics, 2300 Zanker Rd., San Jose, CA 95131: Free catalog ■ Test equipment and electronics components. 408–943–9773.

Amprobe Test Equipment, Box 329, Lynbrook, NY 11563: Free catalog ■ Multimeters, volt-amp-ohmmeters, and other test equipment. 516–593–5600.

C & S Sales, Inc., 1245 Rosewood, Deerfield, IL 60015: Free catalog ■ Test equipment and other suppplies. 800–292–7711; 708–541–0710 (in IL).

Contact East, 335 Willow St. South, North Andover, MA 01845: Free catalog ■ Equipment and accessories for testing, repairing, and assembling electronics equipment. 800–225–5370; 508–682–2000 (in MA).

Davilyn Corporation, 13406 Saticoy St., North Hollywood, CA 91605: Free catalog ■ Multipurpose test equipment. 800–235–6222; 818–787–3334 (in CA).

E.T. Tech, Inc., 15 S. Van Brunt St., Englewood, NJ 07631: Free information ■ Test equipment. 201–569–3339.

Electro Tool, Inc., 9103 Gillman, Livonia, MI 48150: Free information ■ Tools and electronics test equipment. 313–422–1221.

John Fluke Manufacturing Company, P.O. Box 9090, Everett, WA 98206: Free brochure ■ Hand-held meters with analog and digital readout displays. 800–87–FLUKE.

Fordham-Scope Catalog, 260 Motor Pkwy., Hauppage, NY 11788: Free catalog ■ Multipurpose test equipment. 516–435–8080.

Global Specialties, 70 Fulton Terrace, New Haven, CT 06512: Free information ■ Compact multimeters that measure AC and DC voltage, current, resistance, and check diodes and continuity. 800–572–1028.

JDR Microdevices, 2233 Branham Ln., San Jose, CA 95124: Free information ■ Multipurpose test equipment. 408–559–1200.

Joseph Electronics, Inc., 8830 N. Milwaukee Ave., Niles, IL 60648: Catalog $4.95 ■ Multipurpose test equipment. 800–323–5925; 708–297–4200 (in IL).

Kelvin Electronics, 7 Fairchild Ave., Plainview, NY 11803: Free catalog ■ Electronics components, test equipment, accessories, and other supplies. 800–645–9212; 516–349–7620 (in NY).

MCM Electronics, 650 E. Congress Park Dr., Centerville, OH 45459: Free catalog ■ Test equipment, computer accessories, telephone equipment and accessories, speakers, television parts, switches, fuses, and lamps. 800–543–4330.

Westcon, Inc., 5101 N. Interstate Ave., Portland, OR 97217: Free catalog ■ Save up to 50 percent on test probes. 800–547–4515.

Tools & Accessories

Electro Tool, Inc., 9103 Gillman, Livonia, MI 48150: Free information ■ Tools and electronics test equipment. 313–422–1221.

W.S. Jenks & Son, 1933 Montana Ave. NE, Washington, DC 20002: Free catalog ■ Hand and power tools, accessories, and supplies for electronics. 800–638–6405; 202–529–6020 (in DC).

Jensen Tools, Inc., 7815 46th St., Phoenix, AZ 85044: Free catalog ■ Precision tools for electronics technicians, experimenters, and hobbyists. Includes the Jensen's line of over 40 tool kits. 602–968–6231.

Joseph Electronics, 8830 N. Milwaukee Ave., Niles, IL 60648: Free catalog ■ Electronics components and accessories, test instruments, tools, chemicals, and soldering equipment. 800–323–5925; 708–297–4200 (in IL).

Time Motion Tools, 410 S. Douglas St., El Segundo, CA 90245: Free catalog ■ Field service kits and test equipment, production aids, telecommunication equipment, maintenance and repair tools, and work stations. 213–772–8170.

ELECTROPLATING

American Bronzing Company, P.O. Box 6504, Bexley, OH 43209: Free information ■ Bronzing and two-tone antique finish for baby's shoes. 800–345–8112.

Chrome Plating, 7477 SW Freeway, Houston, TX 77074: Free information ■ Chrome, nickel, and gold plating. 713–981–1440.

Edmund Scientific Company, Edscorp Bldg., Barrington, NJ 08007: Free catalog ■ Electroplating kits. 609–573–6260.

Hiles Plating Company, Inc., 2030 Broadway, Kansas City, MO 64108: Free brochure ■ Silver and gold plating, and refinishing with brass, copper, and pewter. 816–421–6450.

Nichols Bronze Supply, 10555 US Hwy. 98, Sebring, FL 33870: Free price list ■ Kits, supplies, and mountings for nonelectric plating of baby shoes and other keepsakes in bronze, gold, silver, or pewter. 813–655–0346.

Plating Service, N3503 Hwy. 55, Chilton, WI 53014: Free information with long SASE ■ Electroplating services.

River Road Industries, 12806 River, Plano, IL 60545: Free information with long SASE ■ Electroplating services.

Texas Platers Supply, 2453 W. Five Mile Pkwy., Dallas, TX 75233: Free information ■ Electroplating kits.

Tropic House, Box 95, Palm Bay, FL 32906: Free details ■ Information on how to plate with gold, silver, copper, nickel, chromium, tin, zinc, cadmium, antimony, other metals, and brass, bronze, and black nickel alloys.

ENGRAVING & ETCHING

Alpha Supply, 1225 Hollis St., Box 2133, Bremerton, WA 98310: Catalog $1 ■ Engraving tools and supplies, casting equipment and supplies, faceting equipment, jewelry-making tools, silver rings, and lapidary equipment and supplies. 206–377–5629.

B. Rush Apple Company, 3855 W. Kennedy Blvd., Tampa, FL 33609: Free information ■ Engraving tools and supplies. 813–870–3180.

Brownells, Inc., 200 S. Front St., Montezuma, IA 50171: Free information ■ Engraving tools. 515–623–5401.

James R. DeMunck, 3012 English Rd., Rochester, NY 14616: Free information with long SASE ■ Engraving tools. 813–385–0647.

Hand Engravers Supply Company, 601 Springfield Dr., Albany, GA 31707: Free information ■ Engraving tools. 912–432–9683.

Indian Jewelers Supply Company, P.O. Box 1774, Gallup, NM 87305: Set of 4 catalogs $5 ■ Precious and base metals; findings in precious and base metals; metalworking, lapidary tools and supplies, and engraving tools and supplies; and semiprecious stones, shells, and coral. 505–722–4451.

Ken Jantz Supply, 222 E. Main, Davis, OK 73030: Free information ■ Engraving tools. 405–369–2316.

J.M. Ney Company, Neycraft Division, 13553 Calimesa Blvd., Yucaipa, CA 92399:

Free information ■ Engraving tools and supplies. 714–795–2461.

EXERCISE EQUIPMENT

American Athletic, Inc., 200 American Ave., Jefferson, IA 50129: Free information ■ Barbells and racks, belts, benches, bicycles, dumbbells, ergometers, home gymnasiums, saunas, rowing machines, slant boards, skip boards, gymnastic bars, floor equipment, and ropes. 800–247–3978.

American Pro Orthopedics, 901 E. 233rd St., Carson, CA 90745: Free information ■ Barbells and benches, belts, dumbells, multifunction home gyms, slant boards, and electric treadmills. 310–715–9360.

Ameri-Fit Corporation, 1237 The Plaza, Charlotte, NC 28205: Free information ■ Barbells and racks, belts, benches, bicycles, dumbbells, ergometers, hand and leg weights, monitors and testers, home gymnasiums, rowing machines, skip ropes, slant boards, treadmills, and weight training equipment 704–372–3294.

Anterion Conditioning Equipment, D.L.C. Fabricating Company, Inc., 4809 Miami St., St. Louis, MO 63116: Free information ■ Barbells and benches, belts, dumbells, hand/leg weights, jogging trampolines, monitors/pulse meters, multi-function home gyms, skip ropes, slant boards, and electric treadmills. 314–351–9778.

Austin Athletic Equipment Corporation, 705 Bedford Ave., Box 423, Bellmore, NY 11710: Free information ■ Barbells and racks, belts, benches, bicycles, dumbbells, ergometers, hand weights, inversion equipment, massage rollers, monitors and testers, home gymnasiums, rowing machines, saunas, skip ropes, slant boards, treadmills, weight training equipment, wheels, gymnastic bars, floor equipment, and ropes. 516–785–0100.

Badger Fitness Equipment, 1010 Davis Ave., South Milwaukee, WI 53172: Free information ■ Barbells, benches, dumbbells, home gymnasiums, and slant boards. 414–764–4068.

Bollinger Fitness Products, 222 W. Airport Freeway South, Irving, TX 75062: Free

information ■ Barbells and racks, belts, benches, dumbbells, hand weights, jogging trampolines, leg weights, home gymnasiums, skip ropes, and treadmills. 800–527–1166; 214–445–0386 (in TX).

California Gym Equipment Company, 3140 E. Pico Blvd., Los Angeles, CA 90023: Free information ■ Barbells and racks, belts, benches, bicycles, dumbbells, ergometers, home gymnasiums, rowing machines, slant boards, and treadmills. 213–264–2715.

Cannon Sports, Inc., P.O. Box 11179, Burbank, CA 91510: Free information ■ Barbells and benches, belts, dumbells, hand/leg weights, gymnastics floor equipment, jogging trampolines, skip ropes, slant boards, and electric treadmills. 800–223–0064; 818–503–9570 (in CA).

Carolina Health & Fitness, 1308 Rainey St., Burlington, NC 27215: Free catalog ■ Aerobic exercise and fitness equipment, exercise wear, personal safety and security products, books, and soft weights. 919–229–1300.

Centurian Sales Company, P.O. Box P, Mountain View, CA 94042: Free information ■ Barbells and racks, benches, bicycles, dumbbells, ergometers, home gymnasiums, and treadmills. 415–968–8910.

Chattanooga Corporation, 4717 Adams Rd., P.O. Box 489, Hixson, TN 37343: Free information ■ Compact exerciser for therapeutic exercising while standing, seated, kneeling, or lying down. Adjusts to the height and arm and leg lengths of the user.

Concept II, Inc., RR 1, Box 1100, Morrisville, VT 05661: Free brochure ■ Exercise rowing machine.

Creative Health Products, Inc., 5148 Saddle Ridge Rd., Plymouth, MI 48170: Free literature and price list ■ Exercise bicycles, rowing machines, stethoscopes, thermometers, digital blood pressure units, scales, lung capacity testers, and pulse monitors. 800–742–4478.

Dynamic Classics, Ltd., 230 5th Ave., New York, NY 10001: Free information ■ Belts, bicycles, dumbbells, hand and leg weights, massage rollers, home gymnasiums, rowing

machines, skip ropes, treadmills, wheels, and gymnastic bars. 212–571–0267.

Enduraciser, 1149 N. Main, Monticello, UT 84535: Free information ■ Total body workout and aerobic exerciser. 800–424–8137.

Fitness Master, Inc., 504 Industrial Blvd., Waconia, MN 55387: Free brochure ■ Cardiovascular fitness and body tone exerciser. 800–328–8995; 612–474–0992 (in MN).

Fitness Systems, Inc., P.O. Box 266, Independence, MO 64501: Free information ■ Motorized and mechanical isokinetic treadmills. 800–821–3126.

Flaghouse, 150 N. MacQuesten Pkwy., Mt. Vernon, NY 10550: Free catalog ■ Physical fitness and gymnastic equipment and supplies, and equipment for camping, playgrounds, and other outdoor activities. 800–221–5185.

Heart-Rate, Inc., 3188 Airway Ave., Ste. E, Costa Mesa, CA 92626: Free brochure ■ Total body aerobic exercise machine. 800–237–2271.

Hi Products, Hofmann Industries, Inc., P.O. Box 2147, Sinking Spring, PA 19608: Free information ■ Barbells and racks, benches, bicycles, dumbbells, hand weights, home gymnasiums, and weight training equipment. 215–678–2626.

Holabird Sports Discounters, 9004 Yellow Brick Rd., Rossville Industrial Park, Baltimore, MD 21237: Free brochure ■ Save up to 40 percent on exercise equipment, sports equipment, clothing and equipment for basketball, tennis, running and jogging, golf, and racquetball. 410–687–6400.

Ivanko Barbell Company, P.O. Box 1470, San Pedro, CA 90733: Free information ■ Barbells and racks, belts, benches, dumbbells, hand and leg weights, and skip ropes. 310–514–1155.

Jayfro Corporation, Unified Sports, Inc., 976 Hartford Tpk., P.O. Box 400, Waterford, CT 06385: Free catalog ■ Wall-mounted gyms, vaulting, boxes, chinning bars, climbing ropes, balance beams, and mat trucks. 203–447–3001.

M.W. Kasch Company, 5401 W. Donges Bay Rd., Mequon, WI 53092: Free information ■ Barbells and benches, belts, dumbells, hand/leg weights, jogging trampolines, Nordic ski machines, monitors/pulse meters, multi-function home gyms, skip ropes, slant boards, stair climbers, stationary cycles/ergometers, and electric treadmills. 414–242–5000.

LifeFitness, Inc., 9601 Jeronimo Rd., Irvine, CA 92718: Free information ■ Aerobic exercise training machine. 800–877–3867.

Monark-Universal Fitness, 50 Commercial St., Plainview, NY 11803: Free information ■ Barbells and racks, belts, benches, bicycles, dumbbells, ergometers, hand weights, isokinetic and isometric units, jogging trampolines, home gymnasiums, rowing machines, saunas, skip ropes, slant boards, treadmills, and wheels. 516–349–8600.

NordicTrack, 141 Jonathan Blvd. North, Chaska, MN 55318: Free brochure ■ Total body exerciser. 800–328–5888.

PCA Industries, Inc., 5642 Natural Bridge, St. Louis, MO 63120: Free information ■ Gymnastic bars, floor equipment, and ropes. 800–727–8180.

The Potomac Company, 29908 S. Stockton, Farmington Hills, MI 48024: Free catalog ■ Clothing and equipment for competitive and recreational rowers. 313–471–4448.

Precore U.S.A., P.O. Box 3004, Bothell, WA 98041: Free information ■ Off-snow, cross-country skier exercise machine. 206–486–9292.

Professional Gym, Inc., P.O. Box 188, Marshall, MO 65340: Free brochure ■ Weight training, body building, and exercise equipment. 800–821–7665; 800–892–2616 (in MO).

Quinton Fitness Equipment, 2121 Terry Ave., Seattle, WA 98121: Free information ■ Fitness bicycles and an upper and lower body workout exercise machine. 206–223–7373.

Rich Marketing Company, Inc., P.O. Box 3828, Albany, GA 31706: Free information ■ Barbells and benches, belts, dumbbells, hand/leg weights, jogging trampolines, multi-function home gyms, slant boards, and electric treadmills. 912–435–2101.

Scientific Sports Systems, 503 Seaport Ct., Port of Redwood City, CA 94063: Free information ■ Off-snow, cross-country skier exercise machine. 800–225–9669.

Sinties Scientific, Inc., 5616–A S. 122 East Ave., Tulsa, OK 74146: Free information ■ Power trainers, with variable resistance and performance computer, for use with wheelchairs or upright chairs. 800–852–6869; 918–599–7828 (in OK).

Spalding & Brothers, 425 Meadow St., P.O. Box 901, Chicopee, MA 01021: Free information ■ Barbells and racks, belts, benches, bicycles, dumbbells, ergometers, hand and leg weights, inversion equipment, isokinetic and isometric units, jogging trampolines, home gymnasiums, rowing machines, saunas, skip ropes, slant boards, and wheels. 413–536–1200.

Sport Club, 615 W. Johnson Ave., Cheshire, CT 06410: Free catalog ■ Fashion designed jogging bras that provide support, fitness clothing for men and women, nutritional supplements, swim wear, exercise equipment, weights, and body shaping equipment.

Theole Manufacturing, Rt. 1, Box 116, Montrose, IL 62445: Free information ■ Exercise machine for quadraplegics, paraplegics, and stroke patients. 217–924–4553.

Trampolking Sporting Goods, P.O. Box 725, Albany, GA 31708: Free brochure ■ Exercise bikes, rowers, other home physical fitness equipment, and trampolines. 800–841–4351; 912–435–2101 (in GA).

Unicare Health & Fitness Company, 273 E. Redondo Beach Blvd., Gardena, CA 90248: Free information ■ Barbells and benches, belts, dumbbells, hand/leg weights, jogging trampolines, monitors/pulse meters, multi-function home gyms, recumbent machines, slant boards, stair climbers, stationary cycles/ergometers, and electric treadmills. 310–538–0905.

Universal Gym Equipment, P.O. Box 1270, Cedar Rapids, IA 52406: Free catalog ■ Weight and exercise equipment, treadmills, computerized aerobic and exercise machines, gymnastic bars, floor equipment, and ropes.

Video Exercise Catalog, 5390 Main St. NE, Minneapolis, MN 55421: Free catalog ■ Workout and exercise equipment, and almost 200 workout video cassettes.

WaterRower, Inc., 255 Armistice Blvd., Pawtucket, RI 02860: Free brochure ■ An exercise rowing machine that uses water resistance to maintain total body fitness. 401–728–1966.

Weider Health & Fitness, 21100 Erwin St., Woodland Hills, CA 91364: Free information ■ Barbells and racks, belts, benches, bicycles, dumbbells, ergometers, hand and leg weights, home gymnasiums, rowing machines, skip ropes, slant boards, weight training equipment, and wheels. 800–535–2149.

Whitland Fitness Corporation, 101 Methuen St., P.O. Box 1049, Lawrence, MA 01842: Free information ■ Gymnastic bars, floor equipment, ropes, and other equipment. 508–685–5109.

Winston Sports Corporation, 200 5th Ave., New York, NY 10010: Free information ■ Barbells and benches, belts, dumbbells, hand/leg weights, jogging trampolines, skip ropes, slant boards, stair climbers, and electric treadmills. 212–255–6870.

FABRIC PAINTING & DYEING

Aljo Dyes, 81 Franklin St., New York, NY 10013: Free catalog ■ Fabric dyes. 212–226–2878.

Badger Air-Brush Company, 9128 W. Belmont Ave., Franklin Park, IL 60131: Free brochure ■ Air brushes and fabric paints. 708–678–3104.

Batik & Weaving Supplier, P.O. Box 451, Arlington, MA 02173: Catalog $2 ■ Supplies and accessories for fabric dyeing and batiking, weaving, knitting, and spinning crafts. 617–646–4453.

Blue Mountain Photo Supply, Box 3085, Reading, PA 19604: Free information ■ Blueprinting materials and supplies.

Blueprint-Printables, 1504 Industrial Way, Belmont, CA 94002: Catalog $3 ■ Fabrics and T-shirts, for blueprinting. Available in kits. 800–356–0445.

Brooks & Flynn, Inc., Box 2639, Rohnert Park, CA 94927: Catalog $3.50 ■ Fabric dyes for painting on silk, Texticolor "Pearlescent" fabric paints from France, silks from China, brushes, T-shirts, and other supplies. 800–822–2372; 800–345–2026 (in CA).

Cerulean Blue, Ltd., P.O. Box 21168, Seattle, WA 98111: Catalog $3 (refundable) ■ Lanaset dyes for wool and silk, instruction books, accessories and equipment, natural fiber fabrics, and supplies for making blueprints on silk. 800–676–8602.

Clothworks, 132 Powell St., Vancouver, British Colombia, Canada V6A 1G1: Free information ■ Premixed textile dyes for silk screening, airbrushing, and handpainting. 604–688–1752.

Createx Colors, 14 Airport Park Rd., East Granby, CT 06026: Free information ■ Fabric dyes. 800–243–2712; 203–453–5505 (in CT).

Decart, Inc., Morrisville, VT 05661: Free information ■ Permanent, machine washable, dry-cleanable fabric paints, paints for use with air brushes, and water-based enamels and paints. 802–888–4217.

Dharma Trading Company, P.O. Box 916, San Rafael, CA 94902: Free catalog ■ Dyes and fabric paints. 800–542–5227.

D.Y.E. Textiles Resources, 3763 Durango Ave., Los Angeles, CA 90034: Free information ■ Blueprinting materials and supplies.

Eastern Craft Supply, P.O. Box 341, Wyckoff, NJ 07481: Catalog $2 ■ Fabric painting kits and supplies. 800–872–3458.

F & R Sales, 1720 Cumberland, Marietta, GA 30067: Free information ■ Slick and glitter paint, iridescent paint, liquid glitter and fashion tints, metallic paint, dyes for tie-dyeing, and paint-writers in glitter, slick, and iridescent colors. 800–745–1562; 404–984–0808 (in GA).

FanciCraft, 686 S. Arroyo Pkwy., Ste. 167, Pasadena, CA 91105: Free catalog ■ Fabric painting kits. 818–241–4202.

Gramma's Graphics, Inc., 20 Birling Gap, Fairport, NY 14450: Catalog $1 with long SASE ■ Blueprinting kits for fabrics. 716–223–4309.

Ivy Crafts Imports, 12213 Distribution Way, Beltsville, MD 20705: Catalog $3.95 ■ Fabric paints, resists, and applicators. 301–595–0550.

Photographers Formulary, P.O. Box 950, Condon, MT 59826: Catalog $1 ■ Materials and supplies for blueprinting on fabric. 800–922–5255.

PRO Chemical & Dye, Inc., P.O. Box 14, Somerset, MA 02726: Free catalog ■ Fabric dyes, dyeing equipment, and accessories. 508–676–3838.

R & J Arts, Inc., 4821 South 1395 East, Salt Lake City, UT 84117: Free information ■ Blueprinting materials and supplies.

Rupert, Gibbon & Spider, Inc., P.O. Box 425, Healdsburg, CA 95448: Free catalog ■ Textile dyes and paints, brushes, resists, silk and cotton fabrics for printing and dyeing, and accessories. 800–442–0455.

Silkpaint Corporation, P.O. Box 18, Waldron, MO 64092: Free brochure ■ French fabric dyes for silk painting. 816–891–7774.

Textile Resources, P.O. Box 90245, Long Beach, CA 90809: Free information ■ Blueprinting materials and supplies.

FABRICS & TRIM

Fabrics

AK Sew & Serge, 1602 6th St. SE, Winter Haven FL 33880: Catalog $2.50 ■ Designer and other fabrics, smocking, Battenberg lace, notions, and accessories. 813–299–3080.

Amici Creative Arts, P.O. Box 163, Rio Vista, CA 94571: Catalog $2 ■ Fabrics, lace and elastic, slip and bra straps, and patterns for making lingerie.

Aurora Silk, 5806 N. Vancouver Ave., Portland, OR 97217: Free brochure; color chart and samples $15 ■ Naturally dyed silk. 503–286–4149.

Baer Fabrics, 515 E. Market St., Louisville, KY 40202: Catalog $2 ■ Ultrasuede, facile, caress, famous designer luxury wools, fashion prints, bridal fabrics, and sewing notions. 502–583–5521.

Bridal-By-The-Yard, P.O. Box 2492, Springfield, OH 45501: Free information ■ Re-embroidered Alencon, Schiffli lace, imported Chantilly and Venice lace, satins, taffeta, organza, millinery supplies, trims, and sewing notions. 513–325–2847.

Bridals International, 45 Albany St., Cazenovia, NY 13035: Catalog $8.50 ■ Imported fabrics and laces for bridal fashions. 800–752–1171.

Calico House, Rt. 4, Box 16, Scottsville, VA 24590: Catalog $3.50 ■ French laces,

English laces, and Swiss eyelets and embroideries

California Bridal Fabrics, 1440 S. Santee St., Los Angeles, CA 90015: Catalog $10 ■ Bridal fabrics. Includes satins, taffeta, French and domestic laces, brocades, sheers, embroideries, trimmings, crowns, and accessories 213–749–6022.

Cerulean Blue, Ltd., P.O. Box 21168, Seattle, WA 98111: Catalog $3 (refundable) ■ Lanaset dyes for wool and silk, instruction books, accessories and equipment, natural fiber fabrics, and supplies for making blueprints on silk. 800–676–8602.

Classic Cloth, The Fountains, 34930 US 19 North, Palm Harbor, FL 34684: Swatches $4 (refundable) ■ Cotton fabrics in 100 percent cotton. 813–785–6593.

Clearbrook Woolen Shop, Box 8, Clearbrook, VA 22624: Free information ■ Wool suitings.

The Cutting Corner, 1815 Freeland Ave., San Angelo, TX 76901: Catalog $10 ■ Fabrics, trims, and lace for bridal and other fashions. 915–942–9780.

D'Anton Leathers, 3079 NE Oasis Rd., West Branch, IA 52358: Catalog $1 ■ Garment leathers. 319–643–2568.

Dazian's, Inc., 2014 Commerce St., Dallas, TX 75201: Free catalog ■ Costume fabrics that include satin brocade, nylon net, organdy, stretch materials, unbleached muslin, lame, and metallics. Other items include trimmings and novelties, leotards, tights, and dance wear. 214–748–3450.

DK Sports, Division Daisy Kingdom, 134 NW 8th Ave., Portland, OR 97209: Free information ■ Rainwear and outerwear fabrics and sewing notions. 800–288–5223.

Exotic Silks, 1959 Leghorn St., Mountain View, CA 94043: Brochure 25¢ ■ Natural silks and scarves in white, solid colors, and printed patterns. 800–845–SILK; 800–345–SILK (in CA).

Fabric Bazaar, P.O. Box 840753, Houston, TX 77284: Information and swatches $3 ■ Silks, designer prints, and other fashion fabrics.

Fabric Center, 485 Electric Ave., Fitchburg, MA 01420: Catalog $2 ■ Decorator fabrics. 508–343–4402.

Fabric Chalet, P.O. Box 25332, Colorado Springs, CO 80936: Samples $5 ■ China silk, cotton velveteen, Swiss lawn, Swiss organdy, English cotton, silk taffeta, Swiss batiste, silk organza, and other fabrics. Other items include Lyn Alexander doll clothes patterns and sewing supplies. 719–632–8862.

Fabric Editions, Ltd., 25 Kenwood Cir., Ste. 4, Franklin, MA 02038: Catalog $3 (refundable) ■ Fabrics in prints and solids. 800–242–5684.

Fabric Gallery, 146 W. Grand River, Williamson, MI 48895: Information $8 ■ Imported and domestic silks, wools, cottons, blends, and synthetics. 517–655–4573.

Fabric Mart, 511 Penn Ave., Sinking Spring, PA 19608: Catalog $5 (refundable) ■ Designer fabrics.

The Fabric Outlet, P.O. Box 2417, South Hamilton, MA 01982: Free information ■ Decorator fabrics. 800–635–9715.

Fabric Shop, 120 N. Seneca St., Shippensburg, PA 17257: Free information with long SASE ■ Antique satins and decorative drapery, slipcover, and upholstery fabrics. Custom makes draperies. 800–233–7012; 800–692–7345 (in PA).

Fabrics by Phone, P.O. Box 309, Walnut Bottom, PA 17266: Brochure $3 ■ Decorator, clothing, and drapery fabrics. Custom makes draperies. 800–233–7012; 800–692–7345 (in PA).

Fabrics Unlimited, 5015 Columbia Pike, Arlington, VA 22204: Free information ■ Imported cotton, silk, wool fabrics, and ultrasuede. 703–671–0324.

Fabric Wholesalers, Inc., P.O. Box 20235, Portland, OR 97220: Free price list ■ Fabrics and sewing notions for clothes, draperies, curtains, and upholstering furniture. 503–666–4511.

Felt People, Box 135, Bloomingdale, NJ 07403: Swatch book $2 (refundable) ■ Wool felt. 800–631–8968; 201–838–1100 (in NJ).

Michel Ferree, P.O. Box 958, Niwot, CO 80544: Samples $12 (refundable) ■ Silk fabrics. 800–488–6170.

Field's Fabrics by Mail, 1695 44th St. SE, Grand Rapids, MI 49508: Free information ■ Genuine ultrasuede and ultraleather and other fabrics. 616–455–4570.

G Street Fabrics, Mail Order Service, 12240 Wilkins Ave., Rockville, MD 20852: Free catalog ■ Decorator, clothing, and drapery fabrics. 301–231–8998.

Gladstone Fabrics, 16 W. 56th St., 2nd Floor, New York, NY 10019: Catalog and swatches $15 ■ Costume fabrics, antique trims, and beading. 212–765–0760.

Green Pepper, 3918 W. 1st Ave., Eugene, OR 97402: Catalog $2 ■ Rainwear and outerwear fabrics, spandex fabrics, sewing notions, and patterns. 503–345–6665.

Gurian Fabrics, 276 5th Ave., New York, NY 10001: Catalog $1 ■ Crewel fabrics. 212–689–9696.

Hambrick's Fabrics, 820 Regal Dr., Huntsville, AL 35801: Free information ■ Corduroy, velvet, cottons, linens, pique, batiste, and other prints. 205–534–4704.

Hancock Fabrics, 3841 Hinkleville Rd., Paducah, KY 42001: Free information ■ Quilting supplies, fabrics, and sewing notions. 800–626–2723.

Home Fabric Mills, Inc., 882 S. Main St., P.O. Box 888, Cheshire, CT 06410: Free brochure ■ Velvets, fabrics for upholstery and draperies, prints, sheers, antique satins, and thermal fabrics. Custom makes draperies. 203–272–3529.

Homespun Weavers, 55 S. 7th St., Emmaus, PA 18049: Brochure 50¢ ■ Fabrics in 100 percent cotton. 215–967–4550.

House of Laird, Box 23778, Lexington, KY 40523: Free information ■ Silk and blends, wool, and rayon suitings. 800–338–4618.

Iowa Pigskin Sales Company, Box 115, Clive, IA 55053: Sample swatches $5 ■ Pigskin leather with velvety suede, smooth full grain, and perforated suede textures. 515–225–2620.

Jehlor Fantasy Fabrics, 730 Andover Park West, Seattle, WA 98188: Catalog $2.50 (refundable) ■ Fabrics and trims for sewing and costume designing. 206–575–8250.

Kagedo, P.O. Box 4593, Seattle, WA 98104: Information and sample swatches $3 ■ Vintage and antique Japanese kimono and obi fabrics. 206–467–9077.

Kalmo Textiles, Inc., 125 W. 45th St., New York, NY 10036: Free information ■ Fabrics and trims for costumes. 212–221–1033.

Labours of Love, 3760 Old Clayburn Rd., Abbotsford, British Colombia, Canada V2S 6B7: Catalog $2 ■ French val lace, Swiss batiste and embroideries, patterns, books, videos, notions, and silk ribbons. 604–853–9132.

Landau Woolen Company, Inc., 239 W. 39th St., New York, NY 10018: Free information ■ Worsted wools, merino jerseys, luxury fibers, rayons, and cottons. 800–553–2292; 212–391–8371 (in NY).

Ledgewood Studio, 6000 Ledgewood Dr., Forest Park, GA 30050: Catalog $2 with long SASE and three 1st class stamps ■ Dress patterns for antique dolls, supplies for recreating period costumes, braids, French laces, silk ribbons, silk taffeta, China silk, Swiss batiste, trims, and sewing notions.

Lee's Mills, 2317 Center Ave., Janesville, WI 53545: Free information ■ Fabrics with long and short pile and light and heavy density. 608–754–0404.

Donna Lee's Sewing Center, 25234 Pacific Hwy. South, Kent, WA 98032: Catalog $4 ■ Swiss batiste, imperial batiste, China silk, silk charmeuse, French val laces, English laces, Swiss embroiders, trims and yardage fabrics, silk ribbon, embroidered ribbon, smocking, French hand-sewing, doll patterns, books, ad sewing supplies. 206–941–9466.

Samuel Lehrer & Company, Inc., 7 Depinedo Ave., Stamford, CT 06902: Free information ■ Wool flannels in three weights, gabardines, linen blends, pinstripes, and plaids for men's and women's clothing. 800–221–2433.

S. Levine & Sons, Inc., P.O. Box 148, Allentown, PA 18105: Free information ■ Fabrics, pound goods, and remnants. 800–523–9452; 215–398–2204 (in PA).

Linen & Lace, 4 Lafayette St., Washington, MO 63090: Catalog $2 ■ Linen and lace fabrics. Custom bed ruffles, canopies, and curtains. 800–332–5223.

The Linen Lady, 5360 H St., Sacramento, CA 95819: Catalog $3 ■ Fabrics and trims. 916–457–6718.

Logan Kits, Rt. 3, P.O. Box 100, Double Springs, AL 35553: Free information with long SASE ■ Lingerie fabrics, lace, and elastic, 205–486–7732.

Looking Good Fashion, Box 58394, Renton, WA 98058: Information $2 with long SASE ■ Lycra fabrics.

Marlene's Decorator Fabrics, 301 Beech St., Hackensack, NJ 07601: Free information ■ Decorator and upholstery fabrics. 800–992–7325.

The Material World, 5700 Monroe St., Sylvania, OH 43560: Swatch collection $7 ■ Imported and domestic silks, wools, cottons, and other fabrics. 419–885–5416.

Mill End Store, 8300 SE McLoughlin Blvd., Portland, OR 97202: Free information ■ Decorator, clothing, and drapery fabrics. 803–236–1234.

Mini-Magic, 3675 Reed Rd., Columbus, OH 43220: Catalog $5 ■ Silks and silk ribbons, cottons and woolens, French laces, Swiss embroideries, and old and tiny buttons.

Monterey Mills Outlet, P.O.Box 271, Janesville, WI 53545: Free information ■ Luxury furs, deep pile fabrics, and stuffing. 800–438–6387; 608–754–8309 (in WI).

Mylar, Inc., P.O. Box 13466, Tallahassee, FL 32317: Catalog $5.50 ■ Fabrics and trims. 800–274–5223.

Nancy's Notions, P.O. Box 683, Beaver Dam, WI 53916: Free catalog ■ Interlock knits, fleece, gabardines, sweater knits, challis, and other fabrics. Other items include sewing notions, threads, books, patterns, and educational videos. 800–833–0690.

Natural Fabrics, 14 E. Cota St., Santa Barbara, CA 93101: Catalog $5 ■ Imported fabrics. 805–965–2572.

New England Quilt Supply, 158 Center St., P.O. Box 633, Pembroke, MA 02359: Free information with long SASE ■ Quilting fabrics, sewing notions, hoops, stands, and other supplies. 617–293–6401.

Nizhonie Fabrics, Inc., P.O. Box 729, Cortez, CO 81321: Free brochure with long SASE ■ Fabrics with silk-screened Indian designs for draperies, dress goods, upholstery, and trims. 303–565–7079.

Norton House, 1836 Country Store Village, Wilmington, VT 05363: Catalog $3 ■ Prints and solids in 100 percent cotton, books on quilting, and other supplies and accessories. 802–464–7213.

Norway Fabric Outlet, Box 703, Norway, ME 04268: Swatches $3 ■ Knit fabrics.

Outdoor Wilderness Fabrics, 16195 Latah Dr., Nampa, ID 83651: Free price list ■ Coated and uncoated nylon fabrics, fleece and blends in coat weights, waterproof Gore-Tex, and Bion II. Includes webbing, patterns, and sewing notions. 208–466–1602.

Pacific States Felt Company, 23850 Clawiter, P.O. Box 5024, Hayward, CA 94540: Free information with long SASE ■ Felt fabrics. 510–783–0277.

Park East Sewing Center, 1358 3rd Ave., New York, NY 10021: Free information ■ Fabrics for sewing and quilting, serger threads, books, and sewing notions. 212–737–1220.

Martha Pullen Company, Inc., 518 Madison St., Huntsville, AL 35801: Catalog $2 ■ Fabrics and trims. 800–547–4176.

Qualin International, P.O. Box 31145, San Francisco, CA 94131: Free information with long SASE ■ Silk fabrics and scarf blanks. Includes natural white silk. 415–647–1329.

Quilt Patch, 208 Brigham St., Marlboro, MA 01752: Catalog $2 ■ Fabrics and quilting supplies. 508–480–0194.

Quilt Patch, 1897 Hanover Pike, Littlestown, PA 17340: Catalog $2 ■ Kits to make quilts, wallhangings, and pillows; prints and solids in 100 percent cotton; calicos and perma-press muslins; and quilting and painting stencils. 717–359–5940.

Quiltwork Patches, P.O. Box 724, Corvallis, OR 97339: Catalog $1 ■ Quilting kits, supplies, tools, stencils, hoops, fabrics, and books. 503–752–4820.

Quintessence, Box 723544, Atlanta, GA 30339: Catalog $3 ■ Exotic leathers, lamb suedes, snakeskin, fabrics, belt buckles, and dressmaker accessories. 404–264–1759.

Rainshed Outdoor Fabrics, 707 NW 11th, Corvallis, OR 97330: Catalog $1 ■ Rainwear, outerwear fabrics, and supplies. Includes cordura, lycra, Thinsulate, polypropylene, Polarfleece, nylons, and Polarplus, sewing notions, webbing, and patterns. 503–753–8900.

Rubin & Green, 290 Grand St., New York, NY 10002: Free information with long SASE ■ Upholstery and decorator fabrics.

Custom makes bedspreads, draperies, and comforters. 212–226–0313.

Donna Salyers' Fabulous-Furs, 700 Madison Ave., Covington, KY 41011: Free brochure ■ Alternatives to natural furs and leather, kits, and patterns. 800–848–4650.

Sawyer Brook Distinctive Fabrics, P.O. Box 909, Boylston, MA 01505: Catalog $5 ■ Natural fiber fabrics, polyesters and blends, wools, silks, and cotton prints. 508–368–3133.

Selwyn Textile Company, Inc., 134 W. 29th St., New York, NY 10001: Free samples and price list ■ Imported linen and cotton canvas, and silk, suede, velveteen, and burlap fabrics. 800–223–3032; 212–564–7992 (in NY).

Serge & Sew, Zachary Square Mall, 11285 96th Ave. North, Maple Grove, MN 55369: Free catalog ■ Serge and sew notions and fabrics. 612–493–2449.

Sew Natural Fabrics by Mail, Rt. 1, Box 428, Middlesex, NC 27557: Swatches $2 ■ French terry, fleece, knits, 100 percent cotton fabrics, denim, corduroy, flannel, and chamois suede. 919–235–2754.

Shama Imports, Box 2900, Farmington Hills, MI 48018: Free catalog and sample swatch ■ Hand-embroidered crewel fabric from India. 313–478–7740.

M. Siegel Company, Inc., 120 Pond St., Ashland, MA 01721: Catalog $2 ■ Luxury leathers and trims. 508–881–5200.

Silks "N" Such, 8224 E. Virginia Ave., Scottsdale, AZ 85257: Catalog $1.50 ■ Swiss batiste, Swiss cotton pique, cotton organdy, velvet and velveteen, silk organza, China silk, Thai silk, taffeta, brocade, French laces, Swiss embroideries, imported trims, French wire edge ribbon, silk ribbon, laces, feathers, ribbons, and buttons. 602–947–5018.

Smocking Bonnet, P.O. Box 555, Cooksville, MD 21723: Catalog series: Big book $5; medium book $3; small book $2 ■ English smocking, French handsewing, fabrics, and laces. 800–524–1678.

Specialties, 236 Cotton Hanlon Rd., Montour Falls, NY 14865: Catalog $2 ■ Lingerie fabrics, sewing notions, and patterns. 607–535–4105.

Stretch & Sew Fabrics, 19725 40th Ave. West, Lynnwood, WA 98036: Free information with long SASE ■ Stretch and sew fabrics, patterns, sewing notions, interfacing, and elastics. 206–774–9678.

Taylor's Cutaways & Stuff, 2802 E. Washington St., Urbana, IL 61801: Brochure $1 ■ Satins, laces, velvet, cottons, felt, calico, trims, sewing notions, polyester squares, other crafts items, books, and patterns.

Testfabrics, Inc., P.O. Box 420, Middlesex, NJ 08846: Free price list ■ Cotton, linen, silk, wool, blend, synthetic, duck, muslin, satin, and twill fabrics. 201–469–6446.

Thai Silks, 252 State St., Los Altos, CA 94022: Free brochure ■ Silk fabrics and linen/cotton and wool gabardine. 800–722–SILK; 800–221–SILK (in CA).

Tioga Mill Outlet, 200 S. Hartman St., York, PA 17403: Information $2 ■ Upholstery, drapery, and other fabrics. Includes damasks, crewel, tapestry, linen, and cotton. 717–843–5139.

The Unique Needle, 539 Blossom Way, Hayward, CA 94541: Brochure $1.50 ■ Imported Swiss fabrics, Swiss embroideries, French laces, other fabrics, trims, patterns, books, and other supplies. 415–727–9130.

Utah Tailoring Fabric Studio, 3080 Washington, Blvd., Ogden, UT 84401: Swatches $5 ■ Imported and domestic fabrics. Includes jacquard, linen, cotton, wool, mohair, ultrasuede, and faile. 801–394–4517.

Utex Trading, 710 9th St., Ste. 5, Niagara Falls, NY 14301: Brochure $1 with long SASE ■ Imported silk fabrics and sewing supplies. 716–282–8211.

Victorian Treasures, 12148 Madison St. NE, Blaine, MN 55434: Catalog $3.50 (refundable) ■ Imported laces, fabrics, Swiss embroideries, notions, and supplies. 612–755–6302.

Warren of Stafford, 645 5th Ave., 17th Floor, New York, NY 10022: Swatches $4 ■ Wool challis, cashmere, camel hair, and other wool fabrics. 212–980–7960.

The Wool Merchant, 2331 Crown Point Executive Dr., Charlotte, NC 28227: Swatches $10 (refundable) ■ Cashmere, camel hair, worsted suitings, linens, and other fabrics. 800–849–WOOL; 704–847–0054 (in NC).

Yardage Shop, 423 Main, Ridgefield, CT 06877: Catalog $1 ■ Ultrasuede and ultraleather, wools, imported cottons and polyester fabrics, Angora wool, cashmere, and others. Includes sewing machine accessories and attachments, monogramming accessories, rufflers, feed attachments, and accessories. 203–438–6100.

Lace & Ribbon

Beggars' Lace, P.O. Box 481223, Denver, CO 80248: Catalog $2 (refundable) ■ Lace-making materials and equipment and lace-making kits. 303–722–5557.

Cindy's Stitches, 588 Roger Williams Ave., Highland Park, IL 60035: Catalog $1 ■ Lace-making and needlework equipment and supplies, and books. 708–433–5183.

Columbine Corner, 11499 E. Evans, Aurora, CO 80014: Free catalog ■ Lace-making and needle crafting supplies and equipment. 303–745–1387.

Creative Trims, Inc., 18 Woodland Dr., Lincroft, NJ 07738: Catalog $1 (refundable) ■ Laces, embroideries, ribbons, venices, bows, and appliques.

The Cutting Corner, 1815 Freeland Ave., San Angelo, TX 76901: Catalog $10 ■ Fabrics, trims, and lace for bridal fashions and other clothes. 915–942–9780.

Elsie's Exquisiques, 513 Broadway, Niles, MI 49120: Free catalog ■ Silk ribbons, trims, novelty ribbons, and ribbon roses. 616–684–7034.

Fabric Barn, 3111 E. Anaheim St., Long Beach, CA 90804: Free catalog ■ Ribbon and lace. 800–544–9374; 310–498–0285 (in CA).

Famous Trading Company, 237 W. 37th St., New York, NY 10018: Free catalog ■ Laces and trims, narrow elastic, jacket zippers, ribbons, plastic scarves and doilies, velcro hooks and loop tape, sequins, and other notions. 800–326–6878; 212–768–9647 (in NY).

The Lacemaker, Lace and Needle Art, 7721 230th SW, Edmonds, WA 98026: Catalog $3 ■ Lace-making tools and supplies. 206–670–1644.

Laces & Lacemaking, 3201 E. Lakeshore Dr., Tallahassee, FL 32312: Catalog $3 ■ Lace-making and sewing supplies, patterns, books, and kits. 904–385–5093.

Laces of the World, P.O. Box 1118, Bellmore, NY 11710: Catalog $3 ■ Polyester lace.

LACIS, 2982 Adeline St., Berkeley, CA 94703: Free information ■ Hairpin lace looms.

The Lavender Rose, P.O. Box 3096, Bellevue, WA 98009: Free catalog with two 1st class stamps ■ Custom lace and embroidery, patterns, kits, and supplies.

The Ribbon Outlet, Inc., 3434 Rt 22 West, Ste 110, Summerville, NJ 08876: Free catalog ■ Over 3000 varieties of ribbons and trims. 800–766–BOWS.

Robbin's Bobbins, Rt. 1, Box 1736, Mineral Bluff, GA 30559: Catalog $1 ■ Pillows, books, pins, threads, and lace-making supplies. 404–374–6916.

Sheu's, 11303 Attingham Ln., Glenn Dale, MD 20769: Free catalog ■ Ready-made lace collars.

Snowgoose, P.O. Box 27805, Denver, CO 80227: Catalog $1 ■ Lace-making kits. 303–934–5168.

Van Sciver Bobbin Lace, 130 Cascadilla Pk., Ithaca, NY 14850: Free catalog with two 1st class stamps ■ Lace-making supplies. 607–277–0498.

Warscokins, 17930 Magnolia, Fountain Valley, CA 92708: Catalog $3.50 ■ Lace, ribbon, sewing notions, accessories, and supplies. 800–225–6356; 714–962–8991 (in CA).

Windsor Vest, P.O. Box 620572, Littleton, CO 80162: Free catalog with two 1st class stamps ■ Custom lace and embroidery patterns, kits, and supplies.

The Woolery, RD 1, Genoa, NY 13071: Free brochure with long SASE ■ Bobbin lace supplies from Belgium. 315–497–1542.

YLI Corporation, P.O. Box 109, Provo, UT 84601: Information $2.50 ■ Silk, spark organdy, synthetic silk, and fancy ribbons; silk thread; and other craft supplies. 800–854–1932.

FANS

AAA-All Factory, Inc., 241 Cedar, Abilene, TX 79601: Brochure $2 (refundable) ■ Ceiling fans and vacuum cleaners. 915–677–1311.

Casablanca Fan Company, 450 N. Baldwin Park Blvd., City of Industry, CA 91746: Free information ■ Ceiling fans. 800–759–3267.

Homestead Products, 114 14th St., Ramona, CA 92065: Free information ■ Ceiling fans. 800–833–8833.

Hunter Fan Company, 2500 Fisco Ave., Memphis, TN 38114: Brochure $1 ■ Ceiling fans, remote control units, lighting fixtures, and electronic thermostats. 901–745–9286.

FAUCETS & PLUMBING FIXTURES

American Standard, Inc., P.O. Box 6820, Piscataway, NJ 08854: Free information ■ Bathroom and kitchen faucets and other plumbing fixtures. 800–821–7700.

Antique Baths & Kitchens, 2220 Carlton Way, Santa Barbara, CA 93109: Brochure $2 ■ Reproduction Victorian-style plumbing fixtures. 805–962–8598.

Chicago Faucet Company, 2100 S. Nuclear Dr., Des Plaines, IL 60018: Free information ■ Decorative bathroom plumbing fixtures. 708–694–4400.

Conservation Concepts, 932 W. 9th St., Upland, CA 91786: Free information ■ Easy-to-install water-saving toilet tank control. 800–825–2522.

Delta Faucet Company, 55 E. 111th St., P.O. Box 40980, Indianapolis, IN 46280: Free information ■ Solid brass plumbing fixtures. Includes washerless faucets. 800–345–3358.

Elkay Manufacturing Company, 2222 Camden Ct., Oak Brook, IL 60521: Free information ■ Faucets with retractable nozzles. 708–574–8484.

Grohe America, Inc., 900 Lively Blvd., Wood Dale, IL 60191: Free information ■ Decorator faucets for kitchen sinks. 708–350–2600.

Kohler Company, Kohler, WI 53041: Catalog $8 ■ Solid brass faucets and other plumbing fixtures. 800–4KOHLER.

MAC the Antique Plumber, 885 57th St., Sacramento, CA 95819: Catalog $6 (refundable) ■ Plumbing fixtures in a 1900s style. 916–454–4507.

Moen, Inc., 377 Woodland Ave., Elyria, OH 44036: Free information ■ Single- and double-handle faucets for bathrooms and kitchens. 800–347–6636.

The Renovator's Supply, Renovator's Old Mill, Millers Falls, MA 01349: Free catalog ■ Plumbing fixtures parts, lamps, lighting fixtures, and hardware. 413–659–2211.

Watercolors, Inc., Garrison on Hudson, NY 10524: Catalog $1 ■ European-style faucets and accessories. 914–424–3327.

FENCES & GATES

Architectural Iron Company, Schocopee Rd., Box 126, Milford, PA 18337: Brochure $4 ■ Reproduction cast-iron 18th- and 19th-century gates, fences, and fountains. 717–296–7722.

California Redwood Association, 405 Enfrente Dr., Ste. 200, Novato, CA 94949: Free information ■ Redwood fences. 415–382–0662.

Cassidy Brothers Forge, Inc., US Rt. 1, Rowley, MA 01969: Brochure $1 ■ Ready-to-use and custom fences, gates, balconies, railings, and spiral stairways. 508–948–7303.

Cat Fence-In, P.O. Box 795, Sparks, NV 89432: Free information ■ Easy-to-install non-electric, narrow netting barrier to prevent cats from climbing over fences and up trees. 702–359–4575.

CCX Fantastic, Inc., 27565 Fantastic Lane, Castaic, CA 91310: Free information ■ Solid wood fencing with polyethylene covering. 800–521–3633; 805–257–3450 (in CA).

Central Tractor Farm & Family Center, 3915 Delaware, Des Moines, IA 50313: Free catalog ■ Fencing supplies. 800–247–1760; 800–247–7508 (in IA).

Color Guard Fence Company, P.O. Box 28, Sheboygan Falls, WI 53085: Free information ■ Custom vinyl fencing. 414–467–8640.

Custom Ironworks, Inc., P.O. Box 180, Union, KY 41091: Brochure $2 ■ Reproduction cast- and wrought-iron fencing in Victorian and other styles. 606–384–4122.

Electric Fence Company, 9735–A Bethel Rd., Frederick, MD 21701: Free price list ■ Fences for animal control. 301–694–6072.

Empire Fencing Systems, 913 Bowman St., Mansfield, OH 44905: Free information ■ Galvanized steel fences. 419–755–3398.

English Garden, Inc., 652 Glenbrook Rd., Stamford, CT 06906: Free information ■ Fences. 203–348–3048.

Freedom Fence, Inc., Box 02061, River Rd., North Adams, MA 01247: Free information ■ Underground fence that prevents pets leaving the yard. 800–828–9089.

Furman Lumber, Inc., P.O. Box 130, Nutting Lake, MA 01865: Free information ■ Factory-assembled picket fences, in heights of 4, 5, and 6 feet. 800–843–9663.

Gallagher Spring-Tight Power Fence, Brookside Industries, Inc., Tunbridge, VT 05077: Free catalog ■ Fencing supplies for power electric fences. Keeps predators out and livestock in. 800–832–9482; 802–889–3737 (in VT).

The Garden Gate, P.O. Box 1117, Cedar Ridge, CA 95924: Free brochure ■ Ready-to-paint gates. 916–272–8109.

Gloucester Street Gate Company, P.O. Box 281, Salisbury, MD 21803: Free brochure ■ Traditional wood gates and hardware. 301–546–4384.

Invisible Fencing, 724 W. Lancaster Ave., Wayne, PA 19087: Free information ■ Invisible radio barrier fence for pets.

Jerith Manufacturing Company, Inc., 3939 G. St., Philadelphia, PA 19124: Free brochure ■ Rust-proof, high-strength aluminum alloy fences with a baked on enamel finish. 800–344–2242.

Moultrie Manufacturing, P.O. Drawer 1179, Moultrie, GA 31776: Catalog $1 ■ Reproduction of "Old South" gates and fences. 800–841–8674.

Northwestern Steel & Wire Company, Communications Services, 121 Wallace St., Sterling, IL 61081: Free information ■ Fences. 815–625–2500.

Nostalgia, Inc., 307 Stiles Ave., Savannah, GA 31401: Free information ■ Gates and fences. 912–232–2324.

Saratoga Fence Company, RD 3, Ballston Spa, NY 12020: Free information ■ Vinyl fencing supplies. 518–885–1882.

Southeastern Wood Products Company, P.O. Box 113, Griffin, GA 30224: Free brochure ■ Wire and wood fences, plant supports, and cold frames. 800–722–7486.

Stewart Iron Works Company, 20 N. 18th St., P.O. Box 2612, Covington, KY 41012: Catalog $2 ■ Custom Victorian-style fences and gates. 606–431–1985.

Triple Crown Fence, P.O. Box 2000, Milford, IN 46542: Free booklet ■ Vinyl fencing supplies. 219–658–9442.

West Virginia Fence Corporation, US Rt. 219, Lindside, WV 24951: Free catalog ■ Permanent and portable electric fences for animal control. 800–356–5458; 304–753–4387 (in WV).

FENCING

American Fencers Supply Company, 1180 Folsom St., San Francisco, CA 94103: Free information ■ Gloves, masks, shoes, uniforms, blades, epees, foils, rapiers, and sabers. 415–863–7911.

Blade Fencing Equipment, Inc., 212 W. 15th St., New York, NY 10011: Free information ■ Gloves, masks, shoes, uniforms, blades, epees, foils, rapiers, and sabers. 212–620–0114.

Genesport Industries, Ltd., Hokkaido Karate Equipment Manufacturing Company, 150 King St., Montreal, Quebec, Canada H3C 2P3: Free information ■ Gloves, masks, uniforms, blades, and sabers for fencers. 514–861–1856.

Renaissance, Ltd., 3170 Hwy. 60, P.O. Box 418, Jackson, WI 53037: Free information ■ Gloves, masks, uniforms and shoes, blades, epees, foils, rapiers, and sabers. 414–677–4113.

FIREPLACES
Accessories & Tools

The Adams Company, 100 E. 4th St., Dubuque, IA 52001: Free catalog ■ Solid brass and black cast iron fireplace tool sets, baskets, screens, andirons, fire backs and lighters, and fenders. 800–553–3012.

An Affair of the Hearth, P.O. Box 95174, Oklahoma City, OK 73143: Free catalog ■ Fireplaces and accessories. 800–755–5488.

Danny Alessandro & Edwin Jackson, 307 E. 60th St., New York, NY 10022: Catalog $5 ■ Antique and reproduction fireplace accessories and 18th-century mantels in limestone, wood, and marble. 212–421–1928.

Art Marble & Stone, 5862 Peachtree Industrial Blvd., Atlanta, GA 30341: Free brochure ■ Glass doors, tools, mantels, and gas logs with glowing embers, for natural or LP gas. 800–476–0298.

Bona Decorative Hardware, 3073 Madison Rd., Cincinnati, OH 45209: Catalog $2 ■ Solid brass hardware and accessories for fireplaces, bathrooms, doors, cabinets, furniture, and kitchens. 513–321–7877.

Century Fireplace Furnishings, Inc., P.O. Box 248, Wallingford, CT 06492: Free information ■ Fireplace screens. 800–284–4328.

Country Iron Foundry, P.O. Box 600, Paoli, PA 19301: Catalog $2 ■ Handcrafted Colonial-style and other firebacks for gas logs and standard fireplaces. 215–296–7122.

Fireplace Accessories, Inc., 1116 Mills Lane Blvd., Savannah, GA 31405: Free information ■ Fireplace furnishings. 800–826–0634; 800–222–2508 (in GA).

Fireside Distributors, Inc., 4013 Atlantic Ave., Raleigh, NC 27604: Free information ■ Fireplace accessories. 800–333–3473; 203–265–1686 (in NC).

Hearth & Home, 3242 Severn at 17th St., Metairie, LA 70002: Free catalog ■ Fireplace accessories, mailboxes, switch plates, and gifts. 504–454–8907.

Lemee's Fireplace Equipment, 815 Bedford St., Bridgewater, MA 02324: Catalog $2 (refundable) ■ Fireplace equipment and accessories. 508–697–2672.

Liberty Forge, 40128 Industrial Park North, Georgetown, TX 78626: Free information ■ Fireplace screens. 512–869–2830.

New England Firebacks, 161 Main St., P.O. Box 268, Woodbury, CT 06798: Free information ■ Solid, hand-cast iron fireback reproductions. 203–263–5737.

Robert H. Peterson Company, 530 N. Baldwin Park Blvd., City of Industry, CA 91744: Free catalog ■ Stone built-in and outdoor barbecues, handcrafted fireplace accessories, ceramic radiant heat gas logs. 818–369–5085.

Plow & Hearth, 301 Madison Rd., P.O. Box 830, Orange, VA 22960: Free catalog ■ Fireplace accessories, gardening tools, birdhouses and feeders, porch and lawn furniture, and other home accessories. 800–866–6072.

Portland Willamette, P.O. Box 13097, Portland, OR 97213: Catalog 25¢ ■ Fireplace screens. 503–288–7511.

Seymour Manufacturing Company, Inc., 500 N. Broadway, P.O. Box 248, Seymour, IN 47274: Free brochure ■ Fireplace tool sets, stove and fireplace repair accessories, brooms, bellows, and fire-starting supplies. 812–522–3320.

Sierra-Tonsina, Ltd., 18620 Old Hwy. 99 SW, Rochester, WA 98579: Free brochure ■ Solid brass trivets, kettles, fireplace tools, and bellows. 206–273–8388.

Fireplaces & Fireplace Kits

Fondis, 334 Raritan Center Pkwy., P.O. Box 6444, Edison, NJ 08818: Free brochure ■ Fireplace inserts. 201–225–7707.

Heat-N-Glo, 6665 W. Hwy. 13, Savage, MN 55378: Free information ■ Fireplaces and accessories. 800–669–4328.

Jotul USA, Inc., P.O. Box 1157, Portland, ME 04104: Free catalog ■ Stoves and fireplaces. 207–797–5912.

Majestic, 1000 E. Market St., Huntington, IN 46750: Free information ■ Fireplaces and accessories. 800–525–1898; 219–356–8000 (in IN).

Nu-Tec Incorporated, P.O. Box 908, East Greenwich, RI 02818: Free brochure ■ Wood burning stoves and fireplace inserts. 800–822–0600.

Sierra West Radiant Heat, P.O. Box 814, Rancho Cordova, CA 95741: Free brochure ■ Outdoor portable fireplace. 800–777–2915.

Superior Fireplace, 4325 Artesia Ave., Fullerton, CA 92633: Free information ■ Fireplaces and accessories. 714–521–7302.

TEMCO Fireplaces, P.O. Box 1184, Nashville, TN 37202: Free information ■ Fireplace kits, pre-cut marble fixings, hearth extensions, and traditional wood mantels. 615–297–7551.

Tulikivi Natural Stone Fireplaces, 30 Glen Rd., West Lebanon, NH 03784: Free brochure ■ Baking ovens, cookstoves, and natural stone fireplaces. 800–843–3473; 804–831–2228 (in VA).

Vermont Castings, Inc., 7095 Prince St., Randolph, VT 05060: Free information ■ Energy-efficient, easy-to-install fireplaces. 800–227–8683.

Mantels

Danny Alessandro & Edwin Jackson, 307 E. 60th St., New York, NY 10022: Catalog $5 ■ Antique and reproduction fireplace accessories and 18th-century mantels in limestone, wood, and marble. 212–421–1928.

Architectural Paneling, Inc., 979 3rd Ave., New York, NY 10022: Catalog $10 ■ Hand-carved wood mantels and moldings. 212–371–9632.

Brill & Walker Associates, Inc., P.O. Box 731, Sparta, NJ 07871: Catalog $3 ■ Stock and custom handcrafted English-style mantels. 201–729–8876.

Colonial Woodworks, P.O. Box 10612, Raleigh, NC 27605: Catalog $5 ■ Hand-crafted fireplace mantels. 919–833–1681.

Dovetail Woodworking, 836 Middle Rd., East Greenwich, RI 02818: Catalog $5 ■ Fireplace mantels, wide pine flooring, and colonial and Victorian entry ways. 401–885–2403.

Driwood Ornamental Wood Moulding, P.O. Box 1729, Florence, SC 29503: Catalog $6 ■ Custom mantels, embossed wood molding, raised paneling, curved stairs, and custom doors. 803–669–2478.

Maizefield Mantels, P.O. Box 336, Port Townsend, WA 98368: Free brochure ■ Traditional and custom mantels with carved ornamentation. 206–385–6789.

Mountain Woodcarvers, P.O. Drawer R, Branson, MO 65616: Free information ■ Handcarved mantels and fireplace accessories. 417–334–1843.

Plantation Mantels, 220 N. Carrollton, New Orleans, LA 70119: Catalog $2.25 ■ Handcrafted wood mantels. 504–486–6822.

Readybuilt Products Company, 1701 McHenry St., Baltimore, MD 21223: Free brochure ■ Hand-carved wood mantels in American and English styles, hand-carved mantel shelves, electric/gas fireplace logs, facings, and fireplaces. 410–233–5833.

Roman Marble Company, 120 W. Kinzie, Chicago, IL 60610: Free brochure ■ Victorian, French, and English-style mantels; and pedestals and statuary. 312–337–2217.

FIRE SAFETY

Escape Ladders

American LaFrance, Box 6159, Charlottesville, VA 22906: Free information ■ Escape ladders. 804–973–4361.

Fire Extinguishers

American LaFrance, Box 6159, Charlottesville, VA 22906: Free information ■ Fire extinguishers. 804–973–4361.

American Safety Products, 631 Mimosa Dr. NW, Cleveland, TN 37311: Free information ■ Fire extinguishers. 615–478–1126.

Black & Decker, 6 Armstrong Rd., Shelton, CT 06484: Free information ■ Fire extinguishers. 203–926–3000.

Fireboy Halon Systems, P.O. Box 152, Grand Rapids, MI 49501: Free information ■ Fire extinguishers for boats. 616–454–8337.

First Alert, 780 McClure Rd., Aurora, IL 60404: Free information ■ Fire extinguishers. 708–851–7330.

Walter Kidde, Division Kidde, Inc., 1394 S. 3rd St., Mebane, NC 27302: Free information ■ Fire extinguishers. 919–563–5911.

Twenty First Century International Fire Equipment & Services Corporation, 3249 W. Story Rd., Irving, TX 75038: Free information ■ Automatic electric and gas-operated stove-top extinguishers.

Smoke Detectors

Black & Decker, 6 Armstrong Rd., Shelton, CT 06484: Free information ■ Smoke alarms. 203–926–3000.

First Alert, 780 McClure Rd., Aurora, IL 60404: Free information ■ Smoke alarms. 708–851–7330.

Jameson Home Products, Inc., 2820 Thatcher Rd., Downers Grove, IL 60515: Free information ■ Smoke alarms. 708–963–2850.

Radio Shack, Division Tandy Corporation, 1500 One Tandy Center, Fort Worth, TX 76102: Free information ■ Smoke alarms. 817–390–3700.

Sanyo Electric, 200 Riser Rd., Little Ferry, NJ 07643: Free information with long SASE ■ Electrostatic air cleaner/ionizer with an automatic smoke sensor. 201–641–2333.

Ultratec, Inc., 6442 Normandy Ln., Madison, WI 53719: Free information ■ Smoke detector for hearing-impaired persons. 608–273–0707 (voice/TDD).

Universal Security Instruments, 10324 S. Dolfield Rd., Owings Mills, MD 21117: Free information ■ Smoke alarms and wireless home security systems. 410–363–3000.

Sprinkler Systems

Central Sprinkler Company, 1100 Howell Ave., Anaheim, CA 92805: Free information ■ Residential sprinkler systems. 800–456–9416.

Grinnell Corporation, 3 Tyco Park, Exeter, NH 03833: Free information ■ Residential sprinkler systems. 603–778–9200.

FIREWORKS

Because regulations governing the purchase and use of fireworks varies from state to state, consumers should check the regulations before ordering from the companies listed below. Consumers should also make sure that they buy fireworks only from licensed or certified vendors who meet applicable requirements governing the sale of fireworks. Using fireworks illegally can result in substantial fines and possible jail sentences.

"Backyard" Fireworks

ACE Fireworks, P.O. Box 221, Conneaut, OH 44030: Catalog $1 ■ Class C "backyard" fireworks. 216–593–4751.

B.J. Alan, 555 W. Federal St., Columbiana, OH 44408: Catalog $1 (refundable) ■ Class C "backyard" fireworks at discount prices. 800–321–9071.

Alonzo Fireworks, 12 Country Rd. 75, Mechansville, NY 12118: Free information ■ Class C "backyard" fireworks. 518–664–9994.

Amazing Fireworks, 852 Drift Rd., Westport, MA 02790: Free information ■ Class C "backyard" fireworks. 508–636–2221.

Bethany Sales Company, P.O. Box 248, Bethany, IL 61914: Free information ■ Class C "backyard" fireworks. 217–665–3396.

Blue Angel Fireworks, P.O. Box 26, Columbiana, OH 44408: Free catalog ■ Class C "backyard" fireworks. 800–321–9071; 216–482–5595 (in OH).

Fireworks of America, 8550 Rt. 224, Deerfield, OH 44411: Free catalog ■ Class C "backyard" fireworks. 800–423–1776.

Fireworks Unlimited, P.O. Box 764, Plainsboro, NJ 08536: Free information ■ Class C "backyard" fireworks. 609–799–9475.

Kellner's Fireworks, P.O. Box 67, Oil City, PA 16301: Free information with long SASE ■ Class C "backyard" fireworks. 800–458–6000.

Neptune Fireworks Company, Inc., 768 E. Dania Beach Blvd., P.O. Box 398, Dania, FL 33004: Free catalog ■ Class C "backyard" fireworks. 800–835–5236; 305–920–6770 (in FL).

New England Fireworks, P.O. Box 3504, Stamford, CT 06905: Free information with long SASE ■ Class C "backyard" fireworks. 203–324–5159.

Olde Glory Fireworks, P.O. Box 2863, Rapid City, SD 57709: Free catalog ■ Class C "backyard" fireworks. 800–843–8758.

Old Southern Trading Post, RD 1, Allendale, SC 29810: Free information ■ Class C "backyard" fireworks. 803–584–3981.

Phantom Fireworks, P.O. Box 66, Columbiana, OH 44408: Free information ■ Class C "backyard" fireworks. 800–777–1699.

Premium Fireworks, 207 Pike St., P.O. Box 703, Covington, KY 41011: Free information with long SASE ■ Class C "backyard" fireworks. 606–431–0606.

Tall Paul, Inc., P.O. Box 248, Eagleville, MO 64442: Catalog $3 ■ Class C "backyard" fireworks. 800–525–4461; 816–867–3354 (in MO).

Fireworks Display Specialists

Atlas Enterprises, Inc., Rt. 25, Box 93 AE, Fort Worth, TX 76135: Free information ■ Class B display fireworks. 817–237–3372.

Fireworks by Grucci, One Grucci Ln., Brookhaven, NY 11719: Free information ■ Class B display fireworks. 516–286–0088.

Kellner's Fireworks, P.O. Box 67, Oil City, PA 16301: Free information ■ Class B display fireworks. 800–458–6000.

Melrose Fireworks, P.O. Box 89, Mokena, IL 60448: Free information ■ Class B display fireworks. 708–349–6677.

Pyro Spectaculars, P.O. Box 2329, Rialto, CA 92377: Free information ■ Class B display fireworks. 714–874–1644.

Ruggieri USA, Inc., 1032 31st St. NW, Washington, DC 20007: Free information ■ Class B display fireworks. 202–337–6556.

Southern International, P.O. Box 8340, Atlanta, GA 30306: Free information ■ Class B display fireworks. 404–924–1777.

Zambelli Internationale, P.O. Box 801, New Castle, PA 16103: Free information ■ Class B display fireworks. 800–245–0397.

Fireworks Memorabilia

American Fireworks News, Star Route Box 30, Dingmans Ferry, PA 18328: Free brochure ■ Books, manuals, and other information for people who collect and research fireworks and fireworks memorabilia. 717–828–8417.

Collectors Trading Service, 1849 E. Guadalupe, #101–103, Tempe, AZ 85283: Price list $1.50 ■ Fireworks collectibles and memorabilia, patriotic paper Americana, labels, posters, catalogs, advertising items, empty boxes, signs, and other items. Does not sell live fireworks. 602–839–7842.

Dennis C. Manochio, Curator, 4th of July Americana & Fireworks Museum, P.O. Box 2010, Saratoga, CA 95070: Free information ■ Buys, sells, and trades old fireworks catalogs, packages and boxes of fireworks, literature, toys, and related items. 800–456–5732; 408–996–1963 (in CA).

FISHING & FLY-TYING

Abel Reels, 165 Avlador St., Camarillo, CA 93010: Free brochure ■ Precision-engineered fly reels. 805–484–8789.

Abu-Garcia, 21 Law Dr., Fairfield, NJ 07004: Free catalog ■ Saltwater spinning reels and rods, plug and bait casting reels, spin casting reels, and fishing lines. 201–227–7666.

Akin Tackle & Technologies, Box 765, Claremore, OK 74018: Free information ■ Float fishig supplies. 918–341–8383.

All Star Graphite Rods, Inc., 9750 Whithorn, Houston, TX 77095: Free catalog ■ Plug and bait casting rods. 713–855–9603.

Ande, Inc., 1310 53rd St., West Palm Beach, FL 33407: Free brochure ■ Fishing lines. 407–842–2474.

George Anderson's Yellowstone Angler, Hwy. 89 South, P.O. Box 660, Livingston, MT 59047: Free catalog ■ Tackle and fly-fishing supplies and fishing and hunting videos. 406–222–7130.

Angler's Covey, Inc., 917 W. Colorado Ave., Colorado Springs, CO 80905: Catalog $2 ■ Fly-fishing, bass fishing, saltwater fishing supplies; fishing and hunting videos; and leather wading boots in sizes 6 to 15. 719–471–2984.

Angler's Sport Group/Airflo, 6619 Oak Orchard Rd., Elba, NY 14058: Free information ■ Fishing lines and leaders. 800–332–3937.

Angler's Workshop, Box 1044, Woodland, WA 98674: Free catalog ■ Rods, tackle, reels, supplies; other equipment; and fishing and hunting videos. 206–225–9445.

Bagley Baits, P.O. Box 810, Winter Haven, FL 33882: Free information ■ Crayfish-simulating lures for panfish and smallmouths. 813–294–4271.

The Bagmaker, 1515 N. 13th St., Boise, ID 83702: Free information ■ Tackle bags. 208–343–3904.

Dan Bailey's Fly Shop, P.O. Box 1019, Livingston, MT 59047: Free catalog ■ Tackle and fly-tying supplies, fishing and hunting videos, and other accessories. 800–356–4052.

The Bass Pond, P.O. Box 82, Littleton, CO 80160: Catalog $1 ■ Flies, fly-tying components, fly rods, reels, lines, leaders, floats, and clothing.

Bass Pro Shops, 1935 S. Campbell, Springfield, MO 65898: Catalog $3 ■ Float fishing equipment, fishing supplies and accessories, and equipment for other outdoor activities. 800–BASS–PRO.

Bead Tackle, 600 Main St., Monroe, CT 06468: Catalog $1 ■ Spinning rods and saltwater lures. 203–459–1213.

Bob Beale Custom Tackle, 1100 NW 53rd St., Bay 2, Fort Lauderdale, FL 33334: Brochure $1 ■ Handcrafted custom rods. 800–833–RODS.

L.L. Bean, Freeport, ME 04033: Free catalog ■ Fly-fishing, bass fishing, saltwater fishing supplies; fly-tying accessories; and fishing and hunting videos. 800–221–4221.

Berkeley, Inc., One Berkeley Dr., Spirit Lake, IA 51360: Free catalog ■ Spinning rods, plug and bait casting rods, saltwater rods, fishing and fly lines, and fly leaders. 800–237–5539; 712–336–1520 (in IA).

Best American Duffel, Box 71, Marine on St. Croix, MN 55047: Free information ■ Tackle bags. 800–424–BAGS.

Big Foot Mountaineering, 2500 New Stine Rd., Bakersfield, CA 93309: Free information ■ Fly fishing supplies and tackle. 805–834–4314.

Bitterroot River Products, 20390 Carlton Creek Rd., Florence, MT 59833: Free information ■ Tackle bags. 800–523–9834.

Blue Fox Tackle, 645 N. Emerson, Cambridge, MN 55008: Free information ■ High-speed trolling lures. 612–869–3402.

Blue Ribbon Flies, Box 1037, West Yellowstone, MT 59758: Free catalog ■ Fly-tying materials.

B'n'M Pole Company, Box 231, West Point, MS 39773: Free information ■ Graphite and fiberglass poles and rods for crappie fishing. 800–647–6363; 601–494–5092 (in MS).

Bomber Bait, c/o PRADCO, Box 1587, Fort Smith, AR 72901: Free information ■ High-speed trolling lures. 800–422–FISH.

Browning Company, Dept. C006, Morgan, UT 84050: Catalog $2 ■ Saltwater spinning reels, spinning rods, and plug and bait casting reels and rods. 800–333–3288.

Burke Fishing Lures, 1969 S. Airport Rd., Traverse City, MI 49684: Free information ■ Large-mouth bass and pike lures. 616–947–5010.

Cabela's, 812 13th Ave., Sidney, NE 69160: Free catalog ■ Float fishing supplies, other fishing accessories, and equipment and

supplies for hunting and outdoor activities. 800–237–4444.

Capt. Harry's Fishing Supplies, 100 NE 11th St., Miami, FL 33132: Catalog $3 ■ Supplies for fly-fishing, saltwater fishing, and bass fishing; fly-tying supplies; and fishing and hunting videos. 305–374–4661.

Class Tackle, Box 837, Minden, LA 71058: Free information ■ Float-fishing supplies. 318–371–2151.

Cold Spring Anglers, Box 633, Boiling Springs, PA 17007: Free catalog ■ Flies, tackle, and fly-tying materials and tools. 800–248–8937.

The Colorado Angler, 1457 Nelson, Lakewood, CO 80215: Free information ■ Fly fishing supplies and video tapes on fishing and hunting. 303–232–8298.

Compleat Angler, 1320 Marshall Lane, Helena, MT 59601: Free information ■ Tackle bags. 406–442–1973.

Cortland Line Company, P.O. Box 5588, Cortland, NY 13045: Free catalog ■ Fly reels, fly lines, and fly leaders. 607–756–2851.

Countrysport, 415 S. Union, Traverse City, MI 49684: Free information ■ Fly fishing supplies and video tapes on fishing and hunting. 616–929–3252.

Custom Jigs & Spins, 1504 Highwood, Pekin, IL 61554: Free information ■ Ice fishing tackle.

Daiwa Corporation, 7421 Chapman Ave., Garden Grove, CA 92641: Catalog $1 ■ Saltwater spinning reels, spinning rods, plug and bait casting reels and bait rods, saltwater reels and rods, and spin casting reels. 714–895–6645.

Dame Juliana, Inc., 1261 Grandview Ave., Columbus, OH 43212: Free information ■ Fly fishing supplies and video tapes on fishing and hunting. 614–488–4844.

Dan's Fly Shop, Box 118, Lake City, CO 81235: Catalog $1 ■ Fly-tying supplies and video tapes on fishing and hunting. 303–944–2281.

Dan's Tackle Service, 2237 W. Mclean Ave., Chicago, IL 60647: Free information ■ Fly fishing supplies, tackle, and video tapes on fishing and hunting. 312–276–5562.

East Fork Fly Fishing Store, 2192 Dupont Dr., Irvine, CA 92715: Free catalog ■ Rods,

reels, flies, and fly-tying and rod-building materials. 714–724–8840.

EdgeWater Fishing Products, 35 N. 1000 West, Clearfield, UT 84015: Free catalog ■ Handmade flies and components for custom fly-tying. 800–584–7647.

Egger's, P.O. Box 1344, Cumming, GA 30130: Free catalog ■ Fly-tying supplies, tools, and net kits.

Fenwick Corporation, 5242 Argosy Dr., Huntington Beach, CA 92649: Catalog $1 ■ Saltwater spinning reels, spinning rods, plug and bait casting rods, and fly rods. 714–897–1066.

The Fish Hawk, 283 Buckhead Ave., Atlanta, GA 30305: Free information ■ Fly fishing supplies, tackle, and video tapes on fishing and hunting. 404–237–3473.

J. Kennedy Fisher, Inc., P.O. Box 3147, Carson City, NV 89702: Free information ■ Fishing rods. Includes 34 travel models, 79 blank models, and 79 kits. 702–246–5220.

Fishing Tackle Grab Bag, 5521 N. State Rd., Davison, MI 48423: Free information ■ Fly fishing supplies and tackle. 313–653–4777.

Flambeau, P.O. Box 745, Manistee, MI 49660: Free information ■ Tackle boxes.

Flies Only, 78 North Rt. 303, Congers, NY 10920: Free catalog ■ Handcrafted flies.

The Fly Box, 923 SE 3rd St., Bend, OR 97702: Catalog $1 ■ Fly fishing supplies and video tapes on fishing and hunting. 503–388–3330.

Flyfisher's Paradise, Pike St., P.O. Box 448, Lemont, PA 16851: Catalog 50¢ ■ Fly-fishing and bass fishing supplies and video tapes on fishing and hunting. 814–234–4189.

The Fly Fisher's Place, 230 Main St., P.O. Box 1179, Sisters, OR 97759: Free information ■ Fly fishing supplies and video tapes on fishing and hunting. 503–549–FISH.

Fly Fishing Outfitters #2, 463 Bush St., San Francisco, CA 94108: Free information ■ Fly fishing supplies, tackle, and video tapes on fishing and hunting. 415–781–3474.

The Fly Rod Shop, Rt. 100 South, Box 960, Stowe, VT 05672: Free information ■ Fly fishing supplies, tackle, and video tapes on fishing and hunting. 802–253–7346.

The Fly Shop, 4140 Churn Creek Rd., Redding, CA 96002: Free information ■ Fly fishing supplies, tackle, and video tapes on fishing and hunting. 800–669–3474.

Frying Pan Anglers, 6692 Frying Pan Rd., Basalt, CO 81621: Free information ■ Fly fishing supplies and video tapes on fishing and hunting. 303–927–3441.

Gander Mountain, Inc., P.O. Box 248, Gander Mountain, Wilmot, WI 53192: Free catalog ■ Outdoor sports equipment and clothing for fishing, hunting, and camping. 800–558–9418.

Gudebrod, Box 357, Pottsdown, PA 19464: Free information: Fishing lines. ■ 215–327–4050.

Hackle & Tackle, 1 W. Bridge St., Saugerties, NY 12477: Free information ■ Rod building supplies. 914–246–0245.

Harrison-Hohe Industries, Inc., 200 Wilson St., Port Jefferson Station, NY 11776: Free catalog ■ Fishing lures. 800–852–0925.

Hildebrandt Corporation, Box 50, Logansport, IN 46947: Free information ■ Fly-fishing supplies and unweighted fly-rod spinners and spoons. 219–722–4455.

Hi-Line Enterprise, Inc., 14 Extra St., Guelph, Ontario, Canada N1H 1Y9: Free information ■ Float-fishing supplies. 519–837–3095.

Hi-Seas Industries, Inc., 18–22 Minetta Ln., New York, NY 10012: Free brochure ■ Fishing lines. 212–924–0463.

Hook & Tackle Company, 7 Kaycee Loop Rd., Plattsburgh, NY 12901: Free catalog ■ Fly-fishing tackle and accessories, fly-tying and fly rod building components and supplies, hand-tied flies, and clothing and wading shoes. 800–552–8342.

Hopkins Fishing Tackle, 1130 Boissevain Ave., Norfolk, VA 23507: Free information ■ Saltwater lures. 804–622–0977.

Hunter Banks Company, 29 Montford Ave., Asheville, NC 28801: Free information ■ Fly fishing and video tapes on fishing and hunting.

Hunter's Angling Supplies, One Central Square Box 300, New Boston, NH 03070: Catalog $3 ■ Fly-fishing, bass fishing, and saltwater fishing supplies; fly-tying supplies; other fishing equipment; and video tapes on fishing and hunting. 603–487–3388.

International Angler, 503 Freeport Rd., Pittsburgh, PA 15215: Catalog $1 ■ Fly fishing supplies, tackle, and video tapes on fishing and hunting. 412–782–2222.

Jann's Sportsman's Supplies, P.O. Box 996, Toledo, OH 43609: Free catalog ■ Lures, rods, and fly-tying supplies.

Jerry's Bait & Tackle, 604 12th St., Highland, IL 62249: Free information ■ Fly fishing supplies, tackle, fly-tying supplies, and video tapes on fishing and hunting. 618–654–3235.

K & K Flyfisher's Supply, 3129 Main, Kansas City, MO 64111: Free catalog ■ Fly-fishing supplies. 800–821–5374.

Kaufmann's Streamborn, P.O. Box 23032, Portland, OR 97223: Free catalog ■ Fly-fishing, bass fishing, and saltwater fishing supplies; fly-tying supplies; and video tapes on fishing and hunting. 800–442–4FLY.

Kunnan Sports Technology, Tackle Division, 9590 Candida St., San Diego, CA 92126: Catalog $1 ■ Spinning rods, plug and bait casting rods, and saltwater rods. 619–566–9200.

L & S Bait Company, 1500 E. Bay Dr., Largo, FL 34641: Free information ■ Freshwater, saltwater, and high-speed trolling lures. 813–584–7691.

Lakeside Fishing Shop, 10 Mile & Jefferson, St. Clair Shores, MI 48081: Free information ■ Fishing supplies, tackle, and video tapes on fishing and hunting. 313–777–7003.

Li'l Mac Molds, P.O. Box 670, Wilsonville, OR 97070: Free catalog ■ Fishing sinker molds, down riggers, jigs, and hooks.

G. Loomis Company, P.O. Box E, Woodland, WA 98674: Catalog $1 ■ Spinning rods, fly rods, and plug and bait casting rods. 206–225–6516.

Lure-Craft Industries, Inc., P.O. Box 1, Solsberry, IN 47459: Catalog $2 ■ Plastic worm-making and lure-making supplies.

Madison River Fishing Company, Box 627, Ennis, MT 59729: Free catalog ■ Fresh and saltwater fly tackle, fly-tying materials, rod building supplies, and books on fishing. 800–227–7127.

Madison River Outfitters, 117 Canyon St., P.O. Box 1106, West Yellowstone, MT 59758: Free information ■ Fly fishing sup-

plies, tackle, and video tapes on fishing and hunting. 406–646–9644.

Magnuflex, 2200 NW 25th St., Miami, FL 33142: Free catalog ■ Plug and bait casting rods. 305–633–6360.

Main Stream Fly Fishing, 8260 Market St., Boardman, OH 44512: Free catalog ■ Equipment and supplies for fresh and saltwater fly fishing and fly-tying. 216–792–3744.

Mann's Bait Company, 603 State Docks Rd., Eufaula, AL 36027: Free information ■ High-speed trolling lures. 205–687–5716.

Marriott's Flyfishing Store, 2700 W. Orangethorpe, Fullerton, CA 92633: Catalog $3 ■ Fly-fishing, bass fishing, and saltwater fishing supplies; fly-tying supplies; and video tapes on fishing and hunting. 800–535–6633; 800–367–2299 (in CA).

Martin Reel Company, 30 E. Main St., Mohawk, NY 13407: Free information ■ Fly reels. 800–322–7335.

Master Fishing Tackle, Inc., 1009 E. Bedmar, P.O. Box 5247, Carson, CA 90746: Free catalog ■ Plug and bait casting rods. 310–631–5188.

The Midge Fly Shop, Inc., 271 State St., Los Altos, CA 94022: Free information ■ Fly fishing supplies and video tapes on fishing and hunting. 415–941–8871.

Mikes Fly Desk, 2395 S. 150 East, Bountiful, UT 84010: Free catalog ■ Fly-tying materials.

MillStream, 722 E. Industrial Park Dr., Manchester, NH 03103: Free information ■ Tackle boxes. 603–647–4003.

Mister Twister, Inc., P.O. Drawer 1152, Minden, LA 71058: Free catalog ■ Fishing tackle, lures, spinners, and accessories. 318–377–8818.

Murray's Fly Shop, 121 Main St., P.O. Box 156, Edinburg, VA 22824: Free catalog ■ Tackle and video tapes on fishing and hunting. 703–984–4212.

National Fiberglass Products Company, Inc., 979 Saw Mill River Rd., Yonkers, NY 10710: Free information ■ Plug and bait casting rods. 914–969–5774.

Netcraft Company, Box 5510, Toledo, OH 43613: Free catalog ■ Kits for making nets, traps, spinners, lures, and rods. 419–472–9826.

Normark/Rapala, 1710 E. 78th St., Minneapolis, MN 55423: Free information ■ High-speed trolling lures. 612–869–3291.

Northland Tackle Company, 3209 Mill St. NE, Bemidji, MN 56601: Free information ■ Tackle for ice fishing.

On the Fly, 3628 Sage Dr., Rockford, IL 61111: Free catalog ■ Fly-fishing supplies and video tapes on fishing and hunting. 815–877–0090.

Orvis Manchester, Historic Rt. 7A, Manchester, VT 05254: Free catalog ■ Fly-fishing rods, reels, leaders, neoprene waders, tackle boxes, and lures. 800–548–9548.

Pace Industries, Inc., P.O. Box 5127, Fort Lauderdale, FL 33310: Free information ■ Cork floats, rod handles, floats, bait bodies, and other supplies. 305–975–6333.

Penn Fishing Tackle, 3028 W. Hunting Park Ave., Philadelphia, PA 19132: Catalog $2 ■ Saltwater spinning reels, spinning rods, plug and bait casting reels and rods, and saltwater reels and rods. 215–229–9415.

Ramsey Outdoor Store, 226 Rt. 17, P.O. Box 1689, Paramus, NJ 07652: Free catalog ■ Fly-tying, other fishing supplies, and video tapes on fishing and hunting. 201–261–5000.

Rizuto's Fly Shop, 42´1 E. Main St., Farmington, NM 87402: Free catalog ■ Fly fishing equipment and supplies. 505–326–0664.

Roaring River Lodge, Hwy. 112 South, Cassville, MO 65625: Free information ■ Fly fishing supplies, tackle, and video tapes on fishing and hunting. 417–847–2330.

The Rod Rack, 181 Thomas Johnson Dr., Frederick, MD 21701: Free information ■ Fly fishing supplies, tackle, and video tapes on fishing and hunting. 301–694–6143.

Ryobi America Corporation, 5201 Pearman Dairy Rd., Anderson, SC 29625: Free catalog ■ Saltwater spinning reels and rods, plug and bait casting reels and rods, saltwater reels and rods, and spin casting reels. 800–323–4615; 803–226–6511 (in SC).

Scientific Anglers, 3M Center, Bldg. 225–3N–04, St. Paul, MN 55144: Free information ■ Reels and other fishing accessories, and how-to cassettes on bass fishing, fly-fishing, deer hunting, waterfowl hunting, and turkey hunting. 612–733–0973.

Scott Powr-Ply Company, 707 Heinz St., Berkeley, CA 94710: Free information ■ Graphite fly rods. 510–841–2444.

Shakespeare Company, 3801 Westmore Dr., Columbia, SC 29223: Catalog $1 ■ Saltwater spinning reels and rods, plug and bait casting reels and rods, spin casting reels, and fishing lines. 803–754–7000.

Sheldon's, Inc., 626 Center St., Antigo, WI 54409: Free information ■ Freshwater lures. 715–623–2382.

Shimano America, P.O. Box 19615, Irvine, CA 92718: Free catalog ■ Saltwater spinning reels, plug and bait casting reels and rods, and saltwater reels and rods. 800–833–5540.

Silstar America Corporation, 1411 Silstar Rd., West Columbia, SC 29179: Catalog $2 ■ Saltwater spinning reels and rods, and plug and bait casting reels and rods.

Snag Proof, 11387 Deerfield Rd., Cincinnati, OH 45232: Free information ■ Bass and northern pike lures. 513–489–6483.

South Bend Sporting Goods, 1950 Stanley St., Northbrook, IL 60065: Catalog $2 ■ Saltwater spinning reels, spinning rods, plug and bait casting rods and rods, and high-speed trolling lures. 708–564–1900.

South Creek, Ltd., P.O. Box 981, Lyons, CO 80540: Catalog $1 ■ Hand-planed, custom 1–, 2– and 3–piece bamboo rods. 800–354–5050.

Sportsman & Ski Haus, 40 E. Idaho St., Kalispell, MT 59901: Free information ■ Fly fishing supplies, tackle. 406–755–6484.

Storm Company, Box 720265, Norman, OK 73070: Free information ■ High-speed trolling lures. 405–329–5894.

Tackle-Craft, P.O. Box 280, Chippewa Falls, WI 54729: Free catalog ■ Fly- and jig-tying supplies. 715–723–3645.

The Tackle Shop, Box 830369, Richardson, TX 75080: Free catalog ■ Tackle components, rod building supplies, lure components, plastic lures, and video tapes on fishing and hunting. 214–231–5982.

Taylor Creek Fly Shops, Box 1295, 189 Basalt Center Cir., Basalt, CO 81621: Free information ■ Fly-fishing supplies. 303–927–4374.

R.D. Taylor Rodmakers, P.O. Box 54, Turners Falls, MA 01376: Free brochure ■

Handcrafted bamboo fly rods. 413–863–8608.

Teton Rod Manufacturing Company, 521 Main Ave., St. Maries, ID 83861: Free information ■ Graphite rods and blanks. 208–245–4442.

Thill Fishing Tackle, Box 721, Urbana, IL 61801: Free information ■ Float-fishing supplies. 217–586–3545.

Thomas & Thomas, P.O. Box 32, Turner Falls, MA 01376: Catalog $3 (refundable) ■ Fly-tying equipment and supplies. 413–863–9727.

Thorn Brothers, 7500 University Ave. NE, Minneapolis, MN 55432: Free information ■ Custom graphite ice fishing rods.

Tuppens, Inc., 1002 N. Dixie Hwy., Lake Worth, FL 33460: Free information ■ Fly fishing supplies and tackle. 407–582–9012.

Westbank Anglers, P.O. Box 523, Teton Village, WY 83025: Free catalog ■ Fly fishing supplies and equipment. 307–733–6483.

R.L. Winston Rod Company, Drawer T, Twin Bridges, MT 59754: Free catalog ■ Salt water salmon rods and handcrafted bamboo, glass, and graphite fly rods. 406–684–5674.

World Class Angler, Inc., P.O. Box 1543, Marathon, FL 33050: Catalog $5 ■ Fly-tying, fly-fishing, and saltwater fishing supplies, and other gear and video tapes on fishing videos. 305–743–6139.

World Wide Sportsman, Inc., 82245 Overseas Hwy., Islamorada, FL 33036: Catalog $1 ■ Fly-fishing tackle and accessories, rods, reels, and saltwater fishing gear. 305–664–4613.

Wright & McGill Company, P.O. Box 16011, Denver, CO 80216: Free catalog ■ Saltwater spinning reels and rods, plug and bait casting rods, saltwater rods, and spin casting reels. 303–321–1481.

Wyoming River Raiders, 601 Wyoming Blvd., Casper, WY 82609: Free catalog ■ Fishing gear, clothing for outdoors, camping and river expedition equipment, hiking equipment, and books. 800–247–6068; 307–235–8624 (in WY).

Yakima Bait Company, P.O. Box 310, Granger, WA 98932: Free information ■ High-speed trolling lures. 509–854–1311.

Yeagers Sporting Goods & Marine, 3101 Northwest Ave., Bellingham, WA 98225: Free information ■ Fishing supplies, tackle, and video tapes on fishing and hunting. 206–733–1080.

Zebco Corporation, P.O. Box 270, Tulsa, OK 74101: Free catalog ■ Saltwater spinning reels and rods, plug and bait casting reels and rods, and spin casting reels. 918–836–5581.

Zetabait, P.O. Box 7985, Jacksonville, FL 32210: Free information ■ Fishing lures. 904–731–9012.

FLAGS & FLAG POLES

Ace Flag & Pennant Factory, 224 Haddon Rd., Woodmere, Long Island, NY 11598: Free information ■ Boating flags, pennants, and gifts. 516–295–2358.

American Flag & Gift, 737 Manuela Way, Arroyo Grande, CA 90277: Free catalog ■ Flags and banners, bunting, flag poles, and accessories. 800–448–3524; 805–473–0395 (in CA).

American Flagpoles & Flags, 100 Liberty Hall Rd., Ste. 102, Goose Creek, SC 29445: Free catalog ■ Flagpoles and American, state, international, nautical, and historical flags. 800–777–1706.

Broward Flag Company, P.O. Box 8593, Asheville, NC 28814: Catalog $2 (refundable) ■ American, state and territorial, foreign, historic, display, church, marine, confederate, custom flags, flag poles, decorations, pennants and banners, and decals. 704–258–9295.

Flag America Company, 2708 Long Beach Blvd., Ship Bottom, NJ 08008: Free catalog ■ Flags and banners, windsocks, and flag poles. 609–494–2626.

Flag Factory, 4156 Library Rd., Pittsburgh, PA 15234: Catalog $2 ■ United States, state, international, nautical, historical, mini, and custom-made flags. Includes flag poles. 412–341–FLAG.

Flags & Flagpoles, Division Associated Builders Specialties, 7106 Mapleridge, Houston, TX 77081: Free information ■ Flags and fiberglass flagpoles. 713–666–2371.

Flags Unlimited, Inc., 1490 Lake Dr. SE, Grand Rapids, MI 49506: Free information ■ Flags and fiberglass flagpoles. 616–458–4200.

The Flying Dutchman Flag Works, P.O. Box 1221, Clarksville, TN 37040: Catalog $2 ■ Flags and accessories.

Fuller Regalia & Flag Company, 1023 Main St., Holden, MA 01520: Free information ■ United States flags and sets, flag poles, banners, and ornaments. 800–448–4491; 800–822–FLAG (in MA).

House of Flags, P.O. Box 8410, Warwick, RI 02888: Free brochure ■ American, historical, state, foreign, holiday, seasonal, nautical, and other flags. Also flagpoles, weather vanes, and eagles. 800–45–FLAGS.

Martin's Flag Company, P.O. Box 1118, Fort Dodge, IA 50601: Free catalog ■ Flags and accessories. 800–992–3524; 800–248–3524 (in IA).

Marvin Display, 322 Boston Post Rd., Milford, CT 06460: Free information ■ United States, historical, state, foreign, nautical, and fun flags, and poles, hardware, and accessories. 800–322–8587.

Safety Flag Company of America, P.O. Box 1005, Pawtucket, RI 02862: Free catalog ■ Flags, vests, belts, and other safety equipment for boats. 401–722–0900.

U.S. Flag Service, 5741 Elmer Derr Rd., Frederick, MD 21701: Free information ■ Flags and accessories. 800–USA–FLAG.

Vaughn Display, 5050 W. 78th St., Minneapolis, MN 55435: Free catalog ■ United States, foreign, state, territorial, and religious flags, and flagpoles, bunting, pennants, floor stands, holders, and brackets. 800–328–6120.

FLOWERS & PLANTS
Artificial Flowers

Bailey's Wholesale Floral Supply, P.O. Box 591, Arcadia, IN 46030: Catalog $3 (refundable) ■ Silk flowers and supplies. 317–984–3663.

John Cornwell Floral & Gift Products, P.O. Box 6610, San Diego, CA 92106: Free brochure ■ Silk flowers, plants, and trees. 619–223–2524.

Florakits, 242 S. 600 East, Alpine, UT 84004: Free information ■ Silk floral arrangement kits. 801–756–2610.

Hammond House, 118 E. Lake Rd., Hamilton, NY 13346: Free catalog ■ Handmade floral arrangements with realistic beauty. 315–824–1585.

International Manufacturing Company, P.O. Box 405, Lillian Springs, FL 32351: Catalog $1 ■ Silk plants, trees, flower arranging supplies, potpourri, and other arts and crafts supplies. 904–875–2918.

Lamrite's Floral & Craft Supply, 565 Broadway, Bedford, OH 44146: Catalog $2 ■ Silk flowers and supplies for making arrangements and other arts and crafts supplies. 216–232–9300.

Petals, 1 Aqueduct Rd., White Plains, NY 10606: Free catalog ■ Silk floral arrangements, decorative flowers and accessories, plants, and trees. 914–328–8600.

Waters of the South, P.O. Box 726, Minden, LA 71058: Free brochure ■ Realistic looking garden greenery. 800–782–5480; 318–377–9394 (in LA).

Dried Flowers

Caswell-Massey Company, Ltd., Catalog Division, 100 Enterprise Pl., Dover, DE 19901: Free catalog ■ Potpourri and pomander mixes, dried flowers, herb plants, essential oils, and perfumery supplies. 800–326–0500.

Country Garden Herb Farm, RD 1, Box 249, Millington, MD 21651: Catalog $1 ■ Dried flowers, plants, and potpourri. 410–928–3190.

The Gathered Herb & Greenhouse, 12114 N. State Rd., Otisville, MI 48463: Catalog $2 ■ Dried flowers, herbs, herb teas, perennials, and potpourri supplies. 313–631–6572.

Goodwin Creek Gardens, Box 83, Williams, OR 97544: Catalog $1 (refundable) ■ Dried floral arrangements, seeds and plants, native American trees, shrubs, and perennial flowers. 503–846–7357.

Hartman's Herb Farm, Old Dana Rd., Barre, MA 01005: Catalog $1 ■ Herbs and herb products, potpourri, and essential oils. 508–355–2015.

Heavenly Scented Acres, P.O. Box 87, Bella Vistra, CA 96008: Free price list ■ Dried flowers and herbs. 916–275–4906.

Home Floral Kits, P.O. Box 70065, Eugene, OR 97401: Free information ■ Kits for making floral decor pieces from dried flowers. 503–746–8497.

Hummingbird Hills Herbal Nursery, 17201 S. Hawkinds, Ashland, MO 65010: Catalog $1 ■ Dried flowers, perennials, everlastings, and organically grown herbs. 314–657–2082.

Sura Kayla Flowers, 484 Broome St., New York, NY 10013: Free information ■ Dried flowers that capture the out-of-doors beauty of the originals. 212–941–8757.

Meadow Everlastings, 149 Shabbona Rd., Malta, IL 60150: Catalog $2 (refundable) ■ Dried flowers, wreath kits, dried flowers, and potpourri. 815–825–2539.

J. Page Basketry, 820 Albee Rd. West, Nokomis, FL 34275: Free catalog ■ Dried and preserved flowers and herbs, pine needle and wheat weaving supplies, basket-making supplies, accessories and tools, and books. 813–485–6730.

Sun-Kempt, P.O. Box 231, Yorkville, NY 13495: Catalog $1 (refundable) ■ Dried flowers and do-it-yourself floral kits. 315–797–9618.

Tom Thumb Workshops, P.O. Box 357, Mappsville, VA 23407: Catalog $1 ■ Potpourri, herbs, spices, essential oils, dried flowers, and other arts and crafts items. 804–824–3507.

Twigs, 381 Bleecker St., New York, NY 10014: Free information ■ Dried flowers that capture the out-of-doors beauty of the originals. 212–620–8188.

VSF Flowers, Inc., 204 W. 10th St., New York, NY 10014: Free information ■ Dried flowers that capture the out-of-doors beauty of the originals. 212–206–7236.

Well-Sweep Herb Farm, 317 Mt. Bethel Rd., Port Murray, NJ 07865: Catalog $2 Potpourri and pomander mixes, dried flowers, and herb plants, 908–852–5390.

William-Wayne & Company, 324 E. 9th St., New York, NY 10003: Free information ■ Dried flowers that capture the out-of-doors beauty of the originals. 212–477–3182.

Zona Flowers, 97 Greene St., New York, NY 10012: Free information ■ Dried flowers that capture the out-of-doors beauty of the originals. 212–925–6750.

FOIL CRAFTS

Guildcraft Company, 3158 Main St., Buffalo, NY 14214: Catalog $1 ■ Colored metal foils and silk-screening, tie dying, stenciling, block printing, chair caning, basket-making, plaster crafts, candle and woodcrafting, leather, and egg crafting supplies. 716–837–9346.

FOOD PROCESSORS

A Cook's Wares, 3270 37th St., Beaver's Falls, PA 15010: Catalog $1.50 ■ Robot-Coupe food processors and accessories, Cuisinart products, cutlery, bakeware, porcelain, French copper pans, and other kitchen aids. 412–846–9490.

Cuisinarts Cookware, 150 Milford Rd., East Windsor, CT 06830: Free information ■ Food processors, attachments, and accessories. 800–726–0190.

European Home Products, P.O. Box 2524, Waterbury, CT 06723: Free catalog ■ Replacement parts and accessories for Cuisinart, Kitchen-Aid, and Robot-Coupe food processors, and other kitchen accessories. 800–225–0760.

Oreck Corporation, 100 Plantation Rd., New Orleans, LA 70123: Free catalog ■ Small kitchen appliances and accessories. 800–989–4200.

Vita-Mix Corporation, 8615 Usher Rd., Cleveland, OH 44138: Free folder ■ Vita-Mix food processor. 800–848–2649.

Zabar's & Company, 2245 Broadway, New York, NY 10024: Free catalog ■ Cookware, food processors, microwave ovens, kitchen tools, and coffee makers. 800–221–3347; 212–787–2000 (in NY).

FOODS
Apple Cider

Aspen Mulling Spices, c/o Wax & Wicks, Inc., P.O. Box 191, Aspen, CO 81611: Free information ■ All-natural mulling spices to make hot and cold cider, wine, or tea.

Berry-Hill Limited, 75 Burwell Rd., St. Thomas, Ontario, Canada N5P 3R5: Free catalog ■ Cider press, canning equipment and supplies, weather vanes, and garden equipment. 519–631–0480.

Growing Naturally, P.O. Box 54, Pineville, PA 18946: Free catalog ■ Cider press for home use. 215–598–7025.

Happy Valley Ranch, Rt. 2, Box 83, Paola, KS 66071: Catalog $1 ■ Home cider presses and fruit grinders. 913–849–3103.

Jaffrey Manufacturing Company, Box 23527, Shawnee Mission, KS 66223: Brochure $1 ■ Solid maple apple cider and wine press. Available assembled or as a kit. 913–849–3139.

Breads & Rolls

Balducci's, 334 E. 11th St., New York, NY 10003: Free catalog ■ Jalapenos and Cheddar, sourdough rye, whole wheat, raisins and walnuts, other breads and food specialties. 212–673–2600.

Baldwin Hill Bakery, Baldwin Hill Rd., Phillipston, MA 01331: Free brochure ■ Whole wheat, sesame wheat, rye, salt-free, raisin, and French varieties of European breads. 508–249–4691.

Boudin Sourdough Bakery, 132 Hawthorne, San Francisco, CA 94107: Free information ■ Sourdough bread in individual loaves or food assortments that include salami, cheese, sparkling cider, and other specialties. 415–882–1800.

Byrd Mill Company, P.O. Box 1638, Gloucester, VA 23061: Free information ■ Flour, cornmeal, cereal, and other all-natural milled grain products. Includes a spoonbread mix, other gourmet specialties, and gift assortments. 800–247–8357.

C'est Croissant, Inc., 22138 S. Vermont Ave., Torrance, CA 90502: Free brochure ■ All-butter croissants. Available plain, fluffy French almond, chocolate, or filled with raspberry preserves. 800–633–2767.

Dean & DeLuca, 560 Broadway, New York, NY 10012: Free information ■ Jalapenos and Cheddar cheese, sourdough rye, and whole wheat breads. 800–999–0306.

Deborah's Country French Bread, 954 W. Washington Blvd., Chicago, IL 60607: Free brochure ■ Overnight delivery of bread from the Poilane bakery in Paris. 800–952–1400; 312–633–4004 (in IL).

DiCamillo Bakery, 811 Linwood Ave., Niagara Falls, NY 14305: Free catalog ■ Italian flat, crisp, and curly breads, and other baked specialties. 800–634–4363; 716–282–2341 (in NY).

H & H Bagels, 2239 Broadway, New York, NY 10024: Free catalog ■ Pumpernickel, white, poppy-seed, sesame-seed, onion, garlic, salt, whole-wheat, sourdough, oat bran, bialy, and cinnamon-raisin bagels. 800–NY–BAGEL.

Manhattan Bagel Company, P.O. Box 580, New York, NY 10014: Free price list ■ Jumbo plain, sesame, onion, cinnamon raisin, whole wheat, poppy, pumpernickel, and egg bagels. 212–691–3041.

Mill City Sourdough Bakery, 2070 Grand Ave., St. Paul, MN 55105: Free brochure ■ Eight traditional European sourdough breads that contain no dairy products, sweeteners, or cholesterol. 800–87–DOUGH.

Moishe's Homemade Kosher Bakery, 181 E. Houston St., New York, NY 10002: Free information ■ Corn bread, challah, and bagels. 212–475–9624.

Orwasher's Bakery, 308 E. 78th St., New York, NY 10021: Free information ■ Black, rye, challah, raisin-pumpernickel, potato, and Irish soda breads. 212–288–6569.

The Pantry Shelf, 896 E. Edwardsville Rd., Wood River, IL 62095: Free information ■ Muffin mixes that include their original flavor, cinnamon fudge, country spice, natural bran, poppy seed, and fruit flavors. 618–254–2234.

Plantation Pride Bakeries, 1002 Apperson Dr., Salem, VA 24153: Free information ■ Nutritious high-fiber bread. 800–729–2732.

Rubschlager Baking Corporation, 3320 W. Grand Ave., Chicago, IL 60651: Free information ■ European-style breads with whole rye chops and stone-ground whole wheat. 312–826–1245.

Sunberry Baking Company, 757 Kohn St., Norristown, PA 19401: Free information ■ All-natural, low-fat, and low-calorie San Francisco-style sourdough bread. Available baked and sliced, or frozen for baking yourself. 800–833–4090.

Wolferman's, One Muffin Ln., P.O. Box 15913, Lenexa, KS 66215: Free catalog ■ English muffins, in original, light wheat, cinnamon-raisin, blueberry, and Cheddar cheese varieties. 800–999–0169.

Ye Olde Sweet Shoppe, P.O. Box 1672, Shepherdstown, WV 25443: Free information ■ European-style breads made from all-natural grain flours free of additives, preservatives, sugar, and shortening. 304–876–2432.

Cakes & Cookies

American Maple Products, Newport, VT 05855: Free price list ■ Baking mixes for breads and muffins; cookie and cake mixes; medium and dark amber maple syrup; maple candy, sugar, and butter; country fudge and other candy specialties; and tea and salad dressings. 800–343–0837; 800–548–1221 (in VT).

Bittersweet Pastries, 460 Piermont Ave., Piermont, NY 10968: Free information ■ All-natural truffle cakes made with bittersweet chocolate. Includes Original Chocolate, Chocolate-Raspberry, Mocha Hazelnut, and Chocolate with Grand Marnier. 800–537–7791; 914–359–7103 (in NY).

Bocock-Stroud Company, 501 W. 4th St., Winston-Salem, NC 27101: Free catalog ■ Sugar crisps and ginger cookies. 919–724–2421.

Byrd Cookie Company, 2233 Norwood Ave., P.O. Box 13086, Savannah, GA 31406: Free brochure ■ Preservative-free, Southern-style cookies and confections by Savannah's cookie maker, Benjamin "Cookie" Byrd. 912–355–1716.

Cafe Beaujolais, Box 730, Mendocino, CA 95460: Free catalog ■ Pastries and desserts. 707–964–0292.

Caroline's Cookies, 544 Michigan Ave., Ste. 2, Evanston, IL 60202: Free information ■ Ready-to-bake frozen cookie dough with chunky chocolate, chunky chocolate with pecans, and chunky white chocolate with macadamia nuts. 708–475–4799.

Charleston Cake Lady, 774 Woodward Rd., Charleston, SC 29407: Free catalog ■ Cakes made with fresh, natural ingredients. Includes poppyseed, macaroon, Charles-towne pound, chocolate pound, banana-pineapple, marble pound, and brown sugar nut. 803–763–2551.

Chocolate Catalogue, 3983 Gratiot, St. Louis, MO 63110: Free catalog ■ French petit fours double dipped in chocolate, with lemon, orange, mocha, and buttercream fillings. 800–325–8881; 314–534–2402 (in MO).

Chocolate Collection, One Chocolate Collection Blvd., P.O. Box 310, Camanche, IA 52730: Free catalog ■ Pecan pies, chocolate decadence, rum cakes, coffee cakes, macadamia nut tortes, Grand Marnier cake, and candies from Geneva, Paris, New York, Munich, Brussels, Madrid, London, and Rome. 800–654–0095.

The Classic Cookie, 409 W. Gregory, Kansas City, MO 64114: Free brochure ■ Fresh-baked chocolate chip, oatmeal raisin nut, oatmeal raisin chocolate chip, chocolate peanut butter chip, and peanut butter cookies, and "snickerdoodles" for children. 816–444–1933.

Collin Street Bakery, 401 W. 7th Ave., Box 515, Corsicana, TX 75110: Free brochure ■ Fruitcakes, cheesecake, pecan pie, and chocolate cake. 800–525–1008.

Crabtree & Evelyn Limited, P.O. Box 167, Woodstock Hill, CT 06281: Catalog $3.50 ■ English biscuits and cookies in assorted flavors, gingerbread, ginger and butter-ginger cookies, Scottish shortbread, Belgian chocolates, cheese wafers and biscuits from Holland, Italian biscuits, preserves, marmalades, jellies, honey, English sauces, spices and condiments, herbs, tea, and candy. 203–928–2766.

Cryer Creek Kitchens, P.O. Box 5079, Corsicana, TX 75110: Free catalog ■ Cheesecakes, pecan pies, rum cakes, pecan fudge pies, pecan and macadamia cakes, fruitcakes, and cookies. 800–468–0088; 903–872–8411 (in TX).

DiCamillo Bakery, 811 Linwood Ave., Niagara Falls, NY 14305: Free catalog ■ Almond macaroons, sesame-coated red wine biscuits, butter cookies, cakes, breads, and finger biscuits made with white wine, champagne, and hazelnuts. 800–634–4363; 716–282–2341 (in NY).

Divine Delights Bakery & Cafe, 1125 Magnolia Ave., Larkspur, CA 94939: Free information ■ Mocha, marzipan roll, plum square, and triple chocolate petit fours. 800–4-HEAVEN; 415–461–2999 (in CA).

Leora Dunga's Chocolates & Sweets, 3466 N. Downer Ave., Milwaukee, WI 53211: Free information ■ Three-layer Grand Marnier-drenched chocolate cake and hand-dipped chocolates. 414–962–3216.

Eilenberger's Butter Nut Baking Company, P.O. Box 710, Palestine, TX 75802: Free brochure ■ Gourmet cakes that include their famous Australian apple cake, fruitcake, pecan cake, and apricot cake. 903–729–2253.

Fantasia Confections, 3465 California St., San Francisco, CA 94118: Free catalog ■ Fruitcakes and cookies. 415–752–0825.

Mrs. Fields Cookies Express Gifts, P.O. Box 4000, Park City, UT 84068: Free catalog n Chocolate chip, chocolate chip with macadamia nuts, and other cookies and pastries. 801–649–1304.

Food of Our Own Design, 1988 Springfield Ave., Maplewood, NJ 07040: Free information ■ Brownie pie with chocolate chips and walnuts; ruggalah filled with apricot, cinnamon, raspberry, or chocolate chips; and apricot, raspberry, toffee, and truffle crunch bars. 800–722–2328.

Funnel Cake Factory, Inc., P.O. Box 3562, Princeton, NJ 08543: Free information ■ Funnel cake kits. 609–683–5400.

Godiva Direct, P.O. Box 4339, Reading, PA 19606: Free catalog ■ Cakes, other pastries, and chocolate candies. 800–447–9393.

Miss Grace Cake Company, 422 N. Canon Dr., Beverly Hills, CA 90210: Free brochure ■ Chocolate chip and lemon pecan cookies, and lemon, macadamia nut, carrot, apple, banana, and orange cakes. 310–274–2879.

Grandma's Fruit Cake, Division Metz Baking Company, Box 457, Beatrice, NE 68310: Free brochure ■ Fruitcake with fancy golden raisins, pecans, California English walnuts, cherries, pineapple, brandy, rum, bourbon, and almonds. 800–228–4030; 402–223–2358 (in NE).

William Greenberg Desserts, Inc., 1377 3rd Ave., New York, NY 10021: Free catalog ■ Baked-to-order brownies, butter cookies, cheese straws, pound cake, schnecken, Danish pastries, kugelhopf, coffee and chocolate yeast loaves, muffins, pecan rings, angel food cake, and carrot cake. 800–255–9278; 212–861–1340 (in NY).

Gwetzli Foods, P.O. Box 20298, Oakland, CA 94620: Free brochure ■ All-butter, coffee-flavored chocolate torte with macadamia nuts and other desserts. 415–863–4367.

Harry & David, P.O. Box 712, Medford, OR 97501: Free catalog ■ Cakes, baklava, cinnamon pastries, tortes, candies, preserves, fresh and dried fruits, and other gourmet specialties. 800–345–5655.

Hearty Mix Company, 1231 Madison Hill Rd., Rahway, NJ 07065: Free catalog ■ Baking mixes for diet-conscious eaters,

without preservatives, cholesterol, or saturated fat products. Includes cookies, cakes, and other dessert pastries; salt-free bread; and wheat-free products. 908–382–3010.

Highland Hill, RR 1, Box 192, Walpole, NH 03608: Free information ■ All-butter shortbread and oatcakes. 603–756–3925.

Holland Honey Cake Company, 420 W. 17th St., Holland, MI 49423: Free information ■ Sodium-free and low-calorie, honey-sweetened cake that contains no sugar, artificial sweeteners, preservatives, fats, or cholesterol. 616–396–6311.

Hunt Country Foods, Inc., P.O. Box 876, Middleburg, VA 22117: Free information ■ Buttery shortbread cookies. 703–364–2622.

Immaculate Heart Hermitage, Big Sur, CA 93920: Free brochure ■ Date-nut cakes and a fruitcake with cherries, pineapples, California raisins, walnuts, dates, Georgia pecans, and dipped in California grape brandy. 408–667–2456.

Jake's Famous Products, Inc., 4910 N. Basin, Portland, OR 97217: Free brochure ■ Chocolate truffle cake and seafood products that include their world famous clam chowder, seafood sauces, smoked white sturgeon, smoked rainbow trout, and several varieties of salmon. 503–226–1420.

Lindy's Food Products, 290 Dyckman St., New York, NY 10034: Free information ■ Lindy's famous all-natural cheesecake. 800–922–7878.

Lush Desserts, P.O. Box 31307, St. Louis, MO 63131: Free information ■ Chocolate amaretto cognac, chocolate brandy alexander, chocolate mint pina colada, and apple rum raisin cakes. 314–349–1008.

Mary of Puddin Hill, P.O. Box 241, Greenville, TX 75401: Free catalog ■ Fruitcakes, other cakes, pies, and chocolates. 903–455–2651.

Monastery Bakery, Holy Cross Abbey, Rt. 2, Box 3870, Berryville, VA 22611: Free information ■ Traditional fruitcakes baked by Trappist Monks at the Holy Cross Abbey. 703–955–1425.

Moravian Sugar Crisp Company, Inc., Rt. 2, Box 431, Clemmons, NC 27012: Free brochure ■ Handmade crisp cookies flavored with sugar, ginger, lemon, butterscotch, or chocolate. 919–764–1402.

Mother Myrick's Confectionary, P.O. Box 1142, Manchester Center, VT 05255: Free brochure ■ Hot fudge sauce, maple cheesecake, linzer torte, stollen, fudge, buttercrunch, truffles, dipped Australian apricots, and caramels. 802–362–1560.

Neal's Cookie & Chocolate Company, Inc., 5700 Savoy, Houston, TX 77036: Free brochure ■ Chocolate and milk chocolate chunk, pecan chocolate, pecan milk chocolate chunk, peanut butter chocolate chunk, white chocolate macadamia nut, oatmeal raisin, and white chocolate macadameroon cookies. 713–784–2722.

Pennysticks, 5200 6th Ave., Altoona, PA 16602: Free information ■ Lightly salted or unsalted, all-natural, cholesterol and sugar-free oat bran pretzel nuggets. 800–344–GIFT.

Pepper Patch, 1250 Old Hillsboro Rd., Franklin, TN 37064: Free brochure ■ Southern-style favorites that include "spirit" cakes, candies, dessert sauces, cocktail jellies and sauces, fresh fruit butters, marmalades, pickles, and relishes. 615–790–1012.

Pittman & Davis, 801 N. Expressway, Harlingen, TX 78552: Free catalog ■ Fruitcakes, cheese, smoked hams, turkeys, ruby-red grapefruit from Texas and Florida, oranges, citrus fruit packs, and pecans. 512–423–2154.

Arnold Reuben Jr's Cheese Cakes, 158 S. 12th Ave., Mt. Vernon, NY 10550: Free information ■ Chocolate, amaretto, marble, chocolate chip, black forest, brandy Alexander, white chocolate chips, and strawberry swirl cheesecakes. 800–648–2253.

Rowena's, 758 W. 22nd, Norfolk, VA 23517: Free information ■ Almond pound cake, preserves, and sauces. 800–627–8699.

Santa Fe Cookie Company, 110 W. San Francisco St., Santa Fe, NM 87501: Free brochure ■ Shortbread with pinon, chocolate chip, peanut butter, chocolate chip with walnuts, and white chocolate chip cookies. 800–243–0353; 505–983–7707 (in NM).

Send a Cake, Inc., 1855 38th St., Boulder, CO 80302: Free information ■ Sends cakes to anyone, anywhere in the United States, in 48 hours or less. 800–338–7840.

Stringham & Smith, 317 SW Morrison, Portland, OR 97204: Free brochure ■ Milk chocolate hazelnut, chocolate raspberry, pecan caramel, and other brownies. 800–888–1487.

Sweet & Almost Sinful Cheesecake, 108 W. College St., Warsaw, NC 28398: Free brochure ■ Homemade cheesecakes, with a choice of 20 flavors. 800–84–CAKES; 919–293–4841 (in NC).

The Sweetery, P.O. Box 243, Anderson, SC 29622: Free brochure ■ Carolina cheesecake, praline cheesecake, chocolate amaretto cheesecake, southern butter pecan chews, chocolate chip cookies, carrot cake, fruitcakes, and brownies. 803–752–1188.

Sweet Exchanges, 259 W. 19th St., New York, NY 10011: Free information ■ Chocolate truffles and chocolate amaretto, Chardonnay, Irish whiskey, and plum spice cakes. 800–527–2216; 212–242–7692 (in NY).

Wolferman's, One Muffin Ln., P.O. Box 15913, Lenexa, KS 66215: Free catalog ■ English muffins in original, light wheat, cinnamon-raisin, blueberry, and Cheddar cheese flavors. 800–999–0169.

The World's Best Chocolate Cake Company, 160 N. Landing Rd., Rochester, NY 14625: Free information ■ Chocolate-chocolate cake for chocolate lovers. 800–743–3530.

YA-HOO! Cake Company, 5302 Texoma Pkwy., Sherman, TX 75090: Free catalog ■ Cakes with Texas pecans, liqueur cakes, caramel and chocolate chunky pecan candies, truffles, fruitcakes, chocolate chip cookies, tea cakes, and brunch breads. 903–771–5624.

Candy & Dessert Sauces

Marcel Akselrod, 530 W. 25th St., New York, NY 10001: Free information ■ Imported Valrhona chocolates. 212–675–7777.

American Maple Products, Newport, VT 05855: Free price list ■ Medium and dark amber maple syrup; pure maple candy, sugar, and butter; and fudge and other candy specialties. 800–343–0837; 800–548–1221 (in VT).

Andre's Boillier, Ltd., 5018 Main St., Kansas City, MO 64112: Free brochure ■ Handmade truffles and chocolate candies. 816–561–3440.

Aplets & Cotlets Factory, P.O. Box C, Cashmere, WA 98815: Catalog $1 (refundable) ■ Washington's famous fruit and nut

confection, Aplets and Cotlets. 509–782–2191.

Astor Chocolate Corporation, 4825 Metropolitan Ave., Glendale, NY 11385: Free brochure ■ Chocolate dessert shells, mocha cups, liqueur cups, dinner mints, truffles, and chocolate greeting cards. 718–386–7400.

Beaux Chocolat, 11041 Weddington St., North Hollywood, CA 91601: Free brochure ■ Chocolates and other candies made with no preservatives, additives, or compound coatings. 818–761–9966.

Belgian Chocolatier Piron, 509 Main St., Evanston, IL 60202: Free information ■ Candies made with chocolate from Belgium's Company Callebaut. 708–864–5504.

Karl Bissinger's French Confections, 3983 Gratiot, St. Louis, MO 63110: Catalog 25¢ ■ Chocolates, fruit and nut bars, jellies, jams, cheese, meat, and tea. 800–325–8881; 314–534–2401 (in MO).

Blue Planet Trading Company, 717 Simundson Dr., Point Roberts, WA 98281: Free information ■ Chocolate candy with Brazil nuts and cashews. 604–251–4277.

Maude Borup, 20 W. 5th St., St. Paul, MN 55102: Free catalog ■ Homemade candies. 612–293–0530.

Chocolat Candy, 2547 9th St., Berkeley, CA 94710: Free information ■ Grand Marnier, Dark on Dark, Toasted Almond, and other truffles. Flavors change monthly and are shipped from October to April. 510–843–1182.

Chocolate Catalogue, 3983 Gratiot, St. Louis, MO 63110: Free catalog ■ Handmade chocolates, and petit fours double dipped in chocolate with lemon, orange, mocha, and other fillings. 800–325–8881; 314–534–2402 (in MO).

Chocolate Collection, One Chocolate Collection Blvd., P.O. Box 310, Camanche, IA 52730: Free catalog ■ Candies and desserts from Geneva, Paris, New York, Munich, Brussels, Madrid, London, and Rome. 800–654–0095.

Chocolate Photos, 637 W. 27th St., New York, NY 10001: Free catalog ■ Custom-molded chocolate novelties. 212–714–1880.

Chocolaterie Corne Toioson D'Or, Trump Tower, Garden Level, 725 5th Ave., New York, NY 10022: Free information ■ Cocoa

nuggets, hazelnut pralines, sugar-glazed truffles, and other candies from Belgium. 212–308–4060.

Chocolates by M, 61 W. 62nd St., New York, NY 10023: Free information ■ Handmade Belgium chocolate candy. 212–307–0777.

Clearbrook Farms, 5514 Fair Ln., Fairfax, OH 45227: Free brochure ■ Semi-sweet chocolate sauces and fruit spreads and preserves made with only fruit and sugar. Includes strawberry, raspberry, tart cherry, blueberry, apricot, peach, boysenberry, black cherry, plum, and orange marmalade. 800–888–3276; 513–271–2053 (in OH).

Cocolat, 2547 9th St., Berkeley, CA 94710: Free information ■ Truffles, triple chocolate almonds, chocolate mint almonds, triple chocolate hazelnuts, almond butter toffee, bittersweet chocolate bark, and chocolate desserts. 800–274–2499.

Community Products, Inc., RD 2, Box 1950, Montpelier, VT 05602: Free information ■ Buttery confection with tropical cashews and Brazil nuts. 802–229–1840.

Corr's Confections, Inc., P.O. Box 64, Midlothian, VA 23113: Free brochure ■ Chocolate covered snacks, potato chips, pretzels, peanut brittle, nuts, and fruits. 804–739–7861.

de Geneve Chocolatier, P.O. Box 7906, Madison, WI 53707: Free catalog ■ Chocolates from Europe and United States. 608–837–0534.

Delty, Inc., 7924 Ronson Rd., San Diego, CA 92111: Free information ■ Sugar-free milk chocolate, milk chocolate with almonds, chocolate coconut, chocolate peanut clusters, dark chocolate, dark chocolate with almonds, and peanut butter cups. 800–962–3355.

Discriminating Tastes, Inc., P.O. Box 515, Murrysville, PA 15668: Free information ■ Homemade English toffee. 412–325–1063.

Leora Dunga's Chocolates & Sweets, 3466 N. Downer Ave., Milwaukee, WI 53211: Free information ■ Three-layer Grand Marnier-drenched chocolate cake and hand-dipped chocolates. 414–962–3216.

Estee Candy Company, Inc., 169 Lackawanna Ave., Parsippany, NJ 07054: Free catalog ■ Sugarless candies and cookies. 201–335–1000.

Ethel M Chocolates, P.O. Box 98505, Las Vegas, NV 89193: Free catalog ■ Milk and dark chocolate truffles, liqueur flavors, buttercreams, nuts, and holiday favorites, and other candies. 800–438–4356.

Fannie May Candy Shops, Inc., 1137 W. Jackson Blvd., Chicago, IL 60607: Free brochure ■ Chocolates, nut candies, nuts, hard candies, and other favorites. 800–999–3629.

Figi's, 3200 S. Maple, Marshfield, WI 54404: Free catalog ■ Candies, holiday assortments, and other gifts. 715–384–6101.

Fralinger's, Inc., 1325 Boardwalk, Atlantic City, NJ 08401: Free brochure ■ Saltwater taffy, mints, filled centers, fudge, peanut butter chews, chocolates, chocolate covered marshmallows, and almond macaroons. 609–345–2177.

Ghirardelli Chocolate Company, 900 Northpoint, San Francisco, CA 91109: Free catalog ■ Chocolate candies and novelties. 415–474–1413.

Godiva Direct, P.O. Box 4339, Reading, PA 19606: Free catalog ■ Chocolate candies and pastries. 800–447–9393.

Gourmand Candy, 636 S. Pickett St., Alexandria, VA 22304: Free information ■ Imported Valrhona chocolates. 703–461–0600.

Grand Finale Confections, 200 Hillcrest Rd., Berkeley, CA 94705: Free brochure ■ Preservative-free candies made with natural ingredients. Includes buttercream caramels, triple-chocolate truffles, and dessert sauces. 800–748–6271; 415–655–8414 (in CA).

Harbor Candy Shop, P.O. Box 498, Ogunquit, ME 03907: Free catalog ■ Chocolate-covered apricots, peaches, and oranges, and caramel turtles in rich dark or milk chocolate, over pecans or cashews. 207–646–8078.

Harbor Sweets, Inc., Palmer Cove, 85 Leavitt St., Salem, MA 01970: Free catalog ■ Handmade chocolates. 508–745–7648.

Harry & David, P.O. Box 712, Medford, OR 97501: Free catalog ■ Candies, cakes, baklava, cinnamon pastries, tortes, preserves, fresh and dried fruits, and other gourmet specialties. 800–345–5655.

Hawaiian Plantations, 650 Iwilei Rd., Honolulu, HI 96817: Free catalog ■ Candies, jams, syrups, dressings, and condiments. 800–767–4650.

Hay Day Market, 2460 Dixwell Ave., Hamden, CT 06514: Free information ■ Imported Callebaut chocolates. 203–288–3148.

Hershey's Chocolate World, P.O. Box 800, Hershey, PA 17033: Free catalog ■ Hershey candies and novelties. 800–544–1347.

Huwyler Candies Chicago, 535 N. Michigan Ave., Chicago, IL 60611: Free information ■ Candies made with natural ingredients and air shipped weekly from Switzerland. 312–923–0028.

Huwyler Candies New York, 510 Madison Ave., New York, NY 10022: Free information ■ Candies made with natural ingredients and air shipped weekly from Switzerland. 212–308–1311.

Indian Wells Date Gardens & Chocolatier, 365 N. Palm Canyon Dr., Palm Springs, CA 92264: Free catalog ■ Candies, nuts, dates, and date specialties. 619–346–2914.

Jinil Au Chocolat, 414 Central Ave., Cedarhurst, NY 11516: Free information ■ Kosher custom molded chocolate and gift baskets. 800–541–5166; 516–295–2550 (in NY).

Kendall Cheese Company, P.O. Box 686, Atascadero, CA 93423: Free information ■ Creme Fraiche dessert topping. 805–466–7252.

Lake Champlain Chocolates, 431 Pine St., Burlington, VT 05401: Free brochure ■ Almond butter crunch, truffles, original Lake Champlain chocolates, honey caramels, maple crunch, mint crunch, chocolate covered fruits and nuts, and chocolate sauces. 800–854–1808.

Lammes Candies, P.O. Box 1885, Austin, TX 78767: Free catalog ■ Texas Chewie Pecan Pralines. 800–252–1885; 512–835–6791 (in TX).

Liberty Orchards Company, Inc., 117 Mission St., P.O. Box C, Cashmere, WA 98815: Free catalog ■ Aplets and Cotlets, and handmade, all-natural candies and fruit specialties. 800–888–5696.

Li-Lac Chocolates, 120 Christopher St., New York, NY 10014: Free information ■ Handmade chocolates, French mints, hazelnut butter truffles, chocolate covered fruits, and walnut cremes. 212–242–7374.

Maillard Corporation, P.O. Box 1158, Bethlehem, PA 18016: Free information ■ Jelly beans. 215–867–7568.

Marshall's Fudge Shops, 308 E. Central Ave., Mackinaw City, MI 49701: Free catalog ■ Preservative-free fudge, other homemade candies, and nuts. 800–343–8343.

Mary of Puddin Hill, P.O. Box 241, Greenville, TX 75401: Free catalog ■ Chocolates, fruitcakes, pies, and other baked goods. 903–455–2651.

MEB Distributing, 390 Swift Ave., #22, San Francisco, CA 94080: Free information ■ Imported Callebaut chocolates. 415–589–1180.

Minerva Street Chocolates, 1052 Olivia, Ann Arbor, MI 48104: Free information ■ Hand-dipped truffles. Shipped from October to May. 313–665–8661.

Moonshine Trading Company, P.O. Box 896, Winters, CA 95694: Free catalog ■ Honeys and butters, and semisweet chocolate crunch, white chocolate cashew creme, white chocolate almond dream, and milk chocolate almond crunch nut spreads. 916–753–0601.

Mother Myrick's Confectionary, P.O. Box 1142, Manchester Center, VT 05255: Free brochure ■ Maple cheesecake, linzer torte, stollen, fudge, buttercrunch, truffles, dipped Australian apricots, caramels, and hot fudge sauce. 802–362–1560.

Pecan Street Sweets, Inc., P.O. Box 561224, Dallas, TX 75356: Free brochure ■ Pecan candies, peanut brittle and nut logs, other nut candues, and divinity fudge. 800–882–6887.

Plumbridge, 30 E. 67th St., New York, NY 10021: Free brochure ■ Chocolates, mints, spiced nuts, candied fruits, and other favorites. 212–744–6640.

Ann Raskas Candies, P.O. Box 13367, Kansas City, KS 66113: Free information ■ Candy for dieters, with 14 calories each piece. 913–422–7230.

Sarris Candies, 511 Adams Ave., Canonsburg, PA 15317: Catalog $2 (refundable) ■ Candies made with all-natural ingredients. 800–255–7771.

Sawyer's Sweets, 55 Summett Ave., Jersey City, NJ 07304: Free information with long SASE ■ Handcrafted, individually wrapped red or white chocolate roses.

See's Candies, P.O. Box S, Culver City, CA 90231: Free price list ■ "Old time" candies that include boxed assortments, other favorites, seasonal and holiday specialties, and lollipops. 800–347–7337.

Select Origins, Box N, Southampton, NY 11968: Free catalog ■ Dessert sauces, oils, vinegars, sauces, marinades, relishes and condiments, herbs and spices, preserves, and coffee and tea. 800–822–2092 516–924–5447 (in NY).

Standard Candy Company, Attention: Mail Order Dept., 715 Massman Dr., Nashville, TN 37210: Free brochure ■ Tennessee's favorite, the Goo Goo Cluster, an original combination of chewy caramel, creamy marshmallow, roasted peanuts, and pure milk chocolate; and Goo Goo Supremes made with pecans; and King Leo stick candies. 615–889–6360.

Teuscher Chocolates of Switzerland, 620 5th Ave., New York, NY 10020: Free information ■ Swiss chocolates flown in weekly from Switzerland. 212–246–4416.

Top Hat Company, Box 66, Wilmette, IL 60091: Free brochure ■ Hot fudge, raspberry fudge, mocha fudge, mint fudge, caramel, and butterscotch dessert sauces. 708–256–6565.

Trappistine Creamy Caramels, Abbey of Our Lady of the Mississippi, RR 3, Dubuque, IA 52001: Free brochure ■ Vanilla, chocolate, licorice caramels, and creamy mints. 319–556–6330.

Trappistine Quality Candy, Mount Saint Mary's Abbey, 300 Arnold St., Wrentham, MA 02093: Free brochure ■ Butter nut munch, caramels, chocolate fudge with walnuts, almond bark, and penuche. 617–528–1282.

Valrhona-Tekla Chocolates, 1456 N. Dayton St., Chicago, IL 60622: Free information ■ Imported Valrhona chocolates. 312–943–0691.

Wilds of Idaho, 1308 W. Boone, Spokane, WA 99201: Free price list ■ Peanut brittle, and wild huckleberry jam, topping, and syrup. 509–326–0197.

J. Wolsk & Company, 87 Ludlow St., New York, NY 10002: Free information with long SASE ■ Dried fruits and nuts, and chocolates and other candies by Lindt, Perugina, and Droste. 212–475–7946.

Young Pecans, P.O. Drawer 6709, Florence, SC 29502: Free brochure ■ Butter roasted and salted pecans and cashews,

double-dipped chocolate pecan halves, butter toffee pecan popcorn, praline pecans, sugar and orange pecans, sugar and spiced pecans, Cheddar cheese pecans, and pecan divinity logs. 803–729–8004.

Caviar

California Sunshine Fine Foods, Inc., 144 King St., San Francisco, CA 94107: Free information ■ American Golden, Beluga, Mandarin Osetra, Caspian Sea Sevruga, Tsar Nicoulai Imperial Mandarin, Tsar Nicoulai American Sturgeon, Tsar Nicoulai Mandarin Osetra caviar, and other caviar; Tobiko flying fish roe; fresh and smoked seafoods; and fresh and smoked game birds. 415–543–3007.

Caspian Caviars, Highland Mill, P.O. Box 876, Camden, ME 04843: Free information ■ Russian Beluga caviar. 800–332–4436; 207–236–4436 (in ME).

Caviar Direct Company, 524 W. 46th St., New York, NY 10036: Free information ■ American sturgeon and Russian Beluga caviar. 800–472–4456; 212–757–8990 (in NY).

Caviar Express, 4397 W. Bethany Rd., Glendale, AZ 85301: Free information ■ Russian Beluga and other caviar. 800–544–2266; 602–937–1000 (in AZ).

Caviar House, Inc., 687 NE 79th St., Miami, FL 33138: Free catalog ■ Smoked scottish salmon, caviar, foie gras, and truffles. 800–522–8427.

Caviar King, 47–39 49th St., Woodside, NY 11377: Free brochure ■ Domestic and imported caviar, smoked salmon, whole smoked trout, smoked sturgeon, Spanish tuna in olive oil, and shad roe. 800–654–7264; 718–784–3344 (in NY).

Caviarteria, Inc., 29 E. 60th St., New York, NY 10022: Free catalog ■ Beluga and Sevruga caviar; American whitefish, sturgeon, and salmon caviar; smoked fish; and other specialties. 800–4–CAVIAR; 212–759–7410 (in NY).

The Forst Mountain Smokehouse, CPO Box 1000P, Kingston, NY 12401: Free brochure ■ Osetra and Sevruga caviar, smoked ham, smoked turkey, filet mignon steaks, strip steaks, boneless sirloin strip steaks, smoked pheasant, Canadian bacon, and aged Cheddar cheese. 800–453–4010; 914–331–3500 (in NY).

Hansen Caviar Company, 391A Grand Ave., Englewood, NJ 07631: Free information ■ American sturgeon and Russian Beluga caviar. 201–568–9659.

J & K Trading Company, 10808 Garland Dr., Culver City, CA 90230: Free price list ■ Lump fish caviar, crab meat, escargots, hearts of palm, button mushrooms, and other gourmet specialties. 213–836–3334.

Mitchell & Winter Caviar, Highland Mill, P.O. Box 876, Camden, ME 04843: Catalog $2 ■ Beluga, Sevruga, Osetra, and American caviar. 207–236–8313.

Petrossian Shop, 182 W. 58th St., New York, NY 10019: Free information ■ Caviar, foie gras, truffles, and smoked salmon. 800–828–9241.

Poriloff Caviar, 47–39 49th St., Woodside, NY 11377: Free information ■ American sturgeon and Russian Beluga caviar. 800–654–7264; 718–784–3344 (in NY).

Cheese

Alleva Dairy, 188 Grand St., New York, NY 10013: Free information ■ Old-fashioned Italian mozzarella, smoked and fresh ricotta, and other cheese. 212–226–7990.

Bandon Foods, Inc., P.O. Box 1668, Bandon, OR 97411: Free brochure ■ Medium and aged sharp Cheddar, Jalapeno Jack, Monterey Jack, Baja Cheddar, sharp Cheddar, garlic Cheddar, onion Cheddar, and Cajun Cheddar cheese. 800–548–8961.

Blue Heron French Cheese Company, 2001 Blue Heron Dr., Tillamook, OR 97141: Free brochure ■ Domestic Brie cheese. 503–862–8281.

Cabot Creamery, Box 128, Cabot, VT 05647: Free information ■ All-natural cheese with half the fat and cholesterol and 33 percent fewer calories than Cheddar. 802–563–2231.

Calef's Country Store, Rt. 9, Box 57, Barrington, NH 03825: Free brochure ■ Homemade cheese, maple syrup, and candy. 603–664–2231.

Cheese Junction, 1 W. Ridgewood Ave., Ridgewood, NJ 07450: Free catalog ■ Domestic and diet cheese. 201–445–9211.

Cheese of All Nations, 153 Chambers St., New York, NY 10007: Catalog $1 ■ Imported and domestic cheese. 212–732–0752.

Laura Chenel's Chevre, 1550 Ridley Ave., Santa Rosa, CA 95401: Free brochure ■ Handmade American and French-style goat cheese. 707–575–8888.

Coach Dairy Goat Farm, Pine Plains, NY 12567: Free information ■ Goat cheese and yogurt. 518–398–5325.

Crowley Cheese, Healdville, VT 05758: Free brochure ■ Mild, medium, and sharp Crowley cheese and Spiced Crowley Cheese with garlic, hot pepper, caraway, or dill. 802–259–2340.

Eichten's Hidden Acres Cheese Farm, 16705 310th St., Center City, MN 55012: Free brochure ■ European-style Dutch Gouda, Baby Swiss, Tilsit, and Cheddar cheese. 612–257–4752.

Formagg, Northgate Industrial Park, P.O. Box 5204, New Castle, PA 16105: Free information ■ Low-fat, low-cholesterol cheese. 800–441–9419.

Gibbsville Cheese Sales, Shenoygan Falls, WI 53085: Free price list ■ Cheese, beef sticks, and summer sausages. 414–454–3242.

Goat Folks Farm, 8528 Tunison Rd., Interlaken, NY 14847: Free brochure ■ American-made French-style goat cheese. 607–532–4343.

Grafton Village Cheese Company, P.O. Box 87, Grafton, VT 05146: Free brochure ■ Cheddar cheese. 802–843–2221.

Heluva Good Cheese, Inc., 6152 Barclay Rd., P.O. Box C, Sodus, NY 14551: Free catalog ■ Gourmet cheese. 800–338–2316 (October 1 to January 31); 315–483–2223 (after February 1).

Hickory Farms, P.O. Box 75, Maumee, OH 43537: Free brochure ■ Cheese, smoked meats, and other specialties. 800–222–4438.

Hollow Road Farms, Inc., Hollow Rd., Box 93, Stuyvesant, NY 12173: Free information ■ Cheese--plain or with herbs--made from ewe's milk. 518–758–7214.

Ideal Cheese Shop, 1205 2nd Ave., New York, NY 10021: Free catalog ■ Imported cheese. 212–688–7579.

Imperia Foods, 234 St. Nicholas Ave., South Plainfield, NJ 07080: Free information ■ Imported grated Romano and Parmesan cheese in regular or reduced fat and low-cholesterol varieties. 908–756–7333.

Kolb-Lena Cheese Company, 301 W. Railroad St., Lena, IL 61048: Free catalog ■ Imported and domestic cheese. 815–369–4577.

Lynn Dairy, Inc., Rt. 1, Box 177, Granton, WI 54436: Free price list ■ Wisconsin cheese, cheese spreads, and beef summer sausage sticks. 715–238–7129.

Marin French Cheese Company, P.O. Box 99, Petaluma, CA 94953: Free brochure ■ French Camembert, Schloss, Breakfast, and Fromage De Brie cheese. 707–762–6001.

Maytag Dairy Farms, Inc., P.O. Box 806, Newton, IA 50208: Free catalog ■ Blue cheese, natural white Cheddar, Cheddar cheese spreads, brick cheese, baby Swiss, Edam, and other favorites. 800–247–2458; 800–258–2437 (in IA).

Mozzarella Company, 2944 Elm St., Dallas, TX 75226: Free brochure ■ Rindless crescenza cheese; queso fresco, a crumbly cheese that resembles farmer's cheese; semi-soft, herb-like caciotta; creamy variety of mascarpone; and other cheese made from cow's, goat's, and sheep's milk. 214–741–4072.

Nauvoo Cheese Company, Young and Wells Streets, P.O. Box 188, Nauvoo, IL 62354: Free brochure ■ Blue cheese that includes a premium wheel, baby blue wheel, cold pack squares, wedges, and crumbles. 800–358–9143; 217–453–2213 (in IL).

Plymouth Cheese Corporation, Box 1, Plymouth, VT 05056: Free brochure ■ Old-fashioned aged and naturally cured Vermont granular curd cheese. 802–672–3650.

Rogue River Valley Creamery, P.O. Box 3606, Central Point, OR 97502: Free brochure ■ Low-fat cheese. 503–664–2233.

Shelburne Farms, Harbor Rd., Shelburne, VT 05482: Free brochure ■ Smoked and soft Cheddar cheese spread, naturally leavened bread made with organic wheat, smoked ham and bacon, honey, maple syrup, and preserves. 802–985–8686.

Sonoma Cheese Factory, 2 Spain St., Sonoma, CA 95476: Free brochure ■ Cheese with reduced fat, cholesterol, calories, and salt. Includes lite garlic, hot pepper, and Jack cheese. 800–535–2855.

Soyco Foods, Division Galaxy Cheese Company, P.O. Box 5181, New Castle, PA 16105: Free information ■ Casein-free cheese alternative for people who want to avoid dairy products. 800–441–9419.

Sugarbush Farm, RFD 2, Box 568, Woodstock, VT 05091: Free brochure ■ Cheddar cheese made with natural ingredients and aged 18 to 24 months, maple syrup, and candy. 802–457–1757.

Swiss Cheese Shop, Hwy. 69 North, P.O. Box 429, Monroe, WI 53566: Free brochure ■ Blue cheese, muenster, smoked Swiss cheese, caraway muenster, brick, limburger, port salut, Colby, Monterey Jack, Cheddar, hot pepper cheese, and others. 608–325–3493.

Swiss Colony, Catalog Request Department, Madison, WI 53793: Free catalog ■ Cheese, meats, sausages, pastries, nuts, candies, and snacks.

Tillamook Cheese, P.O. Box 313, Tillamook, OR 97141: Free catalog ■ Cheese, exotic and international favorites, snacks, candies, meats and fowl, smoked fish, and jellies and preserves. 503–842–4481.

Vermont Butter & Cheese Company, Pitman Rd., P.O. Box 95, Websterville, VT 05678: Free information ■ American-made cheese. 802–479–9371.

WSU Creamery, Washington State University, Troy Hall 101, Pullman, WA 99164: Free brochure ■ Includes WSU Cheddar, Cougar Gold, mild flavored Viking, and Hot Pepper cheese made by the Washington State University Creamery. 509–335–4014.

Western Dairymen Cooperative, Inc., P.O. Box 155, Smithfield, UT 84335: Free brochure ■ Mild, medium, and sharp Cheddar cheese. Others include Swiss, taco, green onion, salami, and hot pepper. 801–563–3281.

Wisconsin Cheeseman, P.O. Box 1, Madison, WI 53701: Free catalog ■ Aged Wisconsin natural cheese, sausage, cookies and pastries, fruits, nuts, and other specialties. 608–837–4100.

Creole & Cajun

Cajun Fixin's, Inc., P.O. Box 956, Abita Springs, LA 70420: Free information ■ Louisiana cajun spices and seasonings, mixes, chow-chow, and other specialties. 800–443–2621.

Comeaux's Grocery & Market, 1000 Lamar, Lafayette, LA 70501: Free information ■ Cajun food specialties that include andouille, boudin (regular, crawfish, and seafood), and tasso. 800–323–2492; 318–234–6159 (in LA).

Community Kitchens, P.O. Box 3778, Baton Rouge, LA 70821: Free catalog ■ Cajun spices, Creole seasonings, French Quarter binet mixes, Louisiana corn bread mix, jambalaya seasoning and rice, and tea and coffee. 800–535–9901.

Creole Delicacies, 533 Saint Ann St., New Orleans, LA 70116: Free brochure ■ Pecan pralines, remoulade sauce, hot pepper jelly, Creole seasonings, and specialties from Brennan's restaurant. 800–786–0941; 504–523–6425 (in LA).

K-Pauls Louisiana Enterprises, P.O. Box 770034, New Orleans, LA 70117: Catalog 50¢ ■ Jambalaya, seasoned meats and seafood, etouffee, smoked turkey, and other specialties. 800–4K–PAULS; 504–947–6712 (in LA).

Luzianne Blue Plate Foods, P.O. Box 60296, New Orleans, LA 70160: Free brochure ■ Luzianne coffee and tea, and New Orleans-style jambalaya, gumbo, Creole, and etouffee dinners. 800–692–7895.

Oak Grove Smokehouse, Inc., 17618 Old Jefferson Hwy., Prairieville, LA 70769: Free catalog ■ Cajun and creole mixes and smoked meats. 504–673–6857.

Poche's Meat Market & Restaurant, Rt. 2, Box 415, Breaux Bridge, LA 70517: Free information ■ Cajun specialties that include andouille, cracklins, stuffed pork roast and pork chops, tasso and other sausages, chaudin, grillades, homemade roux, and stuffed tongue. 318–332–2108.

Ethnic

Anzen Importers, 736 NE Union Ave., Portland, OR 97232: Free information ■ Thai food specialties. 503–233–5111.

Francois Carrier, 5353 W. Alabama, Ste. 200, Houston, TX 77056: Free information ■ Duck and goose foie gras, with and without truffles. 713–963–0787.

Casados Farms, P.O. Box 1269, San Juan Pueblo, NM 87566: Free brochure with long SASE ■ Chiles, corns, flours, nuts, and spices. 505–852–2433.

Chili Pepper Emporium, 328 San Felipe NW, Albuquerque, NM 87104: Free catalog ■ Ristras, chili wreaths, chili seeds and powder, and chili jams. 505–242–7538.

Chinese Kitchen, P.O. Box 218, Stirling, NJ 07980: Catalog $1 ■ Supplies for Chinese cooking. 201–665–2234.

Dewildt Imports, Inc., Rt. 3, Bangor, PA 18013: Free catalog ■ Oriental, Dutch, and Indonesian foods. 800–338–3433.

Duangrat Market, 5888 Leesburg Pike, Falls Church, VA 22041: Free information ■ Oriental foods and specialties. 703–578–0622.

El Paso Chile Company, 100 Ruhlin Ct., El Paso, TX 79922: Free information ■ Medium-hot cactus salsa made from vine-ripened tomatillos, onions, fresh cilantro, mild chile, fiery jalapeno, vinegar, spices, and nopalitos. 915–544–3434.

Ferrara Foods & Confections, Inc., 195 Grand St., New York, NY 10013: Free brochure and price list ■ Italian specialties that include coffee, candy, syrups, breadsticks, sauces, vegetables, and pastas. 212–226–6150.

Frigo Food Products Company, Inc., P.O. Box 446, Torrington, CT 06790: Free price list ■ Italian cheese, pasta, salami, pepperoni, prosciutto ham, sopressata, pesto sauce, imported dried tomatoes, saffron, and dried mushrooms. 203–482–8127.

Gaston Dupre, Inc., 7904 Hopi Pl., Tampa, FL 33634: Free information ■ Hand-folded and rolled fettucine and angel hair pasta. Includes beet, tomato and basil, lemon and pepper, tarragon and chives, chocolate, wild mushroom, saffron, squid ink, and curry flavors. 800–937–9445.

Gourmail, Inc., 816 Newton Rd., Berwyn, PA 19312: Free catalog ■ Foods and spices from India. 215–296–4620.

Great Valley Mills, 687 Mill Rd., Telford, PA 18969: Free catalog ■ Pennsylvania Dutch foods. 800–688–6455.

Hard Times Chili, 310 Commerce St., Alexandria, VA 22314: Free information with long SASE ■ Texas Roadhouse Chili and Cincinnati Chile mixes. 703–836–7449.

Jardine's Texas Foods, P.O. Box 18868, Austin, TX 78760: Free catalog ■ Chili fixings, salsas, hand-stuffed olives, and spicy Bloody Mary mix. 800–544–1880.

Josie's Best, 1130 Agua Fria St., P.O. Box 5525, Santa Fe, NM 87501: Free price list ■ Mexican and Southwest Indian cooking condiments. Includes white and blue corn tortillas, tortillas flour, sopapilla mix, corn husks, Indian fried bread mix, posole, salsa, chicos, and red and green chile puree. 505–983–6520.

La Palma Mexicatessan, 2884 24th St., San Francisco, CA 94110: Free information ■ Mexican canned and dried chiles, tomatillos, and fresh tortillas. 415–647–1500.

Los Chileros de Nuevo Mexico, P.O. Box 6215, Santa Fe, NM 87502: Free brochure ■ Cascabel, arbol, negro, ancho, chipotle, jalapeno, and pasilla peppers for Mexican cooking. 505–471–6967.

Louisiana's Cajun Marketplace, 10557 Cherry Hill Ave., Baton Rouge, LA 70816: Free price list ■ Jambalaya, etouffee, creole gumbo, dirty rice, and other creole and Cajun quick-to-fix mixes. 800–321–5571.

Malibu Greens, P.O. Box 6286, Malibu. CA 90264: Free information ■ Thai food specialties. 800–383–1414.

Manganaro Foods, 488 9th Ave., New York, NY 10018: Free information ■ Italian salami, prosciutto ham, and cheese; panettone, amaretti, colomba, and torrone desserts. 800–472–5264.

Morgan's Mexican Lebanese Foods, 736 S. Robert St., St. Paul, MN 55107: Free information ■ Mexican canned and dried chiles, tomatillos, masa, and fresh tortillas. 612–291–2955.

Morisi's Pasta, 647 5th Ave., Brooklyn, NY 11215: Catalog $2.50 (refundable) ■ All-natural pasta with over 50 flavors and 65 shapes. 800–253–6044.

Nine Ninety Nine Kosher Provisions, 15 Rivington St., New York, NY 10002: Free brochure ■ Fresh-frozen kosher veal and beef, delicatessen meats, all-beef franks, and other kosher products. 212–254–5994.

Old Southwest Trading Company, P.O. Box 7545, Albuquerque, NM 87194: Free catalog ■ Exotic and domestic chiles, featuring the Habanero Chiles, one of the hottest varieties. 505–836–0168.

Oriental Food Market & Cooking School, Inc., 2801 W. Howard St., Chicago, IL 60645: Catalog $2 (refundable) ■ Oriental foods and cooking specialties. 312–274–2826.

Oriental Food Mart, 909 Race St., Philadelphia, PA 19107: Free information ■ Oriental foods and specialties. 215–922–5111.

The Oriental Market, 502 Pampas St., Austin, TX 78752: Free information ■ Oriental foods and specialties. 512–453–9058.

The Oriental Pantry, 423 Great Rd., Acton, MA 01720: Free catalog ■ Oriental foods and specialties. 508–263–6922.

Pacific Mercantile Company, Inc., 1925 Lawrence St., Denver, CO 80202: Free information ■ Oriental foods. Includes noodle specialties. 303–295–0293.

Pastorelli Food Products, Inc., 162 Sangamon St., Chicago, IL 60607: Free information ■ Add a professional chef's taste to pizza, pasta, hamburgers, snacks, and omelets with a pizza sauce made with olive oil and all-natural ingredients. 312–666–2041.

Pendery's, Inc., 304 E. Belknap St., Fort Worth, TX 76102: Free price list ■ Mexican spices, seasonings, flavorings, and other specialties. 817–332–3871.

Poo Ping Corporation, 81A Bayard St., New York, NY 10013: Free information ■ Oriental foods and specialties. 212–349–7662.

G.B. Ratto & Company, International Grocers, 821 Washington St., Oakland, CA 94607: Catalog $1 (refundable) ■ Imported ethnic and specialty foods. 800–228–3515.

Rossi Pasta, P.O. Box 759, Marietta, OH 45750: Free brochure ■ Handmade pasta, that includes black olive, linguine, garlic fettuccini, saffron linguine, and others. 800–227–6774.

Scandinavian Foods, 244 Main St., Farmington, CT 06032: Free catalog ■ Scandinavian foods. 203–677–1881.

Schaller & Weber, Inc., 22–35 46th St., Long Island City, NY 11105: Free brochure ■ German-style smoked bacon and ham, and sausage that includes wursts, salami, and cervelats. 718–879–3047.

Sorrenti Family Farms, 14033 Steinegul Rd., Escalon, CA 95320: Free information ■ California wild rice and pasta combinations. 209–838–1127.

Southwestern Flavor Company, P.O. Box 315, Red River, NM 87558: Free information ■ Cactus salsa, chile honey, chile, and corn ristras. 505–754–2221.

Sultan's Delight, Inc., P.O. Box 253, Staten Island, NY 10314: Free catalog with long

SASE ■ Coffee, baked goods, candies, nuts, and grains from the Middle East. 718–720–1557.

Thailand Food Corporation, 4821 N. Broadway St., Chicago, IL 60640: Free information ■ Oriental foods and specialties. 312–728–1199.

Dai Thanh Market, 420 S. 2nd St., San Jose, CA 95113: Free information ■ Oriental foods and specialties. 408–287–3744.

Truzzolino Food Products Company, P.O. Box 4226, Butte, MT 59702: Free information ■ Mexican beef enchiladas, refried beans, beef and turkey tamales, chili, salsa, and hickory-smoked Montana rainbow trout. 406–494–3132.

Tsang & Ma Wokery, P.O. Box 5644, Redwood City, CA 94063: Free catalog ■ Oriental herbs and spices, vegetables, mustards, stir-fry sauces, seasoning oils, and sauces. Also cooking equipment that includes woks, tempura racks, and steamers. 415–595–2270.

Uwajimaya, 519 6th Ave. South, Seattle, WA 98104: Free information ■ Oriental noodles, seaweed, dried vegetables and fish, sauces, and condiments. 206–624–6248.

Viet Hoa Market, 676 S. Jackson St., Seattle, WA 98104: Free information ■ Oriental foods and specialties. 206–621–8499.

Vietnam House, 242 Farmington Ave., Hartford, CT 06105: Free information ■ Thai food specialties. 203–524–0010.

May Wah Trading Company, 1230 Stockton, San Francisco, CA 94133: Free information ■ Oriental foods and specialties. 415–433–3095.

Fruits & Vegetables

Alamo Fruit, P.O. Box 666, Alamo, TX 78516: Free catalog ■ Fruit and smoked meats. 512–787–3548.

Aguajitoos Avocado Ranch, P.O. Box 2267, Goleta, CA 93118: Free brochure ■ Avocados. 805–968–2772.

Apricot Farm, Inc., 2620 Buena Vista Rd., Hollister, CA 95023: Free catalog ■ California dried fruit. 800–233–4413; 408–637–6388 (in CA).

Atkinson's Vidalia Onions, Box 121, Garfield, GA 30425: Free information ■ Vidalia onions. 800–241–3408; 912–763–2149 (in GA).

Bess' Beans, P.O. Box 1542, Charleston, SC 29402: Free brochure ■ Bean specialties that include soups. 800–233–2326; 803–722–4559 (in SC).

Bland Farms, P.O. Box 506, Glennville, GA 30427: Free information ■ Vidalia onions, marinated mushrooms, relishes, sauces, pickled items, salad dressings, meats, peanuts, nut candies and fudge, and Georgia pecans. 800–843–2542.

Blue Heron Fruit Shippers, 3221 Bay Shore Rd., Sarasota, FL 34234: Free brochure ■ Florida citrus, candies, marmalades, pecans, and honey. 800–237–3920.

Davis Citrus Farms, US 27 North, Sebring, FL 33871: Free catalog ■ Citrus fruit. 800–822–8777.

Delegeane Garlic Farms, P.O. Box 2561, Yountville, CA 94599: Free brochure ■ Fresh garlic, chili ristras, salt-free herb seasonings, and California wildflower honeys. 707–944–8019.

Delftree Farm, Hidden Valley Rd., P.O. Box 460, Pownal, VT 05261: Free price list ■ Fresh shiitake mushrooms. 800–243–3742.

Forest Foods, Inc., 355 N. Ashland Ave., Chicago, IL 60607: Free brochure ■ Morels, porcini wild mushrooms, shiitake mushrooms, and oyster mushrooms; cream of wild mushroom soup and other soup mixes; wild rice; and wild mushroom caviar. 312–421–3676.

G.I.M.M. Dry Yard, P.O. Box 1016, Winters, CA 95964: Free catalog ■ California dried fruit. 916–795–2919.

Gracewood Fruit Company, 1626 90th Ave., P.O. Box 2590, Vero Beach, FL 32961: Free information ■ Navel oranges and ruby red grapefruit. 800–678–1154.

Susan Green's California Cuisine, 3501 Taylor Dr., P.O. Box 8505, Ukiah, CA 95482: Free catalog ■ California dried and fresh fruit, nuts, deli favorites, baked goods, hams, and candy. 800–753–8558.

Hadley Fruit Orchards, P.O. Box 495, Cabazon, CA 92230: Free catalog ■ Dried fruit, nuts, candy, honey, and jellies. 714–849–4668.

Hale Indian River Groves, Indian River Plaza, Wabasso, FL 32970: Free catalog ■ Jumbo navel oranges, sweet ruby red grapefruits, and nova tangelos. 800–289–4253.

Harry & David, P.O. Box 712, Medford, OR 97501: Free brochure ■ Oregold peaches, Alphonse LaValle grapes, Royal Riviera pears, Crisp Mountain apples, and other fruits and gourmet specialties. 800–345–5655.

Hart's Crestview Groves, 9030 17th Pl., Vero Beach, FL 32966: Free information ■ Florida oranges and tree-ripened ruby red grapefruit. 800–285–8488.

Hendrix Farms, P.O. Box 175, Metter, GA 30439: Free information ■ Vidalia onions. 800–752–1551.

Hyatt Fruit Company, Box 639, Vero Beach, FL 32961: Free catalog ■ Oranges, grapefruits, candies, and jellies. 800–327–5810; 407–567–3766 (in FL).

Jaffe Brothers Natural Foods, P.O. Box 636, Valley Center, CA 92082: Free catalog ■ Grains and grain products, nuts, fruit, honey, and other natural foods. 619–749–1133.

Jones-Berry Farms, Rt. 1, Mt. Vernon, GA 30445: Free brochure ■ Vidalia sweet onions, sweet onion pickles, and relishes. 912–583–2549.

Kennedy Groves, P.O. Box 968, Vero Beach, FL 32961: Free catalog ■ Indian River grapefruit, valencia and navel oranges, tangerines, and tangelos. Other specialties include preserves, marmalades and jellies, citrus candy, baked goods, and dried fruit. 800–327–4768.

Lone Star Farms, P.O. Box 685, Mercedes, TX 78570: Free information ■ Texas sweet onions. 800–552–1015.

Lundberg Family Farms, P.O. Box 369, Richvale, CA 95974: Free information ■ Premium brown rice, organic brown rice, rice syrup, rice flower, salted and unsalted rice cakes, and rice cereals. 916–882–4551.

The Maples Fruit Farm, P.O. Box 167, Chewsville, MD 21721: Free list with long SASE ■ Fruit and nuts. 301–733–0777.

Mission Orchards, P.O. Box 6947, San Jose, CA 95150: Free catalog ■ Comice pears, red dessert grapes, California navel oranges, red grapefruit, cherries, plums, tangelos, pineapples, and kiwi fruit. Other specialties include cheese, candy, dried fruit, nuts, truffles, fruit cakes and pastries, and smoked meats and seafood. 800–333–1448.

Northern Lakes Wild Rice Company, P.O. Box 28, Cass Lake, MN 56633: Free information ■ Hand-harvested native wild rice. 218–335–6369.

Oasis Date Gardens, P.O. Box 757, Thermal, CA 92274: Free information ■ Medjool and Noor dates, dried figs, and candied apricots. 619–399–5665.

Old Southwest Trading Company, P.O. Box 7545, Albuquerque, NM 87194: Free catalog ■ Habanero Chiles and other exotic and domestic chiles. 505–836–0168.

The Onion Country Store, Inc., P.O. Box 1043, Vidalia, GA 30474: Free information ■ Vidalia onions. 912–583–2294.

Pinnacle Orchards, 441 S. Fir, Medford, OR 97501: Free catalog ■ Comice pears and other specialties. 800–879–7327.

Pittman & Davis, 801 N. Expressway, Harlingen, TX 78552: Free catalog ■ Ruby red grapefruit from Texas and Florida, and oranges, pecans, fruit cakes, cheese, and smoked hams and turkeys. 512–423–2154.

Poinsettia Groves, 1481 South US Hwy. 1, P.O. Box 1388, Vero Beach, FL 32961: Free brochure ■ Oranges and grapefruits. 800–627–3230.

Radcliffe's Mushrooms, P.O. Box 1712, Southeastern, PA 19399: Free information with long SASE ■ Mushrooms. 800–673–7811.

Red Cooper, Rt. 3, Box 10, Alamo, TX 78516: Free catalog ■ Grapefruits, oranges, pineapples, avocados, apples, persimmons, tangelos, dates, pears, and dried fruit. 800–876–4733.

Robinson Ranch, P.O. Box 1018, Walla Walla, WA 99362: Free information ■ Shallots. 509–525–6589.

Sphinx Date Ranch, 3039 N. Scottsdale Rd., Scottsdale, AZ 85251: Free brochure ■ Medjool dates, pitted and hand-dipped in creamy milk chocolate, stuffed with walnuts, rolled in powdered sugar, or for cooking; date-pecan loaves; trail mixes; fruit cakes; jellies; and nuts. 800–482–3283; 602–941–2261 (in AZ).

Spyke's Grove, 7250 Griffin Rd., Davie, FL 33314: Free catalog ■ Florida oranges, mangos, avocados, and Nova, Navel, Honeybell, Temple, Murcott, Valencia, and Ruby Red grapefruit. 800–327–9713.

Sullivan Victory Groves, P.O. Box 10, Cocoa, FL 32923: Free brochure ■ Florida navel oranges. 800–ORANGE–1.

Sun Ripe Tomatoes, 813 E. Bloomingdale Blvd., Brandon, FL 33511: Free information ■ Hand-picked farm-fresh tomatoes. 800–283–0606.

Sweet Energy, P.O. Box G, Essex Center, VT 05451: Free list ■ Dried fruit. 802–655–4440.

Timber Crest Farms, 4791 Dry Creek Rd., Healdsburg, CA 95448: Free catalog ■ Organic apples, apricots, dates, figs, cherries, dried tomato products, fruit butters, nuts, and trail mixes. 707–433–8251.

Tri-Tex Citrus Company, Rt. 2, Box 50, Weslaco, TX 78596: Free brochure ■ Ruby red grapefruit and oranges. 800–888–1957.

USA Evans Farm, P.O. Box 913, Fort Valley, GA 31030: Free brochure ■ Tree-ripened peaches. 800–321–0640.

Walker Indian River Groves, Box 536, Vero Beach, FL 32961: Free catalog ■ Oranges and other fruits. 407–689–2670.

Walla Walla Gardener's Association, 210 N. 11th Ave., Walla Walla, WA 99362: Free information ■ Sweet Walla Walla onions. 800–553–5014; 509–525–7070 (in WA).

Gift Assortments & Gourmet Specialties

Austin Street Market, 2296 Senter Rd., P.O. Box 4758, San Jose, CA 95150: Free catalog ■ Meats, seafood, breads, cakes, pies, and candies. 800–527–7654.

Balducci's, 334 E. 11th St., New York, NY 10003: Free catalog ■ Jalapenos and Cheddar, sourdough rye, whole wheat, raisins and walnuts, other breads and food specialties. 212–673–2600.

Baskets Because, Box 27800, Albuquerque, NM 87114: Catalog $2 ■ Southwestern food specialties. 505–898–9092.

Bland Farms, P.O. Box 506, Glennville, GA 30427: Free information ■ Vidalia onions, marinated mushrooms, relishes, sauces, pickled items, salad dressings, meats, peanuts, nut candies and fudge, and Georgia pecans. 800–843–2542.

Brumwell Flour Mill, P.O. Box 126, South Amana, IA 52334: Free brochure ■ Pancake, muffin, biscuit and granola mixes; maple syrup and sorghum; and apple butter. 319–622–3455.

Burberry's Limited, 9 E. 57th St., New York, NY 10022: Free catalog ■ International tea, preserves and marmalades, chutney, mustards and horseradish sauces, cakes, and shortbread biscuits. 212–371–5010.

Callaway Gardens Country Store, Pine Mountain, GA 31822: Free catalog ■ Southern-style bacon, ham, other meats, and jellies. 800–282–8181.

Cavanaugh Lakeview Farms, Ltd., P.O. Box 580, Chelsea, MI 48118: Free catalog ■ Honey-cured and smoked poultry; smoked ham and bacon; fresh-frozen poultry, steaks, and game; smoked seafood; and desserts and popcorn. 800–243–4438.

Cherry Hill Cooperative Cannery, Inc., Barre-Montpelier Rd., Barre, VT 05641: Free information ■ Applesauces and apple butters, pickles, maple syrup and honey, salsa, conserves, marinara sauce, barbecue sauce, and mustards. 802–479–2558.

Clearview Farms, Inc., RD 1, Box 5070, Enosburg Falls, VT 05450: Free catalog ■ Maple syrup and sugar, maple apple sauce and apple pie, maple brandy sauce, maple-sugared nuts, mustards, barbecue sauces and glazes, preserves, relishes and pickles, and salad dressings. 802–933–2537.

Coastal Express Food & Spirits, 1501 14th St. NW, Washington, DC 20005: Free catalog ■ Fruit, chocolates, cakes, spirits and wines, and other favorites. 800–243–7466; 202–387–6492 (in DC).

Community Kitchens, P.O. Box 3778, Baton Rouge, LA 70821: Free catalog ■ Imported coffee and tea, Cajun spices, Creole seasonings, French Quarter binet mixes, Louisiana corn bread mix, jambalaya seasoning and rice, and candy. 800–535–9901.

Corr's Confections, Inc., P.O. Box 64, Midlothian, VA 23113: Free brochure ■ Chocolate covered snacks, potato chips, pretzels, peanut brittle, nuts, and fruits. 804–739–7861.

Dakin Farm, Rt. 7, Ferrisburg, VT 05456: Free catalog ■ Vermont smoked ham and bacon, maple syrup, and aged Cheddar cheese. 802–425–3971.

Festive Foods of Virginia, Ltd., 20 Carrollton Rd., Sterling, VA 22170: Free catalog ■ Pastry and baking products, chocolate and cocoa, herbs and spices, teas, wild mush-

rooms, oils and vinegars, jams and preserves, dried fruit, flavorings and oils, and other specialties. 703–450–4504.

Figi's, 3200 S. Maple, Marshfield, WI 54404: Free catalog ■ Baked goods, meats, cheese, candies, jams and jellies, and nuts. 715–384–6101.

Fin 'n Feather, 11 S. 2nd Ave., P.O. Box 487, St. Charles, IL 60174: Free catalog ■ Smoked game birds, hams and other meats, cheese, jellies and jams, and cookies. 800–628–2242.

Fraser-Morris Fine Foods, 931 Madison Ave., New York, NY 10021: Free catalog ■ Meats, cookies and other pastries, candy, fruit, seafood, cheese, nuts, preserves, coffee and tea, caviar, pates, soups, spices and other condiments, mustards, truffles, and mushrooms. 212–988–6700.

G & R Farms of Georgia, Rt. 3, Box 35A, Glennville, GA 30427: Free catalog ■ Fruits and vegetables, baked goods, popcorn specialties, salad dressings, Georgia pecans and peanuts, nut candies, sauces, and condiments. 800–522–0567.

Thomas Garraway, Ltd., United States Customer Service Center, Madison, WI 53779: Free catalog ■ Gourmet sauces, pastas, mustards, dressings, coffee, tea, cheese, and preserves. 800–356–7070.

Gazin's Cajun Creole Foods, 2910 Toulouse St., P.O. Box 19221, New Orleans, LA 70179: Catalog 50¢ ■ Gourmet specialties from New Orleans. 800–262–6410; 504–482–0302 (in LA).

Goodies from Goodman, 12102 Inwood Rd., Dallas, TX 75244: Free catalog ■ Fruit, cheese, nuts, candy, popcorn specialties, and smoked meats and fish. 800–535–3136; 214–387–4804 (in TX).

Great Valley Mills, 687 Mill Rd., Telford, PA 18969: Free brochure ■ Pennsylvania Dutch country cheese, ham, bacon, sausage, beef, preserves, fruitcakes, stollen, flour, cereals, and meals. 800–688–6455.

Susan Green's California Cuisine, 3501 Taylor Dr., P.O. Box 8505, Ukiah, CA 95482: Free catalog ■ California dried and fresh fruit, nuts, deli favorites, baked goods, hams, and candy. 800–753–8558.

Hannah's Choice, P.O. Box 943, Shelburne, VT 05482: Free brochure ■ Vermont maple syrup, whole grain pancake mixes,

honey, and homemade jams and jellies. 203–574–0667.

Harman's Cheese & Country Store, Sugar Hill, NH 03585: Free catalog ■ Cheddar cheese, maple syrup, fruit preserves, salad dressings, plain and pate smoked salmon, crab meat, honey, smoked herring fillets, pancake mixes, maple butter, and candy. 603–823–8000.

Harrington Ham Company, 295 Main St., Richmond, VA 05477: Free catalog ■ Spiral-sliced, cob-smoked, maple-glazed hams and other smoked meats that include bacon, turkey breast, and pheasant. Other specialties include cheese, maple syrup, pastries, plum pudding, fruitcakes, and dried fruit. 802–434–4444.

Harry & David, P.O. Box 712, Medford, OR 97501: Free catalog ■ Fruit, cakes, baklava, cinnamon pastries, tortes, candy, and preserves. 800–345–5655.

Heartland/Minnesota, 1791 Glen Lake Station, Minnetonka, MN 55345: Free catalog ■ Swedish baked goods, apple cider syrup, wild rice sausage, smoked pheasant, apple-smoked hams, preserves, and wild turkey. 800–544–8661.

Hickins, Black Mountain Rd., RFD 1, Box 293, Brattleboro, VT 05301: Free catalog ■ Jams and jellies, pickles, fruit syrups, maple syrup, fruit cakes, candies, and cheese. 802–254–2146.

Hickory Farms, P.O. Box 75, Maumee, OH 43537: Free catalog ■ Cheese, meats, candies, pastries, deli specialties, seafood, nuts, truffles, fruit cakes, liqueur cakes, tea and coffee, dried fruit, jellies and preserves, fresh fruit, and popcorn. 800–222–4438.

House of Webster, 1013 N. 2nd, Rogers, AR 72756: Catalog $1 ■ Preserves and jellies, cheese, country cured and smoked bacon, biscuit and pancake mixes, candy, syrups, wild honey, and country sorghum. 501–636–4640.

Improv Gourmet Food Baskets & Gifts, 17320 Germantown Rd., Germantown, MD 20874: Free brochure ■ Ready-made or custom gift assortments that include beverages and juices, cakes and cookies, breads, pates, nibbling delights, candies, pickles and relishes, tea, soup mixes, and other international gourmet favorites. 800–322–4438; 301–428–1010 (in MD).

It's from Oregon, 8065 SW Cirrus Dr., Beaverton, OR 97005: Catalog $1 (refundable) ■ Smoked Chinook salmon, desserts and dessert sauces, and other specialties. 800–247–0727.

J & K Trading Company, 10808 Garland Dr., Culver City, CA 90230: Free price list ■ Escargots, crab meat, lump fish caviar, hearts of palms, button mushrooms, and other gourmet specialties. 213–836–3334.

Kenyon Corn Meal Company, Inc., P.O. Box 221, West Kingston, RI 02892: Free brochure ■ Stone-ground meals and flours and New England delicacies that include mince meat, clam and corn chowder, pancake syrups, pickle relishes, Indian pudding, and minced clams. 401–783–4054.

Knott's Berry Farm, P.O. Box 1989, Placentia, CA 92670: Free catalog ■ Jellies and preserves, cheese, sausage, candy, cakes, cookies, and dried fruit. 800–877–6887.

Kozlowski Farms, 5566 Gravenstein Hwy., North Forestville, CA 95436: Free brochure ■ Marmalades, jams, and preserves; honey and mustards; barbecue sauce and fruit butters; sugar-free berry vinegars; conserves; and chutney. 707–887–1587.

Madeline & Sylvia's Fancy Food Emporium, 89 Middletown Rd., Holmdel, NJ 07733: Free catalog ■ Smoked salmon, pasta, honey-glazed ham, coffee and tea, breads, jellies and jams, and candies. 908–946–2711.

Maison Glass Delicacies, 111 E. 58th St., New York, NY 10022: Catalog $5 ■ Smoked meats and fish. 800–822–5564; 212–755–3316 (in NY).

Market Square Food Company, Inc., 1642 Richfield Ave., Highland Park, IL 60035: Free information ■ Oils, vinegars, and sauces; confections and baked goods; wild rice from Minnesota; and smoked, boneless sockeye salmon from Alaska. 800–232–2299.

Matthews 1812 House, 250 Kent Rd., P.O. Box 15, Cornwall Bridge, CT 06754: Free brochure ■ Cakes, nuts, chocolates, jams, tea, condiments, and smoked meats. 800–662–1812.

Mid South Pecan Company, P.O. Box 882, Ruston, LA 71273: Free information ■ Natural in-the-shell and cracked pecans. 800–345–1148.

New England Country Fare, 378 Washington St., Westwood, MA 02090: Free information ■ Gift assortments with food products from New England food producers. 800–274–FARE.

Pan Handler Products, RR 4, Box 399, Stowe, VT 05672: Free brochure ■ Mexican specialties, Belgian dessert sauces, chutney, conserves, cheese, jams and jellies, and Vermont maple syrup. 802–253–7138.

Pepperidge Farm, P.O. Box 917, Clinton, CT 06413: Free catalog ■ Soups, cookies and other pastries, crackers, candy, cheese and sausage, popcorn, and breakfast mixes. 800–243–9314.

Pepper Patch, 1250 Old Hillsboro Rd., Franklin, TN 37064: Free brochure ■ Cakes, candies, dessert sauces, cocktail jellies and sauces, fresh fruit butters, marmalades, pickles, and relishes. 615–790–1012.

Perfect Nut Company, Mail Order Division, 1348 Busch Pkwy., Buffalo Grove, IL 60089: Free catalog ■ Chocolates from California, Hawaii, Switzerland, and Belgium; nuts and snack items in tins, bags, and baskets; fresh fruit; and smoked meats, poultry, and fish. 800–451–2051; 708–459–2590 (in IL).

Petrossian Shop, 182 W. 58th St., New York, NY 10019: Free information ■ Caviar, foie gras, truffles, and smoked salmon. 800–828–9241.

Pfaelzer Brothers, 281 W. 83rd St., Burr Ridge, IL 60521: Catalog $2 ■ Gourmet food specialties. 800–621–0226.

Pinnacle Orchards, 444 S. Fir, Medford, OR 97501: Free catalog ■ Comice pears and other gourmet specialties. 800–879–7327.

Rossi Pasta, P.O. Box 759, Marietta, OH 45750: Free brochure ■ Handmade black olive, linguine, garlic fettuccini, saffron linguine, and other pastas. 800–227–6774.

S.E. Rykoff & Company, 3501 Taylor Dr., Ukiah, CA 95482: Free catalog ■ Gourmet foods and professional-quality cookware for home chefs. 800–333–1448.

San Antonio River Mill, P.O. Box 1470, San Antonio, TX 78295: Free catalog ■ Chili, preserves, southern biscuit and other

baking mixes, jellies, and cooking accessories. 800–627–6455.

Seyco Fine Foods, 1645 Donlon St., Ste. 106, Ventura, CA 93003: Free catalog ■ Pates, sauces, preserves, desserts, soups, olives, pickles and relishes, sweet pickled fruit, oils, vinegars, dressings, jellies and marmalades, specialty and spirited fruits, candy, and nuts. 800–423–2942.

Silver Palate, 274 Columbus Ave., New York, NY 10023: Price list $2 ■ Spices, condiments, and other delicacies. 212–799–6340.

Snack World, Inc., P.O. Box 13026, Reading, PA 19612: Free brochure ■ Pennsylvania Dutch Country chocolate coated pretzels and shoofly pies, cheese and plain pretzels, smoked bolognas, Cheddar cheese, candy, nuts, and sesame sticks. 215–929–5219.

A Southern Season, Eastgate, Chapel Hill, NC 27514: Free catalog ■ Irish whiskey cake, shortbread, imported coffee, nuts and candies, fruit cakes and other baked goods, condiments, preserves, and pastas. 800–253–3663; 919–929–7133 (in NC).

Sutton Place Gourmet, 10323 Old Georgetown Rd., Bethesda, MD 20814: Free catalog ■ International and domestic seafoods, coffee and tea, fruit, caviar, foie gras, champagnes, nuts, wild rices, condiments and syrups, meats, dried fruit, cheese, deli specialties, sauces, candies, and wines. 800–346–8763.

Swiss Colony, Catalog Request Department, Madison, WI 53793: Free catalog ■ Cheese, meats, sausages, pastries, nuts, candies, and snacks.

Tillamook Cheese, P.O. Box 313, Tillamook, OR 97141: Free catalog ■ Cheese, exotic delicacies, candies, prepared meats and fowl, smoked fish, and jellies and preserves. 503–842–4481.

Todaro Brothers, 555 2nd Ave., New York, NY 10016: Catalog $1 ■ Cheese, pastas, breads, meats, confections, spices, coffee, and other specialties. 212–679–7766.

Valley View Blueberries, 21717 NE 68th St., Vancouver, WA 98682: Free information ■ Blueberry syrup, blueberry spiced jam, blueberry amaretto glaze, dried blueberries, and blueberry trail mix. 206–892–2839.

War Eagle Mill, Rt. 5, Box 411, Rogers, AR 72756: Free catalog ■ Stone-ground flours and meals, whole grain mixes for biscuits, corn bread, buckwheat pancakes and waffles, hush puppies, muffins, jellies, preserves and fruit butters, country sorghum, and clover honey. 501–789–5343.

Whet Your Appetite, P.O. Box 1282, Goleta, CA 93116: Free catalog ■ Gift assortments that include specialty foods from around the world. 800–228–9438.

Zabar's & Company, 2245 Broadway, New York, NY 10024: Free catalog ■ Smoked fish, condiments and spices, candies, crackers, and other specialties. Includes cookware, food processors, microwave ovens, kitchen tools, and coffee makers. 800–221–3347; 212–787–2000 (in NY).

Gingerbread Houses

Fantasy Cookie Company, 12800 Arroyo St., Sylmar, CA 91342: Free information ■ Easy-to-assemble gingerbread house kits. Complete with baked parts and decorations. 800–354–4488; 818–361–6901 (in CA).

Health & Natural

Ahler's Organic Date Garden, P.O. Box 726, Mecca, CA 92254: Free information ■ Dates and date products. 619–396–2337.

Allergy Resources, Inc., 195 Huntington Beach Dr., Colorado Springs, CO 80921: Free catalog ■ Wheat-free and gluten-free products, and other organic foods. 719–488–3630.

American Forest Foods Corporation, P.O. Box 1258, Henderson, NC 27536: Free catalog ■ Oyster and shiitake mushrooms, spices, and other organic foods. 919–438–2674.

American Spoon Foods, 411 E. Lake St., Petoskey, MI 49770: Free literature ■ Pancake and waffle mix made with organic-grown Indian blue corn, wild rice, wild berry preserves, and wild pecans. 800–222–5886.

Arjoy Acres, HCR Box 1410, Payson, AZ 85541: Free literature ■ Garlic varieties and shallots. 602–474–1224.

Asha Foods, 115 Dundas St. East, Napance, Ontario, Canada K7R 1J2: Catalog $1 ■ Organic grains, beans, seeds, nuts, herbs, and teas. 613–354–5987.

Better Foods Foundation, 200 N. Washington, Greencastle, PA 17225:

Catalog $1 ■ Cereals, cookies, and snacks. 717–597–7127.

Be Wise Ranch, 9018 Artesian Rd., San Diego, CA 92127: Free literature ■ Limes, lemons, oranges, and avocados. 619–756–4851.

Blue Heron Farm, P.O. Box 68, Rumsey, CA 95679: Free information ■ Organic oranges, other citrus fruits, and nuts. 916–796–3799.

Bread Alone, Rt. 28, Boiceville, NY 12412: Free information ■ Rye, wheat, and sourdough breads. 914–657–3328.

Brier Run Farm, Rt. 1, Box 73, Birch River, WV 26610: Free information ■ Soft goat cheese. 304–649–2975.

Brown Company, P.O. Box 69, Tetonia, ID 83452: Free information ■ Idaho potatoes and seed potatoes. 208–456–2500.

Brownville Mills, Brownville, NE 68321: Free price list ■ Natural flour and meals, grain and cereal, beans, nuts, seeds, oils, honey and syrups, dried fruit, and spices. 402–825–4131.

Brumwell Flour Mill, P.O. Box 126, South Amana, IA 52334: Free brochure ■ Pancake, muffin, biscuit, and granola mixes; maple syrup; sorghum; apple butter; and specialties made with milled yellow, white, and blue corn, wheat, rye, oats, buckwheat, barley, and soybeans. 319–622–3455.

Cabot Creamery, Box 128, Cabot, VT 05647: Free information ■ All-natural cheese with half the fat and cholesterol and 33 percent fewer calories than Cheddar. 802–563–2231.

Capay Fruits & Vegetables, Star Route, Box 3, Capay, CA 95607: Free information ■ Herbs, peaches, and dried tomatoes. 916–796–4111.

Cascadian Farm, P.O. Box 568, Concrete, WA 98237: Free information ■ Fruit conserves and dill pickles. 206–853–8175.

Chieftain Wild Rice Company, P.O. Box 1080, Hayward, WI 54843: Free information ■ Long-grain wild rice. 800–262–6368; 715–634–3702 (in WI).

Coleman Natural Beef, 5140 Race Court, Denver, CO 80217: Free information ■ Antibiotic- and hormone-free meat. 303–297–9393.

Cooks Maple Products, Bashan Hill Rd., Worthington, MA 01098: Free information ■ Maple syrup. 413–238–5827.

Country Grown/Health Rich, 12202 Woodbine, Redford, MI 48239: Free information ■ Wheat-free organic snacks that contain no preservatives or dairy products. 313–535–9222.

Country Life Natural Foods, 109 52nd Ave., Pullman, MI 49450: Free information ■ Beans, grains, seeds, nuts, and raisins. 616–236–5011.

Covalda Date Company, P.O. Box 908, Coachella, CA 92236: Free information ■ Dried fruits, dates, and nuts. 619–398–3441.

Daisyfresh Dairy Cultures, Box 36, Santa Cruz, CA 95063: Free price information ■ Dairy cultures for making home-style Bulgarian yogurt, extra mild Swiss acidophilus, home-style Danish sour cream, and Irish country buttermilk.

Dakota Lean Meats, Inc., 136 W. Tripp Ave., Winner, SD 57580: Free information ■ Hormone-free meat. 800–727–5326.

Deer Valley Farm, RD 1, Guilford, NY 13780: Free information ■ Beef, pork, chicken, turkey, eggs, fruit, grains, herbs, juices, pasta, oil, seasonings, baked goods, confections, and nuts. 607–764–8556.

Delwick Candy Company, P.O. Box 39, Short Hills, NJ 07078: Free information ■ Sugar-free candy that contains no sorbitol or salt.

Dharma Farma, Star Route Box 140, Osage, AR 72638: Free information ■ Apples and pears. 501–553–2550.

Diamond Organics, Freedom, CA 95019: Free information ■ Organic lettuce, greens, roots, herbs, and fruits. 800–922–2396.

Dutch Mill Cheese, 2001 N. State Rd. I, Cambridge City, IN 47327: Free information ■ Organic cheese. 317–478–5847.

Eagle Agricultural Products, 407 Church Ave., Huntsville, AR 72740: Free information ■ Fresh and dried produce, beans, flour, pasta, and grains. 501–738–2203.

Ecology Sound Farms, 42126 Rd. 168, Orosi, CA 93647: Free literature ■ Kiwi fruit, persimmons, Asian pears, plums, oranges, dried fruit, and garlic. 209–528–3816.

Eden Foods, 701 Tecumseh, Clinton, MI 49236: Free information ■ Low-sodium organic soy sauces. 517–456–7424.

Famous Idaho Potatoes, Star Rt., Moyie Springs, ID 83845: Free information ■ Organic vegetables. 208–267–7938.

Fiddler's Green Farm, RR 1, Box 656, Belfast, ME 04915: Free literature ■ Pancake, muffin, and spice cake mixes, and a breakfast gift package that includes pancake and muffin mix, maple syrup, and honey. 207–338–3568.

Four Chimneys Farm Winery, RD 1, Hall Rd., Himrod-on-Seneca, NY 14842: Free information ■ Wine, grape juice, wine vinegar, and champagne. (Note: alcohol products cannot be shipped out of state.) 607–243–7502.

J. Francis Company, Rt. 3, Box 54, Atlanta, TX 75551: Free information ■ Pecans. 903–796–5364.

Frankferd Farms Food, RD 1, 318 Love Rd., Valencia, PA 16059: Free catalog ■ Organic grains, beans, flours, pancake mixes, cereals, soy foods, macrobiotic supplies, cheese, dried fruit, juices, and nut butters. 412–898–2242.

French Meadow Bakery, 2610 Lyndale Ave., Minneapolis, MN 55408: Free catalog ■ Organic European sourdough breads that contain no yeast, dairy products, oil, or sweeteners. 612–870–4740.

Frontier Cooperative Herbs, P.O. Box 299, Norway, IA 52318: Free literature ■ Herbs and spices. 319–227–7991.

Garden Spot Distributors, 438 White Oak Rd., New Holland, PA 17557: Free information ■ Poultry and organic meat products. 717–354–4936.

Gem Cultures, 30301 Sherwood Rd., Fort Bragg, CA 95437: Free catalog ■ Food cultures and starters for tempeh, misos, shoyu, villi, sourdough, and kefir. Other specialties include tofu coagulants, books, sea vegetables, and reusable culture items. 707–964–2922.

Genesee Natural Foods, RD 2, Box 105, Genesee, PA 16923: Free ordering information ■ Beans, seeds, flour, pasta, corn chips, rice cakes, raisins, prunes, prune and apple juice, and peanut, almond, hazelnut, and cashew nut butters. 814–228–3200.

Giusto's Specialty Foods, Inc., 241 E. Harris Ave. South, San Francisco, CA 94080:

Free literature ■ Breads, cakes, grains, spices, cereals, flour, oil, seeds, and cookies. 415–873–6566.

Golden Acres Orchard, Rt. 2, Box 2450, Front Royal, VA 22630: Free information ■ Apples, apple cider vinegar, and apple juice. 703–636–9611.

Gold Mine Natural Food Company, 1947 30th St., San Diego, CA 92102: Free information ■ Organic brown rice and beans. 800–647–2929; 619–234–9711 (in CA).

Gravelly Ridge Farms, Star Rt. 16, Elk Creek, CA 95939: Free catalog ■ Organic fresh fruit, dried fruit, vegetables, and grains. 916–963–3216.

Greek Gourmet, Ltd., 195 Whiting St., Hingham, MA 02043: Free information ■ Extra virgin olive oil and olives. 617–749–1866.

Green Earth Natural Foods, 2545 Prairie Ave., Evanston, IL 60201: Free information ■ Fresh produce, grains, meats, and other organic food products. 800–322–3662; 708–864–8949 (in IL).

Green Knoll Farm, P.O. Box 434, Gridley, CA 95948: Free information ■ Kiwi fruit. 916–846–3431.

Hardscrabble Enterprises, Inc., Box 42, Cherry Grove, WV 26804: Catalog $3 (refundable) ■ Shiitake mushrooms. 304–567–2727.

Hawthorne Valley Farm, RD 2, Box 225A, Ghent, NY 12075: Free information ■ Organic cheese. 518–672–7500.

Health Valley Natural Foods, 700 Union St., Montebello, CA 90604: Free information ■ Nutritious grains. 213–724–2211.

Herb Pharm, P.O. Box 116, Williams, OR 97544: Free information ■ Herbal extracts, herbs, and teas. 503–846–7178.

Hill & Dale Farms, West Hill-Daniel Davis Rd., Putney, VT 05346: Free information ■ Apples and apple cider vinegar. 802–387–5817.

Homestead Organic Produce, Rt. 1, 2002 Rd. 7 NW, Quincy, WA 98848: Free ordering information ■ Sweet onions. 509–787–2248.

Hugh's Gardens, Rt. 1, Box 67, Buxton, ND 58218: Free information ■ Carrots, onions, and potatoes. 701–942–3345.

International Yogurt Company, 628 N. Doheny Dr., Los Angeles, CA 90069: Free brochure ■ Yogurt tablets, acidophilus capsules, yogurt culture, acidophilus milk culture, cheese culture, and Kefir grains and culture. 310–274–9917.

S.M. Jacobson, 1505 Doherty, Mission, TX 78572: Free information ■ Organic oranges and other citrus fruits. 512–585–1712.

Jaffe Brothers Natural Foods, P.O. Box 636, Valley Center, CA 92082: Free catalog ■ Organic dried foods that contain no preservatives or other chemical additives. Includes dried fruit, nuts, brown rice, pasta, oil, grains, beans peas, seeds, olives, and candy. 619–749–1133.

Krystal Wharf Farms, RD 2, Box 191A, Mansfield, PA 16933: Free information ■ Dried fruits, fresh produce, nuts, beans, and grains.

Living Farms, Box 50, Tracey, MN 56175: Free information ■ Grains, beans, rice, wheat, sunflowers, and alfalfa, clover, and radish sprouting seeds. 800–533–5320; 800–622–5235 (in MN).

Maine Coast Sea Vegetables, Shore Rd., Franklin, ME 04634: Free information ■ Sea chips, kelp, dulse, and nori. 207–565–2907.

Mercantile Food Company, P.O. Box 1140, Georgetown, CT 06829: Free information ■ Hot and cold breakfast cereals.

Mill City Sourdough Bakery, 2070 Grand Ave., St. Paul, MN 55105: Free brochure ■ European sourdough breads that contain no dairy products, sweeteners, or cholesterol. 800–87–DOUGH.

Millstream Natural Health Supplies, 1310–A E. Tallmadge Ave., Akron, OH 44310: Free information ■ Fruits, vegetables, and nuts. 216–630–2700.

Moksha, 724 Palm Ave., P.O. Box 1168, Watsonville, CA 95077: Free catalog ■ Dried organic-grown fruits, olives, herb vinegars and oils, and hand-rolled pastas. 800–274–8778.

Morningland Dairy, Rt. 1, Box 188–B, Mountain View, MO 65548: Free information ■ Raw milk cheese. 417–469–3817.

Mountain Ark Trading Company, 120 S. East Ave., Fayetteville, AR 72701: Free literature ■ Vegetables, miso, seasonings, rice, pasta, fruit, spreads, oils, beans, and soups. 800–643–8909.

Natural Lifestyle Supplies, 16 Lookout Dr., Asheville, NC 28804: Free catalog ■ Cereals and grains, prepared foods, nuts and seeds, seasonings, condiments, oils, other natural food products, and natural baby and body care products. 800–752–2775.

Natural Way Mills, Inc., Rt. 2, Box 37, Middle River, MN 56737: Free information ■ Flours, cereals, whole grains, and other organic foods. 218–222–3677.

New England Natural Bakers, 107 Long Plain Rd., RFD 1, South Deerfield, MA 01373: Free information ■ Nut granola made with Brazil nuts, cashews, honey, coconut, and cinnamon. 413–665–8599.

Northwest Select, 14724 184th St. NE, Arlington, WA 98223: Free information ■ Organic herbs, vegetables, edible flowers, and other food items. 206–435–8577.

Nu-World Amaranth, Inc., P.O. Box 2202, Naperville, IL 60504: Free information ■ Nutritious grains. 501–298–3297.

Organic Foods Express, Inc., 11003 Emack Rd., Beltsville, MD 20705: Free catalog ■ Organic and natural grains, beans, cheese, milk, meats, breads, juices, coffees, snacks, vegetables, and fruits. 301–937–8608.

Paul's Grains, 2475–B 340 St., Laurel, IA 50141: Free information ■ Whole grains and grain products, chicken, turkey, lamb, and beef. 515–476–3373.

Steven Pavich & Sons, Rt. 2, Box 291, Delano, CA 03215: Free information ■ Organic grapes. 805–725–1046.

Peace Valley Premium Beef, 125 Hosea Ave., Cincinnati, OH 45220: Free information ■ Antibiotic- and hormone-free meat. 513–861–2455.

Piedmont Foods, 7419 Hwy. 64 East, Knightdale, NC 27545: Free information ■ Organic pork and beef. 919–269–5858.

Rein Farms, 812 Cedar Ave., Metarie, LA 70001: Free information ■ Organic vegetables. 504–888–5763.

Rising Sun Distributors, P.O. Box 627, Milesburg, PA 16853: Free information ■ Beef, poultry, lamb, pork, fruit and vegetables, beans, seeds, and grains. 814–355–9850.

1788 Tuthilltown Grist Mill, Albany Post Rd., P.O. Box 62, Gardiner, NY 12525: Free brochure ■ Stone-ground flours, meals and cereal products, and old-fashioned health foods. 914–255–5695.

Sleepy Hollow Farm, 44001 Dunlap Rd., Miramonte, CA 93641: Free information ■ Organic herbs and apples. 209–336–2444.

Joe Soghomonian, 8624 S. Chestnut, Fresno, CA 93725: Free information ■ Raisins, grapes, and walnuts. 209–834–2772.

Southern Brown Rice, P.O. Box 185, Weiner, AR 72479: Free catalog ■ Rice products fresh from the farm. 800–421–7423.

Soyco Foods, Division Galaxy Cheese Company, P.O. Box 5181, New Castle, PA 16105: Free information ■ Casein-free cheese alternative for people who want to avoid dairy products. 800–441–9419.

Specialty Grain Company, Box 2458, Dearborn, MI 48123: Free information ■ Grains, seeds, beans, dried fruits, and nuts. 313–535–9222.

Sprout Delights, 13090 NW 7th Ave., Miami, FL 33168: Free information ■ Bakery items. 800–334–2253; 305–687–5880 (in FL).

Stapelman's Meats, 2nd & State Streets, Box 358, Osman, NE 68765: Free information ■ Antibiotic- and hormone-free beef and pork. 402–985–2470.

Starr Organic Produce, Inc., P.O. Box 561502, Miami, FL 33256: Free information ■ Organic oranges and other citrus fruits. 305–262–1242.

Sunrise Farm Health Food Store, 17650 Torrence Ave., Lansing, IL 60438: Free information ■ Organic foods. 708–474–6166.

Thee Six B Farms, 4998 Centerville Rd. North, Greens Fork, IN 47345: Free brochure ■ Ham, bacon, and pork that contain no additives, preservatives, or growth hormones. 800–473–PORK.

Timber Crest Farms, 4791 Dry Creek Rd., Healdsburg, CA 95448: Free catalog ■ Dried fruit, dried tomato products, fruit butters, nuts, and trail mixes. 707–433–8251.

Walnut Acres Natural Foods, 438 Wite Oak Rd., Penns Creek, PA 17862: Free catalog ■ Fresh and canned vegetables; canned fruits, grains, baked goods, natural cheese, fruit and vegetable juices. dried fruit, nuts, jams and preserves, and other specialties. 800–433–3998.

Water Wheel Sugar House, Rt. 2, Jefferson, NH 03583: Free information ■ Maple syrup. 603–586–4479.

Wax Orchards, 22744 Wax Orchards Rd. SW, Vashon, WA 98070: Free information ■ Food products sweetened with a blend of concentrated natural fruit juices, conserves, smooth apple butters, fruit syrups, and dessert toppings. 800–634–6132; 206–682–8251 (in WA).

Weiss Kiwifruit, 594 Pasco Companeros, Chico, CA 95928: Free information ■ Kiwi fruit. 916–343–2354.

Whole Foods SoHo, 117 Prince St., New York, NY 10012: Free information ■ Organic grains and beans, macrobiotic specialties, allergy-free products, and fresh organic chicken, turkeys, eggs, and meats. 212–673–5388.

Wilton's Organic Potatoes, Box 28, Aspen, CO 81612: Free information ■ Potatoes. 303–925–3433.

Maple Syrup

American Maple Products, Newport, VT 05855: Free price list ■ Medium and dark amber maple syrup; maple candy, sugar, and butter; fudge; tea; salad dressings; and cookie and cake mixes. 800–343–0837; 800–548–1221 (in VT).

Branon Maple Syrup, La Plante Rd., Rt. 2, Box 27A, West Chazy, NY 12992: Free information ■ Maple sugar and syrup. 518–493–7090.

Butternut Mountain Farm, Johnson, VT 05656: Free information ■ Maple syrup and sugar. 800–828–2376.

Clearview Farms, Inc., RD 1, Box 5070, Enosburg Falls, VT 05450: Free catalog ■ Maple syrup maple sugar, maple apple sauce and apple pie, maple brandy sauce, maple-sugared nuts, mustards, barbecue sauces and glazes, preserves, relishes and pickles, and salad dressings. 802–933–2537.

Grafton Village Apple Company, RR 3, Box 236D, Grafton, VT 05146: Free catalog ■ Maple syrup and sugar. 800–843–4822.

Green Mountain Sugar House, Box 341, Ludlow, VT 05149: Free catalog ■ Maple syrup, maple sugar candy and nut brittle, cheese, smoked slab bacon, fudge, pancake mix, mincemeat, Vermont grist mill products, and homemade jams. 802–228–7151.

Maple Grove Farms of Vermont, 167 Portland St., St. Johnsbury, VT 05819: Free information ■ Maple sugar and syrup. 802–748–3136.

Northern Wisconsin Maid Sugarbush, Rt. 3, Box 357, Park Falls, WI 54552: Free information ■ Maple syrup from Wisconsin. 800–627–5777.

Palmer's Maple Syrup, Waitsfield, VT 05673: Free information ■ Maple sugar and syrup. 802–496–3696.

Sugarbush Farm, RFD 1, Box 568, Woodstock, VT 05091: Free brochure ■ Maple syrup and candy and Cheddar cheese aged 18 to 24 months. 802–457–1757.

Vermont Country Maple, Inc., P.O. Box 53, Jericho Center, VT 05465: Free information ■ Maple sugar and syrup. 802–864–7519.

Wick's Maple Products, RD 1, Box 14, Harrisville, NY 13648: Free information ■ Maple syrup, maple creams, and maple sugar cakes. 315–543–2737.

Wood's Cider Mill, RFD 2, Box 477, Springfield, VT 05156: Free brochure ■ Maple syrup, cider jelly and syrup, and boiled cider. 802–263–5547.

Meats

Aidells Sausage Company, 1575 Minnesota St., San Francisco, CA 94107: Free brochure ■ Filler- and preservative-free fresh and hickory-smoked sausage. 415–285–6660.

Alamo Fruit, P.O. Box 666, Alamo, TX 78516: Free catalog ■ Smoked meats and fruit. 512–787–3548.

All-American Prime Food Company, Interchange West, 435 Ford Rd., Minneapolis, MN 55426: Free information ■ Hand-carved tenderloin cuts of meat. 800–755–3575.

Amana Meat Shop & Smokehouse, 1854 Smokehouse Ln., Amana, IA 52203: Free brochure ■ Ham, bacon, sausage, cheese, and other specialties. 800–373–MEAT; 319–622–3111 (in IA).

Basse's Choice Plantation, P.O. Box 1, Smithfield, VA 23430: Free information ■ Cured, smoked, and aged Smithfield ham, or the less salty Williamsburg ham. 804–292–2773.

Beck's Jackson Hole Buffalo Meat Products, 1655 W. Berger Ln., P.O. Box 2100, Jackson, WY 83001: Free catalog ■ Fresh buffalo steaks, smoked buffalo sausage, salami, and jerky. 307–733–8343.

Benton's Smoky Mountain Country Hams, Hwy. 411 North, Rt. 3, Madisonville, TN 37354: Free information ■ Well-aged country hams. 615–442–5003.

Boyle Meat Packing Company, 500 E. 3rd St., Kansas City, MO 64106: Free brochure ■ Hand-carved rib eye steaks and other meats. 800–821–3626; 800–892–5844 (in MO).

Brae Beef, Level 3, Stamford Town Center, 100 Greyrock Pl., Stamford, CT 06901: Free price list ■ Beef, lamb, cold cuts, turkey, and chicken. Does not use additives, hormones, steroids, or other chemicals, and meats are low in fat, calories, and cholesterol. 800–323–4484; 203–323–4482 (in CT).

Broadbent's B & B Food Products, 6321 Hopkinsville Rd., Cadiz, KY 42211: Free catalog ■ Smoked, hand-cured country hams, bacon, and sausage; jams and jellies; and cheese. 800–841–2202; 502–233–5294 (in KY).

Burgers' Ozark Country Cured Hams, Inc., Rt. 3, Box 126, California, MO 65018: Free catalog ■ Hickory-smoked, sugar-cured ham and ham steaks, bacon, and turkeys; barbecued chickens; sausage; and cheese. 314–796–3134.

Cameron Meat Market, 162 Kearney Ave., Kearney, NJ 07032: Free information ■ Haggis. 201–991–2985.

Cavanaugh Lakeview Farms, Ltd., P.O. Box 580, Chelsea, MI 48118: Free catalog ■ Honey-cured and smoked poultry; smoked hams and bacons; fresh frozen poultry; steaks and game; and smoked seafood. 800–243–4438.

Classic Steaks of Omaha, 4430 S. 110th St., Omaha, NE 68137: Free catalog ■ USDA choice steaks. 800–288–2783.

Czimer Game & Seafood, Rt. 7, Orland Park, IL 60462: Free brochure ■ Oven-ready game birds, antelope, moose, bear, zebra, eland, lion, camel, wild mountain goat, possum, rabbit, venison, buffalo, wild boar, and exotic seafood. 708–460–7152.

Dakin Farm, Rt. 7, Ferrisburg, VT 05456: Free catalog ■ Smoked ham and bacon, maple syrup, and Cheddar cheese. 802–425–3971.

D'Artagnan, 399–419 St. Paul Ave., Jersey City, NJ 07306: Free catalog ■ Fresh American foie gras, Muscovy duck, other game birds, rabbit, and venison. 800–327–8246.

S. Wallace Edwards & Sons, Inc., P.O. Box 25, Surry, VA 23883: Catalog $1 ■ Hickory-smoked Virginia hams, bacon, and sausage; preserves from the Blue Ridge Mountains; and seafood from the Eastern Shore. 800–222–4267.

Folk's Folly Prime Cut Shoppe, 551 S. Mendenhall, Memphis, TN 38117: Free catalog ■ Choice cuts of meat. 800–467–0245.

The Forst Mountain Smokehouse, CPO Box 1000P, Kingston, NY 12401: Free brochure ■ Osetra and Sevruga caviar, smoked ham, smoked turkey, filet mignon steaks, strip steaks, boneless sirloin strip steaks, smoked pheasant, Canadian bacon, and aged Cheddar cheese. 800–453–4010; 914–331–3500 (in NY).

Fortuna's Deli, Franklin Shopping Plaza, Westerly, RI 02891: Free information ■ Dried-cured, lean, hot, sweet, extra-hot, garlic, and other sausage. 800–722–2328.

Four Oaks Farm, Inc., P.O. Box 987, Lexington, SC 29072: Free catalog ■ Country-style hams and bacon, sausage products, jams, jellies, pickles, relishes, and pecans and peanuts. 803–356–3194.

Douglas Freeman, 605 New Hope Rd., Cadiz, KY 42211: Free information ■ Aged country hams. 502–522–8900.

Game Exchange, 107 Quint St., San Francisco, CA 94124: Free information ■ Exotic meats that include camel, lion, water buffalo, pheasant, and squab. 415–282–7878.

Gaspar's Sausage Company, P.O. Box 436, North Dartmouth, MA 02747: Free information ■ Hot and mild Portuguese-style sausage, sweet breads, and sliced meats. 800–343–8086; 508–998–2012 (in MA).

Golden Trophy Steaks, Division of the Bruss Company, 3548 N. Kostner Ave., Chicago, IL 60641: Free catalog ■ Steaks, milk-fed veal, veal chops, rack of lamb, lamb chops, roast duckling, beef Wellington, smoked whole turkey and turkey breast, chicken, Cornish hens, and shrimp. 800–621–3882; 312–282–2900 (in IL).

Gould's Country Smokehouse, River Rd., Piedmont, NH 03779: Free information ■ Corncob-cured precooked hams with a smoky flavor. 603–272–5856.

Great Valley Mills, 687 Mill Rd., Telford, PA 18969: Free brochure ■ Dutch country cheese, ham, bacon, sausage, beef, preserves, fruitcakes, stollen, flour, cereals, and meals. 800–688–6455.

Pink ("Tiny") Guier, Jr., 2385 Canton Rd., Cadiz, KY 42211: Free information ■ Aged country hams. 502–522–6145.

Harrington Ham Company, 295 Main St., Richmond, VA 05477: Free catalog ■ Spiral-sliced, cob-smoked, maple-glazed hams and other smoked meats that include bacon, turkey breast, and pheasant; cheese; maple syrup; pastries and fruitcakes; plum pudding; and dried fruit. 802–434–4444.

High Valley Farm, Inc., 14 Alsace Way, Colorado Springs, CO 80906: Free brochure ■ Hickory-smoked poultry. 719–634–2944.

Hoffman's Quality Meats, Rt. 6, Box 5, Hagerstown, MD 21740: Free brochure ■ Country ham and bacon, Delmonico steaks, boneless New York strip steaks, and country sausage. 800–356–3193.

Honey Baked Ham Company, Inc., 4501 Erskin, Ste. 120, Cincinnati, OH 45242: Free brochure ■ Spiral-sliced, hickory-smoked hams with a honey-spice glaze; smoked turkeys and turkey breasts; barbecued pork back ribs; and Canadian-style bacon. 513–984–9600.

Inman Wild Game, Box 616, Aberdeen, SD 57401: Free brochure ■ Fresh, frozen, and smoked pheasant; wild turkey; buffalo sausage; and quail and partridge. 800–843–1962.

Jamison Farm, 161 Jamison Ln., Latrobe, PA 15650: Free brochure ■ Young, milk-fed lamb. 800–237–LAMB.

Jordan's Virginia Ham Company, Mail Order Dept., P.O. Box 447, Smithfield, VA 23430: Free catalog ■ Smithfield spiral-sliced honey-glazed ham, center cut ham slices, Smithfield half slab bacon, ham sausage, and smoked turkey breast. 804–357–4321.

Lucky Star Ranch, RR 1, Box 273, Chaumont, NY 13622: Free brochure ■ Venison roasts with bone in, stew meat, steaks, rib chops, and other cuts. 607–836–4766.

Maurice's Flying Pig, P.O. Box 6847, West Columbia, SC 29171: Free information ■ Hickory pit-cooked all-ham barbecue and barbecue sauce. 800–MAURICE; 803–791–5887 (in SC).

Meadow Farms Country Smokehouse, P.O. Box 1387, Bishop, CA 93514: Free brochure ■ Mahogany-smoked ham and fowl, slab bacon, loin chops, whole Tom turkey breast, sirloin beef tip, sausage, beef jerky, Polish Kolbase, Cheddar cheese, knockwurst, Italian salami, and hot sticks. 619–873–5311.

Myers Meats, RR 1, Box 132, Parshall, ND 58770: Free information ■ Country-style sausage, beef jerky, country-cured dried beef, beef sticks, and other specialties. 800–ND–JERKY; 701–743–4451 (in ND).

New Braunfels Smokehouse, P.O. Box 311159, New Braunfels, TX 78131: Free catalog ■ Bin-cured and hickory-smoked turkeys, ham, sausage, bacon, chicken, and beef. 800–537–6932.

New Skete Farms, P.O. Box 128, Cambridge, NY 12816: Catalog $1 ■ Smoked whole ducks and chickens, turkey and chicken breasts, bacon, ham, and sausage, and Cheddar cheese and cheese spreads. 518–677–3928.

Colonel Bill Newsom's Kentucky Country Hams, 127 N. Highland Ave., Princeton, KY 42445: Free brochure ■ Virginia-style, hickory-smoked country hams that are nitrate- and preservative-free. 502–365–2482.

Nine Ninety Nine Kosher Provisions, 15 Rivington St., New York, NY 10002: Free brochure ■ Fresh-frozen kosher veal and beef, delicatessen meats, all-beef franks, and other kosher products. 212–254–5994.

North Country Smokehouse, P.O. Box 1415, Claremont, NH 03743: Free brochure ■ All-natural, old-fashioned cob-smoked meats and other favorites that include ham, slab bacon, Canadian bacon, pork chops, sausage, spareribs, boneless lamb, whole turkeys and turkey breasts, duck, pheasant, smoked sharp Vermont cheese, and smoked mozzarella cheese. 800–258–4304.

Nueske's Hillcrest Farm Meats, RR 2, Wittenberg, WI 54499: Free brochure ■ Smoked hams, sausage, bacon, smoked shanks, pork loins, pork chops, duck, turkeys and turkey breasts, cornish game hens, and chicken and

chicken breasts. 800–382–2266; 800–372–2266 (in WI).

Oak Grove Smokehouse, Inc., 17618 Old Jefferson Hwy., Prairieville, LA 70769: Free catalog ■ Smoked meats and Cajun and Creole mixes. 504–673–6857.

Oakridge Smokehouse Restaurant, P.O. Box 146, Schulenburg, TX 78956: Free information ■ Peppered beef tenderloins, smoked pork tenderloins, and baby-back smoked pork spare ribs. 800–548–6325.

Omaha Steaks International, P.O. Box 3300, Omaha, NE 68103: Free catalog ■ Aged steaks and beef. 800–228–9055.

Ozark Mountain Smoke House, Inc., P.O. Box 37, Farmington, AR 72730: Free catalog ■ Smoked poultry and meats. 800–643–3437; 800–632–0155 (in AR).

Pittman & Davis, 801 N. Expressway, Harlingen, TX 78552: Free catalog ■ Smoked hams and turkeys, fruitcakes, cheese, ruby red grapefruit from Texas, pecans, and Florida oranges. 512–423–2154.

Ranch House Meat Company, 300 San Saba, Menard, TX 76859: Free catalog ■ Beef, pork tenderloins, and other meats. 915–396–4536.

Roland & Son, P.O. Box 278, South Barre, VT 05670: Free information ■ Maple-cured smoked ham and smoked bacon. 800–457–6066.

The Sausage Maker, Inc., 26–50 Military Rd., Buffalo, NY 14207: Free catalog ■ Equipment and supplies for making sausage at home. 716–876–5521.

Schaller & Weber, Inc., 22–35 46th St., Long Island City, NY 11105: Free brochure ■ German-style wursts, salami, cervelats, and smoked bacon and ham. 718–879–3047.

Schiltz Goose Farm, 7 W. Oak St., P.O. Box 267, Sisseton, SD 57262: Free information ■ Geese, from early October through the holidays, packaged for the freezer. 605–698–7651.

Scott Hams, Box 114, Rt. 4, Greenville, KY 42345: Free information ■ Aged country hams. 502–338–3402.

Sinai Kosher Foods Corporation, 1000 W. Pershing Rd., Chicago, IL 60609: Free information ■ Kosher beef, lamb, veal, roasts, steaks, chops, and ground beef, packaged for freezers. 800–621–5044; 312–650–6330 (in IL).

Skylark Meats, 4430 S. 110th St., Omaha, NE 68137: Free information ■ Thick, center-cut steaks. 800–28–TASTE.

Smithfield Ham & Products Company, P.O. Box 487, Smithfield, VA 23430: Free information ■ Country-style Red Eye hams and Amber Smithfield hams. 800–628–2242; 804–357–5407 (in VA).

Stock Yards Packing Company, 340 N. Oakley Blvd., Chicago, IL 60612: Free catalog ■ Foods and meat specialties. 800–621–3687.

Summerfield Farm, SR 4, Box 195A, Brightwood, VA 22715: Free information ■ Naturally raised, milk-fed veal, pheasant, young lamb, and fresh squab. 703–948–3100.

Texas Wild Game Cooperative, P.O. Box 530, Ingram, TX 78025: Free information ■ Venison and other gourmet foods. 800–962–4263.

Thee Six B Farms, 4998 Centerville Rd. North, Greens Fork, IN 47345: Free brochure ■ Ham, bacon, and pork that contain no additives, preservatives, or growth hormones. 800–473–PORK.

Thundering Herd Buffalo Products, P.O. Box 1051, Reno, NV 89504: Free catalog ■ Ranch-raised Wyoming buffalo meat. 800–525–9730.

Union Stockyards, 4538 S. Marshfield Ave., Chicago, IL 60609: Free catalog ■ Gourmet meats. 800–257–2977.

U.S. Bison Company, Ltd., 119 Central Ave., Owen, WI 54460: Free catalog ■ Buffalo, bison, alligator, wild boar, bear, venison, rattlesnake, kangaroo, muscovy duck, poussin, pheasant, quail, and other exotic meats. 715–229–2115.

Usinger's Famous Sausage, 1030 N. Old World 3rd St., Milwaukee, WI 53203: Free catalog ■ Over 75 varieties of sausage. 800–558–9999; 414–276–9105 (in WI).

Virginia Diner, P.O. 310, Wakefield, VA 23888: Free catalog ■ Virginia bacon and ham, fudge, homemade jellies and jams, and peanuts and peanut specialties. 800–868–NUTS; 804–899–3196 (in VA).

Whistling Wings, 113 Washington St., Hanover, IL 61041: Free brochure ■ Hickory-smoked Mallard ducks. 815–591–3512.

Wimmer's Meat Products, 126 W. Grant, West Point, NE 68788: Free catalog ■ Hams, sausage, bacon, and other meats cured with a European flavor using old-world spice recipes. 800–358–0761.

Wylie Hill Farm, P.O. Box 35, Craftsbury Common, VT 05827: Free brochure and recipes ■ Wine-cured, hickory-smoked pheasant and other fresh game birds. 802–586–2887.

Nuts

A & B Milling Company, Inc., Box 327, Enfield, NC 27823: Free information ■ Shelled and fried peanuts, chocolate peanut clusters, and other nut favorites. 800–843–0105; 919–445–3161 (in NC).

Ace Pecan Company, 900 Morse Ave., Elk Grove Village, IL 60007: Free catalog ■ Pecans and pecan candies. 800–323–9754.

Almond Plaza, P.O. Box 500, Sacramento, CA 95803: Free catalog ■ Almonds and candy specialties. 800–225–6887.

Bacon's Castle Supply, Rt. 1, Box 101, Surry, VA 23883: Free brochure ■ Virginia peanuts in gift boxes, bags, and bulk. 804–357–6159.

Bates Brothers Nut Farm, Inc., 15954 Woods Valley Rd., Valley Center, CA 92082: Free price list ■ Walnuts, pecans, cashews, macadamias, and pistachios; fresh apricots, prunes, and dates; old-fashioned candies; granolas; dried fruits; preserves; and honey. 619–749–3333.

Blue Diamond Nuts, 1701 C St., Sacramento, CA 95814: Free information ■ Salted, onion-garlic flavored, hickory-smoked flavored, barbecue flavored, roasted blanched-salted, and cheese flavored almonds. 800–225–6887.

Brewer Pistachio Farms, 1265 S. Lyon Ave., Mendota, CA 93640: Free price list ■ Fresh roasted California pistachios. 209–655–4949.

Buchanan Hollow Nut Company, 6510 Minturn, Le Grand, CA 95333: Free information ■ Fresh roasted pistachios. 800–532–1500; 209–389–4594 (in CA).

Cal-Almond, 6049 Leedom Rd., Hughson, CA 95326: Free brochure ■ Whole natural and hickory-smoked almonds. 209–883–0478.

Clark Hill Plantation, Rt. 1, Box 344A, Garfield, GA 30425: Free information ■ Georgia pecan halves and shelled nuts. 800–822–9696.

Country Estate Pecans, P.O. Box 7, Sahuarita, AZ 85629: Free information ■ Pecans. 800–327–3226.

Dixie Nut Company, 512 E. Central Ave., P.O. Box 159, Fitzgerald, GA 31750: Free brochure ■ Shelled pecan halves. 800–423–1262.

Dundee Orchards, P.O. Box 327, Dundee, OR 97115: Free information ■ Roasted hazelnuts and walnut hazelnut, peanut hazelnut, chocolate hazelnut, and mocha hazelnut butters. 503–538–8105.

Durey-Libby Nuts, Inc., P.O. Box 345, Carlstadt, NJ 07072: Free brochure ■ Walnuts, cashews, pecans, macadamia nuts, almonds, and pistachios. 201–939–2775.

Ellis Brothers Pecans, Rt. 3, Exit 36, I-75, Vienna, GA 31092: Free brochure ■ Pecan halves, shelled and unshelled nuts, raw or roasted pecans, pecan pieces, glazed and spiced pecans, roasted jumbo peanuts in the shell. 912–268–9041.

Fran's Pecans, 110 N. Hicks St., P.O. Box 188, Harlem, GA 30814: Free brochure ■ Pecan halves, praline pecans, roasted and salted pecans, and honey-roasted and cinnamon-sugared specialties. 800–476–6887; 404–556–9172 (in GA).

From the Rainforest, 270 Lafayette St., Ste. 1000, New York, NY 10012: Free information ■ Preservative-free roasted cashews and a mixture of papaya, banana chips, mango, Brazil nuts, cashews, pineapple, and coconut. 800–EAR–TH96.

Golden Kernel Pecan Company, Inc., Box 613, Cameron, SC 29030: Free brochure ■ Pecans and pecan specialties. 800–845–2448; 803–823–2311 (in SC).

Goodbee Pecan Plantations, P.O. Box 6709, Florence, SC 29502: Free catalog ■ Pecans and pecan specialties. 800–729–7006.

Gourmet Nut Center, 1430 Railroad Ave., Orland, CA 95963: Free brochure ■ Gift nut assortments. 916–865–5511.

Henry's Farm, 1216 E. Henry Rd., Newberg, OR 97132: Free information ■ Oregon-grown hazelnuts and filbert butternuts. 503–538–5244.

Houston's Peanut Outlet, P.O. Box 160, Dublin, NC 28332: Free brochure ■ Extra-large, raw, blanched, salted-in-the-shell, gourmet oil-roasted peanuts. 800–334–8383.

The Maples Fruit Farm, P.O. Box 167, Chewsville, MD 21721: Free list with long SASE ■ Nuts, nut assortments, candies, and fruits. 301–733–0777.

Mariani Nut Company, 709 Dutton St., P.O. Box 664, Winters, CA 95694: Free information ■ Cholesterol-free California almonds.

Mauna Loa Macadamia Nut Corporation, Mainland Expediting Center, 6523 N. Galena Rd., P.O. Box 1772, Peoria, IL 61656: Free catalog ■ Macadamia nuts in milk or dark chocolate; honey roasted, salted and unsalted nuts and white confection coated; truffles and other candies; and Kona coffee. 800–832–9993.

Mid South Pecan Company, P.O. Box 882, Ruston, LA 71273: Free information ■ Toasted or natural in-the-shell and cracked pecans and other nuts, dried fruits, candies, cakes, cookies, jam, jelly, popcorn, and wild rice. 800–345–1148.

Missouri Dandy Pantry, P.O. Box A, Stockton, MO 65785: Free brochure ■ Cashews, pistachios, black walnuts, other nutmeats, and candy. 800–872–6879.

Nunes Farms Almonds, P.O. Box 311, Newman, CA 95360: Free catalog ■ California fresh almonds, roasted salted almonds, honey glazed almonds, and cheddar almonds. 800–255–1641.

Nuts D'Vine, P.O. Box 589, Edenton, NC 27932: Free catalog ■ Peanut brittle and farm fresh peanuts raw in the shell, roasted in the shell, salted in the shell, home-style, unsalted home-style, and red skins. 800–334–0492.

Peanut Patch, Inc., 111 N. Main St., P.O. Box 186, Courtland, VA 23837: Free brochure ■ Peanut and peanut candy assortments, raw peanuts in bulk, and dry-cured hams. 800–544–0896.

Pecan Producers International, P.O. Box 1301, Corsicana, TX 75110: Free information ■ Texas native pecans and California pistachios. 903–872–1337.

Theodore Pehnec, 12650 Hoover St., Garden Grove, CA 92641: Free catalog ■ Hickory-roasted, dry-roasted, salted, and whole natural almonds. 714–897–2277.

P-R Farms, Inc., 2917 E. Shepherd, Clovis, CA 93612: Free information ■ Shelled almonds.

Priester's Pecans, 227 Old Fort Dr., Fort Deposit, AL 36032: Free catalog ■ Roasted, salted, and salt-free pecans; brittles, pecan candies, and butter balls; variety assortments and party fixings; pecan brownies and pie; and sugar-free pecan clusters. 800–277–3226.

Pueblo to People, P.O. Box 2545, Houston, TX 77252: Free information ■ Brazil nuts. 800–843–5257.

Ross-Smith Pecan Company, Inc., 710 Oak St., McRae, GA 31055: Free brochure ■ Pecans. 800–841–5503; 912–868–5693 (in GA).

Senor Pistachio, 23320 Ave. 95, Terra Bella, CA 93720: Free information ■ Roasted salted and unsalted pistachios. 800–468–1319; 800–437–8067 (in CA).

J.H. Sherard, P.O. Box 75, Sherard, MS 38669: Free brochure ■ Shelled and unshelled pecans, pistachios, and other nuts. 800–647–5518; 205–227–4301 (in MS).

South Georgia Pecan Company, P.O. Box 5366, Valdosta, GA 31603: Free information ■ Giant cashews, natural pistachios, cinnamon-spiced pecans, mixed nuts, and other favorites. 800–841–4449.

The Squire's Choice, 2000 W. Cabot Blvd., Langhorne, PA 19047: Free catalog ■ Nuts, coffee, and other specialties. 800–523–6163.

Sun Burst Farms, P.O. Box 983, Tifton, GA 31793: Free brochure ■ Georgia pecans and peanuts. 800–358–9412.

Sunnyland Farms, Inc., P.O. Box 8200, Albany, GA 31706: Free catalog ■ Pecans and other nuts, candies, cakes and dried fruits, maple syrup, honey, jellies, and gift assortments. 912–883–3085.

Sun River Packing Company, 1329 Hazeldean Rd., Waterford, CA 95386: Free information ■ Fresh, blanched, and hickory-smoked almonds. 800–334–NUTS.

TAP Almonds, 12700 E. Graves Rd., Manteca, CA 95336: Free information ■ Shelled almonds for snacking or baking. 209–599–7248.

H.M. Thames Pecan Company, P.O. Box 2206, Mobile, AL 36652: Free catalog ■ Nuts and nut products, candy, baked goods, pralines, and fruit cakes. 800–633–1306.

Vetsch Farms, P.O. Box 9126, Bakersfield, CA 93389: Free information ■ Farm-fresh, shelled almonds. 805–831–3094.

Virginia Diner, P.O. 310, Wakefield, VA 23888: Free catalog ■ Peanuts and peanut specialties, peanut pie, homemade jellies and jams, fudge, and Virginia bacon and ham. 800–642–NUTS; 804–642–3106 (in VA).

Westnut, P.O. Box 125, Dundee, OR 97115: Free brochure ■ Fresh and shelled hazelnuts. 503–538–2161.

Young Pecans, P.O. Box 6709, Florence, SC 29502: Free brochure ■ Pecan halves, butter roasted and salted pecans, chocolate pecan halves, butter toffee pecan popcorn, praline pecans, sugar and orange pecans, sugar and spice pecans, Cheddar cheese pecans, pecan cake, pecan divinity logs, and cashews. 800–729–8004.

Popcorn

Culpepper Popcorn & Candy, Inc., Dinard Ave., Santa Fe Springs, CA 90670: Free catalog ■ Flavored popcorn. 213–921–7961.

Fisher's Popcorn, 200 S. Boardwalk, Ocean City, MD 21842: Free price list ■ Caramel popcorn. 410–289–5638.

Mallard Pond Farms, 746 Mallard Pond Dr., Boulder, CO 80303: Free catalog ■ Popping corn, popcorn flour, popcorn pancakes, popcorn bread, and wildflower seed mix. 800–533–2676; 494–3551 (Denver area).

Popcorn Factory, Mail Order Dept., One Harvest Ln., Peoria, IL 61614: Free catalog ■ Popcorn covered with butter flavor, aged Cheddar cheese, homemade caramel, and other flavors. Other specialties include gummy and chocolate teddy bears. 800–541–2676.

Popcorn World, Inc., 2303 Princeton Rd., P.O. Box 507, Trenton, MO 64683: Free brochure ■ Popcorn specialties that include butter, caramel, cheese, cinnamon, cinnamon with almonds and pecans, and vanilla butter with almonds and pecans. 800–443–8226.

Rocky Mountain Popcorn Factory, Tiffany Plaza, 7400 E. Hampden Ln., Denver, CO 80231: Free brochure ■ Seven flavors of popcorn packaged in decorator canisters or classic burlap bags and salted-in-the-shell peanuts. 303–771–0632.

Velvet Creme Popcorn, 4710 Belinder, Shawnee Mission, KS 66205: Free brochure ■ Unsalted popcorn, or as extra-large, ready-to-pop kernels. 913–236–7742.

What's Poppin, 990 N. Amelia, San Dimas, CA 91773: Free catalog ■ Popcorn in reusable containers. 800–344–2676; 800–338–2676 (in CA).

Preserves, Jellies & Honey

Alaska Wildberry Products, 528 E. Pioneer Ave., Homer, AK 99603: Free brochure ■ Wild lingonberry, raspberry, mossberry, and salmonberry jams. 907–235–8858.

American Spoon Foods, Inc., 411 E. Lake St., Petoskey, MI 49770: Free catalog ■ Blackberry, chokeberry-apple, elderberry, and grape jellies; thimbleberry, apricot, damson plum, nectarine, and peach preserves; pumpkin butter; rhubarb marmalade; and strawberry-rhubarb and winter pear conserve. 800–222–5886.

Bainbridge's Festive Foods, P.O. Box 50805, Nashville, TN 37215: Free information ■ Fruit preserves. 615–383–5157.

Bear Meadow Farm, Moore Rd., Rt. 2, Florida, MA 01247: Free catalog ■ Country-style cinnamon cider jelly, peach jam, and raspberry preserves. 413–663–9241.

A.M. Braswell Food Company, P.O. Box 485, Statesboro, GA 30458: Free brochure ■ Low-sugar jams; preserves, jellies, and marmalades; fruit butters; relishes and chow-chow pickles; and fruit and chocolate dessert toppings. 912–764–6191.

Cape Cod Sampler, 199 Main St., P.O. Box 98, East Orleans, MA 02643: Free information ■ Jams and jellies and a Cape Cod "favorite recipe" cookbook. 508–255–1949.

Clearbrook Farms, 5514 Fair Ln., Fairfax, OH 45227: Free brochure ■ Semi-sweet chocolate sauces and strawberry, raspberry, tart cherry, blueberry, apricot, peach, boysenberry, black cherry, plum, and orange marmalade fruit spreads made with only fruit and sugar. 800–888–3276; 513–271–2053 (in OH).

Crabtree & Evelyn Limited, P.O. Box 167, Woodstock Hill, CT 06281: Catalog $3.50 ■ English biscuits and cookies in assorted flavors, gingerbread, ginger and butter-ginger cookies, Scottish shortbread, Belgian chocolates, cheese wafers and biscuits from Holland, Italian biscuits, preserves, marmalades, jellies, honey, English sauces, spices and condiments, herbs, tea, and candy. 203–928–2766.

Glorybee Honey & Supplies, P.O. Box 2744, Eugene, OR 97402: Catalog 50¢ ■ Honey and honey-prepared foods. Other specialties include beekeeping and honey-processing equipment and supplies. 800–456–7923; 503–689–0913 (in OR).

Hadley Fruit Orchards, P.O. Box 495, Cabazon, CA 92230: Free catalog ■ Fruit jams and jellies, dried fruits, nuts, candy, and honey. 714–849–4668.

Harry & David, P.O. Box 712, Medford, OR 97501: Free brochure ■ Fruit preserves, fruits, cakes, and other desserts. 800–345–5655.

Hawaiian Plantations, 650 Iwilei Rd., Honolulu, HI 96817: Free catalog ■ Candies, jams, syrups, dressings, and condiments, all made with authentic Hawaiian ingredients. 800–767–4650.

Helen's Tropical Exotics, 3519 Church St., Clarkston, GA 30021: Free brochure ■ Dips, marinades, sauces, Jamaican pimento, tropical spices, and hot peppers. 800–544–JERK.

Honey Acres, Ashippun, WI 53003: Free information ■ Natural honey, honeycombs, honey-fruit spreads, candies, beeswax candles, mustards, gifts, and cookbooks. 414–474–4411.

Knott's Berry Farm, P.O. Box 1989, Placentia, CA 90620: Free catalog ■ Gourmet jellies and preserves, cheese, sausage, candy, cakes, cookies, and dried fruit. 800–877–6887.

Kozlowski Farms, 5566 Gravenstein Hwy., North Forestville, CA 95436: Free brochure ■ Marmalades, jams, and preserves; honey and mustards; barbecue sauce and fruit butters; sugar-free berry vinegars; conserves; and chutney. 707–887–1587.

Latta's Oregon Delicacies, P.O. Box 1377, Newport, OR 97365: Free catalog ■ Homemade preserves, gourmet seafoods, dried fruits, and nuts. 503–265–7675.

Lollipop Tree, Inc., 319 Vaughan St., Portsmouth, NH 03801: Free brochure ■ All-natural preserves, condiments, and baking mixes. 800–842–6691.

Maury Island Farm, P.O. Box L, Vashon, WA 98070: Free brochure ■ Gourmet preserves. 800–356–5880.

Moon Shine Trading Company, P.O. Box 896, Winters, CA 95694: Free catalog ■ Sweet Clover, Yellow Star Thistle, Sunflower, Eucalyptus Honey; Almond butter; and Semisweet Chocolate Crunch, White Chocolate Cashew Creme, White Chocolate Almond Dream, and Milk Chocolate Almond Crunch nut spreads. 916–753–0601.

Old Southern Touch Muscadine, 2212 B St., Meridian, MS 39301: Free catalog ■ Sugar-free muscadine jams, jellies, preserves, toppings, syrups, and sauces. 800–233–1736.

Panhandler Products, Inc., RR 4, Box 399, Stowe, VT 05672: Free brochure ■ Conserves, jams, and jellies. Include Strawberry Amaretto, Blueberry Bourbon, Apple Cranberry Maple, Apple Blueberry, Brandied Peach, Apple Rum Walnut, Raspberry Apple, and Peach Melba. 802–253–7138.

Pepper Patch, 1250 Old Hillsboro Rd., Franklin, TN 37064: Free brochure ■ Marmalades, fresh fruit butters, "spirit" cakes, candies, dessert sauces, cocktail jellies and sauces, pickles, and relishes. 615–790–1012.

Pine Ridge Country Honey, Box 9A, Crawford, NE 69339: Free pamphlet ■ Natural creamed honeys flavored with lemon or spices. 800–658–3285.

Rocky Top Farms, RR 1, Essex Rd., Ellsworth, MI 49729: Free information ■ All-natural, additive-free cherry, seedless raspberry, and strawberry preserves, and peach, blueberry, cherry, and apricot butters. 800–862–9303.

Sarabeth's Kitchen, 423 Amsterdam Ave., New York, NY 10024: Free brochure ■ Additive- and preservative-free lemon-pear butter; peach-apricot preserves; chunky apple butter; cranberry relish; a melange of figs, pears, lemons, and spices; orange-apricot marmalade; and chunky strawberry preserves. 212–580–8335.

Spruce Mountain Preserves, P.O. Box 68, Rockport, ME 04865: Free brochure ■ Blueberry conserve and wild blueberry chutney, plain or with almonds and raisins. 207–236–3538.

Virginia Diner, P.O. 310, Wakefield, VA 23888: Free catalog ■ Homemade jellies and jams, Virginia bacon and ham, fudge, peanuts, and peanut specialties. 800–642–NUTS; 804–899–3106 (in VA).

Wilds of Idaho, 1308 W. Boone, Spokane, WA 99201: Free price list ■ Wild huckleberry jam, topping, and syrup, and peanut brittle. 509–326–0197.

Wood's Cider Mill, RFD 2, Box 477, Springfield, VT 05156: Free brochure ■ Maple syrup, and cider jelly and syrup, and boiled cider. 802–263–5547.

Salt-free

Avalon Foods Corporation, 2914 Coney Island Ave., Brooklyn, NY 11235: Free brochure ■ Salt-free cakes and cookies and low-calorie and sugar-free foods. 718–332–6000.

Ener-G Foods, P.O. Box 84887, Seattle, WA 98124: Free information ■ Low-sodium non-allergenic and dietetic foods. 800–331–5222; 800–325–9788 (in WA).

Hearty Mix Company, 1231 Madison Hill Rd., Rahway, NJ 07065: Free catalog ■ Baking mixes for diet-conscious eaters, without preservatives, cholesterol, or saturated fat products. Includes cookies, cakes and other dessert pastries, salt-free bread, and wheat-free items. 908–382–3010.

Seafood

Abbott's Lobster, 117 Pearl St., P.O. Box 285, Noank, CT 06340: Free brochure ■ North Atlantic lobsters shipped overnight. 800–325–3346; 800–423–3861 (in CT).

Byrd's Famous, P.O. Box 547, Crisfield, MD 21817: Free brochure ■ Chesapeake Bay blue crabs, lump crab meat, and backfin, claw, and crab fingers. 410–968–1666.

California Sunshine Fine Foods, Inc., 144 King St., San Francisco, CA 94107: Free information ■ Fresh and smoked seafoods, caviar, smoked game birds, and Aidells sausage. 415–543–3007.

Carolina Mountain, Rt. 1, Box 287, Andrews, NC 28901: Free information ■ Fresh and smoked salmon and trout. 800–722–9477.

Carolina Smoked Specialties, Inc., 118 S. Cypress, Mullins, SC 29574: Free information ■ Hand-cut, oak-apple smoked trout fillets. 800–776–8731.

Caviar House, Inc., 687 NE 79th St., Miami, FL 33138: Free catalog ■ Smoked scottish salmon, caviar, foie gras, and truffles. 800–522–8427.

Chesapeake Express, Rt. 1, Box 38, Centreville, MD 21617: Free brochure ■ Maryland's Eastern Shore backfin meat crab cakes, oysters, and soft shell crabs. Delivered ready to heat and serve. 800–282–2722.

Chief Seattle Seafood, 672 S. Orcas, Seattle, WA 98108: Free information ■ Indian-style smoked Pacific Northwest smoked salmon. 800–426–0001; 206–762–4165 (in WA).

Clambake Celebrations, 5 Giddiah Hill, Orleans, MA 02653: Free information ■ Cape Cod seafood dinners with live lobsters, shellfish, and fresh corn. Ready to cook, they are shipped via air directly to your door. 800–423–4038.

Coastline Marketing, 264 H St., Ste. 3110, Blaine, WA 98230: Free brochure ■ Smoked salmon, oysters, clams, and coho salmon.

Cotuit Oyster Company, P.O. Box 563, Cotuit, MA 02635: Free price list ■ New England oysters and cherrystone clams. 508–428–6747.

Crawford Lobster Company, 62 Badgers Island, Kittery, ME 03904: Free catalog ■ Lobster, clams, salmon, and oysters. 207–439–0920.

Deanie's Seafood, 1713 Lake Ave., Metairie, LA 70005: Free catalog ■ Ready-to-eat crawfish. 504–834–1225.

Downeast Seafood Express, Rt. 176, Box 138, Brooksville, ME 04617: Free brochure ■ Live Maine lobsters, ocean-fresh lobster meat, fresh Maine crab meat, fresh sea scallops, and Maine steamer clams (when available). 800–556–2326.

Ducktrap River Fish Farm, Inc., RFD 2, Box 378, Lincolnville, ME 04849: Free brochure ■ Preservative- and additive-free smoked seafood that includes salmon, rainbow trout, and a seafood sampler of mussels and scallops. 800–828–3825.

Dutchess Farms, Old Indian Rd., RD 1, Box 95, Milton, NY 12547: Free catalog ■

Imported Norwegian salmon and other delicacies. 914–795–2175.

Ekone Oyster Company, Star Route, Box 465, South Bend, WA 98586: Free information ■ Grows their own oysters and harvests them fresh, smokes them over red alderwood, then vacuum packs to seal in natural flavors. Uses no preservatives. 206–875–5494.

Graffam Brothers, Box 340, Rockport, ME 04856: Free information ■ Handpicked live Maine lobsters. 207–236–3396.

Great Northern Products, Ltd., P.O. Box 7622, Warwick, RI 02887: Free information ■ Pre-sliced and ready for freezing Lochinvar Scottish smoked salmon and other gourmet seafoods. 401–885–7740.

Green River Trout Farm, RR 1, Box 267, Mancelona, MI 49659: Free brochure ■ Smoked and fresh rainbow trout, smoked turkey breast and turkey roll, pheasant, chicken, and cornish game hens. 616–584–3486.

Green Turtle Cannery, P.O. Box 585, Islamorada, Florida Keys 33036: Free information ■ Turtle soup, turtle chowder, conch chowder, Manhattan clam chowder, New England fish chowder, and New England clam chowder. 305–664–9595.

Handy Softshell Crawfish, P.O. Box 309, Crisfield, MD 21817: Free brochure ■ Softshell crabs and crawfish. 800–426–3977.

Hawaiian Abalone Farms, P.O. Box A, Kailua-Kona, HI 96745: Free brochure ■ Farm-grown baby abalone. Shipped fresh in the shell. 800–442–6690; 808–329–7345 (in HI).

Hegg & Hegg, 801 Marine Dr., Port Angeles, WA 98362: Free brochure ■ Pacific Northwest smoked salmon, nova-style smoked salmon, Puget Sound red sockeye salmon steaks, sturgeon, shrimp, baby clams, tuna, smoked shad, dungeness crab meat, and seafood appetizers and sampler assortments. 800–435–3474; 206–457–3344 (in WA).

Homarus, Inc., 76 Kisco Ave., Mount Kisco, NY 10549: Free brochure ■ Cured salmon smoked in pastrami spices, smoked trout, and Norwegian smoked salmon. 800–23–SALMON.

Horton's Seafood, P.O. Box 430, Waterboro, ME 04087: Free catalog ■ Naturally smoked Maine salmon, mussels, trout, shrimp, mackerel, and blue fish. 800–346–6066; 207–247–6900 (in ME).

J & K Trading Company, 10808 Garland Dr., Culver City, CA 90230: Free price list ■ Crab meat, lump fish caviar, escargot, hearts of palm, and button mushrooms. 213–836–3334.

Jake's Famous Products, Inc., 4910 N. Basin, Portland, OR 97217: Free brochure ■ Chocolate truffle cake and seafood products that include their world famous clam chowder, seafood sauces, smoked white sturgeon, smoked rainbow trout, and several varieties of salmon. 503–226–1420.

Josephson's Smokehouse & Dock, 106 Marine Dr., P.O. Box 412, Astoria, OR 97103: Free catalog ■ Smoked salmon and oysters, scallops, boneless trout and sturgeon, salmon steaks, and sturgeon caviar. 800–772–3474, 800–828–3474 (in OR).

Kathy Ann, Inc., 18th St. & Bayview Ave., Barnegat Light, NJ 08006: Free information ■ Preservative-free scallops. 800–325–SEAS.

Killer Whale Fish Company, P.O. Box 82, Burlington, WA 98233: Free catalog ■ Gourmet foods and seafood specialties. 206–757–7717.

Latta's Oregon Delicacies, P.O. Box 1377, Newport, OR 97365: Free catalog ■ Homemade preserves, seafood, dried fruits, and nuts. 503–265–7675.

Legal Sea Foods, 33 Everett St., Allston, MA 02134: Free brochure and price list ■ Imported smoked salmon from Ireland and smoked bluefish pate. 800–343–5804.

Live from Maine Lobster Company, 7 Fox Ct., Portland, ME 04101: Free information ■ Overnight shipping of live Maine lobsters and steamer clams complete with cooking instructions, claw crackers, picks, and seafood forks. 800–766–6246.

Lobster Company, 7 Fox Ct., Portland, ME 04101: Free information ■ Live Maine lobsters and steamers. 800–766–MAINE.

Lobster Connection, Inc., P.O. Box 508, Kittery, ME 03904: Free information ■ Lobster and seafood combinations. Overnight shipment, air express delivery. 603–778–9093.

Mitchell & Winter Caviar, Highland Mill, P.O. Box 876, Camden, ME 04843: Catalog $2 ■ Maine seafood specialties and Beluga,

Sevruga, Osetra, and lobster caviar. 207–236–8313.

Mountain Springs, P.O. Box 861, Prineville, OR 97754: Free brochure ■ Low-salt and smoke-flavored rainbow trout fillets. 800–542–2303.

Murray's Sturgeon Shop, 2429 Broadway, New York, NY 10024: Free catalog ■ Smoked and canned sturgeon. 212–724–2650.

Nantucket Specialty Seafood Company, Box 2013, Nantucket, MA 02584: Free information ■ Fresh bay scallops. 800–344–BAYS.

Nelson Crab, Inc., P.O. Box 520, Tokeland, WA 98590: Free brochure ■ Dungeness crab, smoked sturgeon, Albacore tuna, Chinook and Blueback salmon, minced Razor clams, smoked shad, and Pacific shrimp. 800–262–0069.

Ocean Kingdoms, 456 Suydam St., Brooklyn, NY 11237: Free catalog ■ Fresh salmon and smoked salmon fillets in whole sides, pre-sliced, and steaks. 800–955–2430.

Olde Maine Lobster Company, Vinalhaven Island, ME 04863: Free brochure ■ Lobsters shipped overnight. 800–562–7909.

Outer Banks Seafood, P.O. Box 2119, Manteo, Roanoke Island, NC 27954: Free information ■ Seafood entrees that serve 4 people. Includes seasoning and marinating ingredients, and cooking suggestions. 800–852–3028.

Ozark Trout Company, 2915 Kavanaugh, Ste. 435, Little Rock, AR 72207: Free information ■ Ready-to-eat smoked trout fillets. 800–835–2246.

Petrossian Shop, 182 W. 58th St., New York, NY 10019: Free information ■ Smoked salmon, caviar, foie gras, truffles, and other specialties. 800–828–9241.

Red-Wing Meadow Farm, Inc., 187 N. Maine St., Sunderland, MA 01375: Free information ■ Lemon Pepper Smoked Trout and fresh trout raised in their own pools. 800–321–4118; 413–549–4118 (in MA).

Rent Mother Nature, P.O. Box 193, Cambridge, MA 02238: Free information ■ Clambake-seafood dinners for two and four. Includes clams, lobster, mussels, cod, onions, potatoes, and corn (when in season), in a reusable enamelled pot. 617–354–5430.

Sea Farm Washington, P.O. Box 2499, Port Angeles, WA 98362: Free catalog ■ Fresh and smoked salmon fillets or whole fish, and white sturgeon fillets. 800–328–0140.

Seafood Direct to You, P.O. Box 2345, Boston, MA 02130: Free price list ■ Idaho trout, bay scallops, mussels, Maine shrimp, Norwegian salmon, bluefish, and lemon-pepper mackerel. 617–524–7446.

Seafood Emporium, Inc., 336 Bayside Rd., Greenland, NH 03840: Free brochure ■ Ready-to-cook clams and lobsters. 603–431–3300.

Sea Island Mercantile, 928 Bay St., P.O. Box 100, Beaufort, SC 29901: Free information ■ She-crab soup and other specialties. 800–735–3215.

Simply Shrimp, 7794 NW 44th St., Fort Lauderdale, FL 33351: Free information ■ Seafood from the Gulf and around the world. When in season, features Florida stone-crab claws. 800–833–0888.

Smoked Salmon, P.O. Box 27739, Seattle, WA 98125: Free information ■ Fresh-caught, alder-smoked Alaskan salmon. 800–551–7371.

Specialty Seafoods, 605 30th St., Anacortes, WA 98221: Free catalog ■ Alderwood-smoked Pacific Northwest sockeye salmon and smoked oysters. 800–645–3474.

Starfish Seafood Emporium, 233 9th Ave., New York, NY 10001: Free catalog ■ Shrimp, caviar, oysters, clams, and scallops, other seafoods, and steaks. 800–553–9703.

Stonington Lobster Co-op, P.O. Box 87, Stonington, ME 04681: Free information ■ Lobsters, scallops, crab meat, clams, mussels, and shrimp. 207–367–2286.

Totem Smokehouse, 1906 Pike Place Market, Seattle, WA 98101: Free brochure ■ Alderwood-smoked salmon and other seafoods. 800–9–SALMON; 206–443–1710 (in WA).

Truzzolino Food Products Company, P.O. Box 4226, Butte, MT 59702: Free information ■ Hickory-smoked Montana rainbow trout and Mexican specialties that include enchiladas, refried beans, beef and turkey tamales, chili, and salsa. 406–494–3132.

Weathervane Seafoods, Public Landing, Belfast, ME 04915: Free information ■ Live Maine lobsters and mussels. 207–338–1777.

Wisconsin Fishing Company, P.O. Box 965, Green Bay, WI 54305: Free brochure ■ Shrimp, lobster, crab, and other seafoods. 414–437–3582.

Seasonings & Condiments

Almond Plaza, P.O. Box 500, Sacramento, CA 95803: Free catalog ■ California herbs, almonds, and candy. 800–225–6887.

Alyce's Herbs, P.O. Box 9563, Madison, WI 53715: Catalog $1 ■ Herb vinegars and herb-infused oils for cooking and salads. 608–274–4911.

Amon Orchids, 7404 US 31 North, P.O. Box 1551, Traverse City, MI 49685: Free information ■ Old-fashioned cherry butter, cherry almond butter, jam and jelly, mustard, hot pepper jelly, and dessert sauces. 616–938–1644.

Arizona Champagne Sauces, Sugar's Kitchen, P.O. Box 41886, Tucson, AZ 85717: Free brochure ■ Salt-free picante sauce, vegetable dip, verde sauce, herbal spice dip mix, mustard sauce, Cajun mustard sauce, hot mustard sauce, and mild and hot jalapeno jellies. 602–299–6027.

Charles Baldwin & Sons, Depot St., West Stockbridge, MA 01266: Free information ■ Pure vanilla extract made from the Madagascar Bourbon Vanilla Bean. 413–232–7785.

Bear Meadow Farm, Moore Rd., Rt. 2, Florida, MA 01247: Free brochure ■ Fruit and herb jellies, jams, preserves, chutney, fruit vinegars, relishes, mustards, salt-free sauces, and brandied fruits. 413–663–9241.

Beaverton Foods, Inc., P.O. Box 687, Beaverton, OR 97075: Free brochure ■ Oregon-grown horseradish, mustards, sauces, and condiments. 503–646–8138.

Bickford Flavors, 282 S. Main St., Akron, OH 44308: Free brochure ■ Nonalcoholic, sugar- and salt-free flavorings, and natural orangeade, grapeade, lemonade, and fruit punch concentrates. 216–762–4666.

Norman Bishop, 111 N. Market St., Ste. 1066, San Jose, CA 95113: Free brochure ■ Low-sodium, preservative-free mustards and mayonnaise. 408–292–1089.

Blanchard & Blanchard, Ltd., P.O. Box 1080, Norwich, VT 05055: Free information ■ Preservative-free natural salad dressings, dessert sauces, mustards, glazes, and marinades. 802–649–1327.

Boetje's Foods, Inc., 2736 12th St., Rock Island, IL 61201: Free information ■ Stone ground mustards. 309–788–4352.

A.M. Braswell Food Company, P.O. Box 485, Statesboro, GA 30458: Free brochure ■ Low-sugar jams, preserves, jellies, marmalades, fruit butters, relishes, chowchow pickles, and fruit and chocolate dessert toppings. 912–764–6191.

Bresse Bleu, N2002 Hwy. 26, Watertown, WI 53094: Free information ■ Goat's milk cheese sauce in herb, cajun, or mushroom flavors. 800–262–3886.

Cajun Fixin's, Inc., P.O. Box 956, Abita Springs, LA 70420: Free information ■ Louisiana cajun spices and seasonings, gourmet mixes, chowchow, and other specialties. 800–443–2621.

Chalif, Inc., P.O. Box 27220, Wyndmoor, PA 19118: Free catalog ■ Low-salt condiments that include a stir-fry sauce, honey-mustard, and lemon-dill mayonnaise. 215–233–2023.

Chicama Vineyards, Stoney Hill Rd., West Tisbury, MA 02575: Free information ■ Oak-aged white wine, red wine, and fruit wine vinegars. Other specialties include preserves, salad dressings, mustards and mustard sauce, ice cream sauces, and oils. 508–693–0309.

Cinnabar Specialty Foods, 1134 W. Haining St., Prescott, AZ 86301: Free information ■ Tomato, tomato-mint, mango, peach, and pear-cardamom chutney. 800–824–4563; 602–778–3687 (in AZ).

Clearview Farms, Inc., RD 1, Box 5070, Enosburg Falls, VT 05450: Free catalog ■ Maple syrup and sugar, maple apple sauce and apple pie, maple brandy sauce, maple-sugared nuts, mustards, barbecue sauces and glazes, preserves, relishes and pickles, and salad dressings. 802–933–2537.

Commissariat Imports, Inc., 2641 Veteran Ave., Los Angeles, CA 90064: Free information ■ Curry, ginger, chutney, and other condiments and ingredients for Indian-style cooking. 310–475–5628.

Crabtree & Evelyn Limited, P.O. Box 167, Woodstock Hill, CT 06281: Catalog $3.50 ■ English mustards and chutney, herbs and spices, French mustard and mustard sauces, oils and vinegars, fruit vinegars and syrups, preserves, biscuits and cookies, and candy. 203–928–2766.

Cultured Foods Corporation, 973 Linda Vista Ave., Mountain View, CA 94043: Free information ■ Ready-to-use mixes for making pickles in 3 days without canning, or for making sauerkraut and pickled peppers. 415–961–5456.

Delegeane Garlic Farms, P.O. Box 2561, Yountville, CA 94599: Free brochure ■ Fresh garlic, chili ristras, salt-free herb seasonings, and California wildflower honeys. 707–944–8019.

Desert Rose Salsa Company, P.O. Box 5391, Tucson, AZ 85703: Free brochure ■ Salsa, from medium to one with a "fiery" flavor, and several in between. Other specialties include spicy mesquite honey-based barbecue sauce, spicy Italian peppers, and tortilla chips. 602–743–0450.

Eden Foods, 701 Tecumseh, Clinton, MI 49236: Free information ■ Low-sodium and organic soy sauces. 517–456–7424.

El Paso Chile Company, 100 Ruhlin Ct., El Paso, TX 79922: Free brochure ■ Chili and spice blends that include Chili Con Carne Powder, Barbecue Meat Marinade, Salsa Primera, Cactus Salsa, Tequila Bar-B-Q Sauce, Beer Bar-B-Q Sauce, and Snakebite Salsa. 915–544–3434.

Fredericksburg Herb Farm, 310 E. Main St., Fredericksburg, TX 78624: Catalog $1 (does not include herb plants) ■ Herb plants, seeds, flowers, toiletries, oils, and seasonings. 512–997–8615.

Get Sauced, 508 Monroe St., Detroit, MI 48226: Free catalog ■ Barbecue sauces, from mild and smooth to very hot; other hot sauces; low-salt and low-cholesterol sauces; and mustards, ketchup, and other condiments. 800–765–TASTE.

Gourmet Foods, Inc., P.O. Box 419, Knoxville, TN 37901: Free brochure ■ Spicy pepper sauce, Worcestershire sauce, hot pepper sauce, beef and burger sauce, Cajun hot pepper sauce, liquid smoke, and oyster and shrimp sauce. 615–970–2982.

Hawaiian Plantations, 650 Iwilei Rd., Honolulu, HI 96817: Free catalog ■ Candies, jams, syrups, dressings, and condiments, all made with authentic Hawaiian ingredients. 800–767–4650.

Helen's Tropical Exotics, 3519 Church St., Clarkston, GA 30021: Free brochure ■ Dips, marinades, sauces, Jamaican pimento, tropical spices, and hot peppers. 800–544–JERK.

Herb Hollow, Safford Rd., East Otto, NY 14729: Catalog $1 (refundable) ■ Herbal teas, seasonings, potpourris, handmade soaps and toiletries, and other herbal products. 716–257–5105.

Herb & Spice Collection, P.O. Box 118, Norway, IA 52318: Free catalog ■ Culinary herbs and spices, herbs and tea, natural herbal body care products, and potpourris. 800–365–4372.

House of Spices, 76–17 Broadway, Jackson Heights, NY 11373: Free catalog ■ East Indian foods and spices. 718–476–1577.

Judyth's Mountain, 1737 Lorenzen Dr., San Jose, CA 95124: Free information ■ Sauces and condiments. Includes their Pepper Olive Sauce with Walnuts for use with meat and cheese, and California Almond Sauce with Capers and Leeks for use with chicken, lamb, or beef. 408–264–3330.

Kelchner's, P.O. Box 245, Dublin, PA 18917: Free information ■ Horseradish cocktail sauce, horseradish tartar sauce, and hot mustard with horseradish. 215–249–3439.

J.R. Kelly Company, Box 471, Collinsville, IL 62234: Free information ■ Horseradish and horseradish sauces. Includes grated plain, hot, grated beet, hot dog relish, shrimp and seafood sauce, creamy smooth sauce, and tartar sauce. 618–344–2910.

Kozlowski Farms, 5566 Gravenstein Hwy., North Forestville, CA 95436: Free brochure ■ Condiments and mustards, sugar-free berry vinegars, barbecue sauce, conserves, mustards, chutney, old-fashioned jams, marmalades, and honey. 707–887–1857.

Le Saucier, 632 Hyde Park Ave., Boston, MA 02131: Free information ■ Sauces, marinades, mustards, vinegars, curry from Thailand, and other condiments. 800–328–7282.

Magic Seasoning Blends, P.O. Box 770034, New Orleans, LA 70177: Free catalog with long SASE ■ All-natural blends of Chef Paul Prudhomme's cajun gourmet seasonings with no MSG, sugar, or preservatives. 800–4–K–PAULS; 504–947–6712 (in LA).

Morris Farms, Rt. 1, Hwy. 56 East, Uvalda, GA 30473: Free catalog ■ Vidalia onion relish, relish with mustard, barbecue sauce, onion pickles, and sweet onion vinaigrette. 800–447–9338.

The Olive Company, 11746 Rt. 108, Clarksville, MD 21029: Free information ■ Gourmet olive specialties. Includes Marinated Olives with Anchovies, Marinated Olives with Garlic, Mild and Spicy Marinated Olives, and Hot and Sassy Marinated Olives. 410–531–5332.

Pendery's Inc., 304 E. Belknap St., Fort Worth, TX 76102: Free price list ■ Spices, seasonings, and flavorings for Mexican cooking. 817–332–3871.

Rafal Spice Company, 2521 Russell, Detroit, MI 48207: Free catalog ■ Spices, decaffeinated coffee beans, tea, and flavoring extracts. 313–259–6373.

Raven's Nest, 4539 Iroquois Trail, Duluth, GA 30136: Catalog $1 ■ Spices and herbs, potpourris and extracts, essential oils, and herbal gifts.

Ray's Brand Products, Inc., 1920 S. 13th St., P.O. Box 1000, Springfield, IL 62705: Free information ■ Chile with beans and all-beef hot dog sauce. 217–523–2777.

The Rosemary House, 120 S. Market St., Mechanicsburg, PA 17055: Catalog $2 ■ Gourmet spices. 717–697–5111.

San Francisco Herb Company, 250 14th St., San Francisco, CA 94103: Free catalog ■ Herbs and spices for gourmet cooking. 800–227–4530; 800–622–0768 (in CA).

San Francisco Mustard Company, 4049 Petaluma Blvd. North, Petaluma, CA 94952: Free information ■ All-natural salt-free whole seed mustards. 707–769–0866.

Santa Barbara Olive Company, 1661 Mission Dr., Solvang, CA 93463: Free information ■ Handpicked olives, specialty olive oils, salad dressings, garlic nectar, and other condiments. 800–624–4896.

Schmidt & Sons Company, 6100 Virginia Dr., Auburn, CA 95603: Catalog $2 ■ Dried herbs, potpourris, teas, and medicinals. 916–878–0967.

Sechler's Fine Pickles, St. Joe, IN 46785: Free information ■ Sweet mixed candied pickles. 219–337–5461.

Select Origins, Box N, Southampton, NY 11968: Free catalog ■ Kitchen-tested vanilla, cooking sweets, dessert sauces, oils, vinegars, sauces, marinades, relishes and condiments, herbs and spices, preserves, and coffee and tea. 800–822–2092; 516–924–5447 (in NY).

Shoffeitt Gourmet Seasoning Corporation, P.O. Box 785, Healdsburg, CA 95448: Free information ■ Gourmet seasonings and sauces for steak, vegetables and salads, fish, lamb, pasta, and beef. 707–433–5555.

Southwestern Flavor Company, P.O. Box 315, Red River, NM 87558: Free information ■ Cactus salsa, chile honey, chile and corn ristras, and other Mexican favorites. 505–754–2221.

Spectacular Sauces, Inc., P.O. Box 30010, Alexandria, VA 22310: Free information ■ Sauces, marinades, and condiments. 800–999–4949.

Spice Merchant, P.O. Box 524, Jackson Hole, WY 93001: Free catalog ■ Spices, herbs, and flavoring condiments from China, Japan, Indonesia, Thailand, and other countries. 307–733–7811.

C.S. Steen Syrup Mill, P.O. Box 339, Abbeville, LA 70510: Free information ■ Flavored vinegar for use in salads, cooking, or as a seasoning. 318–893–1654.

Sweet Adelaide Enterprises, Inc., 3457–A S. La Cienega Blvd., Los Angeles, CA 90016: Free information ■ Low-salt all-natural herb vinegars and herb seasonings with no sugar, MSG, or other additives and preservatives. Other specialties include cold-pressed French walnut oil and red-hot pecan oil with red peppers, black peppercorns, and garlic. 310–559–6196.

Talk O'Texas, 1610 Roosevelt St., San Angelo, TX 76905: Free information ■ Hot and mild crisp okra pickles. 800–749–6572.

Tommy Tangs Thai Seasonings, 7829 Melrose Ave., Los Angeles, CA 90046: Free information ■ Seasonings with no MSG and artificial ingredients. 213–874–3883.

Taste Buds, 7400 N. Federal, Boca Raton, FL 33431: Free catalog ■ Barbecue sauces, dressings, toppings, hot sauces, salsa, mustards, and marinades. 800–765–TASTE.

TLC of Idaho, Inc., 449 N. Steelhead Way, Boise, ID 83704: Free information ■ Mild hickory, sweet and sour, and cajun barbecue sauces. 208–378–9525.

Varney's Chemist Laden, 310 E. Main St., Fredericksburg, TX 78624: Catalog $1 ■ Seasonings and spices, herbs and oils, toiletries, and books. 800–284–0526.

Vieux Carre Foods, Inc., P.O. Box 50277, New Orleans, LA 70150: Free brochure ■

Cajun and Creole flavorings. Includes a Praline Sauce, Shrimp Remoulade Sauce, Creole Mustard, Creole Steak Sauce, Shrimp and Crab Boil, Ground Garlic Cloves, Barbecue Sauce, and Seafood Sauce. 504–822–6065.

VMM of Locust Company, 1555 Birch Hill Rd., Locust Valley, NY 11560: Free information ■ Salt- and preservative-free dried tomatoes, tomato pesta, and elephant garlic. 516–671–1519.

Watkins Manufacturing, 150 Liberty St., P.O. Box 5570, Winona, MN 55987: Free catalog ■ Seasonings, spices, flavors, and extracts. 800–553–8018.

Sugar-free & Dietetic

Delty, Inc., 7924 Ronson Rd., San Diego, CA 92111: Free information ■ Sugar-free chocolate. 800–962–3355.

Estee Candy Company, Inc., 169 Lackawanna Ave., Parsippany, NJ 07054: Free catalog ■ Sugarless candies and cookies. 201–335–1000.

Hearty Mix Company, 1231 Madison Hill Rd., Rahway, NJ 07065: Free catalog ■ Baking mixes for diet-conscious eaters, without preservatives, cholesterol, or saturated fat products. Includes cookies, cakes and other dessert pastries, salt-free bread, and wheat-free items. 908–382–3010.

Ann Raskas Candies, P.O. Box 13367, Kansas City, KS 66113: Free information ■ Candy for dieters, with 14 calories each piece. 913–422–7230.

Tea, Coffee & Cocoa

American Coffee, Inc., 800 Magazine St., New Orleans, LA 70130: Free information ■ New Orleans famous French Market coffee.

Aspen Mulling Spices, c/o Wax & Wicks, Inc., P.O. Box 191, Aspen, CO 81611: Free information ■ All-natural mulling spices to make hot or cold cider, wine, or tea.

Barclay's Coffee & Tea Company, 9030 Tampa Ave., Northridge, CA 91324: Free catalog ■ Freshly roasted coffee and tea and brewing and serving accessories. 818–885–7744.

Barnie's Coffee & Tea Company, 340 N. Primrose Dr., Orlando, FL 32803: Free information ■ Exotic teas and coffees. 407–894–1416.

Baronet Gourmet Coffee, 77 Weston St., Hartford, CT 06120: Free catalog ■ Over 90 specialty coffees and accessories. 800–253–7374.

Bean Bag, 10400 Old Georgetown Rd., Bethesda, MD 20814: Free catalog ■ Over 60 exotic blends of gourmet coffee and tea. 301–530–8090.

Boyar's International, 5095 Paris St., Denver, CO 80239: Free catalog ■ Exotic, flavored and nonflavored, caffeinated and decaffeinated, 100 percent Arabica gourmet coffee blends in whole bean, ground, and tea-bag style. Other items include air-tight canisters, espresso makers, grinders, coffee filters, thermal carafes, and gourmet gift baskets. 800–284–5776; 303–375–0828 (in CO).

Brown & Jenkins Trading Company, P.O. Box 1570, Burlington, VT 05402: Free catalog ■ Over 50 gourmet coffees that are fresh roasted daily and shipped direct. Includes mocha java, Colombia supreme, Colombian, Costa Rican, Vermont breakfast blend, decaffeinated Mexican, decaffeinated Colombian, and special blends. 802–862–2395.

Cafe La Semeuse, P.O. Box 429, Brooklyn, NY 11222: Free brochure ■ Regular or water-processed whole bean decaffeinated Cafe La Semeuse, the award-winning hand-roasted coffee. 800–242–6333.

Cocolat, 2547 9th St., Berkeley, CA 94710: Free information ■ Gourmet cocoa for chocolate and dessert creations. 800–274–2499.

Confetti, Embarcadero Center 4, San Francisco, CA 94111: Free information ■ Droste and Ghirardelli cocoa for chocolate and dessert creations. 415–362–1706.

Culinary Emporium, 4740 Interstate Dr., Cincinnati, OH 45246: Free information ■ Over 60 varieties of freshly roasted caffeinated and decaffeinated blended coffees and flavored coffees. 513–874–7469.

Dean & DeLuca, 560 Broadway, New York, NY 10012: Free information ■ Bensdorp and Droste cocoa for chocolate and dessert creations. 800–999–0306.

Desert Tea, Box 328, Whitehorn, CA 95489: Free information ■ Caffeine- and alkaloid-free wild herb tea. 800–955–4832.

First Colony Coffee & Tea Company, Box 11005, Norfolk, VA 23517: Free information ■ Raspberry, peach orchard, apple or-

chard, orange and cinnamon, black current, tangy apricot, and strawberry patch tea. 800–446–8555.

Georgetown Coffee, Tea & Spice, 1330 Wisconsin Ave. NW, Washington, DC 20007: Free catalog ■ Imported coffee, unroasted green beans, herbal bulk tea, decaffeinated tea, brewing equipment, coffee filters, and replacement beakers. 202–338–3801.

Gevalia Kaffe, P.O. Box 10851, Des Moines, IA 50336: Free catalog ■ Exotic blends of gourmet coffees from around the world.

Gillies Coffee Company, 150 19th St., Brooklyn, NY 11232: Free brochure ■ Imported coffee and tea from around the world. 718–499–7766.

Gourmet Roasters, Inc., 4947 Windhaven Ct., Atlanta, GA 30338: Free list ■ Gourmet specialty coffees prepared from whole beans roasted fresh daily. 404–698–0626.

Green Mountain Coffee Roasters, Mail Order Division, 33 Coffee Ln., Waterbury, VT 05676: Free brochure ■ Freshly roasted Colombian Peaberry and other gourmet coffees. 800–223–6768.

Harney & Sons, Ltd., P.O. Box 676, Salisbury, CT 06068: Free price list ■ Gourmet tea that is available loose, in tea bags, gift canisters, and hotel-style packaging. 203–435–9218.

Harris & Holmes Tea Merchants, 11444 Gravelly Lake Dr., P.O. Box 99146, Tacoma, WA 98499: Free brochure ■ Black teas, green and semi-fermented teas, and blended and scented teas. 206–588–0655.

Harvest Blend Coffees, 1029 Davis St., Evanston, IL 60201: Free brochure ■ Custom-roasted gourmet coffee in 33 blends. 708–475–1121.

Herb Hollow, Safford Rd., East Otto, NY 14729: Catalog $1 (refundable) ■ Herbal teas, seasonings, potpourris, handmade soaps and toiletries, and other herbal products. 716–257–5105.

Mackinlay Teas, 5025 Venture Dr., Ann Arbor, MI 46108: Free information ■ Decaffeinated teas in exotic flavors. 800–TEA–FOR–U.

McNultys Tea & Coffee Company, 109 Christopher St., New York, NY 10014: Free brochure ■ Imported tea and coffee from the around world and brewing accessories. 800–356–5200; 212–242–5351 (in NY).

Northwestern Coffee Mills, 217 N. Broadway, Milwaukee, WI 53202: Catalog 50¢ ■ Imported and domestic coffee and tea. 414–276–1031.

O'Mona International Tea Company, 9 Pine Ridge Rd., Rye Brook, NY 10573: Free catalog ■ Over 200 teas from worldwide sources. 914–937–8858.

Rafal Spice Company, 2521 Russell, Detroit, MI 48207: Free catalog ■ Coffee, coffee beans, tea, spices, and flavoring extracts. 313–259–6373.

Richard's Gourmet Coffee, P.O. Box 202, Chestnut Hill, MA 02167: Free information ■ Gourmet coffee. 617–327–2132.

Schapira Coffee Company, 117 W. 10th St., New York, NY 10011: Free information ■ Gourmet coffee. 212–675–3733.

Simpson & Vail, Inc., 38 Clinton St., P.O. Box 309, Pleasantville, NY 10570: Free catalog ■ Gourmet coffee and tea flavored with rum, almond, lotus, coconut, and others. 914–747–1336.

Starbucks Coffee Company, 2010 Airport Way South, Seattle, WA 98134: Free catalog ■ Over 30 blends fresh-roasted and decaffeinated coffee from around the world, brewing machines, mugs, thermos containers, coasters, and tea. 206–447–1575.

Stash Tea, 9040 SW Burnham, Tigard, OR 97223: Catalog $2 ■ Tea in traditional, herb, decaffeinated, and spiced varieties. 800–826–4218; 503–684–7944 (in OR).

Steamer Hot Cocoa, Inc., 175 5th Ave., Ste. 2546, New York, NY 10010: Free information ■ All-natural gourmet hot cocoa mixes that include a traditional hot chocolate mix and a white hot chocolate variety. 800–444–5860.

Sunberry Farms, 1830 Jefferson St., Napa, CA 94559: Free information ■ Refined sugar- and artificial sweetener-free low-fat cocoa mix and natural caffeinated or decaffeinated ice tea mixes. 800–622–8800.

The Ultimate Herb & Spice Shoppe, 111 Azalea, P.O. Box 395, Duenweg, MO 64841: Catalog $2 ■ Bulk herbs and spices, tea blends, potpourris, soaps, and sundries. 417–782–0457.

Williams-Sonoma, Mail Order Department, P.O. Box 7456, San Francisco, CA 94120: Free information ■ Pernigotti and Dark Jersey cocoa for chocolate and dessert creations. 415–541–1262.

FOOTBALL

Clothing

Advantage Uniforms, Inc., 115 W. Main, P.O. Box 186, Manchester, MI 48158: Free information ■ Uniforms, jerseys, pants, and clothing for coaches. 313–428–8522.

Allied Corporation, Fibers Division, 1411 Broadway, New York, NY 10018: Free information ■ Uniforms, jackets, jerseys, pants, shoes, and clothing for coaches. 212–391–5000.

Apsco, Inc., 1st Ave. & 50th St., Building 57, Brooklyn, NY 11232: Free information ■ Uniforms, jerseys, jackets, and pants. 718–965–9500.

Betlin Manufacturing, 1445 Marion Rd., Columbus, OH 43207: Free information ■ Uniforms, jerseys, jackets, pants, and clothing for coaches. 614–443–0248.

Bomark Sportswear, Bomark Group, 5804 S. Rice, Houston, TX 77081: Free information ■ Uniforms, jackets, jerseys, pants, and clothing for coaches. 800–231–3351; 800–392–0616 (in TX).

Champion Products, Inc., 3141 Monroe Ave., Rochester, NY 14618: Free information ■ Uniforms, jackets, jerseys, pants, shoes, socks, and clothing for coaches. 716–385–3200.

De Long, 733 Broad St., P.O. Box 189, Grinnell, IA 50112: Free information ■ Uniforms, jackets, jerseys, pants, shoes, and clothing for coaches. 800–733–5664; 515–236–3106 (in IA).

Empire Sporting Goods Manufacturing Company, 443 Broadway, New York, NY 10013: Free information ■ Uniforms, jackets, jerseys, pants, socks, and clothing for coaches. 800–221–3455; 800–EMPIRE–6 (in NY).

Fab Knit Manufacturing, Division Anderson Industries, 1415 N. 4th St., Waco, TX 76707: Free information ■ Uniforms, jackets, jerseys, pants, and clothing for coaches. 800–433–3380; 817–752–2511 (in TX).

Kajee, Inc., 101 E. Wayne St., Franklin, IN 46131: Free information ■ Uniforms, jackets, jerseys, pants, and clothing for coaches. 800–428–4314; 317–736–8032 (in IN).

MacGregor Sporting Goods, 336 Trowbridge Dr., P.O. Box 910, Fond du Lac, WI 54935: Free information ■ Uniforms, jerseys, pants, and clothing for coaches. 414–921–8200.

Midwest Sales Group, 5055 Liberty Ave., P.O. Box 456, Vermillion, OH 44089: Free information ■ Jackets and uniforms. Will custom make. 216–967–7355.

Southland Athletic Manufacturing Company, P.O. Box 280, Terrell, TX 75160: Free information ■ Jackets and uniforms. Will custom make. 214–563–3321.

T-Shirt Ink, Inc., 5624 Lincoln Dr., Edina, MN 55436: Free information ■ Uniforms, jackets, jerseys, pants, shoes, socks, and clothing for coaches. 612–938–1116.

Venus Knitting Mills, Inc., 140 Spring St., Murray Hill, NJ 07974: Free information ■ Uniforms, jerseys, pants, socks, and clothing for coaches. 800–955–4200; 201–464–2400 (in NJ).

Wilson Sporting Goods, 2233 West St., River Grove, IL 60171: Free information ■ Uniforms, jackets, jerseys, pants, shoes, socks, and clothing for coaches. 800–323–1552.

Equipment

Adams USA, P.O. Box 489, Cookeville, TN 38501: Free information ■ Protective gear. 800–251–6857; 615–526–2109 (in TN).

Alchester Mills Company, Inc., 314 S. 11th St., Camden, NJ 08103: Free information ■ Protective gear. 609–964–9700.

Austin Athletic Equipment Corporation, 705 Bedford Ave., Box 423, Bellmore, NY 11710: Free information ■ Goal posts, markers, and marking machines. 516–785–0100.

Baden Sports, Inc., 1120 SW 16th, Renton, WA 98055: Free information ■ Leather, rubber covered, synthetic, and juvenile footballs. 206–235–1830.

Bike Athletic Company, Kazmaier Associates, Inc., 2801 Red Dog Dr., P.O. Box 666, Knoxville, TN 37901: Free information ■ Protective gear. 800–251–9230; 615–546–4703 (in TN).

Body Glove International, Dive N' Surf, Inc., 530 6th St., Hermosa Beach, CA 90254: Free information ■ Protective gear. 310–374–4074.

H.D. Brown Enterprises, Ltd., 23 Beverly St. East, P.O. Box 190, St. George, Ontario, Canada N0E 1N0: Free information ■ Leather, rubber covered, synthetic, and juvenile footballs. 519–448–1381.

Casco USA, 80 Common Rd., Dresden, ME 04342: Free information ■ Protective gear. 800–327–9285; 207–737–8516 (in ME).

Cannon Sports, P.O. Box 11179, Burbank, CA 91510: Free information ■ Protective gear. 800–223–0064; 818–503–9570 (in CA).

Gerry Cosby & Company, 3 Pennsylvania Plaza, Madison Square Garden, New York, NY 10001: Free information ■ Protective gear. 800–548–4003; 212–563–6464 (in NY).

Cougar Sports, 7954 Wallace Rd., Eden Prairie, MN 55344: Free information ■ Protective gear. 800–445–2664; 612–934–5384 (in MN).

Cramer Products, Inc., 153 W. Warren St., P.O. Box 1001, Gardner, KS 66030: Free information ■ Protective gear. 800–255–6621; 913–884–7511 (in KS).

Dreier Company, 375 Turnpike Rd., East Brunswick, NJ 08816: Free information ■ Protective gear. 908–257–0400.

Eastern Sports Sales, 676 Elm St., Concord, MA 01742: Free information ■ Protective gear. 508–369–7111.

Fisher Athletic Equipment, Inc., Rt. 8, Box 602, Salisbury, NC 28144: Free information ■ Blockers and chargers, blocking sleds, kicking cages, and tackling dummies. 704–636–5713.

Franklin Sports Industries, Inc., 17 Campanelli Pkwy., P.O. Box 508, Stoughton, MA 02072: Free information ■ Leather, rubber covered, synthetic, and juvenile footballs. 617–344–1111.

Gared Sports, Inc., 1107 Mullanphy St., St. Louis, MO 63106: Free information ■ Goal posts, markers, and marking machines. 800–325–2682; 314–421–0044 (in MO).

GeorGI-Sports, Richmat, Inc., P.O. Box 1107, Lancaster, PA 17604: Free information ■ Leather, rubber covered, synthetic,

and juvenile footballs, and protective gear. 800–338–2527; 717–291–8924 (in PA).

Marty Gilman, Inc., P.O. Box 97, Gilman, CT 06336: Free information ■ Blockers and chargers, charging and blocking sleds, kicking cages, and tackling dummies. 800–243–0398; 203–889–7334 (in CT).

Grid, Inc., NDL Products, 2313 NW 30th Pl., Pompano Beach, FL 33069: Free information ■ Protective gear. 800–543–1810; 800–843–3022 (in FL).

Hutch Sporting Goods, 1835 Airport Exchange Blvd., Ste. 100, Erlanger, KY 41018: Free information ■ Footballs, helmets, and shoulder guards. 606–282–9000.

Jayfro Corporation, Unified Sports, Inc., 976 Hartford Tpk., P.O. Box 400, Waterford, CT 06385: Free catalog ■ Goals, training equipment, and field markers. 203–447–3001.

Leisure Marketing, Inc., 2204 Morris Ave., Ste. 202, Union, NJ 07083: Free information ■ Leather, rubber covered, synthetic, and juvenile footballs. 908–851–9494.

McDavid Knee Guard, Inc., 5420 W. Roosevelt Rd., Chicago, IL 60650: Free information ■ Protective gear. 800–237–8254; 312–626–7100 (in IL).

Markwort Sporting Goods Company, 4300 Forest Park Ave., St. Louis, MO 63108: Free information ■ Footballs, face masks, gloves, helmets, and shoulder guards. 314–652–3757.

Dick Martin Sports, Inc., 201 River Rd., P.O. Box 931, Clifton, NJ 07014: Free information ■ Footballs. 800–221–1993; 201–473–0757 (in NJ).

Maxpro, Inc., 6846 Alamo Downs Pkwy., San Antonio, TX 78238: Free information ■ Protective gear. 512–680–5256.

Molten USA, Inc., Adidas Sport Balls. P.O. Box 70310, Reno, NV 89570: Free information ■ Leather, rubber covered, synthetic, and juvenile footballs. 800–666–5836; 702–358–4060 (in NV).

Mueller Sports Medicine, Inc., One Quench Dr., Prairie du Sac, WI 53578: Free information ■ Protective gear. 800–356–9522; 608–643–8530 (in WI).

New South Athletic Company, Inc., 1010 N. Maine St., P.O. Box 398, Lowell, NC

28098: Free information ■ Protective gear. 800–438–9934; 704–824–4678 (in NC).

Olympia Sports, School Tech., Inc., 745 State Cir., Ann Arbor, MI 48108: Free information ■ Blockers and chargers, charging and blocking sleds, kicking cages, and tackling dummies. 313–761–5135.

Pennsylvania Sporting Goods, 1360 Industrial Hwy., P.O. Box 451, Southampton, PA 18966: Free information ■ Protective gear. 800–535–1122.

Rawlings Sporting Goods Company, P.O. Box 22000, St. Louis, MO 63126: Free information ■ Leather, rubber covered, synthetic, and juvenile footballs, and protective gear. 314–349–3500.

Reda Sports Express, 44 N. 2nd St., P.O. Box 68, Easton, PA 18044: Free information ■ Footballs and protective equipment. 215–258–2957.

Regent Sports Corporation, 45 Ranick Rd., Hauppage, NY 11787: Free information ■ Leather, rubber covered, synthetic, and juvenile footballs. 516–234–2948.

Royal Textile Mills, Inc., Firetower Rd., P.O. Box 250, Yanceyville, NC 27379: Free information ■ Protective gear. 800–334–9361; 919–694–4121 (in NC).

Spalding & Brothers, 425 Meadow St., P.O. Box 901, Chicopee, MA 01021: Free information ■ Leather, rubber covered, synthetic, and juvenile footballs. 413–536–1200.

Star Specialty Knitting Company, Inc., 266 Union Ave., 2nd Floor, Laconia, NH 03246: Free information ■ Protective gear. 603–528–STAR.

Venus Knitting Mills, Inc., 140 Spring St., Murray Hill, NJ 07974: Free information ■ Uniforms, jerseys, pants, socks, clothing for coaches, and protective gear. 800–955–4200; 201–464–2400 (in NJ).

Voit Sports, 1451 Pittstand-Victor Rd., 100 Willowbrook Office Park, Fairport, NY 14450: Free information ■ Leather, rubber covered, synthetic, and juvenile footballs. 800–367–8648; 716–385–2390 (in NY).

Whitland Fitness Corporation, 101 Methuen St., P.O. Box 1049, Lawrence, MA 01842: Free information ■ Goal posts, markers, marking machines, blockers and chargers, charging and blocking sleds, kicking cages, and tackling dummies. 508–685–5109.

Wilson Sporting Goods, 2233 West St., River Grove, IL 60171: Free information ■ Leather, rubber covered, synthetic, and juvenile footballs. Includes uniforms, jackets, jerseys, pants, shoes, socks, and clothing for coaches. 800–323–1552.

Winston Sports Corporation, 200 5th Ave., New York, NY 10010: Free information ■ Leather, rubber covered, synthetic, and juvenile footballs. 212–255–6870.

FOUNTAINS

Bench Manufacturing Company, 390 Pond St., South Weymouth, MA 02190: Free catalog ■ Fountains, cast-iron and wood benches, trash receptacles, clocks, light poles, and sculptures. 617–436–3080.

Moultrie Manufacturing, P.O. Drawer 1179, Moultrie, GA 31776: Catalog $3 ■ Cast-aluminum tables, chairs, settees, planters, urns, fountains, chaises, and lighting fixtures. 800–841–8674.

Otto Wendt & Company, 417A Gentry Rd., Spring, TX 77373: Brochure $2 ■ Cast-aluminum lighting equipment, benches, mailboxes, fountains, patio sets, urns, and plant stands. 713–288–8295.

FRAMES

American Frame Corporation, 1340 Tomahawk Dr., Maumee, OH 43537: Free information ■ Metal picture frames. 800–537–0944.

Artemis Wood Products, Inc., P.O. Box 766, Jefferson City, TN 37760: Free catalog ■ Handcrafted, solid hardwood frames. 615–475–5669.

ASF Sales Corporation, 1340 Tomahawk Dr., Maumee, OH 43537: Free brochure ■ Picture-framing supplies and equipment, frame kits, colored mat boards and backing materials, and cutters. 800–537–0944.

Colorado Frame Manufacturing, 1230 Blue Spruce Dr., Fort Collins, CO 80524: Free information ■ Readymade and custom frames and framing materials. 800–762–3342.

Contemporary Frame Company, 346 Scott Swamp Rd., P.O. Box 514, Farmington, CT 06032: Free information ■ Aluminum section frames. 203–677–7787.

Cos-Tom Picture Frames, 1121 Bay Blvd., Chula Vista, CA 92011: Free catalog ■ Frames at factory-direct prices.

Country Frames, Box 284, Rochert, MN 56578: Free flyer ■ Country-style frames. 800–289–8883.

Crown Art Products Company, 90 Dayton Ave., Passaic, NJ 07055: Free catalog ■ Metal section frames and framing supplies. 201–777–6010.

Decor Frame Company, 4307 Metzger Rd., Fort Pierce, FL 34982: Free information ■ Aluminum section frames with hardware for assembly. Springs and hangers optional. 800–826–7969.

Documounts, 3709 W. 1st Ave., Eugene, OR 97402: Free catalog ■ Wood picture frames and bevel-edged mats. 800–942–9191.

Exposures, 2800 Hoover Rd., Stevens Point, WI 54481: Free catalog ■ Albums and frames. 800–572–5750.

E-Z Frame, P.O. Box 23748, Tucson, AZ 85734: Catalog $2.50 ■ Ready-to-assemble frames. Custom sizes available.

Fletcher-Terry Company, 65 Spring Ln., Farmington, CT 06032: Free information ■ Easy-to-use picture framing tool that won't tear or dent backing materials, or cause frames to split. 800–THE–FTCO 203–677–7331 (in CT).

Florida Frames, Inc., 12011 44th St. North, Clearwater, FL 34622: Free catalog ■ Solid oak and teak frames. Will custom make. 800–878–3946.

Frame Factory, 1909 W. Diversey Pkwy., Chicago, IL 60614: Free catalog ■ Frames and framing supplies. 800–621–6570.

Frame Fit Company, P.O. Box 8926, Philadelphia, PA 19135: Free information ■ Custom aluminum picture frames and hangers. 800–523–3693; 215–332–0683 (in PA).

Frames by Mail, 11551 Adie Rd., St. Louis, MO 63043: Free catalog ■ Wood and metal picture frames. 800–3322–2467.

Franken Frames, 214 W. Holston Ave., Johnson City, TN 37604: Free catalog ■ Frames and moldings. 800–322–5899.

GM Enterprises, 3511 136th St. NE, Marysville, WA 98270: Free catalog ■ Oak picture frames. 800–345–3576.

Gold Leaf Studios, P.O. Box 50156, Washington, DC 20004: Free brochure with long SASE ■ Custom frames. 202–638–4660.

Graphik Dimensions, Ltd., 41–23 Haight St., Flushing, NY 11355: Free catalog ■ Frames and framing supplies. 800–221–0262.

The Mettle Company, P.O. Box 525, Fanwood, NJ 07023: Free information ■ Free information ■ Aluminum frames. 800–621–1329.

New England Frameworks, Rt. 1, Wilton, NH 03086: Free catalog with long SASE ■ Wooden frames and display domes. 603–878–1633.

Old Tyme Picture Frames, P.O. Box 2308, Temecula, CA 92593: Catalog $1 ■ Reproduction antique frames. 714–699–9622.

Plaid Enterprises, P.O. Box 7600, Norcross, GA 30091: Free information ■ Frame-making supplies and accessories.

Pootatuck, P.O. Box 24, Windsor, VT 05089: Free catalog ■ Framing accessories. 802–674–5984.

Press-On-Products, 1020 S. Westgate, Addison, IL 60101: Free catalog ■ Framing accessories and mat boards. 800–323–1745.

Putnum Distributors, P.O. Box 477, Westfield, NJ 07091: Free catalog ■ Picture frames. 800–631–7330; 908–232–9200 (in NJ).

Skolnick Photo Frames, 29245 Dequindra Ave., Madison Heights, MI 48071: Free catalog ■ Metal, wooden, and plastic frames, and framing accessories, mat boards, and mat cutters. 313–547–0347.

Daniel Smith Art Supplies, Inc., 4130 1st Ave. South, Seattle, WA 98134: Catalog $3 ■ Metal frames, framing accessories, and mat boards. 206–223–9599.

Stu-Art Supplies, 2045 Grand Ave., Baldwin, NY 11510: Free catalog ■ Mats, plastic and glass for custom framing; pre-assembled frames; aluminum and wood frame-making components; shrink wrap; plastic picture saver panels; and other framing supplies. 800–645–2855.

Taylor Frame Company, 13401 Sherman Way, North Hollywood, CA 91605: Free catalog ■ Frames and framing supplies. 800–423–2620; 818–982–0610 (in CA).

Tennessee Moulding & Frame Company, 1188 Antioch, Nashville, TN 37211: Catalog $5 ■ Metal, wood, laminates, and formica frames, and mats and framing equipment and tools. 800–821–5483.

World Frame Distributors, 107 Maple St., Denton, TX 76201: Free brochure ■ Framing supplies and ready-made frames that include gallery ornates. 817–382–3442.

FUND-RAISING

Ace Pecan Company, 900 Morse Ave., Elk Grove Village, IL 60007: Free information ■ Fund-raising programs with pecans, walnuts, pistachios, almonds, cashews, and Brazil nuts. 800–323–9754.

Acme Premium Supply Corporation, 4100 Forest Park, St. Louis, MO 63108: Free catalog ■ Specialty merchandise for fund-raising, carnivals, incentive and premium programs, and bingo. 800–325–7888.

America's Best, P.O. Box 91717, Mobile, AL 36691: Free information ■ Merchandise for fund-raising programs. 800–633–6750.

Classic American Fund Raisers, Cookbook Plan, 11184 Antioch, Ste. 415, Overland Park, KS 66210: Free information with long SASE ■ Personalized fund-raising cookbook plan. 800–821–5745.

Cookbook Publishers, Inc., P.O. Box 1260, Olathe, KS 66061: Free information ■ Describes how to raise funds by putting together personalized cookbooks. 800–227–7282.

Cookbooks by Morris Press, P.O. Box 1681, Kearney, NE 68848: Free information ■ Fund-raising cookbook plan. 800–445–6621; 800–652–9314 (in NE).

Foreign Candy Company, Inc., 451 Black Forest Rd., Hull, IA 51239: Free catalog ■ Fund-raising programs for schools, churches, social, and civic groups. 712–439–1496.

Fuller Fund Raising Company, P.O. Box 4957, Montgomery, AL 36103: Free information ■ Fund-raising program with nationally advertised candies and gift wrappings. 800–633–5732.

Fundcraft, P.O. Box 340, Collierville, TN 38017: Free information ■ Fund-raising program with community cookbooks. 800–351–7822.

Hale Indian River Groves, Indian River Plaza, Wabasso, FL 32970: Free information ■ Fund-raising program with Hale Indian River oranges and grapefruit. 800–289–4253.

Tracy Hamilton, Inc., 20 Maple Place, Freeport, NY 11520: Sample $2 ■ Fund-raising program with calendars. 516–223–2534.

KD Enterprises, 5 Manmar Dr., Ste. 495, Plainville, MA 02762: Catalog $5 (refundable with $25 order) ■ Fund-raising programs with everything from decorative hardware to jewelry, burglar alarms to porcelain figurines, music boxes and trinkets to miniatures, auto care items, tools, office accessories, knives, leather goods, and toys. 508–695–1613.

Krum's Chocolatier, 4 Dexter Plaza, Pearl River, NY 10965: Free catalog ■ Fund-raising program with kosher chocolates. 800–ME–CANDY.

Manhattan Chocolates, Division Shufra Chocolates, 580 Union Ave., Brooklyn, NY 11211: Free brochure ■ Kosher chocolates, truffle filled chocolate bars in milk or dark chocolate, boxed marshmallows, candy clusters, mints, and fudge squares for fund-raising by Jewish organizations. 718–388–5420.

Mascot Pecan Company, P.O. Box 765, Glennville, GA 30427: Free information ■ Fund-raising program with pecans and pecan candies. 800–841–3985; 912–654–2195 (in GA).

Nestle-Beich, P.O. Box 2914, Bloomington, IN 61702: Free information ■ Fund-raising program with boxed chocolates and other candies. 800–431–1248

Oriental Trading Company, Inc., P.O. Box 3407, Omaha, NE 68103: Free catalog ■ Fund raisers, toys, giftwares, novelties, carnival supplies, and holiday and seasonal items. 800–228–0475.

Passover Pastries, Inc., 21301 Powerline Rd., Ste, 309, Boca Raton, FL 33433: Free information ■ Fund-raising program selling pareve and kosher Passover pastries baked under Rabinical supervision of the Orthodox Union. 800–825–3743; 407–451–8336 (in FL).

Revere Company, N. South Rd., Scranton, PA 18504: Free catalog ■ Fund-raising program with household items. 800–876–9967.

Spirit of America Fund Raisers, P.O. Box 621, Montgomery, AL 36101: Sample $2 ■ Fund-raising program with 2–year daily planners with memo pads. 800–628–3671.

Sunny South Pecans, P.O. Box 192, Staresboro, GA 30458: Free information ■ Fund-raising program with packaged pecans. 912–764–5337.

Tic-La-Dex, 3443 Camino Del Rio South, Ste. 326, San Diego, CA 92108: Free information ■ Custom recycled plastic book covers for schools, organizations, associations. 800–827–9467; 619–281–7242.

U.S. Pen Fund Raising Company, P.O. Box 1027, Montgomery, AL 36101: Free information ■ Fund-raising program for schools, churches, and other organizations, that involves selling popular home, office, and school products. 800–633–8738.

Walter's Cookbooks, 215 5th Ave. SE, Waseca, MN 56093: Free information ■ Fund-raising program with custom-made cookbooks. 800–447–3274; 507–835–3691 (in MN).

FURNACES & HEATING SYSTEMS

Cal-K, Inc., 7411 Laurel Canyon Blvd., North Hollywood, CA 91605: Free information ■ Programmable setback thermostats. 818–764–3288.

Carrier Corporation, P.O. Box 4808, Syracuse, NY 13221: Free information ■ Combination gas/electric heating and cooling system, gas and electric furnaces, heat pumps, and air conditioners. 800–CARRIER.

Central Environmental Systems, York International Corporation, P.O. Box 1592, York, PA 17405: Free information ■ Gas furnaces. 717–771–7890.

Empire Comfort Systems, Inc., 918 Freeburg Ave., Belleville, IL 62222: Free information with long SASE ■ Wall furnaces. Includes 25,000 and 35,000 BTU single wall models and a 50,000 BTU dual wall unit. 618–233–7420.

Hunter Fan Company, 2500 Fisco Ave., Memphis, TN 38114: Brochure $1 ■

Programmable electronic thermostat. 901–745–9286.

Intertherm, Inc., 10820 Sunset Office Dr., St. Louis, MO 63127: Free brochure ■ Intertherm portable heaters. 314–822–9600.

Jameson Home Products, 2820 Thatcher Rd., Downers Grove, IL 60515: Free information ■ Programmable, electronic thermostats. 708–963–2850.

Sears, Roebuck & Company, Catalog Division, 925 S. Homan Ave., Chicago, IL 60607: Free catalog ■ Heating and cooling equipment. (Catalog also available from local stores.) 312–875–2500.

Suburban Manufacturing Company, P.O. Box 399, Dayton, TN 37321: Free information ■ Easy-to-install, wall mounted heating units for use with natural or LP gas. 615–775–2131.

York International Corporation, P.O. Box 1592, York, PA 17405: Free information ■ Gas furnaces. 717–771–7890.

FURNITURE

Beds

American Starbuck, P.O. Box 15376, Lenexa, KS 66215: Free catalog ■ Custom pencil post beds. 913–894–1567.

Amish Country Collection, RD 5, Sunset Valley Rd., New Castle, PA 16105: Catalog $5 (refundable) ■ Rustic bedroom furniture with an Early American look. 800–232–6474.

Bartley Collection, Ltd., 3 Airpark Dr., Easton, MD 21601: Free catalog ■ Reproduction furniture kits for 18th-century-style beds. 800–227–8539.

Bedlam Brass, 137 Rt. 4 West, Paramus, NJ 07652: Catalog $1 ■ Brass beds and solid brass mirrors, tables, coat racks, quilt and blanket racks, and other accessories. 201–368–3500.

Bedpost, Inc., 32 S. High St., East Bangor, PA 18013: Catalog $2 ■ Brass beds and furnishings. 215–588–3824.

Brass Bed Factory, 442 Harding Way West, Galion, OH 44833: Brochure $1 ■ Save up to 50 percent on handcrafted brass beds, white iron beds, and daybeds. 419–468–3861.

Brass Beds Direct, 4866 W. Jefferson Blvd., Los Angeles, CA 90016: Free catalog ■ Save from 50 to 70 percent on custom brass beds. 800–727–6865.

Brass Bed Shoppe, 12421 Cedar Rd., Cleveland, OH 44106: Free catalog ■ Save up to 50 percent on brass beds. 216–229–4900.

Cohasset Colonials, 271 Ship St., Cohasset, MA 02025: Catalog $3 ■ Kits for Early American, Shaker, Queen Anne, Chippendale beds, and other furniture. 617–383–0110.

Country Bed Shop, Richardson Rd., RR 1, Box 65, Ashby, MA 01431: Catalog $4 ■ Handcrafted reproductions of 17th- and 18th-century American beds, chairs and tables, bed hangings, and other furniture. 508–386–7550.

Hollingsworth Furniture, P.O. Box 2592, Wilmington, NC 28402: Free brochure ■ American country-style reproduction hand-painted, stained, and unfinished pencil post and sleigh beds and other furniture. 919–251–0280.

Isabel Brass Furniture, 200 Lexington Ave., Room 1010, New York, NY 10016: Catalog $4 ■ Antique-style reproduction brass beds. 800–221–8523.

Leonard's Reproductions & Antiques, 600 Taunton Creek, Seekonk, MA 02771: Catalog $4 ■ Antique beds. 508–336–8585.

Mack Wallbed Systems, 1010 Lakeville St., Petaluma, CA 94952: Free brochure ■ Wall and bed systems that include beds, multi-drawer cabinets, nightstands, and wardrobes. 707–762–7900.

Murphy Door Bed Company, 65 Mall Dr., Commack, NY 11725: Catalog $1 ■ Folding hideaway beds. 516–543–0234.

Roberts Brass Company, 22118 NE 66th Pl., Redmond, WA 98053: Catalog $1.50 ■ Brass beds available with headboards and steel side rails. 206–868–4012.

Charles P. Rogers Brass Beds, 899 1st Ave., New York, NY 10022: Catalog $1 ■ Original 19th- and 20th-century solid brass and iron beds. 800–272–7726; 212–935–6900 (in NY).

Room & Board, 4800 Olson Memorial Hwy., Minneapolis, MN 55422: Free information ■ Handcrafted steel beds and tables. 800–486–6554.

Sico Incorporated, Room Makers Division, 7525 Cahill Rd., P.O. Box 1169, Minneapolis, MN 55440: Free information ■ Wallbeds with mattresses and box springs. 800–328–6138.

Thomasville Furniture, P.O. Box 339, Thomasville, NC 27360: Catalog $3.50 ■ Early American-style beds and other furniture. 919–472–4000.

Lisa Victoria Brass Beds, 17106 S. Crater Rd., Petersburg, VA 23805: Catalog $4 ■ Custom brass beds. 804–862–1491.

Melvin Wolf, 1500 W. Cortland St., Chicago, IL 60622: Free brochure ■ Brass occasional furniture and beds. 312–252–2800.

YankeeWood, 64 Main, Littleton, NH 03561: Free brochure ■ Canopy and pencil post beds. 603–444–5562.

Yorktowne Brass Beds, 2445 S. Queen St., York, PA 17402: Catalog $4 ■ Solid brass beds.

Beds, Adjustable

American Health Manufacturing, P.O. Box 16287, Baltimore, MD 21210: Free brochure ■ Adjustable beds with electric hand controls. 800–622–8806.

Betterest, Inc., 2001 E. Easter Ave., P.O. Box 3065, Littleton, CO 80161: Free information ■ Adjustable beds with electric hand controls. 800–448–5854.

Craftmatic Beds, 2500 Interplex Dr., Trevose, PA 19047: Free information ■ Adjustable beds with electric hand controls. 800–677–8200.

Electropedic Products, 907 Hollywood Way, Burbank, CA 91505: Free brochure ■ Adjustable beds with electric hand controls. 800–662–4548.

Wonderbed Manufacturing Company, P.O. Box 1551, Roswell, GA 30077: Free brochure ■ Adjustable beds with electric hand controls. 800–631–1746.

Children's Furniture

A & B Furniture, 11710 Baltimore Ave., Beltsville, MD 20705: Free information ■ Cribs, chests, and dressers. 301–725–4994.

Boston & Winthrop, 2 E. 93rd St., New York, NY 10128: Catalog $3 ■ Custom handpainted children's furniture. 212–410–6388.

H.U.D.D.L.E. Furniture for Kids, 11159 Santa Monica Blvd., Los Angeles, CA 90025: Free information ■ Adjustable, divisible, convertible, expandable, transformable, and climbable furniture for children. 213–836–8001.

Little Colorado, Inc., 158660 W. 7th Ave., Golden, CO 80401: Catalog $3 ■ Handmade children's furniture in solid wood. 303–278–2451.

MaxiMoms, 5482 Complex St., Ste. 108, San Diego, CA 92123: Free catalog ■ Nursery room and older children's furniture, car seats and baby carriers, soft toys, health and safety aids, nursing accessories, toilet trainers, trampolines, and playtime and educational toys. 619–278–8909.

Furniture Kits

Adams Wood Products, Inc., 974 Forest Dr., Morristown, TN 37814: Free brochure ■ Ready-to-assemble furniture. 615–587–2942.

Bartley Collection, Ltd., 3 Airpark Dr., Easton, MD 21601: Free brochure ■ Kits for antique reproduction furniture. 800–227–8539.

Cohasset Colonials, 271 Ship St., Cohasset, MA 02025: Catalog $5 ■ Kits for Early American, Shaker, Queen Anne, Chippendale beds, and other furniture. 617–383–0110.

Craftsman's Corner Woodcraft, 4012 NE 14th St., P.O. Box AP, Des Moines, IA 50302: Free catalog ■ Oak roll-top desks in pre-cut, partially assembled kits. 515–265–3239.

Cypress Street Center, 350 Cypress St., Fort Bragg, CA 95437: Free catalog ■ Easy-to-assemble outdoor chairs with matching love seats, foot rests, side carts, and tables. 800–222–0343.

Emperor Clock Company, Emperor Industrial Park, P.O. Box 1089, Fairhope, AL 36533: Catalog $1 ■ Do-it-yourself kits for grandfather clocks and furniture. 800–542–0011; 205–928–2316 (in AL).

Pacific Wood Products, 5150 Edison Ave., Chino, CA 91710: Catalog $1 ■ Macrame furniture kits. 800–421–2781; 800–262–1638 (in CA).

Shaker Workshops, P.O. Box 1028, Concord, MA 01742: Catalog $1 ■ Shaker furniture in kits or custom finished, needle crafts, dolls, and miniature furniture. 617–646–8985.

Wood Classics, Box 1, Gardner, NY 12525: Catalog $2 ■ Teak and mahogany outdoor furniture in kits or assembled. 914–255–7871.

Yield House, P.O. Box 5000, North Conway, NH 03860: Free catalog ■ Pre-sanded furniture kits with hardware and other materials. 800–258–4720.

Home Furnishings

Acorn Services Corporation, 346 Still River Rd., Bolton, MA 01740: Catalog $2 ■ Solid redwood garden furniture, plant stands, and potting benches. 508–779–5515.

Stephen Adams, Furnituremakers, Rt. 160, Box 130, Denmark, ME 04022: Catalog $4 ■ Reproduction 18th- and 19th-century furniture. 207–452–2444.

American Furniture Galleries, P.O. Box 60, Montgomery, AL 36101: Brochure $1 ■ Handcrafted, reproduction Victorian furniture. 800–547–5240.

Amish Country Collection, RD 5, Sunset Valley Rd., New Castle, PA 16105: Catalog $5 (refundable) ■ Amish-style oak and hickory twig furniture, rugs, quilts, and wall hangings. 800–232–6474.

Antiquaria, 60 Dartmouth St., Springfield, MA 01109: Catalog $4 ■ Victorian-style furniture and accessories. 413–781–6927.

Backwoods Furnishings, Rt. 28, Box 161, Indian Lake, NY 12842: Free flyer ■ Custom rustic-style tables and chairs, rocking chairs, four-poster beds, and desks. 518–251–3327.

Barne & Barnes Fine Furniture, 190 Commerce Ave., Southern Pines, NC 28387: Free information with long SASE ■ Save up to 50 percent on furniture, accessories, and decorator fabrics. 800–334–8174.

Robert Barrow Furniture Maker, 412 Thames St., Bristol, RI 02809: Catalog $3 ■ Handmade 18th-century Windsor chairs. 401–253–4434.

C.H. Becksvoort, Box 12, New Gloucester, ME 04260: Catalog $5 ■ Handmade cherry furniture and accessories in classic, contemporary, and Shaker designs. 207–926–4608.

Best Furniture Distributors, Inc., 16 W. Main, P.O. Box 489, Thomasville, NC 27360: Free information ■ Save up to 40 percent on furniture and accessories. 800–334–8000.

Big Country, 242 Long John Silver Dr., Wilmington, NC 28405: Free brochure ■ Handcrafted solid wood furniture reproductions. 800–344–4072.

Blackwelder's, US Hwy. 21 North, Statesville, NC 28677: Catalog $7.50 ■ Save from 30 to 50 percent on furniture. 800–438–0201; 704–872–8922 (in NC).

Blake Industries, 390 Pond St., South Weymouth, MA 02190: Free brochure ■ Outdoor and indoor teak furniture and ornamental cast-iron pole lights and fixtures. 617–337–8772.

Bombay Company, P.O. Box 161009, Fort Worth, TX 76161: Free catalog ■ Antique furniture reproductions. 800–829–7789.

Bonita Furniture Galleries, Rt. 5, Box 105, US Hwy. 321 North, Hickory, NC 28601: Free information ■ Furniture and accessories. 704–396–3178.

Brentwood Manor Furnishings, 316 Virginia Ave., Clarksville, VA 23927: Free brochure ■ Furniture, draperies and accessories, clocks, and mirrors. 800–225–6105.

Teri M. Browning, The Wentworth Collection, P.O. Box 131, Wentworth, NH 03282: Catalog $6 ■ Furniture reproductions. 603–764–9395.

Curtis Buchanan, Windsor Chairmaker, 208 E. Main St., Jonesborough, TN 37659: Brochure $2 and long SASE ■ Windsor chairs. 615–753–5160.

Michael Camp, Cabinetmaker, 495 Amelia, Plymouth, MI 48170: Catalog $3 ■ Custom 18th- and 19th-century furniture reproductions. 313–459–1190.

Candlertown Chairworks, P.O. Box 1630, Candler, NC 28715: Catalog $2 ■ Handbuilt country-style adult and children's chairs, benches, and bar stools finished in a worn milk-paint with a 100-year patina. 704–667–4844.

Carolina Furniture Gallery, Rt. 1, Box 37A, Thomasville, NC 27360: Free information ■ Furniture and accessories. 919–475–1309.

Carolina Interiors, 115 Oak Ave., Kannapolis, NC 28081: Catalog $5 ■ Save from 20 to 60 percent on furniture. 704–933–1888.

Carolina Leather House, Inc., P.O. Box 5195, Hickory, NC 28601: Catalog $2 ■ Leather furniture. 704–322–4478.

Cherry & Deen Furniture, 1214 Goshen Mill Rd., Peach Bottom, PA 17563: Brochure $2 ■ Custom period-style furniture. 717–548–3254.

Cherry Hill Furniture, Box 7405, Furnitureland Station, High Point, NC 27264: Furnishings portfolio $5 ■ Save up to 50 percent on furniture. 800–888–0933.

Class Fab Mica Works, 1401 S. 30th Ave., Hollywood, FL 33020: Free information ■ Dining room and bedroom furniture, wall units, desks, TV carts, and mattresses. 305–945–3351.

Coffey Furniture Galleries, Box 141, Granite Falls, NC 28630: Free information ■ Furniture and accessories. 704–396–2900.

Cohasset Colonials, 271 Ship St., Cohasset, MA 02025: Catalog $5 ■ Reproduction furniture in kits, or assembled and finished, fabrics, paints and stains, lighting fixtures, and brass and pewter items. 617–383–0110.

Cole's Appliance & Furniture Company, 4026 Lincoln Ave., Chicago, IL 60618: Free information with long SASE ■ Furniture, audio and video equipment, television sets, and kitchen appliances. 312–525–1797.

Colonial Designs Furniture, Box 1429, Havertown, PA 19083: Catalog $2 ■ Reproduction 18th-century furniture. 215–446–0835.

Colonial Furniture Shops, Box 12007, Winston-Salem, NC 27117: Brochure $1 ■ Reproduction 18th-century furniture. 919–788–2121.

Colonial Williamsburg, P.O. Box 3532, Williamsburg, VA 23187: Catalog $18.95 ■ Williamsburg furniture reproductions. 800–446–9240.

Conran's Mail Order, 475 Oberlin Ave. South, Lakewood, NJ 08701: Catalog $2 ■ Indoor and outdoor furniture, homewares, kitchen equipment, fabrics, linens, wallpaper, lighting fixtures and lamps, and floor coverings. 908–905–8800.

Cornucopia, P.O. Box 30, Harvard, MA 01451: Catalog $2 ■ Early American and primitive style rocking and Windsor chairs, settees, tables, and hutches. 508–772–0023.

Country Bed Shop, Richardson Rd., RR 1, Box 65, Ashby, MA 01431: Catalog $4 ■ Handcrafted reproductions of 17th- and 18th-century American beds, chairs and tables, and bed hangings. 508–386–7550.

Country Furniture Shop, Box 125, Rt. 20E, Madison, NY 13402: Brochure $3 ■ Reproduction 18th-century furniture. 315–893–7404.

Country Store, P.O. Box 17696, Whitefish Bay, WI 53217: Catalog $2 ■ Willow furniture. 414–263–1919.

Country Workshop, 95 Rome St., Newark, NJ 07105: Catalog $1 ■ Finished and ready-to-finish furniture. 800–526–8001; 201–589–3407 (in NJ).

Gerald Curry, Cabinetmaker, Pound Hill Rd., Union, ME 04862: Free brochure ■ Reproduction 18th-century furniture. 207–785–4633.

Frederick Dackloe & Bros., Inc., P.O. Box 427, Portland, PA 18351: Catalog $5 ■ Handcrafted Windsor chairs, rockers, benches, and bar stools. 717–897–6172.

Davis Cabinet Company, P.O. Box 60444, Nashville, TN 37206: Catalog $3 ■ Victorian-style furniture reproductions from the Lillian Russell collection.

Decorum, 235–237 Commercial St., Portland, ME 04101: Free information ■ Antique lighting, roll-top and other desks, file cabinets, period lamps, recycled cabinet and door hardware, and plumbing and bathroom fixtures. 207–775–3346.

Deep River Trading Company, 2436 Willard Rd., High Point, NC 27260: Free information ■ Reproduction 18th-century bedroom and dining room furniture; contemporary, French, Victorian, and country-style furniture; and butcher block tables. 919–885–2436.

Derby Desk Company, 140 Tremont St., Brighton, MA 02135: Free brochure ■ Antique desks that include roll-tops. 617–787–2707.

Designer Secrets, Box 529, Fremont, NE 68025: Catalog $2 (refundable) ■ Save up to 75 percent on furniture and accessories, wall coverings and fabrics, bedspreads, and window treatments. 800–955–2559.

Edgar B Furniture, Box 849, Clemmons, NC 27012: Catalog $15 ■ Furniture and accessories. 800–255–6589; 919–766–6321 (in NC).

Clint Edwards, Cabinetmaker, 5208 Brook Rd., Richmond, VA 23227: Free information with long SASE ■ Handmade reproduction furniture. 804–266–1583.

Fabian House, P.O. Box 86, Bowie, MD 20715: Catalog $1 ■ Furniture, quilts, samplers, Windsor chairs, tables, upholstered pieces, and reproduction lighting. 301–262–6606.

Falcon Designs, 91535 Deadwood Creek Rd., Deadwood, OR 97430: Catalog $3 ■ Heirloom solid cherry furniture. 503–964–3191.

Jeffrey Fiant, Windsor Chairmaker, 260 Golf Rd., Reinholds, PA 17569: Brochure $2 ■ Reproduction Windsor chairs. 215–678–1828.

Frontier Furniture, 260 Kelley Dr., Bigfork, MT 59911: Catalog $4 ■ Handcrafted log furniture, accessories, and log guard rails. 406–837–5194.

The Furniture Barn, 1190 Hwy., 74 Bypass, Springdale, NC 28160: Free information ■ Save up to 50 percent on furniture, bedding, and decor accessories. 704–287–8785.

Furniture Collections of Carolina, Rt. 8, Box 128, Hickory, NC 28602: Free information ■ Furniture for the home and office. 704–294–3593.

Furniture Company, 322 Pine Mountain Rd., Hudson, NC 28638: Free information ■ Save from 40 to 60 percent on furniture and accessories. 704–728–5001.

Furniture Country U.S.A., P.O. Box 946, Granite Falls, NC 28630: Free information ■ Furniture and accessories. 800–331–6724.

Furniture Discount Resource, 274 Eastchester Dr., High Point, NC 27262: Free information ■ Furniture and accessories. 800–768–2535.

Furniture Showcase, 214 N. Main, High Point, NC 27261: Free information ■ Save up to 60 percent on furniture. 800–234–1303.

Genada Imports, P.O. Box 204, Teaneck, NJ 07666: Catalog $1 ■ Modern Danish furniture. 201–790–7522.

Great Meadows Joinery, P.O. Box 392, Wayland, MA 01778: Catalog $4 ■ Handmade reproduction Shaker and country-style furniture. 508–358–4370.

The Guild of Gulden Cabinetmakers, Gulden Gallery Investment Replicas, P.O. Box 66, Aspers, PA 17304: Catalog $20 ■ Hand-carved and hand-finished reproduction 18th-century furniture. 717–677–6146.

Habersham Plantation, 171 Collier Rd., P.O. Box 1209, Toccoa, GA 30577: Catalog $12 ■ Reproduction 17th- and 18th-century country and contemporary furniture. 800–241–0716.

Harvest House Furniture, P.O. Box 1440, Denton, NC 27239: Free information: Free information ■ Save up to 50 percent on furniture. 704–869–5181.

Heart of the Wood Furniture, P.O. Box 3031, Plymouth, MA 02361: Brochure $1 ■ Reproduction 17th-century furniture. 508–888–3552.

Heirloom Fine Furnishings, 1834 W. 5th St., Montgomery, AL 36106: Catalog $2 ■ Victorian and French period furniture reproductions. 800–288–1513.

Hollingsworth Furniture, P.O. Box 2592, Wilmington, NC 28402: Free brochure ■ American country furniture reproductions. 919–251–0280.

Holton Furniture Company, P.O. Box 280, Thomasville, NC 27360: Free information ■ Furniture and accessories. 800–334–3183.

The Home Book, 628 Santa Cruz Ave., Menlo Park, CA 94025: Free catalog ■ Classic and modern furniture, bathroom accessories, tools, hardware, office aids, lamps, and accessories for children's rooms. 800–345–5233.

Homeway Furniture Company, P.O. Box 1548, Mt. Airy, NC 27030: Free information ■ Save up to 45 percent on furniture. 800–334–9094; 919–786–6151 (in NC).

Michael Houle Furniture, P.O. Box 1089, Marstons Mills, MA 02648: Catalog $3 ■ Period furniture reproductions. 508–833–1399.

Martha M. House, 1022 S. Decatur St., Montgomery, AL 36104: Catalog $3 ■ Victorian sofas, chairs, tables, dining, and bedroom furniture. 205–264–3558.

House Dressing Furniture, 2212 Battleground, Greensboro, NC 27408: Free brochure ■ Furniture and accessories. 800–322–5850.

Howerton Antique Reproductions, Clarksville, VA 23927: Catalog $2 ■ Handmade furniture reproductions. 804–374–5715.

Hudson's Discount Furniture, P.O. Box 2547, Hickory, NC 28603: Free information ■ Save up to 50 percent on furniture and accessories. 704–322–5717.

Hunt Galleries, Inc., P.O. Box 2324, Hickory, NC 28603: Catalog $3 ■ Sofas, upholstered chairs, ottomans, benches, lounges, headboards, and other furniture. 800–248–3876; 704–324–9934 (in NC).

Hutchins Furniture, P.O. Box 1427, Kemersville, NC 27285: Free information ■ Furniture and accessories. 800–334–2408.

Ian Ingersoll, Cabinetmakers, Main St., West Cornwall, CT 06796: Brochure $3 ■ Reproduction Shaker furniture and chairs. 800–237–4926.

IKEA, Inc., Plymouth Commons, Plymouth Meeting, PA 19462: Free catalog ■ Swedish designed furniture, flooring and wallpaper, bed linens, and tablewares. 215–834–0150.

Interior Furnishings, Ltd., Box 1644, Hickory, NC 28603: Brochure $3 ■ Save up to 45 percent on furniture and accessories. 704–328–5683.

Irion Company Furniture Makers, 44 N. Valley Rd, Paoli, PA 19301: Free brochure with long SASE ■ Handmade 18th-century furniture reproductions. 215–644–7516.

John-Michael Furniture, 2113 Hickory Blvd., Hudson, NC 28638: Free information ■ Furniture and accessories. 800–669–3801; 704–728–2944 (in NC).

Knight Galleries, P.O. Box 1254, Lenoir, NC 28645: Free information ■ Furniture and accessories. 800–334–4721.

Thomas H. Kramer, Inc., 805 Depot St., Commerce Park, Columbus, IN 47201: Catalog $3 (refundable) ■ Period and country-style furniture and furnishings. 812–379–4097.

James Lea, Cabinetmaker, 9 West St., Rockport, ME 04856: Catalog $5 ■ Handmade reproduction 17th- and 18th-century furniture. 207–236–3632.

Leather Interiors, Box 9305, Hickory, NC 28603: Free information ■ Traditional and contemporary leather furniture. 800–627–4526.

LeFort Furniture, 293 Winter St., Hanover, MA 02339: Portfolio $6 ■ Furniture and accessories. 617–826–9033.

Lenoir Furniture Market, Inc., 2034 Hickory Blvd., Lenoir, NC 28645: Free information with long SASE ■ Indoor and outdoor furniture, beds and bedding, and accessories. 704–728–2946.

Liberty Green, Box 5035, Station 1, Wilmington, NC 28403: Catalog $3 (refundable) ■ Handcrafted reproduction pine furniture from the past. 800–255–9704.

Lincoln House Furniture, 3105 Sulphur Springs Rd. NE, Hickory, NC 28601: Catalog $5 ■ Handmade leather furniture. 704–322–4478.

Loftin Black Furniture Company, 111 Sedgehill Dr., Thomasville, NC 27360: Free information with long SASE ■ Furniture and accessories. 800–334–7398; 919–472–6117 (in NC).

Mack & Rodel Cabinet Makers, Leighton Rd., RR 1, Box 88, Pownal, ME 04069: Brochure $4 ■ Custom furniture. 207–688–4483.

Magnolia Hall, 725 Andover, Atlanta, GA 30327: Catalog $3 ■ Carved furniture. 404–237–9725.

Mahogany Craft, Park Alley Building, 16 E. Patrick St., Frederick, MD 21701: Catalog $5 ■ Reproduction 18th-century Chippendale chairs and bedroom and dining room furniture. 301–663–4611.

David & Susan Margonelli, RR 1, Box 25852, Edgecomb, ME 04556: Portfolio $9 ■ Handmade furniture. 207–633–3326.

Mathias & Coutler, 1735 Pennsylvania Ave., P.O. Box 2173, Hagerstown, MD 21742: Catalog $3 ■ Reproduction 18th-century American colonial-style furniture. 301–791–2956.

Maynard House Antiques, 11 Maynard St., Westborough, MA 01581: Catalog $2 ■ Handcrafted American country sofas and wing chairs, from the 1780s to 1820s. 508–366–2073.

Mecklenburg Furniture Shops, 520 Providence Rd., Charlotte, NC 28207: Free brochure ■ Furniture and accessories. 704–333–5891.

Miya Shoji & Interiors, Inc., 109 W. 17th St., New York, NY 10011: Free brochure ■ Custom Japanese Shoji screens. 212–243–6774.

E.T. Moore Company, 3100 N. Hopkins Rd., Richmond, VA 23224: Free information ■ Custom furniture and cabinets; pine mantels; and columns, flooring, moldings, paneling, and hand-hewn beams. 804–231–1823.

Thos. Moser Cabinetmakers, 415 Cumberland Ave., Portland, ME 04101: Catalog $9 ■ Handcrafted furniture for homes and offices. 207–774–3791.

Moultrie Manufacturing, P.O. Drawer 1179, Moultrie, GA 31776: Catalog $# ■ Southern-style furniture reproductions for homes and gardens. 800–841–8674.

Murrow Furniture Galleries, P.O. Box 4337, Wilmington, NC 28406: Free brochure ■ Save up to 40 percent on furniture. 919–799–4010.

North Woods Chair Shop, 237 Old Tilton Rd., Canterbury, NH 93224: Catalog $3 ■ Handcrafted Shaker furniture. 603–783–4595.

Olde Mill House Shoppe, 105 Strasburg Pike, Lancaster, PA 17602: Catalog $1 ■ Country-style handcrafted furniture, braided rugs, homespun table linens, and bathroom accessories. 717–299–0678.

Old Wagon Factory, P.O. Box 1427, Clarksville, VA 23927: Catalog $2 ■ Chippendale furniture, Victorian railings and brackets, and Victorian and Chippendale storm screen doors. 804–374–5787.

Orleans Carpenters, P.O. Box 217, Orleans, MA 02653: Catalog $3 ■ Shaker and colonial furniture reproductions. 508–255–2646.

Oxford Woodworks, 80 Holsenbeck Dr., Oxford, GA 30267: Catalog $2 ■ Ready-to-finish furniture. 404–786–4159.

Parkway Furniture Galleries, Hwy. 105 South, Box 2450, Boone, NC 28607: Free information ■ Furniture and accessories. 704–264–3993.

Plaza Furniture Gallery, 241 Timberbrook Ln., Hwy. 321, Granite Falls, NC 28630:

Free information ■ Furniture and accessories. 704–396–8150.

Plexi-Craft Quality Products, 514 W. 24th St., New York, NY 10011: Catalog $2 ■ Save up to 50 percent on Lucite and Plexiglas furniture, accessories, and fixtures. Will custom make. 800–24–PLEXI, 212–924–3244 (in NY).

Priba Furniture Sales & Interiors, P.O. Box 13295, Greensboro, NC 27415: Free information ■ Save up to 45 percent on furniture and accessories. 919–855–9034.

Ralston Furniture Reproductions, Box 144, Cooperstown, NY 13326: Brochure $3.50 ■ Reproduction 18th-century furniture. 607–547–2675.

Rhoney Furniture, 2401 Hwy. 70 SW, Hickory, NC 28602: Free brochure ■ Save up to 50 percent on traditional and contemporary furniture. 704–328–2034.

Dana Robes Wood Craftsmen, Lower Shaker Village, P.O. Box 707, Enfield, NH 03748: Catalog $2 ■ Shaker reproduction furniture. 603–632–5385.

Mario Rodriguez Cabinetmaker, 419 Manhattan Ave., Brooklyn, NY 11222: Brochure $3.50 ■ Handcrafted reproduction 18th-century furniture. 718–387–6685.

William James Roth, P.O. Box 355, Yarmouthport, MA 02675: Catalog $4 ■ Handcrafted period furniture reproductions. 508–362–9235.

St. Charles Furniture, P.O. Box 2144, High Point, NC 27261: Free information ■ Furniture and accessories. 800–545–3287.

Sawtooth Valley Woodcrafts, 4600 Ginzel, Boise, ID 83703: Free brochure ■ Custom, handcrafted log furniture. 208–342–5265.

Shakercraft, Box 253, Hawesville, KY 43348: Brochure $1 ■ Handcrafted Shaker reproduction furniture.

Shaker Workshops, P.O. Box 1028, Concord, MA 01742: Catalog $1 ■ Shaker furniture in kits or custom finished, needle crafts, dolls, and miniature furniture. 617–646–8985.

Shaw Furniture Galleries, P.O. Box 576, Randleman, NC 27317: Free information ■ Furniture and accessories. 919–498–2628.

Shoji Workshop, 21–10 31st Ave., Astoria, NY 11106: Send two 1st class stamps for

free brochure ■ Shoji screens. 718–274–9351.

Solway Furniture, Inc., 120 Perimeter Park Dr., Knoxville, TN 37922: Free information ■ Furniture and accessories. 800–422–8011.

Southampton Antiques, 172 College Hwy., Rt. 10, Southhampton, MA 01073: Catalog $25 ■ Antique American oak and Victorian furniture. 413–527–1022.

Strafford House, 43 VanSant Rd., New Hope, PA 18938: Catalog $2 ■ Handcrafted and hand-painted reproduction pine furniture. 215–598–0259.

Straw Hill Chairs, RFD 1, Straw Hill, West Unity, NH 03743: Brochure $2 ■ Windsor chairs. 603–542–4367.

Sutton-Council Furniture, P.O. Box 3288, Wilmington, NC 28406: Catalog $5 ■ Furniture and accessories. 919–799–1990.

Taos Furniture, 232 Galisteo St., Taos, NM 87501: Free brochure ■ Handmade drum tables, pedestals, and Indian chairs.

Chapin Townsend Furniture, P.O. Box 628, West Kingston, RI 02892: Brochure $2 ■ Custom handmade 18th-century furniture. 401–783–6614.

R. Trammell & Son Cabinetmakers, 8519½ Chestnut Ave., Historic Old Bowie, MD 20715: Catalog $3 ■ American Shaker furniture in cherry or aged milk-painted finishes. 301–745–9347.

Marion Travis, P.O. Box 292, Statesville, NC 28677: Catalog $1 ■ Handwoven fiber rush seats on native hardwood. 704–528–4424.

Triplett's Furniture Fashions, 2084 Hickory Blvd., Lenoir, NC 28645: Free brochure ■ Furniture and accessories. 704–728–8211.

Trott Furniture Company, P.O. Box 7, Richlands, NC 28574: Catalog $5 ■ Furniture and Oriental rugs in an 18th-century style. 800–682–0095; 919–324–3660 (in NC).

Turner-Tolson, Inc., P.O. Drawer 1507, New Bern, NC 28560: Brochure $2 ■ Furniture and accessories. 800–334–6616; 919–638–2121 (in NC).

Tysinger Furniture Gallery, P.O. Box 10339, Wilmington, NC 28406: Free information ■ Furniture and accessories. 919–799–8137.

Varner Furniture Sales, 2605 Uwharrie Rd., High Point, NC 27263: Free information ■ Save from 40 to 50 percent on furniture and accessories. 800–334–3894.

Village Furniture, P.O. Box 1148, Huntersville, NC 28078: Catalog $5 (refundable) ■ Shaker-style furniture.

Walpole Woodworkers, 767 East St., Walpole, MA 02081: Catalog $6 ■ Handcrafted natural cedar New England-style furniture. Includes some wicker items. 508–668–2800.

Max Wardlow, RR 1, Fillmore, MO 64449: Catalog $2 ■ Windsor and ladderback chairs in traditional designs. 816–487–3385.

Wellington's Furniture, P.O. Box 2178, Boone, NC 28607: Free information ■ Leather furniture. 800–262–1049.

The Wentworth Collection, P.O. Box 131, Wentworth, NH 03282: Information $3 ■ Period furniture reproductions. 603–764–9395.

White of Mebane, Box 367, Mebane, NC 27302: Free brochure ■ Classic 18th-century English- and American-style furniture. 919–563–1217.

Whitson Furniture, Rt. 3, Box 157, Hwy. 64–70W, Newton, NC 28658: Free brochure ■ Save up to 50 percent on furniture. 704–464–4596.

Willsboro Wood Products, S. Ausable St., Keeseville, NY 12996: Free catalog ■ Foldaway Adirondack chairs, rocking chairs, and other country-style furniture. 800–342–3373.

Windrift Furniture Gallery, 145 Industrial Ave., Greensboro, NC 27406: Free brochure ■ Save up to 40 percent on furniture and accessories. 919–379–8895.

Windsor Chairmakers, RR 2, Box 7, Lincolnville, ME 04849: Free information ■ Handcrafted Windsor furniture. 207–789–5188.

Windsors by Bill Wallick, 41 N. 7th St., Wrightsville, PA 17368: Brochure $2 ■ Handcrafted reproduction Windsor chairs. 717–252–1240.

Melvin Wolf, 1500 W. Cortland St., Chicago, IL 60622: Free brochure ■ Brass occasional furniture and beds. 312–252–2800.

Woodshop, 2966 Bay Rd., Redwood City, CA 94063: Free brochure ■ Custom hand-

crafted reproductions of oak roll-top desks and file cabinets. 415–365–1110.

Workshops of David T. Smith, 3600 Shawhan Rd., Morrow, OH 45152: Catalog $5 ■ Reproduction furniture, pottery, lamps, and chandeliers. 513–932–2472.

Lift Chairs

American Stair-Glide Corporation, 4001 E. 138th St., Grandview, MO 64030: Free fact kit ■ Cushioned chairs that lift people to a standing position. 800–383–3100.

Cushion-Lift of New England, 195 Maple St., Stratford, CT 06497: Free information ■ Push-button controlled, cushioned lift chairs. 800–243–9707.

Ortho-Kinetics, The Independence Company, 1 Mobility Centre, P.O. Box 1647, Waukesha, WI 53187: Free information ■ Combination power recliner/lounger/lift chair. 800–446–4522.

Whitakers, 1 Odell Plaza, Yonkers, NY 10703: Free brochure ■ Lifts for transporting people with physical disabilities up and down and into the bathtub. 800–44–LIFTS; 800–924–LIFT (in NY).

Office Furniture

Alfax Wholesale Furniture, 370 7th Ave., Ste. 1101, New York, NY 10001: Free catalog ■ Office furniture, equipment, and supplies. 212–947–9560.

Basil & Jones Cabinetmakers, 1150 17th St. NW, Ste. 600, Washington, DC 20036: Free brochure ■ Custom wood or leather-finished stand-up desks in period and contemporary styles. 202–337–4369.

Business & Institutional Furniture Company, 611 N. Broadway, Milwaukee, WI 53202: Free catalog ■ Office furniture and equipment. 800–558–8662; 414–272–6080 (in WV).

Derby Desk Company, 140 Tremont St., Brighton, MA 02135: Free brochure ■ Antique desks that include roll-tops. 617–787–2707.

Frank Eastern Company, 599 Broadway, New York, NY 10012: Free catalog ■ Office furniture, equipment, and supplies. 212–219–0007.

Franz Stationery Company, Inc., 1601 Algonquin Rd., Arlington Heights, IL 60005: Free catalog ■ Office equipment and furni-

ture, stationery, and other supplies. 800–323–8685.

Jacobs Gardner Office Products & Furniture, 5121 Buchanan St., Hyattsville, MD 20781: Free catalog ■ Furniture and supplies for home and business offices. 800–638–0983.

National Business Furniture, Inc., 222 E. Michigan St., Milwaukee, WI 53202: Free catalog ■ Office furniture and supplies. 800–558–1010.

Pyramid of Urbana, 2107 N. High Cross Rd., Urbana, IL 61801: Free catalog ■ Office furniture and supplies, arts and crafts supplies, and school equipment. 217–328–3099.

Reliable Home Office, P.O. Box 804117, Chicago, IL 60607: Free catalog ■ Furniture and supplies for home and business offices. 800–326–6230.

Scan Office Interiors, 8406 Greenwood Pl., Savage, MD 20763: Free catalog ■ Contemporary office furniture. 301–953–2050.

The Stand-Up Desk Company, 5207 Baltimore Ave., Bethesda, MD 20816: Free brochure ■ Handcrafted stand-up desks and stools. 301–657–3630.

Staples, Inc., P.O. Box 160, Newton, MA 02195: Free catalog ■ Office furniture, drafting equipment, fax machines, typewriters, and supplies. 617–965–7030.

Stuart-Townsend-Carr Furniture, P.O. Box 373, Limington, ME 04049: Catalog $4 ■ Classic furniture for offices and dens. 800–637–2344; 207–793–4522 (in ME).

Woodshop, 2966 Bay Rd., Redwood City, CA 94063: Free brochure ■ Handcrafted reproduction file cabinets and desks. Includes roll-tops. 415–365–1110.

Outdoor Furniture

Adirondack Designs, 350 Cypress St., Fort Bragg, CA 95437: Free catalog ■ Redwood chairs, love seats, swings, and tables. 800–222–0343.

Adirondack Store & Gallery, 109 Saranac Ave., Lake Placid, NY 12946: Free catalog ■ Oak or maple outdoor furniture. 518–523–2646.

AK Exteriors, 298 Leisure Ln., Clint, TX 79836: Catalog $2 (refundable) ■ Cast-aluminum, Victorian-style outdoor furniture and lighting fixtures. 915–851–2594.

Alfresco Porch Swing Company, P.O. Box 1336, Durango, CO 81302: Free brochure ■ Redwood porch swings, Adirondack chairs, and garden benches. 303–247–9739.

Allibert, Customer Service, 1200 Hwy. 27 South, Stanley, NC 28164: Free information ■ Outdoor furniture. 704–263–9155.

Amish Country Collection, RD 5, Sunset Valley Rd., New Castle, PA 16105: Catalog $5 (refundable) ■ Amish-style furniture in oak and hickory twigs, rugs, quilts, and wall hangings. 800–232–6474.

Bench Manufacturing Company, 390 Pond St., South Weymouth, MA 02190: Free catalog ■ Cast-iron and wood benches, trash receptacles, clocks, light poles, sculptures, and fountains. 617–436–3080.

Brown-Jordan, P.O. Box 5688, El Monte, CA 91734: Free information ■ Welded aluminum furniture and accessories. 818–443–8971.

Canterbury Designs, Inc., P.O. Box 5730, Sherman Oaks, CA 91413: Free information ■ Cast-iron and aluminum benches. 213–936–7111.

Charleston Battery Bench, 191 King St., Charleston, SC 29401: Free price list ■ Reproduction cast-iron and cypress benches from the 1880s. 803–722–3842.

Clappers, P.O. Box 2278, West Newton, MA 02165: Free information ■ Teak furniture for gardens, patios, and breezeways. 617–244–7900.

Coppa Woodworking, Inc., 1231 Paraiso Ave., San Pedro, CA 90731: Free brochure ■ Adirondack chairs and screen doors. 310–548–4142.

Country Casual, 17317 Germantown Rd., Germantown, MD 20874: Catalog $3 ■ Imported English teakwood benches, swings, chairs, tables, and planters. 301–540–0040.

Cypress Street Center, 350 Cypress St., Fort Bragg, CA 95437: Free catalog ■ Easy-to-assemble outdoor chairs with matching love seats, foot rests, side carts, and tables. 800–222–0343.

Fib-Con Corporation, Box 3387, Silver Spring, MD 20918: Free catalog ■ Planters, benches, waste receptacles, and patio furni-

ture made of reinforced fiberglass. 301–572–5333.

Flanders Industries, Inc., P.O. Box 1788, Fort Smith, AR 72902: Free brochure ■ Casual and outdoor pool furniture. 800–843–7532.

The Golden Rabbit, 115 S. Royal St., Alexandria, VA 22314: Free information ■ Wooden outdoor furniture and accessories. 703–276–1495.

Green Enterprises, 43 S. Rogers St., Hamilton, VA 22068: Brochure $1.50 ■ Swings, gliders, tables and benches. 703–338–3606.

Hamptons of Bristol, P.O. Box 1104, West Concord, MA 01742: Brochure $1 ■ Teakwood outdoor furniture and planters. 508–371–1526.

Holiday Pool & Patio, P.O. Box 727, Hudson, NC 28638: Free information ■ Patio furniture. 704–728–2637.

Irving & Jones, Village Center, Colebrook, CT 06021: Brochure $2 ■ Furniture and other garden furnishings. 203–379–9219.

Kingsley-Bate, Ltd., P.O. Box 6797, Arlington, VA 22206: Brochure $1 ■ Teak planters, window boxes, and other garden furniture. 703–931–9200.

La Jolla Sales Company, 6910 Dennison St., San Diego, CA 92122: Catalog $2 ■ Aluminum outdoor benches, lamp posts and lighting units, and planters. 619–452–2044.

Landscape Forms, Inc., 431 Lawndale Ave., Kalamazoo, MI 49001: Free information ■ Outdoor furniture. 800–521–2546; 616–381–0396 (in MI).

Kenneth D. Lynch & Sons, Inc., P.O. Box 488, Wilton, CT 06897: Catalog $4 ■ Outdoor benches in cast- and wrought-iron, stone, concrete, and wood. 203–762–8363.

Lyon-Shaw, 1538 Jake Alexander Blvd., Salisbury, NC 28144: Free information ■ Wrought-iron furniture that includes glider sofas, glider chairs, end tables, coffee tables, glider settees, and dining room pieces. 704–636–8270.

Mel-Nor Industries, 303 Gulf Bank, Houston, TX 77037: Information $1 ■ Hanging lawn and porch swings, park benches, and old-time lamp posts. 713–445–3485.

Moultrie Manufacturing, P.O. Drawer 1179, Moultrie, GA 31776: Catalog $3 ■ In-

door and outdoor aluminum furniture. 800–841–8674.

Pittman & Davis, 801 N. Expressway, Harlingen, TX 78552: Free brochure ■ Folding tables and other outdoor furniture and accessories. 512–423–2154.

Plow & Hearth, 301 Madison Rd., P.O. Box 830, Orange, VA 22960: Free catalog ■ Porch and lawn furniture, birdhouses and feeders, fireplace accessories, and other items. 800–866–6072.

Roberts Furniture, 115 East Putnam Ave., P.O. Box 433, Greenwich, CT 06836: Catalog $6 ■ Brown Jordan furniture and accessories. 800–899–4610.

Robinson Iron Corporation, P.O. Box 1119, Alexander City, AL 35010: Free information ■ Cast-iron benches. 205–329–8486.

Rustic Furnishings, 3280 Broadway, New York, NY 10027: Catalog $3 ■ Custom rustic-style furniture. 212–926–3880.

Santa Cruz Foundry, N. Douty St., Hanford, CA 93230: Free brochure ■ Cast-iron furniture made using 100-year-old patterns. 209–584–1541.

Smith & Hawken, 25 Corte Madera, Mill Valley, CA 94941: Free catalog ■ Garden furniture. 415–383–6399.

Victor Stanley, Inc., P.O. Box 144, Dunkirk, MD 20754: Free information ■ Indoor and outdoor furniture. 800–368–2573; 301–855–8300 (in MD).

Telescope Casual Furniture, 85 Church St., Granville, NY 12832: Free information ■ Outdoor furniture. 518–642–1100.

Tropitone Furniture Company, P.O. Box 3197, Sarasota, FL 33578: Catalog $3 ■ Patio and casual furniture. 813–355–2715.

Walpole Woodworkers, 767 East St., Walpole, MA 02081: Catalog $6 ■ Handcrafted lawn and garden cedar furniture. Includes porch and children's swings. 508–668–2800.

Otto Wendt & Company, 417A Gentry, Spring, TX 77373: Catalog $2 ■ Cast-aluminum lighting equipment in an early 1900s style. 713–288–8295.

Wicker Works, 267 8th St., San Francisco, CA 94103: Free information ■ Outdoor furniture. 415–626–6730.

Dan Wilson & Company, Inc., P.O. Box 566, Fuquay-Varina, NC 27526: Catalog $2

■ Handcrafted garden furniture. 919–552–4945.

Winston Furniture Company, P.O. Box 868, Haleyville, AL 35565: Free information ■ Outdoor furniture. 205–486–9211.

Wood Classics, Box 1, Gardner, NY 12525: Catalog $2 ■ Teak and mahogany outdoor furniture in kits or assembled. 914–255–7871.

Zircon, 1580 Dell Ave., Campbell, CA 95008: Free information ■ Folding tables ready for painting or staining. 408–866–8600.

Wicker & Rattan

Bielecky Brothers, Inc., 306 E. 61st St., New York, NY 10021: Free information ■ Outdoor and indoor rattan, cane, and wicker furniture. 212–753–2355.

Deutsch, Inc., 31 E. 32nd St., New York, NY 10016: Catalog $3 ■ Rattan furniture. 800–223–4550; 212–683–8746 (in NY).

Ellenburg's Wicker & Casual, P.O. Box 5628, Statesville, NC 28677: Catalog $3 ■ Wicker and rattan furniture and accessories with optional upholstered cushions, padding, and custom covers. 704–873–2900.

Fran's Basket House, 295 Rt. 10, Succasunna, NJ 07876: Catalog 50¢ ■ Imported wicker and rattan furniture and accessories. 201–584–2230.

Masterworks Furniture, P.O. Box M, Marietta, GA 30061: Catalog $2.50 ■ Bent-willow rockers, chairs, porch swings, beds, tables, chaises, and children's furniture. 404–426–6538.

Michael's Classic Wicker, 8532 Melrose Ave., Los Angeles, CA 90069: Brochure $4 ■ Reproduction Victorian wicker furniture. 310–659–1121.

Wicker Gallery, 8009 Glenwood Ave., Raleigh, NC 27612: Free brochure ■ Wicker and rattan furniture and accessories. 919–781–2215.

Wicker Warehouse, Inc., 195 S. River St., Hackensack, NJ 07601: Free information ■ Save from 30 to 50 percent on wicker furniture and accessories. 201–342–6709.

Wicker Works, 267 8th St., San Francisco, CA 94103: Free information ■ Outdoor furniture. 415–626–6730.

GARAGE DOORS & OPENERS

Atlas Roll-Lite, 10407 Rocket Blvd., Orlando, FL 32824: Free information ■ Insulated raised-panel garage doors.

Clopay Corporation, Consumer Affairs Department, 101 E. 4th St., Cincinnati, OH 45202: Free information ■ Garage doors with raised panel surfaces. 800–992–8700.

Overhead Door, P.O. Box 809046, Dallas, TX 75380: Free information ■ Garage door opener with a microprocessor controller program to detect obstructions and insulated steel overhead doors. 800–543–2269.

Philips Home Products, 22790 Lake Park Blvd., Alliance, OH 44601: Free information ■ Garage door openers with an option for controlling house lights. 800–654–3643.

Raynor Garage Doors, P.O. Box 448, Dixon, IL 61021: Free information ■ Wood-grained steel garage doors with raised panels. 800–545–0455.

Ridge Doors, New Rd., Monmouth, NJ 08852: Free information ■ Solid wood garage doors with carved or plain panels and other optional trims and glass. 800–631–5656; 800–872–4980 (in NJ).

Wayne-Dalton Corporation, P.O. Box 67, Mount Hope, OH 44660: Free information ■ Insulated steel garage doors. 216–674–7015.

GARDENING EQUIPMENT & SUPPLIES

Beneficial Insects & Organisms

Applied Bionomics, 11074 W. Saanich Rd., Sidney, British Columbia, Canada V8L 3X0: Free brochure ■ Beneficial insects. 604–656–2123.

Arbico, Inc., P.O. Box 4247CRB, Tucson, AZ 85738: Free catalog ■ Beneficial insects. 800–767–2847.

Biofac, P.O. Box 87, Mathis, TX 78368: Free catalog ■ Beneficial insects. 512–547–3259.

Bozeman Bio-Tech, 1612 Gold Ave., Box 3146, Bozeman, MT 59772: Free catalog ■ Beneficial insects. 800–289–6656; 406–587–5891 (in MT).

W. Atlee Burpee & Company, 300 Park Ave., Warminster, PA 18974: Free catalog ■ Beneficial insects. 215–674–1793.

Farmer Seed & Nursery Company, 818 NW 4th St., Faribault, MN 55021: Free catalog ■ Beneficial organisms. 507–334–1623.

Henry Field's Seed & Nursery, 415 N. Burnett, P.O. Box 700, Shenandoah, IA 51602: Free catalog & Beneficial organisms. 605–665–9391.

Gardener's Supply Company, 128 Intervale Rd., Burlington, VT 05401: Free catalog ■ Beneficial insects. 800–944–2250.

Harmony Farm Supply, P.O. Box 460, Graton, CA 95444: Catalog $2 (refundable) ■ Beneficial insects. 707–823–9125.

M & R Durango, Inc., P.O. Box 886, Bayfield, CO 81122: Free catalog ■ Beneficial insects. 800–526–4075; 303–259–3521 (in CO).

Mellinger's, 2328 W. South Range Rd., North Lima, OH 44452: Free catalog ■ Beneficial organisms. 216–549–9861.

Natural Gardening Company, 217 San Anselmo Ave., San Anselmo, CA 94960: Free catalog ■ Beneficial insects. 800–755–4769.

Natural Gardening Research Center, 125 Highway 48, P.O. Box 149, Sunman, IN 47041: Free information ■ Beneficial organisms. 812–623–4201.

Necessary Trading Company, P.O. Box 305, New Castle, VA 24127: Catalog $2 (refundable) ■ Beneficial insects. 703–864–5103.

Orcon, 5132 Venice Blvd., Los Angeles, CA 90019: Free brochure ■ Beneficial insects. 213–937–7444.

Peaceful Valley Farm Supply, P.O. Box 2209, Grass Valley, CA 95945: Catalog $2 (refundable): Beneficial organisms. 916–272–4769.

Rincon-Vitova Insectaries, Inc., P.O. Box 95, Oak View, CA 93022: Free brochure ■ Beneficial insects. 800–248–2847; 805–643–5407 (in CA).

Unique Insect Control, P.O. Box 15376, Sacramento, CA 95851: Free brochures ■ Beneficial insects. 916–961–7945.

Carts

Ayres Yard-Cart, RD 1, Wawaka, IN 46794: Free information ■ Yard and garden carts. 219–761–3511.

BCS America, P.O. Box 1739, Matthews, NC 28105: Free catalog ■ Garden carts, chippers and shredders, tillers, sprayers, and mowers. 800–873–1913.

Country Manufacturing, P.O. Box 104, Fredericktown, OH 43019: Free information ■ Quick-dump carts, lawn brooms, pressure sprayers, turf spreaders, wagons, and trailers. 614–694–9926.

Gardener's Supply Company, 128 Intervale Rd., Burlington, VT 05401: Free catalog ■ Garden carts, composters, sprayers for pest control, watering systems and controls, weeding and cultivating tools, organic fertilizers and other chemical preparations, leaf mulchers, furniture, and canning and preserving supplies. 800–944–2250.

Garden Way, 9th Ave. & 102nd St., Troy, NY 12179: Free catalog ■ Carts, tillers, clippers, sickle bar mowers, garden composters, and other equipment. 800–535–6001.

Homestead Carts, 6098 Topaz St. NE, Salem, OR 97305: Free brochure ■ Garden carts and composters. 503–390–5586.

Norway Industries, 809 W. Main St., Stoughton, WI 53589: Free brochure ■ Garden carts with removable front doors. 608–873–8664.

Chippers & Shredders

Al-Ko Kober Company, 25784 Birg Rd., Elkhart, IN 46514: Free information ■ Electric chipper/shredder.

Amerind MacKissic, Inc., P.O. Box 111, Parker Ford, PA 19457: Free information ■ Gasoline-operated chipper/shredder. 800–344–4030; 800–342–0052 (in PA).

Gardener's Supply Company, 128 Intervale Rd., Burlington, VT 05401: Free information ■ Gasoline-powered chipper/shredder. 800–944–2250.

Garden Way, 9th Ave & 102nd St., Troy, NY 12180: Free information ■ Compact chipper/shredder. 800–535–6001.

Kemp Company, 160 Koser Rd., Lititz, PA 17543: Free information ■ Chipper/shredder that reduces almost anything organic into small pieces. 717–627–7979.

The Kinsman Company, River Rd., Point Pleasant, PA 18950: Free information ■ Electric chipper/shredder. 800–733–5613.

Mantis Company, 1458 County Line Rd., Huntingdon Valley, PA 19006: Free information ■ Gasoline and electric-powered chipper/shredders. 800–366–6268.

White Outdoor Products Company, P.O. Box 361131, Cleveland, OH 44136: Free information ■ Gasoline-powered chipper/shredder.

Fertilizers & Plant Food

Koos, Inc., 4500 13th Ct., Kenosha, WI 53141: Free information ■ Lawn and garden fertilizers, herbicides, insecticides, and organic plant foods. 414–654–5301.

Natural Gardening Research Center, Hwy. 48, P.O. Box 149, Sunman, IN 47041: Free catalog ■ Organic fertilizers, plant foods, application equipment, propagation supplies, foods for attracting insect-eating birds, and pest barriers. 812–623–4201.

Necessary Trading Company, P.O. Box 305, New Castle, VA 24127: Catalog $2 (refundable) ■ Soil testing supplies, plant nutrients, fertilizers, and pest control preparations. 703–864–5103.

Ringer, 9959 Valley View Rd., Eden Prairie, MN 55344: Free catalog ■ Chemical treatments and fertilizers, tools, growing aids, propagation supplies, pest control preparations, and patio accessories. 800–654–1047.

Shore Fertilizer Company, 307 S. Evers St., Plant City, FL 33566: Free information ■ Lawn and garden fertilizers. 800–329–2203.

Sudbury Laboratories, Inc., 572 Dutton Rd., Sudbury, MA 01776: Free brochure ■ Soil testing kits, fertilizers, animal repellents, and other supplies. 508–443–8844.

Greenhouses

American Solar Systems, 31740 Enterprise, P.O. Box 2865, Livonia, MI 48150: Catalog $3 ■ Greenhouses and solariums.

Bramen Company, P.O. Box 70, Salem, MA 01970: Free information ■ Automatic solar-vent for cold frames and greenhouses. 508–745–7765.

Collier Warehouse, Inc., 1485 Bayshore Blvd., San Francisco, CA 94124: Free information ■ Greenhouses, accessories, and solar products. 415–467–9590.

Cropking Greenhouses, P.O. Box 310, Medina, OH 44258: Free catalog ■ Greenhouses. 216–725–5656.

Dixie Greenhouse Manufacturing Company, Rt. 1, Box 339, Alapaha, GA 31622: Free information ■ Build-it-yourself greenhouse kits. 800–346–9902; 912–532–4600 (in GA).

Elite Greenhouses, Ltd., RD 2, Crooked St., Scotia, NY 12302: Free catalog ■ Aluminum frame greenhouses and accessories. 518–384–1224.

Four Seasons Solar Products, 5005 Veterans Memorial Hwy., Holbrook, NY 11741: Free catalog ■ Greenhouses and accessories. 800–368–7732.

Gardener's Supply Company, 128 Intervale Rd., Burlington, VT 05401: Free information ■ Greenhouses. 800–944–2250.

General Aluminum Corporation, 1001 W. Crosby Rd., Dallas, TX 75006: Free information ■ Window greenhouse with adjustable shelves, screen tops, and removable bottom pans. 214–242–5271.

Gothic Arch Greenhouses, P.O. Box 1564, Mobile, AL 36633: Free brochure ■ Redwood/fiberglass greenhouse kits. 800–628–4974.

Greenhouse Designs, Division of San Antonio Tent & Awning Company, P.O. Box 200426, San Antonio, TX 78220: Free information ■ Build-it-yourself greenhouse kits. 800–531–7230.

Habitek, 102 Queens Dr., King of Prussia, PA 19406: Free brochure ■ Window greenhouses and solariums. 215–962–0240.

Jacobs Greenhouse Manufacturing, 2315 Whirlpool St., Box 106, Niagara Falls, NY 14305: Catalog $2 ■ Greenhouses with tempered glass and automatic roof vents. 519–582–2880.

Janco Greenhouses, 9390 Davis Ave., Laurel, MD 20707: Catalog $5 ■ Greenhouses and accessories. 800–323–6933.

Lindal Cedar Homes, P.O. Box 24426, Seattle, WA 98124: Information package $15 ■ Window greenhouses and sunrooms. 800–426–0536.

National Greenhouse Company, P.O. Box 100, Pana, IL 62557: Free catalog ■ Greenhouses. 800–826–9314; 217–562–9333 (in IL).

Northwest Eden Greenhouses, 14219 NE 167th St., Woodenville, WA 98072: Free information ■ Greenhouses. 800–545–3336.

Peerless Products, Inc., P.O. Box 2469, Shawnee Mission, KS 66201: Free literature ■ Window greenhouses. 913–432–2778.

Progressive Building Products, P.O. Box 866, East Longmeadow, MA 01028: Catalog $5.95 ■ Greenhouses and solarium components. 800–776–2534.

Santa Barbara Greenhouses, 1115–J Ave. Acaso, Camarillo, CA 93010: Free catalog ■ Redwood greenhouses. 800–544–5276.

Skytech Systems, P.O. Box 763, Bloomsburg, PA 17815: Catalog $3 ■ Greenhouses, window greenhouses, and solariums. 717–752–1111.

Solar Components Corporation, 121 Valley St., Manchester, NH 03103: Brochure $1 ■ Build-it-yourself greenhouse kits, in lean-to or free-standing models. 603–668–8186.

Sturdi-Built Manufacturing Company, 11304 SW Boones Ferry Rd., Portland, OR 97219: Free catalog ■ Greenhouses, cold frames, and sunrooms. 503–244–4100.

Sundome Greenhouses, 42125 Blackhawk Plaza Circle, Danville, CA 94506: Free brochure ■ Portable greenhouses. 800–786–7831.

Sunglo Solar Greenhouses, 4441 26th Ave. West, Seattle, WA 98199: Free information ■ Solar greenhouses and solariums. 800–647–0606; 206–284–8900 (in WA).

Sun Room Company, 322 E. Main St., P.O. Box 301, Leola, PA 17540: Free information ■ Window greenhouses, free-standing greenhouses, and solariums. 800–426–2737; 717–656–9391 (in PA).

Sun System Greenhouses, 75 Austin Blvd., Commack, NY 11725: Free catalog ■ Aluminum, double pane-covered greenhouses. 516–543–7600.

Texas Greenhouse Company, 2524 White Settlement Rd., Fort Worth, TX 76107: Catalog $3 ■ Greenhouses and accessories. 817–335–5447.

Troy-Bilt Manufacturing Company, 9th Ave & 102nd St., Troy, NY 12180: Free in-formation ■ Greenhouses and accessories. 800–535–6001.

Turner Greenhouses, US 13, Goldsboro, NC 27530: Free catalog ■ Greenhouses and accessories. 800–672–4770.

Under Glass Manufacturing Corporation, Market Street Industrial Park, P.O. Box 323, Wappingers Falls, NY 12590: Free information ■ Greenhouses, solariums, and accessories. 914–298–0645.

Vegetable Factory, Inc., P.O. Box 1353, Stamford, Ct. 06904: Catalog $2 ■ Solar greenhouses. 203–324–0010.

Victory Garden Supply, 1428 E. High St., Charlottsville, VA 22901: Free brochure ■ Aluminum-frame greenhouses with double strength glass and space-saving sliding doors. 804–293–2298.

Hydroponic Gardening Supplies

Alternative Garden Supply, Inc., 297 N. Barrington Rd., Streamwood, IL 60107: Free catalog ■ Hydroponic supplies. 800–444–2837.

Applied Hydroponics, 3135 Kerner Blvd., San Rafael, CA 94901: Free catalog ■ Hydroponic equipment and supplies. 800–634–9999; 415–459–7897 (in CA).

Aquaculture, Inc., 700 W. 1st St., Tempe, AZ 85281: Free catalog ■ Hydroponic systems, lights, plant food, and other accessories. 800–633–2137; 602–966–6429 (in AZ).

Brew & Grow, 8179 University Ave. NE, Fridley, MN 55432: Free information ■ Hydroponic equipment and home brewing supplies for making beer. 612–780–8191.

Central Washington Hydroponics, 1001 Fruitvale Blvd., Yakima, WA 98902: Free catalog ■ Hydroponic and greenhouse equipment and supplies. 800–247–6905; 509–452–9760 (in WA).

Circle City Hydroponics, 10812 DeAmdra Dr., Zionsville, IN 46077: Free price list ■ Indoor gardening equipment and accessories. 800–232–7271; 317–873–2355 (in IN).

Diamond Gardening Products, 628 Lindaro St., San Rafael, CA 94901: Free catalog ■ Hydroponic nutrients and other supplies. 800–331–3994; 415–459–3994 (in CA).

Discount Garden Supply, Inc., E. 14109 Sprague, Ste. 5, Spokane, WA 99216: Free catalog ■ Hydroponic systems, lights, nutrients and fertilizers, nutrient controls, propagation aids, and other accessories. 800–444–4378.

East Coast Hydroponics, 432 Castleton Ave., Staten Island, NY 10301: Free catalog ■ Hydroponic and outdoor gardening supplies. 800–255–0121; 718–727–9300 (in NY).

Eco Enterprises, 2821 NE 55th St., Seattle, WA 98105: Free catalog ■ Hydroponic equipment and supplies. 800–426–6937.

Foothill Hydroponics, 10705 Burbank Blvd., North Hollywood, CA 91601: Free information ■ Nutrients, growlights, climate control and test equipment, rock wool, and irrigation equipment. 818–760–0688.

Future Garden Supply, Inc., 12605 Pacific Ave., Tacoma, WA 98444: Free catalog ■ Hydroponic supplies and equipment. 800–237–6672.

Gold Coast Hydroponics Greenhouse Supply, 5794 Bird Rd., Miami, FL 33155: Free information ■ Hydroponic supplies and lighting equipment. 800–780–7371.

Green Thumb Hydro-Gardens, 3312 Lakeshore Dr., Sheboygan, WI 53081: Free catalog ■ Automatic, programmable closed-loop hydroponic gardens. 414–459–8405.

Halide of Oregon, 9220 SE Stark, Portland, OR 97216: Free information ■ Hydroponic systems. 800–433–6805; 503–256–2400 (in OR).

Hamilton Technology Corporation, 14902 S. Figueroa St., Gardena, CA 90248: Free catalog ■ Lights, hydroponic systems, gardening supplies, and accessories. 800–447–9797.

Harvest Moon Hydroponics, Inc., Airport Plaza, 4214 Union Rd., Cheektowaga, NY 14225: Free catalog ■ Hydroponic supplies. 800–635–1383, 716–634–8290 (in NY).

Hollisters Hydroponics, P.O. Box 16601, Irvine, CA 92713: Free information ■ Hydroponic supplies and equipment. 714–552–1728.

Home Harvest Garden Supply, Inc., 13426 Occoquan Rd., Woodbridge, VA 22191: Free catalog ■ Indoor horticultural lighting systems and hydroponic equipment and supplies. 703–494–2917.

Hydro-Gardens, Inc., P.O. Box 1097, Colorado Springs, CO 80932: Free catalog ■ Hydroponic supplies and equipment.

Light Manufacturing Company, 1634 SE Brooklyn, Portland, OR 97202: Free catalog ■ Hydroponic systems, lights, and nutrient controls. 800–NOW–LITE.

New Earth, Inc., 4422 East Hwy. 44, Sheperdsville, KY 40165: Free catalog ■ Hydroponic and outdoor gardening supplies. 800–462–5953; 502–543–5933 (in KY).

Southern Lights & Hydroponics, 6200 Buford Hwy., Building 1–C, Norcross, GA 30071: Free catalog ■ Hydroponic supplies. 800–551–8371.

Superior Growers Supply, 4870 Dawn Ave., East Lansing, MI 48823: Free catalog ■ Hydroponic supplies. 800–227–0027.

Urban-Tek Growers Supply, Inc., 2911 W. Wilshire, Oklahoma City, OK 73116: Free catalog ■ Organic gardening supplies and lighting equipment for greenhouses and indoor gardens. 405–843–1888.

Virginia Hydroponics, 1291 N. King St., Hampton, VA 23669: Free information ■ Hydroponic supplies and equipment. 804–766–1324.

Worm's Way, 3151 South Hwy. 446, Bloomington, IN 47401: Free catalog ■ Hydroponic and organic gardening supplies. 812–331–0300.

Indoor Gardening Supplies

Alternative Garden Supply, Inc., 297 N. Barrington Rd., Streamwood, IL 60107: Free catalog ■ Indoor lighting systems, growing kits and supplies, and biological pest control supplies. 800–444–2837.

DoDe's Gardens, Inc., 1490 Saturn St., Merritt Island, FL 32953: Free catalog with two 1st class stamps ■ African violets, growing supplies, and how-to books. 407–452–5670.

Florist Products, Inc., 2242 N. Palmer Dr., Schaumburg, IL 60173: Free catalog ■ Horticultural supplies and tools. 800–828–2242.

Indoor Gardening Supplies, P.O. Box 40567, Detroit, MI 48240: Catalog 25¢ ■ Indoor gardening supplies, stands, lights, books, and accessories. 313–426–9080.

Janellco Products, Inc., 700 Museum Dr., Charlotte, NC 28207: Free catalog ■ Brack-

ets and hangers for indoor gardens. 704–375–0662.

McKee's House Plant Corner, P.O. Box 96, Northfield, NJ 08225: Catalog $1 ■ Equipment and supplies for indoor gardening. 609–646–6063.

Plant Collectibles, 103 Kenview Ave., Buffalo, NY 14217: Catalog $2 ■ Plastic pots, hanging baskets, starter trays, waterers, plant foods and insecticide sprays, and lighting units.

Landscaping Stone

Allan Block, 7400 Metro Blvd., Ste. 102, Edina, MN 55435: Free brochure ■ Mortarless concrete blocks for retaining walls, curves, corners, stairways, and terraces. 612–835–5309.

Stone Company, Inc., Rt. 1, Eden, WI 53019: Free information ■ Natural building and landscaping cobblers, granite boulders, wall stone, steppers, flagstone, and others. 414–477–2521.

Urdl's Waterfall Creations, Inc., 1010 NW 1st St., Delray Beach, FL 33444: Free information ■ Manufactured hollow concrete rocks for landscaping waterfall settings and custom waterfalls. 305–278–3320.

Lawn Ornaments & Statues

Ballard Designs, 1670 DeFoor Ave. NW, Atlanta, GA 30318: Catalog $3 ■ Castings for indoor and outdoor settings, furniture, lamps, fireplace accessories, pillows, and art prints. 404–351–5099.

BowBends, P.O. Box 900, Bolton, MA 01740: Information $3 ■ Arched garden bridges in any width, from 8 to 40 feet. 508–779–2271.

Robert Compton, Ltd., RD 3, Box 3600, Bristol, VT 05443: Brochure $2 ■ Original stone fountains. 802–453–3778.

East/West Gardens, 1259 El Camino Real, Menlo Park, CA 94025: Free catalog ■ Handcrafted landscape accessories from foreign countries. Includes bronze and marble animals, Chinese relics, porcelain fishbowls, planters, pottery, stone lanterns, and garden stools. 415–321–2571.

Florentine Craftsmen, 46–24 28th St., Long Island City, NY 11101: Catalog $4 ■ Ornamental sculpture, fountains, birdbaths, and furniture. 718–937–7632.

Form Products, Division of Wausau Tile, Inc., P.O. Box 1520, Wausau, WI 54402: Free catalog ■ Concrete garden and landscaping accessories. 800–992–8728.

Garden Concepts Collection, P.O. Box 241233, Memphis, TN 38124: Catalog $3 ■ Landscaping and outdoor statuary, fountains, urns and vases, pedestals, planters, mahogany furniture, and garden structures. 901–682–1109.

Hermitage Garden Pools, P.O. Box 361, Canastota, NY 13032: Catalog $1 ■ Fiberglass rocks and waterfalls, giant redwood water wheels, wooden bridges, and bubbling fantasias. 315–697–9093.

Lazy Hill Farm Designs, Lazy Hill Rd., Colerain, NC 27924: Free information ■ Handcrafted garden accessories. 919–356–2828.

Machin Designs by Amdega, P.O. Box 713, Glenview, IL 60025: Catalog $3 ■ Landscaping buildings and ornaments. 203–834–9566.

New England Garden Ornaments, 38 E. Brookfield Rd., North Brookfield, MA 01535: Catalog $6 ■ Garden ornaments and furniture. 508–867–4474.

Southern Statuary & Stone, 901 33rd St. North, Birmingham, AL 35222: Catalog $5 ■ Stone castings for garden landscaping. 205–322–0379.

Stickney's Garden Houses, One Thompson Square, P.O. Box 34, Boston, MA 02129: Brochure $3 ■ Handcrafted garden houses with carved details and optional seats. 617–242–1711.

Strassacker Bronze, Inc., P.O. Box 931, Spartanburg, SC 29304: Catalog $10 (refundable) ■ Contemporary and abstract bronze sculptures, fountains, and lighting equipment. 803–573–7438.

Samuel Welch Sculpture, Inc., P.O. Box 55, Cincinnati, OH 45201: Free portfolio ■ Modern sculpture in bronze, aluminum, steel, concrete, marble, and granite. 513–321–8882.

Mowers, Trimmers & Blowers

American Honda Motor Company, Inc., 100 W. Alondra Blvd., Gardena, CA 80247: Free information ■ Walk-behind and riding mowers.

American Yard Products, Inc., 931 Broad St., Augusta, GA 30901: Free information ■ Riding mowers.

Ariens Company, 655 W. Ryan St., Brillion, WI 54110: Free information ■ Self-propelled mower and riding mowers with electric start engines. 414–756–2141.

BCS America, P.O. Box 1739, Matthews, NC 28105: Free catalog ■ Chippers and shredders, tillers, garden carts, sprayers, and mowers. 800–873–1913.

Billy Goat Industries, 1803 S. Jefferson, P.O. Box 308, Lee's Summit, MO 64063: Free information with long SASE ■ Indoor/outdoor power vacuum. 816–524–9666.

Black & Decker, 10 N. Park Dr., P.O. Box 798, Hunt Valley, MD 21030: Free information ■ Portable vacuums and blowers in gasoline-powered and cordless electric models, electric hedge trimmers, and electric lawn mowers. 800–762–6672; 410–683–7000 (in MD).

Country Home Products, Ferry Rd., Box 89, Charlotte, VT 05445: Free information ■ Power trimmer on wheels. 802–446–8746.

John Deere & Company, 1400 3rd Ave., Moline, IL 61265: Free information with long SASE ■ Lawn sweepers, self-propelled walk-behind mowers, and mulching attachments. 800–544–2122.

Dixon Industries, Inc., P.O. Box 1569, Coffeyville, KS 67337: Free information ■ Riding mowers.

Echo, Inc., 400 Oakwood Rd., Lake Zurich, IL 60047: Free information ■ Walk-behind mowers.

Excel Industries, Inc., P.O. Box 7000, Hesston, KS 67062: Free information ■ Riding mowers.

Garden Way, 9th Ave & 102nd St., Troy, NY 12180: Free information ■ Carts, tillers, clippers, sickle bar mowers, garden composter, and other equipment. 800–535–6001.

Homelite Sales, Box 7047, Charlotte, NC 28273: Free information with long SASE ■ Push and riding mowers, lawn tractors, electric and gasoline-operated trimmers, hedge trimmers, gasoline-powered blowers, vacuums, sprayers, cutoff saws, and snow removal equipment. 800–242–4672; 704–588–3200 (in NC).

Husqvarna Power Products, 907 W. Irving Park Rd., Itasca, IL 60143: Free information ■ Walk-behind and riding mowers.

Kubota Tractor Corporation, 550 W. Artesia Blvd., Compton, CA 90224: Free information ■ Walk-behind mowers.

Lawn-Boy, P.O. Box 152, Plymouth, WI 53073: Free information ■ Walk-behind and riding mowers.

Mainline of North America, P.O. Box 526, London, OH 43140: Free brochure ■ All-gear driven tiller with no belts or chains and optional sickle bar, hydraulic log splitter, cart, and snow thrower. 614–852–9733.

Poulan, Division White Consolidated Industries, 5020 Flournoy-Lucas Rd., Shreveport, LA 71129: Free information with long SASE ■ Gasoline-powered, hand-held blowers and lawn trimmer. 318–687–0100.

Simplicity Manufacturing, Inc. 500 N. Spring St., Port Washington, WI 53074: Free information ■ Walk-behind and riding mowers.

Snapper Power Equipment, P.O. Box 777, McDonough, GA 30253: Free information ■ Walk-behind mowers and riding mowers.

Tanaka, Ltd., 22322 E. Imperial Hwy., Bothell, WA 98021: Free information ■ Hand-held, gasoline-operated string trimmers with electric starters. 206–481–2000.

Toro Company, 5300 Shoreline Blvd., Mound, MN 55463: Free information ■ Riding trimmers. 800–336–0242.

White Outdoor Products Company, P.O. Box 361131, Cleveland, OH 44136: Free information ■ Walk-behind mowers and riding mowers.

Organic Gardening Supplies

Gardens Alive, 5100 Schenley Pl.,Lawrenceburg, IN 47025: Free catalog ■ Organic gardening supplies. 812–537–8651.

Garden-Ville, 6266 Hwy. 290 West, Austin, TX 78735: Free catalog ■ Organic gardening supplies and equipment. 512–892–0002.

Koos, Inc., 4500 13th Ct., Kenosha, WI 53141: Free information ■ Lawn and garden fertilizers, plus herbicides, insecticides, and organic plant foods. 414–654–5301.

Pots & Planters

Cambridge Designs, P.O. Box 765, Hillsdale, MI 49242: Free information ■ Landscaping benches, planters, receptacles, fountains, and pedestrian control screens. 517–439–4348.

Hamptons of Bristol, P.O. Box 1104, West Concord, MA 01742: Catalog $1 ■ Teak-wood outdoor furniture and planters. 508–371–1526.

Heritage Crafters, 1303 Gaston Way, Dallas, NC 28034: Catalog $2 ■ Solid wood planters, oak porch swings, and handcrafted wood reproduction chests and trunks. 704–922–9253.

Kingsley-Bate, Ltd., P.O. Box 6797, Arlington, VA 22206: Brochure $1 ■ Hand-carved and traditional teak planters, window boxes, and garden furniture. 703–931–9200.

Plant Collectibles, 103 Kenview Ave., Buffalo, NY 14217: Catalog $2 ■ Plastic pots, hanging baskets, starter trays, waterers, plant foods, insecticide sprays, and lighting units.

Syracuse Pottery, 6551 Pottery Rd., Warners, NY 13164: Free catalog ■ Stoneware, ceramic, brass, and terra cotta indoor and outdoor planters. 315–487–6066.

TerraCast, 1136 Samuelson St., City of Industry, CA 91748: Free information ■ Unbreakable, lightweight planters for indoor and outdoor gardens. 800–423–8539; 818–965–5095 (in CA).

Violet House of Pots, Box 1274, Gainesville, FL 32601: Free catalog ■ Indoor and outdoor plastic pots, hanging baskets, seeds for growing violets, insecticides, fertilizers, potting soils, perlite vermiculite, books, and trays. 904–377–8465.

Soil Testing

Cascade Analytical, 3019 G.S. Center Rd., Wenatchee, WA 98801: Free information ■ Soil and garden testing services.

Earth-Rite, RD 1, Box 243, Gap, PA 17527: Free information ■ Soil and garden testing services.

Freedom Soil Lab, P.O. Box 1144, Freedom, CA 95019: Free information ■ Soil and garden testing services. 408–724–4427.

Necessary Trading Company, P.O. Box 305, New Castle, VA 24127: Catalog $2 (refundable) ■ Soil and garden testing services, testing supplies and equipment, plant nutrients, fertilizers, and pest control preparations. 703–864–5103.

Soil & Plant Laboratory, 4173–18 Joe Miller Rd., Malaga, WA 98828: Soil and garden testing services.

Sudbury Laboratories, Inc., 572 Dutton Rd., Sudbury, MA 01776: Free brochure ■ Soil testing kits, fertilizers, animal repellents, and other garden supplies. 508–443–8844.

Tillers

American Honda Motor Company, Inc., 100 W. Alondra Blvd., Gardena, CA 80247: Free information ■ Power-operated tillers.

American Yard Products, Inc., 931 Broad St., Augusta, GA 30901: Free information ■ Power-operated tillers.

Ariens Company, 655 W. Ryan St., Brillon, WI 54110: Free information ■ Power-operated tillers. 414–756–2141.

BCS America, P.O. Box 1739, Matthews, NC 28105: Free catalog ■ Chippers and shredders, tillers, garden carts, sprayers, and mowers. 800–873–1913.

Black & Decker, Inc., 10 N. Park Dr., Hunt Valley, MD 21030: Free information ■ Power-operated tillers. 800–762–6672; 410–683–7000 (in MD).

Ford New Holland, Inc., 300 Schaefer Rd., P.O. Box 6011, Dearborn, MI 48121: Free information ■ Power-operated tillers.

Garden Way, 9th Ave & 102nd St., Troy, NY 12180: Free information ■ Power operated tiller-power composter for small gardens. 800–535–6001.

Husqvarna Power Products, 907 W. Irving Park Rd., Itasca, IL 60143: Free information ■ Power-operated tillers.

Kubota Tractor Corporation, 550 W. Artesia Blvd., Compton, CA 80224: Free information ■ Power-operated tillers.

Lawn-Boy, P.O. Box 152, Plymouth, WI 53070: Free information ■ Power-operated tillers.

Mainline of North America, P.O. Box 526, London, OH 43140: Free brochure ■ All-gear driven tiller with no belts or chains and optional sickle bar, hydraulic log splitter, cart, and snow thrower. 614–852–9733.

Mantis Manufacturing Company, 1458 County Line Rd., Huntingdon Valley, PA 19006: Free information ■ Electric powered tiller with optional border edger, planter furrower, lawn aerator, and thatch remover. 800–366–6268.

Masport, Inc., 6140 McCormick Dr., Lincoln, NE 68507: Free information ■ Power-operated tillers.

Poulan, Division White Consolidated Industries, 5020 Flournoy-Lucas Rd., Shreveport, LA 71129: Free information with long SASE ■ Gasoline-powered, hand-held blowers and lawn trimmer. 318–687–0100.

Roto-Hoe, 100 Auburn Rd., Newbury, OH 44065: Free information ■ Easy-handling tillers. 216–564–2294.

White Outdoor Products Company, P.O. Box 361131, Cleveland, OH 44136: Free information ■ Power-operated tillers.

Tools & Sprayers

Alsto Company, P.O. Box 1267, Galesburg, IL 61401: Free catalog ■ Garden tools and accessories. 800–447–0048.

Amerind MacKissic, Inc., P.O. Box 111, Parker Ford, PA 19457: Free information ■ Sprayers for fruit trees, shrubs, ornamentals, gardens, and lawns. 800–344–4030; 800–342–0052 (in PA).

Brookstone Company, 5 Vose Farm Rd., P.O. Box 5, Petersborough, NH 03458: Free catalog ■ House and garden tools. 800–846–3000.

W. Atlee Burpee & Company, 300 Park Ave., Warminster, PA 18974: Free catalog ■ Garden supplies, tools, equipment, growing aids, and accessories. 215–674–1793.

Charley's Greenhouse Supply, 1569 Memorial Hwy., Mt. Vernon, WA 98273: Catalog $2 ■ Shading materials, fans, watering and misting equipment, insulation, and propagating supplies. 206–428–2626.

Clapper's, P.O. Box 2278, West Newton, MA 02165: Free catalog ■ Spreaders, sprayers, sprinkling and full-flow watering systems, outdoor furniture, landscaping ornaments, and outdoor lighting. 617–244–7900.

Duraco Products, 109 E. Lake St., Streamwood, IL 60103: Free information ■ Garden accessories. 800–888–POTS.

Environmental Concepts, 710 NW 57th St., Fort Lauderdale, FL 33309: Free catalog with long SASE ■ Meters that measure soil temperature, pH, light intensity, and the need for fertilizer. 305–491–4490.

Gardener's Eden, Mail Order Department, P.O. Box 7307, San Francisco, CA 94120: Free catalog ■ Garden tools, landscaping accessories, growing and transplanting aids, and furniture. 800–822–9600.

Gardener's Supply Company, 128 Intervale Rd., Burlington, VT 05401: Free catalog ■ Composters, pest control sprayers, watering systems and controls, weeding and cultivating tools, organic fertilizers, garden carts, leaf mulchers, furniture, and canning and preserving accessories. 800–944–2250.

Gro-Tek, 36 Mohawk Trail, Guilford, CT 06437: Catalog 50¢ ■ Seedling starter kits, tools, and accessories for greenhouses, solariums, and gardening.

Harris Seeds, 60 Saginaw Dr., P.O. Box 22960, 3670 Buffalo Rd., Rochester, NY 14692: Free catalog ■ Gardening equipment, seeds, plants, and other supplies. 716–442–0410.

House of Wesley, 2200 E. Oakland, Bloomington, IL 61701: Free catalog ■ Gardening tools, supplies, and plants and seeds. 309–663–9551.

Indoor Gardening Supplies, P.O. Box 40567, Detroit, MI 48240: Free catalog ■ Gardening supplies, lights, books, and other accessories. 313–426–9080.

Johnny's Selected Seeds, Foss Hill Rd., Albion, ME 04910: Free information ■ Tools, growing aids, and supplies. 207–437–4301.

Kemp Company, 160 Koser Rd., Lititz, PA 17543: Free information ■ Garden composters. 717–627–7979.

The Kinsman Company, River Rd., Point Pleasant, PA 18950: Free information ■ Composters, compost bins, chipper-shredders, rose arbors, garden arches, plant supports, and tools. 800–733–5613.

Langenbach Fine Tool Company, 38 Millbrook-Stillwater Rd., P.O. Box 453, Blairstown, NJ 07825: Free catalog ■ Garden tools and accessories. 800–362–1991

A.M. Leonard, Inc., 6665 Spiker Rd., Piqua, OH 45356: Catalog $1 ■ Tools, sprayers, and gardening supplies. 800–543–8955.

MacKenzie Nursery Supply, Inc., P.O. Box 322, Perry, OH 44081: Free information ■ Gardening tools and accessories.

Mainline of North America, P.O. Box 526, London, OH 43140: Free brochure ■ All-gear driven tiller with no belts or chains and optional sickle bar, hydraulic log splitter, cart, and snow thrower. 614–852–9733.

Mantis Manufacturing Company, 1458 County Line Rd., Huntingdon Valley, PA 19006: Free information ■ Portable power sprayer for garden, washing windows and outside walls, and other uses. 800–366–6268.

Mellinger's, Inc., 2310 W. South Range Rd., North Lima, OH 44452: Free catalog ■ Gardening tools and accessories, plants and seeds, and growing aids. 216–549–9861.

Modern Homesteader, 1825 Big Horn Ave., Cody, WY 82414: Free catalog ■ Gardening equipment and supplies, clothing and hats, tools, truck and automotive accessories, and canning equipment. 800–443–4934; 307–587–5946 (in WY).

Natural Gardening Company, 217 San Anselmo Ave., San Anselmo, CA 94960: Catalog $1 ■ Tools, seeds, fertilizers, pest controls, birdhouses, and books. 800–755–4769.

L.L. Olds Seed Company, P.O. Box 7790, Madison, WI 53707: Catalog $2.50 ■ Tools and equipment, growing aids, and seeds and plants. 608–249–9291.

Park Seed Company, Cokesbury Rd., P.O. Box 46, Greenwood, SC 29648: Free catalog ■ Gardening tools and accessories, plants and seeds, and growing aids. 803–223–7333.

PeCo, Inc., P.O. Box 1197, Arden, NC 28704: Free information ■ Battery-powered sprayer with charger and wand. 800–438–5823; 704–684–1234 (in NC).

Pinetree Garden Seeds, Rt. 100, New Gloucester, ME 04260: Free information ■ Sprayers for pest control. 207–926–3400.

Plow & Hearth, 301 Madison Rd., P.O. Box 830, Orange, VA 22960: Free catalog ■ Gardening tools, outdoor furniture, bird houses and feeders, and birdbaths. 800–866–6072.

Poulan, Division White Consolidated Industries, 5020 Flournoy-Lucas Rd., Shreveport, LA 71129: Free information with long SASE ■ Gasoline-powered, hand-held blowers and lawn trimmer. 318–687–0100.

Ringer, 9959 Valley View Rd., Eden Prairie, MN 55344: Free catalog ■ Garden tools, chemical treatments and fertilizers, growing aids, propagation supplies, compost-making equipment, lawn care supplies, and planters. 800–654–1047.

Smith & Hawken, 25 Corte Madera, Mill Valley, CA 94941: Free information ■ Tools, equipment, sprayers, and greenhouse supplies. 415–383–2000.

Stern's Miracle-Gro, P.O. Box 888, Port Washington, NY 11050: Free information ■ Sprayers for pest control. 516–883–6550.

Stokes Seeds, Inc., Box 548, Buffalo, NY 14240: Free catalog ■ Greenhouse tools and supplies. 416–688–4300.

Topiary Frames

Fancy Plants Farms, P.O. Box 1126, Lake Placid, FL 33852: Free information ■ Wire forms and other supplies. 813–699–1990.

Fox Hill Farm, 444 W. Michigan Ave., Box 9, Parma, MI 49269: Catalog $1 ■ Herbal topiary standards and supplies. 517–531–3179.

Ivy League, P.O. Box E, Wakefield, MA 01880: Free catalog ■ Wire forms in different shapes planted with small vines. Empty frames available. 617–246–3635.

The Kinsman Company, River Rd., Point Pleasant, PA 18950: Free information ■ Cone and ball wire forms. 800–733–5613.

Topiary, Inc., 41 Bering, Tampa, FL 33606: Free brochure ■ Wire and stuffed wire forms in geometric and animal shapes. 813–837–2841.

Tractors

American Honda Motor Company, Inc., 100 W. Alondra Blvd., Gardena, CA 80247: Free information ■ Lawn and garden tractors.

American Yard Products, Inc., 931 Broad St., Augusta, GA 30901: Free information ■ Lawn and garden tractors.

Ariens Company, 655 W. Ryan St., Brillon, WI 54110: Free information ■ Lawn and garden tractors. 414–756–2141.

BCS America, P.O. Box 1739, Matthews, NC 28105: Free information ■ Lawn and garden tractors. 800–873–1913.

John Deere & Company, 1400 3rd Ave., Moline, IL 61265: Free information ■ Lawn and garden tractors. 800–544–2122.

Ford New Holland, Inc., 300 Schaefer Rd., P.O. Box 6011, Dearborn, MI 48121: Free information ■ Lawn and garden tractors.

Garden Way, 9th Ave. & 102nd St., Troy, NY 12180: Free information ■ Lawn and garden tractors. 800–535–6001.

Husqvarna Power Products, 907 W. Irving Park Rd., Itasca, IL 60143: Free information ■ Lawn and garden tractors.

Kubota Tractor Corporation, 550 W. Artesia Blvd., Compton, CA 80224: Free information ■ Lawn and garden tractors.

Lawn-Boy, P.O. Box 152, Plymouth, WI 53070: Free information ■ Lawn and garden tractors.

Poulan, Division White Consolidated Industries, 5020 Flournoy-Lucas Rd., Shreveport, LA 71129: Free information ■ Lawn and garden tractors. 318–687–0100,

Simplicity Manufacturing, Inc., 500 N. Spring St., Port Washington, WI 53074: Free information ■ Lawn and garden tractors.

Snapper Power Equipment, P.O. Box 777, McDonough, GA 30253: Free information ■ Lawn and garden tractors.

White Outdoor Products Company, P.O. Box 361131, Cleveland, OH 44136: Free information ■ Lawn and garden tractors.

Yamaha Outdoor Power Equipment Division, 6555 Katella Ave., Cypress, CA 90630: Free information ■ Lawn and garden tractors.

Water Gardening Supplies

Belik Creation, 1610 Mulcahy, Rosenberg, TX 77471: Free information ■ Interior and exterior water fountains. 713–341–7197.

Cambridge Designs, P.O. Box 765, Hillsdale, MI 49242: Free information ■ Landscaping benches, planters, receptacles, fountains, and pedestrian control screens. 517–439–4348.

Continental Custom Bridge Company, Rt. 5, Alexandria, MN 56308: Free information

■ Prefab bridges for garden settings. 800–328–2047; 612–852–7500 (in MN).

Dolphin Outdoors, Dolphin Pet Village, 1808 W. Campbell Ave., Campbell, CA 95008: Free brochure with long SASE ■ Fiberglass ponds for water gardens, filters, plants, and fish. 408–379–7600.

Federal Fountain Supply, 6029 Fourteen Mile, Sterling Heights, MI 48077: Catalog $3 ■ Easy-to-assemble garden fountains with cascading water return. 313–264–7460.

Hermitage Garden Pools, P.O. Box 361, Canastota, NY 13032: Catalog $1 ■ Fiberglass garden pools, rock waterfalls, redwood waterwheels, wooden bridges, and bubbling fantasias. 315–697–9093.

Hydro Dramatics, 918 S. 4th St., St. Louis, MO 63102: Free information ■ Floating and site fountains and underwater lighting equipment. 314–231–9806.

Lilypons Water Gardens, P.O. Box 10, Buckeystown, MD 21717: Catalog $5 ■ Supplies and equipment for aquatic gardens. 800–723–7667.

Maryland Aquatic Nurseries, 3427 N. Furnace Rd., Jarrettsville, MD 21084: Catalog $2 ■ Plants for water garden settings, ornamental grasses, and Japanese irises. 410–557–7615.

Paradise Water Gardens, 34 May St., Whitman, MA 02382: Catalog $3 ■ Fountains, pools, pumps, goldfish, aquatic plants, and books. 617–447–4711.

S. Scherer & Sons, 104 Waterside Rd., Northport, NY 11768: Free price list ■ Water lilies, aquatic plants, pools, pumps, waterfalls, and fish and supplies for water gardens. 516–261–7432.

Slocum Water Gardens, 1101 Cypress Gardens Rd., Winter Haven, FL 33884: Catalog $1 ■ Water gardening supplies. 813–293–7151.

Somethin' Fishy, 5103 Kingston Pike, Knoxville, TN 37919: Catalog $2 ■ Water gardening supplies. 615–584–1925.

Urdl's Waterfall Creations, Inc., 1010 NW 1st St., Delray Beach, FL 33444: Free information ■ Custom waterfalls and other water equipment for garden settings. Includes manufactured hollow concrete rocks for landscaping waterfall settings. 305–278–3320.

Van Ness Water Gardens, 2460 N. Euclid, Upland, CA 91786: Catalog $6 ■ Water lilies, other aquatic plants, waterfalls, and gardening supplies. 714–982–2425.

Waterford Gardens, 74 E. Allendale Rd., Saddle River, NJ 07458: Catalog $5 ■ Water lilies, lotus and bog plants, pools, and fish. 201–327–0721.

Western Wood Structures, Inc., P.O. Box 130, Tualatin, OR 97062: Free information ■ Pedestrian, equestrian, and golf course bridges, from 20– to 100–foot spans. 503–692–6900.

Watering & Irrigation Equipment

Acu-Drip Water System, Wade Manufacturing Company, P.O. Box 8769, Portland, OR 97208: Free information ■ Easy-to-install custom drip watering systems. 800–222–7246.

Drip Irrigation Garden, 16216 Raymer St., Van Nuys, CA 91406: Free catalog ■ Watering system kits, outdoor irrigation supplies, and soaker hoses. 818–989–5999.

Full Circle, P.O. Box 6, Redway, CA 95560: Catalog $2 ■ Watering system kits, outdoor irrigation supplies, and soaker hoses. 800–426–5511.

Gardena, Inc., 6031 Culligan Way, Minnetonka, MN 55345: Free catalog ■ Watering system kits, outdoor irrigation supplies, and soaker hoses. 612–933–2445.

Harmony Farm Supply, P.O. Box 460, Graton, CA 95444: Catalog $2 ■ Watering system kits, outdoor irrigation supplies, and soaker hoses. 707–823–9125.

International Irrigation Systems, P.O. Box 160, Niagara Falls, NY 14304: Free catalog ■ Watering system kits, outdoor irrigation supplies, and soaker hoses. 416–688–4090.

Mel-Nor Industries, Inc., 303 Gulf Bank, Houston, TX 77037: Free information with long SASE ■ Time-controlled sprinklers, hose reel carts, hanging lawn and porch swings, park benches, and old-time lamp posts. 713–445–3485.

Miser Irrigation Systems, Box 94616, Lincoln, NE 68509: Free information ■ Watering systems for gardens. 402–467–1369.

Moss Products, Inc., P.O. Box 72, Palmetto, FL 33561: Free catalog and guide ■

Watering systems for gardens. 813–729–5433.

Nitron Industries, Inc., P.O. Box 1447, Fayetteville, AR 72702: Free catalog ■ Watering system kits, outdoor irrigation supplies, and soaker hoses. 501–750–1777.

Plastic Plumbing Products, 17005 Manchester Rd., P.O. Box 186, Grover, MO 63040: Catalog $1 (refundable) ■ Drip irrigation systems, outdoor irrigation supplies, and soaker hoses. 314–458–2226.

Raindrip, Inc., P.O. Box 2173, Chatsworth, CA 91313: Free catalog ■ Watering system kits, outdoor irrigation supplies, and soaker hoses. 800–544–3747; 800–367–3747 (in CA).

Skagit Gardens, 1695 Johnson Rd., Mt. Vernon, WA 98273: Catalog $2 ■ Watering system kits, outdoor irrigation supplies, and soaker hoses. 206–424–6760.

Submatic Irrigation Systems, P.O. Box 246, Lubbock, TX 79048: Free catalog ■ Standard and custom irrigation systems. 800–692–4100.

Trickle Soak Systems, 8733 Magnolia, Ste. 100, Santee, CA 92071: Catalog $4 ■ Watering system kits, outdoor irrigation supplies, and soaker hoses. 619–449–6408.

Urban Farmer Store, 2833 Vicente St., San Francisco, CA 94116: Catalog $1 ■ Watering system kits, outdoor irrigation supplies, and soaker hoses. 415–661–2204.

USA Drip, P.O. Box 429, Goodland, KS 67735: Free brochure ■ Irrigation system for the home gardener. 800–USA–DRIP.

VC & C Products, Rt. 3, Box 438, Hereford, TX 79045: Free catalog ■ Adjustable lawn and garden sprinkler. 806–276–5338.

Weiss Brothers Nurseries, 11690 Colfax Hwy., Grass Valley, CA 95945: Free information ■ Drip irrigation supplies. 916–272–7657.

GARDENING—PLANTS & SEEDS

African Violets & Gesneriads

Alice's Violets, Rt. 6, Box 233, Waynesville, MO 65583: Free catalog with long SASE ■ African violets. Includes single, double, semi-double, miniature, and semi-miniature varieties. 314–336–4763.

Bowman African Violets, P.O. Box 6712, Malibu, CA 90264: Free catalog ■ African violets and self-watering pots. 310–456–8370.

Elizabeth Buck African Violets, 9255 Lake Pleasant Rd., Clifford, MI 48727: Free catalog ■ African violet leaves. 517–761–7382.

Buell's Greenhouse, Inc., Weeks Rd., P.O. Box 218, Eastford, CT 06242: Free catalog ■ African violets, exotic gesneriads, and growing supplies. 206–829–1811.

Cape Cod Violetry, 28 Minot St., Falmouth, MA 02540: Catalog $1 (refundable) ■ African violet plants and leaves. 508–548–2798.

Davidson-Wilson Greenhouses, Rt. 2, Box 168, Crawfordsville, IN 47933: Catalog $1 ■ African violets, houseplants, and geraniums. 317–364–0556.

DoDe's Gardens, Inc., 1490 Saturn St., Merritt Island, FL 32953: Send two 1st class stamps for catalog ■ African violet and houseplant growing supplies. 407–452–5670.

Fischer Greenhouses, Blackman Rd. & Poplar Ave., Bargaintown, NJ 08221: Catalog 35¢ ■ African violet plants or leaves, and gesneriads. 609–927–3399.

Jeannette's Jesneriads, 2173 Leslie St., Terrytown Gretna, LA 70056: Catalog $1 ■ Standard to large-size African violets. 504–393–6977.

JoS Violets, 402 Dundee St., Victoria, TX 77904: Free catalog with long SASE ■ Standard, semi-miniature, miniature, and trailing African violets; and growing supplies and pots. 512–575–1344.

Kartuz Greenhouses, 1408 Sunset Dr., Vista, CA 92083: Catalog $2 ■ Gesneriads, begonias, and miniature terrarium and unusual tropical plants. 619–941–3613.

Lauray of Salisbury, Undermountain Rd., Salisbury, CT 06068: Catalog $2 ■ Ges-

neriads, begonias, orchids, cacti and succulents, and other plants. 203–435–2263.

Lyndon Lyon Greenhouses, Inc., 14 Mutchler St., Dolgeville, NY 13329: Catalog $1 ■ African violets and exotic houseplants. 315–429–8291.

Mighty Minis, 7318 Sahara Ct., Sacramento, CA 95828: Catalog $1 (refundable) ■ Miniature African violet plants or leaves. 916–421–7284.

Miree's Gesneriads, 70 Enfield Ave., Toronto, Ontario, Canada M8W 1T9: Catalog $1 (refundable) ■ Miniature begonias, African violets, and gesneriads. 416–251–6369.

Tiki Nursery, 2325 Valley Rd., Fairview, NC 28730: Catalog 50¢ ■ African violets, gesneriads, begonias, fuchsias, and rare exotics. 704–628–2212.

Tinari Greenhouses, P.O. Box 190, Huntingdon Valley, PA 19006: Catalog 35¢ ■ African violets in standard, miniature, trailer, and variegated species. 215–947–0144.

Travis Violets, P.O. Box 42, Ochlochnee, GA 31773: Catalog $1 (refundable) ■ Hybrid African violets, other varieties, growing supplies, and pots. 912–574–5167.

Violet Showcase, 3147 S. Broadway, Englewood, CO 80110: Catalog $1 ■ African violet plants. Includes standards, trailers, pinwheels, and miniatures. 303–761–1770.

Volkmann Bros. Greenhouses, 2714 Minert St., Dallas, TX 75219: Free catalog with long SASE ■ African violets and growing supplies. 214–526–3484.

West Coast Violets, 2692 E. 45th Ave., Vancouver, British Columbia, Canada V5R 3C1: Catalog $1 ■ Growing supplies and miniature, semi-miniature, standard, trailer, and chimera varieties of African violets. 604–435–6382.

Wilson Plant Sales, 202 S. Indiana St., Roachdale, IN 46172: Free catalog ■ African violets, geraniums, and exotic houseplants. 317–522–1320.

Wilson's Violet Haven, 3900 Carter Creek Pkwy., Bryan, TX 77802: Catalog $1.50 ■ African violets. Includes standards, trailers, and a few miniatures. 409–846–8970.

Zaca Vista Nursery, 1190 Alamo Pintado Rd., Solvang, CA 93463: Catalog $1 (refundable) ■ African violet plants, seed, and leaves; growing supplies; and books. 805–688–2585.

Aquatic Plants

Eco-Gardens, P.O. Box 1227, Decatur, GA 30031: Price list $1 ■ Water garden plants, perennials, wildflowers, ferns, daylilies, trees and shrubs, and ferns. 404–294–6468.

Kester's Birdseed, Inc., P.O. Box 516, Omro, WI 54963: Catalog $2 ■ Aquatic plants. 800–558–8815; 414–685–2929 (in WI).

Lilies of the Valley, P.O. Box 22363, Carmel, CA 93922: Catalog $1.50 ■ Water lilies and other aquatic plants. 408–624–5279.

Maryland Aquatic Nurseries, 3427 N. Furnace Rd., Jarrettsville, MD 21084: Catalog $2 ■ Marginal and bog plants for aquatic gardens. 410–557–7615.

S. Scherer & Sons, 104 Waterside Rd., Northport, NY 11768: Free price list ■ Water lilies, other aquatic plants, pools, pumps, waterfalls, fish, and water gardening supplies. 516–261–7432.

William Tricker, Inc., 7125 Tanglewood Dr., Independence, OH 44131: Catalog $3 ■ Water lilies, aquatic plants, and exotic fish for indoor and outdoor water gardens. 216–524–3491.

Waterford Gardens, 74 E. Allendale Rd., Saddle River, NJ 07458: Catalog $5 ■ Water lilies, lotus and bog plants, pools, and accessories. 201–327–0721.

Wicklein's Aquatic Farm & Nursery, Inc., 1820 Cromwell Bridge Rd., Baltimore, MD 21234: Catalog $1 ■ Water lilies, other aquatic plants, and perennials. 410–823–1335.

Azaleas & Rhododendrons

Bovees Nursery, 1737 SW Coronado, Portland, OR 97219: Catalog $2 (refundable) ■ Parent type and hybridizer azaleas and rhododendrons. 503–244–9341.

Cardinal Nursery, Rt. 1, Box 316, State Rd., NC 28676: Free catalog ■ Rhododendrons for woodland landscapes and rock gardens. 919–874–2027.

Carlson's Gardens, Box 305, South Salem, NY 10590: Catalog $2 (refundable) ■ Dwarf rhododendrons and landscape-size azaleas that include Exbury, Windsor, Robin Hill, North Tisbury, Glenn Dale, Gable, natives, and fragrant yellows. 914–763–5958.

Chambers Nursery, 26874 Ferguson Rd., Junction City, OR 97448: Free catalog ■ Rhododendrons and azaleas. 503–998–2467.

Clifford's Perennial & Vine, Rt. 2, Box 320, East Troy, MI 53120: Catalog $1 (refundable) ■ Azaleas, rhododendrons, irises, Oriental poppies, peonies, daylilies, other perennials, and flowering vines. 414–968–4040 (April-September); 414–642–7156 (October-March).

Crownsville Nursery, P.O. Box 797, Crownsville, MD 21032: Catalog $2 (refundable) ■ Ferns, wildflowers, azaleas, ornamental grasses, and other perennials. 410–923–2212.

Cummins Garden, 22 Robertsville Rd., Marlboro, NJ 07746: Catalog $2 ■ Dwarf rhododendrons, evergreens and deciduous azaleas, dwarf conifers, and companion plants. 908–536–2591.

Daystar, Rt. 2, Box 250, Litchfield, ME 04350: Catalog $1 ■ Perennials, rhododendrons, trees and shrubs, and other plants. 207–724–3369.

Eastern Plant Specialties, P.O. Box 40, Colonia, NJ 07067: Catalog $2 ■ Rare, choice, and new rhododendrons and azaleas; companion and dwarf plants; and laurels and conifers. 908–388–3101.

Eco-Gardens, P.O. Box 1227, Decatur, GA 30031: Price list $1 ■ Azaleas, perennials, wildflowers, ferns, daylilies, water garden plants, trees and shrubs, and ferns. 404–294–6468.

Flora Lan Nursery, Rt. 1, Box 357, Forest Grove, OR 97116: Free catalog ■ Azaleas and rhododendron hybrids. 503–357–3500.

Girard Nurseries, P.O. Box 428, Geneva, OH 44041: Free catalog ■ Azaleas and rhododendrons. 216–466–2881.

The Greenery, 14450 NE 16th Pl., Bellevue, WA 98007: Catalog $1 (refundable) ■ Azaleas and rhododendrons. 206–641–1458.

Greer Gardens, 1280 Goodpasture Island Rd., Eugene, OR 97401: Catalog $3 ■ Azaleas and rhododendrons, trees and shrubs, Japanese maples, and bonsai. 503–686–8266.

Hall Rhododendrons, 6924 Hwy. 38, P.O. Box 62, Drain, OR 97435: Catalog $1 ■ Rhododendron hybrids and species varieties. 503–836–2290.

Hillhouse Nursery, 90 Kresson-Gibbsboro Rd., Voorhees, NJ 08043: Free catalog ■ Double and semi-double varieties of azalea plants. 609–784–6203.

Justice Gardens, 107 Hight Dr., Watkinsville, GA 30677: Free catalog with long SASE ■ Azalea and rhododendron hybrids. 404–769–8379.

Oak Hill Farm, 204 Presley St., Clover, SC 29710: Free catalog with long SASE ■ Species azaleas. 803–222–4245.

Roslyn Nursery, 211 Burrs Ln., Dix Hills, NY 11746: Catalog $2 ■ Rhododendrons. 516–643–9347.

Stubbs Shrubs, 23225 SW Bosky Dell Ln., West Linn, OR 97068: Catalog $2 (refundable) ■ Evergreen azalea hybrids. 503–638–5048.

Bamboo

American Bamboo Company, 345 W. 2nd St., Dayton, OH 45402: Free catalog ■ Bamboo plants.

David C. Andrews, P.O. Box 10358, Ocon Hill, MD 20750: Free information with long SASE ■ Bamboo plants.

A Bamboo Shoot, 1462 Darby Rd., Sebastopol, CA 95472: Catalog $1 ■ Bamboo plants. 707–823–0131.

Bamboo Sourcery, 666 Wagnon Rd., Sebastopol, CA 95472: Catalog $1 ■ Bamboo plants. 707–823–5866.

Kurt Bluemel, Inc., 2740 Greene Ln., Baldwin, MD 21013: Catalog $2 ■ Bamboo plants, perennials, ferns, and ornamental grasses. 410–557–7229.

Burt Associates, Box 719, Westford, MA 01886: Informative booklet $2 (refundable) ■ Bamboo plants.

Endangered Species, P.O. Box 1830, Tustin, CA 92681: Catalog $5 ■ Giant, medium-sized, and dwarf green and variegated bamboo plants, and other rare plants. 714–544–9505.

Gardens of the Blue Ridge, P.O. Box 10, Pineola, NC 28662: Catalog $2 ■ Bamboo plants. 704–733–2417.

Garden World's Exotic Plants, 2503 Garfield St., Laredo, TX 78043: Catalog $1 ■ Bamboo, bananas, citrus trees, cacti, and other tropical growing stock. 512–724–3951.

Louisiana Nursery, Rt. 7, Box 43, Opelousas, LA 70570: Free information with long SASE ■ Bamboo plants and books. 318–948–3696.

New England Bamboo Company, P.O. Box 358, Rockport, MA 01966: Free information with long SASE ■ Bamboo plants. 508–546–3581.

Northern Groves, 3328 SE Kelly, Portland, OR 97202: Free catalog with long SASE ■ Bamboo plants. 503–232–1860.

Orion Trading Company, 820 Coventry Rd., Kensington, CA 94707: Catalog $1 ■ Bamboo poles. 510–540–7136.

Steve Ray's Bamboo Gardens, 909 79th Pl. South, Birmingham, AL 35206: Catalog $2 ■ Bamboo plants. 205–833–3052.

Tradewinds Nursery, P.O. Box 70, Calpella, CA 95418: Free list with long SASE ■ Bamboo plants. 707–485–0835.

Tripple Brook Farm, 37 Middle Rd., Southampton, MA 01073: Free catalog ■ Bamboo plants, exotic fruits, trees, perennials, and shrubs. 413–527–4626.

Upper Bank Nurseries, P.O. Box 486, Media, PA 19063: Free information ■ Bamboo plants. 215–566–0679.

Banana Plants

The Banana Tree, 715 Northampton St., Easton, PA 18042: Catalog $3 ■ Banana and other tropical plants. 215–253–9589.

Garden World's Exotic Plants, 2503 Garfield St., Laredo, TX 78043: Catalog $1 ■ Banana and bamboo plants; cacti; and pineapple and citrus trees. 512–724–3951.

W.O. Lessard Nursery, 19201 SW 248th St., Homestead, FL 33031: Catalog $1 ■ Banana plants. 305–247–0397.

Begonias

Antonelli Brothers, 2545 Capitola Rd., Santa Cruz, CA 95062: Free catalog ■ Tuberous and miniature begonias. 408–475–5222.

Glasshouse Works, Church St., Box 97, Stewart, OH 45778: Catalog $1.50 ■

Begonias and rare tropical plants. 614–662–2142.

Kartuz Greenhouses, 1408 Sunset Dr., Vista, CA 92083: Catalog $2 ■ Begonias, miniature terrarium plants, and unusual tropical plants. 619–941–3613.

Lauray of Salisbury, Undermountain Rd., Salisbury, CT 06068: Catalog $2 ■ Begonias, gesneriads, orchids, cacti and succulents, and other plants. 203–435–2263.

Miree's Gesneriads, 70 Enfield Ave., Toronto, Ontario, Canada M8W 1T9: Catalog $1 (refundable) ■ Miniature begonias, African violets, and gesneriads. 416–251–6369.

The Plant Shop's Botanical Gardens, 18007 Topham St., Reseda, CA 91335: Catalog $3.50 (refundable) ■ Cacti and succulents, species orchids, begonias, bulbs, and other plants. 818–881–4831.

Berry Plants

Ahrens Strawberry Nursery, Rt. 1, Huntingburg, IN 47542: Free booklet ■ Strawberry, gooseberry, raspberry, blueberry, and blackberry plants; fruit trees; and grapevines, rhubarb, and currants. 612–683–3055.

Alexander's Nurseries, 376 Wareham St., Middleborough, MA 02346: Free catalog with long SASE ■ Highbush blueberry root cuttings and two- to four- year-old plants. 508–947–6390.

Allen Company, P.O. Box 1577, Salisbury, MD 21801: Free catalog ■ Strawberry, asparagus, raspberry, blueberry, and thornless blackberry plants. 410–742–7122.

Vernon Barnes & Son Nursery, P.O. Box 250, McMinnville, TN 37110: Free catalog ■ Berry plants, flowering trees and shrubs, shade trees, fruit trees, wildflowers, nut trees, hedges, and vines. 615–668–8576.

Blueberry Hill, RR 1, Maynooth, Ontario, Canada K0L 2S0: Free catalog ■ Hardy, native lowbush blueberry plants for cold climates.

Blue Star, Rt. 3, P.O. Box 173, Williamstown, NY 13493: Free catalog ■ Earliblue, Spartan, Blueray, Bluetta, Patriot, and Northland varieties of blueberry bushes. 315–964–2295.

Boston Mountain Nurseries, Rt. 2, Box 405–A, Mountainburg, AR 71946: Free

catalog with first class stamp ■ Plants for strawberries, blueberries, cane berries, and table grapes. 501–369–2007.

Bountiful Ridge Nurseries, Inc., P.O. Box 250, Princess Anne, MD 21853: Free catalog ■ Berry plants, fruit and nut trees, and grapevines. 410–651–0400.

Brittingham Plant Farms, P.O. Box 2538, Salisbury, MD 21801: Free catalog ■ Strawberry, blueberry, raspberry, thornless blackberry, grape, and asparagus plants. 410–749–5153.

W. Atlee Burpee & Company, 300 Park Ave., Warminster, PA 18974: Free catalog ■ Berry plants, seeds, bulbs, and other gardening aids. 215–674–1793.

The Conner Company, P.O. Box 534, Augusta, AR 72006: Free catalog ■ Strawberry plants. 501–347–2561.

DeGrandchamp's Blueberry Farm, 15037 77th St., South Haven, MI 49060: Free catalog ■ Blueberry plants. 616–637–3915.

Dutch Mountain Nursery, 7984 N. 48th St., Augusta, MI 49012: Free catalog ■ Berry plants. 616–731–5232.

Dyke Brothers Nursery, Rt. 1, Box 251, Vincent, OH 45758: Free catalog with long SASE ■ Blueray, Berkeley, Colville, and Jersey blueberry, and Cheyenne blackberry growing stock. 614–678–2192.

Emlong Nurseries, Stevensville, MI 49127: Free catalog ■ Thornless blackberries, other berry plants, dwarf and standard fruit trees, nut trees, ornamental trees and shrubs, flowers, landscaping plants, and roses. 616–429–3612.

Enoch's Berry Farm, Rt. 2, Box 227, Fouke, AR 71837: Free price list ■ Plants and root cuttings for Shawnee, Rosborough, and Cheyenne blackberries. 501–653–2806.

Farmer Seed & Nursery Company, 818 NW 4th St., Faribault, MN 55021: Free catalog ■ Berry plants, vegetable seeds, flowering bulbs, fruit and shade trees, ornamental shrubs and hedges, and roses. 507–334–1623.

Henry Field's Seed & Nursery, 415 N. Burnett, P.O. Box 700, Shenandoah, IA 51602: Free catalog ■ Strawberry and other berry plants, vegetable and flower seeds, fruit and nut trees, shade trees, hedges, ornamental shrubs, and roses. 605–665–9391.

Fig Tree Nursery, P.O. Box 124, Gulf Hammock, FL 32639: Catalog $1 ■ Berry plants, ornamentals, and grapes for southern climates. 904–486–2930.

Dean Foster Nurseries, P.O. Box 127, Hartford, MI 49057: Free catalog ■ Strawberry, blackberry, and raspberry plants; fruit and nut and shade trees; evergreens; and grape, rhubarb, and asparagus plants. 616–621–2419.

Harris Seeds, Inc., 60 Sainaw Dr., P.O. Box 22960, Rochester, NY 14692: Free catalog ■ Berry plants and seeds. 716–442–0410.

Hartmann's Plantation, 310 60th St., P.O. Box E, Grand Junction, MI 49056: Catalog $2.25 (refundable) ■ Blueberry plants. 616–253–4281.

Highlander Nursery, P.O. Box 177, Pettigrew, AR 72752: Free catalog ■ Hardy, low-chill blueberry plants. 501–677–2300.

Ison's Nursery, Rt. 1, Brooks, GA 30205: Free catalog ■ Muscadine grapevines; blackberry, blueberry, raspberry, and strawberry plants; and fruit and nut trees that include apples, pears, figs, peaches, walnuts, and pecans. 800–733–0324.

Johnny's Selected Seeds, Foss Hill Rd., Albion, ME 04910: Free catalog ■ Strawberry plants, flower and vegetable seeds for northern climates; and gardening tools and supplies. 207–437–4301.

Johnson Nursery, Rt. 5, Box 296, Ellijay, GA 30540: Free catalog ■ Strawberry plants, grapevines, and apple, plum, pear, cherry, apricot, walnut, and almond nut trees. 404–276–3187.

Kelly Nurseries, Catalog Division, P.O. Box 10, Louisiana, MO 63353: Free catalog ■ Berry plants and grapevines, heavily rooted fruit and nut trees, landscaping trees and shrubs, ornamentals, and flowers. 800–325–4180.

Krider Nurseries, P.O. Box 29, Middlebury, IN 46540: Free catalog ■ Berry plants, roses, and bulbs. 219–825–5714.

Krohne Plant Farms, Rt. 6, Box 586, Dowagiac, MI 48197: Free brochure ■ Strawberry plants. 616–424–3450.

Makielski Berry Nursery, 7130 Platt Rd., Ypsilanti, MI 48197: Free catalog ■ Raspberries, thornless blackberries, strawberries, currants, rhubarb, gooseberries, and blueberries. 313–434–3673.

Earl May Seeds & Nursery Company, N. Elm St., Shenandoah, IA 51603: Free catalog ■ Vegetable and flower seeds, bulbs, fruit and nut trees, roses, berry plants, grapevines, shade and ornamental trees, flowering shrubs, other plants, and gardening aids. 712–246–1020.

Mellinger's, Inc., 2310 W. South Range Rd., North Lima, OH 44452: Free catalog ■ Fruit and nut trees, ornamental and shade trees, flowering shrubs and hedges, perennials, wildflowers, berry plants, and gardening supplies. 216–549–9861.

J.E. Miller Nurseries, Inc., 5060 West Lake Rd., Canandaigua, NY 14424: Free catalog ■ Berry plants, fruit trees, and grapevines. 716–396–2647.

W.K. Morse & Son, Rt. 2, Boxford, MA 01921: Free brochure ■ Strawberry and raspberry plants and grapevines. 617–352–2633.

New York State Fruit Testing Cooperative, West North St., Geneva, NY 14456: Catalog and membership $10 ■ Berry plants. 315–787–2205.

Nichols Garden Nursery, 1190 Pacific West, Albany, OR 97321: Free catalog ■ Vegetable and herb seeds; strawberry plants; and saffron crocus, garlic, and shallot growing stock. 503–928–9280.

Nourse Farms, Box 485 RFD, South Deerfield, MA 01373: Free catalog ■ Raspberry, strawberry, asparagus, and rhubarb plants. 413–665–2568.

Pacific Berry Works, 963 Thomas Rd., Bow, WA 98232: Free list ■ Raspberries, strawberries, and blackberries for northern climates. 206–757–4385.

Park Seed Company, Inc., Cokesbury Rd., P.O. Box 46, Greenwood, SC 29648: Free catalog ■ Strawberry plants, other seeds and bulbs, and gardening tools and accessories. 803–223–7333.

Patrick's Nursery, P.O. Box 1300, Ty Ty, GA 31795: Free catalog ■ Vegetable seeds for southern climates, fruit and nut trees, berry plants, and grapevines. 912–386–1919.

Peaceful Valley Farm Supply, P.O. Box 2209, Grass Valley, CA 95945: Catalog $2 (refundable) ■ Berry plants. 916–272–4769.

Pense Nursery, Rt. 2, Box 330–A, Mountainburg, AR 72946: Free information ■ Thornless blackberries, red and black raspberries, blueberries, boysenberries, elderberries, and seedless grapevines.

Rayner Brothers, Inc., P.O. Box 1617, Salisbury, MD 21801: Free catalog ■ Strawberry plants; raspberry, blueberry, and asparagus plants; and dwarf fruit tree and evergreen seedlings. 410–742–1594.

Savage Farms Nursery, P.O. Box 125, McMinnville, TN 37110: Free catalog ■ Berry plants, fruit trees, flowering trees and shrubs, shade trees, evergreens, and nursery and gardening supplies. 615–668–8902.

R.H. Shumway, Seedsman, P.O. Box 1, Graniteville, SC 29829: Catalog $1 ■ Berry plants, fruit trees, roses, seeds and bulbs, ornamental shrubs and plants, and gardening supplies. 803–663–9771.

Stark Bro's. Nurseries & Orchards Company, P.O. Box 10, Louisiana, MO 63353: Free catalog ■ Berry plants; fruit, nut and shade trees; and gardening supplies. 314–754–5511.

Thompson & Morgan, Inc., P.O. Box 1308, Jackson, NJ 08527: Free catalog ■ Strawberry plants and vegetable and flower seeds. 908–363–2225.

White Flower Farm, Rt. 63, Litchfield, CT 06759: Catalog $5 ■ Bulbs, perennials, shrubs, strawberry plants, other seeds and plants, books, tools, and gardening supplies. 800–888–7756.

Bonsai

Artistic Plants, P.O. Box 1165, Burleson, TX 76028: Catalog $1 ■ Bonsai, bonsai pots and tools, succulents, terrarium mixtures, and other supplies. 817–295–0802.

Bonsai Creations, P.O. Box 7511, Fort Lauderdale, FL 33338: Catalog $2.50 ■ Japanese pottery, trees, tools, stands, books, soils, and supplies. 305–463–8783.

Bonsai Farm, P.O. Box 130, Lavernia, TX 78121: Catalog $1 ■ Bonsai trees, indoor and outdoor bonsai plants, books, tools, and pots. 512–649–2109.

The Bonsai Gardener, 1909 Slaton Ct., Columbus, OH 43235: Catalog $1 (refundable) ■ Bonsai supplies. 614–764–9680.

Bonsai Master-Line, 1584 W. 182nd St., Gardena, CA 90248: Free catalog ■ Bonsai tools and supplies.

Bonsai of Brooklyn, 2433 McDonald Ave., Brooklyn, NY 11223: Free information ■ Potted and established bonsai, trained and semi-trained pre-bonsai stock, tools, books, pottery, and other supplies. 800–9–BONSAI; 718–339–8252 (in NY).

Bonsai of Georgia, David Cook, 4096 Clairmont Rd., Atlanta, GA 30341: Free information with long SASE ■ Bonsai supplies. 404–451–5356.

Bonsai Products, Jim Barrett, 480 Oxford Dr., Arcadia, CA 91006: Free information with long SASE ■ Bonsai supplies. 818–445–4529.

The Bonsai Shop, 43 William St., Smithtown, NY 11787: Free catalog ■ Finished bonsai, growing supplies, tools, and books. 516–724–3055.

Bonsai West, 100 Great Rd., P.O. Box 1291, Littleton, MA 01460: Free information with long SASE ■ Bonsai growing supplies, pots, tools, and books. 508–486–3556.

Brussel's Bonsai Nursery, 8365 Center Hill Rd., Olive Branch, MS 38654: Catalog $1 (refundable) ■ Bonsai, bonsai plants, pots, growing supplies. 601–895–7457.

The China Bonsai Company, 119 S. Jackson St., Seattle, WA 98104: Catalog $2 ■ Bonsai plants, pots, and books. 206–622–2858.

Coenosium Gardens, 6642 S. Lone Elder Rd., Aurora, OR 97002: Catalog $3 (refundable) ■ Conifers, dwarf conifers, Japanese maples, beeches, kalmias, and other bonsai plants. 503–266–5471.

Dallas Bonsai Garden, 5301 Beltline Rd., Dallas, TX 75240: Catalog 25¢ ■ Bonsai and supplies. 214–661–98021.

ETI-Electra Tech International, Inc., Imports Division, 2302 Parkside, Irving, TX 75061: Free information with long SASE ■ Bonsai containers from China. 214–986–0706.

Five Towns Bonsai, P.O. Box 461, Inwood, NY 11696: Free information ■ Genuine handcrafted rocks for bonsai. 718–868–0488.

Forestfarm, 990 Tetherow Rd., Williams, OR 97544: Catalog $3 ■ Plants, ornamental trees and shrubs, and perennials for use in bonsai. 503–846–6963.

Giacobbe's, 108 N. Main St., Mauldin, SC 29662: Free information with long SASE ■ Bonsai trees. 803–234–0274.

Girard Nurseries, P.O. Box 428, Geneva, OH 44041: Free catalog ■ Bonsai trees, ornamental trees and shrubs, and evergreen seeds and trees. 216–466–2881.

Greer Gardens, 1280 Goodpasture Island Rd., Eugene, OR 97401: Catalog $3 ■ Bonsai, azaleas and rhododendrons, trees and shrubs, Japanese maples, and succulents. 503–686–8266.

Hortica Gardens, P.O. Box 308, Placerville, CA 95667: Catalog 50¢ ■ Trees and shrubs, azalea hybrids, and other plants that can be trained for bonsai. 916–622–7089.

Jope's Bonsai, Box 594, Wenham, MA 01984: Catalog $1 (refundable) ■ Unusual dwarf plants, tools, pots, supplies, and books.

Maple Leaf Nursery, 4236 Greenstone Rd., Placerville, CA 95667: Catalog $1.50 ■ Bonsai training stock. 916–622–2265.

Marrs Tree Farm, 9802 52nd Ave., Payallup, WA 98373: Catalog $1 (refundable) ■ Bonsai plants. 206–848–4833.

Matsu-Momiji Nursery, P.O. Box 11414, Philadelphia, PA 19111: Catalog $2 ■ Japanese maple, black pine, and spruce trees for bonsai training and culture. 215–722–6286.

Miniature Plant Kingdom, 4125 Harrison Grade Rd., Sebastopol, CA 95472: Catalog $2.50 ■ Miniature roses and Japanese maples, conifers, and other plants for Bonsai. 707–874–2233.

Mountain Maples, 5901 Spyrock Rd., Laytonville, CA 95454: Catalog $1 ■ Japanese maples for bonsai.

New England Bonsai Gardens, 89 Pleasant St., South Natick, MA 01760: Free price list ■ Tropical, sub-tropical, and juniper bonsai in ceramic bonsai pots; pots and tools; and other supplies. 800–457–5445.

New Leaf Nursery, 800 Vine Maple Dr., Myrtle Creek, OR 97457: Free information ■ Rooted and foliage-pruned plants that are established in pots. 503–863–5767.

Panzai Enterprise, P.O. Box 1326, San Jose, CA 95109: Catalog $3 ■ Bonsai and supplies, bonsai pots, tools, and books. 408–374–7754.

Petals & Buds, 10798 County Rd. 3101, Winona, TX 75792: Catalog $2 ■ Blossoming apple tree, a replica of Japanese bonsai. 903–877–3724.

Pine Garden Pottery, 20331 SR 530 NE, Arlington, WA 98223: Free catalog ■ Stoneware bonsai containers. 206–435–5995.

Prime Material & Supply Corporation, P.O. Box 681685, Houston, TX 77268: Free information ■ Haydite aggregate selected and graded for bonsai. 713–353–1230.

Rakestraw's Gardens, 3094 S. Term St., Burton, MI 48529: Catalog $1 ■ Bonsai and perennials. 313–742–2685.

Shanti Bithi Nursery, 3047 High Ridge Rd., Stamford, CT 06903: Catalog $3 ■ Bonsai plants, growing supplies, tools, and pots. 203–329–0768.

Spring Hill Nurseries, 6523 N. Galena Rd., P.O. Box 1758, Peoria, IL 61656: Free catalog ■ Bonsai, perennials, roses, annuals, ground covers, small fruits, houseplants, other seeds and plants, and gardening supplies. 309–691–4616.

Tansu Woodworking, 321 Main St. West, Girard, PA 16417: Free brochure ■ Teak and cypress potting benches and bonsai containers, handcrafted Oriental furniture, and display stands for indoor and outdoor use. 814–286–3714.

Tru North Bonsai, 1154 Bank St., Ottawa, Ontario, Canada K1S 3X6: Free price list with long SASE ■ Pre-bonsai plants, imported pots and stands, and tools. 613–567–2610.

Waterstone, P.O. Box 671143, Houston, TX 77267: Free information ■ Bonsai wire in most sizes. 617–444–5911.

Wildwood Gardens, 14488 Rock Creek Rd., Chardon, OH 44024: Catalog 50¢ ■ Imported and domestic bonsai and pre-bonsai plants. 216–286–3714.

Woodview Gardens, HC 68, Box 405H, St. Francisville, LA 70775: Free catalog ■ Bonsai, pre-bonsai plants, pots, tools, and supplies. 504–635–4220.

Cacti & Succulents

Abbey Garden, 4620 Carpinteria Ave., Carpinteria, CA 93013: Catalog $2 ■ Cacti and succulents. 805–684–5112.

Apacha Cactus, 3441 Road B, Redwood Valley, CA 95470: Catalog 50¢ ■ Cacti for dish gardens. 707–485–7088.

Aztekakti/Desertland Nursery, 11306 Gateway East, P.O. Box 26126, El Paso, TX 79926: Free catalog with three 1st class stamps ■ Rare seeds for North and South American and Mexican cacti and succulents. 915–858–1130.

Betsy's Brierpatch, 1610 Ellis Hollow Rd., Ithaca, NY 14850: Free catalog with long SASE ■ Cacti, succulents, and foliage. 607–273–6266.

Cactus by Dodie, 934 E. Mettler Rd., Lodi, CA 95242: Catalog $1 (refundable) ■ Cacti and succulents. 209–368–3692.

Cactus by Mueller, 10411 Rosedale Hwy., Bakersfield, CA 93312: Catalog $1 (refundable) ■ Cacti and succulents. 805–589–2674.

Cactus Gem Nursery, 5485 White Dr., Batesville, AR 72501: Catalog $1 ■ Exotic cacti plants. 501–698–2011.

Cactus Patch, RR 2, Box 159, Radium, KS 67550: Free catalog with first class stamp ■ Winter-hardy cacti. 316–982–4670.

Cactus Unlimited, 21030 Gardena Dr., Cupertino, CA 95014: Catalog $1 ■ Cacti and succulents. 408–257–1047.

California Epi Center, P.O. Box 1431, Vista, CA 92083: Catalog $1 ■ Cacti. Includes flowering varieties. 714–758–4290.

Catalog of Unusual Succulents, 553 Buena Creek, San Marcos, CA 92069: Catalog $1 ■ Unusual succulents. 619–744–8191.

Christa's Cactus, 529 W. Pima, Coolidge, AZ 85228: Free catalog with 1st class stamp ■ Cacti and succulents, desert trees, and shrubs. 602–723–4185.

Desert Nursery, 1301 S. Copper, Deming, NM 88030: Free catalog with 1st class stamp ■ Cacti and succulents. 505–546–6264.

Desert Plant Company, P.O. Box 880, Marfa, TX 79843: Catalog $2 ■ Native-grown cacti. 915–729–4943.

Desert Theatre, 17 Behler Rd., Watsonville, CA 95076: Catalog $2 ■ Cacti and succulents. 408–728–5513.

Flechsig Cacti & Succulents, 619 Opheus Ave., Encinitas, CA 92024: Catalog $1 (refundable) ■ Nursery-grown cacti, aloes, cerepegias, and other succulents. 619–753–5942.

Garden World's Exotic Plants, 2503 Garfield St., Laredo, TX 78043: Catalog $1 ■ Cacti; bamboo, banana, and pineapple plants; and citrus trees. 512–724–3951.

Greenlife Gardens Greenhouse, 101 County Line Rd., Griffin, GA 30223: Catalog $2 ■ Succulents and cacti plants. 404–228–3669.

Grigsby Cactus Gardens, 2354 Bella Vista, Vista, CA 92084: Catalog $2 (refundable) ■ Rare cacti and succulents, sansevierias, and euphorbias. 619–727–1323.

Robert B. Hamm, 10065 River Mist Way, Rancho Cordova, CA 95670: Free catalog ■ Cacti and succulents, scented geraniums, and other plants. 206–435–9206.

Henrietta's Nursery, 1345 N. Brawley, Fresno, CA 93722: Catalog 50¢ ■ Cacti and succulents. 209–275–2166.

Intermountain Cactus, 2344 S. Redwood Rd., Salt Lake City, UT 84119: Free price list with long SASE ■ Winter-hardy cacti. 801–972–5149.

K & L Cactus/Succulent Nursery, 12712 Stockton Blvd., Galt, CA 95632: Catalog $2 (refundable) ■ Cacti and seeds. 209–745–4756.

Kimura International, 18435 Rea Ave., P.O. Box 327, Aromas, CA 95004: Free catalog ■ Cacti and succulents. 408–726–3223.

Lauray of Salisbury, Undermountain Rd., Salisbury, CT 06068: Catalog $2 ■ Cacti and succulents, begonias, gesneriads, and orchids. 203–435–2263.

Mesa Flora Nursery, Box 4159, Yucca Valley, CA 92284: Catalog $2 (refundable) ■ Seeds and plants for cacti and succulents. 619–364–2232.

Mesa Garden, Box 72, Belen, NM 87002: Free price list with two 1st class stamps ■ Cacti and succulent seeds and plants. 505–864–3131.

New Mexico Cactus Research, 1132 E. River Rd., P.O. Box 787, Belen, NM 87002: Free list with first-class stamp ■ Cacti, succulents, and other exotic plants. 505–864–4027.

The Plant Shop's Botanical Gardens, 18007 Topham St., Reseda, CA 91335: Catalog $3.50 (refundable) ■ Cacti and succulents, species orchids, begonias, bulbs, and other plants. 818–881–4831.

Rainbow Gardens, 1444 E. Taylor St., Vista, CA 92084: Catalog $2 (refundable) ■ Cacti, hoyas, and books on cacti. 619–758–4290.

Rocky Waters Farm, 4383 Pool Rd., Winston, GA 30187: Catalog $1 (refundable) ■ Cacti and succulent seedlings, root cuttings, and mature plants. 404–942–3114.

The Seed Shop, Tongue River Stage, Miles City, Montana 59301: Catalog $2 ■ Seeds for cacti and succulents.

Succulenta, P.O. Box 480325, Los Angeles, CA 90048: Price list $1 ■ Rare and unusual cacti and succulents. 213–933–8676.

Y.O. Ranch Cactus Company, P.O. Box 1443, Ingram, TX 78025: Free catalog ■ Rare and unusual plants from Texas, Mexico, South America, and South Africa. 512–367–5110.

Carnivorous Plants

Carolina Exotic Gardens, Rt. 5, Box 283-A, Greenville, NC 27834: Catalog $1 ■ Carnivorous plants and seeds and terrarium plant groupings. 919–758–2600.

Cedar Ridge Nurseries, Cedar Ridge Rd., Allison Park, PA 15101: Free catalog ■ Tropical pitcher plants. 412–443–6060.

Peter Pauls Nurseries, 4665 Chapin Rd., Canandaigua, NY 14424: Free catalog ■ Carnivorous and woodland terrarium plants. 716–394–7397.

World Insectivorous Plants, P.O. Box 70513, Marietta, GA 30007: Catalog 50¢ ■ Carnivorous plants. 404–973–1554.

Chrysanthemums

Dooley Mum Gardens, Rt. 1, Hutchinson, MN 55350: Free list ■ New and old varieties of chrysanthemums. 612–587–3050.

Huff's Gardens, P.O. Box 187, Burlington, KS 66839: Free catalog $1 ■ Chrysanthemums. 316–364–2933.

King's Chrysanthemums, P.O. Box 368, Clements, CA 94227: Catalog $1 ■ Chrysanthemum rooted cuttings. 209–759–3571.

Lamb Nurseries, 101 E. Sharp Ave., Spokane, WA 99202: Free catalog ■ Chrysanthemums, perennials, and rock garden plants. 509–328–7956.

Reno Nurseries, 2718 Washington, Dubuque, IA 52001: Free price list ■ New varieties of cushion chrysanthemums. 319–556–4503.

Thon's Garden Chrysanthemums, Oak St., Crystal Lake, IL 60014: Free catalog ■ Exhibition, football, and spider varieties of chrysanthemums. 815–923–4644.

Citrus & Exotic Fruits

Alberts & Merkel Brothers, Inc., 2210 S. Federal Hwy., Boynton Beach, FL 33435: Catalog $1 ■ Citrus and exotic fruits. 305–732–2071.

The Banana Tree, 715 Northampton St., Easton, PA 18042: Catalog $3 ■ Citrus and exotic fruits. 215–253–9589.

Burgess Seed & Plant Company, 905 Four Seasons Rd., Bloomington, IL 61701: Free catalog ■ Citrus and exotic fruits. 309–653–9551.

W. Atlee Burpee & Company, 300 Park Ave., Warminster, PA 18974: Free catalog ■ Exotic fruits. 215–674–1793.

Edible Landscaping, P.O. Box 77, Afton, VA 22920: Catalog 50¢ ■ Exotic fruits. 804–361–9134.

Exotica Rare Fruit Nursery, P.O. Box 160, Vista, CA 92083: Catalog $2 ■ Tropical fruit, nut, palm, and other trees. 619–724–9093.

Henry Field's Seed & Nursery, 415 N. Burnett, P.O. Box 700, Shenandoah, IA 51602: Free catalog ■ Exotic fruits. 605–665–9391.

Fig Tree Nursery, P.O. Box 124, Gulf Hammock, FL 32639: Catalog $1 ■ Exotic fruits. 904–486–2930.

Garden of Delights, 2018 Mayo St., Hollywood, FL 33020: Catalog $2 (refundable) ■ Tropical fruits and nuts. 305–923–2087.

Garden World's Exotic Plants, 2503 Garfield St., Laredo, TX 78043: Catalog $1 ■ Exotic fruits. 512–724–3951.

Glasshouse Works, 10 Church St., Box 97, Stewart, OH 45778: Catalog $1.50 (refundable) ■ Citrus and exotic fruits. 614–662–2142.

Gurney Seed & Nursery Company, 110 Capitol St., Yankton, SD 57079: Free catalog ■ Citrus and exotic fruits. 605–665–1930.

House of Wesley, 2200 E. Oakland, Bloomington, IL 61701: Free catalog ■ Citrus and exotic fruits. 309–663–9551.

Kartuz Greenhouses, 1408 Sunset Dr., Vista, CA 92083: Catalog $2 ■ Citrus and exotic fruits. 619–941–3613.

Logee's Greenhouses, 141 North St., Danielson, CT 06239: Catalog $3 (refundable) ■ Citrus and exotic fruits. 203–774–8038.

Mellinger's, Inc., 2310 W. South Range Rd., North Lima, OH 44452: Free catalog ■ Citrus and exotic fruits. 216–549–9861.

Northwoods Nursery, 28696 S. Cramer Rd., Molalla, OR 97038: Free catalog ■ Citrus and exotic fruits. 503–651–3737.

Oregon Exotica Nursery, 1065 Messinger Rd., Grants Pass, OR 97527: Free catalog ■ Subtropical fruit trees.

Richard Owen Nursery, 2300 E. Lincoln St., Bloomington, IL 61701: Catalog $1 ■ Citrus and exotic fruits. 309–663–9551.

Pacific Tree Farms, 4301 Lynnwood Dr., Chula Vista, CA 92010: Catalog $2 ■ Citrus and exotic fruits. 619–422–2400.

Peaceful Valley Farm Supply, P.O. Box 2209, Grass Valley, CA 95945: Catalog $2 (refundable) ■ Citrus fruits. 916–272–4769.

Raintree Nursery, 391 Butts Rd., Morton, WA 98356: Free information ■ Citrus and exotic fruits. 206–496–6400.

South Seas Nursery, P.O. Box 4974, Ventura, CA 93007: Free information with long SASE ■ Guavas, feijoas, sapotes, cherimoyas, and other tropical and subtropical fruit trees. 805–647–2262.

Tripple Brook Farm, 37 Middle Rd., Southampton, MA 01073: Free catalog ■ Bamboo plants, exotic fruits, trees, perennials, and shrubs. 413–527–4626.

Van Bourgondien Bros., 245 Farmingdale Rd., Rt. 109, P.O. Box A, Babylon, NY 11702: Free catalog ■ Citrus and exotic fruits. 800–873–9444.

Daffodils

Bonnie Brae Gardens, 1105 SE Christensen Rd., Corbett, OR 97019: Free catalog ■ Novelty daffodils that include some show varieties. 503–695–5190.

Cascade Daffodils, 1790 Richard Cir., West St. Paul, MN 55118: Free catalog ■ Standard, miniature, and show varieties of daffodils. 612–455–6177.

Cooper's Garden, 212 W. County Rd. C, Roseville, MN 55113: Free catalog ■ Species daffodils, Siberian and Louisiana irises, daylilies, perennials, and wildflowers. 501–347–2026.

The Daffodil Mart, Rt. 3, Box 794, Gloucester, VA 23061: Catalog $1 (refundable) ■ Novelty, miniature, hybridized, and species daffodils. 804–693–3966.

Hatfield Gardens, 22799 Ringgold Southern Rd., Stoutsville, OH 43154: Catalog $2 ■ Daffodils, daylilies, bearded irises, hostas, ornamental grasses, and perennials. 614–474–5719.

Grant Mitsch Novelty Daffodils, P.O. Box 218, Hubbard, OR 97032: Catalog $3 (refundable) ■ Exhibition and garden varieties of pink and hybrid daffodils. 503–651–2742.

Oregon Trail Daffodils, 3207 SE Mannthey Rd., Corbett, OR 97019: Free catalog ■ New and novelty daffodils. 503–695–5513.

Quality Dutch Bulbs, 50 Lake Dr., P.O. Box 225, Hillsdale, NJ 07642: Free catalog ■ Daffodils, irises, tulips, and other ornamental bulbs. 201–391–6586.

Dahlias

Alpen Gardens, 173 Lawrence Ln., Kalispell, MT 59901: Free price list ■ Dahlias. Includes competition winners. 406–257–2540.

Bedford Dahlias, 65 Leyton Rd., Bedford, OH 44146: Free catalog with first class stamp ■ Dahlias. 216–232–2852.

Blue Dahlia Gardens, P.O. Box 316, San Jose, IL 62682: Free catalog ■ Dahlias. 309–247–3210.

Cornellis, 10216 40th Ave. East, Tacoma, WA 98446: Catalog $2 (refundable) ■ Dahlias from worldwide sources.

Dahlias by Phil Traff, 10717 Orting Hwy. East, Puyallup, WA 98373: Free catalog ■ Prize winning dahlias. 206–863–0542.

Evergreen Acres Dahlia Gardens, 682 Pulaski Rd., Greenlawn, NY 11740: Catalog 50¢ ■ Established dahlia cultivars and new introductions from the United States, England, Canada, Japan, and New Zealand. 516–261–1024.

Garden Valley Dahlias, 406 Lower Garden Rd., Roseburg, OR 97470: Free price list with 1st class stamp ■ Dahlias. 503–673–2426.

Kordonowy's Dahlias, P.O. Box 568, Kalama, WA 98625: Free catalog ■ Dahlias. 206–673–2426.

Lamson's Dahlias, Rt. 4, P.O. Box 4275, Selah, WA 98942: Free catalog with two 1st class stamps ■ Dahlias. 509–697–8552.

Shackleton's Dahlias, 30535 Division Dr., Troutdale, OR 97060: Free catalog with 1st class stamp ■ New dahlia varieties. 503–663–7057.

Swan Island Dahlias, P.O. Box 700, Canby, OR 97013: Catalog $3 ■ Dahlias. 503–266–7711.

Ferns

Kurt Bluemel, Inc., 2740 Greene Ln., Baldwin, MD 21013: Catalog $2 ■ Ferns, perennials, bamboo plants, and ornamental grasses. 410–557–7229.

Busse Gardens, Rt. 2, Box 238, Cokato, MN 55321: Catalog $2 (refundable) ■ Siberian irises, ferns, and other seeds and plants. 612–286–2654.

Conley's Garden Center, Boothbay Harbor, ME 04538: Catalog $1.50 ■ Hardy wildflowers and seeds, ferns, native perennials, bulbs, orchids, and ground covers. 207–633–5020.

Crownsville Nursery, P.O. Box 797, Crownsville, MD 21032: Catalog $2 (refundable) ■ Ferns, wildflowers, azaleas, ornamental grasses, and other perennials. 410–923–2212.

Gardens of the Blue Ridge, P.O. Box 10, Pineola, NC 28662: Catalog $2 ■

Wildflower seeds, ferns, trees, plants, shrubs, and bulbs. 704–733–2417.

Russell Graham Plants, 4030 Eagle Crest Rd. NW, Salem, OR 97304: Catalog $2 (refundable) ■ Ferns, ornamental grasses, lily bulbs, irises, daffodils, and other plants. 503–362–1135.

Griffey's Nursery, 16870 Hwy. 25–70, Marshall, NC 28753: Free catalog ■ Appalachian wildflowers, ferns and vines, rock and bog plants, and orchards. 704–656–2334.

Holiday Seeds, 4276 Durham Cir., Stone Mountain, GA 30083: Catalog $1 ■ Hosta plants and cultivars, ferns, irises, lilies, and daylilies. 404–294–6594.

Jerry Horne, 10195 SW 70th St., Miami, FL 33173: Free list with long SASE ■ Aroids, bromeliads, cycads, ferns, and palms. 305–270–1235.

Lamb Nurseries, 101 E. Sharp Ave., Spokane, WA 99202: Free catalog ■ Perennials, ferns, other plants, and shrubs. 509–328–7956.

Oakridge Nursery, P.O. Box 182, East Kingdom, NH 03872: Catalog $1 ■ Ferns and wildflowers. 603–642–8227.

Orchid Gardens, 2232 139th Ave. NW, Andover, MN 55304: Catalog 50¢ ■ Ferns and wildflowers. 612–755–0205.

Rice Creek Gardens, 1315 66th Ave. NE, Minneapolis, MN 55432: Catalog $2 ■ Ferns, vines, ornamental shrubs, and rock garden plants and supplies. 612–574–1197.

Geraniums

Cook's Geranium Nursery, 712 N. Grand, Lyons, KS 67554: Catalog $1 (refundable) ■ New, old, and unusual geraniums. 316–257–5033.

Dabney Herbs, P.O. Box 22061, Louisville, KY 40222: Catalog $2 ■ Ginseng, herbs, scented geraniums, perennials, and wildflowers. 502–893–5198.

Davidson-Wilson Greenhouses, Rt. 2, Box 168, Crawfordsville, IN 47933: Catalog $1 ■ African violets, geraniums, and other houseplants. 317–364–0556.

Fox Hill Farm, 444 W. Michigan Ave., Box 9, Parma, MI 49269: Catalog $1 ■ Easy-to-grow geraniums. 517–531–3179.

Good Hollow Greenhouse & Herbarium, Rt. 1, Box 116, Taft, TN 38488: Catalog $1

■ Herbs, perennials, wildflowers, scented geraniums, essential oils and potpourris, teas, and dried herbs and spices. 615–433–7640.

Robert B. Hamm, 10065 River Mist Way, Rancho Cordova, CA 95670: Free catalog ■ Cacti and succulents, scented geraniums, and other plants. 206–435–9206.

Happy Hollow Nursery, 221 Happy Hollow Rd., Villa Rica, GA 30180: Catalog $1 (refundable) ■ Scented geraniums and herb plants. 404–459–4144.

Holbrook Farm & Nursery, Rt. 2, Box 223–B, Fletcher, NC 28732: Catalog $2 ■ Geraniums, native wildflowers, trees and shrubs, garden perennials, and hostas. 704–891–7790.

Lake Odessa Greenhouse, 1123 Jordan Lake St., Lake Odessa, MI 48849: Free price list ■ Scented geraniums. 616–374–8848.

Lily of the Valley Herb Farm, 3969 Fox Ave., Minerva, OH 44657: Catalog $2 ■ Herbs, everlasting, perennial, scented geranium plants, and herbal products. 216–862–3920.

Rasland Farm, N.C. 82 at US 13, Godwin, NC 28344: Catalog $2.50 ■ Herb plants, scented geraniums, and dried flowers. 919–567–2705.

Sandy Mush Herb Nursery, Surret Cove, Rt. 2, Leicester, NC 28748: Catalog $2 (refundable) ■ Geraniums. 704–683–2014.

Shady Hill Gardens, 821 Walnut St., Batavia, IL 60510: Catalog $2 (refundable) ■ Over 800 varieties of geraniums. 708–879–5665.

Sunnybrook Farms Nursery, 9448 Mayfield Rd., Chesterland, OH 44026: Catalog $1 (refundable) ■ Geraniums, herb plants, ivies, and houseplants. 216–729–7232.

Well-Sweep Herb Farm, 317 Mt. Bethel Rd., Port Murray, NJ 07865: Catalog $2 ■ Geraniums. 908–852–5390.

Wilson Plant Sales, 202 S. Indiana St., Roachdale, IN 46172: Free catalog ■ Geraniums, African violets, and exotic houseplants. 317–522–1320.

Young's Mesa Nursery, 2755 Fowler Ln., Arroyo Grande, CA 93420: Catalog $2 (refundable) ■ Miniature geraniums and other regular-size plants. 805–489–0548.

Ginseng

American Ginseng Gardens, Box 440, Flag Pond, TN 37657: Catalog $1 ■ Ginseng seedlings and growing information. 615–743–3700.

William H. Collins Gardens, Box 48, Viola, IA 52350: Free information ■ Seed roots for growing ginseng.

Dabney Herbs, P.O. Box 22061, Louisville, KY 40222: Catalog $2 ■ Ginseng, herbs, scented geraniums, perennials, and wildflowers. 502–893–5198.

HSU's Ginseng Enterprises, Inc., P.O. Box 509, Wausau, WI 54402: Free information ■ American and Canadian stratified ginseng seed, planting rootlets, American ginseng health products and extracts, ginseng novelties, Chinese gift hand soaps, and books. 800–826–1577; 715–675–2325 (in WI).

Wilcox Drug Company, Inc., P.O. Box 391, Boone, NC 28607: Free information ■ Ginseng. 704–264–3615.

Gladioli

Gladside Gladiolus, 61 Main St., Northfield, MA 01360: Catalog $1 ■ New gladioli and older cultivars.

Kingfisher Glads, 11734 Road 33–1/2, Madera, CA 93638: Free catalog ■ New gladioli and older cultivars.

Mellinger's, Inc., 2310 W. South Range Rd., North Lima, OH 44452: Free catalog ■ Gladioli, fruit and nut trees, shade and ornamental trees, flowering shrubs, hedges, irises, wildflowers, and gardening equipment. 216–549–9861.

Noweta Gardens, 900 Whitewater Ave., St. Charles, MN 55972: Free catalog ■ New gladioli and older cultivars.

Skolaski's Glads, 4821 Trunk Hwy. Q, Waunakee, WI: Catalog $1 ■ New gladioli and older cultivars.

Squire's Bulb Farm, 3419 Eccles Ave., Ogden, UT 84403: Free catalog ■ New gladioli and older cultivars.

Alex Summerville, RD 1, Box 449, Glassboro, NJ 08028: Free catalog ■ Gladioli. 609–881–0704.

Waushara Gardens, Rt. 2, Box 570, Plainfield, WI 54966: Catalog $1 ■ Gladioli. 715–335–4462.

Gourds

H. Bankhead Gourds, Rt. 2, Box 60, Roscoe, TX 79545: Free information with long SASE ■ Seeds for large luffa gourds.

Roy Bell Gourd Seed, Rt. 2, Box 195, Linden, TN 37096: Free information with long SASE ■ Gourd seed mixtures.

Lena Braswell Gourds, Rt. 1, Box 73, Wrens, GA 30833: Free information with long SASE ■ Gourds. 404–547–6784.

Edmond O. Brown, Rt. 1, Box 135, Reeds, MO 64859: Free information with long SASE ■ Big dipper gourd seeds.

Linda Fisher Gourds, Rt. 1, Box 282, Nashville, NC 27856: Free price list with long SASE ■ Seeds for growing gourds. 919–443–0715.

The Gourd Factory, P.O. Box 55311, Stockton, CA 95205: Free information with long SASE ■ Dried gourds. 209–943–5852.

Fred & Clarita Hayes Gourds, Rt. 8, Box 828, Gilmer, TX 75644: Free information with long SASE ■ Gourds for crafting. 903–734–5204.

J.L. Hudson, Seedsman, Box 1058, Redwood City, CA 94064: Catalog $1 ■ Gourd seeds.

O.V. Maynor, Rt. 2, Box 424, Pisgah, AL 35765: Free information with long SASE ■ Luff and long handle dipper gourd seed.

Nichols Garden Nursery, 1190 N. Pacific Hwy., Albany, OR 97321: Free catalog ■ Gourd seeds. 503–928–9280.

The Pumpkin Farm & Gourd Place, 101 Creston Rd., Paso Robles, CA 93446: Free information with long SASE ■ Gourds for crafting. 805–238–0624.

James Stephens Gourds, 501 Lee St., Attalia, AL 35954: Free information with long SASE ■ Dried gourds for crafting. 205–538–7030.

William Swirin, 3 Henderson Ct., Greensboro, NC 27410: Free information with long SASE ■ Seed for birdhouse bushel basket gourds. 919–854–4227.

Frank Wheeler Gourds, 8285 Johnstown-Utica Rd., Johnstown, OH 43031: Free information with long SASE ■ Basketball, cannon ball, and martin house gourd seeds.

Grapes

Ahrens Strawberry Nursery, Rt. 1, Huntingburg, IN 47542: Free booklet ■ Grapevines, strawberries, other berry plants, fruit trees, rhubarb plants, and currants. 612–683–3055.

Bountiful Ridge Nurseries, Inc., P.O. Box 250, Princess Anne, MD 21853: Free catalog ■ Berry plants, fruit and nut trees, and grapevines. 410–651–0400.

Boordy Nursery, Box 38, Riderwood, MD 21139: Catalog 50¢ ■ Wine grapes.

California Nursery Company, P.O. Box 2278, Fremont, CA 94536: Free information ■ Table and wine grapevines grapes and fruit and nut trees. 510–797–3311.

Fig Tree Nursery, P.O. Box 124, Gulf Hammock, FL 32639: Catalog $1 ■ Berry plants, ornamentals, and grapevines for southern climates. 904–486–2930.

Ison's Nursery, Rt. 1, Brooks, GA 30205: Free catalog ■ Muscadine grapevines, berries, and fruit and nut trees. 800–733–0324.

Lon's Oregon Grapes, P.O. Box 7632, Salem, OR 97303: Free catalog with long SASE ■ Grapevines. 503–393–5165.

Earl May Seeds & Nursery Company, N. Elm St., Shenandoah, IA 51603: Free catalog ■ Grapevines, berry plants, fruit and nut trees, roses, shade and ornamental trees, flowering shrubs, and gardening aids. 712–246–1020.

J.E. Miller Nurseries, Inc., 5060 West Lake Rd., Canandaigua, NY 14424: Free catalog ■ Grapevines, berry plants, and fruit trees. 716–396–2647.

W.K. Morse & Son, Rt. 2, Boxford, MA 01921: Free brochure ■ Grapevines and strawberry and raspberry plants. 617–352–2633.

Patrick's Nursery, P.O. Box 1300, Ty Ty, GA 31795: Free catalog ■ Grapevines, vegetable seeds, berry plants, and fruit and nut trees. 912–386–1919.

Grasses & Ground Covers

Kurt Bluemel, Inc., 2740 Greene Ln., Baldwin, MD 21013: Catalog $1 ■ Ornamental grasses, water garden plants, and perennials. 410–557–7229.

Bluestone Perennials, 7269 Middle Ridge Rd., Madison, OH 44057: Free catalog ■ Groundcovers. 800–852–5243.

W. Atlee Burpee & Company, 300 Park Ave., Warminster, PA 18974: Free catalog ■ Ornamental grasses. 215–674–1793.

Classic Groundcovers, Inc., 405 Belmont Rd., Athens, GA 30605: Free catalog ■ Groundcovers. 800–248–8424; 404–543–0145 (in GA).

Conley's Garden Center, Boothbay Harbor, ME 04538: Catalog $1.50 (refundable) ■ Groundcovers, wildflowers, ferns, and vines. 207–633–5020.

Country Gardens, Rt. 2, Box 455A, Crivitz, WI 54114: Catalog $1 ■ Ornamental grasses. 715–757–2045.

Crownsville Nursery, P.O. Box 797, Crownsville, MD 21032: Catalog $2 (refundable) ■ Ferns, wildflowers, azaleas, ornamental grasses, and perennials. 410–923–2212.

Evergreen Nursery, 1220 Dowdy Rd., Athens, GA 30606: Free information ■ Bare root and potted ground covers. 800–521–7267; 404–548–7781 (in GA).

Gilson Gardens, P.O. Box 277, US Rt. 20, Perry, OH 44081: Free catalog ■ Ground covers.

Russell Graham Plants, 4030 Eagle Crest Rd. NW, Salem, OR 97304: Catalog $2 (refundable) ■ Ferns, ornamental grasses, lily bulbs, irises, daffodils, and other plants. 503–362–1135.

Greenlee Nursery, 301 E. Franklin Ave., Pomona, CA 91766: Free catalog ■ Ornamental grasses. 904–795–3785.

Hatfield Gardens, 22799 Ringgold Southern Rd., Stoutsville, OH 43154: Catalog $2 ■ Daffodils, daylilies, bearded irises, hostas, ornamental grasses, and perennials. 614–474–5719.

Heritage Gardens, 1 Meadow Ridge Rd., Shenandoah, IA 51601: Free catalog ■ Ornamental grasses, perennials, foliage plants, hostas, shade garden plants, ferns, lilies, rock garden plants, shrubs, azaleas and rhododendrons, roses, and flowering trees. 605–665–5188.

Horizon Seeds, Inc., P.O. Box 886, Hereford, TX 79045: Free catalog ■ Seeds for prairie grasses. 806–258–7280.

Joyce's Garden, 64640 Old Bend Redmond Hwy., Bend, OR 97701: Catalog $2 ■ Groundcovers. 503–388–4680.

Maryland Aquatic Nurseries, 3427 N. Furnace Rd., Jarrettsville, MD 21084: Catalog $2 ■ Plants for water gardens, ornamental grasses, and Louisiana and Japanese irises. 410–557–7615.

Park Seed Company, Inc., Cokesbury Rd., P.O. Box 46, Greenwood, SC 29648: Free catalog ■ Ornamental grasses. 803–223–7333.

Perry's, P.O. Box 442, Carpinteria, CA 93013: Catalog $3 ■ Groundcovers. 805–684–5468.

Plants of the Southwest, Rt. 6, Box 11A, Santa Fe, NM 87501: Catalog $1 ■ Native grasses, wildflowers, trees and shrubs, and other plants for the southwest. 505–983–1548.

Prairie State Commodities, P.O. Box 6, Trilla, IL 62469: Catalog 50¢ ■ Seeds for annual varieties, perennial rye grass, redtop, and Park Kentucky bluegrass; corn; and clover and alfalfa. 217–235–4322.

Prentiss Court Ground Covers, P.O. Box 8662, Greenville, SC 29604: Catalog 25¢ ■ Groundcovers. 803–277–4037.

Rocknoll Nursery, 7812 Mad River Rd., Hillsboro, OH 45133: Free catalog with two 1st class stamps ■ Groundcovers, rock garden plants, wildflowers, perennials, dwarf evergreens, flowering shrubs, and ivies. 513–393–1278.

Stock Seed Farms, Rt. 1, P.O. Box 112, Murdock, NE 68407: Free catalog ■ Seed for grasses and native wildflowers. 402–867–3771.

Thompson & Morgan, Inc., P.O. Box 1308, Jackson, NJ 08527: Free catalog ■ Ornamental grasses. 908–363–2225.

Van Hise Nursery, 30688 SE Waybill Rd., Boring, OR 97009: Free information ■ Ground covers, perennials, and shrubs. 503–663–6123.

Herbs

ABC Nursery & Greenhouse, Rt. 1, Box 313, Lecoma, MO 65540: Free price list with 1st class stamp ■ Herb plants. 314–435–6389.

Aphrodesia Products, 228 Bleeker St., New York, NY 10014: Catalog $3 ■ Dried herbs, herb products, and books. 800–221–6898; 212–989–6440 (in NY).

Bears, Herbs, Hearts & Flowers, 81 E. Raymond-Willapa Rd., Raymond, WA 98577: Catalog $2 ■ Fragrant herbs. 206–942–2122.

Capriland's Herb Farm, 534 Silver St., Coventry, CT 06238: Free catalog with long SASE ■ Plants, seeds, books, potpourris, wreaths, and other herb products. 203–742–7244.

Casa Yerba Gardens, 3459 Days Creek Rd., Days Creek, OR 97429: Catalog $1 (refundable) ■ Seeds for rare and unusual herbs. 503–825–3534.

Caswell-Massey Company, Ltd., Catalog Division, 100 Enterprise Place, Dover, DE 19901: Free catalog ■ Herb products. 800–326–0500.

Catnip Acres Herb Nursery, 67 Christian St., Oxford, CT 06483: Catalog $2 ■ Herb plants and scented geraniums. 203–888–5649.

Companion Plants, 7247 N. Coolville Ridge, Athens, OH 45701: Catalog $2 ■ Seeds for exotic and other herb and native plants. 614–592–4643.

Comstock, Ferre & Company, 236 Main St., P.O. Box 125, Wethersfield, CT 06109: Catalog $2 ■ Vegetable, flower, and herb seeds. 203–529–3319.

Dabney Herbs, P.O. Box 22061, Louisville, KY 40222: Catalog $2 ■ Ginseng, herbs, scented geraniums, perennials, and wildflowers. 502–893–5198.

T. DeBaggio Herbs, 923 N. Ivy St., Arlington, VA 22201: Catalog $1 ■ Herbs. 703–243–2498.

Dutch Mill Herb Farm, Rt. 2, Box 190, Forest Grove, OR 97116: Free catalog with long SASE ■ Herbs. 503–357–0924.

Earthstar Herb Gardens, 438 W. Perkinsville Rd., Chino Valley, AZ 86323: Catalog $1 (refundable) ■ Organically grown herb plants, dried flowers, scented geraniums, and garlic. 602–636–2565.

Flowery Branch, P.O. Box 1330, Flowery Branch, GA 30542: Catalog $2 ■ Rare and exotic herb seeds.

Fox Hill Farm, 440 W. Michigan Ave., Box 9, Parma, MI 49269: Catalog $1 ■ Container-grown herb plants that include culinary, medicinals, fragrants, everlastings, and others. 517–531–3179.

Garden-Ville, 6266 Hwy. 290 West, Austin, TX 78735: Free catalog ■ Herbs and gardening supplies. 512–892–0002.

The Gathered Herb & Greenhouse, 12114 N. State Rd., Otisville, MI 48463: Catalog $2 ■ Herbs, herb teas, perennials, dried flowers, and potpourri supplies. 313–631–6572.

Good Hollow Greenhouse & Herbarium, Rt. 1, Box 116, Taft, TN 38488: Catalog $1 ■ Herbs, perennials, wildflowers, scented geraniums, essential oils, potpourris, teas, and dried herbs and spices. 615–433–7640.

Goodwin Creek Gardens, P.O. Box 83, Williams, OR 97544: Catalog $1 ■ Dried floral arrangements, herb plants, container-grown native American trees and shrubs, and perennial flowers. 503–846–7357.

Greenfield Herb Garden, Depot & Harrison, P.O. Box 437, Shipshewana, IN 46565: Catalog $1.50 ■ Herb books and herb plants. 219–768–7110.

Halcyon Herbs, P.O. Box 75, Wexford, PA 15090: Catalog $1 ■ Herb seeds.

Happy Hollow Nursery, 221 Happy Hollow Rd., Villa Rica, GA 30180: Catalog $1 (refundable) ■ Scented geraniums and herb plants. 404–459–4144.

Hartman's Herb Farm, Old Dana Rd., Barre, MA 01005: Catalog $1 ■ Herbs and herb products, potpourris, essential oils, and wreaths. 508–355–2015.

The Herbfarm, 32804 Issaquah-Fall City Rd., Fall City, WA 98024: Free catalog ■ Herb plants, herb seed, and unique herbal items. 206–886–HERB.

Herb Place, 120 Anita Dr., Monroe, LA 71202: Catalog 50¢ ■ Scented geraniums, potpourri, and fresh-cut herb plants. 318–322–3527.

The Herb Shop, 111 Azalea, Duenweg, MO 64841: Free information ■ Bulk herbs and spices, tea blends, potpourris, and soaps and sundries. 417–782–0457.

Hummingbird Hills Herbal Nursery, 17201 S. Hawkinds, Ashland, MO 65010: Catalog $1 ■ Organically grown herbs, perennials, everlastings, and dried flowers. 314–657–2082.

Indiana Botanic Gardens, P.O. Box 5, Hammond, IN 46325: Catalog $1 ■ Herbs, essential oils, and herb seeds. 800–348–6434; 219–931–2480 (in IN).

Le Jardin du Gourmet, P.O. Box 75, St. Johnsbury Center, VT 05863: Catalog $1 ■ Herb plants and seeds and vegetable seeds.

Lily of the Valley Herb Farm, 3969 Fox Ave., Minerva, OH 44657: Catalog $2 ■ Herb plants, everlastings, perennials, scented geraniums, and herbal products. 216–862–3920.

Lost Prairie Herb Farm, 805 Kienas Rd., Kalispell, MT 59901: Catalog $1 ■ Herb plants. 406–756–7741.

Meadowbrook Herb Gardens, Rt. 138, Wyoming, RI 02898: Catalog $1 ■ Herb seeds. 401–539–7603.

Meadowsweet Herb Farm, 729 Mount Holly Rd., Shrewsbury, VT 05738: Catalog $1 ■ Kitchen, medicinal, household, wedding, potpourris, and ornamental herbs; seeds for windowsill herbs; dried flowers; and scented basils. 802–492–3565.

Nichols Garden Nursery, 1190 Pacific West, Albany, OR 97321: Free catalog ■ Seeds, plants, and miscellaneous herb products. 503–928–9280.

Planta Dei Medicinal Herb Farm, Millville, New Brunswick, Canada E0H 1M0: Catalog $2 (refundable) ■ Biologically grown teas, medicinal herbs, healing tea mixtures, cosmetics, natural ointments, and massage oils. 506–463–8169.

Rasland Farm, N.C. 82 at U.S. 13, Godwin, NC 28344: Catalog $2.50 ■ Herb plants, scented geraniums, dried flowers, and herbal products. 919–567–2705.

Redwood City Seed Company, P.O. Box 361, Redwood City, CA 94064: Catalog $1 ■ Herb and vegetable seeds from worldwide sources. 415–325–7333.

The Rosemary House, 120 S. Market St., Mechanicsburg, PA 17055: Catalog $2 ■ Plants, seeds, herb products, and books. 717–697–5111.

Sandy Mush Herb Nursery, Surret Cove, Rt. 2, Leicester, NC 28748: Catalog $4 (refundable) ■ Herbs and plants. Includes culinary and tea herbs, other herbs, scented geraniums, and flowering perennials. 704–683–2014.

Sunnybrook Farms Nursery, 9448 Mayfield Rd., Chesterland, OH 44026: Catalog $1 (refundable) ■ Herb plants, ivies, scented geraniums, other seeds, and herbal products. 216–729–7232.

Taylor's Herb Gardens, Inc., 1535 Lone Oak Rd., Vista, CA 92084: Catalog $3 ■ Herb plants and seeds. 619–727–3485.

Tinmouth Channel Farm, Box 428B, Tinmouth, VT 05773: Catalog $1 ■ Vermont certified organic plants and seeds. 802–446–2812.

The Ultimate Herb & Spice Shoppe, 111 Azalea, P.O. Box 395, Duenweg, MO 64841: Catalog $2 ■ Herbs and spices, tea blends, potpourris, soaps, and sundries. 417–782–0457.

Well-Sweep Herb Farm, 317 Mt. Bethel Rd., Port Murray, NJ 07865: Catalog $2 ■ Seeds for herbs, plants, and perennials. 908–852–5390.

Wrenwood of Berkeley Springs, Rt. 4., Box 361, Berkeley Springs, WV 25411: Catalog $1.50 ■ Herbs and perennials. 304–258–3071.

Hostas

American Daylily & Perennials, P.O. Box 210, Grain Valley, MO 64029: Catalog $3 ■ Hostas, dwarf cannas, and daylilies. 816–224–2852.

Carroll Gardens, P.O. Box 310, Westminster, MD 21158: Catalog $2 (refundable) ■ Hostas plants and cultivars. 410–876–7336.

Coastal Gardens & Nursery, 4611 Socastee Blvd., Myrtle Beach, SC 29575: Catalog $2 (refundable) ■ Hostas, Siberian and Japanese irises, daylilies, ground covers, perennials, woodland and bog plants, and aquatic plants. 803–293–2000.

Crownsville Nursery, P.O. Box 797, Crownsville, MD 21032: Catalog $2 (refundable) ■ Hosta plants and cultivars. 410–849–2212.

Donnelly's Nursery, Rt. 7, Box 420, Fairview, NC 28730: Free catalog ■ Hostas. 704–298–0851.

Hatfield Gardens, 22799 Ringgold Southern Rd., Stoutsville, OH 43154: Catalog $2 ■ Daffodils, daylilies, bearded irises, hostas, ornamental grasses, and perennials. 614–474–5719.

Holbrook Farm & Nursery, Rt. 2, Box 223–B, Fletcher, NC 28732: Catalog $2 ■ Geraniums, native wildflowers, trees and shrubs, perennials, and hostas. 704–891–7790.

Holiday Seeds, 4276 Durham Cir., Stone Mountain, GA 30083: Catalog $1 ■ Hosta plants and cultivars, ferns, irises, lilies, and daylilies. 404–294–6594.

Homestead Division of Sunnybrook Farms, 9448 Mayfield Rd., Chesterland, OH 44026: Catalog $1 ■ Hosta plants and cultivars. 216–729–9838.

Klehm Nursery, Rt. 5, Box 197, South Barrington, IL 60010: Catalog $2 (refundable) ■ Hosta plants and cultivars. 800–551–3336.

Rocknoll Nursery, 7812 Mad River Rd., Hillsboro, OH 45133: Free catalog with two 1st class stamps ■ Hosta plants and cultivars, perennials, ivies, dwarf plants, and groundcovers. 513–393–1278.

Andre Viette Nurseries, Rt. 1, Box 16, Fisherville, VA 22929: Catalog $2 ■ Hostas plants and cultivars. 703–943–2315.

Wayside Gardens, 1 Garden Ln., Hodges, SC 29695: Catalog $1 ■ Hosta plants and cultivars. 800–845–1124.

Houseplants

Davidson-Wilson Greenhouses, Rt. 2, Box 168, Crawfordsville, IN 47933: Free catalog ■ Exotic houseplants. 317–364–0556.

Gardener's Choice, Country Rd. 687, P.O. Box 8000, Hartford, MI 49057: Catalog $1 ■ Houseplants, vegetables, flowers, and trees. 616–621–2481.

Lauray of Salisbury, Undermountain Rd., Rt. 41, Salisbury, CT 06068: Catalog $2 ■ Begonias, orchids, cacti, and succulents. 203–435–2263.

Logee's Greenhouses, 141 North St., Danielson, CT 06239: Catalog $3 (refundable) ■ Begonias, geraniums, exotics, herbs, and other houseplants. 203–774–8038.

Lyndon Lyon Greenhouses, Inc., 14 Mutchler St., Dolgeville, NY 13329: Catalog $1 ■ African violets and exotic houseplants. 315–429–8291.

Merry Gardens, Mechanic St., P.O. Box 595, Camden, ME 04843: Catalog $2 ■ Houseplants. Flowering plants, herbs, ivies, gesneriads, ferns and mosses, impatiens, and geraniums. 207–236–9064.

Plant Kingdom, Box 7273, Lincoln Acres, CA 92047: Catalog $1 ■ Gesneriads, begonias, miniature plants, dwarf plants, exotics, and other houseplants. 619–267–1991.

Rhapis Palm Growers, 31350 Alta Vista, P.O. Box 84, Redlands, CA 92373: Catalog $2 ■ Rhapis palms. 714–794–3823.

Spring Hill Nurseries, 6523 N. Galena Rd., P.O. Box 1758, Peoria, IL 61656: Free catalog ■ Houseplants, perennials, roses, annuals, ground covers, and bonsai. 309–691–4616.

Sunnybrook Farms Nursery, 9448 Mayfield Rd., Chesterland, OH 44026: Catalog $1 (refundable) ■ House and herb plants, ivies, scented geraniums, seeds, and herbal products. 216–729–7232.

Wilson Plant Sales, 202 S. Indiana St., Roachdale, IN 46172: Free catalog ■ Exotic houseplants, geraniums, and African violets. 317–522–1320.

Ivies & Vines

Bluestone Perennials, Inc., 7269 Middle Ridge Rd., Madison, OH 44057: Free catalog ■ Ivies and vines, perennial flowers, and ground covers. 800–852–5243.

Conley's Garden Center, Boothbay Harbor, ME 04538: Catalog $1.50 (refundable) ■ Vines and ivies, wildflowers, ferns, and other gardening aids. 207–633–5020.

Park Seed Company, Inc., Cokesbury Rd., P.O. Box 46, Greenwood, SC 29648: Free catalog ■ Vines and strawberry plants, seeds, bulbs, and gardening tools. 803–223–7333.

Plant Kingdom, Box 7273, Lincoln Acres, CA 92047: Catalog $1 ■ Vines, gesneriads, begonias, miniature plants, dwarf plants, and exotics. 619–267–1991.

Rice Creek Gardens, 1315 66th Ave. NE, Minneapolis, MN 55432: Catalog $2 ■ Rock garden plants, vines, ferns, and ornamental shrubs. 612–574–1197.

Rocknoll Nursery, 7812 Mad River Rd., Hillsboro, OH 45133: Free catalog with 2 first class stamps ■ Rock garden plants, ivies, perennials, dwarf plants, and groundcovers. 513–393–1278.

Sunnybrook Farms Nursery, 9448 Mayfield Rd., Chesterland, OH 44026: Catalog $1 (refundable) ■ Ivies, scented geraniums, herb plants, seeds, herbal products, and other gardening aids. 216–729–7232.

Lilacs

Hastings, P.O. Box 115535, Atlanta, GA 30310: Free catalog ■ Lilacs. 404–755–6580.

Heard Gardens, Ltd., 5355 Merle Hay Rd., Johnston, IA 50131: Catalog $2 (refundable) ■ Lilacs. 515–276–4533.

Marigolds

W. Atlee Burpee & Company, 300 Park Ave., Warminster, PA 18974: Free catalog ■ Marigolds. 215–674–1793.

Hastings, P.O. Box 115535, Atlanta, GA 30310: Free catalog ■ Marigolds. 404–755–6580.

Park Seed Company, Cokesbury Rd., P.O. Box 46, Greenwood, SC 29648: Free catalog ■ Marigolds. 803–223–7333.

Stokes Seeds, Inc., Box 548, Buffalo, NY 14240: Free catalog ■ Marigolds. 416–688–4300.

Thompson & Morgan, Inc., P.O. Box 1308, Jackson, NJ 08527: Free catalog ■ Marigolds. 908–363–2225.

Mushrooms

American Forest Foods Corporation, P.O. Box 1258, Henderson, NC 27536: Free catalog with two 1st class stamps ■ Shiitake and oyster mushroom growing kits. 919–436–2674.

Choice Edibles, 584 Riverside Park Rd., Carlotta, CA 95528: Free list with long SASE ■ Morel mushroom spawn and cultures. 707–768–3135.

Far West Fungi, P.O. Box 428, South San Francisco, CA 94083: Free catalog with long SASE ■ Mushroom growing supplies and kits. Includes mushroom spawn for shiitake, button, tree-oyster, almond, and other varieties. 415–871–5424.

Field & Forest Products, Inc., N3296 Kuzuzek Rd., Peshtigo, WI 54157: Catalog $2 (refundable) ■ Mushroom-growing supplies. 715–582–4997.

Full Moon Mushroom Company, P.O. Box 6138, Olympia, WA 98502: Free brochure ■ Button mushroom spawn. 206–866–9362.

Fungi Perfecti, P.O. Box 7634, Olympia, WA 98507: Catalog $3 (refundable) ■ Mushroom-growing supplies and spawn. 206–426–9292.

Gourmet Mushrooms, P.O. Box 515, Graton, CA 95444: Free information ■ Morel mushroom spawn for backyard gardens. 707–829–7301.

Hardscrabble Enterprises, Inc., Box 42, Cherry Grove, WV 26804: Catalog $3 (refundable) ■ Shiitake mushroom-growing supplies. 304–567–2727.

H-S Farming Company, P.O. Box 724, Healdsburg, CA 95448: Free information ■ Kit for growing exotic oyster mushrooms at home. 707–838–4570.

Mushroom-people, P.O. Box 220, Summertown TN 38483: Free catalog ■ Mushroom-growing kits, supplies, and how-to books. 615–964–2200.

Nurseries

Each of the companies in this section offers a wide variety of seeds and plants, gardening supplies, tools, and equipment.

Burgess Seed & Plant Company, 905 Four Seasons Rd., Bloomington, IL 61701: Free catalog ■ 309–653–9551.

W. Atlee Burpee & Company, 300 Park Ave., Warminster, PA 18974: Free catalog ■ 215–674–1793.

Henry Field's Seed & Nursery, 415 N. Burnett, P.O. Box 700, Shenandoah, IA 51602: Free catalog ■ 605–665–9391.

Harris Seeds, Inc., 60 Saginaw Dr., P.O. Box 22960, Rochester, NY 14692: Free catalog ■ 716–442–0410.

J.W. Jung Seed Company, 335 High St., Randolph, WI 53957: Free catalog ■ 414–326–4100.

Orol Ledden & Sons, P.O. Box 7, Sewell, NJ 08080: Free catalog ■ 609–468–1000.

Letherman's Seeds, 1221 Tuscarawas St. East, Canton, OH 44707: Free catalog ■ 216–452–5704.

Earl May Seeds & Nursery Company, N. Elm St., Shenandoah, IA 51603: Free catalog ■ 712–246–1020.

Mellinger's, 2310 W. South Range Rd., North Lima, OH 44452: Free catalog ■ 216–549–9861.

Nichols Garden Nursery, 1190 Pacific West, Albany, OR 97321: Free catalog ■ 503–928–9280.

L.L. Olds Seed Company, P.O. Box 7790, Madison, WI 53707: Catalog $2.50 ■ 608–249–9291.

Park Seed Company, Inc., Cokesbury Rd., P.O. Box 46, Greenwood, SC 29648: Free catalog. 803–223–7333.

Shady Oaks Nursery, 700 19th Ave. NE, Waseca, MN 56093: Catalog $1 (refundable) ■ 507–835–5023.

R.H. Shumway, Seedsman, P.O. Box 1, Graniteville, SC 29829: Catalog $1 (refundable) ■ 803–663–9771.

Stark Bro's. Nurseries & Orchards Company, P.O. Box 10, Louisiana, MO 63353: Catalog $1 ■ 314–754–5511.

Otis Twilley Seed Company, P.O. Box 65, Trevose, PA 19047: Catalog $1 ■ 215–627–7333.

Orchids

A & P Orchids, 110 Peters Rd., Swansea, MA 02777: Free catalog ■ Hybrid orchids. 508–675–1717.

Adagent Acres, 2245 Floral Way, Santa Rosa, CA 95403: Free catalog with 1st class stamp ■ Hybrid orchids. 707–575–4459.

Alberts & Merkel Brothers, Inc., 2210 S. Federal Hwy., Boynton Beach, FL 33435: Catalog $1 ■ Orchid plants and growing supplies. 407–732–2071.

The Angraecum House, P.O. Box 976, Grass Valley, CA 95945: Free catalog ■ Hybrid and species Angraecum orchids from Africa. 916–273–9426.

Baker & Chantry Orchids, P.O. Box 554, 18611 132nd St. NE, Woodinville, WA 98072: Free catalog with long SASE and two 1st class stamps ■ Hybrid orchids. 206–483–0345.

Beal Orchid Company, 3400 Academy Dr. SE, Auburn, WA 98002: Free catalog ■ Orchids. 206–735–1140.

Breckinridge Orchids, 6201 Summit Ave., Brown Summit, NC 27214: Free price list with long SASE ■ Blooming orchids. 919–656–7991.

Carter & Holmes, Inc., 1 Old Mendenhall Rd., P.O. Box 668, Newberry, SC 29108: Catalog $1.50 (refundable) ■ Unusual hybrids and orchid growing supplies. 803–276–0579.

Cloud Forest Orchids, P.O. Box 370, Honokaa, HI 96727: Free catalog ■ Species and hybrid orchids. 808–775–9850.

Creole Orchids, P.O. Box 24458, New Orleans, LA 70184: Free catalog ■ Orchids. 504–282–5191.

Fennell's Orchid Jungle, 26715 SW 157th Ave., Homestead, FL 33031: Catalog $2 ■ Orchids. 303–247–4824.

Fox Orchids, 6615 W. Markham, Little Rock, AR 72205: Free catalog ■ Orchids, staghorn ferns, bromeliads, fertilizers, potting mixes, and books. 501–663–4246.

G & B Orchid Lab & Nursery, 2426 Cherimoya Dr., Vista, CA 92084: Free catalog ■ Cymbidium, dendrobium, phalenopsis, and cattleya orchids; growimg supplies and fertilizers; and growing media. 619–727–2611.

Golden Orchid, 9100 Fruitville Rd., Sarasota, FL 34240: Free brochure ■ Orchid hybrids. Includes mostly cattleyas and cattleya-like mericlones, and a few vandas, phalaenopsis, epidendrums, and dendrobiums. 813–377–1058.

Greenleaf Orchids, 158 S. Winterset Ave., Crystal River, FL 32629: Catalog $2 ■ Cattleya, angraecum, vandas, phalaenopsis orchids, and miniature and dwarf varieties. 904–795–3785.

Green Valley Orchids, Green Valley Rd., Folsom, LA 70437: Catalog $1 (refundable) ■ Orchid seedlings. Includes phalaenopsis, cattleya alliance meristems, and other genera. 504–796–5785.

Island Biotropix, S.R. 6021, Keaau, HI 96749: Free brochure ■ Kits and other supplies for growing orchids at home. 808–966–6367.

J & L Orchids, 20 Sherwood Rd., Easton, CT 06612: Catalog $1 ■ Orchids from around the world. Hybrid species; rare and unusual orchids; and easy-to-grow miniatures. 203–261–3772.

J.E.M. Orchids, 6595 Morikami Park Rd., Delray Beach, FL 33446: Catalog $2 (refundable) ■ Mini-cats, oncidium intergenerics, catasetum, and species breeding orchids.

Jones & Scully, 18955 SW 168th St., Miami, FL 33187: Catalog $5 (refundable) ■ Orchids. 305–238–7000.

Kensington Orchids, 3301 Plyers Mill Rd., Kensington, MD 20895: Free price list ■ Orchid plants. 301–933–0036.

Lauray of Salisbury, Undermountain Rd., Salisbury, CT 06068: Catalog $2 ■ Orchids, begonias, gesneriads, and cacti and succulents. 203–435–2263.

Rod McLellan Company, 1450 El Camino Real, South San Francisco, CA 94080: Catalog $2 ■ Orchid plants and growing supplies. 415–871–5655.

Mellinger's, Inc., 2310 W. South Range Rd., North Lima, OH 44452: Free catalog ■ Orchids, daylilies, gladioli, irises, trees, shrubs, and gardening equipment and supplies. 216–549–9861.

Miami Orchids, 22150 SW 147th Ave., Miami, FL 33170: Catalog $1 ■ Cattleya, phalaenopsis, vanda, oncidium, and dendrobium orchids in 3–inch pots. 305–258–2664.

Orchid Plant-A-Month Club, Box 4115, Boynton Beach, FL 33424: Free brochure ■ Club members receive a different plant each month with instructions for care. 800–338–5319.

Orchids by Hauserman, Inc., Addison Rd., Villa Park, IL 60126: Catalog $1.25 ■ Orchid plants and growing supplies. 708–543–6855.

Penn Valley Orchids, 239 Old Gulph Rd., Wynnewood, PA 19096: Catalog $1 ■ Exotic and rare orchids. 215–642–9822.

The Plant Shop's Botanical Gardens, 18007 Topham St., Reseda, CA 91335: Catalog $3.50 (refundable) ■ Cacti and succulents, species orchids, begonias, bulbs, and other plants. 818–881–4831.

Shaffer's Tropical Gardens, 1220 41st Ave., Capitola, CA 95010: Catalog $2 ■ Orchid plants and books. 408–475–3100.

Stewart Orchids, 3376 Foothill Rd., P.O. Box 550, Carpinteria, CA 93013: Catalog $2 ■ Orchids. 805–684–5448.

Teas Nursery Company, 4400 Bellaire Blvd., Bellaire, TX 77401: Catalog $1 (refundable) ■ Orchid starter collections, growing supplies, and books. 713–664–4400.

Tonkin's Orchids, 119 St. Albans Rd., Kensington, CA 94708: Free catalog ■ Paphiopedilum hybrids. 510–526–1371.

Zuma Canyon Orchids, 5949 Bonsall Dr., Malibu, CA 90265: Catalog $3 ■ Orchid plants. 310–457–9771.

Palms

The Green Escape, P.O. Box 1417, Palm Harbor, FL 34682: Catalog $6 ■ Rare and uncommon varieties of indoor and outdoor palms. 813–784–1132.

Neon Palm Nursery, 1560 Sebastopol Rd., Santa Rosa, CA 95407: Free catalog ■ Palms, cycads, rare and unusual plants, and foliage for interior settings. 707–578–7467.

Rhapis Gardens, 101 Rhapis Rd., Gregory, TX 78359: Catalog $1 ■ Dwarf indoor rhapis excella plants. Includes green and variegated types. 512–643–2061.

Rhapis Palm Growers, 31350 Alta Vista, P.O. Box 84, Redlands, CA 92373: Catalog $2 ■ Rhapis palms. 714–794–3823.

Peonies, Irises & Daylilies

Adamgrove, Rt. 1, Box 246, California, MO 65018: Catalog $2 (refundable) ■ Bearded, beardless, Siberian, arilbred, and species irises.

Alpine Valley Gardens, 2627 Calistoga Rd., Santa Rosa, CA 95404: Free price list with long SASE ■ Daylilies. 707–539–1749.

American Daylily & Perennials, P.O. Box 210, Grain Valley, MO 64029: Catalog $3 ■ Daylilies, hostas, and dwarf cannas. 816–224–2852.

Anderson Iris Gardens, 22179 Keather Ave. North, Forest Lake, MN 55025: Catalog 50¢ ■ Herbaceous peonies and tall bearded irises. 612–433–5268.

B & D Lilies, 330 P St., Port Townsend, WA 98368: Catalog $2 (refundable) ■ Species and hybrid lilies and special heirloom collections. 206–385–1738.

Barnee's Garden, Rt. 10, Box 2010, Nacogdoches, TX 75961: Free catalog with 1st class stamp ■ Registered daylily cultivars. 409–564–2920.

Bay View Gardens, 1201 Bay St., Santa Cruz, CA 95060: Free catalog ■ Tall bearded, spuria, Pacific coast, and Louisiana irises. 408–423–3656.

Borbeleta Gardens, 15980 Canby Ave., Faribault, MN 55021: Catalog $3 ■ Daylilies, bearded and Siberian irises, and lilies. 507–334–2807.

Lee Bristol Nursery, Bloomingfields Farm, Rt. 55, Gaylordsville, CT 06755: Free catalog ■ Daylilies. 203–354–6951.

The Bulb Crate, 2560 Deerfield Rd., Riverwoods, IL 60015: Free catalog ■ Peonies, dwarf and tall bearded irises, hybrid lilies, daffodils, and species tulips. 708–317–1414.

Busse Gardens, Rt. 2, Box 238, Cokato, MN 55321: Catalog $2 (refundable) ■ Siberian irises and ferns. 612–286–2654.

Caprice Farm Nursery, 15425 SW Pleasant Hill Rd., Sherwood, OR 97140: Catalog $1 (refundable) ■ Rare hybrids, daylilies, Japanese irises, and hostas. 503–625–7241.

Clifford's Perennial & Vine, Rt. 2, Box 320, East Troy, MI 53120: Catalog $1 (refundable) ■ Azaleas, rhododendrons, irises, Oriental poppies, peonies, daylilies, perennials, and flowering vines. 414–968–4040 (April-September); 414–642–7156 (October-March).

Coburg Planting Fields, 573 E. 600 North, Valparaso, IN 46383: Free catalog ■ Old and new varieties of daylilies. 219–462–4288.

Comanche Acres Iris Gardens, Rt. 1, Box 258, Gower, MO 64454: Catalog $3 (refundable) ■ Tall bearded and intermediate irises. 816–424–6436.

Cooley's Gardens, 11553 Silverton Rd. NE, P.O. Box 126, Silverton, OR 97381: Catalog $2 (refundable) ■ Irises. 800–225–5391.

Cooper's Garden, 212 W. County Rd. C, Roseville, MN 55113: Free catalog ■ Species daffodils, Siberian and Louisiana

irises, daylilies, perennials, and wildflowers. 501–347–2026.

Cordon Bleu Farms, 418 Buena Vista Rd., San Marcos, CA 92069: Catalog $1 ■ Daylilies and irises. 714–744–3851.

Cottage Gardens, 11314 Randolph Rd., Wilton, CA 95693: Catalog 50¢ ■ New tall bearded irises. 916–687–6134.

Country View Gardens, 13253 McKeighan Rd., Chesaning, MI 48616: Free catalog with long SASE and two 1st class stamps ■ Miniature and standard dwarf, miniature and standard tall bearded, and Siberian irises. 517–845–7556.

Eco-Gardens, P.O. Box 1227, Decatur, GA 30031: Price list $1 ■ Perennials, wildflowers, ferns, daylilies, water garden plants, trees and shrubs, and ferns. 404–294–6468.

Greenwood Gardens, Inc., 4905 Pioneer Blvd., Ste. 10, Whittier, CA 90601: Free catalog ■ Daylilies.

Greenwood Nursery, P.O. Box 1610, Goleta, CA 93116: Catalog $3 ■ Barefoot daylily plants. 805–964–2040.

Hatfield Gardens, 22799 Ringgold Southern Rd., Stoutsville, OH 43154: Catalog $2 ■ Daffodils, daylilies, bearded irises, hostas, ornamental grasses, and perennials. 614–474–5719.

Hildenbrandt's Iris Gardens, HC 84, Box 4, Lexington, NE 68850: Free catalog with two 1st class stamps ■ Peonies, Oriental poppies, lilies and dwarf irises that include medians, arilreds, and tall bearded varieties. 308–324–4334.

Holiday Seeds, 4276 Durham Cir., Stone Mountain, GA 30083: Catalog $1 ■ Hosta plants and cultivars, ferns, irises, lilies, and daylilies. 404–294–6594.

Honeywood Lilies, Box 63, Parkside, Saskatchewan, Canada S0J 2A0: Catalog $4 ■ Herbaceous peonies. 306–747–3776.

Iris Test Gardens, 1010 Highland Park Dr., College Place, WA 99324: Catalog 50¢ ■ Tall, intermediate, and dwarf irises.

Jernigan Gardens, Rt. 6, P.O. Box 593, Dunn, NC 28334: Free price list with long SASE ■ Lilies, hostas, and irises. 919–567–2135.

Klehm Nursery, Rt. 5, Box 197, South Barrington, IL 60010: Catalog $4 (refundable) ■

Peonies, irises, daylilies, and perennials. 800–551–3336.

Long's Garden, P.O. Box 19, Boulder, CO 80306: Free catalog ■ Tall, intermediate, and dwarf irises.

Louisiana Nursery, Rt. 7, Box 43, Opelousas, LA 70570: Catalog $5 ■ Daylily and iris cultivars. 318–948–3696.

Maryland Aquatic Nurseries, 3427 N. Furnace Rd., Jarrettsville, MD 21084: Catalog $2 ■ Plants for water gardens, ornamental grasses, and Louisiana and Japanese irises. 410–557–7615.

Maryott's Gardens, 1073 Bird Ave., San Jose, CA 95125: Catalog $1 (refundable) ■ Bearded, ruffled, and laced irises. 408–971–0444.

Mellinger's, 2310 W. South Range Rd., North Lima, OH 44452: Free catalog ■ Daylilies, gladioli, irises, other plants, and gardening equipment and supplies. 216–549–9861.

The New Peony Farm, P.O. Box 18235, St. Paul, MN 55118: Free booklet ■ Peony cultivars in singles, doubles, semi-doubles, and Japanese varieties. 612–457–8994.

Oakes Daylilies, 8204 Monday Rd., Corryton, TN 37721: Price list $2 ■ Daylily cultivars. 615–687–3770.

Powell's Gardens, Hwy. 70, Rt. 3, Box 21, Princeton, NC 27569: Catalog $2.50 ■ Irises, daylilies, perennials, rock garden plants, dwarf evergreens, and rare shrubs and trees. 919–936–4421.

Quality Dutch Bulbs, 50 Lake Dr., P.O. Box 225, Hillsdale, NJ 07642: Free catalog ■ Irises, daffodils, tulips, and other ornamental bulbs. 201–391–6586.

Reath's Nursery, 100 Central Blvd., Vulcan, MI 49892: Catalog $1 ■ Herbaceous peonies. 906–563–9321.

Roris Gardens, 7851 Carmencita Ave., Sacramento, CA 95829: Catalog $2 ■ Irises. 916–689–7460.

Schreiner's Gardens, 3625 Quinaby Rd. NE, Salem, OR 97303: Catalog $3 ■ Dwarf and tall bearded irises. 800–525–2367.

Smirnow's Son, 11 Oakwood Dr. West, Rt. 1, Huntington, NY 11743: Catalog $2 ■ Tree peonies. 516–421–0836.

Tischler Peony Gardens, 1021 E. Division St., Faribault, MN 55021: Free catalog ■ Herbaceous peonies. 507–334–7242.

Tranquil Lake Nursery, 45 River St., Rehoboth, MA 02769: Free catalog with 1st class stamp ■ Daylilies and irises. 508–336–6491.

Wayside Gardens, 1 Garden Ln., Hodges, SC 29695: Catalog $1 ■ Siberian irises. 800–845–1124.

White Flower Farm, Rt. 63, Litchfield, CT 06759: Free catalog ■ Herbaceous peonies. 800–888–7756.

Gilbert H. Wild & Son, Inc., P.O. Box 338, Sarcoxie, MO 64862: Catalog $3 ■ Peonies, irises, and daylilies. 417–548–3514.

Perennials

Kurt Bluemel, Inc., 2740 Greene Ln., Baldwin, MD 21013: Catalog $2 ■ Perennials, ferns, bamboo plants, and ornamental grasses. 410–557–7229.

Bluestone Perennials, Inc., 7269 Middle Ridge Rd., Madison, OH 44057: Free catalog ■ Perennial flowers, ground covers, ivies, and vines. 800–852–5243.

Butchart Gardens, Station A, Box 4010, Victoria, British Columbia, Canada V8X 3X4: Catalog $1 (refundable) ■ Seeds for annuals and perennials. 604–652–4422.

Canyon Creek Nursery, 3527 Dry Creek Rd., Oroville, CA 95965: Catalog $1 ■ Perennials. 916–533–2166.

Clifford's Perennial & Vine, Rt. 2, Box 320, East Troy, MI 53120: Catalog $1 (refundable) ■ Azaleas, rhododendrons, irises, Oriental poppies, peonies, daylilies, perennials, and flowering vines. 414–968–4040 (April-September); 414–642–7156 (October-March).

Colorado Alpines, P.O. Box 2708, Avon, CO 81620: Catalog $2 ■ Perennial plants for cold regions. 303–949–6464.

Cooper's Garden, 212 W. County Rd. C, Roseville, MN 55113: Free catalog ■ Species daffodils, Siberian and Louisiana irises, daylilies, perennials, and wildflowers. 501–347–2026.

Country Gardens, Rt. 2, Box 455A, Crivitz, WI 54114: Catalog $1 ■ Seeds for annuals and perennials. 715–757–2045.

Crownsville Nursery, P.O. Box 797, Crownsville, MD 21032: Catalog $2 (refundable) ■ Ferns, wildflowers, azaleas, ornamental grasses, and perennials. 410–923–2212.

Daystar, Rt. 2, Box 250, Litchfield, ME 04350: Catalog $1 ■ Perennials, trees and shrubs, and rhododendrons. 207–724–3369.

Donaroma's Nursery & Landscape Services, Box 2189, Edgartown, MA 02539: Free brochure ■ Perennials and perennial wildflowers shipped potted and ready for planting. 508–627–8366.

Eco-Gardens, P.O. Box 1227, Decatur, GA 30031: Price list $1 ■ Perennials, wildflowers, ferns, daylilies, water garden plants, trees and shrubs, and ferns. 404–294–6468.

Fieldstone Gardens, Inc., 620 Quaker Ln., Vassalboro, ME 04989: Catalog $1.50 ■ Nursery-propogated perennials. 207–923–3836.

Garden Place, 6780 Heisley Rd., P.O. Box 388, Mentor, OH 44061: Catalog $1 ■ Perennials. 216–255–3705.

Gary's Perennials, 1122 Welsh Rd., Ambler, PA 19002: Free information ■ American and European herbaceous perennials. 215–628–4070.

Good Hollow Greenhouse & Herbarium, Rt. 1, Box 116, Taft, TN 38488: Catalog $1 ■ Herbs, perennials, wildflowers, scented geraniums, essential oils and potpourris, teas, and dried herbs and spices. 615–433–7640.

Heritage Gardens, 1 Meadow Ridge Rd., Shenandoah, IA 51601: Free catalog ■ Perennial plants for all climates, ornamental grasses, foliage plants, hostas, shade garden plants, ferns, lilies, rock garden plants, shrubs, azaleas and rhododendrons, roses, and flowering trees. 605–665–5188.

Hummingbird Hills Herbal Nursery, 17201 S. Hawkinds, Ashland, MO 65010: Catalog $1 ■ Organically grown herbs, perennials, everlastings, and dried flowers. 314–657–2082.

Indigo Knoll Perennials, 16236 Compromise Ct., Mt. Airy, MD 21771: Catalog $1 (refundable) ■ Field-grown plants that include dianthus. 410–442–7656.

Klehm Nursery, Rt. 5, Box 197, South Barrington, IL 60010: Catalog $4 (refundable) ■ Perennial plants. 800–551–3336.

Lamb Nurseries, 101 E. Sharp Ave., Spokane, WA 99202: Free catalog ■ Perennials, ferns, shrubs, and other plants. 509–328–7956.

Lily of the Valley Herb Farm, 3969 Fox Ave., Minerva, OH 44657: Catalog $2 ■ Herb, everlasting, perennial, and scented geranium plants. 216–862–3920.

Mellinger's, 2310 W. South Range Rd., North Lima, OH 44452: Free catalog ■ Perennials, wildflowers, berry plants, orchids, trees and shrubs, and gardening equipment and supplies. 216–549–9861.

Milaeger's Gardens, 4838 Douglas Ave., Racine, WI 53402: Catalog $1 ■ Perennials. 414–639–2371.

Mohns, Inc., P.O. Box 2301, Atascadero, CA 93423: Free catalog with two 1st class stamps ■ Perennial poppies for western gardens. 805–466–4362.

Niche Gardens, 1111 Dawson Rd., Chapel Hill, NC 27516: Catalog $3 ■ Nursery-propagated wildflowers, perennials, trees, and shrubs. 919–967–0078.

Patrick's Nursery, P.O. Box 130, Ty Ty, GA 31795: Free catalog ■ Perennials, vegetables, fruit and nut trees, berry plants, and grapevines for southern climates. 912–386–1919.

Rakestraw's Gardens, 3094 S. Term St., Burton, MI 48529: Catalog $1 (refundable) ■ Bonsai supplies and perennials for rock gardens. 313–742–2685.

Rocknoll Nursery, 7812 Mad River Rd., Hillsboro, OH 45133: Free catalog with 2 first class stamps ■ Perennials, ivies, dwarf plants, groundcovers, and plants for rock gardens. 513–393–1278.

Spring Hill Nurseries, 6523 N. Galena Rd., P.O. Box 1758, Peoria, IL 61656: Free catalog ■ Perennials, roses, annuals, ground covers, bonsai, and houseplants. 309–691–4616.

Stanek's Garden Center, 2929 27th Ave. East, Spokane, WA 99203: Catalog 25¢ ■ Perennials, roses, bulbs, evergreens, shade trees, shrubs, and gardening supplies. 509–535–2939.

Surry Gardens, P.O. Box 145, Surry, ME 04684: Catalog $2 ■ Herbaceous borders and other supplies for rock gardens. 207–667–4493.

Vandenberg, Black Meadow Rd., Chester, NY 10918: Catalog $2 (refundable) ■ Perennials, hybrid lilies, seeds, and bulbs. 914–469–2633.

Van Hise Nursery, 30688 SE Waybill Rd., Boring, OR 97009: Free information ■ Perennials, ground covers, and shrubs. 503–663–6123.

Andre Viette Nurseries, Rt. 1, Box 16, Fisherville, VA 22939: Catalog $2 ■ Flowering perennials, rock garden perennials, woodland plants, and daylilies. 703–943–2315.

Wayside Gardens, 1 Garden Ln., Hodges, SC 29695: Catalog $1 ■ Perennials, trees and shrubs, ground covers, and gardening supplies and equipment. 800–845–1124.

Weiss Brothers Nursery, 11690 Colfax Hwy., Grass Valley, CA 95945: Catalog $1 (refundable) ■ Perennials and drip irrigation supplies. 916–272–7657.

Wrenwood of Berkeley Springs, Rt. 4., Box 361, Berkeley Springs, WV 25411: Catalog $1.50 ■ Perennials and herbs. 304–258–3071.

Rock Garden Plants

Carroll Gardens, P.O. Box 310, Westminster, MD 21158: Catalog $2 ■ Rock garden and alpine plants. 410–876–7336.

Daystar, Rt. 2, Box 250, Litchfield, ME 04350: Catalog $1 ■ Rock garden plants, supplies, and growing aids. 207–724–3369.

Endangered Species, P.O. Box 1830, Tustin, CA 92681: 4 catalogs a year for $5 ■ Rare and unusual rock garden plants. 714–544–9505.

Rice Creek Gardens, 1315 66th Ave. NE, Minneapolis, MN 55432: Catalog $2 ■ Rock garden plants and supplies, vines, ferns, and ornamental shrubs. 612–574–1197.

Rocknoll Nursery, 7812 Mad River Rd., Hillsboro, OH 45133: Free catalog with 2 first class stamps ■ Rock garden plants, ivies, perennials, dwarf plants, groundcovers, and other gardening aids. 513–393–1278.

Siskiyou Rare Plant Nursery, 2825 Cummings Rd., Medford, OR 97501: Catalog $2 (refundable) ■ Dwarf and other plants for rock gardens and woodland and alpine settings. 503–772–6846.

Twombly, Inc., 163 Barn Hill Rd., Monroe, CT 06468: Catalog $2 ■ Dwarf conifers, from miniatures for rock gardens to stately specimens. 203–261–2133.

We-Du Nursery, Rt. 5, Box 724, Marion, NC 28752: Catalog $1 (refundable) ■ Plants and supplies for rock gardens. 704–738–8300.

Roses

Antique Rose Emporium, Rt. 5, Box 143, Brenham, TX 77833: Catalog $5 ■ Antique roses for southern climates. 800–441–0002.

BDK Nursery, 2091 Haas Rd., P.O. Box 628, Apopka, FL 32712: Free catalog ■ Miniature roses. 305–889–3053.

County Bloomers Nursery, 20091 E. Chapman Ave., Orange, CA 92669: Free catalog ■ Miniature and old roses. 714–633–7222.

Gloria Del, 36 East Rd., High Falls Park, High Falls, NY 12440: Free catalog ■ New miniature roses. 914–687–9981.

Jackson & Perkins, P.O. Box 1028, Medford, OR 97501: Free catalog ■ Roses. 800–292–4769.

Krider Nurseries, P.O. Box 29, Middlebury, IN 46540: Free catalog ■ Roses. Cultivars, floribunda, and miniature roses. 219–825–5714.

Earl May Seeds & Nursery Company, N. Elm St., Shenandoah, IA 51603: Free catalog ■ Roses, shade and ornamental trees, flowering shrubs, vegetable and flower seeds, bulbs, and other gardening aids. 712–246–1020.

Miniature Plant Kingdom, 4125 Harrison Grade Rd., Sebastopol, CA 95472: Catalog $2.50 ■ Miniature roses and Japanese maples, conifers, and other plants for bonsai. 707–874–2233.

Mini-Roses of Texas, P.O. Box 267, Denton, TX 75202: Free catalog ■ Miniature roses. 817–566–3034.

NorEast Miniature Roses, Inc., 58 Hammond St., Rowley, MA 01969: Free catalog ■ Miniature roses. 508–948–7964.

Oregon Miniature Roses, 8285 SW 185th Ave., Beaverton, OR 97007: Free information ■ Micro-mini, climbing miniature, and miniature patio tree roses. 503–649–4482.

Pickering Nurseries, Inc., 670 Kingston Rd., Pickering, Ontario, Canada L1V 1A6: Catalog $2 ■ Hybrid tea, floribunda, grandiflora, climber, shrub roses, and antique roses. 416–839–2111.

Rosehill Farm, Gregg Neck Rd., Galena, MD 21635: Free catalog ■ Roses. 410–648–5538.

Roses by Fred Edmunds, 6235 SW Kahle Rd., Wilsonville, OR 97070: Free catalog ■ Roses. 503–682–1476.

Roses of Yesterday & Today, 803 Brown's Valley Rd., Watsonville, CA 95076: Catalog $4 ■ Old, rare, and unusual varieties of roses. 408–724–3537.

Savage Farms Nursery, P.O. Box 125, McMinnville, TN 37110: Free catalog ■ Roses. 615–668–8902.

Sequoia Nursery/Moore Miniature Roses, 2519 E. Noble Ave., Visalia, CA 93277: Free brochure ■ Miniatures, tree roses, climbing miniatures, and roses for hanging baskets. 209–732–0190.

R.H. Shumway, Seedsman, P.O. Box 1, Graniteville, SC 29829: Catalog $1 (refundable) ■ Roses, berry plants, fruit trees, seeds and bulbs, ornamental shrubs and plants, and gardening supplies. 803–663–9771.

Spring Hill Nurseries, 6523 N. Galena Rd., Peoria, IL 61632: Free catalog ■ Old roses, miniatures, and other roses; perennials and annuals; trees and shrubs; and ground covers, bonsai, and houseplants. 309–691–4616.

Stanek's Garden Center, 2929 27th Ave. East, Spokane, WA 99203: Catalog 25¢ ■ Perennials, roses, bulbs, evergreens, shade trees, shrubs, and gardening supplies. 509–535–2939.

Stocking Rose Nursery, 785 N. Capital Ave., San Jose, CA 95133: Free catalog ■ Hybrid teas, floribundas, grandifloras, miniatures, and old roses. 408–258–3606.

Thomasville Nurseries, Inc., P.O. Box 7, Thomasville, GA 31799: Free catalog ■ Hybrid tea roses. 912–226–5568.

Sassafras

Vernon Barnes & Son Nursery, P.O. Box 250, McMinnville, TN 37110: Free catalog ■ Sassafras trees, flowering trees and shrubs, shade trees, fruit trees, wildflowers, nut trees, hedges, vines, and berry plants. 615–668–8576.

Dutch Mountain Nursery, 7984 N. 48th St., Augusta, MI 49012: Free catalog with long SASE ■ Sassafras trees. 616–731–5232.

Forestfarm, 990 Tetherow Rd., Williams, OR 97544: Catalog $3 ■ Sassafras trees. 503–846–6963.

Louisiana Nursery, Rt. 7, Box 43, Opelousas, LA 70570: Catalog $5 ■ Sassafras trees. 318–948–3696.

Seeds & Bulbs

Abundant Life Seed Foundation, P.O. Box 772, Port Townsend, WA 98368: Catalog $1 ■ Organic and untreated vegetable, grain, herb, wildflower, and other seeds. 206–385–5660.

Amaryllis, Inc., P.O. Box 318, Baton Rouge, LA 70821: Catalog $1 ■ Amaryllis bulbs. 504–924–5560.

American Horticultural Society, 7931 East Blvd. Dr., Alexandria, VA 22308: Free list for members ■ Hard-to-find and heirloom seeds donated by members and commercial growers. 703–768–5700.

Archia's Seed Store, 106 E. Main St., Sedalia, MO 65301: Free catalog ■ Vegetable and flower seeds, gardening supplies, nursery stock, and beekeeping equipment and supplies. 816–826–1330.

Bakker of Holland, U.S. Bulb Reservation Center, Louisiana, MO 63353: Free catalog ■ Dutch bulbs. 314–754–4525.

The Banana Tree, 715 Northampton St., Easton, PA 18042: Catalog $3 ■ Rare seeds from temperate and tropical climates. 215–253–9589.

Walter Baxter Seed Company, P.O. Box 8175, Weslaco, TX 78596: Free price list ■ Seeds for "Texas" vegetables. 512–968–3187.

Bonnie Brae Gardens, 1105 SE Christensen Rd., Corbett, OR 97019: Free catalog ■ Narcissus bulbs. 503–695–5190.

Bountiful Gardens, 19550 Walker Rd., Willits, CA 95490: Free catalog ■ Untreated, open-pollinated seeds for flowers, herbs, and vegetables.

Breck's Dutch Bulbs, Mail Order Reservation Center, 6523 N. Galena Rd., P.O. Box 1757, Peoria, IL 61656: Catalog $1 ■ Holland spring flower bulbs. 309–691–4616.

John Brudy Exotics, 3411 Westfield Dr., Brandon, FL 33511: Catalog $2 (refundable) ■ Seeds for rare trees and shrubs. Includes the rare Adenium plant. 813–684–4302.

The Bulb Crate, 2560 Deerfield Rd., Riverwoods, IL 60015: Free catalog ■ Peonies, dwarf and tall bearded irises, hybrid lilies, some daffodils, and species tulips. 708–317–1414.

Bundles of Bulbs, 112 Greenspring Valley Rd., Owings Mills, MD 2117: Catalog $2 ■ Spring-flowering bulbs. 410–581–2188.

Burgess Seed & Plant Company, 905 Four Seasons Rd., Bloomington, IL 61701: Free catalog ■ Seeds, bulbs, and plants. 309–653–9551.

W. Atlee Burpee & Company, 300 Park Ave., Warminster, PA 18974: Free catalog ■ Seeds and bulbs. 215–674–1793.

D.V. Burrell Seed Company, P.O. Box 150, Rocky Ford, CO 81067: Free catalog ■ Seeds and other gardening aids. 719–254–3318.

Butterbrooke Farm, 78 Barry Rd., Oxford, CT 06483: Catalog 50¢ ■ Chemically untreated, open-pollinated, short-maturity seeds. 203–888–2000.

Comstock, Ferre & Company, 236 Main St., P.O. Box 125, Wethersfield, CT 06109: Catalog $2 ■ Vegetable, flower, and herb seeds. 203–529–3319.

The Cook's Garden, P.O. Box 53528, Londonberry, VT 05148: Catalog $1 ■ Seeds for baby vegetables, lettuce, and Italian-style vegetables. 802–824–3400.

Country Gardens, Rt. 2, Box 455A, Crivitz, WI 54114: Catalog $1 ■ Seeds for annuals and perennials. 715–757–2045.

The Daffodil Mart, Rt. 3, Box 794, Gloucester, VA 23061: Catalog $1 ■ Daffodils, tulips, autumn flowering and forcing bulbs, other bulbs, and growing supplies. 804–693–3966.

Dan's Garden Shop, 5821 Woodwinds Cir., Frederick, MD 21701: Free catalog ■ Seeds for annuals, perennials, and vegetables. 301–695–5966.

DeGiorgi Seed Company, Inc., 6011 N St., Omaha, NE 68117: Catalog $1 ■ Seeds. 402–731–3901.

deJager Bulbs, Inc., 188 Ashbury St., South Hamilton, MA 01982: Free catalog ■ Holland-grown bulbs. 617–468–1622.

Dutch Gardens, Inc., P.O. Box 200, Adelphia, NJ 07710: Free catalog ■ Tulip, hyacinth, crocus, iris, amaryllis, and other bulbs. 908–780–2713.

Evergreen Y.H. Enterprises, P.O. Box 17538, Anaheim, CA 92817: Catalog $2 (refundable) ■ Oriental vegetable seeds from China, Japan, and other Asian countries; gardening tools; and Oriental cookbooks.

Farmer Seed & Nursery Company, 818 NW 4th St., Faribault, MN 55021: Free catalog ■ Vegetable seeds, flowering bulbs, fruit and shade trees, ornamental shrubs and hedges, berry plants, and roses. 507–334–1623.

Far North Gardens, 16785 Harrison, Livonia, MI 48154: Catalog $2 (refundable) ■ Rare flower seeds from worldwide sources and primroses, orchids, wildflowers, and ferns. 313–422–0747.

Henry Field's Seed & Nursery, 415 N. Burnett, P.O. Box 700, Shenandoah, IA 51602: Free catalog ■ Vegetable and flower seeds, fruit and nut trees, shade trees, berry plants, hedges, ornamental shrubs, and roses. 605–665–9391.

Fisher's Garden Store, P.O. Box 236, Belgrade, MT 59714: Free catalog ■ Seeds and plants for high altitude gardening or short growing seasons. 406–388–6052.

The Fragrant Path, P.O. Box 328, Fort Calhoun, NE 68023: Catalog $1 ■ Seeds for prairie wildflowers, grasses, ferns, trees and shrubs, and climbing plants.

Gardener's Choice, Country Rd. 687, P.O. Box 8000, Hartford, MI 49057: Catalog $1 ■ Seeds for vegetables, flowers, house plants, and trees. 616–621–2481.

Garden Solutions, 2535 Waldorf Ct. NW, Grand Rapids, MI 49550: Free catalog ■ Bulbs, flowering perennials, trees, vines, shrubs, hedges, and other plants. 616–771–9540.

Gary's Perennials, 1122 Welsh Rd., Ambler, PA 19002: Free brochure ■ Tulips, daffodils, hyacinths, and minor bulbs. 215–628–4070.

Russell Graham Plants, 4030 Eagle Crest Rd. NW, Salem, OR 97304: Catalog $2 (refundable) ■ Ferns, ornamental grasses, lily bulbs, irises, daffodils, and other plants. 503–362–1135.

Greenleaf Seeds, P.O. Box 98, Conway, MA 01341: Catalog 50¢ ■ Seeds for root and green leafy vegetables.

Grianan Gardens, P.O. Box 14492, San Francisco, CA 94114: Catalog $1 (refundable) ■ Sky-blue poppies, old-fashioned English sweet peas, and other garden flowers from England, Europe, and North America.

Gurney Seed & Nursery Company, 110 Capitol St., Yankton, SD 57079: Free catalog ■ Seeds and bulbs, and apple trees that include semi-dwarf and standard varieties. 605–665–1930.

Harris Seeds, 60 Saginaw Dr., P.O. Box 22960, Rochester, NY 14692: Free catalog ■ Seeds and other gardening aids. 716–442–0410.

Hastings, P.O. Box 115535, Atlanta, GA 30310: Free catalog ■ Seeds for vegetables and plants for southern climates. 404–755–6580.

Heirloom Seeds, P.O. Box 245, West Elizabeth, PA 15088: Catalog $1 ■ Unusual and old-fashioned flower and vegetable seeds.

Hortigifts, Box 31073, Tampa, FL 33631: Free information with long SASE ■ Exotic caladium bulbs. Includes the sun-loving dwarf varieties.

J.L. Hudson, Seedsman, Box 1058, Redwood City, CA 94064: Catalog $1 ■ Seeds from around the world.

Jackson & Perkins, P.O. Box 1028, Medford, OR 97501: Free catalog ■ Seeds, plants, and roses. 800–292–4769.

Johnny's Selected Seeds, Foss Hill Rd., Albion, ME 04910: Free catalog ■ Strawberry plants and flower and vegetable seeds for cool, northern climates. 207–437–4301.

J.W. Jung Seed Company, 335 High St., Randolph, WI 53957: Free catalog ■ Seeds and gardening supplies. 414–326–4100.

Kitazawa Seed Company, 1748 Laine Ave., Santa Clara, CA 95051: Free price list ■ Chinese and Japanese vegetable seeds. 408–249–6778.

Krider Nurseries, P.O. Box 29, Middlebury, IN 46540: Free catalog ■ Berry plants, roses, and bulbs. 219–825–5714.

Lagomarsino Seeds, 5675–A Power Inn Rd., Sacramento, CA 95824: Catalog 50¢ ■ Seeds for vegetables, trees, and flowers. 916–381–1024.

D. Landreth Seed Company, P.O. Box 6426, Baltimore, MD 21230: Catalog $2 ■ Vegetable and flower seeds. 410–727–3923.

Le Jardin du Gourmet, P.O. Box 75, St. Johnsbury Center, VT 05863: Catalog $1 ■ Herb plants and seeds, and vegetable seeds.

Orol Ledden & Sons, P.O. Box 7, Sewell, NJ 08080: Free catalog ■ Seeds for cantaloupes, corn, and tomatoes. 609–468–1000.

Letherman's Seeds, 1221 Tuscarawas St. East, Canton, OH 44707: Free catalog ■ Vegetable, flower, and grass seeds; landscaping tools; and gardening supplies. 216–452–5704.

Liberty Seed Company, P.O. Box 806, New Philadelphia, OH 44663: Free catalog ■ Flower and vegetable seeds. 216–364–1611.

Lindenberg Seeds, Ltd., 803 Princess Ave., Brandon, Manitoba, Canada R7A 0P5: Catalog $1 ■ Vegetable and flower seeds and gardening supplies.

McClure & Zimmerman, P.O. Box 368, Friesland, WI 53935: Free catalog ■ Tulip bulbs.

Earl May Seeds & Nursery Company, N. Elm St., Shenandoah, IA 51603: Free catalog ■ Vegetable and flower seeds, bulbs, fruit and nut trees, roses, grapes, and flowering shrubs. 712–246–1020.

Mellinger's, 2310 W. South Range Rd., North Lima, OH 44452: Free catalog ■ Vegetable and flower seeds, fruit and nut trees, ornamental and shade trees, flowering shrubs and hedges, perennials, wildflowers, and berry plants. 216–549–9861.

Michigan Bulb Company, 1950 Waldorf NW, Grand Rapids, MI 49550: Free catalog ■ Bulbs, perennials, foliage plants, trees and shrubs, exotic house plants, hedges and climbers, and roses.

Netherland Bulb Company, 13 McFadden Rd., Easton, PA 18042: Free catalog ■ Imported Dutch bulbs. 215–253–8879.

Nichols Garden Nursery, 1190 N. Pacific West, Albany, OR 97321: Free catalog ■ Vegetable and herb seeds and plants, saffron crocus, garlic and shallots, and strawberry plants. 503–928–9280.

L.L. Olds Seed Company, P.O. Box 7790, Madison, WI 53707: Catalog $2.50 ■ Vegetable, herb, and flower seeds. 608–249–9291.

Oregon Bulb Farms, 14071 NE Arndt Rd., Aurora, OR 97002: Catalog $2 (refundable) ■ Lily bulbs. 503–678–1272.

Park Seed Company, Cokesbury Rd., P.O. Box 46, Greenwood, SC 29648: Free catalog ■ Bulbs, vegetable and flower seeds; gardening tools; and supplies. 803–223–7333.

Patrick's Nursery, P.O. Box 1300, Ty Ty, GA 31795: Free catalog ■ Vegetable and flower seeds, fruit and nut trees, berry plants, and grapevines for southern climates. 912–386–1919.

Pepper Gal, Box 12534, Lake Park, FL 33403: Free list with long SASE ■ Seeds for peppers.

Pinetree Garden Seed' Rt. 100, New Gloucester, ME 04260: Free catalog ■ Seeds for vegetables, herbs, flowers, house plants, and perennials. 207–926–3400.

Pleasant Valley Glads, P.O. Box 494, Agawam, MA 01001: Free catalog ■ Gladioli bulbs. 413–786–9146.

Pony Creek Nursery, Tilleda, WI 54978: Free catalog ■ Seeds for vegetables and flowers, trees and shrubs, and gardening supplies. 715–787–3889.

Porter & Son Seedsmen, P.O. Box 104, Stephenville, TX 76401: Free catalog ■ Seeds for vegetables, fruits, and flowers. 817–965–5600.

Quality Dutch Bulbs, 50 Lake Dr., P.O. Box 225, Hillsdale, NJ 07642: Free catalog ■ Iris, daffodil, tulip, and other ornamental bulbs. 201–391–6586.

Rex Bulb Farms, P.O. Box 774, Port Townshend, WA 98368: Catalog $1 (refundable) ■ Lilies for garden and greenhouse growing. 206–385–4280.

P.L. Rohrer & Brothers, Inc., P.O. Box 25, Smoketown, PA 17576: Free catalog ■

Vegetable and flower seeds in individual packets or by the pound; grass seed by the sack. 717–299–2571.

John Scheepers, Inc., Phillipsburg Rd., RD 6, Middletown, NY 10940: Catalog $3 ■ Tulip bulbs.

Seeds Blum, Idaho City Stage, Boise, ID 83706: Catalog $3 ■ Hybrid and heirloom vegetable seeds. 208–343–2202.

Seedway, Inc., Box 250, Hall, NY 14463: Free catalog ■ Seeds for hybrid vegetables and flowers. 716–526–6391.

Select Seeds, 180 Stickney Hill Rd., Union, CT 06076: Catalog $2 ■ Seeds for foxgloves, mignonetta, balloon flowers, hollyhocks, sweet peas, nicotiana, and other "old-fashioned" flowers.

Shepherd's Garden Seeds, 30 Irene St., Torrington, CT 06790: Catalog $1 ■ Seeds for baby, Mexican, Italian, Oriental, and French vegetables. 203–482–3638.

R.H. Shumway, Seedsman, P.O. Box 1, Graniteville, SC 29829: Catalog $1 (refundable) ■ Seeds and bulbs, berry plants, fruit trees, roses, ornamental shrubs and plants, and gardening supplies. 803–663–9771.

Southern Oregon Organics, 1130 Tetherow Rd., Williams, OR 97544: Free catalog ■ Open-pollinated vegetable seeds. 503–846–7173.

Stark Bros. Nurseries & Orchards Company, P.O. Box 10, Louisiana, MO 63353: Free catalog: Fruit, nut, and shade trees; grapevines and berry plants; ornamentals; roses; and seeds. 314–754–5511.

Stokes Seeds, Box 548, Buffalo, NY 14240: Free catalog ■ Vegetable and flower seeds. 416–688–4300.

Sunrise Enterprises, P.O. Box 330058, West Hartford, CT 06110: Catalog $2 (refundable) ■ Seeds for Oriental vegetables and other plants. 203–666–8071.

Thompson & Morgan, Inc., P.O. Box 1308, Jackson, NJ 08527: Free catalog ■ Vegetable and flower seeds. 908–363–2225.

Tsang & Ma International, P.O. Box 5644, Redwood City, CA 94063: Free catalog ■ Seeds for Oriental vegetables. 415–595–2270.

Otis Twilley Seed Company, P.O. Box 65, Trevose, PA 19047: Free catalog ■ Seeds for

fruits, vegetables, and flowers. 800–622–7333.

U.S. Bulb Reservation Center, Louisiana, MO 63353: Free catalog ■ Dutch bulbs. 314–754–4525.

Van Bourgondien Bros., 245 Farmingdale Rd., Rt. 109, P.O. Box A, Babylon, NY 11702: Free catalog ■ Save up to 50 percent on flowering bulbs. 800–873–9444.

Vandenberg, Black Meadow Rd., Chester, NY 10918: Catalog $2 (refundable) ■ Perennials, hybrid lilies, seeds, and imported bulbs. 914–469–2633.

Van Engelen, Inc., Stillbrook Farm, 307 Maple St., Litchfield, CT 06759: Free catalog ■ Imported Dutch tulips, daffodils, narcissi, crocuses, hyacinths, irises, muscari, and other bulbs. 203–567–8734.

Mary Mattison Van Schaik, P.O. Box 32, Cavendish, VT 05142: Catalog $1 (refundable) ■ Old favorites, novelty, and miniature varieties of tulip, daffodil, and hyacinth bulbs. 802–226–7653.

Vermont Bean Seed Company, Rt. 7, Charlotte, Fair Haven, VT 05445: Free catalog ■ Bean seeds. 802–425–3500.

Mary Walker Bulb Farm, Box 256, Omega, GA 31775: Free catalog ■ Bulbs. 912–386–1919.

Wayside Gardens, 1 Garden Ln., Hodges, SC 29695: Catalog $1 ■ Bulbs. 800–845–1124.

White Flower Farm, Rt. 63, Litchfield, CT 06759: Catalog $5 ■ Bulbs, shrubs, strawberry plants, books, tools, and gardening supplies. 800–888–7756.

Willhite Seed Company, P.O. Box 23, Poolville, TX 76076: Free catalog ■ Seeds. 817–599–8656.

Wyatt-Quarles Seed Company, P.O. Box 739, Garner, NC 27529: Free catalog ■ Seeds. 919–832–0551.

Shrubs

Farmer Seed & Nursery Company, 818 NW 4th St., Faribault, MN 55021: Free catalog ■ Ornamental shrubs and hedges, vegetable seeds, flowering bulbs, fruit and shade trees, berry plants, and roses. 507–334–1623.

Holbrook Farm & Nursery, Rt. 2, Box 223–B, Fletcher, NC 28732: Catalog $2 (refundable) ■ Herbaceous perennials, trees and shrubs, and native wildflowers. 704–891–7790.

Inter-State Nurseries, Inc., 1800 Hamilton Rd., Bloomington, IL 61704: Free catalog ■ Plants, shrubs, flowering bulbs, and trees.

Lamb Nurseries, 101 E. Sharp Ave., Spokane, WA 99202: Free catalog ■ Plants, shrubs, perennials, ferns, and other gardening items. 509–328–7956.

Rice Creek Gardens, 1315 66th Ave. NE, Minneapolis, MN 55432: Catalog $2 ■ Ornamental shrubs, vines, ferns, rock garden plants, and gardening supplies. 612–574–1197.

R.H. Shumway, Seedsman, P.O. Box 1, Graniteville, SC 29829: Catalog $1 (refundable) ■ Ornamental shrubs and plants, berry plants, fruit trees, roses, seeds and bulbs, and gardening supplies. 803–663–9771.

Stark Bros. Nurseries & Orchards Company, P.O. Box 10, Louisiana, MO 63353: Free catalog ■ Plants and shrubs. 314–754–5511.

Van Hise Nursery, 30688 SE Waybill Rd., Boring, OR 97009: Free information ■ Shrubs, perennials, and ground covers. 503–663–6123.

Terrariums

Allgrove, Box 459, Wilmington, MA 01887: Catalog 50¢ ■ Woodland terrarium plants, kits, and supplies. 508–658–4869.

Carolina Exotic Gardens, Rt. 5, Box 283–A, Greenville, NC 27834: Catalog $1 ■ Carnivorous plants, seeds, terrarium plants, and soil. 919–758–2600.

Kartuz Greenhouses, 1408 Sunset Dr., Vista, CA 92083: Catalog $2 ■ Miniature terrarium, rare and tropical, flowering and foliage, and begonia plants. 619–941–3613.

Peter Pauls Nurseries, 4665 Chapin Rd., Canandaigua, NY 14424: Free catalog ■ Woodland terrarium and carnivorous plants. 716–394–7397.

Trees

Adams County Nursery, Inc., P.O. Box 108, Aspers, PA 17304: Free catalog ■ Plum trees and antique apples in dwarf and standard sizes. 717–677–8105.

Vernon Barnes & Son Nursery, P.O. Box 250, McMinnville, TN 37110: Free catalog ■ Flowering trees and shrubs, shade trees, fruit trees, wildflowers, nut trees, sassafras trees, hedges, vines, and berry plants. 615–668–8576.

Bear Creek Nursery, P.O. Box 41175, Northport, WA 99157: Catalog $1 ■ Fruits and nuts. Includes a selection of old apples. 509–732–6219.

Burford Brothers, Monroe, VA 24574: Catalog $8 (refundable); brochure $1 ■ Modern and antique apples. 804–929–4950.

California Nursery Company, P.O. Box 2278, Fremont, CA 94536: Free catalog ■ Fruit and nut trees and table and wine grapevines. 510–797–3311.

Carino Nurseries, Box 538, Indiana, PA 15701: Free catalog ■ Christmas trees, seedlings, and transplants. 412–463–3350.

Catalpa Nursery, P.O. Box 1599, Easton, MD 21601: Free brochure ■ Cypress trees. 800–673–8514.

Chestnut Hill Nursery, Inc., Rt. 1, Box 341, Alachua, FL 32615: Free brochure ■ Oriental persimmons and hybrid American-Chinese Chestnuts. 904–462–2820.

Colvos Creek Nursery & Landscaping, 1931 2nd Ave., Seattle, WA 98101: Catalog $2 (refundable) ■ Trees, shrubs, and bamboo plants. 206–441–1509.

Daystar, Rt. 2, Box 250, Litchfield, ME 04350: Catalog $1 ■ Perennials, trees and shrubs, and rhododendrons. 207–724–3369.

Eco-Gardens, P.O. Box 1227, Decatur, GA 30031: Price list $1 ■ Perennials, wildflowers, ferns, daylilies, water garden plants, trees and shrubs, and ferns. 404–294–6468.

Edible Landscaping, P.O. Box 77, Afton, VA 22920: Free catalog ■ Dwarf citrus trees. (Does not ship to California.) 804–361–9134.

Farmer Seed & Nursery Company, 818 NW 4th St., Faribault, MN 55021: Free catalog ■ Fruit and shade trees, vegetable seeds, flowering bulbs, ornamental shrubs and hedges, berry plants, and roses. 507–334–1623.

Henry Field's Seed & Nursery, 415 N. Burnett, P.O. Box 700, Shenandoah, IA 51602: Free catalog ■ Fruit and nut trees and shade

trees; berry plants; hedges and ornamental shrubs; roses; plum trees; and dwarf, standard, and seedling apple trees. 605–665–9391.

Dean Foster Nurseries, P.O. Box 127, Hartford, MI 49057: Free catalog ■ Dwarf, semi-dwarf, standard, or seedling apple trees; fruit and nut trees and shade trees; evergreens; grapevines; and rhubarb and asparagus plants. 616–621–2419.

Four Wind Growers, P.O. Box 3538, Fremont, CA 94539: Free catalog with long SASE ■ Dwarf citrus trees. (Does not ship to Arizona, Florida, or Texas.) 510–656–2591.

Fowler Nurseries, Inc., 525 Fowler Rd., Newcastle, CA 95658: Catalog $2 ■ Asian pear trees, berry plants, and vines. 916–645–8191.

Frysville Farms, 300 Frysville Rd., Ephrata, PA 17522: Free catalog ■ Trees. 800–422–FRYS.

Gardener's Choice, Country Rd. 687, P.O. Box 8000, Hartford, MI 49057: Catalog $1 ■ Vegetables, flowers, house plants, and trees. 616–621–2481.

Garden World's Exotic Plants, 2503 Garfield St., Laredo, TX 78043: Catalog $1 ■ Citrus trees, bamboo, bananas, pineapples, and cacti. 512–724–3951.

Girard Nurseries, P.O. Box 428, Geneva, OH 44041: Free catalog ■ Baby evergreen seeds and seedlings, shade trees, and flowering shrubs. 216–466–2881.

Goodwin Creek Gardens, P.O. Box 83, Williams, OR 97544: Catalog $1 ■ Container-grown native American trees, shrubs, and perennial flowers. 503–846–7357.

Gossler Farms Nursery, 1200 Weaver Rd., Springfield, OR 97478: Catalog $1 ■ Magnolias; and new, rare, and unusual trees and shrubs that include maples, stewartias, and styrax. 503–746–3922.

Greer Gardens, 1280 Goodpasture Island Rd., Eugene, OR 97401: Free information ■ Asian pear trees. 503–686–8266.

Gurney Seed & Nursery Company, 110 Capitol St., Yankton, SD 57079: Free catalog ■ Apple trees in semi-dwarf and standard varieties. 605–665–1930.

Harmony Farm Supply, P.O. Box 460, Graton, CA 95444: Catalog $2 ■ Miniature and standard size fruit and nut trees. 707–823–9125.

Hilltop Trees, Newark Nurseries, P.O. Box 578, Hartford, MI 49057: Free catalog ■ Standard and dwarf fruit trees. 616–621–3135.

Inter-State Nurseries, 1800 Hamilton Rd., Bloomington, IL 61704: Free catalog ■ Flowering, shade, and fruit trees. Other items include shrubs, berry plants, roses, and perennials.

Ison's Nursery, Rt. 1, Brooks, GA 30205: Free catalog ■ Apple, pear, fig, peach, walnut and pecan trees; muscadine grapevines; and blackberry, strawberry, blueberry, and raspberry plants. 800–733–0324.

Johnson Nursery, Rt. 5, Box 296, Ellijay, GA 30540: Free catalog ■ Apple, plum, pear, cherry, apricot, walnut, almond, and other fruit and nut trees; strawberry plants; and grapevines. 404–273–3187.

Kelly Nurseries, Catalog Division, P.O. Box 10, Louisiana, MO 63353: Free catalog ■ Heavily rooted fruit and nut trees, landscaping trees and shrubs, ornamentals, berry plants, grapevines, and flowers. 800–325–4180.

Lawson's Nursery, Box 472, Ball Ground, GA 30107: Free list ■ Antique apple trees. 404–893–2141.

Henry Leuthardt Nurseries, Box 666, East Moriches, NY 11940: Free catalog ■ Dwarf fruit trees that grow full-size fruit. 516–878–1387.

Earl May Seeds & Nursery Company, N. Elm St., Shenandoah, IA 51603: Free catalog ■ Fruit and nut trees, shade and ornamental trees, flowering shrubs, berry plants, roses, and seeds for vegetables and fruit. 712–246–1020.

Mellinger's, 2310 W. South Range Rd., North Lima, OH 44452: Free catalog ■ Fruit and nut trees, ornamental and shade trees, flowering shrubs and hedges, perennials, wildflowers, berry plants, and gardening supplies. 216–549–9861.

J.E. Miller Nurseries, Inc., 5060 W. Lake Rd., Canandaigua, NY 14424: Free catalog ■ Semi-dwarf hybrid antique apples, in spring and fall varieties; other fruit trees; berry plants; and grapevines. 716–396–2647.

Musser Forests, P.O. 340, Indiana, PA 15701: Free catalog ■ Evergreen hardwood seedlings and transplants, other trees and shrubs, and ground covers. 412–465–5685.

National Arbor Day Foundation, 100 Arbor Ave., Nebraska City, NE 68410: Free catalog ■ Standard and dwarf fruit trees, nut trees, berry plants, flowering shrubs and trees, evergreens, and flowering bulbs. 402–474–5655.

Newark Nurseries, P.O. Box 578, Hartford, MI 49057: Free catalog ■ Standard and dwarf fruit trees. 616–621–3135.

New York State Fruit Testing Cooperative, West North St., Geneva, NY 14456: Catalog and membership $10 ■ Apple and other fruit trees. 315–787–2205.

Niche Gardens, 1111 Dawson Rd., Chapel Hill, NC 27516: Catalog $3 ■ Nursery-propagated wildflowers, perennials, and trees and shrubs. 919–967–0078.

Nolin River Nut Tree Nursery, 797 Port Wooden Rd., Upton, KY 42784: Free price list ■ Grafted or budded Black and Persian walnut, chestnut, heartnut, pecan, and butternut trees. 502–369–8551.

Northwoods Nursery, 28696 S. Cramer Rd., Molalla, OR 97038: Free catalog ■ Growing stock for figs, persimmons, kiwis, Asian pears, passion fruit, and pomegranates. 503–651–3737.

Pacific Tree Farms, 4301 Lynwood Dr., Chula Vista, CA 92010: Catalog $2 ■ Miniature trees, genetic dwarf avocados, and exotic ornamentals. 619–402–2400.

Patrick's Nursery, P.O. Box 1300, Ty Ty, GA 31795: Free catalog ■ Vegetable seeds for southern climates, fruit and nut trees, berry plants, and grapevines. 912–386–1919.

Peaceful Valley Farm Supply, P.O. Box 2209, Grass Valley, CA 95945: Catalog $2 (refundable) ■ Miniature fruit and nut trees, tools, propagation supplies, seeds, and farming equipment. 916–272–4769.

Pikes Peak Nurseries, Box 75, Penn Run, PA 15765: Free catalog ■ Evergreen and deciduous seedlings and transplants, nut trees, dwarf fruit trees, and flowering trees. 412–463–7747.

Raintree Nursery, 391 Butts Rd., Morton, WA 98356: Free information ■ Asian pear trees. 206–496–6400.

Savage Farms Nursery, P.O. Box 125, McMinnville, TN 37110: Free catalog ■ Fruit trees, flowering trees and shrubs, shade trees, evergreens, berry plants, and gardening supplies. 615–668–8902.

F.W. Schumacher Company, 36 Spring Hill Rd., Sandwich, MA 02563: Catalog $1 ■ Fir and other evergreen trees. 508–888–0659.

Sonoma Antique Apple Nursery, 4395 Westside Rd., Healdsburg, CA 95448: Free catalog ■ Old-time apple and pear trees on semi-dwarf root stocks. 707–433–6420.

Southmeadow Fruit Gardens, Lakeside, MI 49116: Catalog $8 ■ Apples, rare grapes and gooseberries, medlars, nectarines, pears, peaches, cherries, plums, apricots, currants, quince, and other trees and shrubs. 616–469–2865.

Stark Bros. Nurseries & Orchards Company, P.O. Box 10, Louisiana, MO 63353: Free catalog ■ Fruit, nut, and shade trees; and berry plants; and gardening aids. 314–754–5511.

Tripple Brook Farm, 37 Middle Rd., Southampton, MA 01073: Free catalog ■ Bamboo plants, exotic fruits, trees, perennials, and shrubs. 413–527–4626.

Ty Ty South Orchards, Box 130, Ty Ty, GA 31794: Free catalog ■ Peach, pear, plum, cherry, apples, nectarine, apricot, and nut trees; dwarf trees; berry plants; bulbs; and grapes. 912–386–2211.

Vans Pines, Inc., 7550 144th Ave., West Olive, MI 49460: Free catalog ■ Evergreen and deciduous trees. Includes pine, spruce, fir, oak, cherry, walnut, ash, and hybrid poplar. 616–399–1620.

Van Well Nursery, Inc., P.O. Box 1339, Wenatchee, WA 98801: Free catalog ■ Apple, pear, peach, cherry, plum, nectarine, and apricot fruit trees; dwarf trees; berry plants; grapevines; and nut trees. 509–663–8189.

Washington Evergreen Nursery, P.O. Box 388, Leicester, NC 28748: Catalog $2 (refundable) ■ Dwarf conifers. 803–747–1641.

Waynesboro Nurseries, P.O. Box 987, Waynesboro, VA 22980: Free information ■ Antique apples in dwarf and standard sizes; fruit and nut trees; flowering and shade trees; and ornamentals. 703–942–4141.

Wayside Gardens, 1 Garden Ln., Hodges, SC 29695: Catalog $1 ■ Container-grown trees ready for transplanting. 800–845–1124.

Western Maine Nurseries, One Evergreen Dr., Fryeburg, ME 04037: Free catalog ■

Evergreen trees. 800–447–4745; 207–935–2161 (in ME).

Womack's Nursery Company, Rt. 1, Box 80, De Leon, TX 76444: Free catalog ■ Peach, apricot, fig, pear, plum, and persimmon trees. 817–893–6497.

M. Worley Nursery, 98 Braggtown Rd., York Springs, PA 17372: Free catalog ■ Dwarf, semi-dwarf, and standard trees for peaches and old-time apples. 717–526–4519.

Vegetable Plants

Alfrey Seeds, P.O. Box 415, Knoxville, TN 37901: Free catalog with long SASE ■ Seeds for sweet and hot peppers, tomatoes, okras, gourds, and luffas.

Becker's Seed Potatoes, RR 1, Trout Creek, Ontario, Canada P0H 2L0: Free information ■ Seed potatoes.

Brown's Omaha Plant Farms, Inc., P.O. Box 787, Omaha, TX 75571: Free catalog ■ Onion, cauliflower, cabbage, broccoli, and brussel sprouts plants. 903–884–2421.

Delegeane Garlic Farms, P.O. Box 2561, Yountville, CA 94599: Free catalog ■ Garlic cloves for planting. 707–944–8019.

Fedco Seeds, 52 Mayflower Hill Dr., Waterville, ME 04901: Catalog $1 ■ Heirloom hybrid vegetable and herb seeds.

Filaree Farm, Rt. 1, Box 162, Okanogan, WA 98840: Free information ■ Garlic varieties.

Fred's Plant Farm, P.O. Box 707, Dresden, TN 38225: Free price list with long SASE ■ Sweet potato seeds and plants. 901–364–5419.

Heirloom Seeds, P.O. Box 245, West Elizabeth, PA 15088: Catalog $1 (refundable) ■ Old-time vegetable and flower seeds.

Horticultural Enterprises, P.O. Box 810082, Dallas, TX 75381: Free price list ■ Hot and sweet peppers, jicama, and herbs for Mexican cooking.

Hurov's Tropical Seeds, P.O. Box 1596, Chula Vista, CA 91912: Price list $1 ■ Seeds for exotic plants from worldwide locations.

Illinois Foundation Seeds, Box 722, Champaign, IL 61824: Free price list ■ Seeds for sweet corn. 217–485–6260.

Jersey Asparagus Farms, Inc., RD 5, Box 572, Newfield, NJ 08344: Free information ■ Seeds and crowns for all-male asparagus. 609–358–2548.

Kalmia Farm, P.O. Box 3881, Charlottesville, VA 22903: Free catalog ■ Hard-to-find shallots, multiplier onions, and garlic varieties.

Moose Tubers, 52 Mayflower Hill Dr., Waterville, ME 04901: Free information ■ Maine-certified seed potatoes.

Piedmont Plant Company, P.O. Box 424, Albany, GA 31703: Free catalog ■ Field-grown pepper, onion, tomato, cabbage, cauliflower, and broccoli plants. 912–883–7029.

Redwood City Seed Company, P.O. Box 361, Redwood City, CA 94064: Catalog $1 ■ Herb and vegetable seeds from worldwide sources. 415–325–7333.

Ronniger's Seed Potatoes, Star Rt. 10, Moyie Springs, ID 83845: Catalog $2 ■ Heirloom and European varieties of seed potatoes.

Seeds Blum, Idaho City Stage, Boise, ID 83706: Catalog $3 ■ Seed potatoes. 208–343–2202.

Southern Oregon Organics, 1130 Tetherow Rd., Williams, OR 97544: Free catalog ■ Open-pollinated vegetable seeds. 503–846–7173.

Steele Plant Company, 212 Collins St., P.O. Box 191, Gleason, TN 38229: Catalog 50¢ ■ Sweet potato plants for northern and southern climates. Other plants include brussels sprouts, onion, cabbage, cauliflower, and broccoli. 901–648–5476.

Tomato Growers Supply Company, P.O. Box 2237, Fort Myers, FL 33902: Free catalog ■ Tomatoes, peppers, books, and garden supplies.

The Tomato Seed Company, Inc., P.O. Box 323, Metuchen, NJ 08840: Free catalog ■ Huge, extra-large, large, medium, small, and cherry tomatoes.

Wood Prairie Farm, RFD 1, Box 164, Bridgewater, ME 04735: Free catalog ■ Seed potatoes.

Wildflowers & Native Plants

Appalachian Wildflower Nursery, Rt. 1, Box 275A, Reedsville, PA 17084: Catalog $1.25 (refundable) ■ Wildflower plants, trees, and shrubs. 717–667–6998.

Applewood Seed Company, P.O. Box 10761, Edgemont Station, Golden, CO 80401: Free catalog ■ Individual packets of wildflower seeds and custom mixtures. 303–431–6283.

Vernon Barnes & Son Nursery, P.O. Box 250, McMinnville, TN 37110: Free catalog ■ Wildflowers, nut trees, sassafras trees, hedges, vines, and berry plants. 615–668–8576.

Beersheba Wildflower Gardens, Stone Door Rd., P.O. Box 551, Beersheba Springs, TN 37305: Free catalog ■ Wildflowers from east of the Mississippi. 615–692–3575.

Bernardo Beach Native Plant Farm, 1 Sanchez Rd., Veguita, NM 87062: Free catalog with four 1st class stamps ■ Wildflower seeds and plants from the southwest. Other items include trees, shrubs, and vines for high-elevation growing. 505–345–6248.

Botanic Garden Seed Company, 9 Wyckoff St., Brooklyn, NY 11201: Catalog $1 (refundable) ■ Wildflower seeds. 718–624–8839.

Brookside Wildflowers, Rt. 3, Box 740, Boone, NC 28607: Catalog $2 ■ Native perennials.

Bullbay Creek Farm, Rt. 2, Box 381, Tallahassee, FL 32301: Free price list ■ Wildflowers from southeastern areas. 904–878–6688.

Conley's Garden Center, Boothbay Harbor, ME 04538: Catalog $1.50 ■ Wildflowers and seeds, ferns, native perennials, bulbs, orchids, ground covers, and vines. 207–633–5020.

Cooper's Garden, 212 W. County Rd. C, Roseville, MN 55113: Free catalog ■ Species daffodils, Siberian and Louisiana irises, daylilies, perennials, and wildflowers. 501–347–2026.

Crownsville Nursery, P.O. Box 797, Crownsville, MD 21032: Catalog $2 (refundable) ■ Ferns, wildflowers, azaleas, ornamental grasses, and perennials. 410–923–2212.

Dabney Herbs, P.O. Box 22061, Louisville, KY 40222: Catalog $2 ■ Ginseng, herbs, scented geraniums, perennials, and wildflowers. 502–893–5198.

Donaroma's Nursery & Landscape Services, Box 2189, Edgartown, MA 02539: Catalog $3 ■ Perennial wildflowers shipped as 3–inch potted plants. 508–627–8366.

E & H Products, 78260 Darby Rd., Bermuda Dunes, CA 92201: Free information ■ Individual species and mixes of wildflower seeds. 619–345–0147.

Far North Gardens, 16785 Harrison, Livonia, MI 48154: Catalog $2 (refundable) ■ Plants for woodland settings, prairies, and rock gardens; rare plants; and herbs and ornamentals. 313–422–0747.

Forestfarm, 990 Tetherow Rd., Williams, OR 97544: Catalog $3 ■ Native and unusual ornamental American plants, shrubs, and trees. 503–846–6963.

The Fragrant Path, P.O. Box 328, Fort Calhoun, NE 68023: Catalog $1 ■ Seeds for prairie wildflowers and grasses, ferns, trees and shrubs, and climbing plants.

Gardens of the Blue Ridge, P.O. Box 10, Pineola, NC 28662: Catalog $2 ■ Wildflower seeds, ferns, trees, plants, shrubs, and bulbs. 704–733–2417.

Good Hollow Greenhouse & Herbarium, Rt. 1, Box 116, Taft, TN 38488: Catalog $1 ■ Herbs, perennials, wildflowers, scented geraniums, essential oils and potpourris, teas, and dried herbs and spices. 615–433–7640.

Green Horizons, 218 Quinlan, Ste. 571, Kerrville, TX 78028: Free information with long SASE ■ Texas wildflowers. 512–257–5141.

Griffey's Nursery, 16870 Hwy. 25–70, Marshall, NC 28753: Free catalog ■ Appalachian wildflowers, ferns and vines, and rock and bog plants. 704–656–2334.

Holbrook Farm & Nursery, Rt. 2, Box 223–B, Fletcher, NC 28732: Catalog $2 ■ Geraniums, native wildflowers, trees and shrubs, garden perennials, and hostas. 704–891–7790.Lafayette Home Nursery, La-Fayette, IL 61449: Catalog 25¢ ■ Seeds for prairie plants, grasses, and flowers. 309–995–3311.

Las Pilitas Nursery, Star Rt., Box 23, Santa Margarita, CA 93453: Catalog $4 ■ Native plants and seeds from California. 805–438–5992.

Mellinger's, 2310 W. South Range Rd., North Lima, OH 44452: Free catalog ■ Wildflowers, trees, flowering shrubs and hedges, perennials, berry plants, vegetable seeds, and gardening equipment and supplies. 216–549–9861.

Midwest Wildflowers, P.O. Box 64, Rockton, IL 61072: Catalog $1 ■ Woodland wildflowers.

Missouri Wildflowers Nursery, Rt. 2, Box 373, Jefferson City, MO 65109: Catalog 50¢ ■ Wildflower seeds.

Moon Mountain Wildflowers, P.O. Box 34, Morro Bay, CA 93442: Catalog $1 ■ Regional wildflower seed mixtures. 805–772–2473.

New England Wildflower Society, Garden in the Woods, Hemenway Rd., Framingham, MA 01701: Free catalog with long SASE and two 1st class stamps ■ Wildflower seeds native to New England. 508–877–7630.

Niche Gardens, 1111 Dawson Rd., Chapel Hill, NC 27516: Catalog $3 ■ Nursery-propagated wildflowers, perennials, trees, and shrubs. 919–967–0078.

Oak Ridge Nurseries, P.O. Box 182, East Kingston, NH 03827: Catalog $2 ■ Wildflowers, hardy native ferns, and aquatic and bog plants. 603–642–8227.

Orchid Gardens, 2232 139th Ave. NW, Andover, MN 55304: Catalog 50¢ ■ Wildflower and fern plants. 612–755–0205.

Plants of the Southwest, Rt. 6, Box 11A, Santa Fe, NM 87501: Catalog $1.50 ■ Wildflowers and native plants from the southwest. 505–983–1548.

Prairie Moon Nursery, Rt. 3, Box 163, Winona, MN 55987: Catalog $1 ■ Plants and seeds for prairie wildflowers and grasses. 507–452–1362.

Prairie Nursery, P.O. Box 306, Westfield, WI 53964: Catalog $3 ■ Plants and seeds for prairie wildflowers and grasses. 608–296–3679.

Prairie Restorations, P.O. Box 327, Princeton, MN 55371: Free catalog ■ Wildflowers. 608–296–3679.

Prairie Ridge Nursery, 9738 Overland Rd., Mount Horeb, WI 53572: Catalog 50¢ ■ Wildflowers. 608–437–5245.

The Primrose Path, RD 2, Box 110, Scottsdale, PA 15683: Catalog $1.50 ■ Alpine and woodland plants. 412–887–6756.

Putney Nursery, Inc., Rt. 5, Putney, VT 05346: Catalog $1 (refundable) ■ Wildflowers, ferns, herbs, perennials, orchids, and gardening supplies. 802–387–5577.

Rice Creek Gardens, 1315 66th Ave. NE, Minneapolis, MN 55432: Catalog $2 ■ Wildflower seeds and mixtures for meadow growing, dwarf conifers, ground covers, colorful rock garden plants, and rhododendrons. 612–574–1197.

Clyde Robin Seed Catalog, P.O. Box 2366, Castro Valley, CA 94546: Catalog $2 ■ Wildflower seeds, trees, and shrubs. 510–785–0425.

Sunlight Gardens, Rt. 1, Box 600, Andersonville, TN 37705: Catalog $1 ■ Nursery-grown wildflowers for the north and south, planting in the sun or shade, or for wet or dry locations. 615–494–8237.

Vermont Wildflower Farm, Rt. 7, P.O. Box 5, Charlotte, VT 05455: Free catalog ■ Seeds for wildflowers and annual and perennial flowers. 802–425–3500.

We-Du Nursery, Rt. 5, Box 724, Marion, NC 28752: Catalog $1 (refundable)* Japanese and American wildflowers, woodland and rock garden plants, unusual perennials, and irises. 704–738–8300.

Wildseed, Inc., P.O. Box 308, Eagle Lake, TX 77434: Free catalog ■ Wildflower seeds. 409–234–7353.

GAZEBOS

Walter J. Bass Company, 1432 W. Grand River, P.O. Box 397, Williamston, MI 48895: Free catalog ■ Easy-to-assemble cedar gazebo kits. 800–345–5735.

Bow House, Inc., P.O. Box 900, Bolton, MA 01740: Catalog $6 ■ Easy-to-assemble gazebos, bridges, and arbors. 508–779–6464.

California Redwood Association, 405 Enfrente Dr., Ste. 200, Novato, CA 94949:

Free information ■ Easy-to-build redwood gazebos. 415–382–0662.

Cedar Gazebo, Inc., 10432 Lyndale, Melrose Park, IL 60164: Brochure $2 ■ Handcrafted western red cedar gazebos with optional screens. 708–455–0928.

Cumberland Woodcraft Company, Inc., P.O. Drawer 609, Carlisle, PA 17013: Catalog $4.50 ■ Gazebo kits, in 10–, 12–, and 16–feet diameters. 717–243–0063.

Dalton Pavilions, Inc., 7260 Oakley St., Philadelphia, PA 19111: Catalog $3 ■ Western red cedar gazebos. 215–342–9804.

English Garden, 652 Glenbrook Rd., Stamford, CT 06906: Catalog $6 ■ Victorian-style gazebos, screens, and other accessories. 203–348–3048.

K-D Wood Products, 180 Front St., Bath, ME 04530: Free information ■ Gazebo kits with lattice-paneled sides and roofs. 207–443–6000.

Kloter Farms, Inc., 216 West Rd., Ellington, CT 06029: Brochure $3 ■ Handcrafted gazebos. 203–871–1048.

Springhill Products, Inc., 120 S. 6th St., Ste. 2518, Minneapolis, MN 55402: Free brochure ■ Easy-to-assemble western red cedar prefab gazebo kits. 612–349–5218.

Sun Designs, P.O. Box 6, Oconomowoc, WI 53066: Free information with long SASE ■ Plans for gazebos, bridges, doghouses, arbors, lawn furniture, swings and other outdoor play structures, and birdhouses. 414–567–4255.

Vintage Wood Works, Hwy. 34, Box R, Quinlan, TX 75474: Catalog $2 ■ Pre-assembled gazebos with bolt-together solid wood panels.

Vixen Hill, Main St., Elverson, PA 19520: Catalog $3 ■ Pre-engineered gazebos for easy assembly by non-carpenters. 215–286–0909.

GENEALOGY

Alabama Department of Archives and History, 624 Washington Ave., Montgomery, AL 36130: Free information ■ Genealogical information about individuals

and organizations, from the 19th- and early 20th-century. 205–261–4361.

Alaska State Archives & Records Management, 141 Willoughby, Juneau, AK 99801: Free information ■ Alaska executive, legislative, and judicial records, from 1880 to the present. 907–465–2275.

American Family Records Association, 311 E. 12th St., Kansas City, MO 64106: Free information ■ Genealogical information and publications about Missouri. 816–373–6570.

Arizona State Genealogical Society, P.O. Box 42075, Tucson, AZ 85733: Free information ■ Arizona census and hospital death records.

Arkansas Professional Genealogists Association, 270 Midland Rd., Alexander, AR 72002: Free information ■ Arkansas genealogy information. 501–470–1120.

Braintree Historical Society, Inc., 786 Washington St., Braintree, MA 02184: Free information ■ Massachusetts genealogical information. 617–846–1640.

California State Library, 915 Capitol Mall, Sacramento, CA 94237: Free information ■ Genealogy information about California. 916–445–4149.

Central Florida Genealogical & Historical Society, Inc., P.O. Box 177, Orlando, FL 32802: Free information ■ Genealogical information about Florida.

Clarke Historical Library, Central Michigan University, Mount Pleasant, MI 48859: Free information ■ Michigan genealogical information. 517–774–3352.

Colorado Genealogical Society, P.O. Box 9671, Denver, CO 80209: Free information ■ Records extraction, indexing and publishing, and genealogical information about Colorado.

Connecticut Society of Genealogists, Inc., 2906 Main St., Glastonbury, CT 06033: Free information ■ Connecticut genealogical information. 203–633–4203.

Church of Jesus Christ of Latter-Day Saints, Family History Department, 50 E. North Temple, Salt Lake City, UT 84150:

Free information ■ Genealogical data from around the world. 801–531–2331.

Delaware County Historical Society, Widener University, Chester, PA 19013: Free information ■ Delaware genealogical information. 215–874–6444.

Florida State Archives, 500 S. Bronough St., R.A. Gray Building, Tallahassee, FL 32399: Free information ■ Genealogical information from state government records. 904–487–2073.

Florida State Genealogical Society, P.O. Box 10249, Tallahassee, FL 32302: Free information ■ Florida genealogical information.

Genealogical Publishing Company, Inc., 1001 N. Calvert St., Baltimore, MD 21202: Free list ■ Genealogy text books, manuals, how-to books, general references and finding aids, and state guide books. 800–727–6687.

The Genealogy Store, 8405 Richmond Hwy., Alexandria, VA 22309: Catalog $1 ■ Genealogical software, preservation materials, coats of arms, maps, and gravestone rubbing materials.

Genealogy Unlimited, Inc., 789 S. Buffalo Grove Rd., Buffalo Grove, IL 60089: Free catalog ■ Books, supplies, and European maps for genealogists. 800–666–4363.

Georgia Historical Society, 501 Whitaker St., Savannah, GA 31499: Free information ■ Georgia records and genealogical information. 912–651–2128.

Goodspeed's, 7 Beacon St., Boston, MA 02108: Catalog $5 ■ Genealogy books and other publications. 617–523–5970.

Hawaii Maui Historical Society, 2375–A Main St., Wailuku, HI 96793: Free information ■ Hawaii genealogical information. 808–244–3326.

Heraldic Imports, Inc., 21 W. 46th St., New York, NY 10036: Booklet $2 ■ Coat of arms drawings of names used most frequently in the United States. 212–719–4204.

Heritage Books, Inc., 1540. E. Pointer Ridge Place, Ste. 180, Bowie, MD 20716: Free information with long SASE ■ Books and periodicals arranged by state and subject. 301–390–7709.

Historical Society of Delaware, 505 Market St., Wilmington, DE 19801: Free information ■ General information about Delaware's history and genealogy. 302–655–7161.

Idaho State Historical Society, 610 N. Julia Davis Dr., Boise, ID 83702: Free information ■ Information about Idaho history and the Northwest. 208–334–3356.

Illinois State Genealogical Society, P.O. Box 10195, Springfield, IL 62791: Free information ■ Illinois genealogy information and educational activities for the public. 217–789–1968.

Iowa State Historical Society, 600 E. Locust, Des Moines, IA 50319: Free information ■ Genealogical information from Iowa archives. 515–279–9711.

Kentucky Genealogical Society, P.O. Box 153, Frankfort, KY 40601: Free information ■ Kentucky genealogical information and publications.

Kentucky Museum and Library, Western Kentucky University, Bowling Green, KY 42101: Free information ■ Genealogical information about Kentucky. 502–745–2592.

Le Comite des Archives de la Louisiane, P.O. Box 44370, Baton Rouge, LA 44370: Free information ■ Genealogy and historical information, books, guides, and other records about Louisiana.

Louisiana Evangeline Genealogical and Historical Society, W. Main St., P.O. Box 664, Ville Platte, LA 70586: Free information ■ Genealogical and historical information across the U.S.

Louisiana Genealogical and Historical Society, P.O. Box 3454, Baton Rouge, LA 70821: Free information ■ Genealogical information about Louisiana.

Marion Public Library, 600 S. Washington St., Marion, IN 46953: Free information ■ Indiana genealogical information, from 1884 to the present. 317–664–7363.

Maryland State Archives, Hall of Records, 350 Rowe Blvd., Annapolis, MD 21401: Free information ■ Maryland genealogical records from 1634 to the present. 410–974–3914.

Minnesota Genealogical Society, 1101 Fort Rd., St. Paul, MN 55116: Free information ■ Minnesota genealogical information and publications. 612–222–6929.

Mississippi Department of Archives and History, P.O. Box 571, Jackson, MS 39205: Free information ■ Information about Mississippi genealogy and history. 601–359–6850.

Missouri State Historical Society, 1020 Lowry St., Columbia, MO 65201: Free information ■ Missouri genealogy information and history. 314–882–7083.

Montana Historical Society, 225 N. Roberts St., Helena, MT 59620: Free information ■ Genealogical information, publications, and other history activities about Montana. 406–444–2694.

National Archives & Records Administration, National Archives Books, Washington, DC 20408: Paperbound book $19 ■ Guide to Genealogical Research in the National Archives, a source of valuable information for genealogical research. Includes census records, military service information, passenger ship arrival lists, and other information. 202–523–3164.

National Genealogical Society, 1921 Sunderland Pl. NW, Washington, DC 20036: Free information about services provided ■ Publications about local area history, biographical data, and heraldry information. 202–785–2123.

Nebraska State Historical Society, Box 82554, Lincoln, NE 68501: Free information ■ Information about Nebraska history and genealogy. 402–471–3270.

New England Historic Genealogical Society, 101 Newbury St., Boston, MA 02116: Catalog $1 ■ Genealogical supplies and New England town histories and vital records. 617–536–5740.

New Hampshire Records and Archives, 71 S. Fruit St., Concord, NH 03301: Free information ■ New Hampshire state records, from 1679 and up to the present. 603–271–2236.

New Jersey Historical Society, 230 Broadway, Newark, NJ 07104: Free information ■ New Jersey history and genealogy records. 201–483–3939.

New Mexico Albuquerque Public Library, Special Collections Branch, 423 Central NE, Albuquerque, NM 87102: Free information ■ New Mexico genealogical information. 505–848–1376.

New Mexico Artesia Historical and Genealogical Society, P.O. Box 803, Artesia, NM 88210: Free information ■ New

Mexico genealogical information. 505–746–3101.

New York Genealogy & Biographical Society Library, 122 E. 58th St., New York, NY 10022: Free information about services provided ■ New York genealogy information and family history and biography files. 212–755–8532.

North Carolina Division of Archives and History, 109 E. Jones St., Raleigh, NC 27611: Free information ■ North Carolina genealogy and historical records. 919–733–7305.

North Dakota Cavalier County Historical Society, Langdon, ND 58249: Free information ■ North Dakota records of family histories and genealogical information. 701–283–5284.

North Dakota Department of History, North Dakota State University, Minard Hall, Fargo, ND 58105: Free information ■ North Dakota historical and genealogical information.

Northeastern Nevada Genealogical Society, Willow and College Pkwy., P.O. Box 1903, Elko, NV 89801: Free information ■ Genealogy information about Nevada.

Ohio Genealogical Society, 34 Sturges Ave., Mansfield, OH 44906: Free information ■ Educational and genealogical information about Ohio family histories. 419–522–9077.

Ohio Historical Society, 1985 Velma Ave., Columbus, OH 43211: Free information ■ Genealogical services and historical information about Ohio. 614–297–2300.

Oklahoma Territorial Museum, 406 E. Oklahoma Ave., Guthrie, OK 73034: Free information ■ Information resources about Oklahoma for genealogists and historians. 405–282–3706.

Oregon Historical Society, 1230 SW Park Ave., Portland, OR 97205: Free information ■ Historical resources about Oregon for genealogists and historians. 503–222–1741.

Pennsylvania Dutch Folk Culture Society, Inc., Main and Willow, Lenhartsville, PA 19534: Free information ■ Pennsylvania genealogical information. 215–562–4803.

Jonathan Sheppard Books, Box 2020, ESP Station, Albany, NY 12220: Free information ■ Reprints of original maps that can be used as research tools by genealogists and local historians. Includes state maps circa 1863–1868, American maps, reprints of 1873–1874 maps of central states, and centennial maps from 1880–1881.

The Ships Chandler, Wilmington, VT 05363: Free brochure ■ Thousands of names from 32 countries in report form, genealogical-related paintings, plaques, and needlepoints. 813–355–3000.

South Carolina Historical Society, 100 Meeting St., Charleston, SC 29401: Free information ■ Records and information about South Carolina history. 803–723–3225.

South Dakota State Historical Society, 900 Governors Dr., Pierre, SD 57501: Free information ■ Genealogical information about South Dakota. 605–773–3458.

The Tennessee Historical Society, War Memorial Building, Nashville, TN 37219: Free information ■ Letters, journals, family papers, diaries, and a myriad of other manuscript materials about the cultural history of Tennessee. 615–320–7001.

Tennessee State Library and Archives, 403 7th Ave. North, Nashville, TN 37219: Free information ■ Tennessee genealogical information. 615–741–2764.

Texas General Land Office: Archives and Records Liaison, 1700 N. Congress, Austin, TX 78701: Free information ■ Records management and Texas genealogical information. 512–463–5277.

Vermont Historical Society, Pavilion Building, 109 State St., Montpelier, VT 05602: Free information ■ Vermont genealogical information and history. 802–828–2291.

The Vinalhaven Historical Society, Inc., P.O. Box 339, Vinalhaven, ME 04863: Free information ■ Genealogical information about Maine. 207–863–4969.

Virginia Genealogical Society, P.O. Box 7469, Richmond, VA 23221: Free information ■ Virginia genealogical information. 804–770–2306.

Virginia Wilton House Museum, 215 S. Wilton Rd., P.O. Box 8225, Richmond, VA 23226: Free information ■ Genealogical information about Virginia. 804–282–5936.

Washington State Archives, 12th & Washington, Olympia, WA 98504: Free information ■ Historical records and genealogical information about Washington. 206–753–2580.

Wisconsin State Genealogical Society, Inc., 2109 20th Ave., Monroe, WA 53566: Free information ■ Wisconsin genealogical information.

Wyoming State Archives, Museums & Historical Department, Barrett Building, 24th & Central, Cheyenne, WY 82002: Free information ■ Genealogical information about Wyoming. 307–777–7519.

GIFTS

Children's Gifts

A Baby's Secret Garden, Division of Childbirth Graphics, Ltd., P.O. Box 20508, Rochester, NY 14602: Free catalog ■ Gifts for babies. 716–272–7836.

Disney Catalog, 475 Oberlin Ave. South, CN 2100, Lakewood, NJ 08701: Free catalog ■ Children's clothes, toys, books to read and color, pens and crayons, lamps, videos cassettes, stuffed toys, marionettes, and Disney watches. 908–905–0111.

Hand in Hand, Rt. 26, RR 1, Box 1425, Oxford, ME 04270: Free catalog ■ Teaching toys, travel items, videos, and nursery room furniture that help nurture, teach, and protect children. 800–872–9745.

Hearth Song, P.O. Box B, Sebastopol, CA 95473: Free catalog ■ Books for children, doll house miniatures, toiletries for babies, dolls, party decorations, back yard play structures, art supplies, kites, games, and musical instruments. 800–533–4397.

Heir Affair, 625 Russell Dr., Meridian, MS 39301: Catalog $2 ■ Strollers, car seats, high chairs, swings, nursery monitors, and bathing aids, and gifts for babies and children. 800–332–4347; 601–484–4323 (in MS).

Just for Kids, P.O. Box 29141, Shawnee, KS 66201: Free catalog ■ Toys and games, dolls and doll houses, things for babies, building blocks, science gadgets, arts and crafts, musical instruments, T-shirts, bathing aids, sports and learning toys, school bags, and videos. 800–443–5827.

Metropolitan Museum of Art, Special Services Office, Middle Village, NY 11381: Catalog $1 ■ Children's books, cassettes, records, cards, and games and toys. 800–468–7386.

Pied Piper, 2922 N. 35th Ave., Ste. 4, Drawer 11408, Phoenix, AZ 85061: Free catalog ■ Science toys, musical instruments, books, toddler and nursery toys, and teaching machines that encourage and foster children's creative and intellectual potential. 602–272–1853.

Right Start Catalog, Right Start Plaza, 5334 Sterling Center Dr., Westlake Village, CA 91361: Free catalog ■ Infant, toddler, and preschool toys and games, music and videos, strollers and car seats, swings, crib sets, personal care aids, clothing, bathtime aids, and highchairs. 800–548–8531.

Storybook Heirlooms, 1215 O'Brien Drive, Menlo Park, CA 94025: Free catalog ■ Children's clothing and gifts. 800–899–7666.

Miscellaneous Gifts

Allegra & Coe, P.O. Box CN 1043, South Plainfield, NJ 07080: Free catalog ■ Decor accessories, jewelry, handbags, picture frames, watches, pillows, furniture, clothing, and other gifts. 908–906–0498.

Amazon Drygoods, 2218 E. 11th St., Davenport, IA 52803: Catalog $2 ■ Victorian style clothing, toiletries, books, toys, hats, fans, garden and home accessories, and other gifts. 319–322–6800.

Ambassador, Palo Verde at 34th St., P.O. Box 28807, Tucson, AZ 85726: Free catalog ■ Women's clothing and accessories, jewelry, decor accessories, and kitchen gadgets. 602–748–8600.

American National Parks, P.O. Box 47, Yorktown, VA 23690: Free catalog ■ Gifts that commemorate American history. 800–821–2903; 804–898–3383 (in VA).

Anticipations by Ross Simons, 9 Ross Simons Dr., Cranston, RI 02920: Free catalog ■ Decor accessories, jewelry, rugs, sterling silver flatware, crystal, furniture, artwork, china, gifts for babies, quilts, and porcelain dinnerware. 800–556–7376; 463–3100 (in RI).

Armchair Shopper, P.O. Box 306, Grandview, MO 64030: Free catalog ■ Decor accessories, country crafts, storage and closet aids, toys and gadgets for children, and holiday items. 800–659–7467.

Art Institute of Chicago, The Museum Shop, Michigan Ave. at Adams St., Chicago, IL 60603: Catalog $1 ■ Museum reproductions and publications that relate to the Institute's collections. 312–263–2635.

Artistic Greetings, Inc., 409 William St., P.O. Box 1623, Elmira, NY 14902: Free catalog ■ Personalized stationery, memo and informal note cards, toys and puzzles, kitchen accessories, and gifts for pets. 607–733–6313.

Laura Ashley, Inc., 1300 MacArthur Blvd., Mahwah, NJ 07430: Free catalog ■ Clothing for mothers and children, calendars, note cards, tapestry kits, decor accessories, perfumes and sachets, fine soaps, and other items. 800–223–6917.

Attitudes, Subsidiary of IDEC Corporation, P.O. Box 61148, Sunnyvale, CA 94088: Free catalog ■ Decor accessories, high-tech electronics, sporting equipment, personal care and bathroom aids, kitchen aids, bicycle gadgets, barbecue accessories, telescopes, toys, computer games, travel aids, and other gifts. 800–241–1107.

At Your Leisure, P.O. Box 6196, Bridgewater, NJ 08807: Free catalog ■ Gifts for personal use and the home and office. 800–222–0015.

B & J Company, P.O. Box 67, Georgetown, TX 78627: Catalog $5 ■ Jan Hagara collectible prints, dolls, plates, figurines, cards, and miniatures. 512–863–8318.

Ballet Boutique Mail Order, 7215 Skillman, Dallas, TX 75231: Free catalog ■ Gifts for dancers. 214–475–3033.

William Barthman, 174 Broadway, New York, NY 10038: Free information ■ Jewelry, watches, porcelain, crystal, and sterling. 800–727–9782; 212–227–3524 (in NY).

Benchwarmers, 2870 E. Oakland Park Blvd., Fort Lauderdale, FL 33306: Free catalog ■ Sports memorabilia and collectibles. 305–566–4324.

Bennett Brothers, Inc., 30 E. Adams St., Chicago, IL 60603: Catalog $4 (refundable) ■ Rings, pins and bracelets, pearls, semiprecious and precious stones, lockets, charms, electronic gifts, toys, cameras, and leather goods. 312–263–4800.

Benny's Express, 495 Tiogue Ave., P.O. Box 38, Coventry, RI 02816: Free catalog ■ Toys and games for children and adults, household aids and accessories, decor accessories, gardening aids, novelties, security devices, safety and health aids, automotive

accessories, umbrellas, tools, and holiday items. 800–456–1700.

Best Kept Secrets, P.O. Box 35200, Colorado Springs, CO 80935: Free catalog ■ Stationery and gifts. 800–828–2120.

B-N-Genius, 22121 Crystal Creek Blvd. SE, P.O. Box 3008, Bothell, WA 98041: Free catalog ■ Toys and games, tanning lamps, kitchen accessories and cookware, telephones, cassette recorder/player and television sets, radar detectors, home office aids, stereo equipment, and watches. 206–483–3343.

Bruce Bolind, 711 Bolind Building, P.O. Box 9751, Boulder, CO 80301: Free catalog ■ Novelty and gift merchandise for adults, children, and pets. 303–443–9688.

Brielle Galleries, 707 Union Ave., P.O. Box 475, Brielle, NJ 08730: Free catalog ■ Crystal, silver, bronze, pewter, and porcelain items; watches; and jewelry. 800–631–2156; 908–528–8400 (in NJ).

Brookstone Company, 5 Vose Farm Rd., P.O. Box 5, Peterborough, NH 03458: Free catalog ■ Homewares, tools, travel aids, and other gifts. 800–846–3000.

Buffalo Bill Historical Center, Museum Selections Gift Shop, P.O. Box 2630, Cody, WY 82414: Free catalog ■ Decor accessories that represent the untamed western frontier. 800–533–3838.

Burberry's Limited, 9 E. 57th St., New York, NY 10022: Free catalog ■ Clothing, handbags, luggage, silk scarves and shawls, belts, hats, shoes, tennis accessories, sports bags, and toiletries. 212–371–5010.

By Way of Maine, Main St., P.O. Box 950, Southwest Harbor, ME 04679: Free catalog ■ Gifts from Maine. 207–244–7027.

Camalier & Buckley, P.O. Box 303, Wye Mills, MD 21679: Free catalog ■ Desk accessories, luggage, jewelry, and travel items. 800–233–5000.

P.J. Carroll & Company, Customer Service Center, 2515 E. 43rd St., P.O. Box 23667, Chattanooga, TN 37422: Free catalog ■ Dinnerware, designer clothing, crystal stemware, picnic accessories, leather goods,

decor accessories, art supplies, umbrellas, jewelry, and music boxes. 800–255–3933.

Harriet Carter, Dept. 32, North Wales, PA 19455: Free catalog ■ Unusual gifts for everyone. 215–361–5122.

Casual Living, 5401 Hangar Ct., P.O. Box 32173, Tampa, FL 33631: Free catalog ■ Toys, books, furniture, watches and clocks, puzzles, kitchen accessories, hand-painted portraits from photographs, lamps, mailboxes, music boxes, model construction kits, and computer games. 800–843–1881.

Chamberlain, CN 1041, South Plainfield, NJ 07080: Free catalog ■ Clothing, decor accessories, statuary, clocks, paperweights, porcelain, art, garden and greenhouse accessories, and dolls. 908–906–0071.

Chance Encounter, 2524 Explorers Way, Madison, WI 53794: Free catalog ■ Electronics, audio and video equipment, jewelry, and games. 800–544–8853.

Chiasso, P.O. Box 10399, Chicago, IL 60610: Free catalog ■ Housewares, jewelry, toys, telephones, clocks, and home office items. 800–654–3570.

Choices, 222 SE 2nd Ave., Portland, OR 97214: Free catalog ■ Garden decor accessories, home and office gadgets, holiday favorites and decorations, and toys. 503–234–6556.

CitiShopper, P.O. Box 1016, Trumbull, CT 06611: Free catalog ■ High-tech and electronic devices, toys, playroom furniture, optics and cameras, luggage, furniture, clothing, comforters and bed furnishings, decor accessories, household aids, bicycles, telephones, watches, and computers. 800–TEL–SHOP.

Coach Leatherware Company, 300 Chubb Ave., Lyndhurst, NJ 07071: Free catalog ■ Leather bags, belts, wallets, briefcases, and other accessories. 201–460–4716.

Coldwater Creek, 1123 Lake St., Sandpoint, ID 83864: Free catalog ■ Nature-related and Native American jewelry, clothing, decor accessories, art, pottery, wind chimes, and other gifts. 800–262–0040.

Collector's Guild, 1625 Bathgate Ave., Bronx, NY 10457: Free catalog ■ Art deco pieces and accessories, classic art, etchings, and statuary. 212–901–5271.

Colonial Casting Company, Inc., 443 S. Colony St., Meriden, CT 06450: Catalog $1

■ Handcrafted, lead-free pewter gifts. 203–235–5189.

Colonial Williamsburg, P.O. Box 3532, Williamsburg, VA 23187: Catalog $18.95 ■ Reproduction colonial furnishings and decor accessories. 800–446–9240.

Colorful Images, 6711 Winchester Cir., Boulder, CO 80301: Free catalog ■ Decor accessories, watches and jewelry, pens, personal labels, note cards, cookie jars, wind chimes, desk accessories, novelty telephones, fancy kitchen mugs, calculators, paperweights, and other items. 303–530–4114.

Comforts, 2515 E. 43rd St., P.O. Box 182216, Chattanooga, TN 37422: Free catalog ■ Gifts and novelties. 615–867–9955.

The Company of Women, Inc., 6 S. Broadway, P.O. Box 742, Nyack, NY 10960: Free catalog ■ Gifts for women. 800–937–1193.

The Computer Museum Store, 300 Congress St., Boston, MA 02210: Free catalog ■ Computer-operated toys, bedroom linens, T-shirts, videos and educational toys, books, posters, mugs, and coasters. 617–426–2800.

Conran's Habitat Mail Order, 921 Eastwind Dr., Westerville, OH 43081: Free catalog ■ Furnishings, decor accessories, linens and pillows, lamps and lighting units, bath accessories, kitchen aids, serving pieces, office aids, stemware, and dishes. 800–462–1769.

Country Loft, Mail Order Department, S. Shore Park, Hingham, MA 02043: Free catalog ■ Lamps and chandeliers, cupboards, cabinets, crocks and carriers, Shaker reproductions, whimsical folk art, whirligigs, baskets, buckets, pillows, braided rugs, and other gifts. 800–225–5408.

Sarah Coventry, P.O. Box 1387, Elk Grove Village, IL 60009: Free information ■ Costume jewelry, watches, hair ornaments, sunglasses, scarves, belts, bags, small leather goods, and nail care sets. 800–252–8770.

Crate & Barrel, P.O. Box 9059, Wheeling, IL 60090: Free catalog ■ Personalized stationery, kitchen accessories, storage systems, sound equipment, decor accessories, and other items. 800–323–5461.

The Crow's Nest Birding Shop, 159 Sapsucker Woods Rd., Ithaca, NY 14850: Free catalog ■ Books and gifts for bird enthusiasts. 607–254–2400.

Cumberland General Store, Rt. 3, Box 81, Crossville, TN 38555: Catalog $3.75 ■ Old-fashioned gifts. Includes hand pumps, windmills, wood cooking ranges, gardening tools, cast-iron ware, farm bells, buggies, blacksmithing equipment, and harnesses. 800–334–4640.

The Daily Planet, P.O. Box 1313, New York, NY 10013: Free catalog ■ Novelties, gifts, stationery, musical instruments, T-shirts, jewelry, African accents, reproduction memorabilia from the past, toys, and other items from worldwide locations. 212–334–0006.

Darke & Reinhold, 11 Market Square, Newburyport, MA 01950: Free information ■ Gifts, clothing, and accessories from around the world. 800–822–3623; 508–463–2040 (in MA).

John Deere & Company, 1400 3rd Ave., Moline, IL 61265: Free catalog ■ Planters and outdoor furniture, fireplace and decor accessories, gifts for pets, playthings for children, picnic accessories, lawn care and garden aids, mailboxes, and birdhouses and feeders. 800–544–2122.

Down's Collectors Showcase, 2200 S. 114th St., P.O. Box 27904, Milwaukee, WI 53227: Free catalog ■ Collectible figurines, miniatures, thimbles, music boxes, mugs and steins, country items, plates, art, and porcelain. 800–558–4200.

Walter Drake & Sons, Drake Building, Colorado Springs, CO 80940: Free catalog ■ Personalized stationery, toys, household items, clothing, decor accessories, office accessories, and hundreds of other items. 719–596–3853.

Early Winters, Inc., P.O. Box 4333, Portland, OR 97208: Free catalog ■ Men's and women's outdoor gifts and equipment, ski wear and accessories, and clothing. 800–821–1286.

18th Century Merchant, 3591 Forest Haven Ln., Chesapeake, VA 23321: Free catalog ■ Brass and pewter accents, colonial china, kitchen needs, toiletries, books, music, and needlework. 804–483–6171.

El Paso Saddleblanket Company, Inc., 601 N. Oregon, El Paso, TX 79901: Free information ■ Casas Grandes pottery, folk art, jewelry, antiques, Indian arts and crafts, kachina dolls, baskets, Zapotec rugs, beaded items, leather goods, clothing, weavings, and other hand-loomed items. 800–351–7847; 800–592–1046 (in TX).

Enticements, 570 Franklin Ave., Mount Vernon, NY 10550: Free catalog ■ Clothing, intimate sleeping attire, sweaters, decor accessories, closet storage aids, and kitchen accessories. 800–243–4300.

Especially Maine, Kennebunkport, ME 04046: Free catalog ■ Gifts in a New England-style. 207–985–3749.

Eximious, 1000 Greenbay Rd., Winnetka, IL 60093: Free catalog ■ Travel aids, desk and office accessories, playing cards, garden accessories, and American crafts. 708–446–8171.

Expressions from Potpourri, 120 N. Meadows Rd., Medfield, MA 02052: Free catalog ■ Toys and puzzles for children and adults, jewelry and watches, note cards and stationery, and decor accessories. 508–359–5440.

The Faith Mountain Company, P.O. Box 199, Sperryville, VA 22740: Free catalog ■ Herbs and flowers, clothing, home furnishings, garden accessories, and American crafts. 800–822–7238.

Fingerhut, 11 McLeland Rd., St. Cloud, MN 56395: Free catalog ■ Kitchen accessories, china and flatware, cookware, furniture, curtains and draperies, pillows and bedroom coordinates, bathroom furnishings, jewelry and watches, clothing, decor accessories, tools, high-tech electronics, and toys.

Finishing Touches, 4555 Lyman Dr., Hilliard, OH 43026: Free catalog ■ Kitchen and bathroom accessories and fixtures, handmade finials, oil paintings, music boxes, handmade brass ornaments, lamps and other lighting fixtures, telephones, architectural accouterments, country crafts, and decor accessories. 800–468–2240.

Flying Panda Gifts, 1259 El Camino Real, Ste. 153, Menlo Park, CA 94025: Free catalog ■ Gifts for pets and pet owners. 415–327–5207.

F.O.R.C.E. Technologies, Ltd., 45 Duroux Ln., P.O. Box 755, Basalt, CO 81621: Free catalog ■ High-tech devices, personal care and comfort items, clothing, optics and astronomy equipment, spa and massage equipment, watches, and travel aids. 800–922–3545.

Fordham-Scope Catalog, 260 Motor Pkwy., Hauppauge, NY 11788: Free catalog

■ Exercisers, world globes, clocks, weather forecasting equipment and chronometers, luggage, word processors, compact copying systems, decorator telephones, toys, tools, audio equipment, and typewriters. 516–435–8080.

Roberta Fortune's Almanac, 150 Chestnut St., San Francisco, CA 94111: Catalog $2 ■ High-tech items, decor accessories, homewares, limited edition prints, beach toys, bathroom gadgets, gifts for golfers, jewelry, and other items. 800–321–2232.

Fox Ridge Outfitters, Inc., 400 N. Main St., P.O. Box 1700, Rochester, NH 03867: Free catalog ■ Gifts for outdoor sportsmen. Includes clothing, shooter's gear and accessories, guns and parts, solid pine carvings, cookware, knives and cutlery, and other items. 800–243–4570.

Fox's Glass Works, P.O. Box 1177, Damariscotta, ME 04543: Catalog $1 ■ Engraved glass with free-hand calligraphy for gifts and trophies. 207–563–1474.

Frontgate, 4555 Lyman Dr., Hilliard, OH 43026: Free catalog ■ Housewares, mailboxes, kitchen accessories, outdoor furniture, gardening tools, barbecues and charcoal ovens, gifts for pets, intercoms, scales, shower equipment, dart boards, automobile gadgets, sports equipment, heaters, and floor registers. 800–626–6488.

Geary's, 351 N. Beverly Dr., Beverly Hills, CA 90210: Free catalog ■ Silver sculptures; Waterford, Baccarat, and Lalique crystal; Lladro porcelain; Christofle French silverplate; Halcyon enamels; tapestries; dinnerware; and desk accessories. 800–243–2797; 310–273–3344 (in CA).

Gift World, P.O. Box 72742, Davis, CA 95617: Free catalog ■ Music boxes, sculptures and statuary, porcelain, glass figurines, decorator accents, miniatures, designer glassware, lamps, clocks, knives, toys and dolls, fishing gear, and holiday decorations. 916–758–8731.

Grand Finale, P.O. Box 620049, Dallas, TX 75262: Catalog $2 (refundable) ■ Women's clothing, furniture, luggage, jewelry, bedroom furnishings, and decor accessories. 214–556–6035.

The Great Living Catalog, 5051 Hwy. 7, P.O. Box 16058, Minneapolis, MN 55416: Free catalog ■ Cooking equipment, kitchen aids, bathroom accessories, electronics, telephones, clothing, health aids, travel and

vacation take-alongs, bird houses and feeders, outdoor equipment, furniture, serving pieces, entertainment accessories, and games. 800–631–5050; 612–925–9018 (in MN).

W.M. Green & Company, Hwy. 64 East, P.O. Box 278, Robersonville, NC 27871: Free catalog ■ Gifts for adults and children. 800–482–5050.

Hammacher Schlemmer, Operations Center, 2515 E. 43rd St., P.O. Box 182256, Chattanooga, TN 37422: Free catalog ■ Gifts for the entire family. 800–233–4800.

Hanover House, P.O. Box 2, Hanover, PA 17333: Free catalog ■ Clothing, gardening supplies, household aids, jewelry, and novelties. 717–633–3366.

Haverhills, 139 Townsend St., San Francisco, CA 94107: Free catalog ■ Gifts for the home, traveling, office, and for personal enjoyment. 800–882–3050.

Hawk Meadow of New England, Rt. 1, Box 182B, Perkinsville, VT 05151: Free catalog ■ Handcrafted clothing, art, furniture, quilts, fireplace accessories, dinnerware, and baskets. 802–263–9400.

Heartland America, 6978 Shady Oak Rd., Eden Prairie, MN 55344: Free catalog ■ High-tech electronics, luggage, games, office and home furniture, audio and stereo equipment, optics and astronomy equipment, exercise equipment, household accessories, telephones, computer equipment, tools, and leather goods. 800–966–1233.

The Hemmeter Collection, 1999 Avenue of the Stars, Los Angeles, CA 90067: Free catalog ■ Sculptures, women's clothing, jewelry, decor accessories, ceramics and pottery, lamps, vases, and other gifts. 800–533–9660.

Herrington, 3 Symmes Dr., Londonderry, NH 03053: Catalog $2 ■ Automotive accessories and tools, photographic and video equipment, compact discs, disc and cassette storage cabinets, gifts for music lovers, and astronomy equipment. 603–437–4638.

Hoffritz, 515 W. 24th St., New York, NY 10011: Catalog $1 ■ Optics, knives and scissors, kitchen aids, clocks, travel aids, luggage, flashlights, calculators, games, yogurt makers, and other gifts from worldwide sources. 212–924–7300.

Holst, Inc., Box 370, Tawas City, MI 48764: Catalog $2 (refundable) ■ Country

items, sundials and weather vanes, housewares, figurines, and holiday decorations. 517–362–5664.

The Home Book, 628 Santa Cruz Ave., Menlo Park, CA 94025: Free catalog ■ Decor accessories, lamps, kitchen accessories, serving pieces, tools, bathroom and shower accessories, and home and office furniture. 800–345–5233.

Home Trends, 779 Mt. Read Blvd., Rochester, NY 14606: Free catalog ■ Gifts for adults and children. 800–426–6257.

The Horchow Collection, P.O. Box 620048, Dallas, TX 75262: Free catalog ■ Items for the dining room and kitchen, den and bar, and bedroom. 800–395–5397.

The Horse Connection, P.O. Box 691, Pottsdown, PA 19464: Catalog $1 ■ Equestrian gifts, jewelry, and clothing. 800–782–9491.

House of Tyrol, P.O. Box 909, Alpenland Center, Helen Highway/75 North, Cleveland, GA 30528: Free catalog ■ Musical cuckoo clocks, crystal, porcelain, lamps, music boxes, pillows, knitted items, decor accessories, bar accessories, collector plates, pewter, tapestries, cards, Alpine hat pins, Christmas decorations, and folk music videos. 800–241–5404.

Impact 2000, 60 Irons St., Toms River, NJ 08753: Free catalog ■ Gifts and accessories. 908–370–4422.

Linda Jioia Gifts, 312 Beechvale Ct., San Jose, CA 95119: Free catalog ■ Music boxes, cork sculptures, miniature statuary, stone and wood carvings, handcarved eagles, dollhouse miniatures, novelties, household items, cosmetics and toiletries, and other giftware. 408–225–5655.

Just Cats, 244 E. 60th St., New York, NY 10022: Free information ■ Gifts for cat lovers and their cats. 212–888–CATS.

David Kay, Inc., One Jenni Ln., Peoria, IL 61614: Free catalog ■ Planters, bird houses, furniture, pool and backyard toys, fireplace accessories, games, sculptures, and wind chimes. 800–535–9917.

Charles Keath, Ltd., P.O. Box 48800, Atlanta, GA 30362: Free catalog ■ Women's clothing, jewelry, watches, decor accessories, luggage and purses, and fireplace accessories. 800–388–6565.

Miles Kimball Company, 41 W. 8th Ave., Oshkosh, WI 54901: Free catalog ■

Hundreds of gifts and gadgets from around the world. 414–231–3800.

Lane Luggage, 1148 Connecticut Ave. NW, Washington, DC 20036: Free catalog ■ Luggage, electronic gifts and gadgets, toys and games, desk accessories, and decor accessories. 202–452–1146.

Left Hand Center, 4400 Excelsior Blvd., St. Louis Park, MN 55416: Catalog $1 ■ Gifts for left-handers. 612–926–6033.

Lefthanders International, P.O. Box 8249, Topeka, KS 66608: Catalog $2 ■ Items for lefties. 913–234–2177.

Lembick, 2330 Old Middlefield Way, Mountain View, CA 94043: Free catalog ■ Collectible miniatures, kitchen and table accessories, serving pieces, pottery, music box cake tops, jewelry, children's gifts, and decorator accents. 800–825–1237.

Lynchburg Hardware & General Store, 39 Main St., Lynchburg, TN 37352: Catalog $1 ■ Gifts, novelty items, housewares, tools, and gardening supplies. 615–759–7184.

Markline, P.O. Box 8, Elmira, NY 14902: Free catalog ■ Electronics, desk accessories, telephones, garden aids and tools, furniture, homewares, doll houses, watches, winter sports equipment, games, and automotive accessories. 800–225–8390.

Mature Wisdom, P.O. Box 28, Hanover, PA 17333: Free catalog ■ Kitchen and bathroom aids, baby gifts, desk accessories, shoes, lingerie and clothing, and travel aids. 717–633–3323.

Metropolitan Museum of Art, Special Service Office, Middle Village, NY 11381: Catalog $1 ■ Greeting cards, note cards, ornaments, books, jewelry, ties, frames, calendars, and other reproductions from museum collections. 800–468–7386.

Minneapolis Institute of Art, 2400 3rd Ave. South, Minneapolis, MN 55404: Free catalog ■ Art reproductions and other gifts. 612–870–3046.

Moby Dick Marine Specialties, 27 William St., New Bedford, MA 02740: Catalog $5 ■ Nautical gifts, decor accessories, and scrimshaw. 800–343–8044; 800–732–5700 (in MA).

Morning Mail, P.O. Box 72, Covington, GA 30209: Free information ■ Gifts for the home and office. Includes personalized stationery. 800–241–0854.

Claire Murray, Inc., P.O. Box 1089, North Charlestown, NH 03630: Catalog $5 (refundable) ■ Handpainted ceramics, quilts, and hand-hooked rugs. 800–323–YARN.

Museum Collections, 4555 Lyman Dr., Hilliard, OH 43026: Free catalog ■ Museum replicas. 800–442–2460.

Museum of Fine Arts, Boston, Catalog Sales Dept., P.O. Box 1044, Boston, MA 02120: Catalog $2 ■ Museum replicas of items from collections. 800–225–5592.

Museum of Modern Art New York, Mail Order Department, P.O. Box 2534, West Chester, PA 19380: Catalog $3 ■ Museum replicas of items from collections. 212–708–9888.

Museum Replicas Limited, P.O. Box 840, Conyers, GA 30207: Catalog $1 ■ Reproductions of historic weapons and period battle wear.

Music Stand, 1 Rockdale Plaza, Lebanon, OH 03766: Free catalog ■ Gifts with a music theme, candies, gift baskets, trophies, plaques, and certificates. 802–295–9222.

Mystic Seaport Museum Stores, Mystic, CT 06355: Free catalog ■ Gifts with a seafaring theme. 800–662–6323.

National Geographic Society, P.O. Box 2806, Washington, DC 20013: Free catalog ■ Books, games, videos, maps and globes, travel aids, and magazine subscriptions. 301–869–3485.

The Nature Company, Home Office, 750 Hearst Ave., Berkeley, CA 94710: Free catalog ■ Jewelry made from natural materials, high-tech devices, scientific gadgets, T-shirts, books, sculptures, optics, clocks, garden accessories, puzzles and toys, reproductions of archaeological finds, and other items. 800–227–1114.

Old Village Shop, Hanover, PA 17333–0008: Free catalog ■ Unusual and classic gifts. Toys, religious gifts, kitchen aids, clothing and intimate apparel, and novelties. 717–633–3311.

Oriental Trading Company, Inc., P.O. Box 3407, Omaha, NE 68103: Free catalog ■ Toys, giftwares, novelties, fund raisers, carnival supplies, and holiday and seasonal items. 800–228–0475.

Orvis Manchester, Historic Rt. 7A, Manchester, VT 05254: Free catalog ■ Men's and women's clothing, country gifts,

rugs, fireplace accessories, gifts for the family pet, kitchen accessories, luggage, lamps, and fishing accessories. 800–548–9548.

The Paragon, 89 Tom Harvey Rd., P.O. Box 995, Westerly, RI 02891: Free catalog ■ Casual clothing, housewares, decor accessories, bathroom items, and games and toys. 800–343–3095.

Claudette Penot Collection, 145 W. 86th St., New York, NY 10024: Free catalog ■ Clothing, leather accessories, jewelry, children's gifts, crafts, and other gifts for men. 212–580–2956.

Personal Creations, 231 Frontage Rd., Burr Ridge, IL 60521: Free catalog ■ Frames, office and desk accessories, leather goods, and gifts for sports enthusiasts, brides and grooms, pets, and homes. 800–326–6626.

The Personal Touch, 409 William St., P.O. Box 1623, Elmira, NY 14902: Free catalog ■ Personalized stationery and gifts. 607–733–6313.

Pigxies Enterprises, Inc., P.O. Box 9566, Laguna Beach, CA 92677: Free catalog ■ Everything for pig lovers and collectors. Includes clothing for adults and children, maternity clothing, kitchen accessories, and stationery. 800–752–6901.

Pitt Petri, 378 Delaware Ave., Buffalo, NY 14202: Free catalog ■ Home accessories and crystal, silverware and silver serving pieces, Lladro figurines, personal accessories, porcelain and china, home bar accessories, ceramics, decor accessories, children's clothing, dolls, and other gifts. 800–345–0053.

Plimoth Plantation Museum Shops, P.O. Box 1620, Plymouth, MA 02360: Free catalog ■ Gifts that depict the Colonial, Federal, Frontier, and Civil War periods of American history. 508–746–1622.

Plow & Hearth, 301 Madison Rd., P.O. Box 830, Orange, VA 22960: Free catalog ■ Gardening tools and accessories, birdhouses and feeders, porch and lawn furniture, fireplace accessories, and gifts for pets. 800–866–6072.

Polish Peddler, 1754 Boston Rd., Hinckley, OH 44233: Free catalog ■ Gifts with a Polish theme. Includes folk arts and crafts, novelties, music, literature, clothing, dolls, needle crafts, note cards and stationery, and posters. 216–237–6924.

Post Scripts from Joan Cook, 3200 SE 14th Ave., Fort Lauderdale, FL 33350: Free catalog ■ Women's and children's clothing, toys, home accessories, luggage, personal care items, and electronic gadgets. 305–761–2350.

Potpourri, 120 N. Meadows Rd., Medfield, MA 02052: Free catalog ■ Jewelry, clothing, party items, games, and decor accessories. 508–359–5440.

Pottery Barn, Mail Order Dept., P.O. Box 7044, San Francisco, CA 94120: Free catalog ■ Gifts for home renovation projects, celebrations, and festive occasions. 800–922–9934.

Promises Kept, Inc., 2525 Xenium Ln., P.O. Box 47368, Plymouth, MN 55447: Free catalog ■ Accessories for porches and patios; items for picnics, outings, and outdoor cooking; Ping-Pong, croquet, and other games; T-shirts; walking staffs; luggage and carriers; water aerobic and swimming aids; health and personal care products; furniture; bathroom accessories; home office furniture and organizers; safes; air filters; portable television sets; kitchen accessories; and other family gifts. 800–989–3545.

Rand McNally & Company, P.O. Box 1697, Skokie, IL 60076: Free catalog ■ Gifts for sports enthusiasts, health and exercise equipment, maps, world globes, books, videos, clocks, prints, travel aids, and watches. 800–234–0679.

Red Rose Collection, P.O. Box 1859, Burlingame, CA 94011: Free catalog ■ Books and tapes, art works, jewelry, tools, games, decor accessories, and toiletries. 415–692–4500.

Remington Products, Inc., 40 Main St., P.O. Box 6158, Bridgeport, CT 06606: Free catalog ■ Bathroom aids, office accessories, and gifts for travelers and outdoor enthusiasts. 203–332–9799.

Rodco Products, P.O. Box 944, Columbus, NE 68602: Catalog 50¢ ■ High-tech equipment and accessories for the home and office. 800–323–2799.

L.L. Rue Enterprises, 138 Millbrook Rd., Blairstown, NJ 07825: Free catalog ■ Books, video tapes, and gifts for photographers and outdoor enthusiasts. 908–362–6616.

The Scope Catalog, 260 Motor Pkwy., Hauppauge, NY 11788: Free catalog ■ High-tech items, sporting items, things for the pool and beach, bar accessories, serving pieces, kitchen accessories, personal care items, toys, outdoor items, video and audio aids, tools, and travel accessories. 800–344–6325.

Scully & Scully, Inc., 506 Park Ave., New York, NY 10022: Free catalog ■ Handcrafted reproductions of 18th-century enamels by English artisans, figurines, furniture, books and games, men's clothing and accessories, crystal, and home office aids. 800–223–3717; 212–755–2590 (in NY).

Seacraft Classics, 6615 N. Scottsdale Rd., Scottsdale, AZ 85250: Free catalog ■ Handbuilt, detailed models of 19th-century ships and boats, with hardwood display stands and brass name plates. 800–356–1987; 602–951–9518 (in AZ).

Serengeti, P.O. Box 349, Ester FL 33928: Free catalog ■ Wildlife apparel and gifts. 800–426–2852.

Service Merchandise Catalog Showroom, Mail Order Dept., P.O. Box 24600, Nashville, TN 37202: Free catalog ■ Homewares, toys and games, hobby accessories, and jewelry. 615–251–6666.

SGF Gifts & Furnishings Catalog, P.O. Box 620047, Dallas, TX 75262: Catalog $3 ■ Dining room table accessories and linens, furniture, luggage and attache cases, gifts for children, and jewelry. 214–484–1517.

Sharper Image, 650 Davis St., San Francisco, CA 94111: Catalog $1 ■ Health and exercise equipment, toys, calculators, watches, pet products, clocks, telephones, and sunglasses. 800–344–4444.

Ship's Hatch, 10376 Main St., Fairfax, VA 22030: Brochure $1 ■ Military patches, pin and insignia, official USN ship ball caps, ship's clocks, hatchcover tables, nautical and military gifts, jewelry, lamps, lanterns, ship's wheels, custom military-style tables, and jewelry boxes. 703–691–1670.

Showboat Dancewear & Gifts, 12408 Hesper Rd., Victorville, CA 92392: Free information ■ Shoes, dancewear, gifts, and custom jewels. 619–243–2363.

Signals Catalog, P.O. Box 64428, St. Paul, MN 55164: Free catalog ■ Books, T-shirts, sweatshirts, video tapes, cassette tapes, and other items. 800–669–5225.

Singer Direct, Inc., 135 Raritan Center Pkwy., P.O. Box 1912, Edison, NJ 08818: Free catalog ■ Gifts for the whole family. 800–877–7392.

Sketches, P.O. Box 48350, Norcross, GA 30362: Free catalog ■ Women's clothing and accessories, decor accessories, and other gifts. 800–388–6565; 449–3100 (in Atlanta).

Smithsonian Institution, Dept. 0006, Washington, DC 20073: Free catalog ■ Gifts, toys, games, books, puzzles, and other replicas from Smithsonian Institution collections. 202–357–1826.

Solutions, P.O. Box 6878, Portland, OR 97228: Free catalog ■ Home accessories, tableware, jewelry, exercise equipment, household aids, and travel accessories. 800–821–1279.

Spencer Gifts, P.O. Box 1700, Pleasantville, NJ 08232: Free catalog ■ Personalized stationery, toys, clothing, office and kitchen accessories, and novelties. 800–445–9618.

Sporty's Preferred Living Catalog, Clermont Airport, Batavia, OH 45103: Free catalog ■ Garden aids, outdoor furniture, sundials, mailboxes, gourmet meat smokers, portable refrigerators, kitchen aids and cutlery, embroidered sport shirts, automotive aids, sports equipment, table games, toys, optics, gifts for pets, and weather forecasting equipment. 800–543–8633.

George Stafford & Sons, 808 Smith Ave., P.O. Box 2055, Thomasville, GA 31799: Free catalog ■ Jewelry, luggage, shoes, books on the outdoors, mugs and dishes, men's and women's clothing, and other items. 912–226–4306.

Sturbridge Yankee Workshop, P.O. Box 9797, Portland, ME 04104: Free catalog ■ Home furnishings, country crafts, Victorian- and Shaker-styled items, and kitchen and bathroom accessories. 800–231–8060.

Sundance Catalog, Customer Service Center, 780 W. Layton Ave., Salt Lake City, UT 84104: Free catalog ■ Sculptures, lamps, stoneware, furniture, jewelry, candleholders, decor accessories, clothing, and toys. 800–422–2770.

Super Locomotion, Inc., 1213 Elko Dr., Sunnyvale, CA 94708: Free catalog ■ High-tech gifts, automotive accessories, travel aids, children's gifts, and games. 800–525–2468.

Tapestry, P.O. Box 46, Hanover, PA 17333: Free catalog ■ Decor accessories, nostalgic Americana, office accessories, imported gifts, fun and fantasy items, and holiday specials. 717–633–3319.

Taylor Gifts, 355 E. Conestoga Rd., Wayne, PA 19087: Free catalog ■ Gifts and novelties. 215–293–3613.

Think Big, 390 W. Broadway, New York, NY 10012: Free catalog ■ Unusual and oversized gags and gifts. 800–221–7019; 212–925–7300 (in NY).

Norm Thompson, P.O. Box 3999, Portland, OR 97208: Free catalog ■ Kitchen and bath aids, automotive accessories, storage and closet organizers, clothing, shoes and boots, high-tech gadgets, and other gifts. 800–547–1160.

Thoroughbred Racing Calendar, Warsaw, VA 22572: Free catalog ■ Calendars and limited edition prints with pictures of famous racing horses, handcrafted fiberglass mailboxes, doormats, sweatshirts and T-shirts, mugs, glasses, jewelry, and wall clocks. 800–777–RACE.

Tiffany & Company, Customer Service, 801 Jefferson Rd., Parsippany, NJ 07054: Free catalog ■ Jewelry, lead crystal adapted from Frank Lloyd Wright designs, watches, Tiffany colognes and perfumes, cultured pearls, serving pieces, pens and pencils, and desk accessories. 201–428–0570.

Tonquish Creek Fire Company, Plymouth, MI 48170: Catalog $1 (refundable) ■ Fire fighting-themed books, buckles, needlework, and toys. 313–451–0161.

Touchstone, 5505 36th St. SE, Grand Rapids, MI 49512: Free catalog ■ Colonial-style desk accessories, stained glass, lamps, walking canes, luggage, porcelain, paperweights, bathroom accessories, furniture, music boxes, stoneware, clocks, and pillows. 616–957–1717.

Trifles, P.O. Box 620048, Dallas, TX 75262: Free catalog ■ Clothing and accessories for men, women, and children; jewelry; coffee and tea service sets; personalized stationery; porcelain and bone china; linens; toys; and fireplace accessories, crystal, luggage, and furniture. 214–556–6055.

Troll Family Gift Catalog, 100 Corporate Dr., Mahwah, NJ 07430: Free catalog ■ Clocks, electronic baby sitters, photo albums, stationery, kitchen gadgets, toys, books, cassettes, and other gifts. 800–247–6106.

Tuesday Morning, 16621 Inwood Rd., Dallas, TX 75244: Free catalog ■ Save 50 percent or more on gifts from worldwide sources. 800–999–7061.

Unicef, 1 Children's Blvd., P.O. Box 182233, Chattanooga, TN 37422: Free catalog ■ Thank you, greeting, and note cards; toys; limited edition plates; gifts; and postcards. 800–553–1200.

United States Purchasing Exchange, United States Purchasing Exchange Bldg., North Hollywood, CA 91611: Free catalog ■ Household aids for cleaning and making repairs, novelties and toys, personal care items, clothing and lingerie, telephones, clocks, kitchen accessories, jewelry, automotive aids, tools, bathroom towels and accessories, and other items.

Vermont Country Store, Mail Order Office, P.O. Box 3000, Manchester Center, VT 05255: Free catalog ■ Gifts from New England. Includes clothing, shoes, purses, watches, pillows and linens, bed coverings, travel aids, throw rugs, stove top potpourris, cleaning aids, and cooking accessories. 802–362–2400.

Lillian Vernon, Virginia Beach, VA 23479: Free catalog ■ Holiday specialties, clothing, electronic gadgets, jewelry, closet organizers, toys, baby care accessories, kitchen and cooking aids, luggage, and leather accessories. 804–430–1500.

Voron Gifts, P.O. Box 7094, Philadelphia, PA 19149: Catalog $1 ■ Business cards, leather goods, jewelry, personal care items, automotive accessories, gifts for children, toys and games, sports equipment, and tools. 215–440–6163.

The Wedding Fantastic, 2323 Fillmore St., San Francisco, CA 94115: Free catalog ■ Gifts for holidays, weddings, and special celebrations. 800–527–6566.

Weekender, P.O. Box 1499, Burnsville, MN 55337: Free catalog ■ Garden and landscaping accessories, outdoor cooking aids, clothing and gloves, security devices and alarms, and high-tech electronic gifts. 800–438–5480.

Weston Bowl Mill, P.O. Box 218, Weston, VT 05161: Free catalog ■ Wooden bowls, crafts, and other accessories for the kitchen and dining room. 800–824–6219.

Whale Gifts, Catalog Order Department, P.O. Box 810, Old Saybrook, CT 06475:

Free catalog ■ Gifts that promote public awareness of the need to conserve and protect the ocean and its inhabitants. Includes clothing, jewelry, books, art, wind chimes, sculptures, rugs, pillows, towels, and drinking glasses. 203–388–4436.

Wild Wings, South Hwy. 61, Lake City, MN 55041: Free catalog ■ Art prints, gun cabinets, solid oak wall clocks, outdoor accents, gifts for fishermen and animal lovers, and note cards. 800–445–4833.

Williams-Sonoma, Mail Order Dept., P.O. Box 7456, San Francisco, CA 94120: Free catalog ■ Kitchenware gourmet foods, and other gifts. 800–541–1262.

Winterthur Museum & Gardens, Catalog Division, 100 Enterprise Pl., Dover, DE 19901: Catalog $2 ■ American art, jewelry, playing cards, lamps, dinnerware, clocks, planters, wind chimes, garden sculptures, and other reproductions from the Henry Francis du Pont Winterthur Museum. 800–767–0500.

Wireless, P.O. Box 64422, St. Paul, MN 55164: Catalog $1 ■ T-shirts and sweatshirts, old time radio broadcasts, toy banks, coffee mugs, Disney cartoons on video, books, wind chimes, and electronics. 800–669–9999.

World Wildlife Fund Catalog, P.O. Box 224, Peru, IN 46970: Free catalog ■ Wildlife theme gifts. Includes clothing, books, games, coasters, coffee mugs, puzzles, note pads, kitchen accents, carryall bags, candlesticks, sculptures, wind chimes, braided door rugs, bird feeders, place mats, and umbrellas. 800–833–1600.

Writewell Company, 5850 W. 80th St., Indianapolis, IN 46278: Free catalog ■ Decor accessories, household items, stationery, books, home office supplies, games, rubber stamps, videos, business cards, and other gifts. 317–871–6710.

Adam York, 340 Poplar St., Hanover, PA 17333: Free catalog ■ Computerized games, typewriters and portable word processors, office furniture, bathroom aids, exercise equipment, electronics, telephones, radar detectors, outdoor accessories, and video equipment. 717–633–3333.

Your Exceptional Home, W.M. Green & Company, Hwy. 64 East, P.O. Box 278, Robersonville, NC 27871: Free catalog ■ Gifts and home accessories. 800–482–5050.

Zippo Manufacturing Company, 33 Barbour St., Bradford, PA 16701: Free catalog ■ Pens and pencils, key rings, money clips, knives, wooden desk accessories, lighters, golf balls, and other items. 814–362–4541.

Zucker's Fine Gifts, 151 W. 26th St., New York, NY 10001: Free catalog ■ Save up to 60 percent on Hummel, Swarovski silver and crystal, Waterford crystal, Lladro items, and other gifts. 212–989–1450.

Religious Gifts

Abbey Press, 334 Hill Dr., St. Meinrad, IN 47577: Free catalog ■ Religious gifts and other items for people of Christian faith. 812–357–8251.

Jeffrey Allon, 5 Bayard Rd., Apt. 919, Pittsburgh, PA 15213: Free information ■ Handcrafted Judaic works of art. Includes ketubahs for Jewish weddings and anniversaries. 412–683–8838.

Ascalon Studios, 115 Atlantic Ave., Berlin, NJ 08009: Free information ■ Judaic art that includes stained glass windows, arks, menorahs, eternal lights, sculptures, endowment and Yahrzeit walls, memorials, and tapestries. 609–768–3779.

Biblical Archaeology Society, 3000 Connecticut Ave. NW, Ste. 300, Washington, DC 20008: Free catalog ■ Biblical-themed gifts. 202–387–8888.

Fortress Church Supply Store, 2900 Queen Ln., Philadelphia, PA 19129: Free catalog ■ Religious gifts and other items for people of Christian faith. 215–848–6800.

Gallerie Robin, 6808 Pennywell Dr., Nashville, TN 37205: Free catalog ■ Judaic art, graphics, and handcrafted gifts. 800–635–8279.

Hamakor Judaica, Inc., P.O. Box 48836, Niles, IL 60659: Free catalog ■ Kosher foods, kitchen accessories, Jewish art, watches and pendants, seder dishes, mezuzahs, candelabras, and other items. 800–426–2567.

Jerusalem Products Company, 33 Deer Run Dr., Randolph, NJ 07869: Free information ■ Bar/Bat Mitzvah's haftorahs personalized on parchment scrolled into a carved hardwood case with a velvet bag and lucite stand. 201–895–3231.

Joy Creations, P.O. Box 688, Jacksonville, OR 97530: Free catalog ■ Religious gifts

and other items for people of Christian faith. 503–899–7610.

Trinity Express, Inc., P.O. Box 626, Lutz, FL 33549: Free catalog ■ Christian gifts. Includes bibles, toys and games, jewelry, T-shirts, educational items, and videos and music tapes. 800–741–1463.

YA-EL Imports, Inc., 137 Main St., Danbury, CT 06810: Free catalog ■ Israeli jewelry, handicrafts, and gifts. 203–748–6062.

GLASS COLLECTIBLES

Ruth S. Jordan, Meridale, NY 13806: Free list with long SASE ■ American brilliant period cut glass. 607–746–2082.

Petri's, 731 Bridgeway, Sausalito, CA 94965: Catalog $2 ■ Paperweights, perfume bottles, vases and art glass collectibles, kaleidoscopes, 14K gold jewelry, and Lladro, Chilmark, and Swarovski items. 415–332–6477.

GLOBES

George F. Cram Company, Inc., 301 S. LaSalle St., Indianapolis, IN 46201: Free catalog ■ Maps, atlases, globes, charts, and teaching aids. 800–227–4199; 317–635–5564 (in IN).

Creative Imaginations, 10879 Portal Dr., Los Alamitos, CA 90720: Free information ■ Inflatable globes. 800–942–6487.

Home Library, 160 S. University Dr., Plantation, FL 33324: Free catalog ■ World globes with handcrafted solid wood floor mountings and brass meridians. 305–579–2016.

Replogle Globes, Inc., 2801 S. 25th Ave., Broadview, IL 60153: Free catalog ■ Earth and space globes in desk and floor models. 708–343–0900.

Trippensee Planetarium Company, 301 Cass St., Saginaw, MI 48602: Free catalog ■ World globes in desk and floor models. 517–799–8102.

GO KARTS & MINICARS

CHI Industries, Inc., P.O. Box 1148, Benton Harbor, MI 49022: Free information ■ Utility vehicles with 3 and 4 wheels. 616–849–3400.

Hagstrom's Sales, 2 Dunwoody Park, Atlanta, GA 30338: Catalog $3 ■ Children's miniature classic cars that include a Ford Model T, 1932 Ford Roadster, and 1975 Corvette. 404–393–0363.

Kart World, 1488 Mentor Ave., Painsville, OH 44077: Catalog $3 (refundable) ■ Assembled go karts and minicars, engines, kits, and parts. 216–357–5569.

Performance Speedway, 2810–C Algonquin Ave., Jacksonville, FL 32210: Catalog $5 ■ Electric cars, golf carts, mopeds, moped parts, how-to and repair manuals, and other books.

GOLF

Clothing

Adventure International Corporation, Adventure Gear, 8039 Deering Ave., Canoga Park, CA 91304: Free information ■ Jackets, caps and hats, sweaters, and shirts. 818–594–0380.

All Star Pro Golf Company, Inc., 120 9th St. SW, Clarion, IA 50525: Free information ■ Caps and hats, gloves, jackets, visors, sweaters, and shirts. 800–247–4830; 515–532–2867 (in IA).

Tommy Armour Golf Company, 8350 N. Lehigh Ave., Morton Grove, IL 60053: Free information ■ Gloves, shirts, skirts, slacks, sweaters, and visors. 708–966–6300.

Artcraft Swiss Embroidery Company, 1450 S. Burlington Ave., Los Angeles, CA 90006: Free information ■ Caps and hats, jackets, shirts, sweaters, and visors. 213–385–1646.

Bogner of America, Bogner Dr., Newport, VT 05855: Free information ■ Caps and hats, gloves, jackets, shirts, skirts, slacks, sweaters, and visors. 800–451–4417; 802–334–6507 (in VT).

Broder Brothers, 45555 Port St., Plymouth, MI 48237: Free information ■ Jackets, shirts, sweaters, and visors. 313–454–8971.

Di Fini Knitwear, 395 Brook Ave., Bronx, NY 10454: Free information ■ Shirts, skirts, slacks, socks, and sweaters. 718–993–1122.

E.B. Naturally, Elaine Benedict, Inc., 3050 NW 40th St., Miami, FL 33142: Free information ■ Caps and hats, jackets, shirts, skirts, slacks, socks, sweaters, and visors. 305–634–0463.

Ellesse USA, Inc., 1430 Broadway, New York, NY 10018: Free information ■ Jackets, shirts, skirts, slacks, sweaters, and visors. 212–840–6111.

A.B. Emblem Corporation, P.O. Box 695, Weaverville, NC 28787: Free information ■ Caps and hats, shirts, and sweaters. 800–438–4285; 704–645–3015 (in NC).

Fila Sports, Inc., 145 Park Ln., Brisbane, CA 94006: Free information ■ Caps and hats, gloves, shirts, skirts, slacks, socks, and sweaters. 415–468–6800.

FTM Sports, 14500 SW 119th Ave., Miami, FL 33186: Free information ■ Caps and hats, shirts, skirts, slacks, socks, and sweaters. 800–292–5589; 305–255–2272 (in FL).

M. Handelsman Company, 1323–5 S. Michigan Ave., Chicago, IL 60605: Free information ■ Caps and hats, shirts, socks, sweaters, and visors. 800–621–4454; 312–427–0784 (in IL).

King Louie International, 13500 15th St., Grandview, MO 64030: Free information ■ Caps and hats, jackets, shirts, sweaters, and visors. 800–521–5212; 816–765–5212 (in MO).

Le Coq Sportif, 28 Engelward Dr., Cranbury, NJ 08512: Free information ■ Caps and hats, shoes, shirts, skirts, slacks, socks, and sweaters. 609–655–1515.

Lily's of Beverly Hills, Ltd., 12905 S. Spring St., Los Angeles, CA 90061: Free information ■ Caps and hats, shoes, shirts, skirts, slacks, socks, sweaters, and visors. 800–421–4474; 310–770–0303 (in CA).

MacGregor Golf Clubs, 1601 S. Slappey Blvd., Albany, GA 31708: Free information ■ Caps and hats, shoes, gloves, shirts, skirts, slacks, socks, sweaters, and visors. 912–888–0001.

Marathon Sales, Inc., 6310 Nancy Ridge Rd., San Diego, CA 92121: Free catalog ■ Golf shoes. 800–289–7888.

Marcia Originals, 18324–3 Oxnard St., Tarzana, CA 91356: Free information ■ Jackets, shirts, skirts, slacks, and sweaters. 800–423–5208; 818–881–3588 (in CA).

Munsingwear, Inc., 724 N. 1st St., P.O. Box 1369, Minneapolis, MN 55440: Free information ■ Jackets, shirts, slacks, socks, and sweaters. 612–340–4700.

Ortho-Vent Division, 115 Brand Rd., Salem, VA 24156: Free catalog ■ Golf shoes. 800–848–2929; 703–389–3698 (in VA).

Spalding & Brothers, 425 Meadow St., P.O. Box 901, Chicopee, MA 01021: Free information ■ Caps and hats, gloves, jackets, shirts, skirts, slacks, socks, sweaters, and vests. 413–536–1200.

Sportcap Southeast, 653 W. Michigan St., Orlando, FL 32805: Free information ■ Caps and hats, jackets, shirts, sweaters, and visors. 800–327–9746; 800–356–7734 (in FL).

Teri Sleeper, Inc., Westview Ln., Norwalk, CT 06854: Free information ■ Jackets, shirts, skirts, slacks, socks, sweaters, and visors. 203–854–5561.

T-Shirt City, 4501 W. Mitchell Ave., Cincinnati, OH 45232: Free information ■ Caps and hats, jackets, shirts, sweaters, socks, and visors. 800–543–7230.

Equipment (Manufacturers)

Accuform Golf Clubs, 76 Fordhouse Blvd., Toronto, Ontario, Canada, M8Z 5X7: Free information. 800–668–7873.

Tommy Armour Golf Company, 8350 N. Lehigh Ave., Morton Grove, IL 60053: Free information. 708–966–6300.

Beawood Golf Clubs, 2915 Daimler St., Santa Ana, CA 92705: Free information. 800–PAR–PSSS; 714–756–1220 (in CA).

Bridgestone Golf Clubs, 2760 Pacific Dr., Norcross, GA 30071: Free information. 404–449–6123.

Browning Golf Clubs, 2346 West, 1000 South, Salt Lake City, UT 84104: Free information. 800–666–6033.

Bullet Golf Clubs, Box 25623, Santa Ana, CA 92799: Free information. 800–669–4848.

Cactus Golf Clubs, 14500 SW 119th Ave., Miami, FL 33186: Free information. 800–292–5589.

Callaway Golf Clubs, 2345 Camino Vida Roble, Carlsbad, CA 92008: Free information. 619–931–1771.

Cleveland Golf Clubs, 14508 S. Garfield Ave., Paramount, CA: Free information. 310–630–6363.

Cobra Golf Clubs, 4645 North Ave., Oceanside, CA 92056: Free information. 619–941–9550.

Daiwa Corporation, 7421 Chapman Ave., Garden Grove, CA 92641: Free information. 714–895–6645.

Dunlop Golf Clubs, Box 3070, Greenville, SC 29602: Free information. 803–241–2200.

Ben Hogan Golf Clubs, 2912 W. Pafford St., Fort Worth, TX 76110: Free information. 817–921–2661.

Karsten Manufacturing Golf Clubs, Box 9990, Phoenix, AZ 85068: Free information. 602–277–1300.

Lynx Golf Clubs, 16017 E. Valley Blvd., City of Industry, CA 91749: Free information. 818–961–0222.

MacGregor Golf Clubs, 1601 S. Slappey Blvd., Albany, GA 31708: Free information. 912–888–0001.

Merit Golf Clubs, 4001 Cobb International Blvd., Kenesaw, GA 30144: Free information. 404–499–1415.

Mitsushiba Golf Clubs, 210 W. Baywood Ave., Orange, CA 92665: Free information. 714–282–0137.

Mizuno Corporation, 5125 Peachtree Industrial Blvd., Norcross, GA 30092: Free information. 800–333–7888.

Northwestern Golf Clubs, 4701 N. Ravenswood, Chicago, IL 60640: Free information. 312–275–0500.

Pinseeker Golf Clubs, 3502 S. Susan St., Santa Ana, CA 92704: Free information. 714–979–4500.

PRGR Golf Clubs, 2539 W. 237th St., Ste. D, Torrance, CA 90505: Free information. 310–534–3700.

Progroup Golf Clubs, 6201 Mountain View Rd., Ooltewah, TN 37363: Free information. 615–238–5890.

Pro Select Golf Clubs, 4701 N. Ravenswood, Ste. 1000, Chicago, IL 60640: Free information. 312–275–0500.

RAM Golf Clubs, 2020 Indian Boundary Dr., Melrose Park, IL 60160: Free information. 708–681–5800.

Slotline Golf Clubs, 5252 McFadden Ave., Huntington Beach, CA 92649: Free information. 714–898–2888.

Spalding & Brothers, 425 Meadow St., Chicopee, MA 01021: Free information. 413–536–1200.

Square Two Golf Clubs, 18 Gloria Lane, Fairfield, NJ 07006: Free information. 201–227–7783.

Taylor Made Golf Clubs, 2271 Cosmos Ct., Carlsbad, CA 92009: Free information. 619–931–1991.

Stan Thompson Golf Clubs, 2707 S. Fairfax Ave., Culver City. CA 90232: Free information. 213–870–7228.

Tiger Shark Golf Clubs, 1682 Sabovich St., Mojave, CA 93501: Free information. 805–824–4551.

Titleist Golf Clubs, Box B965, New Bedford, MA 02741: Free information. 508–997–2811.

Ryobi-Toski Golf Clubs, 160 Essex St., Box 576, Newark, OH 43055: Free information. 614–345–9683.

Yamaha Sporting Goods Division, 6600 Orangethorpe Ave., Buena Park, CA 90620: Free information. 800–541–6514; 714–522–9011 (in CA).

Yonex Corporation, 350 Maple Ave., Torrance, CA 90503: Free information. 800–992–6639; 800–772–5522 (in CA).

Equipment (Retailers)

All Star Pro Golf Company, Inc., 120 9th St. SW, Clarion, IA 50525: Free information ■ Clubs, bags and bag covers, grips, head covers, and miscellaneous equipment. 800–247–4830; 515–532–2867 (in IA).

Austad's, 4500 E. 10th St., P.O. Box 1428, Sioux Falls, SD 57196: Free catalog ■ Golfing and other sports equipment and clothing. 800–444–1234.

Auto-Caddy, Inc., P.O. Box 955, Los Altos, CA 94023: Free brochure ■ Battery-operated remote control caddy for golf clubs. 800–782–7535.

B & G Wholesale, 47–09 30th St., Long Island City, NY 11101: Free information ■ Clubs for professional and amateur golfers. 718–706–0100.

Chesal Industries, 2120 W. Florist Ave., P.O. Box 09281, Milwaukee, WI 53209: Free information ■ Golf balls, ball retrievers, ball washers, bags and bag covers, grips, head covers, tubes, miscellaneous equip-ment, and miscellaneous equipment. 414–228–7920.

Custom Golf Clubs, Inc., 10206 North IH–35, Austin, TX 78753: Free catalog ■ Golfing equipment repair supplies, custom golf equipment, clothing, gloves, bags, and accessories. 800–456–3344.

Dorson Sports, Inc., 195 Lauman Ln., P.O. Box 606, Hicksville, NY 11802: Free information ■ Bags and bag covers, grips, head covers, tubes, and other equipment. 800–645–7215; 516–822–2424 (in NY).

Eastern Golf Corporation, 2537 Boston Rd., North Bronx, NY 10467: Free information ■ Golf balls, ball retrievers, golf clubs, and golf course equipment and accessories. 212–547–3918.

Fila Sports, Inc., 145 Park Ln., Brisbane, CA 94006: Free information ■ Clubs, bags and bag covers, grips, and head covers. 415–468–6800.

Florida Golf Warehouse, Inc., 4085 L.B. Mcleod Rd., Orlando, FL 32811: Catalog $1 (refundable) ■ Golfing equipment and supplies, shoes, and shirts. 800–346–6574.

Golf Haus, 700 N. Pennsylvania, Lansing, MI 48906: Free catalog ■ Professional clubs, bags, clothing, umbrellas, and scorekeepers. 517–482–8842.

Golfsmith, 10206 N. Interstate Hwy. 35, Austin, TX 78753: Catalog $1 ■ Golf club components. 800–456–3344.

The Golfworks, P.O. Bx 3008, Newark, OH 43055: Free catalog ■ Components and supplies for customizing and assembling golf clubs, how-to books, and video and audio tapes. 800–848–8358.

Harris International, Inc., 9999 NE Glisan St., Portland, OR 97220: Free information ■ Clubs, bags and bag covers, head covers, and other equipment. 800–547–2880; 503–256–2302 (in OR).

Holabird Sports Discounters, 9004 Yellow Brick Rd., Rossville Industrial Park, Baltimore, MD 21237: Free brochure ■ Save up to 40 percent on equipment and clothing for golf, basketball, tennis, running and jogging, racquetball, and other sports. 410–687–6400.

Jayfro Corporation, Unified Sports, Inc., 976 Hartford Tpk., P.O. Box 400, Waterford, CT 06385: Free catalog ■ Outdoor practice cages, target baffles, and chipping and driving mats. 203–447–3001.

Larry's Golf Discount Center, 21 W. 35th St., New York, NY 10001: Free information ■ Golf equipment and accessories. 212–563–6895.

Las Vegas Discount Golf & Tennis, 5325 S. Valley View Blvd., Ste. 10, Las Vegas, NV 89118: Free catalog ■ Equipment, clothing, and shoes for golf, tennis, racquetball, walking and jogging, and other sports. 702–798–7777.

Al Liebers World of Golf, 146 E. 47th St., New York, NY 10017: Free information ■ Equipment, supplies, and accessories. 212–242–2895.

Lombard's Sporting Goods, 1840 NE 164th St., North Miami Beach, FL 33162: Catalog $1 ■ Professional golf sets, individual clubs, bags, and accessories. 305–944–1166.

Ralph Maltby Enterprises, Inc., P.O. Box 3008, Newark, OH 43055: Free catalog ■ Golf supplies for repair shops, custom club makers, manufacturers, and do-it-yourselfers. 800–848–8358; 800–762–1831 (in OH).

Richard Metz Golf Studio, Inc., 35 E. 50th St., New York, NY 10022: Free information ■ Golf equipment, and accessories, golf club repair services, antique and collectible clubs, video tapes, and books. 212–759–6940.

Nevada Bob's Discount Golf & Tennis, 3333 E. Flamingo Rd., Las Vegas, NV 89121: Free catalog ■ Golf and tennis equipment and supplies. 702–451–3333.

New York Golf Center, 29 W. 36th St., New York, NY 10001: Free information ■ Equipment and accessories. 212–564–2255.

Pennsylvania Sporting Goods, 1360 Industrial Hwy., P.O. Box 451, Southampton, PA 18966: Free information ■ Golf balls, ball retrievers, ball washers, bags and bag covers, grips, head covers, tubes, and other equipment. 800–535–1122.

Prima, 5380 S. Valley View Blvd., Las Vegas, NV 89118: Free information ■ Women's golf clubs. 800–932–1622; 702–736–8801 (in NV).

Professional Golf & Tennis Suppliers, 7825 Hollywood Blvd., Pembroke Pines, FL 33024: Free catalog with long SASE ■ Golf, tennis, and racquetball equipment and supplies. 305–981–7283.

Pro Golf Shop, 8130 N. Lincoln Ave., Skokie, IL 60077: Free catalog ■ Professional equipment. 800–323–4047.

Sam's World of Golf, 7547 Mentor Ave., Mentor, OH 44060: Catalog $2 ■ Golf equipment and accessories. 216–946–3392.

SGD Company, Inc., P.O. Box 5445, Akron, OH 44313: Free information ■ Golf balls, ball retrievers, ball washers, and golf course equipment and accessories. 800–321–3411.

Telepro Golf Shops, 17642 Armstrong Ave., Irvine, CA 92714: Free catalog ■ Professional golf clubs, shoes, carts, and other equipment and accessories. 800–333–9903.

UT Golf, 2346 W. 1500 South, Salt Lake City, UT 84104: Free information ■ Golf club components. 800–666–6033.

Voit Sports, 1451 Pittstand-Victor Rd., 100 Willowbrook Office Park, Fairport, NY 14450: Free information ■ Bags and bag covers, grips, shafts, head covers, tubes, and golf course equipment and accessories. 800–367–8648; 716–385–2390 (in NY).

Wa-Mac, Inc., Highskore Products, Inc., 178 Commerce Rd., P.O. Box 128, Carlstadt, NJ 07072: Free information ■ Golf balls and ball washers, miscellaneous equipment, and golf course equipment and accessories. 800–447–5673; 201–438–7200 (in NJ).

Edwin Watts Golf Shops, P.O. Drawer 1806, Fort Walton Beach, FL 32549: Free catalog ■ Golf clubs, carts, bags, and other equipment and accessories. 800–874–0146.

Wittek Golf Supply Company, Inc., 3650 N. Avondale, Chicago, IL 60618: Free information ■ Clubs, bags and bag covers, grips, head covers, and tubes, and golf course equipment and accessories. 312–463–2636.

Wood Wand Corporation, 2101 Sandhills Blvd., Southern Pines, NC 28387: Free information ■ Golf equipment for amateur and professional golfers. 919–692–2205.

World of Golf, 8130 N. Lincoln Ave., Skokie, IL 60077: Free information ■ Golf equipment, accessories, and supplies for men, women, and juniors. 800–323–4047.

Worthington Golf, 1540 Lowell St., Elyria, OH 44035: Free information ■ Golf balls. 216–322–5401.

Zippo Manufacturing Company, 33 Barbour St., Bradford, PA 16701: Free information ■ Golf balls and golf course equipment and accessories. 814–362–4541.

Left-handed Equipment

Lefties Only, 1972 Williston Rd., South Burlington, VT 05403: Free price list ■ Golf equipment for left-handed persons. 800–533–8437.

Kenneth Smith Golf Clubs, Box 41, Kansas City, MO 64141: Free brochure and fitting chart ■ Left-handed golf clubs. 816–221–6644.

Somerton Springs Golf, 53 Bustleton Pike, Feasterville, PA 19047: Free brochure ■ Left-handed golf clubs, personalized balls, umbrellas, tees, travel covers, putters, jackets, golf bags, and head covers. 800–220–GOLF; 215–355–7276 (in PA).

GREETING CARDS

Frank N. Abate Greeting Cards, 30 E. 42nd St., New York, NY 10017: Free catalog ■ Custom and personalized cards. 212–867–6964.

The Amy Allison Card Shop, P.O. Box 246, Elmira, NY 14902: Free catalog ■ Greeting cards. 607–733–8586.

Amity Hallmark, Ltd., P.O. Box 929, Linden Hill Station, Flushing, NY 11354: Free catalog ■ Business cards, custom stationery, special event cards, and office forms. 718–939–2323.

Associated Photo Company, Box 14270, Cincinnati, OH 45250: Free information ■ Imprinted custom photo Christmas cards. 513–421–6620.

Car Collectables, P.O. Box 221, Madison, CT 06443: Free brochure ■ Christmas cards, note cards, and gifts with an automotive theme. 203–245–2242.

Current, The Current Bldg., Colorado Springs, CO 80941: Free catalog ■ Original designs in greeting cards, stationery, gift wrapping, and decorations; toys; calendars; and other gifts. 800–525–7170; 719–594–4100 (in CO).

The Drawing Board, P.O. Box 620004, Dallas, TX 75262: Free catalog ■ Personalized greeting and calendar cards for all occasions. Available with a stock message, or one you write yourself. 800–845–8575.

Kristin Elliott, Inc., 6 Opportunity Way, Newburyport, MA 01950: Free catalog ■ Boxed notes, gift enclosures, Christmas cards, greeting cards, desk memos, memo pads, postcards, correspondence cards, and gift wrap. 800–922–1899; 508–465–1899 (in MA).

Enfield Stationers, 215 Moody Rd., Enfield, CT 06082: Free catalog ■ Business greeting cards, calendars, and gifts. 203–763–3980.

Faded Rose, P.O. Box 19575, Portland, OR 97219: Brochure $1 ■ Recycled paper greeting cards.

Lady with a Past, Box 365, Seaside, OR 97138: Catalog $1 ■ Nostalgic greeting cards.

Lang Graphics, P.O. Box 99, Delafield, WI 53018: Brochure $3 ■ Wall calendars and greeting cards with a country theme, address books, and engagement calendars. 414–646–2211.

Lazowski Enterprises/Patty Prints, P.O. Box 563, St. Charles, IL 60174: Catalog $1 ■ Greeting cards with a country theme. 708–584–4362.

New England Card Company, Rt. 41, Box 228, West Ossipee, NH 03890: Free brochure ■ Greeting cards with scenes of New England. 800–762–5562; 603–539–5200 (in NH).

Posty Cards, 1600 Olive St., Kansas City, MO 64127: Free catalog ■ Greeting cards. 816–231–9873.

Reindeer House, 3409 W. 44th St., Minneapolis, MN 55410: Free catalog ■ Greeting cards for all occasions and stationery. 800–328–3894.

Renaissance Greeting Cards, P.O. Box 845, Springvale, ME 04038: Free catalog ■ Greeting cards. 800–688–9998; 207–324–4153 (in ME).

Syracuse Cultural Workers, P.O. Box 6367, Syracuse, NY 13217: Free catalog ■ Greeting cards and note cards with environmental, Native American, African American, pacifist themes. 315–474–1132.

Trumble Greetings, c/o Leanin' Tree, 6075 Longbow Dr., Boulder, CO 80301: Catalog $1 ■ Greeting cards that depict America's heritage with country, and wildlife scenes. 800–525–0658; 303–530–7768 (in CO).

Unicef, 1 Children's Blvd., P.O. Box 182233, Chattanooga, TN 37422: Free catalog ■ Thank you, greeting, and note cards; toys; limited edition plates; gifts; and postcards. 800–553–1200.

Victorian Papers, P.O. Box 411332, Kansas City, MO 61141: Free brochure ■ Greeting and note cards for birthdays, holidays and celebrations, graduation, and other special occasions. 816–471–7808.

GUM BALL MACHINES

The Antique Emporium, 1119 Industrial, San Carlos, CA 94070: Free information ■ Jukeboxes, slot machines, pinball machines, candy and gum ball machines, cash registers, and other coin-operated devices. 510–886–1727.

Carousel Industries, Inc., Morton Grove, IL 60053: Free information ■ Gum ball machines, gumballs, and other treats. 800–323–8077.

KAPS Vending, 25137 Lavina Ct., Helmet, CA 92344: Free price list with long SASE ■ Gum ball machines, globes, parts, decals, and gum balls and candies.

GUNS & AMMUNITION

Air Guns & Supplies

Armsport, Inc., P.O. Box 523066, Miami, FL 33152: Free information ■ Air rifles and pistols, scopes, pellets and bb ammunition, and targets. 305–635–7850.

Beeman Precision Arms, Inc., 3440 Airway Dr., Santa Rosa, CA 95403: Catalog $2 ■ Air rifles and pistols, scopes, pellets and bb ammunition, and targets. 707–578–7900.

Benjamin Air Rifle Company, 2678 Chicory Rd., Racine, WI 53403: Free catalog ■ Single shot and repeater air rifles and pistols, scopes, pellets and bb ammunition, and targets. 414–554–7900.

Century International Arms, 80 N. Main St., St. Albans, VT 05478: Free information ■ Air rifles and pistols. 802–527–1252.

Crosman Air Guns, Rt. 5, East Bloomfield, NY 14443: Free information ■ Air rifles and pistols, scopes, pellets and bb ammunition, and targets. 800–828–1495; 716–657–6161 (in NY).

Daisy Manufacturing Company, Inc., P.O. Box 220, Rogers, AR 72757: Free information ■ Air rifles and pistols, scopes, pellets and bb ammunition, and targets. 800–643–3458; 501–636–1200 (in AR).

Dixie Gun Works, Inc., Gunpowder Ln., Union City, TN 38261: Catalog $4 ■ Air rifles and pistols. 800–238–6785.

Eastern Sports Supply, Ltd., P.O. Box 67, Tremont, PA 17981: Free information ■ Air rifles and pistols, scopes, pellets and bb ammunition, and targets. 717–695–3113.

Feline Archery, Inc., 229 Rt. 30 West, Ligonier, PA 15658: Free information ■ Air rifles and pistols, scopes, and targets. 412–238–3673.

Mandall Shooting Supplies, 3616 N. Scottsdale Rd., Scottsdale, AZ 85251: Free information ■ Air guns, scopes, accessories, and ammunition. 602–945–2553.

Ammunition

Activ Industries, Inc., 1000 Zigor Rd., Kearneysville, WV 25430: Free brochure ■ Shotgun shells in a reloadable, all-plastic hull.

Amsec International Ammo Depot, 1849–B Candy Ln. SW, Marietta, GA 30060: Catalog $10 (refundable) ■ Ammunition, camping, hunting, and archery supplies. 800–622–1121.

Badger Shooter's Supply, Inc., 106 S. Harding, Owen, WI 54460: Free catalog ■ Sporting firearms, ammunition, and supplies. 715–229–2101.

Ballistic Products, Inc., 20015 75th Ave. North, Corcoran, MN 55340: Catalog $1 ■ Ammunition supplies. 612–494–WADS.

Blount, Inc., Sporting Equipment Division, P.O. Box 856, Lewiston, ID 83501: Free information ■ Big game hunting bullets and ammunition for rifles and handguns. 800–627–3640.

Broward Shooter's Exchange, 250 S. 60th Ave., Hollywood, FL 33023: Catalog $8 ■ Equipment and supplies for shooting, reloading, and muzzleloading; hunting; and archery. 800–554–9002.

Buffalo Bullet Company, 12637 Los Nietos Rd., Unit A, Santa Fe Springs, CA 90670: Free brochure ■ Bullets for muzzle loaders and other ammunition.

Century International Arms, 80 N. Main St., St. Albans, VT 05478: Free information ■ Ammunition supplies. 802–527–1252.

City Metal Recycling, 4420 N. Santa Fe, Oklahoma City, OK 73118: Free information ■ Bullet-casting metals. 800–228–1266.

Colorado Sutlers Arsenal, P.O. Box 991, Granby, CO 80446: Free information ■ Ammunition supplies. 303–887–2813.

Corbin Manufacturing & Supply, Inc., P.O. Box 2659, White City, OR 97503: Free information with long SASE ■ Ammunition supplies. 503–826–5211.

Dillon Precision Products, Inc., 7442 E. Butherus Dr., Scottsdale, AZ 85260: Free information ■ Reloading equipment. 800–421–7632.

Eastern Sports Supply, Ltd., P.O. Box 67, Tremont, PA 17981: Free information ■ Ammunition supplies. 717–695–3113.

Federal Cartridge Company, 900 Ehlen Dr., Anoka, MN 55303: Free information ■ Ammunition supplies. 612–422–2840.

Feline Archery, Inc., 229 Rt. 30 West, Ligonier, PA 15658: Free information ■ Ammunition supplies. 412–238–3673.

Fisher Enterprises, 655 Main St., Ste. 305, Edmonds, WA 98020: Free information ■ Ammunition supplies. 206–776–4365.

Gander Mountain, Inc., P.O. Box 248, Gander Mountain, Wilmot, WI 53192: Free catalog ■ Reloading supplies. 800–558–9418.

Robert W. Hart & Son, Inc., 401 Montgomery St., Nescopeck, PA 18635: Free information ■ Ammunition supplies. 717–752–3655.

Hogdon Powder Company, Inc., P.O. Box 2934, Shawnee Mission, KS 66201: Free information ■ Propellants for rifle, pistol, and shotgun ammunition.

Hornady Manufacturing Company, Box 1848, Grand Island, NE 68802: Catalog $2 ■ Ammunition supplies. 308–382–1390.

Lawrence Leather Company, 709 E. McNeil St., P.O. Box 1479, Lillington, NC 27546: Free information ■ Ammunition supplies. 800–822–1857; 919–893–2627 (in NC).

Magnus Bullet Company, Inc., P.O. Box 2225, Birmingham, AL 35201: Free information ■ Ammunition supplies. 205–785–3357.

Mayville Engineering Company, Inc., 715 South St., Mayville, WI 53050: Free brochure ■ Shotgun shell reloading equipment. 414–387–4500.

Michaels of Oregon Company, P.O. Box 13010, Portland, OR 97213: Free information ■ Ammunition supplies. 503–255–6890.

Nosler Bullets, Inc., P.O. Box 671, Bend, OR 97709: Free catalog ■ Hunting bullets. 503–382–3921.

Pennsylvania Sporting Goods, 1360 Industrial Hwy., P.O. Box 451, Southampton, PA 18966: Free information ■ Ammunition supplies. 800–523–1132.

Remington Arms Company, Inc., 1007 Market St., Wilmington, DE 19898: Free information ■ Ammunition supplies. 302–773–5292.

Southern Gun & Tackle, Inc., 1349 NW 45th Ave., Opa-Locka, FL 33054: Free information ■ Ammunition supplies. 305–685–8451.

Antique, Muzzleloading & Replica Guns

Antique Arms Company, David F. Saunders, 1110 Cleveland, Monett, MO 65708: Free information ■ Antique muzzleloading guns, accessories, and equipment. 417–235–6501.

Antique Gun Parts, Inc., 1118 S. Braddock Ave., Pittsburgh, PA 15218: Free information ■ Antique muzzleloading guns and parts, accessories, and supplies. 412–241–1811.

Armoury, Inc., Rt. 202, New Preston, CT 06777: Free information ■ Blackpowder handguns and rifles, blackpowder, kits, and replica guns. 203–868–0001.

Armsport, Inc., P.O. Box 523066, Miami, FL 33152: Free information ■ Antique handguns, rifles, kits, and accessories. 305–635–7850.

Collector's Armoury, 800 Slaters Ln., P.O. Box 59, Alexandria, VA 22313: Free information ■ Replica and antique guns. 800–544–3456.

Connecticut Valley Arms, Inc., 5988 Peachtree Corners East, Norcross, GA

30071: Free catalog ■ Reproductions of Sam Colt's mid-1880 handguns, assembled, other blackpowder handguns, rifles, and kits. 404–449–4687.

Daisy Manufacturing Company, Inc., P.O. Box 220, Rogers, AR 72757: Free information ■ Replica guns. 800–643–3458; 501–636–1200 (in AR).

Dixie Gunworks, Inc., Gunpowder Ln., Union City, TN 38261: Catalog $4 ■ Antique and replica blackpowder handguns and rifles, accessories, and blackpowder. 800–238–6785.

Eastern Sports Supply, Ltd., P.O. Box 67, Tremont, PA 17981: Free information ■ Blackpowder rifles and handguns, kits, and accessories. 717–695–3113.

EMF Company, 1900 Warner Ave., Santa Ana, CA 92705: Catalog $1 ■ Replica U.S. Cavalry and U.S. Artillery revolvers. 714–261–6611.

Euroarms of America, Inc., 1501 Lenoir Dr., Winchester, VA 22601: Free information ■ Blackpowder rifles and handguns, replica guns, kits, and accessories. 703–662–1863.

Firearms Import & Export Company, P.O. Box 4866, Hialeah Lakes, FL 33014: Free information ■ Blackpowder and muzzleloading guns. 305–685–5966.

N. Flayderman & Company, Inc., P.O. Box 2446, Fort Lauderdale, FL 33303: Catalog $10 ■ Antique guns, swords, knives, and western, nautical, and other military collectibles. 305–761–8855.

Fulmer's Antique Firearms, Box 792, Detroit Lakes, MN 56501: Catalog $2 ■ Antique firearms.

Golden Age Arms Company, 115 E. High St., Ashley, OH 43003: Catalog $4 ■ Muzzleloading guns, parts, supplies, and books. 614–747–2488.

Hansen Cartridge Company, 244 Old Post Rd., Southport, CT 06490: Free information ■ Replica and antique guns. 203–259–6222.

House of Muskets, Inc., P.O. Box 4640, Pagosa Springs, CO 81157: Free information ■ Replica and antique guns and gun parts. 303–731–2295.

Log Cabin Sport Shop, 8010 Lafayette Rd., Lodi, OH 44254: Catalog $3 ■ Antique and replica guns. 216–948–1082.

Lyman Products Corporation, Rt. 147, P.O. Box 453, Middlefield, CT 06455: Catalog $2 ■ Blackpowder rifles and handguns, kits, and accessories. 800–22–LYMAN.

Miltech, P.O. Box 322, Los Altos, CA 94022: Free brochure ■ Restored vintage military firearms. 415–948–3500.

Mountain State Muzzleloading Supplies, Inc., Rt. 2, Box 154–1, Williamstown, WV 26187: Free information ■ Blackpowder rifles, handguns, kits, and accessories. 304–375–7842.

Muzzle Loaders Etc., Inc., 9901 Lyndale Ave. South, Bloomington, MN 55420: Free information ■ Blackpowder and muzzleloading guns, and accessories. 612–884–1161.

Navy Arms Company, 689 Bergen Blvd., Ridgefield, NJ 07657: Catalog $2 ■ Blackpowder rifles and handguns, replica guns, kits and blackpowder, and accessories. 201–945–2500.

New Orleans Arms Company, 5001 Treasure St., New Orleans, LA 70186: Free information ■ Antique guns. 504–944–3371.

Rice Gun Products, Inc., 235 30th St., West Palm Beach, FL 33407: Free information ■ Blackpowder rifles and handguns, kits, accessories, and blackpowder. 407–848–7771.

S & S Firearms, 74–11 Myrtle Ave., Glendale, NY 11385: Free information ■ Antique guns. 212–497–1100.

C. Sharps Arms Company, P.O. Box 885, Big Timber, MT 59011: Brochure $2 ■ Blackpowder rifles. 406–932–4353.

Shiloh Rifle Manufacturing Company, Inc., P.O. Box 279, Big Timber, MT 59011: Free information ■ Blackpowder and muzzleloading arms. 406–932–4454.

Simmons Gun Specialties, Inc., Jerry's Sport Center, 700 S. Rogers Rd., P.O. Box 100, Olathe, KS 66062: Free information ■ Blackpowder rifles and handguns, kits, accessories, and blackpowder. 800–444–0220; 913–782–3131 (in KS).

South Bend Replicas, Inc., 61650 Oak Rd., South Bend, IN 46614: Catalog $7 ■ Replica and antique guns and gun parts. 219–289–4500.

Springfield Sporter, Inc., RD 1, Penn Ruth, PA 15765: Catalog $2 ■ Replica and antique guns and gun parts. 412–254–2626.

Theme Prints, Ltd., P.O. Box 123, Bayside, NY 11361: Free brochure ■ Books, antique guns, historic documents, and letters and autographs from the Revolutionary War era to the early 20th-century. 718–225–4067.

Thompson/Center Arms Company, P.O. Box 5002, Rochester, NH 03867: Free catalog ■ Muzzleloading rifles, handguns, kits, accessories, and blackpowders. 603–332–2394.

Traditions, Inc., 500 Main St., P.O. Box 235, Deep River, CT 06417: Free information ■ Blackpowder rifles and handguns, kits, accessories, and replica guns. 203–526–9555.

Trail Guns Armoury, P.O. Box 1258, League City, TX 77573: Free information ■ Blackpowder rifles and handguns, kits, and accessories. 713–332–5833.

Racks, Cases & Holsters

Bob Allen Sportswear, 214 SW Jackson, Des Moines, IA 50315: Free information ■ Carrying cases, holsters, and racks. 515–283–2191.

American Import Company, 1453 Mission St., San Francisco, CA 94103: Free information ■ Gun racks, soft cases, and slings. 415–863–1506.

American Sales & Manufacturing, Box 677, Laredo, TX 78042: Catalog $3 ■ Hand-crafted gunbelts and holsters. 512–723–6893.

API Outdoors, Inc., P.O. Box 1432, Tallulah, LA 71282: Free information ■ Gun racks. 318–574–4903.

Assault Systems, 1075 Headquarters Park, Fenton, MO 63026: Free information ■ Canvas carrying and gun storage cases, holsters, and slings. 800–325–3049; 314–343–3575 (in MO).

Beeman Precision Arms, Inc., 3440 Airway Dr., Santa Rosa, CA 95403: Catalog $2 ■ Holsters, slings, and soft cases. 707–578–7900.

Bowhunter Supply, Inc., 1158 46th St., P.O. Box 5010, Vienna, WV 26105: Free information ■ Hard and soft cases and stands for gun storage. 800–624–1923; 800–642–2638 (in WV).

Brauer Brothers Manufacturing Company, 12 Washington Ave., St. Louis, MO 63103: Free information ■ Soft cases, cabinets, slings, and holsters. 314–231–2864.

Browning Company, Dept. C006, Morgan, UT 84050: Catalog $2 ■ Hard and soft cases, holsters, and slings. 800–333–3288.

Chipmunk Manufacturing Company, Oregon Arms, Inc., 164 Schulz Rd., Central Point, OR 97502: Free information ■ Gun cases. 503–664–5588.

DeSantis Holster & Leather Company, 149 Denton Ave., New Hyde Park, NY 11040: Free information ■ Gun holsters. 516–354–8000.

Detroit Safe & Vault Company, 1729 E. 14 Mile Rd., Ste. 220, Troy, MI 48083: Free brochure ■ Gun safes. Includes used models. 800–473–1284.

Eastern Sports Supply, Ltd., P.O. Box 67, Tremont, PA 17981: Free information ■ Hard and soft cases, holsters, racks, slings, and stands. 717–695–3113.

El Dorado Leather, P.O. Box 341, Cortaro, AZ 85652: Free catalog ■ Custom cowhide holsters.

A.G. English, Inc., 708 S. 12th St., Broken Arrow, OK 74012: Free information ■ Gun safes. 800–222–7233.

Feline Archery, Inc., 229 Rt. 30 West, Ligonier, PA 15658: Free information ■ Hard and soft cases, holsters, racks, slings, and stands. 412–238–3673.

Fort Knox Security Products, 1051 N. Industrial Park Rd., Orem, UT 84057: Free information ■ Burglar-proof gun safes. 800–821–5216.

Frontier Safe Company, 1317 Chute St., Fort Wayne, IN 46803: Free information ■ Gun safes. 219–422–4801.

G-S Sales Company, P.O. Box 514, Kent, OH 44240: Free information ■ Gun safes. 800–544–1102; 216–678–3023 (in OH).

Don Hume Leathergoods, Box 351, Miami, OK 74354: Catalog $1 ■ Holsters. 918–542–6604.

Liberty Safe, 316 W. 700 South, Provo, UT 84601: Free brochure ■ Gun safes. 800–247–5625.

National Security Safe Company, P.O. Box 39, American Fork, UT 84003: Free

brochure ■ Gun safes with double steel walls. 800–544–3829.

Penguin Industries, Inc., Airport Industrial Mall, Coatesville, PA 19320: Free information ■ Gun cases and cabinets. 215–384–6000.

Safariland Leather Products, 1941 S. Walker Ave., Monrovia, CA 91016: Free information ■ Gun holsters. 818–357–7902.

Southern Security Safes, 1700 Oak Hills Dr., Kingston, TN 37763: Free information ■ Reinforced, hard plate metal gun safes with protective bolt-locking systems. 800–251–9992.

Tread Corporation, 1764 Granby St., Roanoke, VA 24032: Free information ■ Security gun chests. 800–336–9675; 703–982–6881 (in VA).

Whiteside Safe Sales Company, P.O. Box 11283, Prescott, AZ 86304: Free brochure ■ Gun safes. 800–433–7024.

Wilson Case Company, P.O. Box 1106, Hastings, NE 68902: Free information ■ Gun cases. 800–322–5493.

Scopes, Mounts & Sights

Aimpoint, 203 Elden St., Ste. 302, Herndon, VA 22070: Free brochure ■ Electronic red-dot sight with an optional 3x scope attachment.

American Import Company, 1453 Mission St., San Francisco, CA 94103: Free information ■ Scopes, mounts, and storage racks. 415–863–1506.

B-Square Company, Box 11281, Fort Worth, TX 76109: Free catalog ■ Scope mounts for handguns, rifles, and shotguns.

Maynard P. Buehler, 17 Orinda Way, Orinda, CA 94563: Free catalog ■ Mounting bases and rings for rifle and handgun scopes.

Burris Company, Inc., P.O. Box 1747, Greeley, CO 80632: Free information with 1st class stamp ■ Mounts and spotting scopes. 303–356–1670.

Bushnell Optical, Bausch & Lomb, 300 N. Lone Hill Ave., San Dimas, CA 91107: Free information ■ Spotting scopes and mounts. 714–592–8072.

Conetrol Scope Mounts, Hwy. 123 South, Sequin, TX 78155: Free information ■ Scope mounting systems.

Keng's Firearms Specialty, Inc., 875 Wharton Dr., P.O. Box 44405, Atlanta, GA 30336: Free information ■ Scope mounts and other accessories. 800–848–4671.

Kowa Optimed, Inc., 2001 S. Vermont Ave., Torrance, CA 90502: Free information ■ Spotting scopes for persons with eyeglasses.

Leupold & Stevens, Inc., P.O. Box 688, Beaverton, OR 97075: Free catalog ■ Low-light rifle scope with variable power settings. 503–646–9171.

Millett Industries, 16131 Gothard St., Huntington Beach, CA 92647: Catalog $1 ■ Gun sights. 714–842–5575.

Redfield Company, 5800 E. Jewell Ave., Denver, CO 80224: Catalog $1 ■ Rifle scopes. 303–757–6411.

Simmons Outdoor Company, 14530 SW 119th Ave., Miami, FL 33186: Catalog $2 ■ Rifle scopes.

Tasco Sales, Inc., P.O. Box 523735, Miami, FL 33122: Free information ■ Gun scopes. 305–591–3670.

Warne Manufacturing Company, 9039 SE Jannsen Rd., Clackamas, OR 97015: Free information ■ Easy-to-install, detachable scope mounts for most rifles. 503–657–5590.

Williams Gun Sight Company, 7389 Lapeer Rd., P.O. Box 329, Davison, MI 48423: Free information ■ Scope mounts for rifles, shotguns, and black powder guns. 800–530–9028; 313–742–2120 (in MI).

Sportshooting Rifles & Handguns

American Derringer Corporation, Box 8983, Waco, TX 76714: Free information ■ Sport shooting automatic pistols, derringers, and revolvers. 817–799–9111.

Armoury, Inc., Rt. 202, New Preston, CT 06777: Free information ■ Guns for sport shooting. 203–868–0001.

Badger Shooter's Supply, Inc., 106 S. Harding, Owen, WI 54460: Free catalog ■ Sporting firearms, ammunition, and supplies. 715–229–2101.

Brownells, Inc., 200 S. Front St., Montezuma, IA 50171: Catalog $3.75 ■ Gunsmithing supplies, tools, and services. 515–623–5401.

Browning Company, Dept. C006, Morgan, UT 84050: Catalog $2 ■ Rifles for sport shooting. Includes bolt and lever action models, semiautomatics and single shot rifles, and over/under, side-by-side, and single barrel shotguns. 800–333–3288.

Century International Arms, 80 N. Main St., Albans, VT 05478: Free information ■ Bolt and lever action guns, semiautomatic rifles, single shot rifles, and accessories. 802–5277–1252.

Clark Custom Guns, Inc., 11462 Keatchie Rd., P.O. Box 530, Keithville, LA 71047: Catalog $1 ■ Custom handguns and accessories. 318–925–0836.

Douglas Barrels, Inc., 5504 Big Tyler Rd., Charleston, WV 25313: Free information ■ Rifle barrels in most sizes. 304–776–1341.

Eastern Sports Supply, Ltd., P.O. Box 67, Tremont, PA 17981: Free information ■ Automatic pistols, blank pistols, derringers, shotguns, and revolvers, and bolt and lever action, target, semiautomatic, and single shot rifles. 717–695–3113.

EMF Company, Inc., 1900 E. Warner Ave., Santa Ana, CA 92705: Catalog $1 ■ United States and foreign revolvers, rifles, pistols, and shotguns. 714–261–6611.

Feline Archery, Inc., 229 Rt. 30 West, Ligonier, PA 15658: Free information ■ Lever and bolt action, semiautomatic, single shot, and target rifles. 412–238–3673.

Gun Parts Corporation, Williams Ln., West Hurley, NY 12491: Catalog $5.95 ■ Commercial, military, antique, and foreign gun parts and supplies. 914–679–2417.

Gil Hebard Guns, 125 Public Square, Knoxville, IL 61448: Free catalog ■ Pistols and accessories. 309–289–2700.

Interarms, 10 Prince St., Alexandria, VA 22314: Free information ■ Bolt and lever action, target, semiautomatic, and single shot rifles. 703–548–1400.

Kimber of Oregon, 9039 SE Jannsen Rd., Clackamas, OR 97015: Free information ■ Sporting firearms for deer hunting. 800–842–0852.

Harry Lawson Company, 3328 N. Richey Blvd., Tucson, AZ 85716: Catalog $1 ■ Custom rifles. 602–326–1117.

Liberty Organization, Inc., P.O. Box 306, Montrose, CA 91020: Free information ■

Automatic and blank pistols, derringers, revolvers, and autoloading, automatic, over/under, semiautomatic, side-by-side, and single barrel shotguns. 818–248–0618.

Marlin Firearms Company, 100 Kenna Dr., North Haven, CT 06473: Free information ■ Semiautomatic, single shot, bolt action, and lever action rifles. 203–239–5621.

Midway Arms, Inc., 5875 W. Van Horn Tavern Rd., Columbia, MO 65203: Free catalog ■ Handguns, rifles, and ammunition. 800–243–3220.

Navy Arms Company, 689 Bergen Blvd., Ridgefield, NJ 07657: Catalog $2 ■ Automatic pistols, blank guns, revolvers, and target, bolt and lever action, semiautomatic, and single shot rifles. 201–945–2500.

Remington Arms Company, Inc., 1007 Market St., Wilmington, DE 19898: Free information ■ Autoloading, automatic, over/under, and semiautomatic shotguns. 302–773–5292.

Rice Gun Products, Inc., 235 30th St., West Palm Beach, FL 33407: Free information ■ Revolvers, automatic pistols, derringers, shotguns, and target, bolt and lever action, semiautomatic, and single shot rifles. 407–848–7771.

Savage, Springdale Rd., Westfield, MA 01085: Free information ■ Sporting firearms for deer hunting. 413–568–7001.

Sherwood, 14830 Alondra Blvd., La Mirada, CA 90638: Price list $1 ■ Parts, accessories, and supplies for guns. 800–962–3203.

Simmons Gun Specialties, Inc., Jerry's Sport Center, 700 S. Rogers Rd., P.O. Box 100, Olathe, KS 66062: Free information ■ Automatic pistols, revolvers, derringers, and target, bolt and lever action, semiautomatic, and single shot rifles. 800–444–0220; 913–782–3131 (in KS).

Springfield Armory, 420 W. Main St., Geneseo, IL 61254: Catalog $3 ■ Pistols, handguns, rifles, and accessories. 309–944–5631.

Sturm, Ruger & Company, Inc., 11 Lacey Pl., Southport, CT 06490: Free catalog ■ Semiautomatic and single shot, bolt and lever action, and target rifles. 203–259–7843.

Tex Products Supply, Inc., 1110 Washington Ave., Houston, TX 77002: Free information ■ Revolvers, automatic pistols, and derringers. 713–236–9478.

Ultra Light Arms, Inc., P.O. Box 1270, Granville, WV 26534: Free information ■ Sporting firearms for deer hunting. 304–599–5687.

Weatherby, Inc., 2781 Firestone Blvd., South Gate, CA 90280: Free information ■ Sporting firearms for deer hunting. 213–569–7186.

Targets & Range Supplies

Alco Target Company, 2048 Central Ave., Duarte, CA 91010: Free information ■ Targets and range equipment.

American Target Company, 1346 Jason St., Denver, CO 80223: Free information ■ Targets and range equipment.

Beeman Precision Arms, Inc., 3440 Airway Dr., Santa Rosa, CA 95403: Free information ■ Targets and range equipment. 707–578–7900.

Caswell International Corporation, 10125 Fuller Rd., Eden Prairie, MN 55344: Free information ■ Shooting range supplies and target carriers. 612–379–2000.

Crosman Air Guns, Rt. 5, East Bloomfield, NY 14443: Free information ■ Targets and range equipment. 800–828–1495; 716–657–6161 (in NY).

Daisy Manufacturing Company, Inc., P.O. Box 220, Rogers, AR 72757: Free information ■ Targets and range equipment. 800–643–3458; 501–636–1200 (in AR).

Eagle Target Company, 3734 NW 52nd St., Hialeah, FL 33142: Free information ■ Targets and range equipment.

Freeland's Scope Stands, Inc., 3737 14th Ave., Rock Island, IL 61201: Free catalog ■ Target equipment and accessories. 309–788–7449.

The Gun Rack, Box 181, Tingley, IA 50863: Free information ■ Novelty and silhouette targets.

Marksman Products, 5622 Engineer Dr., Huntington Beach, CA 92649: Free information ■ Targets and range equipment. 800–822–8005; 714–898–7535 (in CA).

National Target Company, P.O. Box 2152, Rockville, MD 20852: Free information ■ Targets and range equipment.

Outers Laboratories, Inc., Onalaska, WI 54650: Free information ■ Targets and range equipment.

Petersons Instant Targets, Inc., 147 West St., Middlefield, CT 06801: Free information ■ Targets. 203–349–3421.

Rocky Mountain Target Company, Box 700, Black Hawk, SD 57718: Free information ■ Targets and range equipment.

Speedwell Targets, 136 Lincoln Blvd., Middlesex, NJ 08846: Free information ■ Targets and range equipment.

U.S. Target Company, 14680 E. Seven Mile Rd., Detroit, MI 48205: Free information ■ Targets and range equipment.

Trap & Skeet Shooting

Ballistic Products, Inc., Box 408, Long Lake, MN 55356: Free information ■ Targets and traps. 612–473–1550.

Beeman Precision Arms, Inc., 3440 Airway Dr., Santa Rosa, CA 95403: Catalog $2 ■ Targets and traps. 707–578–7900.

Boss Traps, P.O. Box 25141, Houston, TX 77265: Free information ■ Clay target traps.

Eastern Sports Supply, Ltd., P.O. Box 67, Tremont, PA 17981: Free information ■ Launchers, targets, and traps. 717–695–3113.

ET Trap Manufacturing, 12411 Ambaum Blvd., Seattle, WA 98146: Free information ■ Clay target traps.

Hunters Pointe, 14809 Timber Lake Rd., Wichita, KS 67330: Free information ■ Clay target traps.

Omark Industries, Blount Sporting Equipment Division, P.O. Box 856, Lewiston, ID 83501: Free information ■ Launchers, traps, and targets. 208–746–2351.

Simmons Gun Specialties, Inc., Jerry's Sport Center, 700 S. Rogers Rd., P.O. Box 100, Olathe, KS 66062: Free information ■ Traps, launchers, and targets. 800–444–0220; 913–782–3131 (in KS).

Trius, Inc., Box 25, Cleves, OH 45002: Free catalog ■ Portable traps and other range equipment.

World of Targets, 9200 Floral Ave., Cincinnati, OH 45242: Free information ■ Traps and targets. 513–791–0917.

HAMMOCKS & SWINGS

Adirondack Store & Gallery, 109 Saranac Ave., Lake Placid, NY 12946: Free catalog ■ Oak and maple porch swings, lawn furniture, and picnic table sets. 518–523–2646.

Alfresco Porch Swing Company, P.O. Box 1336, Durango, CO 81301: Free brochure ■ Custom porch swings, Adirondack chairs, and garden benches. 303–247–9739.

Brushy Mountain Bee Farm, Rt. 1, P.O. Box 135, Moravian Falls, NC 28654: Free catalog ■ Porch swings, birdhouses and feeders, and beekeeping supplies. 800–233–7929.

Country Casual, 17317 Germantown Rd., Germantown, MD 20874: Catalog $3 ■ Porch swings and classic British solid teak garden seats that include the Chippendale Suite, Warwick-National Herb Garden bench, and Sissinghurst Luytens. 301–540–0040.

Daniel's Wicker, 2125 Dedmon Rd., Bowling Green, KY 42101: Catalog $2.50 ■ Handmade solid wicker porch swings with solid oak frames. 502–842–6926.

Gazebo & Porchworks, 728 9th Ave. SW, Puyallup, WA 98371: Catalog $2 ■ Outdoor swings and backyard play structures. 206–848–0502.

Hangouts from Bellartson, P.O. Box 148, Boulder, CO 80306: Free brochure ■ Hammocks. 800–HANGOUT.

Heritage Crafters, 1303 Gaston Way, Dallas, NC 28034: Catalog $2 ■ Oak porch swings, solid wood planters, reproduction chests, and trunks. 704–922–9253.

Lazy Day Hammocks, 8225 Hwy. 64 East, Knightdale, NC 27545: Free brochure ■ Hand-woven, cotton rope hammocks in three sizes; hammock chairs; and swings. 919–266–2819.

Mel-Nor Industries, 303 Gulf Bank, Houston, TX 77037: Information $1 ■ Hanging lawn and porch swings, park benches, and old-time lamp posts. 713–445–3485.

O'Connor's Woodworks, P.O. Box 712, Washington, LA 70589: Brochure $2 ■ Solid cypress porch swings. 800–786–1051.

Marion Travis, Box 292, Statesville, NC 28677: Catalog $1 ■ Wooden porch swings. 704–528–4424.

Twin Oaks Hammocks, Rt. 4, P.O. Box 169, Louisa, VA 23093: Free price list ■ Woven rope hammocks and other furniture. 800–688–8946.

Unique Simplicities, P.O. Box 33906, Philadelphia, PA 19153: Catalog $1 ■ Easy-to-install weatherproof swing for indoors and outdoors. 800–845–1119.

Walpole Woodworkers, 767 East St., Walpole, MA 02081: Catalog $6 ■ Porch swings, covered swings, swing sets for children, chairs, tables, and picnic table sets. 508–668–2800.

HANDBALL

Adidas USA, Inc., 15 Independence Blvd., Warren, NJ 07060: Free information ■ Balls. 908–580–0700.

Baden Sports, Inc., 1120 SW 16th, Renton, WA 98055: Free information ■ Balls. 206–235–1830.

Cannon Sports, P.O. Box 11179, Burbank, CA 91510: Free information ■ Balls and eyeguards. 800–223–0064; 818–503–9570.

Ektelon, 12540 Spindletop Rd., San Diego, CA 92129: Free information ■ Eyeguards and gloves. 619–560–0066.

Professional Gym, Inc., P.O. Box 188, Marshall, MO 65340: Free brochure ■ Eyeguards. 800–821–7665; 800–892–2616 (in MO).

Spalding & Brothers, 425 Meadow St., P.O. Box 901, Chicopee, MA 01021: Free information ■ Balls. 413–536–1200.

Sport World Distributors, 3060 Clermont Rd., P.O. Box 27131, Columbus, OH 44327: Free information ■ Eyeguards and gloves. 614–838–8511.

Standard Merchandising Company, 1125 Wright Ave., Camden, NJ 08103: Free information ■ Eyeguards and gloves. 609–964–9700.

Unique Sports Products, Inc., 840 McFarland Rd., Alpharetta, GA 30201: Free information ■ Eyeguards and gloves. 404–442–1977.

Wa-Mac, Inc., Highskore Products, Inc., 178 Commerce Rd., P.O. Box 128, Carlstadt, NJ 07072: Free information ■ Balls and gloves. 800–447–5673; 201–438–7200 (in NJ).

HARDWARE

Acorn Manufacturing Company, Inc., P.O. Box 31, Mansfield, MA 02048: Catalog $6 ■ Reproduction colonial hardware, sconces, hurricane lamps, fireplace tools and accessories, and bathroom accessories. 800–835–0121; 508–339–4500 (in MA).

American Home Supply, P.O. Box 697, Campbell, CA 95009: Catalog $2 ■ Victorian and contemporary style knobs, cabinet hardware and locks, roll top and other desk hardware, door handles and dead bolts, faucets and bathroom hardware, grills and registers, and restoration items. Many items available in brass. 408–246–1962.

Anglo-American Brass Company, P.O. Box Drawer 9487, San Jose, CA 95157: Catalog $2 ■ Solid brass reproduction hardware. 408–246–3232.

Antique Hardware Catalogue, RD 2, Box A, Kintnersville, PA 18930: Free information ■ Victorian and country-style renovation products. Includes clawfoot tub and shower conversions, sinks, faucets, high-tank toilets, door and cabinet hardware, wrought iron, weather vanes, and builder's brass hardware. 800–422–9982.

Antique Hardware Company, P.O. Box 1592, Torrance, CA 90505: Catalog $3 ■ Handcrafted reproductions of antique hardware. 213–378–5990.

Antique Hardware Store, 9718 Easton Rd., Rt. 611, Kintnersville, PA 18930: Catalog $3 ■ Antique hardware, pedestal sinks, faucets, high tank toilets, cabinet hardware, weather vanes, brass bar rails, and tin and wood chandeliers. 800–422–9982.

Antique Trunk Supply Company, 3706 W. 169th St., Cleveland, OH 44111: Catalog $1 ■ Trunk repair parts. 216–941–8618.

Armor Products, P.O. Box 445, East Northport, NY 11731: Catalog $1 ■ Hardware, lamp parts, wood turnings and parts for toys and other crafts, and replacement clock movements for mantel, banjo, and grandfather clocks. 800–292–8296.

Baldwin Hardware Corporation, 841 E. Wyomissing Blvd., Box 15048, Reading, PA 19612: Bathroom accessories brochure 75¢; lighting fixtures brochure $3; door hardware brochure 75¢; decor hardware brochure 75¢ ■ Forged brass dead bolts, other door hardware, bathroom accessories, lighting fixtures, and decorative hardware. 215–777–7811.

Ball & Ball, 463 W. Lincoln Hwy., Exton, PA 19341: Catalog $5 ■ Brass and wrought-iron reproductions of 1680s to 1900s American hardware. 215–363–7330.

Blaine Hardware International, 1919 Blaine Dr., RD 4, Hagerstown, MD 21740: Catalog $2.50 ■ Replacement hardware for doors, screens, and windows; and grab bars and other aids for people with disabilities. 800–678–1919.

Bona Decorative Hardware, 3073 Madison Rd., Cincinnati, OH 45209: Catalog $2 ■ Solid brass hardware for bathrooms, doors, cabinets, furniture, kitchens, and fireplaces. 513–321–7877.

The Broadway Collection, 1010 W. Santa Fe, Olathe, KS 66061: Free catalog ■ Plumbing fittings and accessories, brass bowls and bar sinks, grab bars, switch plates, railing systems, and cabinet hardware. 800–766–1966.

Camelot Enterprises, Box 65, Bristol, WI 53104: Catalog $1 (refundable) ■ Bolts, screws, and tools. 414–857–2695.

Cirecast, Inc., 380 7th St., San Francisco, CA 94103: Catalog $3 ■ Reproduction and custom solid bronze hardware. 415–863–8319.

Monroe Coldren & Sons, 723 E. Virginia Ave., West Chester, PA 19380: Free information ■ Restored original and custom reproduction of 18th- and 19th-century hardware. 215–692–5651.

Constantine, 2050 Eastchester Rd., Bronx, NY 10461: Catalog $1 ■ Cabinet and furniture wood, hardware, and veneers; plans and how-to books; carving tools and chisels; and inlay designs. 212–792–1600.

Crawford's Old House Store, 550 Elizabeth St., Waukesha, WI 53186: Free literature ■ Reproduction Colonial and Victorian brass, bronze, wrought-iron, and porcelain hardware and other items. 800–556–7878.

18th Century Hardware Company, 131 E. 3rd St., Derry, PA 15627: Catalog $3 ■ Early American and Victorian-style hardware in black iron, porcelain, and brass. 412–694–2708.

Elephant Hill Ironworks, RR 1, Box 168, Turnbrige, VT 05077: Catalog $3 ■

Reproduction 17th-, 18th-, and early 19th-century hardware and ironwork. 802–889–9444.

Elwick Supply Company, 230 Woods Ln., Somerdale, NJ 08083: Free catalog ■ Stainless steel and brass screws and bolts, high speed drill bits, router accessories, metal tubing, and modeling tools and accessories.

Charolette Ford Trunks, Box 536, Spearman, TX 79081: Catalog $3 ■ Supplies, tools, and accessories for restoring trunks. 809–553–2649.

Garbe Industries, Inc., 4137 S. 72nd East Ave., Tulsa, OK 74145: Free brochure ■ Solid-brass hardware. 918–627–0284.

Historic Hardware, Ltd., P.O. Box 1327, North Hampton, NH 03862: Catalog $3 ■ Custom period hardware, decor accessories, strap hinges, bull's eye glass, and fireplace accessories and cranes. 603–964–2280.

Horton Brasses, Nooks Hill Rd., P.O. Box 120, Cromwell, CT 06416: Catalog $3 ■ Brass hardware, knobs, drawer pulls, and hardware for beds. Includes reproductions of Chippendale, Queen Anne, Hepplewhite, Sheraton, Victorian, and early 1900s hardware. 203–635–4400.

Imported European Hardware, 4320 W. Bell Dr., Las Vegas, NV 89118: Catalog $3 ■ Imported hardware from Europe. 702–871–0722.

Kayne & Son Forged Hardware, 76 Daniel Ridge Rd., Candler, NC 28715: Catalog $4 ■ Fireplace tools and hand-forged hardware. 704–667–8868.

Phyllis Kennedy Restoration Hardware, 9256 Holyoke Ct., Indianapolis, IN 46268: Catalog $2 ■ Antique trunk hardware and other supplies. 317–872–6366.

Klockit, P.O. Box 636, Lake Geneva, WI 53147: Free catalog ■ Decorative and functional hardware, Swiss music box movements, music box kits, and clock-building equipment and supplies. 800–556–2548.

Brian F. Leo Hardware, 7532 Columbus Ave. South, Richfield, MN 55423: Catalog $3 ■ Reproduction hardware in bronze and other metals. 612–861–1473.

Meisel Hardware Specialties, P.O. Box 70, Mound, MN 55364: Catalog $1 ■ Hardware, wood parts and accessories, and plans and parts for musical door harps. 800–441–9870.

Merit Metal Products Corporation, 240 Valley Rd., Warrington, PA 18976: Catalog $10 ■ Brass locks and hinges, and hardware for doors, furniture, and cabinets. 215–343–2500.

Old Smithy Shop, Box 336, Milford, NH 03055: Catalog $3 ■ Hand-forged Colonial reproduction hardware and fireplace accessories. 603–673–0132.

Paxton Hardware, Ltd., 7818 Bradshaw Rd., Upper Falls, MD 21156: Catalog $4 ■ Cabinet hardware and hinges. 410–592–8505.

Renaissance Decorative Hardware, P.O. Box 332, Leonia, NJ 07605: Catalog $3 ■ Solid brass hardware and accessories for cabinets, doors, furniture, and bathrooms. 201–568–1403.

The Renovator's Supply, Renovator's Old Mill, Millers Falls, MA 01349: Catalog $3 ■ Old-style hardware, plumbing, lighting fixtures, and decor accessories. 413–659–2211.

Restoration Works, Inc., 810 Main St., Buffalo, NY 14205: Catalog $3 ■ Hardware for furniture and builders, ceiling medallions and trims, plumbing fixtures, and bathroom accessories. 800–735–3535.

Schlage Lock Company, 2401 Bayshore Blvd., San Francisco, CA 94134: Free information ■ Door-lock hardware. 415–330–5547.

Stanley Hardware, 195 Lake St., New Britain, CT 06050: Free information ■ Brass hardware. 203–225–5111.

Stock Drive Products, 55 S. Denton Ave., New Hyde Park, NY 11040: Catalog $5.95 ■ Hardware, parts, and accessories in inches and metric sizes. 516–328–3330.

E.P. Titcomb, 17 Jan Sebastian Way, Sandwich, MA 02563: Catalog $3 ■ Finely wrought reproduction hardware. 508–833–1168.

Garrett Wade Company, 161 Avenue of Americas, New York, NY 10013: Catalog $4 ■ English-made, solid brass hardware, with many patterns similar to those of 100 years ago. 800–221–2942.

Whitechapel Brasses, Ltd., P.O. Box 136, 3650 West Highway 22, Wilson, WY 83014: Catalog $2.50 ■ Locks, handles, and hinges. 307–739–9478.

Williamsburg Blacksmiths, Inc., 1 Buttonshop Rd., Williamsburg, MA 01096: Catalog $5 ■ Reproduction Early American hardware, wrought-iron furniture, and accessories. 800–248–1776.

Wise Company, 6503 St. Claude Ave., P.O. Box 118, Arabi, LA 70032: Catalog $4 ■ Antique restoration materials, hardware, and refinishing supplies to restore or repair furniture. 504–277–7551.

The Woodworkers' Store, 21801 Industrial Blvd., Rogers, MN 55374: Catalog $2 ■ Hardware and woodworking supplies. 612–428–2199.

HATS

Caledonia Company, 300 Chestnut Hill Rd., Stevens, PA 17578: Free information ■ Classic style western hats. 800–338–2410.

Custom Cowboy Shop, 321 N. Main, Sheridan, WY 82801: Free information ■ Custom western-style cowboy hats. 307–672–7733.

Hat Store, 5587 Richmond, Houston, TX 77056: Catalog $1 ■ Custom, hand-shaped western-style hats. 713–780–2480.

J.J. Hat Center, Inc., 1276 Broadway, New York, NY 10001: Free catalog ■ Headwear for men and women. 212–239–4368.

Luskey's Western Stores, Inc., 101 N. Houston St., Fort Worth, TX 76102: Free catalog ■ Hats and boots in a western tradition for the entire family. 817–335–5833.

Priest Hat Company, 342 E. State St., Eagle, ID 83616: Free catalog ■ Western-style custom fur felt hats. 208–939–4287.

Rand's Custom Hatters, 2205 1st Ave., North Billings, MT 59101: Free catalog ■ Custom western-style hats. 406–259–4886.

Riverhouse Hats, 1925 E. Velvet Dr., Tempe, AZ 85284: Free brochure ■ Safari hats for men and women. 602–838–7221.

Rowell's Hat Shop, Box 43, Idaho City, ID 83631: Free catalog ■ Custom western-style hats. 208–392–4438.

Tonto Rim Trading Company, P.O. Box 463, Salem, IN 47167: Catalog $3 ■ Western-style boots and hats. 800–253–4287; 812–883–3023 (in IN).

HEALTH CARE SUPPLIES

AARP Pharmacy Service Center Catalog, 7609 Energy Pkwy., Baltimore, MD 21226: Free catalog for American Association Retired Persons members ■ Over-the-counter medications, cosmetics, vitamins, dental needs, cold remedies, sick room supplies, personal care items, and other health care supplies and equipment. 703–684–0244.

Allergy Control Products, 96 Danbury Rd., Ridgefield, CT 06877: Free catalog ■ Air filters, mattress and pillow covers, face masks, dehumidifiers, and books for allergy-sensitive persons. 800–422–3878; 203–438–9580 (in CT).

American Foundation for the Blind, Inc., Product Center, 100 Enterprise Pl., P.O. Box 7044, Dover, DE 19903: Free catalog ■ Lists products available from the American Foundation for the Blind. Includes watches and clocks, canes, household and personal care aids, calculators, and other items. 800–829–0500.

American Printing House for the Blind, 1839 Frankfort Ave., P.O. Box 6085, Louisville, KY 40206: Free catalog ■ Braille writing and embossing equipment, electronic devices, containers, reading readiness products, educational aids, and other aids for people with visual handicaps. 502–895–2405.

Aqua-Tec Health Care Products, 1003 International Dr., Oakdale, PA 15071: Free information ■ Household water pressure-operated, portable bathtub lift. 412–695–2122.

B & B Company, Inc., 2417 Bank Dr., P.O. Box 5731, Boise, ID 83705: Free information ■ Mastectomy breast forms that fit regular bras. 208–343–9696.

Barrier Free Lifts, Inc., P.O. Box 4163, Manassas, VA 22110: Free information ■ Battery-operated, multi-directional barrier free ceiling lift. 800–582–8732; 703–361–6531 (in VA).

The Braun Corporation, 1014 S. Monticello, P.O. Box 310, Winamac, IN 46996: Free information ■ Van conversion and driving accessories, wheel air lifts, and other equipment. 800–THE–LIFT; 219–946–6153 (in IN).

Bruce Medical Supply, 411 Waverly Oaks Rd., P.O. Box 9166, Waltham, MA 02154: Free catalog ■ Medical and health supplies and equipment for ostomy patients, diabetics, sick rooms, post hospital care, and first aid. 800–225–8446.

Bruno Independent Living Aids, P.O. Box 84, Oconomowoc, WI 53066: Free information ■ Wheelchair and scooter lifts. 800–882–8183.

C & H Sales, Inc., 1141 E. Northwest Hwy., Dallas, TX 75218: Free information with long SASE ■ Mastectomy breast forms. 214–360–9657.

Columbus McKinnon Corporation, Marketing Communications, 140 John James Audubon Pkwy., Amherst, NY 14228: Free information ■ Easy-to-operate mobility and lifting system.

Comfortably Yours, 2515 E. 43rd St., P.O. Box 182216, Chattanooga, TN 37422: Free catalog ■ Mastectomy bras, back support pillows for use in cars or the home, posture braces, and other items for people with physical disabilities. 602–829–0154.

Emergency Medical Products, 9434 Chesapeake Dr., Ste. 1208, San Diego, CA 92123: Free information ■ First-aid kits for backcountry travel and other outdoor activities. 800–228–1538.

Emergency Systems, 1716 W. Main, Ste. 8A, Bozeman, MT 59715: Free information ■ First-aid kits for backcountry travel and other outdoor activities. 406–587–5571.

Enrichments, P.O. Box 579, Hinsdale, IL 60521: Free information ■ Health care products, personal care needs, dressing aids, leisure time helps, and comfort aids. 800–323–5547.

ETAC USA, 2325 Parklawn Dr., Ste. P, Waukesha, WI 53186: Free brochure ■ Walking aids, bath safety equipment, wheelchairs, and other aids to make daily living easier. 800–678–ETAC; 414–796–4600 (in WI).

Frohock-Stewart, Inc., P.O. Box 330, Northborough, MA 01532: Free information ■ Clamp-on bathtub bench and grip for bathing comfort and safety. 800–343–6059.

Grant Waterx Corporation, 1011 High Ridge Rd., Stamford, CT 06905: Free information ■ Pivoting bathtub lift that operates with household water pressure. 800–243–5237.

Guardian Products, Inc., 12800 Wentworth St., Arleta, CA 91331: Free information ■ One-piece, no assembly, height-adjustable shower and commode chair. 800–255–5022; 818–504–2820 (in CA).

Handi-Move, T.E. Herceg, Inc., 98 Ridge Rd., Chester, NY 10918: Free information ■ Remote, hand-operated overhead track or free-standing lift. 914–469–6438.

Health Supplies of America, P.O. Box 1059, Burlington, NC 27834: Free catalog ■ Wheelchairs, wheelchair parts and accessories, and other health care supplies. 800–334–1187.

Home Delivery Incontinent Supplies Company, 325 Paul Ave., Ferguson, MO 63135: Free catalog ■ Incontinence supplies. 800–538–1036.

Home Diagnostics, Inc., 230 Park Ave., New York, NY 10169: Free catalog ■ Home products for radon testing, water analysis, carbon monoxide and formaldehyde testing, blood pressure monitoring, and diabetes screening. 212–986–0101.

Home Health Products, Inc., 1160 Millers Ln., Virginia Beach, VA 23451: Free catalog ■ Health care supplies, skin care products and natural beauty treatments, herbal medications and other preparations, and Edgar Cayce products. 800–284–9123.

Hyland's Standard Homeopathic Company, 210 W. 131st St., Box 61067, Los Angeles, CA 90061: Free information ■ Homeopathic medicines. 800–624–9659; 213–321–4284 (in CA).

Independent Living Aids, Inc./Can-Do Products, 27 East Mall, Plainview, NY 11803: Free catalog ■ Health care equipment and supplies. 800–537–2118; 516–752–8080 (in NY).

Independent Mobility Systems, 4100 W. Piedras, Farmington, NM 87401: Free information ■ Automatic door ramp for automotive vehicles.

I-Tec, 5482 Business Dr., Unit C, Huntington Beach, CA 92649: Free information ■ Ceiling mounted or free-standing electromechanical system for in-the-home mobility. 800–622–ITEC; 714–898–9005 (in CA).

Miles Kimball Company, 41 W. 8th Ave., Oshkosh, WI 54901: Free catalog ■ Bathroom accessories, arthritis aids, clothing, kitchen accessories, canes, and personal care items for people with disabilities. 414–231–3800.

King-Aire Products, P.O. Box 126, Fortfille, IN 46040: Free catalog ■ Air purifiers, humidifiers and dehumidifiers, water filters, and ventilators. 317–485–7771.

Kohler Company, Kohler, WI 53044: Free information ■ Low threshold shower stalls for wheelchair accessibility. 800–4KOH-LER.

Dr. Leonard's Health Care Catalog, 74 20th St., Brooklyn, NY 11232: Free catalog ■ Health care supplies and equipment. 718–768–0010.

Lindustries, P.O. Box 295, Auburndale, MA 02166: Free information ■ Lever convertible adapters for making doors easy to open. 617–237–8177.

Maddak, Inc., Pequannock, NJ 07440: Free catalog ■ Aids for daily living, home health care, rehabilitation, personal hygiene and grooming, transportation, recreation, and household activities. 201–628–7600.

Maxi Aids, P.O. Box 3209, Farmingdale, NY 11735: Free catalog ■ Aids and appliances for people with visual, hearing, and physical impairments. 800–522–6294.

Pillows for Ease, P.O. Box 402113, Miami, FL 33140: Free brochure ■ Special support pillows, body wedges, back rests, cradles,

and other pillow-type supports for treatment of chiropractic, orthopedic, and massage therapy-related conditions. 800–347–1486; 305–538–1210 (in FL).

Power Access Corporation, Bridge St., P.O. Box 235, Collinsville, CT 06022: Free brochure ■ Easily attached remote/manually operated door opener. 800–344–0088; 693–0751 (in CT).

J.A. Preston Corporation, P.O. Box 89, Jackson, MI 49204: Free catalog ■ Exercise equipment, walkers, crutches, mats, body molds and positioning aids, perceptual motor accessories, self-help aids, and professional equipment for the doctor's office. 800–631–7277.

Radio Shack, Division Tandy Corporation, 1500 One Tandy Center, Fort Worth, TX 76102: Free product information ■ Health care equipment and supplies. 817–390–3700.

Rampus, Inc., P.O. Box 37, Coldwater, MI 49036: Free catalog ■ Wheel chair and scooter lifts. 800–876–9498.

Sears Health Care Catalog, 3050 Finley Rd., Downers Grove, IL 60515: Free catalog ■ Health care supplies.

SelfCare Catalog, 5850 Shellmound Ave., Emeryville, CA 94662: Free catalog ■ Health care equipment and supplies. 800–345–3371.

Sense-Sations, 919 Walnut St., Philadelphia, PA 19107: Free catalog in large print, Braille, or cassette ■ Adaptive recorders, computer products, and other services and supplies for people with visual impairments. 215–627–0600.

Space Tables, Inc., P.O. Box 32082, Minneapolis, MN 55432: Free catalog ■ Adjustable tables for wheelchairs. 800–328–2580.

Support Plus, Box 500, Medfield, MA 02052: Free catalog ■ Support hosiery, personal hygiene aids, home health care aids, bath safety products, and walking shoes. 508–359–2910.

Temco Home Health Care Products, Inc., 125 South St., Box 328, Passaic, NJ 07055: Free catalog ■ Home health care supplies and equipment. 201–472–3173.

Thermosport, Ltd., Omniplex, Inc., 5724 W. 3rd St., Ste. 304, Los Angeles, CA 90036: Free brochure ■ Hot and cold therapy wraps, and braces for elbows, knees,

backs, shoulders, and ankles. 800–729–8002; 213–965–8100 (in CA).

Worldwide Home Health Center, Inc., 926 E. Tallmadge Ave., Akron, OH 44310: Free catalog ■ Ostomy appliances and supplies, incontinence supplies, mastectomy breast forms and clothing, skin care products, and other health care accessories. 800–223–5938; 800–621–5938 (in OH).

HEALTH CARE SUPPLIES & AIDS FOR THE DISABLED

Access to Recreation, Inc., 2509 E. Thousand Oaks Blvd., Thousand Oaks, CA 91362: Free catalog ■ Adaptive recreation equipment, devices to help with embroidery and knitting, games, books, video controllers, wheelchair ramps, and an environmental control system. 405–498–7535.

adaptAbility, Dept. 2200, 75 Mill St., Colchester, CT 06415: Free catalog ■ Adaptive home products for independent living. Includes mobility, grooming, dressing, bathing, eating and cooking aids, and exercise and therapy games. 800–243–9232.

AliMed, Inc., 297 High St., Dedham, MA 02026: Free catalog ■ Readers; dressing aids; adapted eating utensils; cuffs; plate guards and adapted dinner plates; adapted cups, mugs, and straws; home and kitchen accessories; bathing and personal care items; toilet seats and commodes; and walkers, walking, and communication aids. 617–329–2900.

AlumiRamp, Inc., 90 Taylor St., Quincy, MI 49082: Free brochure ■ Aluminum ramps. 517–639–4576.

Attainment Company, Inc., P.O. Box 930160, Verona, WI 53593: Free catalog ■ Special needs equipment and supplies for children and adults. 800–327–4269.

Best Book Rest, Box 2745, Jolie, IL 60434: Free brochure ■ Book rests for use with wheelchairs, baths, beds, bed tables, whirlpools, and other situations.

Cleo, Inc., 3957 Mayfield Rd., Cleveland, OH 44121: Free catalog ■ Exercise equipment, blood pressure pillows, walkers and canes, wheelchair accessories, cushions, recreation and rehabilitation aids, heat therapy appliances, bathroom aids, grooming and dressing aids, homemaking and eating accessories, and other self-help products for the physically challenged. 800–321–0595; 216–382–9700 (in OH).

Columbia Medical Manufacturing Corporation, P.O. Box 633, Pacific Palisades, CA 90272: Free catalog ■ Car seats, bath and toilet supports, commodes, exercise equipment, and other items for handicapped children and adults. 310–454–6612.

Consumer Care Products, Inc., P.O. Box 684, Sheboygan, WI 53082: Free catalog ■ Wheelchair trays, positioning aids, do-it-yourself supplies, communication and mobility aids, and other supplies and information for exceptional persons. 414–459–8353.

Crestwood Company, 6625 N. Sidney Pl., Milwaukee, WI 53209: Free catalog: Free catalog ■ Communication aids for children and adults. 414–352–5678.

Flaghouse, 150 N. MacQuesten Pkwy., Mt. Vernon, NY 10550: Free catalog ■ Physical education and recreation, sports and play, and rehabilitation equipment and supplies. 800–221–5185.

Guardian Products, Inc., 12800 Wentworth St., Arieta, CA 91331: Free catalog ■ Walkers and accessories; crutches and canes; home activity aids; beds, lifters, and ramps; and transport assistive equipment. 800–255–5022; 818–504–2820 (in CA).

Handi-Ramp, Inc., P.O. Box 745, 1414 Armour Blvd., Mundelein, IL 60060: Free catalog ■ Ramps for vans and homes, and portable models. 800–876–RAMP.

Imaginart, 307 Arizona St., Bisbee, AZ 85603: Free catalog ■ Special education and assistive materials for preschool language, articulation, thinking skills, adult aphasia, and swallowing and feeding. 800–828–1376; 602–432–5741 (in AZ).

Independent Living Aids/Can-Do Products, 27 East Mall, Plainview, NY 11803: Free catalog ■ Self-help products for individuals with vision impairment and physical disabilities/challenges. 800–537–2118; 516–752–8080 (in NY).

Lumex, 100 Spence St., Bay Shore, NY 11706: Free catalog ■ Bathroom safety products, walking aids, pressure ulcer management devices, daily living aids, stainless steel wheelchairs, and other home health care products. 516–273–2200.

Touch Turner Company, 443 View Ridge Dr., Everett, WA 98203: Free brochure ■ Flashlight battery-powered page turner for magazines and books. 206–252–1541.

Vantage Mini Vans, 2441 E. Chambers Rd., Phoenix, AZ 85040: Free catalog ■ Mini-van conversions for the physically challenged. 800–348–VANS.

HEARING & COMMUNICATION AIDS

Audio Enhancement, 8 Winfield Point Ln., St. Louis, MO 63141: Free information ■ Wireless, auditory assistance device for hearing-impaired persons. 314–567–6141.

Harris Communications, 3255 Hennepin Ave., Ste. 55, Minneapolis, MN 55408: Free catalog ■ Closed caption and cable-ready decoder, TDDs, signalers, clocks, and other devices for hearing-impaired persons. 800–825–6758; 800–825–9187 (TDD).

Hear You Are, Inc., 4 Musconetcong Ave., Stanhope, NJ 07874: Free catalog ■ Smoke alarms, telephone aids, and amplification equipment for hearing-impaired persons. 201–347–7662.

Independent Living Aids, Inc./Can-Do Products, 27 East Mall, Plainview, NY 11803: Free catalog ■ Writing aids, low-vision aids and Braille items, household items, home health care supplies, talking appliances, mobility equipment, and communication aids, for disabled persons. 800–537–2118; 516–752–8080 (in NY).

National Captioning Institute, Inc., 5203 Leesburg Pike, Falls Church, VA 22041: Free brochure ■ Closed captioned equipment for people with hearing impairments. 703–845–1992; 703–998–2400 (TTY).

Nationwide Flashing Signal Systems, Inc., 8120 Fenton St., Silver Spring, MD 20910: Free catalog ■ Visual alerting devices and TDDs for hearing-impaired persons. 301–589–6671; 301–589–6670 (TDD).

One Video Place, 405 Lowell St., Wakefield, MA 01880: Catalog $3.95 ■ Closed-captioned movies on video cassettes.

Phone-TTY, Inc., 202 Lexington Ave., Hackensack, NJ 07601: Free information ■ Computer modems and software for using

computers to talk with TDDs. 201–489–7889; 201–489–7890 (TDD).

Phonic Ear, Inc., 3880 Cypress Dr., Petaluma, CA 94954: Free catalog ■ Sound enhancers for group functions and phonic ear personal FM systems for hearing- impaired individuals. 800–227–0735; 800–772–3374 (in CA).

Potomac Telecom, Inc., 1010 Rockville Pike, Rockville, MD 20854: Free information ■ Special needs devices and accessories for hearing-impaired persons. 301–762–4005; 301–762–0851 (TDD).

Quest Electronics, 510 S. Worthington St., Oconomowoc, WI 53066: Free information ■ Electronic alerting devices for people with hearing impairments. Includes ringing of telephones, door bells, alarm clocks, and other sounds. 800–558–9526.

Radio Shack, Division Tandy Corporation, 1500 One Tandy Center, Fort Worth, TX 76102: Free catalog ■ Special needs devices and accessories for hearing-impaired persons. 817–390–3700.

Science Products, Box 888, Berwyn, PA 19312: Free catalog ■ Voice sensory aids and custom electronics for people with hearing or visual impairments. 800–888–7400; 215–296–2111 (in PA).

Siemans Hearing Instruments, Inc., 10 Corporate Pl. South, Corporate Park 287, Piscataway, NJ 08854: Free information ■ Easy-to-install infrared in-home TV listening system. 908–562–6600.

Silent Call, P.O. Box 16348, Clarkston, MI 48016: Free information ■ Electronically activated wireless personal alert system.

Sonic Technology Products, 120 Richardson St., Grass Valley, CA 95945: Free information ■ Personal portable sound amplifier. 800–247–5548.

Ultratec, Inc., 6442 Normandy Ln., Madison, WI 53719: Free information ■ Smoke detector for hearing-impaired persons. 608–273–0707 (voice/TDD).

Weltbrech Communications, Inc., 2656 29th St., Ste. 205, Santa Monica, CA 90405:

Free information ■ Portable TDDs. 800–233–9130 (voice/TDD); 310–452–8613 (in CA/voice); 310–452–5460 (in CA/TDD).

ZiCom, The Deaf Culture Company, 2485 Coral St., Vista, CA 92083: Free information ■ Portable TDD. 800–748–5633 (voice/TDD).

HEAT EXCHANGERS

Gaylord Industries, Inc., P.O. Box 558, Wilsonville, OR 97070: Free information ■ Air-to-air heat exchangers. 800–547–9696.

Q-DOT Corporation, 701 N. 1st St., Garland, TX 75040: Free information ■ Air-to-air heat exchangers. 214–487–1130.

HOCKEY, FIELD

Action Sport Systems, Inc., P.O. Box 1442, Morgantown, NC 28671: Free information ■ Uniforms, balls, nets and cages, and leg guards. 800–631–1091; 704–874–2249 (in NC).

American Sports, Inc., 22 Longview Dr., Thornton, PA 19373: Free information ■ Uniforms, balls, nets and cages, leg guards, shoes, and hockey sticks. 215–459–8534.

Austin Athletic Equipment Corporation, 705 Bedford Ave., Box 423, Bellmore, NY 11710: Free information ■ Nets and cages. 516–785–0100.

Champion Sports Products Company, P.O. Box 138, Sayreville, NJ 08872: Free information ■ Uniforms, balls, nets and cages, and leg guards. 908–238–0330.

Cran Barry, Inc., 2 Lincoln Ave., Marblehead, MA 01945: Free information ■ Uniforms, balls, nets and cages, leg guards, shoes, and hockey sticks. 617–631–8510.

Doss Shoes, Soccer Sport Supply Company, 1745 1st Ave., New York, NY 10128: Free information ■ Uniforms, balls, nets and cages, leg guards, shoes, and hockey sticks. 212–427–6050.

Pennsylvania Sporting Goods, 1360 Industrial Hwy., P.O. Box 451, Southampton, PA 18966: Free information ■ Balls, nets and cages, leg guards, and hockey sticks. 800–523–1122.

Whitland Fitness Corporation, 101 Methuen St., P.O. Box 1049, Lawrence, MA 01842: Free information ■ Nets and cages. 508–685–5109.

HOCKEY, ICE

Clothing

Active Knitting, Ltd., 89 Tycos Dr., Toronto, Ontario, Canada M6B 1W3: Free information ■ Uniforms for hockey players and clothing for ice skaters. 416–789–1101.

Advantage Uniforms, Inc., 115 W. Main, P.O. Box 186, Manchester, MI 48158: Free information ■ Uniforms and accessories. 313–428–8522.

Betlin Manufacturing, 1445 Marion Rd., Columbus, OH 43207: Free information ■ Uniforms and accessories. 614–443–0248.

Kajee, Inc., 101 E. Wayne St., Franklin, IN 46131: Free information ■ Uniforms and other sportswear. 800–428–4314; 317–736–8032 (in IN).

Loco Athletics/YNot Jackets, 199–B Brook Ave., Deer Park, NY 11729: Free information ■ Uniforms and other sportswear. 515–586–2225.

Majestic Athletic Wear, Ltd., 636 Pen Argyl St., Pen Argyl, PA 18072: Free information ■ Uniforms and other sportswear. 215–863–6161.

T-Shirt Ink, Inc., 5624 Lincoln Dr., Edina, MN 55436: Free information ■ Uniforms and other sportswear. 612–938–1116.

Venus Knitting Mills, Inc., 140 Spring St., Murray Hill, NJ 07974: Free information ■ Uniforms, clothing for ice skaters, and other sportswear. 800–955–4200; 201–464–2400 (in NJ).

Equipment

American Athletic Shoe Company, Inc., 15 South St., Ware, MA 01802: Free information ■ Figure and hockey ice skates and accessories. 413–967–3511.

AmerSport USA, Inc., Clinton County Industrial Park, P.O. Box 1160, Plattsburgh, NY 12901: Free information ■ Guards and pads, helmets, masks, mouth guards, pucks, nets and cages, hockey sticks, and skates. 518–561–0202.

Can/Am Hockey, Ltd., 12834 Gravois Rd., St. Louis, MO 63127: Free information ■ Figure, racing, and hockey skates and accessories, and blade sharpeners. 314–843–3553.

Canstar Sports USA, Inc., 50 Jonergin Dr., Swanton, VT 05448: Free information ■

Figure and hockey ice skates, blade sharpeners, and other accessories. 800–362–3146; 800–451–5120 (in VT).

Cooper International, Inc., 501 Alliance Ave., Toronto, Ontario, Canada M6N 2J3: Free information ■ Guards and pads, helmets, masks, mouth guards, pucks, nets and cages, hockey sticks, figure and hockey ice skates and accessories, and blade protectors. 416–763–3801.

Karhu USA, Inc., P.O. Box 4249, South Burlington, VT 05401: Free information ■ Guards and pads, helmets, masks, hockey sticks, and ice skates. 800–222–1833; 802–864–4519 (in VT).

Lowry's Manufacturing, Ltd., 19 Keith Rd., Winnipeg, Manitoba, Canada R3H 0H7: Free information ■ Figure and hockey ice skates, replacement blades and blade protectors, and accessories. 204–633–6359.

Maska USA, Inc., Pierson Industrial Park, Rt. 25, P.O. Box 381, Bradford, VT 05033: Free information ■ Guards and pads, helmets, masks, pucks and accessories, and figure and hockey ice skates. 800–451–4600; 802–222–4751 (in VT).

National Sporting Goods Corporation, 25 Brighton Ave., Passaic, NJ 07055: Free information ■ Figure and hockey ice skates, blade protectors and sharpeners, and accessories. 201–779–2323.

Oberhamer, Inc., 11975 Portland Ave. South, Ste. 122, Burnsville, MN 55337: Free information ■ Figure and hockey ice skates, blade sharpeners and protectors, and accessories. 612–890–1657.

Riedell Shoes, Inc., P.O. Box 21, Red Wing, MN 55066: Free information ■ Figure, racing, and hockey skates and accessories, and blade sharpeners and protectors. 612–388–8251.

SK Sports Shoes, Ltd., 280 Donlands Ave., Toronto, Ontario, Canada M4J 3R4: Free information ■ Figure, racing, and hockey ice skates and accessories. Includes replacement blades, blade sharpeners, and protectors. 416–465–2784.

USA Skate Company, 157 Grant Ave., Islip, NY 11751: Free information ■ Guards and pads, nets and cages, hockey sticks, and skates and accessories. 800–426–3334; 516–277–1000 (in NY).

HOME BUILDING & IMPROVEMENT

Ceilings

AA-Abbingdon Affiliates, 2149 Utica Ave., Brooklyn, NY 11234: Brochure $1 ■ Tin ceilings cornice moldings. 718–258–8333.

Ceilings, Walls & More, Inc., 124 Walnut St., Box 494, Jefferson, TX 75657: Free brochure ■ Nonporous vinyl or polymer reproductions of original antique metal ceiling panels. 903–665–2221.

Celotex Building Products Division, P.O. Box 31602, Tampa, FL 33631: Free information ■ Sound-absorbing ceiling tiles. 813–873–1700.

Chelsea Decorative Metal Company, 9603 Moonlight Dr., Houston, TX 77096: Catalog $1 ■ Embossed metal for ceilings and walls in art deco tin. 713–721–9200.

Dovetail Woodworking, 836 Middle Rd., East Greenwich, RI 02818: Catalog $5 ■ Easy-to-install ceiling panels, corner pieces, moldings, center medallions, and border friezes. 401–885–2403.

Midwestern Wood Products, 1500 W. Jefferson St., P.O. Box 434, Morton, IL 61550: Free information ■ Easy-to-install suspended hardwood ceiling panels. 800–441–7493.

W.F. Norman Corporation, P.O. Box 323, Nevada, MO 64772: Catalog $3 ■ Metal plates for ceilings and wallcoverings. Includes center plates, corner plates, border plates, cornice, filler plates, and over 1300 sheet metal ornaments. 800–641–4038.

Old Jefferson Tile Company, Twin Oaks Plant, P.O. Box 494, Jefferson, TX 75657: Free brochure ■ High-impact polymer styrene replicas of tin ceilings. 903–665–2221.

Cupolas

Colonial Cupolas, P.O. Box 38, Haslett, MI 48840: Brochure $3 ■ Authentic reproductions of historic cupolas and weather vanes.

Country Cupolas, East Conway, NH 04037: Free brochure ■ Country-style cupolas, assembled or as a kit. 603–939–2698.

Denninger Cupolas & Weathervanes, RD 1, Box 447, Middletown, NY 10940: Catalog $1 ■ Redwood cupolas with copper roofs and weathervanes. 914–343–2229.

Sun Designs, P.O. Box 6, Oconomowoc, WI 53066: Catalog 50¢ ■ Plans for gazebos, bridges, cupolas, and other backyard and landscaping structures. 414–567–4255.

Doors

Andersen Windows, 100 4th Ave., Bayport, MN 55003: Free booklet ■ Energy-efficient windows, roof windows, and patio doors. 612–439–5150.

Architectural Components, 26 N. Leverett Rd., Montague, MA 01351: Brochure $3 ■ Reproduction doors from the 18th and 19th centuries, windows and window frames, sashes, and moldings. 413–367–9441.

Arctic Glass & Window Outlet, Rt. 1 West, Hammond, WI 54015: Catalog $2 (refundable) ■ Windows, entryway doors, patio doors, skylights, and sunrooms. 715–796–2292.

Atrium Door & Window Corporation, P.O. Box 226957, Dallas, TX 75222: Free information ■ Handcrafted energy-efficient wooden doors with solid brass mortise lock sets and hinges. 800–527–5249.

Bel-Air Door Company, 314 S. Date Ave., P.O. Box 829, Alhambra, CA 91802: Brochure $2 (refundable) ■ Handcrafted exterior doors with custom panels and openings and beveled or etched glass. 213–283–3731.

Benchmark Doors Division, P.O. Box 7387, Fredericksburg, VA 22404: Free information ■ Steel doors with a wood-grain finish. 703–898–3800.

Bennett Industries, Inc., 1530 Palisade Ave., Fort Lee, NJ 07024: Free information ■ Red oak and mahogany doors with leaded glass and triple-glazed windows. 201–947–5340.

Beveled Glass Industries, 6006 W. Washington Blvd., Culver City, CA 90232: Free information ■ Wood doors with sidelights and beveled glass. 800–421–0518.

The Bilco Company, P.O. Box 1203, New Haven, CT 06505: Free information ■ All-steel outside doors for basement entrances.

Caradco Corporation, P.O. Box 920, Rantoul, IL 61866: Free information ■ Hinged and sliding wooden and insulated aluminum doors for entryways and patios. 217–893–4444.

Cascade Woodwork, P.O. Box 316, Ouray, CO 81427: Catalog $1 ■ Handcrafted storm and screen doors with removable panels and optional hardware and pre-finishing. 303–325–4780.

Ciro Coppa Doors, 1231 Paraiso Ave., San Pedro, CA 90731: Free catalog ■ Wood screen doors and Adirondack chairs. 310–548–4142.

Colonial Craft, 2772 Fairview Ave., St. Paul, MN 55113: Free catalog ■ Hardwood windows and doors and removable door and window grilles. 800–727–5187; 612–631–2110 (in MN).

Combination Door Company, P.O. Box 1076, Fond du Lac, WI 54936: Free brochure ■ Wooden combination storm and screen doors and basement and garage windows. 414–922–2050.

Crestline, 1725 Indian Wood Cir., Maumee, H 43537: Free information ■ Water repellent French doors with optional glass panels and transoms. 800–552–4111.

Curvoflite, 205 Spencer Ave., Chelsea, MA 02150: Free catalog ■ Spiral and circular oak staircases, paneling, moldings, cabinets, and other millwork. 800–445–7009; 617–889–0007 (in MA).

Customwood Manufacturing Company, P.O. Box 26208, Albuquerque, NM 87125: Free information ■ Carved wooden doors and hardwood interior room dividers. 505–344–1691.

Dovetail Woodworking, 836 Middle Rd., East Greenwich, RI 02818: Catalog $5 ■ Colonial and Victorian entryways, fireplace mantels, and wide pine flooring. 401–885–2403.

Driwood Ornamental Wood Moulding, P.O. Box 1729, Florence, SC 29503: Catalog $6 ■ Custom doors, embossed wood molding, raised paneling, custom mantels, and curved stairs. 803–669–2478.

Eagle Window & Door, 375 E. 9th St., Dubuque, IA 52001: Free information ■ Doors. 319–556–2270.

Elegant Entries, 240 Washington St., Auburn, MA 01501: Free catalog ■ Mahogany and rosewood exterior and interior doors. 800–343–3432.

Elite Interior Doors, Commerce Dr., Mount Vernon, OH 43050: Free information ■ Molded interior doors with the look of wood, in pre-hung or bi-fold models. 614–397–3403.

Entry Systems, 911 E. Jefferson, Pittsburgh, KS 66762: Free information ■ Steel doors with a choice of light and transom designs. 800–835–0364.

Fiberlux, Inc., 59 S. Terrace Ave., Mt. Vernon, NY 10550: Free information ■ Sliding glass and aluminum doors. 800–342–7111.

General Aluminum Corporation, 1001 W. Crosby Rd., Dallas, TX 75006: Free information ■ Insulated aluminum entryway doors, insulated hinged doors for patios, sliding glass doors, and window greenhouses with adjustable shelves, screen tops, and removable bottom pans. 214–242–5271.

Georgia-Pacific, 133 Peachtree St. NE, P.O. 105605, Atlanta, GA 30303: Free information ■ Doors and windows. 404–521–4000.

Grande Entrance Door Company, P.O. Box 5249, Bend, OR 97708: Free information ■ Douglas fir doors with oval-patterned and beveled glass and solid brass came in the door and sidelights. 800–821–10116.

Grand Era Reproduction, P.O. Box 1026, Lapeer, MI 48446: Catalog $2 (refundable) ■ Easy-to-assemble screen and storm door kits in Victorian, Colonial, Cape Cod, ranch, and country styles. 313–664–1756.

Hess Manufacturing Company, Box 127, Quincy, PA 17247: Free information ■ Insulated aluminum entryway doors and windows. 800–541–6666; 800–542–6666 (in PA).

Hurd Millwork Company, 520 S. Whelen Ave., Medford, WI 54451: Free information ■ Windows and hinged and sliding wood and insulated aluminum patio doors. 800–2BE–HURD.

Iberia Millwork, 500 Jane St., New Iberia, LA 70560: Free brochure ■ French doors, interior and exterior shutters, and cabinets. 318–365–5644.

Ideal Company, Inc., P.O. Box 2540, Waco, TX 76702: Free brochure ■ Doors with antique leaded and clear-leaded glass, or divided lights. 817–752–2494.

International Wood Products, 9630 Aero Dr., San Diego, CA 92123: Free information ■ Wood door entry systems with a choice of

transom designs, in single- or double-entry models, and sidelights. 800–468–3667.

Jeld-Wen, 335 Commerce Dr., Mt. Vernon, OH 43050: Free information ■ Pre-finished, or ready-for-finishing provincial and colonial-style bi-fold interior doors. 800–535–3936.

Jessup Door Company, 300 E. Railroad St., Dowagiac, MI 49047: Free information ■ French doors for patios. 616–782–2183.

Joinery Company, P.O. Box 518, Tarboro, NC 27886: Brochure $5 ■ Reproduction antique entryways and doors. 919–823–3306.

Kirby Millworks, 3269 CR 514, Durango, CO 81301: Free brochure; portfolio $12 ■ Interior and exterior solid oak doors and moldings. 800–245–3667.

Kusan Company, Mastic Building, 131 S. Taylor St., P.O. Box 65, South Bend, IN 46624: Free information ■ Entryway surrounds. 209–288–4621.

Leslie-Lock, Inc., 4501 Circle 75 Pkwy., Building D, Ste. 4300, Atlanta, GA 30339: Free information ■ Traditionally styled security storm doors with all-welded steel frames, brass locks, and dead bolts. 404–953–6366.

Mad River Woodworks, 189 Taylor Way, P.O. Box 1067, Blue Lake, CA 95525: Catalog $3 ■ Ready-to-paint or stain, custom reproduction doors from the mid-1800s. 707–668–5679.

Mar-Flo, Inc., 8 Fox Ct., Dumont, NJ 07628: Free information ■ Custom interior, exterior, and cabinet doors. 201–742–4765.

Marvin Windows, Warroad, MN 56763: Free information ■ Windows and doors with divided light and insulated storm windows and transoms. 800–346–5128.

Mastic Corporation, 131 S. Taylor St., South Bend, IN 46624: Free information ■ Easy-to-maintain vinyl doors. 219–288–4621.

Monarch Mirror Doors, P.O. Box 4116, Chatsworth, CA 91313: Free information ■ Mirrored closet doors. 818–998–6444.

Morgan Manufacturing, P.O. Box 2446, Oshkosh, WI 54903: Free information ■ Paneled and carved wooden doors and sliding glass and hinged patio doors. 800–435–7464.

Nicolai Doors, 601 Oregon St., Oshkosh, WI 54901: Free information ■ Solid wood French doors with a choice of glass arrangements.

E.A. Nord Company, Box 1187, Everett, WA 98206: Free information ■ Paneled and carved wooden doors. 206–259–9292.

Old Wagon Factory, P.O. Box 1427, Clarksville, VA 23927: Catalog $2 ■ Victorian and Chippendale storm screen doors, railings and brackets, and Chippendale furniture. 804–374–5787.

Peachtree Windows & Doors, Box 5700, Norcross, GA 30091: Free information ■ Steel, wood, glass, and aluminum doors and windows. 404–497–2000.

Pease Industries, Inc., P.O. Box 14–8001, Fairfield, OH 45014: Free information ■ Steel entryway and hinged patio doors. 800–543–1180.

Pella Information Center, P.O. Box 308, Moline, IL 61265: Free idea booklet ■ Information on how to use doors and windows when building a new house or remodeling.

Perma-Door, 9017 Blue Ash Rd., Cincinnati, OH 45242: Free information ■ Wooden and steel entryway and patio doors. 513–745–6400.

Remodelers & Renovators Supplies, P.O. Box 45478, Boise, ID 83711: Catalog $3 ■ Ready-to-stain screen doors. 800–456–2135.

Season-all Industries, Inc., 1480 Wayne Ave., Indiana, PA 15701: Free information ■ Custom vinyl doors for patio entrances. 800–999–1847.

Sheppard Millwork, Inc., 21020 70th Ave. West, Edmonds, WA 98020: Free catalog ■ Sanded and unfinished doors with optional hardware. 206–771–4645.

Silverton Victorian Millworks, P.O. Box 2987, Durango, CO 81302: Catalog $4 ■ Doors with stained glass or etched glass inserts. 303–259–5915.

Simpson Door Company, P.O. Box 210, McCleary, WA 98557: Catalog 50¢ ■ Paneled, carved, and standard wooden flush-entry doors. 206–495–3291.

Southeastern Insulated Glass, 6477–B Peachtree Industrial Blvd., Atlanta, GA 30360: Free information ■ Sliding glass doors and skylights with optional tempered insulated glass and kits for greenhouses and sunrooms. 800–841–9842; 404–455–8838 (in GA).

Stanley Hardware, 195 Lake St., New Britain, CT 06050: Free information ■ Sliding closet make-your-own door kits. 203–225–5111.

Taylor Brothers, P.O. Box 11198, Lynchburg, VA 24506: Catalog $2 ■ Custom Chippendale storm and screen doors. 800–288–6767.

Temple Products, Inc., P.O. Box 1008, Temple, TX 76503: Free information ■ Paneled and carved entryway and patio doors. 800–634–3667; 800–792–3357 (in TX).

Therma-Tru Corporation, 1684 Woodlands Dr., Maumee, OH 43537: Free product information ■ Insulated doors and windows. 419–537–1931.

Wagon Factory, P.O. Box 1427, Clarksville, VA 23927: Catalog $2 ■ Handcrafted Victorian and Chippendale storm and screen doors. 804–374–5787.

Jack Wallis Door Emporium, Rt. 1, Box 22A, Murray, KY 42071: Catalog $4 ■ Handcrafted doors with optional stained glass. 502–489–2613.

Weather Shield Mfg., Inc., 531 N. 8th St., Medford, WI 54451: Free brochure ■ Wooden windows, patio doors, and steel entryways. 800–477–6808.

Windsor Doors, Division Ceco Corporation, P.O. Box 9770, Little Rock, AR 72209: Free information ■ Doors. 501–562–1872.

Wing Industries, P.O. Box 38347, Dallas, TX 75238: Free information ■ Bi-fold French doors for interiors. 214–699–9900.

Woodstone Company, Patch Rd., P.O. Box 223, Westminster, VT 05158: Brochure $3 ■ Single-, double-, or triple-glazed windows, with palladians and straight and fanned transoms. Other items include solid wooden doors with insulated cores, pegged mortises, and tenon frames. 802–722–9217.

Flooring

Bangkok Industries, Inc., 4562 Worth St., Philadelphia, PA 19124: Free brochure ■ Unfinished and pre-finished exotic hardwood flooring in strips, planks, and parquet patterns. 215–537–5800.

Carlisle Restoration Lumber, Rt. 123, Stoddard, NH 03464: Free information ■ Wide pine flooring and paneling. 603–446–3937.

Country Floors, Inc., 15 E. 16th St., New York, NY 10003: Catalog $10 ■ Hand-molded and painted ceramic tiles. 212–627–8300.

Craftsmen Lumber, 436 Main St., Box 222, Groton, MA 01450: Free information ■ Flooring and reproduction colonial woodwork in pine and red oak. 508–448–6336.

Dovetail Woodworking, 836 Middle Rd., East Greenwich, RI 02818: Catalog $5 ■ Wide-pine flooring, fireplace mantels, and colonial and Victorian entryways. 401–885–2403.

Goodwin Lumber, Rt. 2, Box 119, Micanopy, FL 32667: Free information ■ Heart pine and red cypress flooring, paneling, and beams. 904–373–9663.

Hartco, 716 Parkway, Servierville, TN 37862: Free brochure ■ Oak flooring in parquet, combination, parallel, herringbone, and basket-weave patterns. 800–446–7772; 615–428–5263 (in TN).

Joinery Company, P.O. Box 518, Tarboro, NC 27886: Portfolio and price list $5 (refundable) ■ Antique heart pine tongue-and-groove flooring, paneling, and trim from authentic colonial buildings. 919–823–3306.

Kentucky Wood Floors, P.O. Box 33276, Louisville, KY 40232: Brochure $2 ■ Custom walnut, oak, cherry, and ash borders ready for glue-down installation. 502–451–6024.

Livermore Wood Floors, P.O. Box 146, East Livermore, ME 04228: Free information ■ Wood flooring in cherry, oak, maple, ash, wide pine, walnut, and birch. 207–897–5211.

Memphis Hardwood Flooring Company, 1551 N. Thomas St., P.O. Box 38217, Memphis, TN 38107: Free information ■ Unfinished and finished oak flooring. 800–346–3010.

Old South Company, P.O. Box 7096, Tarboro, NC 27886: Portfolio $5 ■ Original hardwood antique flooring. 919–823–8100.

J.L. Powell & Company, Inc., 600 S. Madison St., Whiteville, NC 28472: Free information ■ Antique heart pine flooring. 800–227–2007.

Quality Woods, Ltd., P.O. Box 205, Lake Hiawatha, NJ 07034: Free brochure ■ Teak lumber, plywood, and teak and Asian rosewood parquet, tongue-and-groove planks, and strip flooring. 201–927–0742.

Robbins/Sykes, Inc., 4777 Eastern Ave., Cincinnati, OH 45226: Free information ■ Solid oak flooring. 513–871–8988.

Tarkett, Box 300, Johnson City, TN 37605: Catalog $1 ■ Pre-finished flooring with beveled edges. 615–928–3122.

Vintage Lumber Company, 9507 Woodsboro Rd., Frederick, MD 21701: Free brochure ■ Remilled antique heart pine, oak, chestnut, oak, cherry, walnut, and poplar flooring. 301–898–7859.

Frames & Beams

Bear Creek Lumber, P.O. Box 669, Winthrop, WA 98862: Brochure $4 ■ Western red cedar building accessories. 509–997–3110.

E.F. Bufton & Son, Builders, Inc., P.O. Box 164, Princeton, MA 01541: Brochure $5 ■ Custom-cut oak post and beam frames. 508–464–5418.

Goodwin Lumber, Rt. 2, Box 119, Micanopy, FL 32667: Free information ■ Heart pine lumber and red cypress flooring, paneling, and beams. 904–373–9663.

Pacific Post & Beam, P.O. Box 13708, San Luis Obispo, CA 93406: Brochure $5 ■ Handcrafted timber frames. 805–543–7565.

Vermont Frames, P.O. Box 100, Hinesburg, VT 05461: Free brochure ■ Post and beam frames. 802–453–3727.

Paint

Antique Color Supply, Inc., P.O. Box 1668, Lunenburg, MA 01462: Free information with long SASE ■ Authentic powdered milk paint for antique restoration. 508–582–6426.

Bay City Paint Company, 2279 Market St., San Francisco, CA 94114: Free information ■ Paints and brushes, glues, and how-to books. 415–431–4914.

Clearwater Color Company, Box 340, Sellersville, PA 18960: Free information ■ Penetrating wood stains. 800–899–5263.

Factory Paint Store, 505 Pond St., South Weymouth, MA 02190: Free information ■

Paint, window shades, lighting fixtures, and wallpaper. 617–331–1200.

Pintchik Homeworks, 2106 Bath Ave., Brooklyn, NY 11214: Free brochure ■ Wallpaper, window treatment supplies, paints, flooring supplies, and hardware. 800–847–4199; 718–996–5580 (in NY).

Paneling

California Redwood Association, 405 Enfrente Dr., Ste. 200, Novato, CA 94949: Free information with long SASE ■ Redwood paneling. 415–382–0662.

Driwood Ornamental Wood Moulding, P.O. Box 1729, Florence, SC 29503: Catalog $6 ■ Embossed wood molding and raised paneling, custom mantels, curved stairs, and custom doors. 803–669–2478.

Georgia-Pacific, 133 Peachtree St. NE, P.O. Box 105605, Atlanta, GA 30348: Free information ■ Wall paneling and pre-hung wallpaper on plywood panels. 404–521–4000.

Goodwin Lumber, Rt. 2, Box 119, Micanopy, FL 32667: Free information ■ Heart pine and red cypress flooring, paneling, and beams. 904–373–9663.

Masonite Corporation, 1 S. Wacker Dr., Chicago, IL 60606: Free information ■ Hardboard paneling that requires no moldings. 312–750–0900.

E.T. Moore Company, 3100 N. Hopkins Rd., Richmond, VA 23224: Free information ■ Pine mantels, columns, flooring, moldings, paneling, hand-hewn beams, custom furniture, and cabinets. 804–231–1823.

Ply-Gem Manufacturing, 201 Black Horse Pike, Haddon Heights, NJ 08035: Free information ■ Plywood and hardboard paneling. 609–546–0704.

Simpson Timber, Box 1169, Arcata, CA 95521: Free information ■ Redwood paneling. 800–637–7077; 707–822–0371 (in CA).

States Industries, Inc., P.O. Box 7037, Eugene, OR 97401: Free information ■ Wood paneling. 800–537–0419.

Weyerhaeuser Paneling Division Headquarters, P.O. Box 9, Klamath Falls, OR 97601: Free information ■ Easy-to-install decorator wall furnishings, from traditional paneling to wallcoverings, wood planking, and tile board. 503–884–2241.

Restoration Materials

Aristocraft Originals, Inc., 6200 Highlands Pkwy. SE, Smyrna, GA 30082: Catalog $3 ■ Reproduction niches, crown molding, trim, fireplaces, ceiling medallions, corbels, archways, columns, porches, and oak beams. 404–333–9934.

Bare Wood, Inc., 106 Ferris St., Brooklyn, NY 11231: Free information ■ Custom 18th- and 19th-century interior and exterior antique doors, mantels, stairway parts, and other architectural millwork. 718–875–9037.

Campbellsville Industries, Inc., P.O. Box 278, Campbellsville, KY 42718: Free information ■ Aluminum cornices, louvers, cupolas, columns, balustrades, and shutters, with an optional baked-on finish. 502–465–8135.

Hartman-Sanders Company, 4340 Bankers Cir., Atlanta, GA 30360: Free information with long SASE ■ Reproduction wood columns. 404–449–1561.

Moorwood, 22 Cottage St., Middletown, NY 10940: Free information ■ Custom wood moldings. 914–341–1924.

E.A. Nord Company, Box 1187, Everett, WA 98206: Free information ■ Fluted or plain hemlock and fir columns. 206–259–9292.

A.F. Schwerd Manufacturing Company, 3215 McClure Ave., Pittsburgh, PA 15212: Free catalog ■ Custom standard and detailed wood columns in seasoned northern white pine, with matching pilasters and aluminum bases. 412–766–6322.

Roofing Materials

C & H Roofing, P.O. Box 2105, Lake City, FL 32056: Free information ■ Red cedar shingles with a thatched look. 800–327–8115.

Cedar Valley Shingle Systems, 943 San Felipe Rd., Hollister, CA 95023: Free brochure ■ Cedar shingle panels in regular or rough-sawn textures. 800–521–9523.

CertainTeed, P.O. Box 860, Valley Forge, PA 19482: Free information ■ Asphalt-based roof shingles that resembles wood shakes. 215–341–7000.

Classic Products, 299 Staunton St., P.O. Box 701, Piqua, OH 45356: Free brochure ■ Aluminum roofing designed to look like wood. 800–543–8938.

Conklin Metal Industries, P.O. Box 1858, Atlanta, GA 30301: Information $3 ■ Roofing supplies and metal roofing shingles in galvanized steel, copper, and other materials. 404–688–4510.

Evergreen Slate Company, 68 E. Potter Ave., Granville, NY 12832: Free brochure ■ Roofing slate, tools, and accessories. 518–642–2530.

FibreCem Corporation, P.O. Box 411368, Charlotte, NC 28246: Free brochure ■ Reinforced cement-base shingles with a slate appearance. 800–346–6147.

GAF Building Materials Corporation, 1361 Alps Rd., Wayne, NJ 07470: Free information ■ Fire-resistant, fiberglass-asphalt roofing shingles. 201–628–3000.

Georgia-Pacific, P.O. Box 2808, Atlanta, GA 30348: Free information ■ Easy-to-install shingles with a textured look of cedar. 404–521–4000.

Ludowici-Celadon, P.O. Box 69, New Lexington, OH 43764: Free information ■ Sculpted French-style clay and ceramic roofing tiles. 614–342–1995.

Masonite Corporation, 1 S. Wacker Dr., Chicago, IL 60606: Free information ■ Wood-fiber shingles with an authentic shake look. 312–750–0900.

Metal Building Components, Inc., 14031 W. Hardy, P.O. Box 38217, Houston, TX 77060: Free information ■ Preformed metal roofs. 713–445–8555.

Metal Sales Manufacturing, 10300 Linn Station Rd., Louisville, KY 40223: Free information ■ Roofing panels in 26–gauge galvanized steel. 502–426–5215.

Met-Tile, Inc., 1745 Monticello Ct., P.O. Box 4268, Ontario, CA 91761: Free information ■ A galvanized-steel roofing system with a look of Spanish tile. 714–947–0311.

Monier Roof Tile, P.O. Box 5567, Orange, CA 92613: Free information ■ Over 100 standard shades of concrete tiles. 714–538–8822.

Oak Crest Manufacturing, P.O. Box 128, Jonesborough, TN 37659: Free information ■ Authentic antique hand-split oak shakes and split- and smooth-sawn oak shingles. 615–753–6599.

Owens-Corning Fiberglas, Fiberglas Tower, Toledo, OH 43659: Free information

■ Fire-protected fiberglass shingles that resemble wood. 800–ROOF–OCF.

ShakerTown Corporation, Box 400, Winlock, WA 98596: Free information ■ Cedar shingles. 800–426–8970.

South Coast Shingle Company, 2220 E. South St., Long Beach, CA 90805: Free brochure ■ Fancy butt shingles. 310–634–7100.

Supradur Manufacturing Corporation, P.O. Box 908, Rye, NY 10580: Free information ■ Fireproof roofing shingles with a natural stone look. 800–223–1948.

U.S. Tile, 215 E. Commonwealth Ave., Ste. F, Fullerton, CA 92632: Free information ■ Ceramic clay tiles. 714–773–9161.

Westile, 8311 W. Carder Ct., Littleton, CO 80125: Free information ■ Concrete roofing tiles. 800–433–8450.

Zappone Manufacturing Company, N. 2928 Pittsburgh, Spokane, WA 99207: Free information ■ Fireproof and watertight copper shingles. 509–483–6408.

Salvaged Building Materials

ADI Architectural Salvage, 2045 Broadway, Kansas City, MO 64108: Catalog $5.50 ■ Architectural salvage from early buildings. Includes ornamental trims, fireplaces, columns, and other items. 816–283–3051.

After the Paint, 2711 Lafayette St., St. Louis, MO 63104: Free information ■ Salvaged building components and other supplies. 314–771–4442.

Aged Woods, 147 W. Philadelphia St., York, PA 17401: Free brochure ■ Antique building materials that include fieldstone and slate. 800–233–9307; 717–843–8104 (in PA).

All State Salvage, 1354 Jackson St., St. Paul, MN 55117: Free information ■ Salvaged building components and trim. 612–488–6675.

American Architectural Antiques, 100 Orange St., New Haven CT 06508: Free information ■ Salvaged architectural building components and decor accessories. 203–624–1009.

Architectural Antiques, 2771 SW 27th Ave., Coconut Grove, FL 33133: Free information ■ Salvaged building components and decor accessories. 305–285–9222.

Architectural Antiques Exchange, 715 N. 2nd St., Philadelphia, PA 19123: Free information ■ Salvaged building components and trim. 215–922–3669.

Architectural Salvage Company, 103 W. Michigan Ave., P.O. Box 401, Grass Lake, MI 49240: Free brochure ■ Architectural antiques from old buildings. Includes hardware, doors, stained glass, woodwork, mantels, lighting fixtures, columns, and other items. 517–522–8516.

Art Directions, 6120 Delmar Blvd., St. Louis, MO 63112: Catalog $2 ■ Salvaged building components and fixtures. 314–863–1895.

The Bank, 1824 Felicity St., New Orleans, LA 70113: Free information ■ Salvaged building components. 504–523–2702.

Berkeley Architectural Salvage, 2741 10th St., Berkeley, CA 94710: Free information ■ Salvaged building components and decor accessories. 510–849–2025.

Cleveland Wrecking, 3170 E. Washington Blvd., Los Angeles, CA 90023: Free information ■ Salvaged building components and accessories. 213–269–0633.

Colonial Antiques, 5000 W. 96th St., Indianapolis, IN 46268: Free information ■ Salvaged building components. 317–873–2727.

1874 House, 8070 SE 13th St., Portland, OR 97202: Free information ■ Salvaged building components and trim. 503–233–1874.

Florida Victorian Architectural Antiques, 112 W. Georgia Ave., Deland, FL 32720: Free information with long SASE ■ Salvaged architectural building components. 904–734–9300.

Great American Salvage Company, 34 Cooper Square, New York, NY 10003: Free information ■ Salvaged building components and trim. 212–505–0070.

Irreplaceable Artifacts, 14 2nd Ave., New York, NY 10003: Free information ■ Salvaged building components. 212–777–2900.

Ohmega Salvage, 2407 San Pablo Ave., Berkeley, CA 94702: Free information ■ Salvaged building components and trim. 510–843–7368.

Olde Theatre Architectural Salvage, 2045 Broadway, Kansas City, MO 64108: Free information ■ Salvaged building components, other components, and decor accessories. 816–283–3740.

Pelnick Wrecking Company, Inc., 1749 Erie Blvd. East, Syracuse, NY 13210: Free information ■ Antique windows and doors, mantels, ornamental building supplies, lumber, sinks, and plumbing. 315–472–1031.

Salvage One, 1524 S. Sangamon St., Chicago, IL 60608: Free information ■ Salvaged building components. 312–725–8243.

Scavenger's Paradise, 4360 Tujunga Ave., North Hollywood, CA 91604: Free information ■ Salvaged building components and trim. 213–877–7945.

Stamford Wrecking, One Barry Pl., Stamford, CT 06902: Free information ■ Windows, doors, and other building components and accessories. 203–324–9537.

Sunrise Salvage, 2204 San Pablo Ave., Berkeley, CA 94702: Free information ■ Salvaged building components and trim. 510–845–4751.

United House Wrecking, Inc., 535 Hope St., Stamford, CT 06906: Free information ■ Salvaged architectural building components and trim. Includes doors, mantels, beveled glass, Victorian gingerbread, paneling, lighting fixtures, dividers, and screens. 203–348–5371.

Urban Archaeology, 285 Lafayette St., New York, NY 10012: Free information ■ Victorian, art nouveau, and art deco architectural antiques and decor accessories. Inventory varies, but often includes staircases, balconies, plaster moldings, windows and skylights, doors, and entrance ways. 212–431–6969.

Wooden Nickel Architectural Antiques, 1410 Central Pkwy., Cincinnati, OH 45210: Free information ■ Salvaged building components and trims. 513–241–2985.

The Wrecking Bar, 292 Moreland Ave. NE, Atlanta, GA 30307: Free information ■ Salvaged building components. 404–525–0468.

Shutters

Alside Corporation, Box 2010, Akron, OH 44309: Free information ■ Shutter sets. 216–929–1811.

American Heritage Shutters, 2345 Dunn Ave., Memphis, TN 38114: Free brochure ■ White pine shutters with movable louvers. Will custom build for round windows. 800–541–1186.

Beech River Mill Company, Old Rt. 16, Centre Ossipee, NH 03814: Catalog $5 ■ Paneled and louvered shutters for exterior and interior installation. 603–539–2636.

European Energy Savers, 14315 Troy Way, Magalia, CA 95954: Free information ■ Retractable patio covers, roll shutters, and window awnings. 916–873–2662.

Hisrich Manufacturing Company, 121 W. 4th St., Dover, OH 44622: Information $1 ■ Custom shutters with fixed or movable louvers. 216–343–8834.

Historic Windows, P.O. Box 1172, Harrisonburg, VA 22801: Catalog $3 ■ Custom handcrafted Victorian-style hardwood shutters. 703–434–5855.

Iberia Millwork, 500 Jane St., New Iberia, LA 70560: Free brochure ■ Interior and exterior shutters, cabinets, and French doors. 318–365–5644.

Inter Trade, Inc., 3175 Fujita St., Torrance, CA 90505: Free catalog ■ Custom roll shutters that provide security and protection from heat, sun, cold, rain, and noise. 213–515–7177.

LaPointe Cabinetmaker, 41 Gulf Rd., Pelham, MA 01002: Free information ■ Custom shutters, cabinets, doors, mantels, and trims. 413–256–1558.

Mastic Corporation, 131 S. Taylor St., South Bend, IN 46624: Free information ■ Shutters made from polystyrene and other materials. 215–288–4621.

REM Industries, P.O. Box 504, Northborough, MA 01532: Catalog $2 ■ Interior and exterior shutters. 508–393–8424.

Shuttercraft, 282 Stepstone Hill Rd., Guilford, CT 06437: Free information ■ Western white pine shutters with movable or fixed louvers, unfinished or primed and painted. 203–453–1973.

Siding

Abitibi-Price Corporation, Troy, MI 48084: Free information ■ Hardboard siding with a look of cross-sawn fir. 313–649–3300.

Alcan Building Products, 11 Cragwood Rd., Woodbridge, NJ 07095: Free information ■ Vinyl siding. 908–381–0900.

Alcoa Building Products, P.O. Box 716, Sidney, OH 45365: Free information ■ Vinyl siding with a rustic wood finish. 513–492–1111.

Black Forest Building Company, 30550 Beaconsfield, Roseville, MI 48066: Free information ■ Custom wooden exterior siding. 313–294–7400.

California Redwood Association, 405 Enfrente Dr., Ste. 200, Novato, CA 94949: Free information with long SASE ■ Redwood siding. 415–382–0662.

Cedar Valley Shingle Systems, 943 San Felipe Rd., Hollister, CA 95023: Free brochure ■ Red cedar shingle panels and decorator shingles. 800–521–9523.

Dryvit Systems, Inc., 1 Energy Way, P.O. Box 1014, West Warwick, RI 02893: Free information ■ Siding that looks like stucco. 800–556–7752.

Georgia-Pacific, 133 Peachtree St. NE, P.O. Box 105605, Atlanta, GA 30303: Free information ■ Hardboard siding with a colonial wood-grain texture. 404–521–4000.

Gold Bond Building Products, 2001 Rexford Rd., Charlotte, NC 28211: Free information ■ Siding with a look of natural wood and a smooth or wood-grain finish. 704–365–7300.

Louisiana-Pacific Corporation, 111 SW 5th Ave., Portland, OR 97204: Free information ■ Treated and weatherized wood siding. 503–221–0800.

Red Cedar Shingle Bureau, 515 116th Ave. NE, Bellevue, WA 98004: Free information ■ Rustic cedar shingles. 206–453–1324.

Reynolds Metals Company, P.O. Box 27003, Richmond, VA 23261: Free information ■ Vinyl-coated aluminum siding. 804–281–4188.

Stucco Stone Products, Inc., P.O. Box 270, Napa, CA 94559: Free information ■ Manufactured interlocking, lightweight stone components for use as siding. 800–255–7462.

USG Corporation, 101 S. Wacker Dr., Chicago, IL 60606: Free information ■ Tex-tured-coated siding for application over cement board. 312–606–4122.

VIPCO, 1441 Universal Rd., P.O. Box 498, Columbus, OH 43216: Free information ■ Solid vinyl exterior siding with a look of carved wood clapboard. 800–366–8472.

Stairways

A.J. Stairs, Inc., 195 Drum Point Rd., Brick, NJ 08723: Brochure $1 ■ Easy-to-assemble, custom spiral and curved stairways. 800–STAIR–85.

American General Products, P.O. Box 395, Ypsilanti, MI 48197: Free catalog ■ Oak stair parts. 800–STAIRS–1; 313–483–1833 (in MI).

American Ornamental Metal, 5013 Kelley St., P.O. Box 21548, Houston, TX 77026: Free brochure ■ Steel spiral stairways. 800–231–3693.

Atlantic Stairworks, P.O. Box 244, Newburyport, MA 01950: Portfolio $2 ■ Custom traditional and contemporary solid wood steps and handrails. 508–462–7502.

Cassidy Brothers Forge, Inc., US Rt. 1, Rowley, MA 01969: Brochure $1 ■ Standard and custom railings and spiral stairways, fences, gates, and balconies. 508–948–7303.

Columns, Inc., P.O. Box 895, Pearland, TX 77581: Free information ■ Aluminum and steel spiral stairs for outdoor or indoor installation. 713–485–3261.

Cooper Stair Company, 1331 Leithton Rd., Mundelein, IL 60060: Free brochure ■ Straight, circular, and spiral wood stairways, in kits or assembled. 312–362–8900.

Driwood Ornamental Wood Moulding, P.O. Box 1729, Florence, SC 29503: Catalog $6 ■ Curved stairs, embossed wood molding, raised paneling, and custom mantels and doors. 803–669–2478.

Duvinage Corporation, P.O. Box 828, Hagerstown, MD 21741: Free catalog ■ Spiral and circular stairways. 301–733–8255.

Goddard Manufacturing, Box 502, Logan, KS 67646: Free brochure ■ Custom spiral staircases with optional wooden railings. 913–689–4341.

Ironcraft, 1000 90th Ave., Oakland, CA 94603: Free information ■ Easy-to-install stairways. 510–632–4612.

The Iron Shop, 400 Reed Rd., P.O. Box 547, Broomall, PA 19008: Brochure $1 ■ Kits for assembling and installing several styles of iron stairs. 800–523–7427.

Midwest Spiral Stair Company, Inc., 113 Adell, Elmhurst, IL 60126: Free information ■ Metal and wood spiral stairways. 708–941–3395.

Mylen Industries, 650 Washington St., Peekskill, NY 10566: Brochure 50¢ ■ Easy-to-install, space-saving indoor and outdoor spiral stairs. 800–431–2155; 914–739–8486 (in NY).

Piedmont Home Products, Inc., P.O. Box 269, Ruckersville, VA 22968: Free information ■ Handcrafted spiral stairs, rails, balusters, starting steps, and newel posts. 800–622–3399; 804–985–8909 (in VA).

Salter Industries, P.O. Box 183, Eagleville, PA 19408: Free brochure ■ Easy-to-install spiral stairs. 215–631–1360.

Spiral Stairs of America, 1718 Franklin Ave., Erie, PA 16510: Free brochure ■ Assembled stairways. 800–422–3700; 814–898–3700 (in PA).

Stairways, Inc., 4166 Pinemont, Houston, TX 77018: Free catalog ■ Custom wood and metal stairways. 800–231–0793.

Steptoe & Wife Antiques, Ltd., 322 Geary Ave., Toronto, Ontario, Canada M6H 2C7: Catalog $3 ■ Easy-to-assemble, interior and exterior cast-iron spiral and straight staircases in Victorian design. 416–530–4200.

Visador Company, 7800 Belfort Pkwy., Ste. 170, Jacksonville, FL 32256: Brochure $2 ■ Custom red oak curved stairs for homes. 800–847–2367.

York Spiral Stairs, Rt. 32, North Vassalboro, ME 04962: Free brochure ■ Spiral stairs in red oak, Honduran mahogany, and other hardwoods. 207–872–5558.

Stucco

Stucco Stone Products, Inc., P.O. Box 270, Napa, CA 94559: Free information ■ Building supplies. 800–225–7462.

Tile & Linoleum

American Olean Tile Company, 1000 Cannon Ave., Lansdale, PA 19446: Brochure 25¢ ■ Easy-to-install ceramic mosaic tiles. 215–855–1111.

Amsterdam Corporation, 150 E. 58th St., 5th Floor, New York, NY 10155: Catalog $2.50 ■ Authentic Dutch hand-painted tiles. 212–644–1350.

Armstrong World Industries, P.O. Box 3001, Lancaster, PA 17604: Free information ■ Tile, linoleum, and other floor coverings, with an optional no-wax surface. 800–233–3823.

Laura Ashley, Inc., 1300 MacArthur Blvd., Mahwah, NJ 07430: Catalog $4 ■ Floor tiles. 800–223–6917.

Color Tile, 515 Houston St., Fort Worth, TX 76102: Free information ■ Ceramic tile for bathroom counter tops and walls. 817–870–9400.

Congoleum, 989 Lenox Dr., Lawrenceville, NJ 08648: Free information ■ Floor coverings and information that explains how to select vinyl flooring. 609–584–3000.

Designs in Tile, P.O. Box 358, Mt. Shasta, CA 96067: Catalog $3 ■ Ceramic tiles and murals featuring historic reproductions, contemporary and traditional patterns, coordinated borders, and corner blocks. 916–926–2629.

Epro Tiles, Inc., 156 E. Broadway, Westerville, OH 43081: Free information ■ Sandstone collection of handmade tiles. 614–882–6990.

Huntington/Pacific International, 5204 Airport Freeway, Fort Worth, TX 76117: Free information ■ Ceramic tiles with a slate look. 817–831–4447.

Italian Tile Center, 499 Park Ave., New York, NY 10022: Free information ■ Italian tile with flowers, fruit, and other patterns. 212–980–8866.

Keniston Tile & Design, 269 Commercial St., Portland, ME 04101: Catalog $5 ■ Tiles with unique designs. 207–775–2238.

Mannington Floors, P.O. Box 30, Salem, NJ 08079: Free information ■ Easy-to-install tiles with a no-wax surface, sheet vinyl flooring, and other floor coverings. 800–FLOOR–US.

Moravian Pottery & Tile Works, Swamp Rd., Doylestown, PA 18901: Catalog $4 ■ Decorative tiles reproduced from British collections and European castles. 215–345–6722.

Tarket Tiles, Inc., 900 Lanidex Plaza, P.O. Box 264, Parsippany, NJ 07054: Free information ■ Ceramic tiles. 201–428–9000.

Terra Designs, 241 E. Blackwell St., Dover, NJ 07801: Catalog $2 ■ Decorator bathroom tiles. 201–539–2999.

Victorian Collectibles, 845 E. Glenbrook Rd., Milwaukee, WI 53217: Brochure $3 ■ Tiles and matching wallpaper, duplicated from 19th-century patterns. 414–352–6971.

Wenczel Ceramic Tile, P.O. Box 5308, Trenton, NJ 08638: Free information ■ Ceramic tiles. 609–599–4503.

Trim & Ornamental Woodwork

American Custom Millwork, Inc., 3904 Newton Rd., P.O. Box 3608, Albany, GA 31706: Catalog $5 ■ Embossed and plain architectural moldings and custom millwork. 912–888–3303.

Anderson-McQuaid Company, Inc., 170 Fawcett St., Cambridge, MA 02138: Free price list ■ Custom and restoration moldings, flooring, paneling, and hardwood lumber. 617–876–3250.

Anthony Wood Products, Inc., P.O. Box 1081, Hillsboro, TX 76645: Catalog $2 ■ Handcrafted Victorian gingerbread. 817–582–7225.

Architectural Components, 26 N. Leverett Rd., Montague, MA 01351: Brochure $3 ■ Custom and reproduction 18th- and 19th-century doors, windows, window frames, sashes, moldings, and French doors and entryways. 413–367–9441.

Architectural Sculpture, Ltd., 242 Lafayette St., New York, NY 10012: Catalog $2 ■ Turn-of-the-century plaster ornaments, plaques, sculptures, and other building and remodeling accouterments. 212–431–5873.

Aristocraft Originals, Inc., 6200 Highlands Pkwy. SE, Smyrna, GA 30082: Catalog $5 ■ Reproduction niches, crown molding, trim, fireplaces, ceiling medallions, corbels, archways, columns, porches, and oak beams. 404–333–9934.

Arvid's Historic Woods, 2820 Rucker Ave., Everett, WA 98201: Catalog $5.95 ■ Interior and exterior historic molding. 800–627–8437.

Barewood Architectural Woodworking, Ltd., 106 Ferris St., Brooklyn, NY 11231:

Free information ■ Interior and exterior 18th- and 19th-century custom architectural millwork. 718–875–9037.

Campbellsville Industries, Inc., P.O. Box 278, Campbellsville, KY 42718: Free information ■ Aluminum cornices, louvers, cupolas, columns, balustrades, and shutters. 502–465–8135.

Classic Architectural Specialties, 3223 Canton St., Dallas, TX 75226: Catalog $4 ■ Colonial, Federal, Greek Revival, and Victorian molding and trim. 800–662–1221.

Country Cupolas, East Conway, NH 04037: Free brochure ■ Country-style cupolas, in kits or assembled. 603–939–2698.

Cross Industries, 3174 Marjan Dr., Atlanta, GA 30341: Free information ■ Vinyl decorative lattice panels with diagonal or rectangular patterns. 800–521–9878.

Cumberland Woodcraft Company, Inc., P.O. Drawer 609, Carlisle, PA 17013: Catalog $4.50 ■ Victorian architectural millwork, carvings, and trims; ceiling treatments; and corbels, brackets, molding, and grilles. 717–243–0063.

Driwood Ornamental Wood Moulding, P.O. Box 1729, Florence, SC 29503: Catalog $6 ■ Embossed wood molding, raised paneling, custom mantels, curved stairs, and custom doors. 803–669–2478.

Empire Woodworks, P.O. Box 717, Blanco, TX 78606: Catalog $3 ■ Country-style and Victorian trim. 512–833–2119.

Raymond E. Enkeboll Designs, 16506 Avalon Blvd., Carson, CA 90746: Free catalog ■ Architectural accouterments carved and sculptured in solid woods. 310–532–1400.

Felber Studios, Inc., 110 Ardmore Ave., Ardmore, PA 19003: Catalog $3 ■ Period and custom plaster cornices, medallions, sculpture, niches, capitals, brackets, and domes. 215–642–4710.

Focal Point, Inc., P.O. Box 93327, Atlanta, GA 30377: Free information ■ Ceiling medallions, cornice moldings, niche caps, and doorway treatments. 800–662–5550.

Fypon Molded Millwork, 22 W. Pennsylvania Ave., Stewartstown, PA 17363: Catalog $2 ■ Molding and trim. 717–993–2593.

Gazebo & Porchworks, 728 9th Ave. SW, Puyallup, WA 98371: Catalog $2 ■ Wood trims, ornamental items, outdoor swings, and backyard play structures. 206–848–0502.

Hampton Decor, 30 Fisk St., Jersey City, NJ 07305: Brochure $3 ■ Polyurethane and plaster ceiling roses, columns, niches, panel moldings, cornices, and door ornaments. 201–433–9002.

Hartman-Sanders Company, 4340 Bankers Cir., Atlanta, GA 30360: Free information with long SASE ■ Reproduction wood columns. 404–449–1561.

Heritage Woodcraft, 1230 Oakland St., Hendersonville, NC 28739: Catalog $2 ■ Corbels, brackets, finials, scrolls, headers, trim, sawn balusters, and turned balusters. 704–692–8542.

Dimitrios Klitsas, Wood Sculptor, 705 Union St., West Springfield, MA 01089: Free information ■ Wood sculptures for decorating. 413–732–2661.

Mad River Woodworks, 189 Taylor Way, P.O. Box 1067, Blue Lake, CA 95525: Catalog $3 ■ Corbels, balusters, trims, brackets, spandrels, wooden gutters, and railings. 707–668–5671.

E.T. Moore Company, 3100 N. Hopkins Rd., Richmond, VA 23224: Free information ■ Mantels, columns, flooring, moldings, paneling, hand-hewn beams, and custom furniture and cabinets. 804–231–1823.

Moorwood, 22 Cottage St., Middletown, NY 10940: Free information ■ Custom wood moldings. 914–341–1924.

E.A. Nord Company, Box 1187, Everett, WA 98206: Free information ■ Fluted or plain hemlock and fir columns. 206–259–9292.

Pagliacco Turning & Milling, P.O. Box 225, Woodacre, CA 94973: Catalog $6 ■ Wood balusters, newel posts, porch posts, railings, and columns. 415–488–4333.

Pasternak's Emporium, 2515 Morse St., Houston, TX 77019: Catalog $1 ■ Victorian gingerbread trim featuring corbels, fretwork, trim, corner brackets, and porch railings. 713–528–3808.

Pennoyer & King Fantastic Forgeries, Ltd., 410 New York Ave., Huntington, NY 11746: Free information ■ Architectural and garden ornaments cast in lightweight, weather-resistant resin-stone. 516–549–0795.

River Bend Turnings, RD 1, River Rd., Box 364, Wellsville, NY 14895: Free information ■ Porch turnings, table legs, chair legs, spoon foot legs, newel posts, balusters, and finials. 716–593–3495.

A.F. Schwerd Manufacturing Company, 3215 McClure Ave., Pittsburgh, PA 15212: Free catalog ■ Custom standard and detailed wood columns in seasoned northern white pine, with matching pilasters and aluminum bases. 412–766–6322.

Sepp Leaf Products, Inc., 381 Park Ave. South, New York, NY 10016: Free information ■ Metal leaf products that include gold, palladium, rolled gold, tools, and kits. 212–683–2840.

Silverton Victorian Millworks, P.O. Box 2987, Durango, CO 81302: Catalog $4 ■ Victorian moldings and millwork. Includes castings, crowns, corner blocks, doors, bases, wainscot, and other architectural accouterments. 303–259–5915.

Sunshine Architectural Woodworks, 2169 Sunshine Dr., Fayettville, AR 72703: Catalog $5 ■ Reproduction 18th-century woodwork. 501–521–4329.

M. Swift & Sons, Inc., 10 Love Ln., Hartford, CT 06141: Free booklet ■ Gold, silver, palladium, aluminum, and composite leaf for decorating and restoring interiors and exteriors of buildings, domes, walls, ceilings, furniture, and works of art. 800–262–9620.

Victorian Millworks, P.O. Box 2987, Durango, CO 81302: Catalog $4 ■ Victorian-style moldings and millwork. Includes casings, bases, crowns, corner blocks, doors, and trims. 303–259–5915.

Vintage Wood Works, Hwy. 34, Box R, Quinlan, TX 75474: Catalog $2 ■ Handcrafted Victorian gingerbread. Includes custom spandrels and shelves, fans, porch posts, balusters, brackets, signs, corbels, headers, and gazebos.

The Woodworkers' Store, 21801 Industrial Blvd., Rogers, MN 55374: Catalog $1 ■ Hardware, ornamentals, woodworking supplies, tools, and accessories. 612–428–2199.

Wallcoverings

American Blind & Wallpaper Factory, 28237 Orchard Lake Rd., Farmington Hills, MI 48018: Free information ■ Save from 35 to 75 percent on wallpaper, wood blinds, vertical blinds, custom roller shades, pleated shades, micro blinds, and mini blinds. 800–735–5300.

American Discount Wallcoverings, 1411 5th Ave., Pittsburgh, PA 15219: Free brochure ■ Save from 15 to 50 percent on decorator wallpapers, window treatments, and upholstery fabrics. 800–777–2737.

Laura Ashley, 1300 MacArthur Blvd., Mahwah, NJ 07430: Catalog $4 ■ Wallpaper reproductions of period patterns with complementing borders and coordinating fabrics. 800–223–6917.

Benington's, 1271 Manheim Pike, Lancaster, PA 17601: Free information ■ Save from 35 to 75 percent on wallpaper. 800–252–5060.

Best Discount Wallcoverings, 417 Jackson St., St. Charles, MO 63301: Free information ■ Save from 35 to 75 percent on wallcoverings. 800–328–5550.

BMI Home Decorating, P.O. Box 25905, Lexington, KY 40524: Free information ■ Save up to 50 percent on decorator fabrics and wallcoverings. 800–999–2091.

Bradbury & Bradbury Wallpapers, P.O. Box 155, Benicia, CA 94510: Catalog $10 ■ Victorian-style wallpapers, hand-printed borders, friezes, ceiling papers, and coordinated wall frills. 707–746–1900.

J.R. Burrows & Company, P.O. Box 522, Rockland, MA 02370: Catalog $5 ■ Artistic wallpaper and fabric, and custom period carpet reproductions by special order. 617–982–1812.

Designer Secrets, Box 529, Fremont, NE 68025: Catalog $2 (refundable) ■ Save up to 75 percent on wallcoverings, fabrics, bedspreads, furniture, window treatments, and accessories. 800–955–2559.

East Carolina Wallpaper Market, 1106 Pink Hill Rd., Kinston, NC 28501: Free information ■ Save from 35 to 50 percent on wallpaper, fabrics, and borders. 800–848–7283.

Eisenhart Wallcoverings Company, Hanover, PA 17331: Free information ■ Wallcoverings and coordinated fabrics. 717–6321–5918.

Factory Paint Store, 505 Pond St., South Weymouth, MA 02190: Free information ■ Wallpaper and paint, window shades, light-ing fixtures, tile, and carpeting. 617–331–1200.

Hang-It-Now Wallpaper Stores, N. Main St., Archdale, NC 27263: Free information ■ Save from 30 to 65 percent on wallcoverings, and up to 40 percent on decorator fabrics. 800–325–9494.

Harmony Supply Company, Inc., P.O. Box 313, Medford, MA 02155: Free information ■ Wallpaper and fabrics for coordinating wall and window treatments. 617–395–2600.

Headquarters Windows & Walls, 8 Clinton Pl., Morristown, NJ 07960: Free information ■ Save up to 50 percent on wallcoverings and window blinds. 800–338–4882.

Marlene's Decorator Fabrics, 301 Beech St., Hackensack, NJ 07601: Free information ■ Decorator fabrics. 800–992–7325.

Mary's Discount Wallpaper, 111 N. Lansdowne Ave., Lansdowne, PA 19050: Free information with long SASE ■ Save up to 75 percent on wallpaper. 800–521–3393.

Mutual Wallpaper & Paint Company, 812 W. Main St., Louisville, KY 40202: Free catalog ■ Wallcoverings, borders, and blinds. 502–583–0525.

National Wholesale Wallcovering, P.O. Box 396, Ledgewood, NJ 07852: Free information ■ Wallcoverings. 800–256–9037.

Nationwide Wallcovering, P.O. Box 40, Hackensack, NJ 07602: Free information ■ Wallcoverings. 800–488–WALL.

Number One Wallpaper, 2914 Long Beach Rd., Oceanside, NY 11572: Free information ■ Save from 40 to 65 percent on wallpaper. 800–423–0084; 516–678–4445 (in NY).

Papers Plus, P.O. Box 204, Countryside, IL 60525: Free information ■ Save from 35 to 75 percent on wallpapers, and up to 30 percent on fabrics. 800–837–8757.

Pintchik Homeworks, 2106 Bath Ave., Brooklyn, NY 11214: Free brochure ■ Wallpapers, window treatment supplies, paints, floor coverings, and hardware. 800–847–4199; 718–996–5580 (in NY).

Post Wallcovering Distributors, Inc., 2065 Franklin, Bloomfield Hills, MI 48013: Free information ■ Save up to 70 percent on wallpaper, and up to 75 percent on window blinds. 800–521–0650.

Robinson's Wallcoverings, 225 W. Spring St., Titusville, PA 16354: Catalog $2 (refundable) ■ Wallcoverings and decorator fabrics. 800–458–2426.

Sanz International, Inc., P.O. Box 1794, High Point, NC 27261: Free information with long SASE ■ Wallcoverings, decorator fabrics, furniture, lamps, and carpeting. 919–886–7630.

Shibui Wall Coverings, P.O. Box 1638, Rohnert Park, CA 94928: Price list $4 ■ Wallcoverings in grasses, jute, cork, and leaf patterns; adhesives; and paper hanging tools. 800–824–3030; 707–526–6170 (in CA).

Shopright Wallcoverings, P.O. Box 24513, St. Louis, MO 63141: Free information ■ Wallcoverings. 800–622–9927.

Silver Wallpaper, Inc., 3001 Kensington Ave., Philadelphia, PA 19134: Free information ■ Save from 30 to 50 percent on wallcoverings. 800–426–6600.

Singer Wallcoverings, Box 300, Kings Island, OH 45034: Free information ■ Vinyl wallcoverings. 800–543–0412; 800–582–1760 (in OH).

Stencils & Seams Unlimited, RR 2, Box 2377, Raymond, ME 04071: Catalog $2.50 (refundable) ■ Stenciled valances and pre-pasted wallpaper borders. 207–655–3952.

Style Wallcovering, P.O. Box 52128, Livonia, MI 48152: Free information ■ Save up to 50 percent on wallcoverings. 800–627–0400.

Valley Forge Wallpaper, Phoenixville, PA 19460: Free information ■ Save up to 40 percent on wallpaper. 800–548–1558; 800–332–WALL (in PA).

Victorian Collectibles, 845 E. Glenbrook Rd., Milwaukee, WI 53217: Brochure $3 ■ Wallpaper in 19th-century patterns with matching tiles. 414–352–6971.

Wallpapers Unlimited, P.O. Box 113, La Fox, IL 60147: Free information ■ Save up to 70 percent on wallpaper. 800–228–0355.

Wallpaper Warehouse, Inc., 1434 Ellis Ave., Jackson, MS 39204: Free information ■ Save up to 50 percent on wallcoverings. 800–523–3503; 800–826–7310 (in MS).

Wallpaperxpress, P.O. Box 4061, Naperville, IL 60567: Free information ■ Save 25 percent on decorator fabrics, 60 percent on mini blinds, and 70 percent on wallcoverings. 800–288–9979.

Yankee Wallcoverings, Inc., 109 Accord Park Dr., Norwell, MA 02061: Free information ■ Save from 35 to 75 percent on wallcoverings and coordinating fabrics. 800–624–7711.

Yield House, P.O. Box 5000, North Conway, NH 03860: Free information ■ Save on wallcoverings. 800–258–4720.

Yorktowne Wallpaper Outlet, 2445 S. Queen St., York, PA 17402: Free information ■ Save from 30 to 50 percent on wallcoverings. 800–847–6142.

Windows

Allied Window, Inc., 2724 W. McMicken Ave., Cincinnati, OH 45214: Free information ■ Windows for all types of installations. 800–445–5411; 513–559–1883 (in OH).

Alside Corporation, P.O. Box 2010, Akron, OH 44309: Free information ■ Outdoor windows with vinyl trim and insulating glass. 216–929–1811.

Andersen Windows, 100 4th Ave., Bayport, MN 55003: Free booklet ■ Energy-efficient windows, roof windows, and patio doors. 612–439–5150.

APC Corporation, P.O. Box 515, Hawthorne, NJ 07507: Free information ■ Weathertight skylights. 201–423–2900.

Arctic Glass & Window Outlet, Rt. 1 West, Hammond, WI 54015: Catalog $2 ■ Windows, doors, patio doors, skylights, and sunrooms. 715–796–2292.

Bristolite Skylights, 401 E. Goetz Ave., P.O. Box 2515, Santa Ana, CA 92707: Free catalog ■ Residential skylights, fixed, or with electric and manual openers. 800–854–8618; 800–422–2131 (in CA).

Cherry Creek Enterprises, Inc., 3500 Blake St., Denver, CO 80204: Catalog $2 ■ Beveled glass in standard or custom designs. 800–338–5725.

Colonial Craft, 2772 Fairview Ave., St. Paul, MN 55113: Free catalog ■ Solid hardwood windows and doors. Other items include custom door and window grilles for regular and sliding patio doors. 800–727–5187; 612–631–2110 (in MN).

Combination Door Company, P.O. Box 1076, Fond du Lac, WI 54936: Free brochure ■ Wooden storm and screen doors, screen doors, and basement and garage windows. 414–922–2050.

Dilworth Manufacturing Company, Box 158, Honey Brook, PA 19344: Free brochure ■ Covers for metal or masonry window wells. 717–354–8956.

Fox Light, 8300 Dayton Rd., Fairborn, OH 45324: Free information ■ Skylights that can be converted from fixed, closed units to opening units. Conversion kits available separately. 800–233–FOXX.

Georgia-Pacific, 133 Peachtree St. NE, P.O. Box 105605, Atlanta, GA 30303: Free information ■ Doors and windows. 404–521–4000.

Great Lakes Windows, P.O. Box 1896, Toledo, OH 43603: Free information ■ Windows for all types of installation. 800–525–5557.

Kolbe & Kolbe, 1323 S. 11th Ave., Wausau, WI 54401: Free information ■ Made-to-order windows.

John F. Lavoie Windows, P.O. Box 15, Springfield, VT 05156: Brochure $2 ■ Reproductions of historical windows. Includes round, oval or quarter-round windows, and transoms. 802–886–8253.

Louisiana-Pacific Corporation, 111 SW 5th, Portland, OR 97204: Free information ■ Windows for many uses. 503–221–0800.

Marvin Windows, Warroad, MN 56763: Free information ■ Doors and windows that include divided light and insulated storm windows and transoms. 800–346–5128.

Midwest Wood Products, 1051 S. Rolff St., Davenport, IA 52802: Free brochure with long SASE ■ Divided light insulated storm windows. 319–323–4757.

NAPCO, 10425 Hampshire Ave. South, Bloomington, MN 55438: Free information ■ Energy-saving insulated windows. 612–944–5120.

New Morning Windows, 10425–A Hampshire Ave., South Bloomington, MN 55438: Free information ■ Custom windows in round styles. 612–944–5120.

PAECO Industries, 1 Executive Dr., Box 968, Toms River, NJ 08753: Free information ■ Insulated glass or double plastic

domed, aluminum-framed roof windows, with optional motorized controls. 908–341–4444.

Pella Information Center, P.O. Box 308, Moline, IL 61265: Free idea booklet ■ Information on how to use doors and windows when building a new house or remodeling.

Pozzi Wood Windows, P.O. Box 5249, Bend, OR 97708: Free information ■ Divided-light windows in standard sizes. 800–323–6474.

PPG Industries, Inc., Sungate Marketing Group, P.O. Box 8727, Harrisburg, PA 17105: Free information ■ Coated glass windows that let in light and heat, and reflect internal heating back into the room. 800–2–GET–PPG.

Reynolds Metals Company, Box 27003, Richmond, VA 23261: Free information ■ Interior and exterior, custom-fitted replacement thermal windows in aluminum and vinyl. 804–281–4188.

Rollamatic Roofs Incorporated, 1441 Yosemite Ave., San Francisco, CA 94124: Free brochure ■ Electrically controlled retractable skylights. 800–345–7392; 415–822–5655 (in CA).

Southeastern Insulated Glass, 6477–B Peachtree Industrial Blvd., Atlanta, GA 30360: Free information ■ Sliding glass doors and skylights with optional tempered insulated glass and greenhouse and sunroom kits. 800–841–9842; 404–455–8838 (in GA).

Therma-Tru Corporation, 1684 Woodlands Dr., Maumee, OH 43537: Free product information ■ Insulated doors and windows. 419–537–1931.

Thermo-Press Corporation, 5406 Distributor Dr., Richmond, VA 23225: Free information ■ Custom-fitted storm windows. 804–231–2964.

Velux-America, Inc., P.O. Box 5001, Greenwood, SC 29648: Free brochure ■ Custom-fitted, weather-tight roof windows and skylights. 800–283–2831.

Ventarama Skylight Corporation, 140 Cantiaque Rock Rd., Hicksville, NY 11801: Free information ■ Ventilating, fixed, and motorized skylights. 516–931–0202.

Wasco Products, P.O. Box 351, Sanford, ME 04073: Free information ■ Easy-to-install wind- and rain-proof operable skylights. 207–324–8060.

Weather Shield Mfg., Inc., 531 N. 8th St., Medford, WI 54451: Free brochure ■ Wooden windows, patio doors, and steel entrance systems. 800–477–6808.

Wenco Windows, Jeld-Wen Corporation, Commerce Dr., Mount Vernon, OH 43050: Free information ■ Exterior windows with operable sides. 614–397–3403.

Wes-Pine Wood Windows, P.O. Box 1157, West Hanover, MA 02339: Free information ■ Divided light insulated storm windows. 617–878–2102.

Woodstone Company, Patch Rd., P.O. Box 223, Westminster, VT 05158: Brochure $3 ■ Single-, double-, or triple-glazed windows, with palladians and straight and fanned transoms. Other items include solid wooden doors with insulated cores, pegged mortises, and tenon frames. 802–722–9217.

HOMES & PREFABS

Conventional Homes

Acorn Structures, Inc., Box 250, Concord, MA 01742: Plan book $15 ■ Solar energy and traditional homes. 508–369–4111.

Cedardale Homes, Inc., 2301 State St., P.O. Box 5427, Hamden, CT 06518: Plan book and catalog $6.95 ■ Traditional homes that include vacation, retirement, and grand estate models. 800–243–3551; 203–562–9981 (in CT).

Classic Post & Beam, P.O. Box 546, York, ME 03909: Portfolio $6 ■ Post and beam homes. 800–872–BEAM.

Daystar Shelter Corporation, 22509 Cedar Dr., Bethel, MN 55005: Catalog $8 ■ Dome kits. 612–753–4981.

Lindal Cedar Homes, P.O. Box 24426, Seattle, WA 98178: Planbook $15 ■ Plans and design tips for customizing existing homes or building a new one. 800–426–0536.

Linwood Homes, P.O. Box 20090, Barrie, Ontario, Canada L4M 6E9: Plan book $10 ■ Post and beam and truss kits. 800–668–6896.

Lumber Enterprises, Inc., P.O. Box 4111, Bozeman, MT 59715: Catalog with floor plans $5 ■ Custom homes. 800–235–4321; 800–421–9946 (in MT).

Miles Homes, P.O. Box 9495, Minneapolis, MN 55440: Catalog $3 ■ Homes with pre-

cut materials and step-by-step instructions. 800–343–2884.

Northern Homes, 51 Glenwood Ave., Queensburg, NY 12804: Catalog $15 ■ Wood frame, domes, and log homes. 518–798–6007.

Pan Abode, Inc., 4350 Lake Washington Blvd. North, Renton, WA 98056: Planning kit $15 ■ Custom cedar homes. 800–782–2633.

Rapid River Rustic, Inc., P.O. Box 8, Rapid River, MI 49878: Catalog $10 ■ Solid cedar homes. 800–422–3327.

Shelter-Kit Incorporated, 24 Mill St., Tilton, NH 03276: Catalog $6 ■ Houses, cabins, barns, and garages with pre-cut framing systems. 603–934–4327.

Mike Tecton, 1469 Spring Vale Ave., McLean, VA 22101: Free brochure ■ Colonial, Georgian, Tudor, and French-style homes. 703–356–5800.

Timberpeg, Box 1500, Claremont, NH 03743: Design portfolio $15 ■ Traditional or contemporary post and beam, single, and multi-level homes. 603–542–7762.

Woodhouse Post & Beam, Inc., P.O. Box 219, Mansfield, PA 16933: Portfolio $10 ■ Custom post and beam homes. 717–549–6232.

Domes

Geodesic Domes, Inc., 10290 Davison Rd., Davison, MI 48423: Catalog $8 ■ Pre-insulated geodesic dome kits that can be assembled in one weekend. 313–653–2383.

Oregon Dome Living, Inc., 3215 Meadow Ln., Eugene, OR 97402: Catalog and planning package $8 ■ Energy-efficient domes. 800–572–8943.

Timberline Geodesics, 2015 Blake St., Berkeley, CA 94704: Information packet $8 ■ Easy-to-assemble dome homes. 800–DOME–HOME

Log Homes

Alta Industries, Ltd., Rt. 30, Box 88, Halcottsville, NY 12438: Product literature $7 ■ Traditional and contemporary log homes. 800–926–ALTA; 914–586–3336 (in NY).

Amerlink Log Homes, P.O. Box 669, Battleboro, NC 27809: Information $9.95 ■ Log

homes. 800–334–5166; 800–682–8127 (in NC).

L.C. Andrew Maine Cedar Log Homes, South Windham, ME 04062: Literature $6 ■ Log homes. 800–341–0405.

Appalachian Log Homes, 11312 Station West, Knoxville, TN 37922: Catalog $7 ■ Traditional and custom log homes in chinked and log-on-log styles. 615–966–6440.

Appalachian Log Structures, Inc., P.O. Box 614, Riley, WV 25271: Portfolio of floor plans $10 ■ Log homes, garages, and condominiums. 800–458–9990; 304–372–6410 (in VA).

Jim Barna Log Systems, 2679 N. Alberta St., Drawer 1011, Oneida, TN 37841: Catalog $6 ■ Log homes. 800–962–4734; 615–569–8559 (in TN).

Beaver Mountain Log Homes, RD 1, Box 32, Hancock, NY 13783: Plan book $4 ■ Pre-cut log home kits. 800–233–2770; 607–467–2700 (in NY).

Cedar Creek Log Homes, 3301 Veterans Dr., Ste. 215, Traverse City, MI 49684: Catalog $9 ■ Log homes. 616–929–4211.

Concept Design Institute, 271 Lonetree Ct., Cheyenne, WY 82009: Design manual $14.95 ■ Log homes. 307–721–5907.

Confederation Log Homes, RR 1, Box 132, Lenoir City, TN 37771: Catalog $10 ■ Traditional and custom log homes. 615–986–0021.

Garland Homes, 2172 Hwy. 93 North, P.O. Box 12, Victor, MT 59875: Catalog $10 ■ Log homes. 800–642–3837.

Gastineau Log Homes, Inc., Old Hwy. 54, Box 248, New Bloomfield, MO 65063: Information $8 ■ Log homes. 800–654–9253; 314–896–5510 (in MO).

Greatwood Log Homes, Hwy. 57, P.O. Box 707, Elkhart Lake, WI 53020: Plan book $7.50 ■ Log homes. 800–558–5812; 800–242–1021 (in WI).

Green Mountain Log Homes, Box 428, Chester, VT 05143: Home design kit $9 ■ Custom log homes. 802–875–2163.

Hearthstone Log Homes, Box 434, Dandridge, TN 37725: Catalog $8 ■ Log homes. 800–247–4442.

Heritage Log Homes, P.O. Box 610, Gatlinburg, TN 37738: Catalog $8 ■ Log homes. 800–456–HOME.

Hiawatha Log Homes, H28 East, P.O. Box 8, Munising, MI 49862: Plan book $6 ■ Log homes. 906–387–4121.

Highland Log Builders, Ltd., P.O. Box 1254, North Bend, WA 98045: Free information ■ Summer cottages, resort lodges, and commercial structures. 206–888–9812.

Holland Log Homes, 13352 Van Buren, Holland, MI 49424: Free brochure; plan book $7 ■ Custom pre-cut log homes. 616–399–9627.

Honest Abe Log Homes, Inc., Rt. 1, Box 84, Moss, TN 38575: Plan book $8 ■ Log homes. 800–231–3695; 615–258–3648 (in TN).

Katahdin Forest Products, P.O. Box 145, Oakfield, ME 04763: Free information ■ Traditional and custom log homes. 207–757–8278.

Kuhns Brothers Log Homes, RD 2, Box 406A, Lewisburg, PA 17837: Catalog $8 ■ Log homes. 717–568–1422.

Log Cabin Homes, Ltd., P.O. Drawer 1457, Rocky Mount, NC 27802: Planning guide $8.95 ■ Custom and traditional log homes. 919–977–7785.

Lok-N-Logs, P.O. Box 677, Sherburne, NY 13460: Catalog $7.50 ■ Log homes. 800–343–8928; 607–674–4447 (in NY).

Majestic Log Homes, P.O. Box 772, 4615 N. Hwy. 287, Fort Collins, CO 80522: Free brochure ■ Log homes. 303–224–4857.

Montana Log Homes, 3212 Hwy. 93 South, Kalispell, MT 59901: Planning guide $6 ■ Log homes. 406–752–2992.

Mountaineer Log Homes, Inc., P.O. Box 251, Downington, PA 19335: Product literature $7 ■ Log homes. 215–229–3078.

New England Log Homes, 2301 State St., P.O. Box 5427, Hamden, CT 06518: Planning kit $15 ■ Log homes. 800–243–3551; 203–562–9981 (in CT).

Northeastern Log Homes, P.O. Box 126, Groton, VT 05046: Planning portfolio $8 ■ Log homes. 800–992–6526.

Real Log Homes, National Information Center, P.O. Box 202, Hartland, VT 05048: Plan book $9 ■ Log homes with optional full basements, garages, slabs, crawl spaces, and piers. 800–732–5564.

Rocky Mountain Log Homes, 1883 Hwy. 93 South, Hamilton, MT 59840: Plan book $10 ■ Log homes. 406–363–5690.

Rustics of Lindbergh Lake, Inc., Star Rt. 2475, Condon, MT 59826: Planning guide booklet $8 ■ Custom log homes. 800–872–5647; 406–754–2222 (in MT).

Satterwhite Log Homes, Rt. 2, Box 256, Longview, TX 75605: Planning guide $4 ■ Log homes. 800–777–7288; 903–663–1729 (in TX).

Southern Cypress Log Homes, Inc., U.S. Hwy. 19 South, P.O. Box 209, Crystal River, FL 32629: Catalog $4.95 ■ Log homes. 904–795–0777.

Southland Log Homes, 7521 Broad River Rd., Irmo, SC 29063: Planning book $7.50 ■ Log homes. 803–781–5100.

Stonemill Log Homes, 7015 Stonemill Rd., Knoxville, TN 37919: Catalog and plans $6 ■ Log homes. 615–693–4833.

Timber Log Homes, Inc., 639 Old Hartford Rd., Colchester, CT 06415: Brochure $10 ■ Log homes. 800–533–5906; 203–537–2393 (in CT).

Vermont Log Buildings, RR 1, Box 69, Hartland, VT 05048: Planbook $8 ■ Log homes. 802–436–2121.

Ward Log Homes, P.O. Box 72, Houlton, ME 04730: Presentation book with plans $8 ■ Log homes. 800–341–1566; 207–532–6531 (in ME).

Wilderness Log Homes, Rt. 2, P.O. Box 902, Plymouth, WI 53073: Planning guide $9 ■ Pre-cut log homes in passive solar and custom models. 800–237–8564; 800–852–5647 (in WI).

Wisconsin Log Homes, Inc., 2390 Pamperin Rd., P.O. Box 11005, Green Bay, WI 54307: Plan book $9.95 ■ Traditional, contemporary, and passive solar log homes. 800–678–9107.

HORSE & STABLE EQUIPMENT

The Australian Stock Saddle Company, P.O. Box 987, Malibu, CA 90265: Catalog $5 ■ Leather saddles. 818–889–6988.

Bargain Corral, P.O. Box 415, Wylie, TX 75098: Free information with long SASE ■ Saddles, stirrups and straps, blankets, spurs, halters, pads, bits, bridles and breast collars, boots, dusters, and rain slickers. 800–955–5616.

Bob's Custom Saddles, Inc., 4202 Lakeside Ln., Scottsdale, AZ 85253: Free information ■ Custom saddles. 602–948–2481.

Bridge Creek Outfitters, P.O. Box 3576, Bozeman, MT 59715: Free catalog ■ Western gear for people and horses. 406–586–7764.

F. Burgess & Company, 200 Pine Place, Red Bank, NJ 07701: Catalog $3 ■ Hand-stitched military saddles and horse equipment.

Chick's Saddle, U.S. Rt. 23, Harrington, DE 19952: Free catalog ■ Horse equipment and supplies. 800–444–2441.

El Paso Saddleblanket Co., 601 N. Oregon, El Paso, TX 79901: Free catalog ■ Western-style saddles and saddleblankets. 800–351–7847; 915–544–1000.

John M. Fallis Custom Saddles, 29301 County Rd. 3, Elizabeth, CO 80107: Catalog $3 ■ Custom saddles. 303–646–4125.

Farnam Equipment Company, P.O. Box 34820, Phoenix, AZ 85067: Free catalog ■ Stable, training, grooming, and feeding equipment and supplies. 800–528–1378; 602–285–1660 (in AZ).

Drs. Foster & Smith, Inc., 2253 Air Park Rd., P.O. Box 100, Rhinelander, WI 54501: Free catalog ■ Pet and equine products and healthcare supplies. 800–826–7206.

Hartmeyer Saddle, 7111 W. Bethel Ave., Muncie, IN 47304: Catalog $2 ■ Saddles, clothing, and tack. 317–759–9507.

Ray Holes Saddle Company, 213 W. Main, Grangeville, ID 83530: Catalog $4 ■ Western saddles, pack equipment, and tack. 208–983–1460.

Horsemen's General Store, P.O. Box 429, Lena/Conover, OH 45317: Catalog $3 (refundable) ■ Everything for horse owners, trainers, breeders, and riders, and for horses. 800–343–0167.

K & B Saddle, Rt. 1, Box 21, Council Bluffs, IA 51501: Catalog $1 ■ Western saddles. 712–366–1026.

H. Kauffman, 139 E. 24th St., New York, NY 10010: Catalog $5 ■ Horseback riding equipment and clothing. 800–872–6687.

Libertyville Saddle Shop, Inc., P.O. Box M, Libertyville, IL 60048: Catalog $3 ■ Saddles and clothing for horseback riding. 800–872–3353.

Marciante Saddle & Leather Company, Inc., 214 Thompson Ave., Glendale, CA 91201: Free information ■ Trail and endurance leather saddles. 818–247–0434.

Bob Marrs Saddle Shop, 2710 E. 3rd St., Amarillo, TX 79104: Brochure $1 ■ Cowboy saddles. 806–372–8439.

Ortho-Flex Saddles, Rt. 2, Box 132, Nevada, MO 64772: Free information ■ Custom anatomically tufted saddles. 417–667–7834.

Outback Ranch, 27407 Schulte Rd., Carmel, CA 93923: Free catalog ■ Australian saddles with optional fittings. 408–625–1417.

Phelan's Equestrian, 10 Liberty Ship Way, Schoonmaker Bldg, Ste. 184, Sausalito, CA 94965: Free catalog ■ Riding equipment, gear, and clothing. 415–332–6001.

Platte Valley Saddle Shop, Inc., 1908 Central Ave., P.O. Box 1683, Kearney, NE 68848: Catalog $4 ■ Custom western-style saddles. 308–234–4015.

Joe Roberts Welding, P.O. Box 777, Ringling, OK 73456: Free information ■ Portable roping arenas. 800–654–4584; 405–662–2071 (in OK).

Rocky Mountain Saddle Company, 1530 W. Main St., Bozeman, MT 59715: Catalog $3 (refundable) ■ Custom saddles and tack. 406–586–2929.

Rohn Agri Products, P.O. Box 2000, Peoria, IL 61656: Free information ■ Heavy-duty horse stalls. 800–447–2264; 309–697–4400 (in IL).

State Line Tack, Inc., P.O. Box 428, Plaistow, NH 03865: Free catalog ■ English and western riding tack and clothing. 800–228–9208.

Texas Outfitters Supply, Inc., Rt. 6, Box 25, Sulphur Springs, TX 75482: Catalog $1 (refundable) ■ Pack equipment for horses and mules. Includes wall tents, folding stoves, panning equipment, saddles, and team and driving harnesses. 903–885–6935.

Western Suppliers, P.O. Box 428, Aubrey, TX 76227: Free catalog ■ Saddles, grooming aids, and other supplies. 817–365–3133.

HORSESHOES

Cannon Sports, P.O. Box 11179, Burbank, CA 91510: Free information ■ Horseshoes and equipment. 800–223–0064; 818–503–9570 (in CA).

Emerson Horseshoe Supply, 2301 Vanceville Rd., Bossier City, LA 71111: Free catalog ■ Horseshoes and equipment. 318–742–5991.

Franklin Sports Industries, Inc., 17 Campanelli Pkwy., P.O. Box 508, Stoughton, MA 02072: Free information ■ Horseshoes and equipment. 617–344–1111.

General Sportcraft Company, Ltd., 140 Woodbine St., Bergenfield, NJ 07621: Free information ■ Horseshoes and equipment. 201–384–4242.

Regent Sports Corporation, 45 Ranick Rd., Hauppage, NY 11787: Free information ■ Horseshoes and equipment. 516–234–2948.

Spalding & Brothers, 425 Meadow St., P.O. Box 901, Chicopee, MA 01021: Free information ■ Horseshoes and equipment. 413–536–1200.

Sport Fun, Inc., 4621 Sperry St., P.O. Box 39150, Los Angeles, CA 90039: Free information ■ Horseshoes and equipment. 800–423–2597; 818–240–6700 (in CA).

HOT TUBS & SAUNAS

Amerec Sauna & Steam, NASSCOR, Inc., P.O. Box 40569, Bellevue, WA 98004: Free information ■ Pre-assembled, easy-to-install free-standing sauna. 800–331–0349; 206–643–7500 (in WA).

AquaGlass Corporation, P.O. Box 412, Industrial Park, Adamsville, TN 38310: Free information ■ Whirlpool baths. 901–632–9011.

Automatic Steam Products, 43–20 34th St., Long Island City, NY 11101: Free information ■ Equipment to convert shower stalls into steam rooms. 800–238–3535.

California Cooperage, 880 Industrial Way, P.O. Box E, San Luis Obispo, CA 93401: Free literature ■ Pre-cut hot tub kits with plumbing. 805–544–9300.

Coleman Spas, Inc., P.O. Box 2920, Chandler, AZ 85244: Free information ■ Spas and hot tubs. 602–895–0598.

Fiat Tubs, Showers & Steam Baths, 1235 Hartrey Ave., Evanston, IL 60202: Free information ■ Multi-jet tubs, showers, whirlpools, and steam baths. 708–864–7600.

Great Lakes Spas, 429 W. 23rd St., Holland, MI 49423: Free information ■ Spas. 616–392–5947.

Helo Saunas from Finland, Box 1339, Minnetonka, MN 55345: Free information ■ Sauna heaters, steam generators, whirlpool baths, spas, and parts. 612–934–4230.

Jacuzzi Whirlpool Bath, P.O. Drawer J, Walnut Creek, CA 94596: Free information ■ Whirlpool baths with hydro massage control and whirlpool spas. 800–227–0710; 800–227–0991 (in CA).

Lyons Industries, P.O. Box 88, Dowagiac, MI 49047: Free information ■ Whirlpools for space–saving corner installation with optional walls and shatter-proof folding shower stall doors. 800–458–9036.

NEMCO, 4655 118th Ave. North, Clearwater, FL 33520: Free information ■ Portable spas with multi-level bench seating. 813–576–6720.

Nordic Sauna, 937 E. San Carlos Ave., San Carlos, CA 94070: Free information ■ Build-them-yourself whirlpool, hot tub, and sauna kits. 415–592–1818.

NoviAmerican, P.O. Box 44649, Atlanta, GA 30336: Free information ■ Extra-deep whirlpool tub with step-by-step, do-it-yourself instructions for installation. 800–521–6080.

Snorkel Stove Company, 108 Elliott Ave., Seattle, WA 98119: Free brochure ■ Wood-fired hot tub kits. No electricity, pumps, or filters needed. 206–283–5701.

Sundance Spas, 13951 Monte Vista Ave., Chino, CA 91710: Free information ■ Spas. 714–590–1791.

Thermasol, 15148 Bledsoe St., Sylmar, CA 91342: Free information ■ Self-cleaning whirlpool baths. 800–423–2477.

Tubmakers, 1830 4th St., Berkeley, CA 94710: Free information ■ Heaters, filters, pumps, and install-them-yourself kits for easy-to-operate hot tubs and spas. 510–843–2000.

Universal Rundle, 303 North St., P.O. Box 29, New Castle, PA 16103: Free information ■ Portable spa that operates by plugging into a standard grounded outlet. 412–658–6631.

Watkins Manufacturing, 1280 Park Center Dr., Vista, CA 92083: Free information ■ Spas. 800–999–4688.

HOT WATER HEATERS

Aqua Star, Controlled Energy Corporation, Fiddler's Green, Waitsfield, VT 05673: Free information ■ Tankless hot water heaters, under-the-sink electric water heaters, and electric instantaneous water heaters. 802–496–4436.

HOUSEWARES

Brookstone Company, 5 Vose Farm Rd., P.O. Box 5, Peterborough, NH 03458: Free catalog ■ Housewares, accessories, and tools. 800–846–3000.

Colonial Garden Kitchens, P.O. Box 66, Hanover, PA 17333: Catalog $2 ■ Housewares, storage aids, bathroom aids, cleaning and cooking aids, furniture, and laundry room aids. 717–633–3330.

Conran's Mail Order, 475 Oberlin Ave. South, Lakewood, NJ 08701: Catalog $2 ■ Housewares, kitchen equipment, fabrics, linens, wallpaper, lighting fixtures, floor coverings, and indoor and outdoor furniture. 201–905–8800.

Joan Cook, 3200 SE 14th Ave., Fort Lauderdale, FL 33350: Free catalog ■ Housewares and accessories for cooking and home care. 305–761–2350.

Hold Everything, Mail Order Dept., P.O. Box 7807, San Francisco, CA 94120: Free catalog ■ Clothing and closet organizers, garment protectors, kitchen and laundry aids, bathroom space makers, and bedroom accessories. 800–421–2285.

HUMIDIFIERS & DEHUMIDIFIERS

Hunter Fan Company, 2500 Fisco Ave., Memphis, TN 38114: Catalog $1 ■ Electronically programmable thermostats. 901–745–9286.

PetroKem Corporation, 101 Oliver St., P.O. Box 1888, Paterson, NJ 07509: Free information ■ Non-electric humidifiers for rooms, closets, and other storage areas. 201–742–6468.

HUNTING
Clothing & Equipment

Amacker Tree Stands, 1212 Main St., Amacker Park, Delhi, LA 71232: Free information ■ Portable and semi-permanent climbing ladders. 318–878–9061.

Ambusher, 2007 W. 7th St., Texarkana, TX 75501: Free information ■ Portable climbing ladders. 800–332–HUNT.

Amsec International Ammo Depot, 1849-B Candy Ln. SW, Marietta, GA 30060: Catalog $10 (refundable) ■ Hunting, camping, archery, and ammunition supplies. 800–622–1121.

API Outdoors, Inc., P.O. Box 1432, Tallulah, LA 71282: Free information ■ Self-climbing tree stands. 318–574–4903.

L.L. Bean, Inc., Freeport, ME 04033: Free catalog ■ Outdoor clothing and equipment. 800–221–4221.

Bear Brand Products, Inc., Box 898, Forrest City, AR 72335: Free information ■ Self-climbing tree stands. 501–633–0410.

Bowhunter's Warehouse, Inc., 1045 Ziegler Rd., Wellsville, PA 17365: Free catalog ■ Equipment and supplies for hunting, bow hunting, camping, and archery. 717–432–8611.

Broward Shooter's Exchange, 250 S. 60th Ave., Hollywood, FL 33023: Catalog $8 ■ Equipment and supplies for shooting, reloading, and muzzleloading; hunting; and archery. 800–554–9002.

Browning Company, Dept. C006, Morgan, UT 84050: Catalog $2 ■ Clothing and equipment for hunters. 800–333–3288.

Buck-Busters, Inc., Rt. 35, Box 1314, Hartselle, AL 35640: Free information ■ Portable climbing ladders. 205–773–2467.

Buckshot, Inc., Box 7127, Wilmington, NC 28406: Free information ■ Self-climbing tree stands. 919–256–3502.

Cabela's, 812 13th Ave., Sidney, NE 69160: Free catalog ■ Hunting, fishing, and other outdoor equipment. 800–237–4444.

Gander Mountain, Inc., Gander Mountain, P.O. Box 248, Wilmot, WI 53192: Free catalog ■ Outdoor and camping equipment, boats, archery supplies, knives, rifle scopes, and videos on hunting. 800–558–9418.

Loc-On Company, 1510 Holbrook St., Greensboro, NC 27403: Free information ■ Portable and semi-permanent climbing ladders. 919–370–4411.

Nite Lite Company, P.O. Box 8210, Little Rock, AR 72221: Free catalog ■ Hunting clothing and accessories, and kennel, training, and hunting supplies for dogs. 800–648–5483; 800–632–6895 (in AR).

Northwest Metals, Inc., Box 532, Hernando, MS 38632: Free information ■ Self-climbing tree stands. 601–368–2239.

Saf-Tree Products, Box 6108, Sheridan, WY 82801: Free information ■ Self-climbing tree stands. 307–672–0493.

Sporting Dog Specialties, Box 900, Brockport, NY 14420: Free catalog ■ Gun dog supplies. Includes dummies, game scents, books, collars and leads, hunting accessories, and camouflage gear. 716–352–1232.

Summit Specialties, Inc., P.O. Box 786, Decatur, AL 35602: Brochure $1 ■ Climbing tree stands.

Trebark Camouflage, 3434 Buck Mountain Rd., Roanoke, VA 24014: Free catalog ■ Camouflage gear for hunters. 800–843–2266.

Warren & Sweat Manufacturing Company, Box 446, Grand Island, FL 32735: Free information ■ Portable and semi-permanent climbing ladders. 904–357–0744.

Woodstream Corporation, P.O. Box 327, Lititz, PA 17543: Free catalog ■ Hunting and shooting accessories. 717–626–2125.

Game Calls, Lures & Scents

Bowhunter Supply, Inc., 1158 46th St., P.O. Box 5010, Vienna, WV 26105: Free information ■ Game calls, decoys, lures, and scents. 800–624–1923; 800–642–2638 (in WV).

Buck Stop Lure Company, Inc., 3600 Grow Rd. NW, Stanton, MI 48888: Free information ■ Scents and lures.

Burnham Brothers, P.O. Box 669, Marble Falls, TX 78654: Free information ■ Game calls. 512–693–3112.

Butski's Game Calls, 453 79th St., Niagara Falls, NY 14304: Free information ■ Turkey calls. 716–283–3504.

Cedar Hill Game Call Company, Rt. 2, Box 236, Downsville, LA 71234: Free information ■ Game calls.

Kelly Cooper, Inc., Kelly Lane, Box 49, Picture Rocks, PA 17762: Free information ■ Turkey calls. 717–584–4422.

Deer Run Products, Inc., 261 Ridgeview Terrace, Goshen, NY 10924: Free information ■ Scents and lures.

Eastern Sports Supply, Ltd., P.O. Box 67, Tremont, PA 17981: Free information ■ Game calls, decoys, lures, and scents. 717–695–3113.

Feline Archery, Inc., 229 Rt. 30 West, Ligonier, PA 15658: Free information ■ Game calls, decoys, lures, and scents. 412–238–3673.

Golden Eagle Archery, 1111 Corporate Dr., Farmington, NY 14425: Free information ■ Game calls, lures, and scents. 716–924–1880.

Hunter's Specialties, Inc., 5285 Rockwell Dr. NE, Cedar Rapids, IA 52402: Free information ■ Game calls, decoys, lures, and scents. 319–395–0321.

Knight & Hale Game Calls, Roger Thomas Dr., Box 468, Cadiz, KY 42211: Free information ■ Turkey calls. 502–522–3651.

Lohman Manufacturing Company, 2901 16th St., Neosho, MO 64850: Free information ■ Game calls. 417–451–4438.

M.L. Lynch Company, Box 377, Liberty, MS 39645: Free information ■ Turkey calls. 601–657–4306.

Mallardtone Game Calls, 2901 16th St., Moline, IL 61265: Free information ■ Game calls. 309–762–8089.

Perfection Turkey Call, Inc., Opequon Ridge, Box 164, Stephenson, VA 22656: Free information ■ Turkey calls. 703–667–4608.

Preston Pittman Game Calls, Box 568, Lucedale, MS 39452: Free information ■ Turkey calls. 601–947–4417.

Primos Wild Game Calls, Inc., Box 12785, Jackson, MS 39236: Free information ■ Turkey calls. 601–366–1288.

Quaker Boy, Inc., 5455 Webster Rd., Orchard Park, NY 14127: Free information ■ Turkey calls. 716–662–3979.

Ray Eye Enterprises, Box 236, Hillsboro, MO 63050: Free information ■ Turkey calls. 314–789–4144.

Eddie Salter Calls, Box 872, Brewton, AL 36427: Free information ■ Turkey calls. 205–867–2584.

Scotch Hunting Products Company, Inc., 6619 Oak Orchard Rd., Elba, NY 14058: Free information ■ Game calls. 716–757–9958.

Simmons Gun Specialties, Inc., Jerry's Sport Center, 700 S. Rogers Rd., P.O. Box 100, Olathe, KS 66062: Free information ■ Game calls, decoys, lures, and scents. 800–444–0220; 913–782–3131 (in KS).

Johnny Stewart Game Calls, Inc., 5100 Fort Ave., Box 7954, Waco, TX 76714: Free information ■ Game calls. 817–772–3261.

Sure-Shot Game Calls, Inc., 6835 Capitol Ave., Groves, TX 77619: Free information ■ Game calls.

Tink's Safariland Hunting Corporation, P.O. Box 244, Madison, GA 30650: Free information ■ Game calls, decoys, lures, and scents. 800–221–5054; 404–342–1916 (in GA).

Ultimate Lures, Rt. 2, 9506 Hwy. Y, Sauk City, WI 53583: Free information ■ Scents and lures.

ICE-CREAM MAKERS

The Chef's Catalog, 3215 Commercial Ave., Northbrook, IL 60062: Free catalog ■ Electric-operated, self-chilling ice-cream maker. 800–338–3232.

Lello Appliances Corporation, 355 Murray Hill Pkwy., East Rutherford, NJ 07073: Free information ■ Electric-powered ice-cream maker. 800–527–4336.

Sun Appliances, 4554 E. Princess Anne Rd., Norfolk, VA 23502: Free information ■ Salt and ice, electric-operated ice-cream maker. 800–347–4197.

White Mountain Freezer, Inc., P.O. Box 459, Winchendon, MA 01475: Free information ■ Old-fashioned, rock salt and ice, electric-operated ice-cream maker. 800–343–0065.

Williams-Sonoma, Mail Order Department, P.O. Box 7456, San Francisco, CA 94120: Free catalog ■ Hand-cranked ice-cream machine. 800–541–1262.

Zabar's & Company, 2245 Broadway, New York, NY 10024: Free catalog ■ Hand-cranked ice-cream maker. 800–221–3347; 212–787–2000 (in NY).

ICE SKATING

American Athletic Shoe Company, Inc., 15 South St., Ware, MA 01802: Free information ■ Figure and hockey ice skates and accessories. 413–967–3511.

Can/Am Hockey, Ltd., 12834 Gravois Rd., St. Louis, MO 63127: Free information ■ Figure, racing, and hockey ice skates, and blade sharpeners. 314–843–3553.

Canstar Sports USA, Inc., 50 Jonergin Dr., Swanton, VT 05448: Free information ■ Figure and hockey ice skates, and blade sharpeners. 800–362–3146; 800–451–5120 (in VT).

Cooper International, Inc., 501 Alliance Ave., Toronto, Ontario, Canada M6N 2J3: Free information ■ Figure and hockey ice skates, and blade protectors. 416–763–3801.

Lowry's Manufacturing, Ltd., 19 Keith Rd., Winnipeg, Manitoba, Canada R3H 0H7: Free information ■ Figure and hockey ice skates, replacement blades, and blade protectors. 204–633–6359.

Maska USA, Inc., Pierson Industrial Park, Rt. 25, P.O. Box 381, Bradford, VT 05033: Free information ■ Figure and hockey ice skates. 800–451–4600; 800–222–4751 (in VT).

National Sporting Goods Corporation, 25 Brighton Ave., Passaic, NJ 07055: Free information ■ Figure and hockey ice skates, blade protectors, and sharpeners. 201–779–2323.

Oberhamer, Inc., 11975 Portland Ave. South, Ste. 122, Burnsville, MN 55337: Free information ■ Figure and hockey ice skates, blade sharpeners, and protectors. 612–890–1657.

Rainbow Sports Shop, 4836 N. Clark St., Chicago, IL 60640: Free catalog ■ Skates and equipment for figure skaters. 312–275–5500.

Riedell Shoes, Inc., P.O. Box 21, Red Wing, MN 55066: Free information ■ Figure, racing, and hockey ice skates, blade protectors, and sharpeners. 612–388–8251.

SK Sports Shoes, Ltd., 280 Donlands Ave., Toronto, Ontario, Canada M4J 3R4: Free information ■ Figure, racing, and hockey ice skates, replacement blades, blade sharpeners, and protectors. 416–465–2784.

INCONTINENCE SUPPLIES

Bruce Medical Supply, 411 Waverly Oaks Rd., P.O. Box 9166, Waltham, MA 02254: Free information ■ An extensive line of health equipment and supplies for disabled and incontinent persons. 800–225–8446.

CarePak, P.O. Box 303, Trabuco Canyon, CA 92679: Free brochure ■ Absorbent products that include underpads, liners, stretch briefs, and tissues. 714–459–1547.

Diskreet Incorporated, 24500 Center Ridge Rd., Westlake, OH 44145: Free catalog ■ Incontinence-bladder control products. 800–422–7431.

Duraline Medical Products, 324 Werner St., P.O. Box 67, Leipsic, OH 45856: Free catalog ■ Reusable and disposable products for children and adults. 800–654–3376.

Fashion Ease, Division M and M Health Care, 1541 60th St., Brooklyn, NY 11219: Free catalog ■ Wheelchair accessories. Also clothing with velcro closures for arthritic, elderly, and handicapped persons, and supplies for incontinent persons. 800–221–8929.

INDIAN ARTS & CRAFTS

Alaska

Alaska Legacy Art Gallery, 311 Mill St., Ste. 202, Ketchikan, AK 99901: Free information with long SASE ■ Northwest Coast masks, paintings, silver and ivory jewelry, baskets, dolls, ivory sculpture, cribbage boards, and scrimshaw. 907–225–1234.

Chilkat Valley Arts, Box 145, Haines, AK 99827: Free price list with long SASE ■ Northwest Coast Tlingit Native American silver jewelry. 907–766–2990.

Eskimo Bow Drill Gallery, P.O. Box 812, Cooper Landing, AK 99572: Free price list with long SASE ■ Ivory sculptures and scrimshaw. 907–595–1221.

Marlinda Dolls, Box 611, Wrangell, AK 99929: Free information with long SASE ■ Eskimo sealskin dolls. 907–874–3854.

Musk Ox Producers Cooperative, 604 H St., Anchorage, AK 99501: Free information with long SASE ■ Hand-knitted Qiviut scarves, caps, tunics, and other clothing, from the underwool of domesticated musk. 907–272–9225.

Nana Museum of the Arctic Craft Shop, P.O. Box 49, Kotzebue, AK 99752: Free information with long SASE ■ Eskimo dolls, masks, birch bark baskets, ivory and whalebone carvings, and jewelry. 907–442–3304.

St. Lawrence Island Original Ivory Cooperative, P.O. Box 189, Gambell, AK 99742: Free price list with long SASE ■ Bracelets, cribbage boards, baleen boats, etchings, and ivory carvings of Arctic animals. 907–985–5112.

Savoonga Native Store, P.O. Box 100, Savoonga, AK 99769: Free price list with long SASE ■ Figurines, scrimshaw, ivory carvings, tusk scenes, jewelry, and cribbage boards.

Taheta Arts & Cultural Group, 605 A St., Anchorage, AK 99501: Catalog $1 ■ Ivory, stone, wood, and bone carvings; grass, birch bark, and baleen baskets; bead, porcupine, quill, silver, ivory, mastodon, and baleen jewelry; Eskimo dance fans; parkas; kuspuks; masks; and etchings, and drawings and prints. 907–272–5829.

Amos Wallace Indian Crafts, P.O. Box 478, Juneau, AK 99802: Free information with long SASE ■ Silver and gold bracelets, earrings and other jewelry, and custom totem poles, masks, and paddles. 907–586–9000.

Yugtarvik Regional Museum Shop, P.O. Box 388, Bethel, AK 99559: Free information with long SASE ■ Grass baskets, mats, trays, plates, wood and ivory masks and carvings, clothing, beaded jewelry, quill and ivory jewelry, dolls, dance fans, and headdresses. 907–543–2098.

Arizona

Dawa's Hopi Arts & Crafts, P.O. Box 127, Second Mesa, AZ 86043: Free information with long SASE ■ Hopi overlay silver jewelry. 602–734–2430.

Hatathli Gallery, Navajo Community College Development Foundation, Tsaile, AZ 86556: Free information with long SASE ■ Jewelry, paintings, rugs, sand paintings, and beadwork. 602–724–3311.

Honani Crafts, Hopi Cultural Center, Shop #4, P.O. Box 317, Second Mesa, AZ 86043: Free information with long SASE ■ Honani silver jewelry; pottery; paintings; baskets; Navajo rugs; and Zuni, Navajo, and Santa Domingo jewelry. 602–734–2238.

Hopi Arts & Crafts, Silvercraft Cooperative Guild, P.O. Box 37, Second Mesa, AZ 86043: Booklet $2.50 ■ Hopi overlay jewelry, coiled and wicker baskets, pottery, and paintings. 602–734–2463.

Hopicrafts, P.O. Box 37, Kykotsmovi, AZ 86039: Free information with long SASE ■ Hopi sterling silver overlay jewelry; Hopi kachinas, pottery, baskets and weavings; and Navajo, Zuni, and Santa Domino turquoise jewelry. 602–734–2484.

Hopi Kiva, P.O. Box 96, Oraibi, AZ 86039: Free information with long SASE ■ Hopi silver and gold overlay jewelry. 602–734–2423.

Kalley Musial, P.O. Box 1335, Flagstaff, AZ 86002: Free information with long SASE ■ Navajo rugs and beadwork. 602–774–2098; 213–839–4465 (in CA).

Albert Long, P.O. Box 40, Lake Havasu City, AZ 86403: Free information with long SASE ■ Gold and other jewelry, sand paintings, rugs, baskets, kachina dolls, and pottery. 602–453–5925.

Navajo Arts & Crafts Enterprise, P.O. Drawer A, Window Rock, AZ 86515: Free information with long SASE ■ Navajo handcrafts, turquoise and silver jewelry, sand paintings, and hand-painted pottery. 602–871–4090.

Percharo Jewelry, 313 Pima Ln., Laveen, AZ 85339: Free information with long SASE ■ Silver and gold jewelry. 602–237–4249.

San Juan Southern Paiute Yingup Weavers Association, P.O. Box 1336, Tuba City, AZ 86045: Free information with long SASE ■ Paiute baskets. 602–526–7143.

Urshel Taylor's Indian Studio, 2254 W. Calle Comodo, Tucson, AZ 87505: Free information with long SASE ■ Original wood sculptures costumed as traditional and contemporary Native American dancers, wood and bronze bear fetishes, oil paintings, and sculptures. 602–887–4021.

Phillip Titla Studio, P.O. Box 497, San Carlos, AZ 85550: Free brochure with long SASE ■ Carved Apache Mountain Spirit Dancers in wood; original oil and watercolor paintings, etchings, serigraphs, and woodcuts; and sculptures in bronze and other metals. 602–475–2361.

Arkansas

Bill & Mary Horn, Rt. 9, Box 227, Pine Bluff, AR 71603: Free information with long SASE ■ Silver, turquoise, and mother-of-pearl jewelry; pottery; baskets; cornhusk dolls; and beadwork and wooden necklaces. 501–879–1066.

California

American Indian Store, 6449 El Cajon Blvd., San Diego, CA 92115: Free catalog ■ Silver and gold jewelry, Sioux star quilts, ribbon shirts, beadwork, quillwork, dance bustles, war bonnets, Southern Plains metalwork, Pueblo pottery, Navajo rugs, and Hopi kachina dolls. 619–583–5389.

De Luna Jewelers, 521 2nd St., Davis, CA 95616: Free information with long SASE ■ Pottery, Navajo rugs, jewelry, baskets, paintings, carvings, and beadwork. 916–753–3351.

Going-to-the-Sun Studio, 1063 Hillendale Ct., Walnut Creek, CA 94596: Free information with long SASE ■ Original paintings, bas relief sculptures, tapestries, block printed fabrics, drums, parfleche containers, dolls, beadwork, ribbon shirts, and shawls. 510–939–8803.

Indian Arts Gift Shop, NCIDC, Inc., 241 F St., Eureka, CA 95501: Free information with long SASE ■ Baskets, silver and shell jewelry, beadwork, paintings and drawings, and carvings. 707–445–8451.

Ophelia Johnson's Indian Variety Shop, 10256 Central Ave., Montclair, CA 91763: Free information with long SASE ■ Silver jewelry, baskets, beadwork, pottery, and dolls. 714–625–2611.

Karok Originals by Vit, P.O. Box 3317, Eureka, CA 95502: Free information with long SASE ■ Jewelry and wall hangings. 707–442–8800.

Chief George Pierre Trading Post, P.O. Box 3202, Torrance, CA 90510: Free infor-

mation with long SASE ■ Rugs, silver and turquoise jewelry, kachina dolls, and beadwork. 213–372–1048.

Tatewin-Petaki American Indian Arts & Crafts, P.O. Box 549, Big Bear City, CA 92314: Free information with long SASE ■ Custom beadwork, peyote stitchery, beaded tapestries, decorated pipes, dolls, and leatherwork. 714–585–1435.

Treasure House of Worldly Wares, P.O. Box 127, Calistoga, CA 94515: Free price list with long SASE ■ Hopi, Navajo, and Zuni silver items; Navajo rugs; and Southwest Native American pottery; baskets, drums, and dolls; and sand paintings and beadwork by special order. 707–942–9976.

Colorado

Ben Nighthorse, P.O. Box 639, Ignacio, CO 81137: Free information with long SASE ■ Contemporary silver and gold jewelry, and silver jewelry inlaid with copper, brass, and German silver. 303–563–4623.

Path-of-the-Sun Images, Gallery & Design Services, 3020 Lowell Blvd., Denver, CO 80211: Free price list with long SASE ■ Paintings, sculptures, traditional and contemporary crafts, and graphic art. 303–477–8442.

District of Columbia

Naica Collectibles, 5223 Wisconsin Ave. NW, Ste. 138, Washington, DC 20015: Free information with long SASE ■ Sterling silver, turquoise, and gold jewelry, carvings, pottery, and beadwork. 202–561–1354.

Florida

Me'shiwi, 433 Harrell Dr., Orlando, FL 32828: Free brochure with long SASE ■ Men's and women's gold and sterling silver jewelry inlaid with natural stones and shell, Zuni pottery, kachina dolls, and paintings. 813–623–3549.

Seminole Arts & Crafts Center, 6073 Sterling Rd., Hollywood, FL 33024: Free brochure with long SASE ■ Patchwork clothing, dolls, wood carvings, baskets, and beadwork jewelry. 305–583–3590.

Seminole Cultural Center, 5221 Orient Rd., Tampa, FL 33610: Free information with long SASE ■ Patchwork jackets, skirts, vests, dresses and purses; sweet grass baskets; and dolls, beadwork, moccasins, and woodcarvings. 813–623–3549.

This N' That, 204 Brevard Ave., Cocoa Village, FL 32922: Free information with long SASE ■ Beadwork, jewelry, pottery, carvings, fetishes, baskets, moccasins, dolls, and Navajo rugs.

Idaho

Kamiakin Krafts, P.O. Box 358, Fort Hall, ID 83203: Free price list with long SASE ■ Beadwork belts, buckles, watch bands, earrings, coin purses, and medallion necklaces; moccasins and slippers; tennis shoes; baseball caps; desk pen sets; salt and pepper shakers; men's and women's clothing; native tanned hides; and cedar or raffia baskets. 208–785–2546.

Trading Post Clothes Horse, P.O. Box 368, Fort Hall, ID 83203: Free brochure with long SASE ■ Beaded and tanned buckskin items that include belt buckles, coin purses, earrings, barrettes, hat bands, bolo ties, gloves, moccasins, dresses, vests, and drums. 208–237–8433.

Indiana

Tisitsistas Free Traders, RR 1, Box 113, Bunker Hill, IN 46914: Catalog $2 (refundable) ■ Handmade reproduction Cheyenne household items, leather and beadwork crafts, spears, flags, and jewelry. 317–689–5031.

Kansas

Laurie Houseman-Whitehawk, RR 3, Box 155–B, Lawrence, KS 66044: Free information with long SASE ■ Original paintings in gouache. 913–842–1948.

Eddie Morrison Wood Carvings & Sculptures, 223 N. Young, Caldwell, KS 67022: Free information with long SASE ■ Wood carvings and stone sculptures. 316–845–2355.

Louisiana

Native American Arts of the South, P.O. Box 217, Elton, LA 70532: Free price list with long SASE ■ Swamp cane and white oak baskets, long-leaf pine needle baskets, and pottery. 318–584–5130.

Maine

Basket Bank, Aroostook Micmac Council, Inc., 8 Church St., Presque Isle, ME 04769: Free brochure with long SASE ■ Potato, pack, clothes, fishing, decorative, shopping, cradle, and sewing baskets. 207–764–1972.

Chief Poolaw Tepee Trading Post, 88 Main St., Old Town, ME 04468: Free information with long SASE ■ Penobscot sweet grass baskets, Passamaquoddy baskets, baskets by other tribes, pottery, moccasins, beadwork, wood carvings, dolls, war clubs, rugs, and jewelry.

Longacre Enterprises, Inc., Old Eastport Rd., P.O. Box 196, Perry, ME 04667: Free price list with long SASE ■ Passamaquoddy birch bark, ash, and sweet grass baskets; balsam Christmas wreaths; bow and arrow racks; incense burners and drift wood lamps; and other crafts. 207–853–2762.

Nowetah's Indian Store & Museum, Rt. 27, Box 40, New Portland, ME 04954: Free brochure with long SASE ■ Rugs and wall hangings, beadwork, leatherwork, moccasins, porcupine quill boxes, birch bark baskets, pottery, leatherwork, drums, dolls, masks, Navajo sand paintings, headdresses, peace pipes, and silver and turquoise jewelry. 207–628–4981.

Wabanaki Arts, P.O. Box 453, Old Town, ME 04468: Free price list with long SASE ■ Penobscot carved canes, war clubs, totem poles, stone tomahawks, baskets, beadwork, and quillwork. 207–827–3447.

Massachusetts

Bluebird Indian Crafts, 130 Glenview St., Upton, MA 01568: Free information with long SASE ■ Porcupine quillwork, beadwork, clothing, and other Native American crafts. 617–937–1818.

Three Feathers, c/o Mary Ann Barros, P.O. Box 3354, Plymouth, MA 02361: Free information with long SASE ■ Fingerwoven bags, moccasins, leather pouches, clothing, beadwork, baskets, and quillwork.

Michigan

Faboriginals by Candi Wesaw Wilcox, 557 Carrier NE, Grand Rapids, MI 49505: Free information with long SASE ■ Native American portraiture and limited edition lithographs. 616–459–8136.

Indian Earth Arts & Crafts Store, 124 W. 1st St., Flint, MI 48502: Free information with long SASE ■ Paintings, pottery, quillwork, black ash baskets, quilts, beadwork, and moccasins. 313–239–6621.

Indian Hills Trading Company & Indian Art Gallery, 1681 Harbor Rd., Petoskey, MI 49770: Free information with long SASE ■ Porcupine quill boxes and pendants, traditional drums, beadwork, buckskin baby moccasins, Navajo rugs, Southwestern silver and turquoise jewelry, Pueblo pottery, Eskimo art, and original Native American paintings. 616–347–3789.

Moon Bear Pottery, c/o Shirley M. Brauker, 6135 E. Broadway, #7, Mt. Pleasant, MI 48858: Free brochure with long SASE ■ Pottery, wall hangings, sculptures, oil paintings and drawings, and dolls. 517–773–2510.

Native American Arts & Crafts Council, Indian Arts & Crafts Store, Goose Creek Rd., P.O. Box 1049, Grayling, MI 49738: Free information with long SASE ■ Porcupine quill boxes, black ash splint and sweet grass baskets, beadwork, birch bark crafts, paintings and drawings, and leatherwork. 517–348–3190.

Passages Express, 141 W. Tamarack St., Ironwood, MI 49938: Free information with long SASE ■ Dolls, porcupine quillwork, and leather crafts. 906–932–4108.

Porcupine Patch, 1737 W. Sheridan Rd., Petoskey, MI 49770: Free price list with long SASE ■ Porcupine quill boxes, paintings, leather crafts, beadwork, and woodcarvings.

Minnesota

Amber Woods Studio, 26570 140th St., Zimmerman, MN 55398: Free information with long SASE ■ Sculptures, wood relief wall hangings, pipestone and marble carvings, graphics, walking sticks, and paintings. 612–856–2328.

Chippewa Indian Craft & Gift Shop, Red Lake Indian Reservation, Goodridge, MN 56725: Brochure $2 with long SASE ■ Carved catlinite peace pipes with decorated stems, pipes with carved effigies, drums, cradleboards, and model birch bark tepees. 218–378–4210.

Elk's Camp Society, 214 S. Hiawatha Ave., Pipestone, MN 56164: Free brochure with long SASE ■ Traditional and contemporary quillwork. 507–825–2052.

Featherstone Products, Inc., 400 N. Hiawatha, P.O. Box 13, Pipestone, MN 56164: Free information with long SASE ■

Bronze sculptures and original paintings. 507–825–4112.

Ikwe Marketing, White Earth Indian Reservation, Rt. 1, Osage, MN 56570: Free brochure with long SASE ■ Birch bark baskets, Ojibway beadwork, star quilts, braided rugs, and quillwork. 218–573–3411.

Lady Slipper Designs, RR 3, Box 556, Bemidji, MN 56601: Free price list with long SASE ■ Birch bark, willow, and black ash baskets; beaded charms; moccasins; birch bark birdhouses; and dream nets. 800–950–5903.

Pipestone Indian Shrine Association, c/o Pipestone National Monument, Box 727, Pipestone, MN 56164: Free brochure with long SASE ■ Pipestone carvings that include pipes, ash trays, jewelry, war clubs, arrowheads, and buffalo and turtle effigies. 507–825–5463.

Mississippi

Choctaw Museum of the Southern Indian Gift Shop, Rt. 7, Box 21, Philadelphia, MS 39350: Free price list with long SASE ■ Baskets, beadwork jewelry, moccasins and traditional Choctaw dresses and shirts by special order, dolls, quilts, pottery, stickball rackets and balls, blowguns, and rabbit sticks. 601–656–5251.

Missouri

Turner Art Works, Rt. 3, Box 460, De Soto, MO 63020: Free information with long SASE ■ Acrylic paintings and handmade traditional and contemporary necklaces, earrings, amulets, and chokers in shell, bone, crayfish pinchers, and turtle shell. 314–586–4105.

Montana

Blackfeet Crafts Association, P.O. Box 51, Browning, MT 59417: Information with long SASE ■ Beadwork jewelry, handbags, dolls, and moccasins.

Blackfeet Trading Post, P.O. Box 626, Browning, MT 59417: Free information with long SASE ■ Moccasins, beadwork, baskets, pottery, shawls, and paintings. 406–338–2050.

Coup Marks, Box 532, Ronan, MT 59864: Free information with long SASE ■ Paintings, sculptures, ribbon shirts, moccasins, beadwork, dolls, shawls, drums, stick games, wing dresses, and cradleboards. 406–246–3216.

Flathead Indian Museum Trading Post & Art Gallery, P.O. Box 464, St. Ignatius, MT 59865: Free information with long SASE ■ Moccasins, beaded buckles, medallions, hair ties, silver and turquoise jewelry, earrings, dance costumes, and Native American paintings. 406–745–2951.

Neeney, Box 84, Joplin, MT 59531: Free information with long SASE ■ Contemporary and traditional beadwork, gemstone necklaces and rings, sacred red rock pipes and fetishes, and native-tanned hides. 406–292–3890.

Northern Plains Indian Crafts Association, P.O. Box E, Browning, MT 59417: Free price list with long SASE ■ Buckskin vests, gloves, handbags and moccasins; beadwork jewelry; beaded belts; dolls; decorated rawhide letter trays, baskets, and wastebaskets; porcupine hair roaches; and native tanned hides. 406–338–5661.

The Tipi Gift Shop, Rt. 62, Box 3110E, Livingston, MT 59047: Free information with long SASE ■ Original paintings, pen and ink sketches, beadwork, pipes, headdresses, baskets, jewelry, bows and arrows, quivers, wall hangings, shields, moccasins, star quilts, and custom knives. 406–222–8575.

Wolf Chief Graphics, 907 C Ave. NW, Great Falls, MT 59404: Free price list with long SASE ■ Watercolor paintings, alabaster and bronze sculptures, and bone chokers. 406–452–4449.

Nebraska

Pilcher's Indian Store, Rt. 2, Box 348A, Fort Calhoun, NE 68023: Free information with long SASE ■ Beadwork, peace pipes, dance roaches, bustles, pottery, kachina dolls, and Navajo silver heishi jewelry. 402–468–5131.

Nevada

Arnold Aragon Sculpture & Illustration, Box 64, Schurz, NV 89427: Free information with long SASE ■ Stone sculptures, drawings, and paintings. 702–773–2542.

Maggi Houten, P.O. Box 265, Nixon, NV 89424: Free information with long SASE ■ Beadwork hair ties, necklaces, bolo ties, watch bands, belt buckles, belts, moccasins, baby baskets, and coin purses. 702–476–0205.

Malotte Studio, South Fork Reservation, Star Rt., Lee, NV 89829: Free information with long SASE ■ Original drawings in all media. 702–744–4305.

Winter Moon Trading Company, P.O. Box 189, Schurz, NV 89427: Free information with long SASE ■ Beaded and silver jewelry, horsehair baskets, pottery, original artwork, and other Native American crafts. 702–773–2510.

New Jersey

Lone Bear Indian Craft Company, 300 Main St., #3F, Orange, NJ 07050: Free price list with long SASE ■ Woodland Native American beadwork, costumes, war bonnets, other headdresses, and authentic Native American collectibles.

New Mexico

Carolyn Bobelu, P.O. Box 443, Zuni, NM 87327: Free information with long SASE ■ Jewelry with faceted and multi-levels of silver, turquoise, coral, and shell. 505–782–2773.

Chi Nah Bah, P.O. Box 122, Brimhall, NM 87310: Information $1 ■ Jewelry, rugs and dolls, Navajo rugs, sand paintings, kachina dolls, leather belts, pottery, baskets, and paintings.

Indian Pueblo Cultural Center, Inc., 2401 12th St. NW, Albuquerque, NM 87102: Free information with long SASE ■ Pueblo pottery, baskets, wood carvings, fabrics, lapidary crafts, stone sculptures, silver and turquoise jewelry, and drums. 505–843–7270.

Jicarilla Arts & Crafts Shop/Museum, P.O. Box 507, Dulce, NM 87528: Free brochure with large stamped manila envelope ■ Beadwork, baskets, leather work, and paintings. 505–759–3515.

Lilly's Gallery, P.O. Box 342, Acoma Pueblo, NM 87034: Free information with long SASE ■ Traditional handcrafted Acoma pottery and figurines made and painted with natural earth materials. 505–552–9501.

Carol G. Lucero, P.O. Box 319, Jemez Pueblo, NM 87024: Free information with long SASE ■ Pottery, storytellers, Nativity sets, Pueblo pottery, baskets, cedar flutes,

kachinas, drums, sculptures, Navajo dolls, sand paintings, and other art. 505–843–9337.

Ted Miller Custom Knives, P.O. Box 6328, Santa Fe, NM 87502: Free price list with long SASE ■ Custom knives with hand-tooled steel blades set in handles of elk or stag horn and bone, and decorated with turquoise or carvings; wood and horn carvings; deer horn pipes and elk horn belt buckles; and bolos. 505–984–0338.

Teresita Naranjo, Rt. 1, Box 455, Santa Clara Pueblo, Espanola, NM 87532: Free information with long SASE ■ Traditional Santa Clara black and red pottery. 505–753–9655.

Navajo Gallery, P.O. Box 1756, Taos, NM 87571: Free information with long SASE ■ Paintings, sculptures, lithographs, and drawings. 505–758–3250.

Oke Oweenge Arts & Crafts, P.O. Box 1095, San Juan Pueblo, NM 87566: Free price list with long SASE ■ Traditional ceremonial mantas, shirts, and sashes; modern vests, shirts, and blouses; and wall hangings and pillows, pottery, dolls, beadwork, silver jewelry, baskets, and paintings. 505–852–2372.

Oklahoma Indian Crafts Company, 4321 Ellison NE, Albuquerque, NM 87109: Free information with long SASE ■ War bonnets and other traditional headdresses, beadwork, traditional and contemporary buckskin and cloth garments, moccasins and boots, original paintings and limited edition prints, pipe bags, and other Native American crafts. 505–345–0796.

Pueblo of Zuni Arts & Crafts, P.O. Box 425, Zuni, NM 87327: Free information with long SASE ■ Pottery, fetishes, contemporary art, and Zuni turquoise, shell, coral, jet, and silver jewelry. 505–782–4481.

Rhonda Holy Bear, P.O. Box 70, Chamisal, NM 87521: Free price list with long SASE ■ Plains and other tribal doll figurines in detailed, handcrafted costumes. 505–587–2018.

Ramona Sakiestewa, Ltd., P.O. Box 2472, Santa Fe, NM 87504: Free brochure with long SASE ■ Handwoven limited edition fabrics, rugs, blankets, and tapestries. 505–982–8282.

Scripsit, c/o Billy, 3089 Plaza Blanca, Santa Fe, NM 87505: Free information with long

SASE ■ Calligraphy crafts on paper and leather. 505–471–1516.

Carol Vigil, P.O. Box 443, Jemez Pueblo, NM 87024: Free information with long SASE ■ Carved and painted Jemez pottery.

Zuni Craftsmen Cooperative Association, P.O. Box 426, Zuni, NM 87327: Information $2 with long SASE ■ Zuni silver and turquoise jewelry, beadwork, fetishes, pottery, and paintings. 505–782–4425.

New York

American Indian Crafts, 719 Broad St., Salamanca, NY 14779: Free information with long SASE ■ Seneca beadwork, masks, rattles, belts, headbands, buckles, cornhusk dolls; Ute dolls and Mohawk baskets; and Zuni and Navajo silver and turquoise jewelry. 716–945–1225.

Black Bear Trading Post, Rt. 9W, P.O. Box 47, Esopus, NY 12429: Free information with long SASE ■ Baskets, pottery, beadwork, kachina dolls, peace pipes, war clubs, soapstone and woodcarvings, dolls, moccasins, cradleboards, paintings, and sterling silver and turquoise jewelry. 914–384–6786.

Chrisjohn Family Arts & Crafts, RD 2, Box 315, Red Hook, NY 12571: Free information with long SASE ■ Masks and other wood carvings, bone jewelry and silver items, cornhusk dolls, and pipes. 914–758–8238.

Peter B. Jones, Box 174, Versailles, NY 14168: Free information with long SASE ■ Original works in clay, one-of-a-kind ceramic sculptures, and wall hangings. 716–532–5993.

Little Feather Trading Post, P.O. Box 3165, Jamaica, NY 11431: Free information with long SASE ■ Beadwork jewelry, silver jewelry, and leatherwork. 212–658–0576.

Mohawk Impressions, Box 20, Mohawk Station, Hogansburg, NY 13655: Free brochure with long SASE ■ Iroquois cornhusk dolls, beadwork with quills and feathers, sweet grass and black ash splint baskets, Mohawk paintings, cradleboards for dolls, and rag dolls. 518–358–2467.

Seneca-Iroquois National Museum Gift Shop, Broad St. Extension, P.O. Box 442, Salamanca, NY 14779: Free price list with long SASE ■ Iroquois beadwork, baskets, wooden false face masks, cornhusk masks

and dolls, rattles, wampum and scrimshaw jewelry, leather crafts, ribbon shirts, and pottery. 716–945–1738.

Sweetgrass Gift Shop, Akwesasne Museum, Rt. 37, Hogansburg, NY 13655: Free brochure with long SASE ■ Black ash splint and sweet grass baskets, pack baskets, laundry baskets, egg baskets, and regular and miniature fancy baskets; beadwork and quillwork; and cradleboards. 518–358–2240.

Tuskewe Krafts, 2089 Upper Mountain Rd., Sanborn, NY 14132: Free brochure with long SASE ■ Women's and men's field and box lacrosse sticks. 716–297–1821.

North Carolina

Haliwa-Saponi Tribal Pottery & Arts, P.O. Box 99, Hollister, NC 27844: Free price list with long SASE ■ Pottery, quilts, beadwork, woodwork, and stonework. 919–586–4017.

Lumbee Indian Arts & Crafts, Rt. 1, Box 310 AA, Rowland, NC 28383: Free information with long SASE ■ Baskets, leatherwork, and beadwork. 919–521–9494.

Qualla Arts & Crafts Mutual, Inc., P.O. Box 277, Cherokee, NC 28719: Free brochure with long SASE ■ River cane, oak splints, and honeysuckle baskets; animal figurines and wood carvings; and masks, beadwork, pottery, dolls, and metalwork. 704–497–3103.

Sacred Hoop Trading Post, 2701 Homestead Rd, #508, Chapel Hill, NC 27516: Free information with long SASE ■ Eastern Cherokee baskets, pottery, wood and stone carvings, and Lumbee paintings and wood carvings. 919–933–7595.

Tuscarora Indians Handcraft Shop, Rt. 4, Box 172, Maxton, NC 28364: Free price list with long SASE ■ Leather boots and moccasins, shirts, hats, vests, handbags, pouches, headbands, belts, necklaces, costumes, sterling silver and brass jewelry, and copper bracelets. 919–844–3352.

Wayah'sti Indian Traditions, P.O. Box 130, Hollister, NC 27844: Free price list with long SASE ■ Beadwork, leather crafts, stone pipes, sculptures, pottery, and bark craft. 919–586–4519.

Robert D. Waynee, Sr., P.O. Box 5232, New Bern, NC 28560: Free information with long SASE ■ Basswood Native American

dance motifs and wood sculptures. 919–637–2546.

Oklahoma

Adams Studio, Rt. 3, Box 615A, Ponca City, OK 74601: Free price list with long SASE ■ Buckles, bracelets, and rings in silver or brass decorated with turquoise and other semi-precious stones; original watercolors, lithographs, serigraphy, and etchings; and beadwork key chains, barrettes, and buckles. 405–765–5086.

American Indian Handicrafts, P.O. Box 533, Meeker, OK 74855: Free brochure with long SASE ■ Ribbon work blankets, shirts, and shawls, and beadwork and feather crafts. 405–279–3343.

Buffalo Sun, 605 E. Central, Box 1556, Miami, OK 74355: Free information with long SASE ■ Traditional and contemporary Native American blouses, skirts, ribbon shirts, dresses, jackets, vests, and coats; buckskin dresses, moccasins and leggings; lamb suede dresses, skirts, blouses, finger-woven belts, shawls, fans, gourds, and jewelry. 918–542–8870.

Cherokee Arts & Crafts Center, P.O. Box 948, Tahlequah, OK 74464: Free information with long SASE ■ Traditional Cherokee tear dresses, ribbon shirts, buckbrush baskets, afghans, beadwork, wood carvings, pottery, grass dolls, rag dolls, quilts, turtle shell rattles, silver and Oochelata stone jewelry, and paintings. 918–456–0511.

Cherokee National Museum Gift Shop, P.O. Box 515, TSA-LA-GI, Tahlequah, OK 74464: Free price list with long SASE ■ Baskets, weapons, and original paintings, prints, and sculptures. 918–456–6007.

Crying Wind Gallery & Framing Company, 400 N. Indiana, Oklahoma City, OK 73106: Free information with long SASE ■ Watercolor portraits, landscapes, still life, and other subjects; Seminole patchwork; and dolls. 405–235–9991.

The Fife Collection, Designer Showroom, P.O. Box 1117, Henryetta, OK 74437: Catalog $1 with long SASE ■ Custom contemporary clothing for men, women, and children that includes dresses, capes, skirts, men's shirts, and Cherokee, Creek, and Seminole traditional dresses; beadwork; small art pieces; jewelry; and wall hangings. 918–652–9607.

Five Civilized Tribes Museum Trading Post, Agency Hill, Honor Heights Dr., Muskogee, OK 74401: Free brochure with long SASE ■ Beaded medallion necklaces, key rings, combs, hair ties, bolo ties, rings, baskets, sculptures, and paintings. 918–683–1701.

The Galleria, 1630 W. Lindsey, Norman, OK 73069: Free information with long SASE ■ Carvings, paintings, bronzes, baskets, jewelry, beadwork, pottery, drawings, and original prints by Native American artists. 405–329–1225.

Bill Glass Studio, Star Route South, Box 39B, Locust Grove, OK 74352: Free information with long SASE ■ Original stoneware sculptures and carvings, pottery, and bronzes. 918–479–8884.

Jack Gregory, Rt. 1, Box 79, Watts, OK 74964: Free information with long SASE ■ Contemporary handmade wooden candle holders, bowls, laminated lamps, rolling pins, jewelry bowls, plates, boxes, and other crafts. 918–723–5408.

Kelley Haney Art Gallery, P.O. Box 103, Seminole, OK 74868: Free brochure with long SASE ■ Original paintings, sculpture, jewelry, baskets, and pottery. 405–382–3915.

Mister Indian's Cowboy Store, 1000 S. Main, Sapulpa, OK 74066: Free information with long SASE ■ Moccasins, fans, shawls, beadwork, ribbon shirts, rugs, pottery, purses, cradleboards, drums, dolls, silver and turquoise jewelry, and paintings. 918–224–6511.

Monkapeme, P.O. Box 457, Perkins, OK 74059: Free information with long SASE ■ Native American contemporary fashions, traditional costumes, moccasins, shawls, headbands, medallions, belts, hair ties, buckskin dresses, leggings, and shirts. 405–547–2948.

Native American Arts, P.O. Box 2103, Ada, OK 74820: Free price list with long SASE ■ Original paintings, jewelry, and sculptures.

Oklahoma Indian Arts & Crafts Cooperative, P.O. Box 966, Anadarko, OK 73005: Free price list with long SASE ■ Beaded moccasins, belts, ties, pins, dance costume accessories and ornaments, suede handbags, war dance bustle ensembles, nickel-silver jewelry, hand-sewn and decorated shirts, aprons, dolls, and paintings by Southern Plains artists. 405–247–3486.

Connie Seaborn Studio, P.O. Box 23795, Oklahoma City, OK 73132: Free information with long SASE ■ Original paintings, drawings, and hand-pulled prints. 405–728–3903.

Seabourn Studio, 6105 Covington Ln., Oklahoma City, OK 73132: Free information with long SASE ■ Original lithographs, serigraphs, and etchings. 405–722–1631.

Snake Creek Workshop, P.O. Box 147, Rose, OK 74364: Free brochure and price list with long SASE ■ Mussel shell gorget necklaces. 918–479–8867.

Supernaw's Oklahoma Indian Supply, P.O. Box 216, Skiatook, OK 74070: Catalog $1 ■ Feather work, nickel-silver jewelry, beadwork, roaches, women's accessories, and other crafts. 918–396–1713.

Tah-Mels, P.O. Box 1123, Tahlequah, OK 74465: Free information with long SASE ■ Little People dolls, beadwork, baskets, quilts, Oochelata pink mussel shell and silver and gold jewelry, wood carvings, and oil and watercolor paintings. 918–456–5461.

Tiger Art Gallery, 2110 E. Shawnee St., Muskogee, OK 74403: Free information with long SASE ■ Traditional and contemporary paintings and sculptures. 918–687–7006.

Touching Leaves Indian Crafts, 927 Portland Ave., Dewey, OK 74029: Catalog $1 with long SASE ■ Beadwork, German silver jewelry, and leatherwork. 918–534–2859.

Two Feathers Indian Shop & Trading Shop, 1304–A N. Elm Pl., Broken Arrow, OK 74012: Free information with long SASE ■ Buckskin dresses and other Native American clothing, blankets, bandoliers, pottery, baskets, flutes, beaded moccasins, and original paintings. 918–258–1228.

Zadoka Pottery, 12515 E. 37th St., Tulsa, OK 74146: Free information with long SASE ■ Earthenware storage vessels, vases, and bowls. 918–663–9455.

Oregon

Klahowya American Indian Gift Shop, 947 S. 1st St., Coos Bay, OR 97420: Free information with long SASE ■ Beadwork, dolls, earrings, wall hangings, drums, feather hair ties, and other crafts. 503–269–7349.

Red Bear Creations, 358 N. Lexington Ave., Brandon, OR 97411: Free information

with long SASE ■ Star quilts, star drum covers, and padded jackets. 503–347–9772.

Nadine Van Mechelen, Rt. 1, Box 270, Pendleton, OR 97801: Free information with long SASE ■ Handmade dolls in authentic Native American costumes. 503–276–2566.

Rhode Island

The Turquoise, Rockland Rd., North Scituate, RI 02857: Free information with long SASE ■ Southwest Native American jewelry, pottery, baskets, rugs, paintings, moccasins, and clothing by Native American designers. 401–647–2579.

South Carolina

Sara Ayers, 1182 Brookwood Cir., West Columbia, SC 29169: Free price list with long SASE ■ Pottery pipes, vases, pitchers, canoes, ash trays, candlesticks, bowls, jardinieres, cups, and bookends. 803–794–5436.

South Dakota

Contemporary Lakota Fashions by Geraldine Sherman, 235 Curtis, #12, Rapid City, SD 57701: Free information with long SASE ■ Ribbon shirts, skirts, dresses, shawls, vests, and king and queen size star quilts. 605–341–7560.

Jackson Originals, Box 1049, Mission, SD 57555: Free price list with long SASE ■ Contemporary men's, women's, and children's leather vests and jackets with beadwork; denim shirts, vests, and jackets with applique or embroidered designs; and traditional Sioux ribbon shirts and dresses. 605–856–2541.

Lakota Jewelry Visions, 909 E. St. Patrick, Ste. 16, Rapid City, SD 57701: Free information with long SASE ■ Traditional and contemporary jewelry and dance accessories. 605–343–0603.

Oyate Kin Cultural Cooperative, c/o Wesley Hare, Jr., Marty, SD 57361: Free information with long SASE ■ Beadwork, feather and leather accessories for dance outfits, Native American star quilts, ribbon shirts, and leather crafts.

Prairie Edge, P.O. Box 8303, Rapid City, SD 57709: Catalog $3 ■ Native American art, artifacts, and jewelry. 605–341–4525.

Rings 'N' Things, P.O. Box 360, Mission, SD 57555: Free information with long

SASE ■ Silver gifts, quillwork, and bead-work. 605–856–4548.

St. Joseph's Lakota Development Council, St. Joseph's Indian School, Chamberlain, SD 57326: Free brochure with long SASE n Dot drawings, jewelry, kachina dolls, leatherwork, beadwork, patchwork quilts, and tote bags. 605–734–6021.

Starboy Enterprises, P.O. Box 33, Rosebud Sioux Reservation, Okreek, SD 57563: Free brochure with long SASE ■ Star quilts. 605–856–4517.

Tipi Shop, Inc., Box 1542, Rapid City, SD 57709: Free price list with long SASE ■ Beaded buckskin moccasins, dance costume accessories, pottery, billfolds, coin purses, beadwork jewelry, quillwork, dolls, parfleche boxes, willow baskets, and paintings by Sioux artists. 605–343–8128.

Texas

Annesley Studio, P.O. Box 3, Missouri City, TX 77459: Free information ■ Limited edition bronze sculptures, original 24K gold and silver point drawings, paintings, and pastels. 713–729–8960.

Crazy Crow Trading Post, 107 N. Fannin, P.O. Box 314, Denison, TX 75020: Catalog $2 ■ Silver items, moccasins, beadwork, and imitation eagle feather war bonnets. 903–463–1366.

Naranjo's World of American Indian Art, P.O. Box 7973, Houston, TX 77270: Free price list with long SASE ■ Jewelry, beadwork, leatherwork, pottery, baskets, rugs, dolls, and kachinas. 713–660–9690.

Tribal Enterprise, Alabama-Coushatta Indian Reservation, Rt. 3, Box 640, Livingston, TX 77351: Free information with long SASE ■ Large and small coiled pine needle baskets and animal effigies, grass baskets, beadwork, pottery, vests, and ribbon shirts. 713–563–4391.

Whitewolf Photography, P.O. Box 297, Redwater, TX 75573: Free information with long SASE ■ Original photographs with Native American and western themes.

Virginia

The Silver Phoenix, Inc., 2946–D Chain Bridge Rd., Oakton, VA 22124: Free information with long SASE ■ Jewelry, sand paintings, pottery, kachinas, rugs, moccasins, and beadwork. 703–255–3393.

Snyder Art Studios, 4502 Hawk Ct., Dale City, VA 22193: Free information with long SASE ■ Paintings, drawings, sculptures, murals, and leather crafts. 703–670–0074.

Via Gambaro Studio, Inc., Retha Walden Gambaro, Sculptor, P.O. Box 1117, Stafford, VA 22554: Free information with long SASE ■ Bronze, wood, stone, and mixed media sculptures; shields; wall hangings; and medicine wheels. 703–659–0130.

Washington

Fran & Bill James, Lummi Indian Craftsmen, 4339 Lummi Rd., Ferndale, WA 98248: Free information with long SASE ■ Northwest Coast Salish wool blankets and cedar bark baskets. 206–384–5292.

Makah Cultural Research Center, P.O. Box 95, Neah Bay, WA 98357: Free price list with long SASE ■ Woven baskets and mats of replicas of archaeological artifacts; carved wooden masks; totem poles; rattles and bowls; shell jewelry, engraved silver bracelets; and miniature basket earrings; painted drums and beadwork; and original serigraphs. 206–645–2711.

March Point Indian Arts, 815 S. March Point Rd., Anacortes, WA 98221: Free information with long SASE ■ Fraser River baskets; Northwest Coast carvings; Haida button blankets; Cowichan sweaters, hats, and mittens; Taos and Minnetonka moccasins; Navajo, Hopi, and Zuni jewelry; Navajo rugs; Ute, Sioux, and Pueblo pottery; and kachinas. 206–293–5632.

Potlatch Gifts, Northwind Trading Company, 708 Commercial Ave., Anacortes, WA 98221: Free brochure with long SASE ■ Salish-style wood carvings, pottery, jewelry, mats, baskets, wool sweaters, hats, mittens, and socks. 206–293–6404.

Sacred Circle Gallery of American Indian Art, c/o Daybreak Star Arts Center, P.O. Box 99100, Seattle, WA 98199: Free information with long SASE ■ Paintings; bronze, wood and stone sculptures; carved and painted wall panels; ceramics; beaded moose hide bags and moccasins; and knives. 206–223–0072.

Suquamish Museum, P.O. Box 498, Suquamish, WA 98392: Free information with long SASE ■ Traditional Suquamish/Puget Sound Salish clam baskets, dolls, whistles, museum replicas, wooden bowls, spoons, canoe bailers, and wood carvings. 206–598–3311.

Tin-Na-Tit Kin-Ne-Ki Indian Arts & Gifts, P.O. Box 1057, Republic, WA 99166: Free price list with long SASE ■ Jewelry, masks, stone carvings, kachina dolls, baskets, pottery, quillwork, beadwork, Cowichan sweaters, mukluks, and sand paintings. 509–775–3077.

Wisconsin

Judith L. Jourdan, 132 Pope St., Seymour, WI 54165: Free information with long SASE ■ Dolls, beadwork, and paintings. 414–833–6469.

Wa-Swa-Gon Arts & Crafts, P.O. Box 477, Lac du Flambeau, WI 54538: Free information with long SASE ■ Beadwork, birch bark items, moccasins, finger weavings, traditional and ceremonial clothes, and carvings. 715–588–7636.

Winnebago Public Indian Museum, P.O. Box 441, Wisconsin Dells, WI 53965: Price list $1 ■ Winnebago baskets, beadwork, deerskin products, pottery, Navajo rugs, and silver items. 608–254–2268.

Wyoming

Fort Washakie Trading Company, 53 N. Fork Rd., P.O. Box 428, Fort Washakie, WY 82514: Free brochure with long SASE ■ Beaded and quilled jewelry, rawhide and smoked skin accessories, dolls, cradleboards, Navajo rugs, southwestern silver and turquoise jewelry, Papago baskets, and Pueblo pottery. 307–332–3557.

La Ray Turquoise Company, P.O. Box 83, Cody, WY 82414: Free information with long SASE ■ Navajo, Zuni, Chippewa, and Hopi silver items; Navajo rugs; and Ojibwa beadwork. 307–587–9564.

INTERCOMS

Aiphone Intercom Systems, 1700 13th Ave. NE, Bellevue, WA 98004: Free information ■ Voice transmission, entry security control, video intercom, and door answering intercoms. 206–445–0510.

Doorking, 120 Glasgow Ave., Inglewood, CA 90301: Free information ■ Intercom with digital keypad for keyless entry security. 310–645–0023.

M & S Systems, Inc., 2861 Congressman Ln., Dallas, TX 75220: Free information ■ Intercom with door chimes and door release. 800–877–6631.

Siedle Communication System of America, 780 Parkway, Broomall, PA 19008: Free information ■ Video intercoms. 215–353–9595.

Talk-A-Phone Company, 5013 N. Kedzie Ave., Chicago, IL 60625: Free information ■ Intercoms for two-way conversation with optional integration with master system. 312–539–1100.

JET SKIS

Aqua-Jet, 2821 W. Chestnut Expy., Springfield, MO 65802: Free information ■ Two-person watercraft. 417–886–2001.

Arizona Jet Ski Center, 2818 E. Bell Rd., Phoenix, AZ 85032: Free information ■ Jet skis, parts, and accessories. 800–245–3875; 602–482–9322 (in AZ).

B.H.I. Racing, 13001 Central Ave. NE, Blaine, MN 55434: Free information ■ New, used, and surplus jet ski parts. 612–757–7110.

Butch's Jet Ski, 3614 S. Division, Grand Rapids, MI 49508: Free information ■ Jet skis, parts, and accessories. 800–54–BUTCH.

Central Manufacturing, 6848 Southeast Blvd., Derby, KS 67037: Free information ■ Jet ski trailers. 316–788–3331.

Competition Accessories, Inc., Rt. 68 North at Rt. 235, Xenia, OH 45385: Catalog $5 (refundable) ■ Watercraft accessories. 800–543–3535.

Dunnavant Performance, 1656 Centerpoint Pkwy., Birmingham, AL 35215: Free information ■ Jet ski parts and accessories. 800–886–SKIS.

Fox Racing, 909 Dell Ave., Campbell, CA 95008: Catalog $1 ■ Men's and women's clothing for watercraft activities.

Hayward Kawasaki, 27185 Mission Blvd., Hayward, CA 94544: Free information ■ Free catalog ■ Jet ski parts and accessories. 510–537–8297.

Hot Sports, 2151 Sampson Ave., Corona, CA 91720: Free information ■ Two-person personal watercraft. 714–279–2884.

Jetco, 2646 Albatross Way, Sacramento, CA 95815: Free information ■ Personal watercraft, parts, and accessories. 915–924–3097.

Jet Ski Parts Warehouse, 31438 Castaic Rd., P.O. Box 85, Castaic, CA 91310: Free information ■ Personal watercraft, parts, and accessories. 805–257–3033.

Jet Trends, P.O. Box 5271, Hialeah Lakes, FL 33014: Free information ■ Men's and women's clothing for watercraft activities and jet ski parts and accessories. 800–231–9279; 305–635–2411 (in FL).

Kawasaki Motor Corporation USA, P.O. Box 25252, Santa Ana, CA 92799: Free information ■ One- and two-person jet skis. 714–770–0400.

L & S Engineering, 9856 Everest, Downey, CA 90242: Free catalog ■ Parts, accessories, and performance products for jet skis. 310–803–5591.

Lee's Kawasaki, 1538 National Hwy., Thomasville, NC 27360: Free catalog ■ Jet ski parts and accessories. 919–889–4667.

Low Dollar Racing, Inc., 3675 S. Santa Fe Dr., Englewood, CO 80110: Free information ■ Personal watercraft, parts, and accessories. 303–761–2471.

Midwest Watercraft, Ltd., 542 Gravois Rd., Fenton, MO 63026: Free catalog ■ Jet ski parts and accessories. 314–343–3565.

Orange County Cycle, 13666 Harbor Blvd., Garden Grove, CA 92643: Catalog $5 (refundable) ■ Jet skis and accessories. 714–530–7340.

Performance Jet Ski, Inc., 4925 E. Hunter, Anaheim, CA 92807: Free information ■ Personal watercraft, parts, and accessories. 714–779–8787.

R & R Jet Tech, Inc., 2811 Evans St., Hollywood, FL 33020: Free catalog ■ Personal watercraft and accessories. 800–833–8445.

Rip Cove, 575 W. Lake Mead Dr., Henderson, NV 89015: Free information ■ Personal watercraft, parts and accessories, wet suits, and swim wear. 702–564–8895.

Scorcher Products, 26943 Ruether Ave., Canyon County, CA 91351: Free information ■ Personal watercraft parts. 805–254–2122.

SOS Express, 6712 N. 54th St., Tampa, FL 33610: Free information ■ Two-person personal watercraft. 813–633–2588.

Top Gun Kawasaki, Rt. 122 South, P.O. Box 429, Wirtz, VA 24184: Free information ■ Jet ski parts. 703–721–4900.

UltraNautics, 620 W. Hueneme Rd., Oxnard, CA 93033: Free information ■ Two-person personal watercraft. 805–986–4812.

VM Boat Trailers, 5200 S. Peach, Fresno, CA 93725: Free information ■ Jet ski trailers. 209–486–0410.

WetJet International, Ltd., 23 Washburne Ave., Paynesville, MN 56362: Free information ■ Personal watercraft, clothing, and accessories. 612–243–3311.

Yamaha Motor Corporation, P.O. Box 6555, Cypress, CA 90630: Free information ■ One- and two-person jet skis. 800–526–6650.

JEWELRY

Adco Earrings Plus, Altid Park, P.O. Box 6531: Free catalog ■ Hypo-allergenic earrings, pierced earrings, and necklaces. 800–933–0260.

Adeler Stone Carvings & Jewelry, P.O. Box 2580, Reston, VA 22090: Free catalog ■ Birthstones and settings. 703–759–4076.

All Ears, 114 5th Ave., New York, NY 10011: Free catalog ■ Save up to 50 percent on earrings and other jewelry.

The Amber Company, 5643 Cahuenga Blvd., North Hollywood, CA 91601: Free price list ■ Amber, beads, fossils, ethnic jewelry, books, faceting and cabbing rough, lapidary supplies, and colored stones. 818–509–5730.

American Silver from the Southwest, 5700 Frederick Rd., Dayton, OH 45414: Free information ■ Native American and contemporary jewelry, pottery, and kachinas. 513–890–0138.

American Talisman, Inc., Catalog Services, P.O. Box 147, Sonoma, CA 95476: Free catalog ■ Birthstone jewelry. 800–777–9940.

Anka, 90 Greenwich Ave., Warwick, RI 02886: Catalog $1 (refundable) ■ Jewelry, buckles, and watches. 401–737–8107.

A.R.C. Traders, Inc., Box 3429, Scottsdale, AZ 85257: Free information ■ Findings, chains, earrings, and sterling silver, gold-filled, and 14k gold beads. 800–528–2374; 602–945–0769 (in AZ).

Arrow Gems & Minerals, Inc., P.O. Box 9068, Phoenix, AZ 85068: Free catalog ■ Pewter figurines, pendants, buckles, and bolas; beads and findings; and mineral specimens and faceted stones. 602–997–6373.

James Avery Craftsman, P.O. Box 1367, Kerrville, TX 78029: Free catalog ■ Jewelry for men and women. 800–283–1770.

Maurice Badler Jewelry, 578 5th Ave., New York, NY 10036: Catalog $3 ■ Save from 25 to 40 percent on jewelry for men and women. 800–M–BADLER; 212–575–9632 (in NY).

Black Hills Artcraft, 603 Main St., Spearfish, SD 57783: Free information ■ Gold, silver, and hammered copper jewelry. 605–642–3752.

Black Hills Gold Jewelry, P.O. Box 2470, Rapid City, SD 57709: Free catalog ■ Traditional and contemporary jewelry made with Black Hills gold. 605–348–1799.

Boston Gem Connection, Inc., 63 Domino Dr., Concord, MA 01742: Free catalog ■ Jewelry from around the world. 800–388–1414.

J.H. Breakell & Company, 69 Mill St., Newport, RI 02840: Catalog $2 ■ Original, handcrafted sterling silver and 14k gold jewelry. 800–767–6411.

Laurel Burch, Inc., 410 Townsend St., San Francisco, CA 94107: Free catalog ■ Custom jewelry and gifts with an animal theme. 800–722–8724.

J.E. Caldwell, 1140 Connecticut Ave. NW, Washington, DC 20036: Free catalog ■ Men's and women's jewelry, watches, crystal, music boxes, vases, carvings, pens, porcelain collectibles, and other gifts. 202–466–6780.

Calstar, Inc., 6470 Sycamore St., Maple Grove, MN 55369: Free catalog ■ Original jewelry with natural gemstones. 800–328–6169.

Circle D Jewelry, 9440 McCombs St., El Paso, TX 79924: Catalog $2 ■ Sterling silver and 14k gold castings and finished jewelry. 915–755–4479.

Christina Cole, Altid Park, P.O. Box 6531, Chelmsford, MA 01824: Free catalog ■ Save up to 60 percent on fashion jewelry close-outs. 800–933–0260.

Collector's Gallery at Kentshire, 37 E. 12th St., New York, NY 10003: Free information ■ Antique jewelry and accessories. 212–673–6644.

A.G.A. Correa, P.O. Box 401, Wiscasset, ME 04578: Free catalog ■ Turk's head jewelry in 14k or 18k gold. Includes head bracelets, rings, necklaces, earrings, cuff links, dress studs, barrettes, brooches, and tie bars. 800–341–0788.

Sarah Coventry, P.O. Box 1387, Elk Grove Village, IL 60009: Free information ■ Costume jewelry, watches, hair ornaments, sunglasses, scarves, belts, bags, small leather goods, and nail care sets. 800–252–8770.

Craftstones, P.O. Box 847, Ramona, CA 92065: Catalog $5 (refundable) ■ Exclusive gemstone jewelry and tumbled gemstones. 619–789–1620.

The Curiosity Shop, P.O. Box 964, Cheshire, CT 06410: Catalog $3 ■ Vintage costume jewelry. 203–271–0643.

Davidson Rock Shop, 531 Randolph St., Traverse City, MI 49684: Catalog $2 ■ Sterling silver and gold-filled pendants. 616–946–4520.

Designs by Romeo, 1550 E. Oakland Park Blvd., Fort Lauderdale, FL 3334: Free information ■ Save up to 50 percent on 14k solid gold rings with semi-precious gemstones. 800–223–7999.

Diamond Essence Company, 6 Saddle Rd., Cedar Knolls, NJ 07927: Free catalog ■ Men's and women's jewelry with simulated diamonds. 201–267–7370.

Diamonds by Rennie Ellen, 15 W. 47th St., Room 401, New York, NY 10036: Catalog $2 ■ Save up to 75 percent on custom-cut diamonds, rubies, sapphires, amethysts, emeralds, pearls, opals, tourmalines, and other gemstones, with optional gold or platinum settings. 212–869–5524.

Eagle Mountain Turquoise Company, 9430 E. Golf Links, Tucson, AZ 85730: Free information ■ Sterling silver and turquoise jewelry. 800–972–1140; 602–296–1090 (in AZ).

Ed's House of Gems, 7712 NE Sandy Blvd., Portland, OR 97213: Free information with long SASE ■ Clocks, clock-making parts and supplies, minerals, gemstones, lapidary equipment and tools, mountings, seashells, gemstone jewelry, and Native American relics. 503–284–8990.

Aaron Faber Gallery, 666 5th Ave., New York, NY 10019: Free catalog ■ Vintage watches and jewelry for men and women. 212–586–8411.

Grafstein & Company, 1851 E. 1st St., 7th Floor, Santa Ana, CA 92705: Free brochure ■ Save up to 60 percent on new and pre-owned Rolex, Cartier, Omega, Ebel, Choppard, Audemars, Patek-Philippe, and other watches. 714–835–6100.

Harmon's Agate & Silver Shop, Box 94, Crane, MT 59217: Catalog $3 ■ Montana moss agate, sapphires, and handmade silver and gold jewelry. 406–482–2534.

Gale Hayman Beverly Hills, 1888 Century Park East, Ste. 1010, Century City, CA 90067: Free catalog ■ Jewelry, accessories, and cosmetics. 800–FOR–GALE.

International Gem Corporation, 3601 Hempstead Tpk., Levittown, NY 11756: Catalog $2 ■ Save up to 40 percent on jewelry with semi-precious gemstones. 516–796–0200.

Ivory Broker, 817 W. 6th Ave., Anchorage, AK 99501: Free information ■ Handcrafted walrus ivory scrimshaw jewelry. 907–274–1664.

Jewelry by Avery, 5134 Chalk Point Rd., West River, MD 20778: Free information with long SASE ■ Handcrafted Zuni, Navajo, and Hopi turquoise jewelry, kachinas, Native American art, mineral specimens, and precious and semi-precious gemstones. 410–867–4752.

James Kaplan Jewelers, 40 Freeway Dr., Cranston, RI 02920: Free catalog ■ Contemporary and classic women's jewelry, gifts for infants and toddlers, Hummel figurines, silver serving pieces, flatware, crystal stemware, and china. 800–343–0712.

Kenya Division, Day & Frick, Inc., 1760 N. Howard St., Philadelphia, PA 19122: Free catalog ■ Men's and women's rings, bracelets, pendants, and other jewelry with Kenya simulated diamonds. 800–523–0158.

Lenox Jewelers, 2379 Black Rock Tpk., Fairfield, CT 06430: Free catalog ■ Watches; porcelain, china, and crystal; figurines; and silver, gold, and diamond jewelry. 800–243–4473; 800–327–9107 (in CT).

Lewis & Roberts, Scientia Park, P.O. Box 6527, Chelmsford, MA 01824: Free catalog

■ Men's and women's watches and costume and fashion jewelry. 800–933–5335.

Majestic Counterfeit Jewels, 9464 Brighton Way, Beverly Hills, CA 90210: Free catalog ■ Jewelry and watches with copies of diamonds and other gemstones set in 14k gold. 310–271–6663.

Carl Marcus & Company, 815 Connecticut Ave. NW, Washington, DC 20006: Free brochure ■ Save from 25 to 50 percent on Rolex, Patek, Phillippe, Audemars Piguet, Baume Mercier, Cartier, watches and jewelry. 800–654–7184; 202–331–0671 (in DC).

Markland's Creations, P.O. Box 1053, Aberdeen, MD 21001: Free information with long SASE ■ Custom wire-wrapped jewelry. 410–272–8260.

Mary Laura's, 701 Carlisle NE, Box 12615, Albuquerque, NM 87195: Catalog $2 ■ Native American jewelry from the Zuni Pueblo. 800–662–4848.

Melanie Collection, 12105 Bermuda NE, Albuquerque, NM 87111: Catalog $2 ■ Silver and bronze replicas of old, new, ancient, and ethnic artifacts. 505–298–7036.

Merlite Industries, Inc., 114 5th Ave., New York, NY 10011: Free catalog ■ Contemporary and classic jewelry for men and women. 212–924–6440.

Merrin, 724 5th Ave., New York, NY 10019: Free catalog ■ Necklaces, chokers, earrings, pins, bracelets, rings, brooches, pendants, and other gemstone and precious metal jewelry. 800–223–5752.

Mindscape Gallery, 1506 Sherman Ave., Evanston, IL 60201: Free information with long SASE ■ Contemporary American jewelry in precious and experimental metals, ceramics, and glass. 708–864–2660.

Museum of Jewelry, 3000 Larkin St., San Francisco, CA 94109: Free catalog ■ Handcrafted jewelry reproductions of historic originals. 800–258–0888.

Nature's Jewelry, 27 Industrial Ave., Chelmsford, MA 01824: Free catalog ■ Leaves, seashells, and other natural objects transformed into jewelry by preservation in precious metals. 800–933–3235.

Navajo Manufacturing Company, 5801 Logan St., Denver, CO 80216: Catalog $2 (refundable) ■ Turquoise jewelry, novelties, and sunglasses. 303–292–8090.

Nelson Rarities, Inc., One City Center, Portland, ME 04101: Free catalog ■ Jewelry previously owned by famous people. 207–775–3150.

Niger Bend, 5261 Irish Ridge Rd., Chittenago, NY 13037: Catalog $3 ■ African beads and jewelry. 800–333–2510.

Oriental Crest, Inc., 6161 Savoy Dr., Ste. 1137, Houston, TX 77036: Free information ■ Semi-precious gemstone jewelry, other jewelry, gemstones and findings, bead-stringing supplies, pendant carvings, and earring jackets. 713–780–2425.

Orr's Jewelers, 690 3rd St., Beaver, PA 15009: Free catalog ■ Fine jewelry and Rolex watches. 412–728–3800.

Pachamama, P.O. Box 7340, Albuquerque, NM 87194: Catalog $4 ■ Sterling silver and beaded pins, crosses, earrings, and other jewelry. 505–247–9669.

Palm Beach International, 6400 E. Rogers Cir., Boca Raton, FL 33499: Free catalog ■ Earrings and other jewelry. 800–633–9803.

Claudette Penot Collection, 145 W. 86th St., New York, NY 10024: Free catalog ■ Clothing, leather accessories, and jewelry. 212–580–2956.

Pizazz, Inc., 770 N. Halstead St., Ste. 107, Chicago, IL 60622: Brochure $3 with long SASE (refundable) ■ Earrings, necklaces, pins, beads, and other jewelry. 312–670–2627.

Plumtree & Smith, Ltd., 3958 Northlake Blvd., Palm Beach Gardens, FL 33140: Free information ■ Handcast antique sterling silver jewelry. 407–687–2457.

Priya Imports, Inc., 7001 Orchard Lake Rd., West Bloomfield, MI 48322: Catalog $1 ■ Silver beads from India. 313–851–3400.

Q-C Turquoise, 3340 E. Washington, Phoenix, AZ 85034: Catalog $2 (refundable) ■ Turquoise nugget jewelry, turquoise nuggets by the strand or pound, and turquoise cutting material and blocks. 602–267–1164.

Rock Art, P.O. Box 278, Yermo, CA 92398: Free information with long SASE ■ Faceted stones, cabochons, amber, necklaces, Gibson opal triplets, 14k and sterling silver rings, pendants, and earrings. 619–254–2022.

Laura Rose Designs, 1780 Rogers Ave., P.O. Box 2064, Glenview, IL 60025: Free

catalog ■ Handcrafted mother-of-pearl, abalone, shell, and crystal jewelry for women. 708–724–7132.

Ross-Simons Jewelers, 9 Ross Simons Dr;, Cranston, RI 02920: Catalog $1 ■ China, crystal, flatware, silver, watches, figurines, and diamond, gold, pearl, and gemstone jewelry. 800–556–7376.

Roussels, 107 Dow, Arlington, MA 02174: Catalog 50¢ ■ Close-out jewelry. 617–643–3388.

Script-Craft Jewelry, P.O. Box 2279, Santa Cruz, CA 95063: Free brochure ■ Handcrafted name pins in 12k rolled gold wire. 800–777–1169.

Second Look, A Silver Works, Inc., 100 Enterprise Pl., P.O. Box 7021, Dover, DE 19903: Free catalog ■ Silver and turquoise earrings, bracelets, necklaces, watch bands, and jewelry by Southwest artisans. 800–544–8200.

Silver Nugget, 416 Juan Tabu NE, Albuquerque, NM 87123: Catalog $2 ■ American Native jewelry. 505–293–6861.

Lucien L. Stern, Inc., 220 5th Ave., New York, NY 10001: Free catalog ■ Precious and semi-precious gemstones, carvings, cubic zirconia gemstones, rings, earrings, pendants, and other jewelry. 212–532–5760.

Tiffany & Company, Customer Service, 801 Jefferson Rd., Parsippany, NJ 07054: Catalog $1 ■ Fine jewelry, silver, china, crystal, watches and clocks, and gifts. 201–428–0570.

T.K.'s Corner, 2155 Verdugo Blvd., #601, Montrose, CA 91020: Catalog $5 ■ Reproduction Victorian necklaces, earrings, bracelets, pins, barrettes, and other items. 818–349–5618.

Tourneau, 488 Madison Ave., New York, NY 10022: Free information ■ Reconditioned and guaranteed pre-owned Rolex, Patek, Piaget, and other watches. 800–542–2389; 212–758–3671 (in NY).

Vanity Fair, S.A. Peck & Company, 55 E. Washington St., Chicago, IL 60602: Free catalog ■ Diamond jewelry. 312–977–0300.

Edith Weber & Company, Place des Antiquaries, 125 E. 57th St., New York, NY 10022: Free information ■ Antique jewelry. 212–688–4331.

Wellington Jewels, 4850 Connecticut Ave. NW, Ste, 103, Washington, DC 20008: Free brochure ■ Fashion jewelry made with synthetic diamonds. 800–424–0100.

Wildflower Collection, Ltd., 5223 S. Ironton Way, Englewood, CO 80111: Brochure $1 ■ Jewelry made from American wildflowers plated with silver or gold. 303–741–4737.

Helena Windsor, 37 11th Ave., Huntington Station., NY 11746: Free catalog ■ Watches and jewelry for men and women. 800–346–9666.

Windsor Collection, 6836 Engle Rd., P.O. Box 94549, Cleveland, OH 44101: Free catalog ■ Fashion watches and other jewelry for men and women. 216–826–1712.

JEWELRY MAKING

Abeada Corporation, 1205 N. Main St., Royal Oak, MI 48067: Free information ■ Semi-precious gemstone beads, freshwater and cultured pearls, glass beads, and gold and silver findings. 800–521–6326; 313–399–6642 (in MI).

Ackley's Rocks & Stamps, 3230 N. Stone Ave., Colorado Springs, CO 80907: Catalog $1 (refundable) ■ Lapidary and silversmithing supplies, and mountings and findings. 719–633–1153.

Aleta's Rock Shop, 1515 Plainfield NE, Grand Rapids, MI 49505: Catalog $1.50 (refundable) ■ Jewelry-making supplies, tumblers, lapidary machines and tools, findings, silicon carbide grits, diamond material, and rocks for cutting, tumbling, and polishing. 616–363–5394.

Allcraft Tool & Supply Company, 666 Pacific St., Brooklyn, NY 11207: Catalog $2.50 ■ Lapidary tools and supplies. 800–645–7124.

Allied Findings, Inc., 3336 Princeton NE, Albuquerque, NM 87107: Free information ■ Bolo tips, bolo backs, button covers, and findings. 505–883–1303.

Alpha Supply, Inc., 1225 Hollis St., Box 2133, Bremerton, WA 98310: Catalog $1 ■ Casting equipment and supplies, faceting equipment, jewelry-making tools, silver rings, wax models, lapidary equipment and supplies, mountings, and clock movements and parts. 206–377–5629.

Amazon Imports, P.O. Box 58, Williston Park, NY 11596: Free price list ■ Amethyst, aquamarine, emerald, garnet, kunzite, blue topaz, imperial topaz, and tourmalines from Brazil. 516–621–7481.

Ambassador, Palo Verde at 34th St., P.O. Box 28807, Tucson, AZ 85076: Free catalog ■ Semi-precious gemstone settings, cloisonne and turquoise settings, sterling silver, 14k gold, onyx, rubies, emeralds, pearls, jade, opals, and zirconia. 602–748–8600.

The Amber Company, 5643 Cahuenga Blvd., North Hollywood, CA 91601: Free price list ■ Amber, beads, fossils, ethnic jewelry, faceting and cabbing rough, lapidary supplies, and colored stones. 818–509–5730.

American Gem Supply, 407 W. Main St., New London, IA 52645: Free information ■ Automatic cabochon machines, vibratory tumblers, trim and slab saws, faceting machines and accessories, and other lapidary equipment. 319–367–2256.

APL Trader, P.O. Box 1900, New York, NY 10185: Free information ■ Precious and semi-precious gemstones, cabochons, carvings, and beads. 718–454–2954.

B. Rush Apple Company, 3855 W. Kennedy Blvd., Tampa, FL 33609: Free information ■ Jeweler's tools and supplies, casting equipment, and findings. 813–870–3180.

A.R.C. Traders, Inc., Box 3429, Scottsdale, AZ 85257: Free information ■ Findings, chains, and earrings, other jewelry, and sterling silver, gold-filled, and 14k gold beads. 800–528–2374; 602–945–0769 (in AZ).

Arizona Gems & Minerals, Inc., 6370 East Hwy. 69, Prescott Valley, AZ 86314: Catalog $4 ■ Chip beads, other beads and findings, silversmithing and lapidary tools, jewelry-making supplies, and mineral specimens. 602–772–6443.

Arrow Gems & Minerals, Inc., P.O. Box 9068, Phoenix, AZ 85068: Free catalog ■ Unusual beads, findings, arrowheads, embedded scorpions, minerals, and faceted stones. 602–997–6373.

Art to Wear, 4202 Water Oaks Ln., Tampa, FL 33624: Catalog $1 ■ Bead-stringing supplies, tools, and jewelry-making kits. 813–265–1681.

B & J Rock Shop, 14744 Manchester Rd., Ballwin, MO 63011: Catalog $3 ■ Jewelry-making supplies, beads and bead-stringing supplies, quartz clock movements, clock-

building kits, and quartz crystals, amethyst crystal clusters, Brazilian agate nodules, geodes, and other imported and domestic gemstones. 314–394–4567.

Baubanbea Enterprises, P.O. Box 1205, Smithtown, NY 11787: Catalog $1 ■ Rhinestones, sequins, beads, and gemstones. 516–724–4661.

Beada Beada, 4262 N. Woodward Ave., Royal Oak, MI 48073: Free catalog ■ Semi-precious beads, cabochons, cultured and freshwater pearls, and 14k gold, gold-filled, and sterling findings. 313–549–1005.

Bead It, P.O. Box 3505, Prescott, AZ 86302: Catalog $3 ■ Czechoslovakian beads, gemstones, charms, bone, findings, supplies, and books. 602–445–9234.

Beadworks, 139 Washington St., South Norwalk, CT 06854: Catalog $10 (refundable) ■ Glass, wood, metal, porcelain, ceramic, bone, plastic, mother-of-pearl, Swarovski crystal, and other beads. 203–852–9194.

Boone Trading Company, 562 Coyote Rd., Brinnon, WA 98320: Catalog $3 ■ Genuine ivory, scrimshaw tusks and netsuke, Oriental and Eskimo carvings, and fossilized walrus and mammoth ivory tusks and pieces. 206–796–4330.

Boston Findings & Jewelers Supply, 387 Washington St., Boston, MA 02108: Catalog $2 ■ Jewelry findings and supplies. 800–225–2436; 617–357–9599 (in MA).

Bourget Bros., 1636 11th St., Santa Monica, CA 90404: Catalog $5 ■ Jewelry-making tools and supplies, gemstones, cabochons, wax patterns, beads and bead-stringing supplies, sterling silver and gold-filled chains, and lapidary tools and equipment. 800–828–3024; 310–450–6556 (in CA).

Brahm Limited, P.O. Box 1, Lake Charles, LA 70602: Catalog $2 ■ Precious and semi-precious costume and designer beads, rhinestones, and accessories and findings.

Brazil Imports, 861 6th Ave., Ste. 316, San Diego, CA 92101: Free information ■ Rubies, sapphires, amethysts, emerald cabochons, calibrated emeralds, tanzite, tourmaline, topaz, quartz, and other gemstones from Brazil. 619–234–3675.

Brown Brothers Lapidary, 2248 S. 1st Ave., Safford, AZ 85546: Catalog $1 ■ Gemstones. 602–428–6433.

Bucks County Classic, 73 Coventry Lane, Langhorne, PA 19047: Price list $1 ■ Gemstone beads, handmade beads, fresh water pearls, Chinese cloisonne, Austrian crystal beads, stone accent beads, metal beads, cabochons, findings, and clasps. 800–942–GEMS.

C & R Enterprises, Inc., 4833 East Park, Springfield, MO 65809: Free catalog ■ Jewelry mountings in sterling silver and 14k gold, lapidary supplies, mineral specimens and cutting material, belt buckles, cut stones, and beads and beading supplies. 417–866–4843.

C & S Gem Shop, 510 Flambeau Ave., Fifield, WI 54524: Price list $1 (refundable) ■ Slabs by the inch or pound, cabbing and tumbling rough, calibrated cabs, jewelry-making kits, findings, and supplies.

Cargo Hold, Inc., P.O. Box 239, Charleston, SC 29402: Free information ■ Bead-stringing thread. 803–722–1377.

Charlie's Rock Shop, 620 J St., Penrose, CO 81240: Catalog $3 ■ Clocks, clock movements, and parts, beads, jewelry-making supplies, and faceted gemstones. 800–336–6923.

Janet Coles Beads, P.O. Box 786, Indianola, PA 15051: Catalog $5 (refundable) ■ Jewelry-making kits, beads and findings, and exclusive ready-to-wear items. 412–767–9404.

Comstock Creations, P.O. Box 2715, Durango, CO 81302: Free information ■ Cut and polished Brazilian agate and geodes. 800–342–2413; 303–247–3836 (in CO).

Contempo Lapidary, 12273 Foothill Blvd., Sylmar, CA 91342: Free information ■ Cabochon machines, rotary tumblers, trim and slab saws, diamond and carborundum grinders, sphere grinders, lapidary supplies, and beads and bead-stringing supplies. 800–356–2441; 818–899–1973 (in CA).

Cord Company, 5611 Virginia, Kansas City, MO 64110: Information and samples $3.50 ■ Silk cords and tassels. 816–333–6851.

Covington Engineering Corporation, 715 W. Colton Ave., P.O. Box 35, Redlands, CA 92373: Catalog $2 ■ Cabochon machines, rotary tumblers, trim and slab saws, faceting machines, flat-lap machines, and sphere grinders. 714–793–6636.

Craftstones, P.O. Box 847, Ramona, CA 92065: Catalog $5 (refundable) ■ Gemstones and exclusive gemstone jewelry. 619–789–1620.

Crystalite Corporation, 13449 Beach Ave., Marina del Ray, CA 90291: Free information ■ Cabochon machines, accessories, and other lapidary equipment. 310–821–6632.

Cupboard Distributing, Box 148, Urbana, OH 43078: Catalog $2 ■ Unfinished wood parts for jewelry-making, crafts, miniatures, toys, tole and decorative painting, and woodworking.

Diamond Pacific Tool Corporation, 25647 W. Main St., Barstow, CA 92311: Free information ■ Cabochon machines, trim and slab saws, jewelry-making supplies, and rockhounding equipment and supplies. 800–253–2954.

Discount Agate House, 3401 N. Dodge Blvd., Tucson, AZ 85716: Free price list on rough rock ■ Rocks and minerals from around the world, lapidary equipment and accessories, sterling silver and metalsmithing supplies, jewelry, and findings. 602–323–0781.

Dremel Manufacturing Company, 4915 21st St., Racine, WI 53406: Free information ■ Tools for grinding and sawing, drilling, carving, shaping, and polishing gemstones. 414–554–1390.

Ebersole Lapidary Supply, Inc., 11417 West Hwy. 54, Wichita, KS 67209: Catalog $2 ■ Tools, findings, mountings, cabochons and rocks, jewelry-making kits, petrified wood, clocks, clock-making parts and accessories, and beads and bead-stringing supplies. 316–722–4771.

Ed's House of Gems, 7712 NE Sandy Blvd., Portland, OR 97213: Free information with long SASE ■ Clocks, clock-making parts and supplies, crystals, minerals, gemstones, lapidary equipment and tools, mountings, seashells, gemstone jewelry, and American Native artifacts. 503–284–8990.

Eloxite Corporation, 806 10th St., Wheatland, WY 82201: Catalog 75¢ ■ Cut gemstones, beads, cabochons, belt buckles,

mountings, tools, and lapidary and clock-making supplies. 307–322–3050.

Ennis Rock House, P.O. Box 293, Ennis, MT 59729: Free price list ■ Montana sapphires and agates, fresh water pearls, rare minerals, and fire agate. 406–682–4689.

Firemountain Gems, 28195 Redwood Hwy., Cave Junction, OR 97523: Catalog $3 ■ Beads, gems, and jewelry-making supplies and tools. 800–423–2319; 503–592–2222 (in OR).

F.J.S. Company, P.O. Box 2218, Fair Oaks, CA 95628: Free catalog ■ Jewelry findings. 916–635–8873.

Florida Jewelry Crafts, Inc., Box 2620, Sarasota, FL 34230: Catalog $2 ■ Jewelry findings, supplies, and tools.

Foredom Electric Company, Rt. 6, P.O. Box 262, Bethel, CT 06801: Free information ■ Tools for grinding and sawing, drilling, carving, shaping, and polishing gemstones. 203–792–8622.

G & G's Miracle House, 5621 W. Hemlock St., P.O. Box 23234, Milwaukee, WI 53223: Free catalog ■ Brushes, buffs, metals, rouges, findings, waxes, frames, burs, and other accessories and supplies. 800–558–5513; 800–242–3403 (in WI).

GBS Distributors, P.O. Box 145, Liverpool, TX 77577: Free catalog ■ Mountings and faceted opals, blue topaz, aquamarines, blue sapphires, rubies, and rhodolite. 713–393–2842.

Gem Center U.S.A., Inc., 4100 Alameda Ave., El Paso, TX 79905: Free price list ■ Geodes and nodules. 915–533–7153.

Gem-Fare, P.O. Box 213, Pittstown, NJ 08867: Price list 50¢ ■ Rare and unusual gemstones and crystals. 908–806–3339.

Gem-Finders, P.O. Box 7068, South Dartmouth, MA 02748: Price list $1 (refundable) ■ Sapphires, zircons, and spinels from Sri Lanka, and other gemstones. 508–990–3470.

Gem-O-Rama, Inc., 150 Recreation Park Dr., Hingham, MA 02043: Free catalog ■ Gemstones, beading supplies, and 14k gold, gold-filled, and sterling silver beads. 617–749–8250.

Gemstone Equipment Manufacturing Company, 750 Easy St., Simi Valley, CA 93065: Free information ■ Vibratory tumblers, trim and slab saws, buffers, cabbing machines, grozers and sculpture routers, and accessories. 805–527–6990.

General Bead, 637 Minna St., San Francisco, CA 94103: Free information ■ Japanese seed beads, fashion accessory components, charms, and items by Swarovski of Austria. 415–621–8187.

Gilman's Lapidary Supply, P.O. Box 103, Hellertown, PA 18055: Free information ■ Lapidary supplies, findings and mountings, silver and gold metal crafting supplies, genuine and synthetic gemstones, tumblers, and polishing equipment. 215–838–8767.

Goodnow's, 3415 S. Hayden St., Amarillo, TX 79109: Free list with long SASE ■ Gem roughs for faceting, cabbing, and tumbling. 806–352–0725.

Graves Company, 1800 Andrews Ave., Pompano Beach, FL 33069: Free information ■ Cabochon machines, rotary tumblers, vibratory tumblers, trim and slab saws, faceting machines, and accessories. 800–327–9103.

Grieger's, P.O. Box 93070, Pasadena, CA 91109: Free catalog ■ Gems, lapidary equipment, jewelry-making supplies, gemstones, mountings, and findings. 800–423–4181; 800–362–7708 (in CA).

Gryphon Corporation, 101 E. Santa Anita Ave., Burbank, CA 91502: Free information ■ Cabochon machines, diamond gem trim and slab saws, accessories, and a 10–in–1 multipurpose lapidary workshop tool. 818–845–7807.

Hardies, P.O. Box 1920, Quartzsite, AZ 85346: Free information ■ Beads, findings, buckles, bolas, Native American jewelry, gems, rocks, and books. 800–962–2775.

Harmon's Agate & Silver Shop, Box 94, Crane, MT 59217: Catalog $3 ■ Montana moss agate, sapphires, and handmade silver and gold jewelry. 406–482–2534.

Hong Kong Lapidary Supplies, 2801 University Dr., Coral Springs, FL 33065: Catalog $3 ■ Semi-precious gemstones and beads. 305–755–8777.

House of Gems, 544 Greenbrae Dr., Sparks, NE 89431: Free information ■ Findings and jewelry-making and lapidary supplies and equipment. 702–359–6448.

House of Onyx, 120 N. Main St., Greenville, KY 42345: Free catalog ■ Jewelry and gemstones, rare gemstones, and jewelry-making supplies. 800–626–8352; 800–992–3260 (in KY).

Indian Jewelers Supply Company, P.O. Box 1774, Gallup, NM 87305: Set of 4 catalogs $5 ■ Precious and base metals; findings in precious and base metals; metalsmithing and lapidary tools and supplies; and semi-precious gemstones, shells, and coral. 505–722–4451.

International Gem Merchants, Inc., 4168 Oxford Ave., Jacksonville, FL 32210: Free information ■ Gemstones, pearls, and synthetic gemstones. 800–633–3653; 904–388–5130 (in FL).

International Import Company, 3340 Peachtree Rd., Atlanta, GA 30326: Free catalog ■ Cut and uncut precious and semi-precious gemstones. 404–266–0255.

Jackson Hole Lapidary, Box 2704, Jackson, WY 83001: Free catalog ■ Beads and bead-stringing supplies, gem trees and kits, and lapidary supplies. 307–733–7672.

Jarvi Tool Company, 1200 N. Jefferson, Anaheim, CA 92807: Free information ■ Lapidary equipment, faceting machines, and accessories. 714–666–2606.

Jewelry Supplies 4 Less, 13001 Las Vegas Blvd. South, Las Vegas, NV 89124: Catalog $4 ■ Jewelry-making supplies.

Kerr Division of Sybron Corporation, 28200 Wick Rd., P.O. Box 455, Romulus, MI 48174: Catalog $2 ■ Lapidary equipment, tools, accessories, and injection wax and molding rubber for making wax patterns. 313–946–7800.

Khalila's House of Beads & Crafts, 114 S. 9th St., Tacoma, WA 98402: Catalog $1.50 ■ Glass beads, findings, shells, brooches, chains, bone, gems, and jewelry-making kits.

Kingsley North, Inc., P.O. Box 216, Norway, MI 49870: Free catalog ■ Jewelry-making tools and supplies, casting equipment, tumblers, slab and trim saws, glass polishing equipment, and rough, cut, and calibrated opals. 800–338–9280.

Krona Gem Merchants, Box 9968, Colorado Springs, CO 80932: Free list ■ Faceted and rare gemstones. 719–597–8779.

Laney Company, 6449 S. 209 East Ave., Broken Arrow, OK 74014: Free brochure ■ German silver jewelry-making supplies. 918–355–1955.

Lapcraft Company, Inc., 195 W. Olentangy St., Powell, OH 43065: Free information ■ Cabochon machines, trim and slab saws, and accessories. 614–764–8993.

Lentz Lapidary, Inc., 11740 S. Oliver, Rt. 2, Box 135, Mulvane, KS 67110: Catalog $2 ■ Buckles, jewelry, mountings, clocks and motors, bookends, and desk sets; rough rock specimens and cabochons; and rockhounding and lapidary equipment. 316–777–1372.

Victor H. Levy, Inc., 1355 S. Flower St., Los Angeles, CA 90015: Catalog $5 ■ Findings, rhinestones, gemstones, braids, and glitter for jewelry-making; and doll-making supplies and accessories. 800–421–8021; 213–749–8247 (in CA).

Lochs, 312 Main St., Emmaus, PA 18049: Catalog $3 ■ Facet rough, faceted gems, 14k gold findings, biron-created emeralds, and polished gemstones. 215–967–3479.

Lonnie's, Inc., 7153 E. Apache Trail, Mesa, AZ 85207: Free information ■ Tools, equipment, and supplies for jewelers, casters, silversmiths, and lapidarists. 602–832–2641.

Lortone, Inc., 2856 NW Market St., Seattle, WA 98107: Free information with long SASE ■ Cabochon machines, rotary tumblers, trim and slab saws, flat-lap machines, and accessories. 206–789–3100.

Lou-Bon Gems & Rocks, Lake Barcroft Plaza, 6341 Columbia Pike, Bailey's Crossroads, VA 22041: Free information ■ Carvings, beads, mineral specimens, fossils, shells, and lapidary and jeweler's equipment and supplies. 703–256–1084.

Maxant Industries, Inc., P.O. Box 454, Ayer, MA 01432: Catalog $1 ■ Cabochon machines, machines, trim and slab saws, accessories, and other lapidary equipment. 508–772–0576.

MDR Manufacturing Company, Box 363, Tujunga, CA 91042: Free price list ■ Faceting machines and accessories. 818–353–6060.

Miami Cork & Supply, 10160 NW 47th St., Sunrise, FL 33351: Free catalog ■ Jewelry-making supplies and equipment. 305–572–8455.

Mimports, 590 Silverado Dr., Lafayette, CA 94549: Free list ■ Synthetic gemstones. 510–284–4196.

Minnesota Lapidary Supply Corporation, 2825 Dupont Ave. South, Minneapolis, MN

55408: Free catalog ■ Lapidary equipment, supplies, and accessories. 612–872–7211.

Mohave Industries, Inc., 2365 Northern Ave., Kingman, AZ 86401: Catalog $1 ■ Automatic cabochon machines, trim and slab saws, and other lapidary equipment and accessories. 602–757–2480.

Neycraft, 13553 Calimesa Blvd., Yucaipa, CA 92399: Free brochure ■ Furnaces for lost wax castings. 714–795–2461.

M. Nowotny & Company, 8823 Callaghan Rd., San Antonio, TX 78230: Free information ■ Gemstones and fossils from worldwide sources; jewelry; pewter figurines; and key chains, scarabs, obsidian eggs, and peacock feathers. 800–950–8276; 512–342–2512 (in TX).

H. Obodda Mineral Specimens, P.O. Box 51, Short Hills, NJ 07078: Free list ■ Rare and semi-precious gemstones. 201–467–0212.

Optional Extras, 150A Church St., Burlington, VT 05401: Catalog $1.50 ■ Jewelry findings and supplies. 802–658–0013.

Oriental Crest, Inc., 6161 Savoy Dr., Ste. 1137, Houston, TX 77036: Free information ■ Semi-precious gemstone jewelry, gemstones and findings, bead-stringing supplies, pendant carvings, earring jackets, and other jewelry. 713–780–2425.

Oso Famoso, Box 654, Ben Lomond, CA 95005: Price list with long SASE and $1 ■ Handmade fossilized ivory beads, scrimshaw, and bulk material. 408–336–2343.

Paradise Diamond Tools, 6267 Becker Way, Paradise, CA 95969: Free information ■ Diamond carving points and drills. 916–877–2597.

Theodore Pehnec, 12650 Hoover St., Garden Grove, CA 92641: Free catalog ■ Pearl, coral, ivory, and gemstone beads. 714–897–2277.

Pioneer Gem Corporation, P.O. Box 1513, Auburn, WA 98071: Free list ■ Cut and polished gemstones. 206–833–2760.

Prospectors Pouch, Inc., P.O. Box 112, Kennesaw, GA 30144: Catalog $2 ■ Rocks and gemstones and jewelry-making supplies. 404–427–6481.

Q-C Turquoise, 3340 E. Washington, Phoenix, AZ 85034: Catalog $2 (refundable) ■ Turquoise nugget jewelry, turquoise nug-

gets by the strand or pound, and turquoise cuttings and blocks. 602–267–1164.

Rainbow's End, P.O. Box 723, Golden, CO 80402: Free information ■ Faceting rough blue topaz, aquamarine, green Tsavorite garnet, tourmaline, orange/pink Malaya garnet, purple Siberian garnet, red/rose rhodolite garnet gems, and polished faceted gemstones. 303–233–6877.

Raytech Industries, 147 West St., Rt. 147, Middlefield, CT 06455: Free information ■ Cabochon machines, trim and slab saws, faceting machines, and accessories. 203–349–3421.

Richardson's Recreational Ranch, Ltd., Gateway Route Box 440, Madras, OR 97741: Free information ■ Rocks and gemstones from worldwide locations, lapidary equipment and supplies, clocks, and clock movements and parts. 503–475–2680.

Rio Grande, 6901 Washington NE, Albuquerque, NM 87109: Free information ■ Jewelry findings and supplies. 800–545–6566.

Rock Art, P.O. Box 278, Yermo, CA 92398: Free information with long SASE ■ Faceted stones, cabochons, amber, necklaces, Gibson opal triplets, and 14k and sterling silver rings, pendants, and earrings. 619–254–2022.

Rock Shop, 5511 Todville Rd., Box 444, Seabrook, TX 77586: Price list $3 ■ Faceted gemstones, cabochons, mineral specimens, geodes, artifacts, and fossils. 713–474–2488.

Running T Trading Company, Hope-Franklin, Inc., 1201 Iron Springs Rd., Ste. 11, Prescott, AZ 86301: Free catalog ■ Prenotched mounts, beads, diamonds, gemstones, chains, safety clasps, and other jewelry-making supplies. 602–778–4274.

Sempert's Jewelry Supplies, P.O. Box 5066, Homosassa Springs, FL 32647: Wire catalog $2; tool catalog $5 ■ Jewelry-making supplies, tools, sterling silver wire and findings, and mountings in sterling silver, gold-filled, and 14k. 904–628–7307.

SESCO, P.O. Box 21406, Reno, NV 89515: Free catalog ■ Findings, gemstones, fossils, and novelties. 702–356–9200.

Fook Shuen Trading Company, Inc., 124 E. 27th St., New York, NY 10016: Free information with long SASE ■ Ivory, jade carvings, netsuke, and jewelry. 212–684–1795.

South Pacific Wholesale Company, 28 Main St., Montpelier, VT 05602: Free price list ■ Beads, semi-precious gemstone settings, findings, gold and silver bracelets, necklaces, and earrings. 802–223–1354.

Lucien L. Stern, Inc., 220 5th Ave., New York, NY 10001: Free catalog ■ Precious and semi-precious gemstones, carvings, cubic zirconia gemstones, rings, earrings, pendants, and other jewelry. 212–532–5760.

Stone Age Industries, Inc., P.O. Box 383, Powell, WY 82435: Catalog $1 ■ Rough gemstones, slabs, cutting and polishing equipment, and lapidary supplies.

Swest, Inc., P.O. Box 540938, Dallas, TX 75354: Free information ■ Jeweler's tools, supplies, equipment, wax patterns, findings, and gemstones. 214–350–4011.

Tagit, P.O. Box 1534, San Juan Capistrano, CA 92675: Free information ■ Automatic cabochon machines, vibratory tumblers, trim and slab saws, and accessories. 310–949–8380.

Tatum Minerals, 3901 Pershing, El Paso, TX 79903: Free catalog ■ Crystals, tourmaline, agates, turquoise, amethyst, citrine, other gemstones, and electroformed jewelry. 915–565–3573.

Terrific Little Crafts, 4140 Oceanside Blvd., Oceanside, CA 92056: Catalog $1 ■ Jewelry findings, quilling supplies, paper clay, and other craft supplies.

Tierracast, 3177 Guerneville Rd., Santa Rosa, CA 95401: Free catalog ■ Jewelry-making findings. 800–222–9939; 707–545–5787 (in CA).

Transworld Trading, 55 W. 47th St., New York, NY 10036: Free price list with long SASE ■ Natural and synthetic precious and semi-precious gemstones, beads, and uncut, cut, faceted, and polished cabochons. 212–302–8487.

Tripp's Manufacturing, P.O. Box 1369, Socorro, NM 87801: Free information ■ Prenotched mounts. 800–545–7962; 1–835–2461 (in NM).

TSI, Inc., P.O. Box 9266, Seattle, WA 98109: Free catalog ■ Jewelry-making tools and supplies. 800–426–9984.

Ultra Tec, 1025 E. Chestnut, Santa Ana, CA 92701: Free information ■ Faceting machines and other lapidary equipment. 714–542–0608.

Wax Factor, 509 Monroe, Oregon City, OR 97045: Catalog $4 ■ Wax patterns and molds for rings, charms, and bracelets. 503–656–0709.

Weidinger's, 19509 Kedzie Ave., Flossmoor, IL 60422: Catalog $2 ■ Mountings, findings, and cut stones. 708–798–6336.

JOKES & NOVELTIES

Funny Side Up, 425 Stump Rd., North Whales, PA 19454: Free catalog ■ Novelty and joke merchandise for birthdays, anniversaries, retirement parties, and other occasions. 215–361–5142.

Global SHAKEUP, 2265 Westwood Blvd., Ste. 618, Los Angeles, CA 90064: Free catalog ■ Finely detailed, slowly settling imported, comical, custom photo, and miscellaneous "snow" domes.

Johnson-Smith Lighter Side Company, 4514 19th St. Court East, P.O. Box 25600, Bradenton, FL 34206: Free catalog ■ Jokes and novelties, tricks, science equipment, sports equipment, hobby supplies, and other entertaining items. 813–747–2356.

Klutz Press, 2121 Staunton Ct., Palo Alto, CA 94306: Free catalog ■ Novelty and fun merchandise, juggling equipment and supplies, and books. 415–857–0888.

Think Big, 390 W. Broadway, New York, NY 10012: Free catalog ■ Unusual and oversized gags, gift items, and home furnishings. 800–221–7019; 212–925–7300 (in NY).

JUGGLING

Abracadabra Magic Shop, P.O. Box 714, Middlesex, NJ 08846: Catalog $3.95 ■ Magician's supplies, close-up and stage magic; juggling equipment; balloons and clown accessories; and costumes, and theatrical make-up. 908–805–0200.

Books by Mail, 1750 California Ave., Ste. 114, Corona, CA 92703: Free book list with two 1st class stamps ■ Books on juggling and clowning. 909–273–0900.

California Juggling Institute, P.O. Box 15651, Westminster, CA 92683: Free catalog with long SASE ■ Jugglebug and Brian Dube juggling equipment and Chasley juggling toys. 714–541–5845.

Chazpro Magic Company, 603 E. 13th, Eugene, OR 97401: Catalog $3 (refundable)

■ Juggling and clown accessories, books, and jokes and novelties. 503–345–0032.

Brian Dube, Inc., 520 Broadway, New York, NY 10012: Free catalog ■ Juggling equipment, accessories, and books. 212–941–0060.

The Entertainers Supermarket, 21 Carol Pl., Staten Island, NY 10303: Free brochure ■ Supplies and props for jugglers, clowns, magicians, balloon sculpturists, face painters, stilt wakers, and other entertainers. 718–494–6232.

Flosso-Hornmann Magic Company, 45 W. 34th St., Room 607, New York, NY 10001: Free information ■ Magic equipment, juggling supplies, tarot cards, crystal balls, and accessories. 212–279–6079.

Ken's Illusionarium, 3288 Main St., Vancouver, British Colombia, Canada V5V 3M5: Free newsletter ■ Books, equipment, and supplies for magicians, mentalists, clowns, jugglers, ventriloquists, and puppeteers. 604–875–9712.

Klutz Press, 2121 Staunton Ct., Palo Alto, CA 94306: Free catalog ■ Novelty and fun merchandise, juggling equipment and supplies, and books. 415–857–0888.

Mecca Magic, Inc., 49 Dodd St., Bloomfield, NJ 07003: Free brochure ■ Juggling supplies, theatrical make-up, clown equipment, balloons, magic, costumes and wigs, puppets, ventriloquism accessories, and custom props. 201–429–7597.

Under the Big Top, P.O. Box 807, Placentia, CA 92670: Catalog $4 ■ Juggling supplies, clown props, costumes, make-up, balloon accessories and supplies, and party supplies. 714–579–1144.

JUKEBOXES

Always Jukin', 221 Yesler Way, Seattle, WA 98104: Catalog $2 ■ Jukebox service manuals and books about jukeboxes and old phonographs and radios. 206–233–9460.

The Antique Emporium, 1119 Industrial, San Carlos, CA 94070: Free information ■ Jukeboxes, slot machines, pinball machines, candy/gumball machines, cash registers, and other coin-operated machines. 510–886–1727.

Classic Coin-Ops, 7038 Hoke Rd., Clayton, OH 45315: Free information with long

SASE ■ Jukeboxes, slot machines, and coke machines. 513–833–5143.

Illinois Antique Slot Machine Company, P.O. Box 542, Westmont, IL 60559: Free information ■ Antique Wurlitzer jukeboxes, nickelodeons, music boxes, slot machines, and other coin-operated machines. 708–985–2742.

Jukebox Classics & Vintage Slot Machines, Inc., 6742 5th Ave., Brooklyn, NY 11220: Free information ■ Antique jukeboxes and coin-operated machines. 718–833–8455.

Jukebox Junction, P.O. Box 1081, Des Moines, IA 50311: Catalog $2.50 ■ Antique jukeboxes. 515–981–4019.

Jukebox Memories, 2518 E. Huntington Dr., Duarte, CA 91010: Free information ■ Jukebox restoration parts. 818–359–8700.

Kremer Kraft, 301 SW 16th St., Fort Lauderdale, FL 33315: Free information ■ Antique jukeboxes. 305–524–5652.

Marvelous Music Machines, 203 Central St., Hudson, NH 03051: Free information with long SASE ■ Vintage jukeboxes, slot machines, pinball machines, and other coin-operated machines. 603–880–1882.

1940 Jukebox & Record Company, 8919 N. Washington St., Thornton, CO 80229: Free information ■ Vintage jukeboxes. 303–288–4230.

Nostalgic Music Company, 58 Union Ave., New Providence, NJ 07974: Free information ■ Restored jukeboxes, from the 1940s and 1950s. 908–464–5538.

Orange Trading Company, 57 S. Main St., Orange, MA 01364: Free list with long SASE ■ Antique coin-operated jukeboxes, pinball and coke machines, and other machines. 508–544–6683.

Ted Salveson, P.O. Box 602, Huron, SD 57350: Free information ■ Manuals for most jukeboxes, slot machines, and other equipment. 605–352–3870.

KALEIDOSCOPES

Ardell Kaleidoscopes, 3672 Douglas Rd., Miami, FL 33133: Free brochure with long SASE ■ Stained glass kaleidoscopes.

Marilyn Endres Kaleidoscopes, 351 Cowpoke Canyon, Driftwood, TX 78619: Free information ■ Handcrafted, one-of-a-kind gemscopes, teleidoscopes, and spinner kaleidoscopes. 512–847–9829.

Gemini Kaleidoscopes, 203 Lindsay Rd., Zelienople, PA 16063: Free information ■ Handcrafted kaleidoscopes. 412–452–8700.

Kaleidoscope Company, 2150 Franklin St., Oakland, CA 94612: Free information ■ Kaleidoscopes. 800–543–6277; 800–368–7600 (in CA).

Light Opera Gallery, Ghirardelli Square, #102, San Francisco, CA 94109: Free brochure ■ Kaleidoscopes. 415–775–7665.

Petri's, 731 Bridgeway, Sausalito, CA 94965: Catalog $2 ■ Art glass, 14k gold jewelry, kaleidoscopes, and Lladro, Chilmark, and Swarovski items. 415–332–6477.

Sir David's Reflections, 966 Calhoun Rd., Cleveland, OH 44145: Free information with long SASE ■ Kaleidoscopes. 216–899–1020.

KITCHEN UTENSILS & COOKWARE

Bay City Sales, 1040 W. Mason St., P.O. Box 11706, Green Bay, WI 54307: Free information ■ Cookware and utensils. 414–494–7280.

Brookstone Company, 5 Vose Farm Rd., P.O. Box 5, Peterborough, NH 03458: Free catalog ■ Homewares and kitchen accessories. 800–846–3000.

Chattanooga Cookery, 725 E. 11th St., Chattanooga, TN 37403: Free catalog ■ Aluminum and stainless cookware and custom pot and glass racks in oak. 615–266–6112.

The Chef's Catalog, 3215 Commercial Ave., Northbrook, IL 60062: Catalog $3 ■ Professional restaurant equipment for home chefs. 800–934–5600.

Colonial Garden Kitchens, P.O. Box 66, Hanover, PA 17333: Catalog $2 ■ Cookware and utensils. 717–633–3330.

Commercial Culinary, P.O. Box 30010, Alexandria, VA 22310: Free catalog ■ Save from 20 to 40 percent on professional cookware, bakeware, and appliances. 800–999–4949.

A Cook's Wares, 3270 37th St., Beaver Falls, PA 15010: Catalog $1.50 ■ Save from 20 to 40 percent on cookware, cutlery, bakeware, porcelain, French copper pans,

and Robot-Coupe food processors and accessories. 412–846–9490.

Corning Incorporated, P.O. Box D, Waynesboro, VA 22980: Free catalog ■ Lightweight dinnerware and cookware. 800–872–7554.

Country Manor, Mail Order Department, Rt. 211, P.O. Box 520, Sperryville, VA 22740: Catalog $2 ■ Kitchen utensils and accessories, rugs, carpets, and decor accessories. 800–344–8354.

Crate & Barrel, P.O. Box 9059, Wheeling, IL 60090: Free catalog ■ Gourmet cooking equipment, utensils, and appliances. 800–323–5461.

Cuisinarts Cookware, 150 Milford Rd., East Windsor, NJ 08520: Free information ■ Cookware and utensils. 800–726–0190.

Cutco Cutlery, 1116 E. State St., P.O. Box 810, Olean, NY 14760: Catalog $1 ■ Replacement cutlery. 800–828–0448.

The Faith Mountain Company, P.O. Box 199, Sperryville, VA 22740: Catalog 50¢ ■ Kitchen utensils and accessories, country-style gifts, folk art reproductions, toys and dolls, handmade Appalachian baskets, and Christmas decorations. 800–822–6238.

Hoffritz, 515 W. 24th St., New York, NY 10011: Catalog $1 ■ Optics, knives and scissors, kitchen aids, clocks, yogurt makers, and other gifts. 212–924–7300.

Kitchen Bazaar, 4455 Connecticut Ave. NW, Washington, DC 20008: Free catalog ■ Cookware and accessories. 202–363–4625.

Lehman Hardware & Appliances, Inc., Box 41, Kidron, OH 44636: Catalog $2 ■ Kitchen accessories and housewares, stoves for heating and cooking, farming and homesteading items, nonelectric appliances, and woodworking and logsmithing tools. 216–857–5441.

Maid of Scandinavia, 3244 Raleigh Ave., Minneapolis, MN 55416: Catalog $2 ■ Utensils and kitchen tools, cake molds and cookie cutters, candy-making molds, and ingredients. 800–328–6722; 800–851–1121 (in MN).

Microwave Times, P.O. Box 1271, Burnsville, MN 55337: Free catalog ■ Microwave cookware, accessories, and cookbooks. 800–328–2846; 612–890–6655 (in MN).

National Presto Industries, Inc., Eau Claire, WI 54703: Free information ■ Cookware and accessories. 715–839–2209.

Pepperidge Farm, P.O. Box 917, Clinton, CT 06413: Free catalog ■ Specialty cookware, microwave cookware, utensils, tools, kitchen gadgets, glassware, silverware, cookbooks, and gourmet foods. 800–243–9314.

S.E. Rykoff & Company, 3501 Taylor Dr., Ukiah, CA 95482: Free catalog ■ Professional gourmet cookware and foods for home chefs. 800–333–1448.

T-Fal Corporation, 208 Passaic Ave., Fairfield, NJ 07004: Free information ■ Cookware and utensils. 201–575–1060.

Tsang & Ma Wokery, P.O. Box 5644, Redwood City, CA 94063: Free catalog ■ Woks and covers, tempura racks, cleavers, steamers, cooking tools, and Oriental foods and supplies. 415–595–2270.

Vermont Country Store, Mail Order Office, P.O. Box 3000, Manchester Center, VT 05255: Free catalog ■ Utensils, equipment, and accessories. 802–362–2400.

Lillian Vernon, Virginia Beach, VA 23479: Free catalog ■ Kitchen equipment and utensils. 804–430–1500.

Williams-Sonoma, Mail Order Department, P.O. Box 7456, San Francisco, CA 94120: Free catalog ■ Specialty cookware for home gourmet chefs, serving pieces, household accessories, books, and gourmet foods. 800–541–1262.

Wilton Enterprise, Inc., 2240 W. 75th St., Woodridge, IL 60517: Catalog $6 ■ Equipment and supplies for making cookies, cakes, and candy. 708–963–7100.

Winterthur Museum & Gardens, Catalog Division, 100 Enterprise Pl., Dover, DE 19901: Catalog $2 ■ Cookware and accessories. 800–767–0500.

Wooden Spoon, Rt. 145, Heritage Park, P.O. Box 931, Clinton, CT 06413: Free catalog ■ Cooking utensils, kitchen tools, and gifts. 203–664–0303.

Zabar's & Company, 2245 Broadway, New York, NY 10024: Free catalog ■ Cookware, food processors, microwave ovens, kitchen tools, coffee makers, and gourmet foods. 800–221–3347; 212–787–2000 (in NY).

KITES

Action Kites, 4202 Sorrento Valley Blvd., San Diego, CA 92121: Free information ■ Kites and accessories. 619–452–6151.

Adventures Kites, 4 Hemlock Trail, Sandy Hook, CT 06482: Free catalog ■ Kites and accessories. 203–426–9786.

Altitude Products, 12945 Duncan Ln., Rockton, IL 61072: Free information with long SASE ■ Ultra-fast line winders that work with all grips and straps.

Big City Kite Company, 1201 Lexington Ave., New York, NY 10028: Catalog $2 (refundable) ■ Kites and accessories. 212–472–2623.

Catch the Wind, 266 SE Hwy. 101, Lincoln City, OR 97367: Free information ■ Kites and accessories. 503–994–9500.

Chinook Winds, P.O. Box 8011, Fort Collins, CO 80526: Free information ■ Windsocks and wind novelties. 303–223–3584.

Coast Kites, Inc., 15953 Minnesota Ave., Paramount, CA 90723: Free information ■ Kites, parts, and accessories. 800–73–KITES.

Colores International, Inc., 1405 132nd Ave. NE, Ste. 2, Bellevue, WA 98005: Free information ■ Standard and fancy kites. 206–454–6323.

Color the Sky, 221 Yoho Dr., Anoka, MN 55303: Free catalog ■ Stunt kites, parafoils, deltas, celled boxes, and other designs. 612–427–9359.

Crowell's Sail Loft., Rt.4, Box 583, Boone, NC 28607: Free information ■ High-performance, aerodynamically designed kites. 704–264–2084.

The Crystal Kite Company, 1320 Lakeview Dr., La Habra, CA 90631: Free information ■ Competition stunt kites. 714–870–4546.

Deerfield Valley Woodworking, P.O. Box 274, Rowe, MA 01367: Free information ■ Kite reels. 413–339–4446.

Dr. Kites Emergency Kite Line, 3502 S. Virginia, #113, Reno, NV 89509: Free catalog ■ Kites and kite-building supplies. 800–622–5483.

Dyna-Kite Corporation, P.O. Box 24, Three Rivers, MA 01080: Free information ■ Kites and accessories. 413–283–2555.

Eurokites, Ltd., P.O. Box 34, Pacific Grove, CA 93950: Catalog $1 ■ Kites and accessories. 408–647–8363.

Fly-Away Kites, 204 Hwy. 71, Brielle, NJ 08730: Free information ■ Kites, accessories, and windsocks. 908–223–2320.

Fly by Night Kite Company, 18 Middle St., Plymouth, MA 02360: Free catalog ■ Kites and accessories. 508–746–0555.

Flying Colors, 815 Spruce St., Boulder, CO 80302: Catalog $1 ■ Kites and banners.

Gasworks Park Kite Shop, 333 Wallingford, Seattle, WA 98103: Free catalog ■ Kites and kite-making supplies. 206–633–4780.

Great Winds Kites, 402 Occidental Ave. South, Seattle, WA 98104: Free catalog ■ Kites and accessories. 206–624–6886.

Hang-Em High Fabrics, 1420 Yale Ave., Richmond, VA 23224: Free information ■ Kite-making supplies. 804–233–6155.

Hearth Song, P.O. Box B, Sebastopol, CA 95473: Free catalog ■ Children's kites, books, dollhouse miniatures, dolls, and art supplies. 800–533–4397.

Hi Fli Kites, Ltd., 12101 E. Iliff, Aurora, CO 80014: Portfolio $5 (refundable) ■ Kites and accessories. 303–755–6105.

High Fly Kite Company, 30 West End Ave., Haddonfield, NJ 08033: Free information ■ Fabric kites, stunt kites, flying lines, reels and handles, and ripstop fabric. 609–429–6260.

Hyperkites, 720–C Gateway Center Dr., San Diego, CA 92102: Free catalog ■ High-performance kites and accessories. 619–262–4712.

Bob Ingraham Kites, 315 N. Bayard St., Silver CIty, NM 88061: Free information ■ Easy-to-assemble and easy-to-fly delta kites. 505–538–9083.

International Connections, 835 Weldon Rd., Santa Barbara, CA 93109: Free information ■ Kites, banners, windsocks, and accessories. 805–963–2964.

Into the Wind/Kites, 1408 Pearl St., Boulder, CO 80302: Catalog $1 ■ Kites and accessories. 800–541–0314.

Keely's Kites, 240 Commercial St., Provincetown, MA 02657: Free catalog ■ Kites, accessories, and wind chimes. 310–396–KITE.

KiteLines, P.O. Box 466, Randallstown, MD 21133: Free catalog ■ Books about kites. 410–922–1212.

The Kite Loft, P.O. Box 551, Ocean City, MD 21842: Free catalog ■ Kites and accessories. 800–345–KITE.

Kitemakers, Mail Order Division, 590 Chestnut St., San Francisco, CA 94133: Free brochure ■ Windsocks and accessories, and Chinese, nylon dragon, Mylar, diamond, delta, and stunt kites. 510–652–1661.

Kites & Fun Things, 615 N. Mill, Plymouth, MI 48170: Free information ■ High-performance stunt kites. 313–454–3760.

The Kite Store, P.O. Box 17672, Denver, CO 80217: Free catalog ■ Kites and accessories. 303–595–8800.

Kitty Hawk Kites, P.O. Box 340, Nags Head, NC 27959: Free information ■ Conventional and stunt kites and accessories. 919–441–4124.

Nevada Kite Company, 1402 Nevada Hwy., Boulder City, NV 89005: Free information ■ Kites, wind socks, wind chimes, and other wind toys. 702–293–5483.

One of Jerry's Kites, P.O. Box 388, Ocean Park, WA 98640: Free information ■ Conventional kites, deltas, and accessories. 206–665–6464.

Peter Powell Kites, Inc., 1040 NE 43rd Ct., Fort Lauderdale, FL 33334: Free information ■ Stunt kites, kite line, handles, and accessories. 305–565–5588.

Premier Kites, Inc., 8673 Cherry Lane, Laurel, MD 20707: Free catalog ■ Kites, stunt kites, windsocks, air toys, and accessories. 301–604–1881.

Renegade Kites, 3769 Peralta Blvd., Fremont, CA 94536: Free information ■ High-performance stunt kites. 510–791–5666.

Shanti Kite Spools, 480 Clementina St., San Francisco, CA 94103: Free information ■ Spools and grips. 415–896–1601.

Sky Delight Kites, 3310 Bridle Path, Austin, TX 78703: Free information ■ Single line stunt kites that collapse for portability. 512–477–1308.

Skyland Kites, P.O. Box 404, Easthampton, MA 01027: Free information ■ Graphite-reinforced V-braced frame stunt kites. 413–527–0624.

Skymaster, Inc., 721 Front St., Louisville, CO 80027: Free information ■ Acrobatic sport kites. 800–525–0980.

Skynasaur, Inc., 726 Front St., Louisville, CO 80027: Free information ■ Kites and accessories. 800–525–0980.

Triby Kites, 65 New Litchfield St., Torrington, CT 06790: Free information ■ Stunt kites and accessories. 800–328–7529.

Windborne Kites, 585 Cannery Row, Monterey, CA 93940: Free catalog ■ Kites and accessories. 800–234–1033.

Wind Related, Inc., P.O. Box 1006, Hamilton, MT 59840: Free information ■ Handcrafted windsocks. 800–735–1885.

Wind Walker Kites, P.O. Box 225, East Bernard, TX 77435: Free information ■ High-performance, dual line stunt kites. 409–335–7503.

KNITTING

Knitting Machines

Chameleon Knitting, 6350 W. 37th St., Indianapolis, IN 46224: Catalog $2 ■ Knitting machines, tools, and accessories; and wool, cotton, mohair, linen, silk, alpaca, rayon, and acrylic yarn on cones. 317–290–1500.

Fiber Studio, 9 Foster Hill Rd., Box 637, Heniker, NH 03242: Catalog $1 ■ Spinning, weaving, and knitting equipment and accessories; natural fibers in cotton, mohair, wool, alpaca, silk, and linen; and spinning fibers, mill ends, and close-outs. 603–428–7830.

Kruh Knits, P.O. Box 1587, Avon, CT 06001: Catalog $5 ■ Knitting machines, accessories, how-to information, yarn winders, yarns, fabric paints, finishing tools, crotchet accessories, elastic thread, patterns, and notions. 203–674–1043.

La Nell's Studio of Lakewood, 1408 W. 117th St., Lakewood, OH 44107: Free information with long SASE and two 1st class stamps ■ Knitting machines, accessories, books, and video tapes. 216–228–4811.

Newton's Knits, 2100 E. Howell Ave., Anaheim, CA 92806: Free information ■ Knitting machines. 714–634–9116.

Passap, 271 W. 2950 South, Salt Lake City, UT 84115: Free information ■ Easy-to-use computerized knitting machines. 800–PAS–KNIT.

Sami's Knit Wit, 6477 Oakwood Dr., Oakland, CA 94611: Catalog $5 ■ Knitting machines; books and supplies; imported and domestic yarns in cones, skeins, and hanks; and discontinued dye lots, mill ends, and closeouts. 515–339–1222.

Sew-Knit Distributors, 9789 Florida Blvd., Baton Rouge, LA 70815: Free price list with long SASE ■ Sewing and knitting machines and knitting accessories. 800–289–5648.

Shannock Tapestry Looms, 10402 NW 11th Ave., Vancouver, WA 98685: Free brochure ■ Heavy-duty, professional tapestry looms with roller beams and other weaving accessories. 206–573–7264.

Studio Knitting Machines, 11760 Berea Rd., Cleveland, OH 44111: Free information ■ Easy-to-operate knitting machines and accessories. 800–367–0518.

Weaving Works, 4717 Brooklyn Ave. NE, Seattle, WA 98105: Catalog $1 ■ Looms, spinning wheels, hand and machine knitting supplies, traditional and fashion yarns, and books. 206–524–1221.

Yarn-It-All, 2223 Rebecca Dr., Hatfield, PA 19440: Free information ■ Knitting machines and accessories and yarn. 215–822–2989.

Patterns & Accessories

Aura Yarns, Box 602, Derby Line, VT 05830: Free information ■ Imported Icelandic wool sweater kits, and alpaca, cashmere, mohair, merino, shetland, silk, and cotton yarns.

Batik & Weaving Supplier, P.O. Box 451, Lexington, MA 02173: Catalog $2 ■ Weaving, spinning, dyeing, batiking, and knitting supplies. 617–646–4453.

Black Sheep Knitting, 101 N. West St., Black Mountain, NC 28711: Free price list ■ Natural fibers in cotton, wool, silk, and blends. 704–669–2802.

Cotton Clouds, Desert Hills, Rt. 2, Safford, AZ 85546: Catalog with yarn samples $10 ■ Cotton yarns, spinning fibers, tools, books, looms, kits, and patterns. 800–322–7888; 602–428–7000 (in AZ).

Martha Hall, 46 Main St., Yarmouth, ME 04096: Catalog $1 ■ Easy-to-knit sweater kits in Maine wools, and hand-dyed yarns in silk, mohair, linen, cotton, cashmere, and alpaca. 207–846–9746.

Herrschners, Inc., Hoover Rd., Stevens Point, WI 54492: Catalog $1 ■ Needle craft kits and supplies, yarns, knitting accessories, and gifts to crochet and hook. 800–441–0838.

Carolyn Lowy Needlecraft, 630 Sun Meadows Dr., Kernersville, NC 27284: Free information with long SASE ■ Needlepoint, knitting, embroidery, and counted cross-stitching patterns. 919–784–7576.

Mary Maxim, Inc., 2001 Holland Ave., P.O. Box 5019, Port Huron, MI 48061: Free catalog ■ Needlecraft kits, yarn, and accessories. 313–987–2000.

Sami's Knit Wit, 6477 Oakwood Dr., Oakland, CA 94611: Catalog $5 ■ Knitting machines, imported and domestic yarns in cones, skeins, and hanks; and discontinued dye lots, mill ends, and closeouts. 515–339–1222.

Stitches East, 55 E. 52nd St., New York, NY 10022: Free information ■ Knitting and needlepoint supplies, yarns, patterns, needles, and canvases. 212–421–0112.

Thumbelina Needlework Shop, P.O. Box 1065, Solvang, CA 93463: Catalog $1 ■ Books, fabrics, threads, yarns, kits, and accessories. 805–688–4136.

Yarns, P.O. Box 434, Uxbridge, MA 01569: Free information ■ European and American knitting kits. 508–278–7733.

KNIVES & KNIFE MAKING

Al Mar Knives, 5755 SW Jean Rd., Ste. 101, Lake Oswego, OR 97035: Free information ■ Knives. 503–635–9229.

Atlanta Cutlery, Box 839, Conyers, GA 30207: Catalog $1 ■ Knife-making supplies. 404–922–3700.

Hugh E. Bartrug, 505 Rhodes St., Elizabeth, PA 15037: Free information ■ Individually created Damascus and Mokume specialty art knives and folders. 412–384–3476.

L.L. Bean, Freeport, ME 04033: Free catalog ■ Knives for hunters, fishermen, and campers. 800–221–4221.

Beretta U.S.A., 17601 Beretta Dr., Accokeek, MD 20607: Free informatiion ■ Lightweight, standard, serrated, and other knives. 301–283–2191.

Briley Cutlery, 306 Blake St., Tuscumbia, AL 35674: Free catalog ■ Knives. 205–386–7774.

Cattle Baron Leather Company, P.O. Box 100724, San Antonio, TX 78201: Catalog $2 ■ Knives and knife-making supplies. 512–697–8900.

Custom Knifemaker's Supply, P.O. Box 308, Emory, TX 75440: Catalog $2 ■ Knives. 903–473–3330.

Cutlery Shoppe, 5461 Kendall St., Boise, ID 83706: Free catalog ■ Save up to 50 percent on knives. 208–376–0430.

Damascus-U.S.A., Rt. 3, Box 39A, Edenton, NC 27932: Brochure $2 ■ Forged-to-shape Damascus steel knives.

Dixie Gun Works, Inc., Gun Powder Ln., Union City, TN 38261: Catalog $4 ■ Knife-making supplies. 800–238–6785.

Doc Hagen, P.O. Box 58, Pelican Rapids, MN 56572: Catalog $2 ■ Handmade forged knives with exotic handle materials and designs. 218–863–8503.

Eagle Brand Farm, Knife Division, 6731 Standifer Gap Rd., Box 23522, Chattanooga, TN 37422: Catalog $3 ■ Low serial number case knives, limited editions, close-outs, club knives, antiques, and books.

Frost Cutlery, P.O. Box 21353, Chattanooga, TN 37421: Free information ■ Knives. 800–251–7768; 615–894–6079 (in TN).

Handcrafted by Chris Reeve, 6147 Corporal Ln., Boise, ID 83704: Brochure $2 ■ Hand-ground knives in 16 blade styles and sizes. 208–375–0367.

Joe Hilliard, P.O. Box 1629, Marysville, CA 95901: Free list with long SASE and 3 stamps ■ Custom knives. 916–743–6404.

Jantz Supply, 222 E. Main, Davis, OK 73030: Catalog $3 ■ Knife-making supplies, tools, and accessories. 800–351–8900.

Ruffin Johnson Knives, 215 La Fonda, Houston, TX 77060: Brochure $2 ■ Knives. 713–448–4407.

Knife & Cutlery Products, Inc., P.O. Box 12480, Kansas City, MO 64116: Catalog $2 ■ Knife-making supplies and equipment. 816–454–9879.

Knife & Gun Finishing Supplies, P.O. Box 458, Lakeside, AZ 85929: Catalog $3 ■ Metal finishing supplies and accessories for making knives. 602–537–8877.

R.C. Knipstein, 731 N. Fielder Rd., Arlington, TX 76012: Brochure $2 ■ Custom knives. 817–265–2021.

Knive's Unlimited, P.O. Box 424, Depoe Bay, OR 97341: Free information ■ Knives. 503–765–2846.

Koval Knives, P.O. Box 26155, Columbus, OH 43226: Catalog $3 ■ Knife-making supplies and equipment. 614–888–6486.

Philip Kretsinger, Jr., 17536 Bakersville Rd., Boonsboro, MD 21713: Information $2 ■ Classic knives forged in Damascus or high carbon steel. 301–432–6771.

Jimmy Lile, 2721 S. Arkansas Ave., Russellville, AR 72801: Free information ■ Custom handmade knives. 501–968–2011.

Masecraft Supply Company, 170 Research Pkwy., P.O. Box 423, Meriden, CT 06450: Free information ■ India stag, pearl, horn, bone, mammoth ivory, and other materials for knife handles. 800–682–5489.

Matthews Cutlery, 4401 Sentry Dr., Tucker, GA 30084: Free information ■ Knives and knife-making supplies. 404–939–6915.

Hanford J. Miller Knives, Box 97, Cowdrey, CO 80434: Catalog $3 ■ Knives.

Lowell R. Oyster Knives, Rt. 1, Box 432, Kenduskeag, ME 04450: Brochure $1 ■ Handcrafted knives.

Parkers' Knife Collectors Service, 5950 Shallowfor Rd., P.O. Box 23522, Chattanooga, TN 37422: Free catalog ■ Collectible knives. 800–251–7687.

R & C Knives, P.O. Box 1047, Manteca, CA 95336: Catalog $3 ■ Custom and collectible knives. 209–239–3722.

Randall-Made Knives, P.O. Box 1988, Orlando, FL 32802: Catalog $2 ■ Knives. 407–855–8075.

A.W. Ray Bladesmith, Rt. 2, Box 705, Lexington, TX 78947: Free catalog with long SASE ■ Handmade knives. 512–446–2278.

Robert Schrap, 7024 W. Wells St., Wauwatosa, WI 53213: Free information ■ Custom leather knife sheaths. 414–771–6472.

Bob Schrimsher's Custom Knifemaker's Supply, P.O. Box 308, Emory, TX 75440: Catalog $2 ■ Knife-making supplies.

Sheffield Knifemakers Supply, P.O. Box 141, Deland, FL 32721: Catalog $5 ■ Knife-making supplies. 904–775–6453.

Silver Dollar City Gun & Knife Shop, Branson, MO 65616: Free brochure ■ Hand-forged knives. 800–282–2489.

Jim Siska Knives, 6 Highland Ave., Westfield, MA 01 085: Free brochure ■ Knives. 413–568–9787.

Smoky Mountain Knife Works, P.O. Box 4947, Sevierville, TN 37864: Free catalog ■ Save up to 60 percent on hunting, collecting, work, and survival knives.

Special Projects, Customer Service, 2128 Knoll Dr., Unit D, Ventura, CA 93003: Free catalog ■ Limited edition knives, cold steel closeout knives, and new knives. 800–258–1655.

Sportsman's Accessory Manufacturing, 615 Reed St., P.O. Box 18091, Philadelphia, PA 19147: Free information ■ Knife cases. 215–336–6464.

Star Sales Company, Inc., 1803 N. Central St., P.O. Box 1503, Knoxville, TN 37901: Catalog $2 ■ Save from 35 to 60 percent on knives. 615–524–0771.

Swiss Armory, 2838 Juniper St., San Diego, CA 92104: Free catalog ■ Swiss army knives. 800–437–5423.

UltraBlade Knives, P.O. Box 710130, Santee, CA 92072: Free information ■ Pocket knives, folding lock-blades, folding fish fillet knives, non-locking knives for hunters, and fixed-blade sheath knives. 800–735–2825.

Wayne Valachovic Bladesmith, RFD 1, Box 213, Hillsboro, NH 03244: Brochure $2 ■ Damascus steel knives. 603–464–5773.

Robert J. White Knifemaker, Rt. 1, Gilson, IL 61436: Brochure $1 ■ Knives. 309–289–4487.

LABORATORY & SCIENCE EQUIPMENT

American Science & Surplus, 601 Linden Pl., Evanston, IL 60202: Catalog 50¢ ■

Surplus science and electromechanical supplies and equipment. 708–475–8440.

Analytical Scientific, 11049 Bandera, San Antonio, TX 78250: Catalog $3 (refundable) ■ Laboratory glassware, chemicals, equipment, books, charts, and other supplies. 512–684–7373.

Anatomical Chart Company, 8221 N. Kimball, Skokie, IL 60076: Catalog $2 ■ Educational anatomical products on health, human anatomy, and other sciences. 800–621–7500; 708–764–7171 (in IL).

Bunting Magnetics Company, P.O. Box 468, Newton, KS 67144: Free catalog ■ Magnets. 316–284–2020.

Edmund Scientific Company, Edscorp Bldg., Barrington, NJ 08007: Free catalog ■ Microscopes, magnifiers, weather forecasting instruments, magnets, telescopes, binoculars and other optics, lasers, and other supplies. 609–573–6260.

Hagenow Laboratories, 1302 Washington, Manitowoc, WI 54220: Catalog $1.50 ■ Economically priced chemicals, glassware, and other supplies. 414–683–3339.

Hubbard Scientific Company, P.O. Box 104, Northbrook, IL 60065: Free catalog ■ Science equipment and supplies for life science, earth science, physical science, energy experiments, health and physiology, topography projects, and health activities. 800–323–8368.

Magnet Sales & Manufacturing Company, 11248 Playa Ct., Culver City, CA 90230: Free brochure ■ Flexible strip, flex dot, button, and bar magnets. 800–421–6692; 213–391–7213 (in CA).

Merrell Scientific/World of Science, 1665 Buffalo Rd., Rochester, NY 14624: Catalog $2 ■ Chemicals, glassware and equipment and supplies for biology, nature experiments, physical and earth science, rockets, and astronomy. 716–426–1540.

The Nature Company, Home Office, 750 Hearst Ave., Berkeley, CA 94710: Free catalog ■ Science supplies, kits, books, toys, novelties, and gifts. 800–227–1114.

LACROSSE

Bacharach Rasin Company, Inc., 802 Gleneagles Ct., Towson, MD 21204: Free information ■ Balls and gloves, goals, protective gear, helmets, and sticks. 410–825–6747.

Brine, Inc., 47 Sumner St., Milford, MA 01757: Free information ■ Balls, gloves, goals, protective equipment, sticks, and uniforms. 800–227–2722; 800–982–6842 (in MA).

Wm. T. Burnett & Company, Inc., 1500 Bush St., Baltimore, MD 21230: Free information ■ Balls and gloves, goals, protective gear, and sticks. 800–368–2250.

Cran Barry, Inc., 2 Lincoln Ave., Marblehead, MA 01945: Free information ■ Balls and gloves, goals, protective gear, and sticks. 617–631–8510.

Jayfro Corporation, Unified Sports, Inc., 976 Hartford Tpk., P.O. Box 400, Waterford, CT 06385: Free catalog ■ Lacrosse and field hockey goals, nets, and other equipment. 203–447–3001.

Sauk Valley Sports Resort, 10750 Prospect Hill, Brooklyn, MI 49230: Free information ■ Balls, gloves, goals, helmets, protective equipment, and sticks. 800–USA–SAUK; 517–467–2061 (in MI).

Sports Dynamics Corporation, 89 Leuning, Unit B–2, South Hackensack, NJ 07606: Free information ■ Balls and gloves, and protective gear. 800–322–DYNA; 201–342–0500 (in NJ).

Tuskewe Krafts, 2089 Upper Mountain Rd., Sanborn, NY 14132: Free brochure with long SASE ■ Women's and men's field and box lacrosse sticks. 717–297–1821.

LADDERS

American LaFrance, Box 6159, Charlottesville, VA 22906: Free product information ■ Escape ladders. 804–973–4361.

Lynn Ladder & Scaffolding Company, Inc., P.O. Box 346, West Lynn, MA 01905: Free information ■ Ladders. 617–598–6010.

Mohberg & Company, 1210 Bay St., Bellingham, WA 98225: Free brochure ■ Stepladder that converts to a chair. 206–733–7569.

Putnam Rolling Ladder Company, Inc., 32 Howard St., New York, NY 10013: Catalog $1 ■ Ladders, library carts, and other furniture. 212–941–1836.

LAMPS & LIGHTING
Chandeliers

A.J.P. Coppersmith & Company, 20 Industrial Pkwy., Woburn, MA 01801: Catalog $3 ■ Handcrafted reproduction colonial lanterns, chandeliers, sconces, cupolas, and weather vanes, in copper, tin, or brass. 617–932–3700.

American Lighting, 2531–108 Eastchester Dr., High Point, NC 27265: Free information ■ Chandeliers. 800–741–0571.

Antique Hardware Store, 9718 Easton Rd., Rt. 611, Kintnersville, PA 18930: Catalog $3 ■ Antique chandeliers, indoor and outdoor lighting fixtures, pedestal sinks, faucets, high tank toilets, cabinet hardware, weather vanes, and brass bar rails. 800–422–9982.

Art Directions, 6120 Delmar Blvd., St. Louis, MO 63112: Catalog $2 ■ Custom lighting fixtures and reproduction and restored chandeliers. 314–863–1895.

Authentic Designs, The Mill Rd., West Rupert, VT 05776: Catalog $3 ■ Handcrafted reproduction 18th-century early American lighting fixtures and chandeliers in brass, copper, and tin. 802–394–7713.

Ball & Ball, 463 W. Lincoln Hwy., Exton, PA 19341: Catalog $5 ■ Reproduction lighting fixtures, chandeliers, and accessories. 215–363–7330.

Brass Light Gallery, 131 S. 1st St., Milwaukee, WI 53204: Catalog $3 ■ Solid brass chandeliers with glass shades, from the early 1900s. 800–243–9595.

Brasslight, Inc., P.O. Box 695, Nyack, NY 10960: Catalog $3 ■ Wall sconces, desk and table lamps, and period chandeliers in solid brass. 914–353–0567.

Copper Lamps by Hutton, Rt. 940, Box 418, Pocono Pines, PA 18350: Free information ■ Electrified reproduction early American lamps in copper, for tables and walls, hanging lamps, post lamps, and chandeliers. 717–646–7778.

The Coppersmith, Rt. 20, P.O. Box 755, Sturbridge, MA 01566: Catalog $3 ■ Handcrafted reproduction chandeliers, lanterns, sconces, and accessories. 508–347–7038.

Country Store, 28 James St., Geneva, IL 60134: Catalog $2 ■ Punched tin chandeliers, ceiling lights, outlet covers, turned wood chandeliers, country-style decor accessories, and braided rugs. 708–879–0098.

Crawford's Old House Store, 550 Elizabeth St., Waukesha, WI 53186: Free information ■ Reproduction Victorian and turn-of-the-century gas and early electric brass chandeliers and wall fixtures. 800–556–7878.

European Classics, 509 N. Virginia Ave., Winter Park, FL 32789: Free information ■ Reproduction period European lighting fixtures. 407–628–8885.

Golden Valley Lighting, 274 Eastchester Dr., High Point, NC 27260: Free information ■ Save up to 50 percent on lighting fixtures, lamps, and accessories. 800–735–3377.

Hammerworks, 6 Fremont St., Worcester, MA 01603: Catalog $3 ■ Handmade colonial reproductions of post lanterns, wall lanterns, chandeliers, and sconces, in copper, brass, iron, or tin. 508–755–3434.

Hubbardton Forge & Wood Corporation, P.O. Box 827, Castleton Corners, Castleton, VT 05735: Brochure $3 ■ Table, wall, and candlestick lamps; wrought-iron and brass chandeliers; hanging pan racks and pan rack bar holders; and bathroom accessories and plant hangers. 802–468–3090.

King's Chandelier Company, P.O. Box 667, Eden, NC 27288: Catalog $3.50 ■ Chandeliers, candelabras, and crystal sconces. 919–623–6188.

Luigi Crystal, 7332 Frankford Ave., Philadelphia, PA 19136: Catalog $1 ■ Crystal accessories and decor table lamps, cut crystal chandeliers, hurricane lamps, and sconces. 215–338–2978.

Nowell's, Inc., 490 Gate 5 Rd., P.O. Box 295, Sausalito, CA 94966: Catalog $4 ■ Reproduction and restored antique chandeliers and other lighting fixtures. 415–332–4933.

Period Lighting Fixtures, 1 W. Main St., Chester, CT 06412: Catalog $3 ■ Reproduction 17th- and early 18th-century lighting fixtures and chandeliers, in pewter, copper, tin, or wood. 203–526–3690.

The Renovator's Supply, Renovator's Old Mill, Millers Falls, MA 01349: Free catalog ■ Solid brass chandeliers. 413–659–2211.

Roy Electric Company, Inc., 1054 Coney Island Ave., Brooklyn, NY 11230: Catalog $6 ■ Victorian-style and turn-of-the-century chandeliers, sconces, and other lighting fixtures. 800–366–3347; 718–434–7002 (in NY).

Saltbox, Inc., 3004 Columbia Ave., Lancaster, PA 17603: Catalog $1.25 ■ Handcrafted colonial-style chandeliers, post lights, lanterns, and foyer lights, in brass, copper, or tin. 717–392–5649.

Studio Steel, P.O. Box 621, Wilton, CT 06897: Catalog $2 ■ Handcrafted French country-style and other chandeliers. 203–846–3978.

Tin Bin, 20 Valley Rd., Neffsville, PA 17601: Catalog $2 ■ Handcrafted antiqued copper or antiqued brass country-style chandeliers. 717–569–6210.

Village Lantern, D.R. Williams, Tinsmith, Box 8, North Marshfield, MA 02059: Brochure 50¢ ■ Handcrafted colonial-style chandeliers. 617–834–8121.

Lt. Moses Willard, Inc., 1156 US 50, Milford, OH 45150: Catalog $3.50 ■ Custom reproduction chandeliers, wall sconces, exterior lighting units, candle holders and lanterns, and wall and table lamps, from the 1700s. 513–831–8956.

Workshops of David T. Smith, 3600 Shawhan Rd., Morrow, OH 45152: Catalog $5 ■ Reproduction furniture, pottery, lamps, and chandeliers. 513–932–2472.

Lamps & Fixtures

A.J.P. Coppersmith & Company, 20 Industrial Pkwy., Woburn, MA 01801: Catalog $3 ■ Handcrafted reproduction colonial lanterns, chandeliers, sconces, cupolas, and weather vanes, in copper, tin, or brass. 617–932–3700.

Alkco Lighting, 11500 W. Melrose Ave., P.O. Box 1389, Franklin Park, IL 60131: Free information ■ Indoor lighting fixtures and accessories. 708–451–0700.

Allied Lighting, Drawer E, Trextertown, PA 18087: Free information ■ Save up to 60 percent on lighting fixtures and accessories. 800–241–6111; 800–322–4468 (in PA).

American Period Showcase, 3004 Columbia Ave., Lancaster, PA 17603: Brochure $1.50 ■ Handcrafted, American period lanterns, table lamps, chandeliers, post lamps, and accessories. 717–392–5649.

Antique Hardware Store, 9718 Easton Rd., Rt. 611, Kintnersville, PA 18930: Catalog $3 (refundable with $20 purchase) ■ Antique-style indoor and outdoor lamps and lighting fixtures, pedestal sinks, faucets, high tank toilets, cabinet hardware, weather vanes, and tin and wood chandeliers. 800–422–9982.

Art Directions, 6120 Delmar Blvd., St. Louis, MO 63112: Catalog $2 ■ Reproduction, restored, and custom chandeliers and lighting fixtures. 314–863–1895.

Authentic Designs, The Mill Rd., West Rupert, VT 05776: Catalog $3 ■ Handcrafted reproduction 18th-century early American lighting fixtures and chandeliers, in brass, copper, or tin. 802–394–7713.

Baldwin Hardware Corporation, 841 E. Wyomissing Blvd., Box 15048, Reading, PA 19612: Bathroom accessories brochure 75¢; lighting fixtures brochure $3; door hardware brochure 75¢; decorative hardware brochure 75¢ ■ Forged brass dead bolts and door hardware, bathroom accessories, lighting fixtures, and decor hardware. 215–777–7811.

Ball & Ball, 463 W. Lincoln Hwy., Exton, PA 19341: Catalog $5 ■ Reproduction lighting fixtures, chandeliers, and accessories. 215–363–7330.

Barap Specialties, 835 Bellows Ave., Frankfort, MI 49635: Catalog $1 ■ Lamp parts, chair caning supplies and tools, turned wood parts, and other craft supplies. 616–352–9863.

Lester H. Berry & Company, P.O. Box 53377, Philadelphia, PA 19105: Free information ■ Reproduction 18th-century chandeliers, wall sconces, hanging lights, and coach lighting fixtures. 215–923–2603.

Brasslight, Inc., P.O. Box 695, Nyack, NY 10960: Catalog $3 ■ Wall sconces, solid brass period chandeliers, and desk and table lamps. 914–353–0567.

Brass'n Bounty, 68 Front St., Marblehead, MA 01945: Free information ■ Antique chandeliers, floor lamps, and sconces, in gas, electric, or combined gas-electric models. 627–631–3864.

Brubaker Metalcrafts, 209 N. Franklin St., P.O. Box 353, Eaton, OH 45320: Free brochure ■ Reproduction 18th-century tin and brass chandeliers, wall sconces, Paul

Revere lanterns, and other fixtures. 513–456–1949.

Century House Antiques & Lamp Emporium, 46785 Rt. 18 West, Wellington, OH 44090: Free information with long SASE ■ Antique lamps and old and custom shades. 216–647–4092.

City Lights, 2226 Massachusetts Ave., Cambridge, MA 02140: Catalog $5 ■ Restored antique lighting units. 617–547–1490.

David L. Claggett, Artistry in Tin, P.O. Box 41, Weston, VT 05161: Catalog $3 ■ Reproduction lighting. 802–824–3194.

Classic Illumination, Inc., 2743 9th St., Berkeley, CA 94710: Catalog $5 ■ Hanging, ceiling, and wall fixtures, and shades. 510–849–1842.

Copper Antiquities, P.O. Box 153, Cummaquid, MA 02637: Brochure $2 ■ Early American-style lanterns handcrafted in copper. 508–775–7704.

Copper Lamps by Hutton, Rt. 940, Box 418, Pocono Pines, PA 18350: Free information ■ Electrified reproduction early American lamps in copper, for tables and walls, hanging lamps, post lamps, and chandeliers. 717–646–7778.

The Coppersmith, Rt. 20, P.O. Box 755, Sturbridge, MA 01566: Catalog $2 ■ Handcrafted reproduction colonial lanterns, sconces, and chandeliers. 508–347–7038.

Crawford's Old House Store, 550 Elizabeth, Waukesha, WI 53186: Free information ■ Reproduction Victorian and turn-of-the-century gas and early electric brass chandeliers and wall fixtures. 800–556–7878.

Dibianco Lighting, 8018 3rd Ave., Brooklyn, NY 11209: Free brochure ■ Contemporary Italian lighting fixtures in Murano glass. 718–238–7153.

Elcanco, Ltd., P.O. Box 682, Westford, MA 01886: Literature $1 ■ Handcrafted electric wax candles with flame-like bulbs. 508–392–0830.

EMC Tiffany, 45 Paris Rd., New Hartford, NY 13413: Catalog $3 ■ Hand-leaded Tiffany lamps. 315–724–2984.

Essex Forge, 5 Old Dennison Rd., Essex, CT 06426: Catalog $2 ■ Reproduction 18th-century indoor and outdoor lighting fixtures. 203–767–1808.

Factory Paint Store, 505 Pond St., South Weymouth, MA 02190: Free information ■ Lighting fixtures, window shades, wallpaper, and paint. 617–331–1200.

David H. Fletcher, Blue Mist Morgan Farm, 68 Liberty St., Haverhill, MA 01830: Catalog $3 ■ Handcrafted copper lanterns and weather vanes. 508–374–8783.

Frombruche, 132 N. Main St., Spring Valley, NY 10977: Photo catalog $4 ■ Handcrafted custom lighting in 1920s, Victorian, traditional, and country French or English styles. Available in solid brass, chrome, pewter, or brass and pewter country-style combination. 800–537–6319.

Genie House, Red Lion Rd., P.O. Box 2478, Vincentown, NJ 08088: Catalog $2 ■ Handcrafted 17th- and 18th-century reproduction lighting fixtures, in copper, tin, and brass. 800–634–3643.

Georgia Lighting Supply Company, Inc., 530 14th St. NW, Atlanta, GA 30318: Free catalog ■ Lighting fixtures in early American, French, English, and Victorian styles. 404–875–4754.

Hammerworks, 6 Fremont St., Worcester, MA 01603: Catalog $3 ■ Handmade colonial reproduction post lanterns, wall lanterns, chandeliers, and sconces, in copper, brass, iron, or tin. 508–755–3434.

Home Decorators Collection, 2025 Concourse Dr., St. Louis, MO 63146: Free catalog ■ Contemporary, traditional, floor, table, halogen lamps, and other lighting units; lamp shades and accessories; and lighting fixtures for the bath, ceiling, wall, and outdoors. 800–245–2217; 314–993–1516 (in MO).

Harry Horn, Inc., 622–624 South St., Philadelphia, PA 19147: Catalog $2 ■ Recess and track lighting. 215–925–6600.

Independence Forge, Rt. 1, Box 1, Whitakers, NC 27891: Brochure $1 ■ Handcrafted country-style iron furniture, chandeliers, and floor, table, and wall lamps. 919–437–2931.

Juno Lighting, Inc., P.O. Box 5065, Des Plaines, IL 60017: Free information ■ Indoor and outdoor lighting fixtures and accessories. 708–827–9880.

Kemp & George, 2515 E. 43rd St., P.O. Box 182230, Chattanooga, TN 37422: Free catalog ■ Lighting fixtures for indoors and outdoors, bathroom fixtures and accessories,

and decor accessories for the home. 800–562–1704.

KML Enterprises, RR 1, Box 234, Berne, IN 46711: Catalog $1 ■ Handcrafted reproductions of 18th-century tinsmith's lanterns, chandeliers, and sconces. 219–589–8853.

Lamp Warehouse & New York Ceiling Fan Center, 1073 39th St., Brooklyn, NY 11219: Free information with long SASE ■ Save from 10 to 35 percent on lamps, lighting fixtures, and ceiling fans. 718–436–8500.

Leviton Manufacturing Company, 59–25 Little Neck Pkwy., Little Neck, NY 11362: Free information ■ Indoor and outdoor lighting fixtures and accessories. 718–229–4040.

Lightolier, 100 Lighting Way, Secaucus, NJ 07096: Free information ■ Indoor and outdoor lighting fixtures and accessories. 201–864–3000.

Luigi Crystal, 7332 Frankford Ave., Philadelphia, PA 19136: Catalog $1 ■ Table lamps, cut crystal chandeliers, hurricane lamps, and sconces. 215–338–2978.

Luma Lighting Industries, Inc., Customer Service, 410 W. Fletcher Ave., Orange, CA 92665: Free information ■ Indoor and outdoor lighting fixtures and accessories. 714–282–1116.

Metropolitan Lighting Fixture Company, Inc., 315 E. 62nd St., New York, NY 10021: Catalog $5 ■ Lighting fixtures in art deco, modern, art nouveau, contemporary, colonial, French historical, country French, and other styles. 212–838–2425.

Mole Hill Pottery, 5011 Anderson Pike, Signal Mountain, TN 37377: Catalog $1 ■ Signed and dated stoneware lamps and pottery. 615–886–4926.

Gates Moore Lighting, 2 River Rd., Silvermine, Norwalk, CT 06850: Catalog $2 (refundable) ■ Early American chandeliers, copper lanterns, and wall sconces. 203–847–3231.

Moultrie Manufacturing, P.O. Box 1179, Moultrie, GA 31776: Catalog $3 ■ Colonial lanterns and other "Old South" reproductions for the home. 800–841–8674.

C. Neri Antiques, 313 South St., Philadelphia, PA 19147: Catalog $5 ■ Antique lighting fixtures and accessories. 215–923–6669.

Newstamp Lighting Company, 227 Bay Rd., North Easton, MA 02356: Catalog $2 ■ Handmade replicas of early American lamps for indoors and outdoors, sconces, chandeliers, and other lighting fixtures. 508–238–7071.

Ocean View Lighting, 2743 9th St., Berkeley, CA 94710: Catalog $5 (refundable) ■ Lighting fixtures and accessories, from Victorian to contemporary styles. 510–841–2937.

Packet Landing Iron Blacksmith, 1022 Rt. 6A, West Barnstable, MA 02668: Free brochure ■ Handcrafted reproduction wrought-iron wall sconces, table lamps, floor lamps, chandeliers, and wall lamps, in 18th-century, early American, English, and other styles. 617–362–2697.

Panet the Tin Man, 195 Riverside Dr., Troy, OH 45373: Catalog $2 ■ Colonial-style lamps in copper, brass, or tin and finished with an aged look. 513–339–2315.

Hurley Patentee Lighting, RD 7, Box 98, Kingston, NY 12401: Catalog $3 ■ Handcrafted replica early American chandeliers, sconces and lamps, and lanterns. 914–331–5414.

Period Lighting Fixtures, 1 W. Main St., Chester, CT 06412: Catalog $3 ■ Reproduction 17th- and early 18th-century lighting fixtures and chandeliers, in pewter, copper, tin, or wood. 203–526–3690.

Progress Lighting, P.O. Box 12701, Philadelphia, PA 19134: Free information ■ Indoor and outdoor lighting fixtures and accessories. 215–289–1200.

Rejuvenation Lamp & Fixture Company, 901 N. Skidmore, Portland, OR 97217: Catalog $3 ■ Authentic reproduction solid brass early 20th-century chandeliers, sconces, and lamps. 503–249–0774.

The Renovator's Supply, Renovator's Old Mill, Millers Falls, MA 01349: Free catalog ■ Ceiling lighting fixtures, hanging lamps, table and floor lamps, wall lamps, and replacement glass shades. 413–659–2211.

Roy Electric Company, 1054 Coney Island Ave., Brooklyn, NY 11230: Catalog $6 ■ Art deco lighting fixtures. 800–366–3347; 718–434–7002 (in NY).

St. Louis Antique Lighting Company, Inc., 801 N. Skinker, St. Louis, MO 63130: Catalog $3 ■ Handcrafted brass reproduction

ceiling fixtures, lamps, and sconces in antique styles. 314–863–1414.

Saltbox, Inc., 3004 Columbia Ave., Lancaster, PA 17603: Catalog $1.25 ■ Handcrafted colonial-style post lights, chandeliers, lanterns, and foyer lights, in brass, copper, or tin. 717–392–5649.

Shadowland Cove Lantern Company, P.O. Box 195, Cheshire, MA 01225: Catalog $2 ■ Chandeliers, lanterns, sconces, and post lights in an early New England style. 413–743–9020.

Task Lighting Corporation, P.O. Box 1094, Kearney, NE 68848: Free information ■ Indoor lighting fixtures and accessories. 800–445–6404.

Victorian Lightcrafters, Ltd., P.O. Box 350, Slate Hill, NY 10973: Catalog $3 ■ Handcrafted Victorian-style lighting fixtures. 914–355–1300.

Victorian Lighting Works, 251 S. Pennsylvania Ave., P.O. Box 469, Centre Hall, PA 16828: Brochure $3 ■ Victorian-style lighting fixtures. 814–364–9577.

Washington Copper Works, 49 South St., Washington, CT 06793: Catalog $3 (refundable) ■ Handcrafted copper lanterns and wall fixtures. 203–868–7527.

Lt. Moses Willard, Inc., 1156 US 50, Milford, OH 45150: Catalog $3.50 ■ Custom reproduction lighting fixtures from styles of the 1700s. Includes chandeliers, wall sconces, exterior lighting units, candle holders and lanterns, wall lamps, and table lamps. 513–831–8956.

Workshops of David T. Smith, 3600 Shawhan Rd., Morrow, OH 45152: Catalog $5 ■ Reproduction lamps and chandeliers, furniture, and pottery. 513–932–2472.

Lamp Shades

American Deluxe Lighting, 13543 Alondra Blvd., Sante Fe Spring, CA 90670: Free catalog ■ Tiffany and Handel-style hand-blown glass shades. 310–802–8910.

Brass Light Gallery, 131 S. 1st St., Milwaukee, WI 53204: Catalog $3 ■ Replacement glass shades and lamps. 800–243–9595.

Burdoch Victorian Lamp Company, 1145 Industrial Ave., San Diego, CA 92025: Brochure $4 with long SASE ■ Lamp bases

and long-fringed lamp shades in satinized polyester. 619–745–3275.

CDR Shade Company, P.O. Box 1030, Great Barrington, MA 01230: Information $2 ■ Shades for use over lighted candles. 413–528–5050.

Century House Antiques & Lamp Emporium, 46785 Rt. 18 West, Wellington, OH 44090: Free information with long SASE ■ Antique lamps, lamp repair supplies, and old-fashioned and custom shades. 216–647–4092.

Classic Illumination, Inc., 2743 9th St., Berkeley, CA 94710: Catalog $5 ■ Lamp shades and hanging, ceiling, and wall fixtures. 510–849–1842.

Diversified Sales & Marketing, 120 Old Mill Run, Ormond Beach, FL 32174: Free information ■ Lamp shades. 800–526–7586.

Einerlei, P.O. Box 679, Chassell, MI 49916: Catalog $1 ■ Lamp shades. 906–523–4612.

Lampshades of Antique, P.O. Box 2, Medford, OR 97501: Catalog $4 ■ Antique styled lamp shades. 503–826–9737.

Lamp Shop, P.O. Box 36, Concord, NH 03302: Catalog $2 ■ Supplies for making lamp shades. 603–224–1603.

Lundberg Studios, P.O. Box C, Davenport, CA 95017: Catalog $3 ■ Hand-blown, antique-style glass globes, gas lights, and filter shades. 408–423–2532.

Mak-A-Shade, 1340 W. Strasburg Rd., West Chester, PA 19382: Brochure $1 ■ Kits, supplies, and tools for making lamp shades. 215–696–2469.

The Renovator's Supply, Renovator's Old Mill, Millers Falls, MA 01349: Catalog $3 ■ Replacement glass shades, ceiling fixtures, hanging lamps, table and floor lamps, and wall lamps. 413–659–2211.

Shady Lady, 418 E. 2nd St., Loveland, CO 80537: Catalog $3.50 ■ Custom lamp shades or will recover old shades. 303–669–1080.

Unique Creations, 28 Cherokee Dr., Newark, DE 19713: Catalog 50¢ ■ Sculptured lamp shades. 302–737–8744.

Outdoor Lighting

Antique Street Lamps, Inc., 8412 S. Congress, P.O. Box 43289, Austin, TX 78745: Free information ■ Lamps in an 1800s and

1900s style, border lights, and lighting and traffic signal posts. 512–282–9780.

Authentic Designs, The Mill Rd., West Rupert, VT 05776: Catalog $3 ■ Outdoor post lighting units and handcrafted reproduction 18th-century Early American light fixtures, in brass, copper, or tin. 802–394–7713.

Brandon Industries, 4419 Westgrove Dr., Dallas, TX 75248: Free brochure ■ Cast aluminum street lamps and old-fashioned pedestal mail boxes with solid brass letter slot and cylinder key lock. 214–250–0456.

BRK Electronics, 780 McClure Rd., Aurora, IL 60504: Free information ■ Controls for converting outdoor lights to an automatic system. 800–323–9005.

Classic Lamp Posts, 3645 NW 67th St., Miami, FL 33147: Free brochure ■ Colonial and Victorian-style lamp posts with single or multiple plastic globes. 800–654–5852; 305–696–1901 (in FL).

Copper Antiquities, P.O. Box 153, Cummaquid, MA 02637: Brochure $2 (refundable) ■ Handcrafted solid copper early American style lanterns. 508–775–7704.

Copper House, RFD 1, Box 4, Epsom, NH 03234: Catalog $2 ■ Handmade copper weather vanes and indoor and outdoor light fixtures. 603–736–9798.

Josiah R. Coppersmythe, 80 Stiles Rd., Boylston, MA 01505: Catalog $3 ■ Handcrafted Early American light fixtures for indoors and outdoors, in brass or copper. 508–869–2769.

Dover Design, Inc., 2175 Beaver Valley Pike, New Providence, PA 17560: Free brochure ■ Handcrafted copper landscape lights. 717–786–8891.

Genie House, P.O. Box 2478, Red Lion Rd., Vincentown, NJ 08088: Free information ■ Indoor and outdoor reproduction lighting fixtures. 609–859–0600.

Heath Company, P.O. Box 8589, Benton Harbor, MI 49023: Free catalog ■ Automatic turn-on and turn-off light controls. 800–44–HEATH.

Heritage Lanterns, 70 Main St., Yarmouth, ME 04096: Free catalog ■ Colonial-style outdoor light fixtures. 800–648–4449.

Herwig Lighting, P.O. Box 768, Russellville, AR 72801: Free information ■ Light fixtures, posts, bollards, street furniture, antique fence posts, custom sand castings, and street clocks. 800–643–9523.

Historic Lighting, P.O. Box 66, Essex Street Station, Boston, MA 02112: Free information ■ Custom lamps in an 1850s to 1930s style. 617–436–3080.

Honeywell, Inc., Residential Division, 1985 Douglas Dr. North, Golden Valley, MN 55422: Free information ■ Motion activated light controls. 800–468–1502.

Hubbell Lighting, 2000 Electric Way, Christiansburg, VA 24073: Catalog $5 ■ Low voltage outdoor lighting systems. 703–382–6111.

Intermatic Lighting, Inc., Intermatic Plaza, Spring Grove, IL 60081: Free information ■ Low voltage outdoor lighting systems. 815–675–2321.

Juno Lighting, Inc., P.O. Box 5065, Des Plaines, IL 60017: Free information ■ Indoor and outdoor light fixtures and accessories. 708–827–9880.

Kelsey-Kane Lighting Manufacturing Company, P.O. Box 4065, Sunrise Station, Fort Lauderdale, FL 33338: Free information ■ Outdoor light fixtures and weatherproof fluorescent floodlights. 305–772–3187.

La Jolla Sales Company, 6910 Dennison St., San Diego, CA 92122: Catalog $2 ■ Cast-aluminum outdoor benches, lamp posts and lighting units, and planters. 619–452–2044.

Leviton Manufacturing Company, 59–25 Little Neck Pkwy., Little Neck, NY 11362: Free information ■ Indoor and outdoor light fixtures and accessories. 718–229–4040.

Lightolier, 100 Lighting Way, Secaucus, NJ 07096: Free information ■ Indoor and outdoor light fixtures and accessories. 201–864–3000.

Liteform Designs, P.O. Box 3316, Portland, OR 97208: Free catalog ■ Low voltage, incandescent, and fluorescent garden, driveway, post and wall mounted lighting units. 800–458–2505.

Loran Nightscaping, Inc., 1705 E. Colton, Redlands, CA 92374: Free information ■ Low voltage outdoor lighting systems. 714–794–2121.

Luma Lighting Industries, Inc., Customer Service, 410 W. Fletcher Ave., Orange, CA 92665: Free information ■ Indoor and outdoor light fixtures and accessories. 714–282–1116.

Mainstreet Lamp Posts, 11020 Berea Rd., Cleveland, OH 44102: Free information ■ Ornamental lamp posts. 216–651–4431.

Mel-Nor Industries, 303 Gulf Bank, Houston, TX 77037: Information $1 ■ Park benches, old time lamp posts, and lawn and hanging porch swings. 713–445–3485.

Moultrie Manufacturing, P.O. Drawer 1179, Moultrie, GA 31776: Catalog $3 ■ Cast-aluminum indoor and outdoor light fixtures, tables, chairs, settees, planters, urns, fountains, and chaises. 800–841–8674.

Progress Lighting, P.O. Box 12701, Philadelphia, PA 19134: Free information ■ Indoor and outdoor light fixtures and accessories. 215–289–1200.

RAB Electric Manufacturing Company, 170 Ludlow Ave., Northvale, NJ 07647: Free information ■ Outdoor light fixtures and accessories. 201–784–8600.

Sentry Electric Corporation, 185 Buffalo Ave., Freeport, NY 11520: Free information ■ Cast-aluminum lamp posts and light fixtures in a colonial and early 1900s style. 516–379–4660.

Specialty Lighting Systems, 31505 Grand River, Farmington, MI 48024: Free catalog ■ Classic and contemporary outdoor and indoor light fixtures in cast-iron, cast-aluminum, and copper coach patterns and lighting poles with an old-fashioned look. 313–474–5888.

Spring City Electrical Manufacturing Company, Hall & Main Sts., Drawer A, Spring City, PA 19475: Free brochure ■ Heavy-duty, cast-iron ornamental lamp posts. 215–948–4000.

Task Lighting Corporation, P.O. Box 1094, Kearney, NE 68848: Free information ■ Indoor light fixtures and accessories. 800–445–6404.

Toro Company, 5300 Shoreline Blvd., Mound, MN 55463: Free information ■ Outdoor lighting units for landscape and security settings, with optional power packs and photo sensors. 800–336–0242.

Tower Lighting Center, P.O. Box 1043, North Adams, MA 01247: Catalog $2 (refundable) ■ Hand-wrought copper lanterns. 413–663–7681.

Valley Iron & Steel Company, 29579 Awbrey Ln., Eugene, OR 97402: Free catalog ■ Outdoor lighting and "streetscaping" fixtures and accessories in traditional and futuristic styles. Includes traffic signals, pedestrian signals, drinking fountains, wall-mounted light units, and lighted or unlighted bollards. 503–688–7741.

Otto Wendt & Company, 417A Gentry Rd., Spring, TX 77373: Brochure $2 ■ Cast-aluminum lighting equipment, in an early 1900s style; benches and mailboxes; and fountains, patio sets, urns, and plant stands. 713–288–8295.

Ultraviolet Light

Alpha Supply, Inc., 1225 Hollis St., Box 2133, Bremerton, WA 98310: Catalog $1 (refundable with $15 order) ■ Ultraviolet light equipment and jewelry-making, prospecting, and rockhounding equipment and supplies. 206–377–5629.

Blacklight Specialties, 1854 Alcatraz, Berkeley, CA 94703: Free information ■ Ultraviolet lamps, fluorescent minerals, papers, paints, inks, and other supplies. 510–653–4424.

Bourget Bros., 1636 11th St., Santa Monica, CA 90404: Catalog $5 ■ Ultraviolet light equipment, rock-polishing supplies and equipment, and jewelry-making tools and supplies. 800–828–3024; 310–450–6556 (in CA).

Cal-Gold, 2569 E. Colorado Blvd., Pasadena, CA 91107: Free catalog ■ Ultraviolet light equipment, metal detectors, supplies for miners and geologists, maps, and books. 818–792–6161.

Ebersole Lapidary Supply, Inc., 11417 West Hwy. 54, Wichita, KS 67209: Catalog $2 ■ Ultraviolet light equipment and jewelry-making, rockhounding, and bead-stringing supplies. 316–722–4771.

Fluorescent Minerals Company, 5106 Walnut Grove Ave., San Gabriel, CA 91776: Free information ■ Ultraviolet light lamps. 800–833–6757.

Gemstone Equipment Manufacturing Company, 750 Easy St., Simi Valley, CA 93065: Free information ■ Ultraviolet light and lapidary equipment and accessories. 805–527–6990.

Graves Company, 1800 Andrews Ave., Pompano Beach, FL 33069: Free catalog ■ Ultraviolet light, rockhounding, and lapidary equipment and supplies. 800–327–9103.

LEATHER CRAFTS

Artway Crafts, Box 699, Tom Bean, TX 75489: Catalog $1 ■ Leather-crafting supplies and tools. 903–546–6755.

Berman Leathercraft, 25 CC Melcher St., Boston, MA 02101: Catalog $3 ■ Chamois, suede, and leather for crafting and upholstering. 617–426–0870.

Leathercrafters Supply Company, 25 Great Jones, New York, NY 10012: Catalog $2 ■ Leather-crafting supplies, equipment, and accessories. 212–673–5460.

Leather Factory, P.O. Box 50429, Fort Worth, TX 76105: Free catalog ■ Leather-crafting kits and supplies, tools, and pictorial stamps. 615–756–4484.

Leather Unlimited, 7155 Country Hwy. B, Belgium, WI 53004: Catalog $2 (refundable) ■ Supplies, kits, and accessories for leather-crafting. 414–999–9464.

Pyramid of Urbana, 2107 N. High Cross Rd., Urbana, IL 61801: Free catalog ■ Leather-crafting kits, tools, how-to books, other craft supplies, office accessories and supplies, art supplies, and school equipment. 217–328–3099.

Quintessence, P.O. Box 723544, Atlanta, GA 30339: Catalog $3 ■ Animal and reptile skins that include snakeskin, fishskin, and lambskin; beads and rhinestones; hand-carved sea shells; and beaded appliques. 404–435–7441.

M. Siegel Company, Inc., 120 Pond St., Ashland, MA 01721: Catalog $2 ■ Leathers, trims, and tools for crafting. 508–881–5200.

Tandy Leather Company, P.O. Box 791, Fort Worth, TX 76101: Free catalog ■ Leather-crafting kits; supplies that include cowhide, chamois, snakeskin, suede, rabbit, lambskin and garment leather; tools; books and patterns; and instructional videos.

Veteran Leather Company, Inc., 204 25th St., Brooklyn, NY 11232: Catalog $2 (refundable) ■ Leather-crafting supplies, tools, and kits. 800–221–7565; 718–768–0300 (in NY).

LEFT-HANDED MERCHANDISE

Aristera, Renovator's Old Mill, Millers Falls, MA 01349: Free catalog ■ Household products and other items for left-handers. 413–659–2211.

Left Hand Center, 4400 Excelsior Blvd., St. Louis Park, MN 55416: Catalog $1 ■ Gifts for left-handers. 612–926–6033.

The Left-Handed Complement, P.O. Box 447, Port Jefferson Station, NY 11776: Catalog $1 ■ Items for left-handers.

Lefthanders International, P.O. Box 8249, Topeka, KS 66608: Catalog $2 ■ Items for lefties. 913–234–2177.

Lefties Only, 1972 Williston Rd., South Burlington, VT 05403: Free price list ■ Equipment for left-handers. 800–523–8437.

Lefty's Corner, P.O. Box 615, Clarks Summit, PA 18411: Catalog $2 (refundable) ■ Items for left-handers. 717–586–LEFT.

Kenneth Smith Golf Clubs, Box 41, Kansas City, MO 64141: Free brochure and fitting chart ■ Left-handed golf clubs. 816–221–6644.

Somerton Springs Golf, 53 Bustleton Pike, Feasterville, PA 19047: Free brochure ■ Left-handed golf clubs, personalized golf balls, umbrellas, jackets, golf bags, and head covers. 800–220–GOLF; 215–355–7276 (in PA).

LOG SPLITTERS

Bailey's Tools & Supplies, P.O. Box 550, Laytonville, CA 95454: Catalog $2 ■ Chain saws, bars, files, protective gear, forestry supplies, log splitters, books, and gifts. 707–984–6133.

Bee Tee Engine Sales, P.O. Box 3037, Hayward, CA 94540: Free literature ■ Automatic, rugged log splitter.

Mobile Manufacturing Company, P.O. Box 250, Troutdale, OR 97060: Free brochure ■ Portable gasoline- or electric-powered saw for cutting logs in any diameter and lengths up to 60 feet. 503–666–5593.

Northern Hydraulics, P.O. Box 1219, Burnsville, MN 55337: Free catalog ■ Log splitters, gas engines, trailer parts, heat magnets, and other tools. 800–533–5545.

Power Equipment Distributors, Inc., 3400 Hubbard, Mt. Clemens, MI 48043: Free brochure ■ Manual hydraulic log splitter. 800–624–2923.

Sperber Tool Works, P.O. Box 1224, West Caldwell, NJ 07007: Free literature ■ Portable sawmills for cutting wood without having to move the log. 201–744–6110.

LUGGAGE & BRIEFCASES

Ace Leather Products, 2211 Ave. U, Brooklyn, NY 11229: Free catalog ■ Leather luggage and small leather goods. 718–891–9713.

Adventure International Corporation, Adventure Gear, 8039 Deering Ave., Canoga Park, CA 91304: Free information ■ Carry-alls, tote bags, duffles, and shoulder bags. 818–594–0380.

Al's Luggage, 2134 Larimer St., Denver, CO 80205: Catalog $2 ■ Luggage carts and luggage. 303–295–9009.

Altman Luggage, 135 Orchard St., New York, NY 10001: Free information ■ Save from 20 to 50 percent on luggage, other leather goods, and pens and pencils. 800–372–3377.

T. Anthony, Ltd., 1201 Connecticut Ave. NW, Washington, DC 20036: Free catalog ■ Leather goods and luggage. 202–LUGGAGE.

Artcraft Swiss Embroidery Company, 1450 S. Burlington Ave., Los Angeles, CA 90006: Free information ■ Carry-alls, tote bags, duffles, and shoulder bags. 213–385–1646.

Asics Tiger Corporation, 10540 Talbert Ave., Fountain Valley, CA 92708: Free information ■ Carry-alls, tote bags, duffles, and shoulder bags. 714–962–7654.

A to Z Luggage, 4627 New Utrecht Ave., Brooklyn, NY 11219: Free catalog ■ Save up to 50 percent on luggage, small leather goods, and accessories. 800–342–5011; 718–435–2880 (in NY).

Bally of Switzerland for Ladies, 689 Madison Ave., New York, NY 10021: Free information ■ Women's shoes, clothing, luggage, small leather goods, and accessories. 212–751–2163.

Bally of Switzerland for Men, 711 5th Ave., New York, NY 10022: Free informa-tion ■ Men's shoes, clothing, luggage, small leather goods, and accessories. 212–751–9082.

Bondy Export Corporation, 40 Canal St., New York, NY 10002: Free information with long SASE ■ Luggage and accessories, small and major appliances, typewriters, cameras, television sets, and video equipment. 212–925–7785.

Bottega Veneta, 635 Madison Ave., New York, NY 10022: Free catalog ■ Wallets, purses and bags, luggage, and other small leather goods. 212–371–5511.

H.D. Brown Enterprises, Ltd., 23 Beverly St. East, P.O. Box 190, St. George, Ontario, Canada N0E 1N0: Free information ■ Carry-alls, tote bags, duffles, and shoulder bags. 519–448–1381.

Buck's Bag, Inc., 2700 W. Idaho, Boise, ID 83702: Free information ■ Carry-alls, tote bags, duffles, and shoulder bags. 208–344–4400.

Coach Leatherware Company, 300 Chubb Ave., Lyndhurst, NJ 07071: Free catalog ■ Leather handbags, gloves, belts, wallets, briefcases, and accessories. 201–460–4716.

Creative House, 100 Business Pkwy., Richardson, TX 75081: Free catalog ■ Luggage, briefcases, attache cases, handbags, and wallets. 800–527–5940; 903–231–3461 (in TX).

Crouch & Fitzgerald, 400 Madison Ave., New York, NY 10017: Free information ■ Leather goods with complimentary monogramming. 800–6–CROUCH; 212–755–5888 (in NY).

Dooney & Bourke, Inc., 1 Regent St., P.O. Box 841, South Norwalk, CT 06856: Free catalog ■ Leather goods and accessories. 800–243–5598.

Everlast Sport Bag, Rose Trunk Manufacturing Company, Inc., 800 Alabama Ave., Brooklyn, NY 11207: Free information ■ Carry-alls, tote bags, duffles, and shoulder bags. 212–993–0100.

Charolette Ford Trunks, Box 536, Spearman, TX 79081: Catalog $3 ■ Trunk repair supplies. 800–553–2649.

Georgetown Leather Design, Catalog Center, 10710 Tucker St., Beltsville, MD 20705: Free catalog ■ Leather clothing for men, women, and children; bags, boots; and attache cases and accessories. 301–937–5111.

Gotcha Bags, 1639 Almaden Rd., San Jose, CA 95125: Free information ■ Carry-alls, tote bags, duffles, and shoulder bags. 408–971–1500.

Hilco, Inc., Hilsport Division, 2102 Fair Park Blvd., Harlingen, TX 78550: Free information ■ Carry-alls, tote bags, duffles, and shoulder bags. 512–423–1885.

Innovation Luggage, 487 Hackensack Ave., River Edge, NJ 07661: Free information ■ Samsonite luggage. 800–722–1800.

Kelty Packs, Inc., P.O. Box 7048–A, St. Louis, MO 63141: Free catalog ■ Cordura nylon backpacks that convert to luggage.

Latonas Luxuries in Leather, P.O. Box 407, Blaistown, NJ 07825: Free catalog ■ Leather wallets, frames, desk accessories, handbags, attache cases, jewel cases, diaries and memorandum books, and luggage. 201–383–6681.

Madden/USA, 2400 Central Ave., Boulder, CO 80301: Free information ■ Carry-alls, tote bags, duffles, and shoulder bags. 303–442–5828.

New England Leather Accessories, P.O. Box 127, Rochester, NH 03867: Brochure $2 (refundable) ■ Leather card cases, diary covers, briefcases and portfolios, handbags and purses, and accessories. 603–332–0707.

North Beach Leather, Catalog Division, P.O. Box 99682, San Francisco, CA 94109: Free catalog ■ Leather clothing and accessories for men and women.

North Face, 999 Harrison St., Berkeley, CA 94710: Free information ■ Carry-alls, tote bags, duffles, and shoulder bags. 510–527–9700.

Remin, 510 Manhattan Rd., Joliet, IL 60433: Free brochure ■ Travel and all-purpose collapsible carts for luggage, cases, and boxes. 815–723–1940.

Rettinger Importing Company, 125 Enterprise, Secaucus, NJ 07096: Free information ■ Carry-alls, tote bags, duffles, and shoulder bags. 800–526–3142; 201–432–7400 (in NJ).

Sports Dynamics Corporation, 89 Leuning, Unit B–2, South Hackensack, NJ 07606: Free information ■ Carry-alls, tote bags, duffles, and shoulder bags. 800–322–DYNA; 201–342–0500 (in NJ).

Sunstar International, Ltd., Sunsport Sporting Goods, 24–16 Queens Plaza South, Long Island City, NY 11101: Free information ■ Carry-alls, tote bags, duffles, and shoulder bags. 718–706–0611.

Tic-La-Dex, 3443 Camino Del Rio South, Ste. 326, San Diego, CA 92108: Free catalog ■ Attaches, briefcases, lap top/overnighter computer case, aluminum cases, and pilot/catalog cases. 800–827–9467; 619–281–7242.

LUMBER

A & M Wood Specialty, Inc., 358 Eagle St. North, Cambridge, Ontario, Canada N3H 4S6: Free information ■ Hardwoods and veneers. 519–653–9322.

Adams Wood Products, Inc., 974 Forest Dr., Morristown, TN 37814: Free brochure ■ Kiln-dried oak, Honduras mahogany, walnut, cherry, maple, and pine turning squares; drawer sides; and carving blanks. 615–587–2942.

Anderson-McQuaid Company, Inc., 170 Fawcett St., Cambridge, MA 02138: Free price list ■ Custom and restoration moldings, flooring, and panelling. 617–876–3250.

The Berea Hardwoods Company, 125 Jacqueline Dr., Berea, OH 44017: Free information ■ Dagame, pear, plum, snakewood, cocobolo, padauk, bloodwood, pau rosa, camphor, bocote, zebrano, osage, tulipwood, mahogany, holly, wenge, and other exotic woods. 800–937–2373.

Boulter Plywood Corporation, 24 Broadway, Somerville, MA 02145: Free catalog ■ Domestic and exotic hardwood, other lumber, and marine plywood. 617–666–1340.

Bristol Valley Hardwoods, 4300 Bristol Valley Rd., Canandaigua, NY 14424: Catalog $1 ■ Exotic domestic and foreign hardwoods. 716–229–5695.

Broad-Axe Beam Company, RD 2, Box 417, West Brattleboro, VT 05301: Brochure $2 ■ Hand-hewn beams in wide pine flooring and beaded edge panelling. 802–257–0064.

Catskill Mountain Lumber Company, P.O. Box 450, Swan Lake, NY 12783: Free catalog ■ Kiln-dried oak, cherry, ash, hard maple, birch, beech, basswood, poplar, knotty and clear pine, and other hardwoods. 800–828–9663.

Center Lumber Company, 85 Fulton St., Box 2242, Paterson, NJ 07509: Free brochure ■ Imported and domestic hardwoods. 201–742–8300.

Certainly Wood, 11753 Big Tree Rd., East Aurora, NY 14052: Free catalog ■ Veneers and custom plywood. 716–655–0206.

Colonial Hardwoods, Inc., 7648 Dynatech Ct., Springfield, VA 22153: Free information ■ Custom cut hardwood and custom moldings. 703–451–9217.

Maurice L. Condon Company, 248 Ferris Ave., White Plains, NY 10603: Catalog $2 ■ Ash, basswood, birch, butternut, cherry, chestnut, ebony, maple, oak, poplar, rosewood, teak, and walnut, and in softwoods that include sugar pine, cypress, cedar, spruce, douglas fir, and hardwood plywood. 914–946–4111.

Constantine, 2050 Eastchester Rd., Bronx, NY 10461: Catalog $1 ■ Cabinet and furniture wood, veneers, plans, hardware, how-to books, carving tools and chisels, inlay designs, and other supplies. 212–792–1600.

Craftsman Wood Service, 1735 W. Cortland Ct., Addison, IL 60101: Catalog $1 ■ Kiln-dried wood, imported rare woods from worldwide sources, veneers, hand and power tools, hardware, finishing materials, clock movements and kits, and other supplies. 708–629–3100.

CraftWoods, 2101 Greenspring Dr., Timonium, MD 21093: Free information ■ Kiln-dried domestic and exotic woods, and woodworking, wood carving, and power tools. 410–561–9444.

D.F. Enterprises, 27 Wills Rd., Connellsville, PA 15425: Catalog $1 ■ Cabinet doors and drawers for do-it-yourself installation and design. 412–626–8870.

Eastwoods Company, RD 1, Hornell, NY 14843: Free information ■ Kiln-dried red oak, cherry flooring, tiger maple, curly cherry, and oak. 607–698–4490.

Fine Woods of Virginia, P.O. Box 160, Crozier, VA 23039: Free catalog ■ Kiln dried oak, cherry, walnut, maple, heart pine, poplar, ash, red cedar, basswood, and chestnut. 800–229–5058.

Gilmer Wood Company, 2211 NW St. Helens Rd., Portland, OR 97210: Free information ■ Rare and exotic woods, in logs, planks, and squares. 503–274–1271.

Groff & Hearne Lumber, 858 Scotland Rd., Quarryville, PA 17566: Free information ■ Walnut, cherry, and other woods. 717–284–0001.

The Harbor Sales Company, Inc., 1401 Russell St., Baltimore, MD 21230: Free information ■ Teak, okoume, sapele, fir, lauan, and other exotic woods. 800–345–1712.

Harper Hardware Company, 1712 E. Broad St., Richmond, VA 23223: Free information ■ Cherry, walnut, and mahogany dowels. 804–643–9007.

Hartwood, E. Golden Ln., P.O. Box 323, New Oxford, PA 17350: Free information ■ Basswood, birch, butternut, mahogany, maple, oak, red oak, white oak, teak, and cherry hardwoods. 717–624–4323.

Henegan's Wood Shed, 7760 Southern Blvd., West Palm Beach, FL 33411: Free list with long SASE ■ Exotic and native hard and soft woods, table slabs, and veneers. 407–793–1557.

Hobbywoods, Division Pioneer Mac Lea, Inc., 1305 Eastern Ave., Baltimore, MD 21231: Free information ■ Foreign and domestic hardwoods, veneers, hardware, and stains and finishes. 410–327–1116.

Joinery Company, P.O. Box 518, Tarboro, NC 27886: Portfolio $5 ■ Reproduction flooring, millwork, cabinets, furniture, and timber frames in antique heart pine. 919–823–3306.

Locust Grove Wood Shop, 375 W. Corrine Rd., West Chester, PA 19382: Free information ■ Walnut, cherry, white oak, red oak, poplar, white ash, curly maple, birdseye maple, curly cherry, and mahogany lumber and turning squares. 215–793–1380.

Marwood Hardwoods, 7790 Rockwell Ave., Philadelphia, PA 19111: Free information ■ Woodworking tools and domestic and imported hardwood and veneers. 800–255–8363; 215–725–0700 (in PA).

E.T. Moore Company, 3100 N. Hopkins Rd., Richmond, VA 23224: Free information ■ Pine mantels, columns, flooring, moldings, paneling, hand-hewn beams, and custom furniture and cabinets. 804–231–1823.

Talarico Hardwoods, RD 3, Box 3268, Mohnton, PA 19540: Free information ■

Kiln-dried white oak and sycamore cut to special sizes. 800–373–6097; 215–775–0400 (in PA).

Unicorn Universal Woods, Ltd., 4190 Steeles Ave. West, Woodbridge, Ontario, Canada L4L 3S8: Free catalog ■ Exotic and domestic woods and veneers. 416–851–2308.

United States Mahogany Corporation, 746 Lloyd Rd., Aberdeen, NJ 07747: Free information ■ Domestic and exotic hardwoods and hardwood plywood. 908–583–6300.

Woodcrafters Supply Company, 7703 Perry Hwy., Rt. 19, Pittsburgh, PA 15237: Free information ■ Domestic and imported woods, veneers, finishes, moldings, carving stock, hardware, inlays and bandings, plans, books, and tools. 412–367–4330.

Wood-Ply Lumber Corporation, 100 Bennington Ave., Freeport, NY 11520: Free price list ■ Exotic and domestic hardwoods. Includes ash, basswood, butternut, cherry, iroko, Philippine and South American mahogany, maple, padauk, red and white oak, wenge, birch, walnut, zebrawood, plywood and veneers. 516–378–2612.

Wood Shed, 1807 Elmwood Ave., Buffalo, NY 14207: Free catalog ■ Veneers. 716–876–4719.

Woodworker's Dream, Division Martin Guitar Company, 510 Sycamore St., Nazareth, PA 18064: Free information ■ Exotic and domestic hardwoods and musical instrument woods that include ebony, rosewood, mahogany, padauk, and others. 800–345–3103; 215–759–2064 (in PA).

Woodworkers Source, 5402 S. 40th St., Phoenix, AZ 85040: Free information ■ Exotic and domestic lumber, plywood, veneers, turning squares, and blanks. 800–423–2450; 602–437–4415 (in AZ).

MACRAME

ADA Village Candle, 3572 Roger B. Chaffee, Grand Rapids, MI 49508: Catalog 50¢ ■ Craft supplies, macrame materials, dough art mediums, candle-making supplies, and books. 616–247–8353.

Al Con Enterprises, P.O. Box 1060, Quincy, FL 32351: Free information ■ Macrame cord, accessories, and how-to books. 904–627–6996.

Craft King Mail Order Dept., P.O. Box 90637, Lakeland, FL 33804: Catalog $2 ■

Save from 40 to 60 percent on craft, needlework, and macrame supplies. 813–686–9600.

International Manufacturing Company, P.O. Box 405, Lillian Springs, FL 32351: Catalog $1 ■ Silk plants, trees, flowers, flower-arranging supplies, macrame cord and supplies, beads, and other craft supplies. 904–875–2918.

Pacific Wood Products, 5150 Edison Ave., Chino, CA 91710: Catalog $1 ■ Kits for building macrame-style furniture. 800–421–2781; 800–262–1638 (in CA).

Wood-Knot Crafts, 36 Chateau Dr., Monorville, NY 11949: Catalog $2 (refundable) ■ Macrame patterns, supplies, and how-to books.

MAGIC TRICKS & VENTRILOQUISM

Abbott's Magic Company, Colon, MI 49040: Catalog $7.50 ■ Magic and props for amateur and professional magicians. 616–432–3235.

Abracadabra Magic Shop, P.O. Box 714, Middlesex, NJ 08846: Catalog $3.95 ■ Magician's props, close-up and stage magic, juggling equipment, balloons, clown accessories, costumes, and make-up. 908–805–0200.

Axtell Expressions, 230 Glencrest Cir., Ventura, CA 93003: Catalog $2 ■ Creative magic for magicians. 805–642–7282.

Books by Mail, 1750 California Ave., Ste. 114, Corona, CA 91719: Free catalog with two first class stamps ■ Books and novelties for clowns, magicians, puppeteers, face painters, and balloon artists. 909-273-0900.

Mike Bornstein Magic, 319 W. 48th St., New York, NY 10036: Free information with long SASE ■ Magic and accessories for amateur and professional magicians.

Captain Dick's Dummy Depot, 2631 NW 95th St., Seattle, WA 98117: Information $2 with long SASE ■ New and used ventriloquist figures and books. 206–784–0883.

Chazpro Magic Company, 603 E. 13th, Eugene, OR 97404: Catalog $3 ■ Innovative magic for amateur and professional magicians. 503–345–0032.

Cosmar Magic, 6765 El Banquero Pl., San Diego, CA 92119: Catalog $7.50 ■ Magic

tricks and illusions for professional and amateur magicians. 619–287–3706.

Daytona Beach Magic Shop, 136 S. Beach St., Daytona Beach, FL 32114: Catalog $5 ■ Magic for amateur and professional magicians. 800–34–MAGIC; 904–672–5467 (in FL).

Flosso-Hornmann Magic Company, 45 W. 34th St., Room 607, New York, NY 10001: Free information ■ Magic tricks, juggling supplies, tarot cards, crystal balls, books, and props. 212–279–6079.

Hades' Seattle Magic Sentre, Box 2242, Seattle, WA 98111: Free information ■ Magic equipment for amateur and professional magicians. 206–624–4287.

Haine's House of Cards, Inc., 2514 Leslie Ave., Norwood, OH 45212: Free information ■ Card magic illusions. 513–531–6548.

Ken's Illusionarium, 3288 Main St., Vancouver, British Colombia, Canada V5V 3M5: Free newsletter ■ Books, magic equipment, and supplies and accessories for magicians, mentalists, clowns, jugglers, ventriloquists, and puppeteers. 604–875–9712.

Klamm Magic, 1412 Appleton, Independence, MO 64052: Free information with long SASE ■ Magic equipment for amateur and professional magicians. 816–461–4595.

Land of Magic & Novelties, Inc., 450 NE 20th St., Ste. 104, Boca Raton, FL 33431: Free information ■ Magic tricks and illusions for professional and amateur magicians, jokes and novelties, and books. 407–393–7352.

Hank Lee's Magic Factory, Mail Order Division, P.O. Box 789, Medford, MA 02155: Catalog $4.50 ■ Magic tricks and illusions, books, props, and jokes and novelties. 617–482–8749.

Magic by Bruce Chadwick, P.O. Box 6106, Fort Worth, TX 76115: Catalog $5 ■ Custom illusions and transporting cases. 817–927–0581.

Maher Studios, P.O. Box 420, Littleton, CO 80160: Catalog $1 ■ Ventriloquist dummies, scripts and dialogues, puppets, and how-to books. 303–798–6830.

Mecca Magic, Inc., 49 Dodd St., Bloomfield, NJ 07003: Free brochure ■ Magic trick, ventriloquism accessories, juggling supplies, make-up, clown equipment, balloons, costumes and wigs, puppets, and custom props. 201–429–7597.

David Meyer Magic Books, Box 427, Glenwood, IL 60425: Catalog $1 ■ New and old books on magic.

Morris Costumes, 3108 Monroe Rd., Charlotte, NC 28205: Catalog $15 + $1.98 (postage) ■ Magic tricks and special effects, costumes, clown props, masks, joke items, novelties, balloons, and books. 704–333–4653.

Morrissey Magic, Ltd., 2882 Dufferin St., Toronto, Ontario, Canada M6B 3S6: Catalog $5 ■ Magic equipment and entertainment supplies. 416–782–1393.

Quality Used & Rare Magic, Ron Allesi, 364 W. Main St., Fredonia, NY 14063: Catalog $3 ■ Used, rare, and antique magic apparatus, early magic sets, books, posters, and other magic memorabilia. 716–679–4073.

Sasco Magic, Inc., 11609 Proctor Rd., Philadelphia, PA 19116: Free catalog ■ Coin and other magic tricks. 215–698–2404.

Show-Biz Services, 1735 E. 26th St., Brooklyn, NY 11229: Free list ■ Books for magicians. 718–336–0605.

Stevens Magic Emporium, 3238 E. Douglas, Wichita, KS 67208: Four catalogs $7.50 ■ Professional magic and books. 316–683–9582.

Sun Magic, 716 E. Camelback Rd., Phoenix, AZ 85014: Catalog $2 ■ Close-up, stage, and parlor magic and illusions, books, and used and collectible magic items. 602–234–3886.

Louis Tannen, Inc., 6 W. 32nd St., 4th Floor, New York, NY 10001: Catalog $10.50 ■ Close-up and parlor magic, illusions, books, and props. 212–239–8383.

U.S. Toys, 2008 W. 103rd Terrace, Leawood, KS 66206: Free catalog ■ Parlor and professional magic illusions and props for magicians. 913–642–8244.

Venture Magic, 106 Main Street, Milford, OH 45150: Catalog $5 ■ Antique and new magic equipment and mental illusions for amateur and professional magicians. 513–248–1666.

Wheeler-Tanner Escapes, P.O. Box 349, Great Falls, MT 59403: Catalog $2 (refundable) ■ Accessories for escape artists. Includes straitjackets, locks and pick sets, handcuffs, leg irons, trick and specialty items, other items, and books. 406–453–4961.

Meir Yedid Magic, P.O. Box 55, Rego Park, NY 11374: Catalog $2 ■ Innovative magical mysteries for magicians.

MAILBOXES

Acorn Manufacturing Company, Inc., P.O. Box 31, Mansfield, MA 02048: Catalog $6 ■ Locking, forged iron mailboxes in vertical and horizontal styles. 800–835–0121; 508–339–4500 (in MA).

Brandon Industries, 4419 West Grove Dr., Dallas, TX 75248: Free brochure ■ Old-fashioned pedestal mailboxes in cast-aluminum, with solid brass letter slots and cylinder key locks; and cast-aluminum street lamps. 214–250–0456.

John Deere & Company, 1400 3rd Ave., Moline, IL 61265: Free catalog ■ Planters, outdoor furniture, fireplace accessories, gifts for pets, playthings for children, picnic accessories, lawn care and garden aids, mailboxes, and birdhouses and feeders. 800–544–2122.

Edisonville Wood Shop, 1916 Edisonville Rd., Strasburg, PA 17579: Brochure $1 ■ Handcrafted all-wood mailboxes with cedar shingles. 717–687–17579.

Frank's Country Store, 162 Washington Ave., North Haven, CT 96473: Free brochure ■ Handcrafted mailboxes with cedar shingle roofs. 800–875–1960.

Hearth & Home, 3242 Severn at 17th St., Metairie, LA 70002: Free catalog ■ Mailboxes, fireplace accessories, switch plates, and gifts. 504–454–8907.

Home Decorators Collection, 2025 Concourse Dr., St. Louis, MO 63146: Free catalog ■ Mailboxes in contemporary and other styles. 800–245–2217; 314–993–1516 (in MO).

Mel-Nor Industries, 303 Gulf Bank, Houston, TX 77037: Catalog $1 ■ Mailboxes, park benches, swings, lights, and other landscaping items. 713–445–3485.

Redwood Unlimited, P.O. Box 8326, Calabasas, CA 91302: Catalog $3 ■ Personalized, custom wood mailboxes. 800–283–1717.

The Renovator's Supply, Renovator's Old Mill, Millers Falls, MA 01349: Catalog $3 ■ Victorian-style solid brass mailboxes, decor accessories, and gifts. 413–659–2211.

Stencil Ease, P.O. Box 1127, Old Saybrook, CT 06475: Free information ■ Mailbox kit ready for finishing. Includes art and alphabet stencils, outdoor stenciling paint, and stenciling brush. 401–339–9500.

York Mountain Mailbox, 3729 N. Claremont, Fresno, CA 93727: Brochure 25¢ ■ Handcrafted wooden mailboxes. 209–291–2878.

MAILING LISTS

Advon, Drawer B, Shelley, ID 83274: Free information ■ Mixed states mailing lists with adhesive labels. 800–992–3866.

American Business Lists, P.O. Box 27347, Omaha, NE 68127: Catalog $2 ■ Mailing lists compiled from the Yellow Pages for businesses, consumers, and other groups. 402–331–7169.

American List Counsel, Inc., 88 Orchard Rd., CN 5219, Princeton, NJ 08543: Free catalog ■ Mailing lists, special high interest databases, and telemarketing lists. 800–ALC–LIST.

Cahners Direct Mail Services, 249 W. 17th St., New York, NY 10011: Free information ■ Mailing lists. 800–537–7930; 212–645–0067 (in NY).

Norman Hill, P.O. Box 1560, Jensen Beach, FL 34958: Free information ■ Computerized mailing lists. 800–554–LIST; 407–334–5205 (in FL).

List Associates, 116 Kellogg Ave., Ames, IA 50010: Free information ■ Zip sorted mailing lists on pressure sensitive labels. 515–232–6789.

List-Masters, Box 750, Wantagh, NY 11793: Free information ■ Mailing lists on adhesive labels. 800–356–8664.

McAfee & Company, 1815 Carpenter St., Bridgeport, TX 76026: Free information ■ Zip-code sorted mailing lists on pressure-sensitive labels. 800–654–5541; 817–683–2462 (in TX).

Quality Lists, P.O. Box 6060, Seaford, NY 11783: Free information ■ Computer-generated mailing lists on peel-and-stick labels in Zip-code order. 800–356–6392.

MAPS

American Map Corporation, Langenscheidt Publishers, Inc., 46–35 54th Rd., Maspeth, NY 11378: Free information ■ Maps, travel guides, and atlases. 718–784–0055.

W. Graham Arader Maps & Prints, 1000 Boxwood Ct., King of Prussia, PA 19406: Free catalog ■ Rare maps and prints for collectors. 215–825–6570.

Bikecentennial, P.O. Box 8308, Missoula, MT 59807: Free catalog ■ Bike touring maps and books. 406–721–1776.

Carta Nova Publishing, P.O. Box 15, New York, NY 10156: Free information ■ United States, European, and world maps. 212–730–0518.

Complete Traveler Bookstore, 199 Madison Ave., New York, NY 10016: Catalog $1 ■ Travel guides, books, and maps. 212–685–9007.

Richard Fitch, 2324 Calle Halcon, Santa Fe, NM 87505: Catalog $3 ■ Antique maps and prints from the United States, Mexico, Canada, North America, and other countries. 505–982–2939.

Gold Bug, P.O. Box 588, Alamo, CA 94507: Free brochure ■ Information on maps published in the 17th and 18th centuries and reproductions of old maps for prospectors and genealogical research buffs.

Hubbard Maps, P.O. Box 400, Chippewa Falls, WI 54729: Free catalog ■ United States, world, and national park maps. Available framed or unframed. 800–323–8368.

Interarts, Ltd., 15 Mount Auburn St., Cambridge, MA 02138: Free information ■ Map books and wall maps. 617–354–4655.

Map Express, P.O. Box 280445, Lakewood, CO 80228: Free catalog ■ Maps and photographs from the United States Geological Service. 800–MAP–0039; 303–987–9384 (in CO).

David Morgan, 11812 Northcreek Pkwy., Ste. 103, Bothell, WA 98011: Free catalog ■ Maps of Great Britain for travel or genealogy research. 206–485–2132.

National Cartographic Information Center, United States Geological Survey, 709 National Center, Reston, VA 22092: Free catalog ■ United States cartographic data and maps. 703–648–5798

Kenneth Nebenzahl, Inc., Glencove, IL 60022: Catalog $3 ■ Rare, old maps from around the world. 708–835–0515.

Northern Map Company, 103 Cherokee Cir., Dunnellon, FL 32630: Catalog $1 ■ Maps from the Civil War; old state, city, railroad, and county maps, from 70 to 120 years old; maps from Canada; and map kits. 904–489–3967.

The Old Print Gallery, 1220 31st St. NW, Washington, DC 20007: Catalog $3 ■ Prints and maps from the 18th- and 19th-century. 202–965–1818.

Philadelphia Print Shop, Ltd., 8441 Germantown Ave., Philadelphia, PA 19118: Catalog $4 ■ Antique maps, prints, and books. 215–242–4750.

Thomas Brothers Maps & Books, 17731 Cowan St., Irvine, CA 92714: Free catalog ■ Atlases, street guides, and maps. 714–863–1984.

Travelers Bookstore, 113 Corporation Rd., Hyannis, MA 02601: Free catalog ■ Maps and books on travel. 800–821–3535; 800–622–3535 (in MA).

United Nations Publications, Room DC2–853, New York, NY 10017: Free information ■ Maps and United Nations publications. 212–963–8323.

MARBLES

Stan Block, P.O. Box 515, Trumbull, CT 06611: Free list with two 1st class stamps ■ Marbles and related items.

Essol's, P.O. Box 176, Sisterville, WV 26175: Free information with long SASE ■ Chinese checker and rainbow glass marbles.

Spice Island Traders, 21546 Golden Triangle Rd., Saugus, CA 91350: Free list with long SASE ■ Marbles and related items.

MARTIAL ARTS

Asian World of Martial Arts, Inc., 917 Arch St., Philadelphia, PA 19107: Free catalog ■ Training and protective equipment, weapons, uniforms, and belts. 215–925–1161.

The Brute Group, 2126 Spring St., P.O. Box 2788, Reading, PA 19609: Free information ■ Equipment and supplies. 800–397–2788; 215–678–4050 (in PA).

Canadian Martial Arts & Sporting Supplies, P.O. Box 518, Milliken Post Office, Milliken, Ontario, Canada L0H 1K0: Catalog $2 ■ Uniforms, books, posters, weapons, and protective equipment for Judo, Karate, Kung-Fu, and Tae Kwon Do.

Century Martial Art Supply, Inc., 1705 National Blvd., Midwest City, OK 73110: Catalog $1 ■ Sparring gear, belts, and clothing. 800–626–2787.

Co-Mart International, P.O. Box 16194, San Francisco, CA 94116: Free information ■ Training equipment, weapons, uniforms, and shoes. 415–759–8640.

Dolan's Sports, Inc., 26 Hwy. 547, P.O. Box 26, Farmingdale, NJ 07727: Free catalog ■ Training equipment, uniforms, custom printed T-shirts, safety equipment, shoes, Samurai swords, heavy bags, and books. 201–938–6656.

J. Ehara International, Inc., 47 Sanford St., Metairie, LA 70006: Free information ■ Clothing, protective gear, shoes, and other equipment. 504–456–2774.

Genesport Industries, Ltd., Hokkaido Karate Equipment Manufacturing Company, 150 King St., Montreal, Quebec, Canada H3C 2P3: Free information ■ Belts, clothing, and equipment. 514–861–1856.

Gym Equipment Company, P.O. Box 144, Ridgewood, NJ 07451: Free information ■ Clothing and belts. 201–447–2884.

Honda Martial Arts Supply, 61 W. 23rd St., New York, NY 10010: Free information ■ Clothing, protective and safety equipment, shoes, books, and training gear. 212–620–4050.

Jhoon Rhee Sports, Inc., 9000 Menden Hall Ct., Columbia, MD 21045: Free information ■ Laceless chops and uniforms and protective gear that includes shin guards, groin cups, footwear, male and female rib protectors, and forearm protectors. 410–381–2900.

John-Paul, Ltd., 314 Broadway, Rt. E1, Saugus, MA 01906: Free information ■ Clothing and belts. 617–233–2399.

Joy Enterprises, 801 Broad Ave., Ridgefield, NJ 07657: Free information ■

Belts, clothing, and equipment. 201–943–5920.

Kiyota Company, Inc., 2326 N. Charles St., Baltimore, MD 21218: Free information ■ Clothing, protective gear, and shoes. 410–366–8275.

K.P. Sporting Goods, 4141 Business Center Dr., Fremont, CA 94538: Free information ■ Chop gloves, foot and instep protectors, chest and rib guards, shin guards, and kicking targets. 800–227–0500.

Macho Products, Inc., 2550 Kirby Ave. NE, Palm Bay, FL 32905: Free catalog ■ Equipment and supplies, belts, and clothing. 800–327–6812; 407–729–6137 (in FL).

Martial Arts Supplies Company, Inc., 10711 Venice Blvd., Los Angeles, CA 90034: Free information ■ Multiple attack stands with lock-in-place hangers, striking bags, belts, and clothing. 213–870–9866.

O'Hara Publications, Inc., 1813 Victory Pl., P.O. Box 7728, Burbank, CA 91510: Free information ■ Books on martial arts. 818–843–4444.

Omaha Martial Arts Supply, 909 S. 27th St., Omaha, NE 68105: Free information ■ Training bag stands. 402–346–7952.

G. Pacillo Company, Inc., P.O. Box 1643, Buffalo, NY 14216: Free information ■ Belts, clothing, and equipment. 716–873–4333.

Panther Productions, 1010 Calle Negocio, San Clemente, CA 92672: Free catalog ■ Training videos for beginners and advanced persons. 800–332–4442.

Pro-Mate USA, 3135 Diablo Ave., Hayward, CA 94545: Free information ■ Clothing and belts. 510–782–8471.

Pro-Tect Manufacturing, Inc., 1251 Ferguson Ave., St. Louis, MO 63133: Free information ■ Protection and safety gear, uniforms, colored belts, and kicking shields. 800–325–1652.

S & P of New York Budo, Inc., 6049 Transit Rd., P.O. Box 2, Depew, NY 14043: Free information ■ Uniforms, equipment, weapons, books, belts, and videotapes for karate, judo, aikido, and kendo. 716–681–7911.

Tho-Ro Products, Inc., Division Eagle Button Company, 335 Paterson Plank Rd.,

Carlstadt, NJ 07072: Free information ■ Clothing and belts. 201–935–3992.

Treco Products, Inc., P.O. Box 6246, Newport News, VA 23606: Free information ■ Power stretching exercise equipment. 804–873–1177.

Uniquity, 215 4th St., P.O. Box 6, Galt, CA 95632: Free information ■ Clothing and belts. 800–521–7771; 209–745–2111 (in CA).

MATCHBOOK COVERS

Political Matchcovers, 3417 Clayborne Ave., Alexandria, VA 22306: Free information ■ Political matchbook covers. 703–768–3932.

Writewell Company, 5850 W. 80th St., Indianapolis, IN 46278: Free information ■ Loose-leaf matchbook cover albums with padded covers of leather-grained vinyl. Personalization available. 317–871–6700.

METAL CRAFTING & SILVERSMITHING

Ackley's Rock & Stamps, 3230 N. Stone Ave., Colorado Springs, CO 80907: Catalog $1 (refundable) ■ Silversmithing supplies. 719–633–1153.

Allcraft Tool & Supply Company, 666 Pacific St., Brooklyn, NY 11207: Catalog $2.50 ■ Tools and supplies for jewelry-making, metal crafting and casting, and silversmithing. 800–645–7124.

Alpha Supply, Inc., 1225 Hollis St., Box 2133, Bremerton, WA 98310: Catalog $1 (refundable with $15 order) ■ Copper wire and sheet, silver wire and sheet, and silversmithing supplies. 206–377–5629.

The Amber Company, 5643 Cahuenga Blvd., North Hollywood, CA 91601: Free catalog ■ Silver and silversmithing supplies. 818–509–5730.

American Art Clay Company, Inc., 4717 W. 16th St., Indianapolis, IN 46222: Free catalog ■ Ceramic and metal-enameling supplies and equipment. Includes clays, kilns, pottery-making equipment, glazes, tools, and coloring materials. 800–428–3239.

ARE, Inc., Rt. 16, Box 8, Greensboro Bend, VT 05842: Catalog $3 ■ Silver, gold, pewter, base metals, tools and equipment, sup-

plies, findings, chains, and semiprecious stones. 800–736–4273.

Bourget Bros., 1636 11th St., Santa Monica, CA 90404: Catalog $5 ■ Copper wire and sheet, gold wire and sheet, silver wire and sheet, and silversmithing supplies. 800–828–3024; 310–450–6556 (in CA).

Campbell Tools Company, 2100 Selma Rd., Springfield, OH 45505: Catalog $2 ■ Lathes, mills, taps, dies, micrometers, miniature screws, cutting tools, and brass, aluminum, steel, and other metals. 513–322–8562.

Cardinal Engineering, Inc., RR 1, Box 163, Cameron, IL 61423: Free brochure ■ Metal working and machining metals and supplies.

Country Accents, P.O. Box 437, Montoursville, PA 17754: Catalog $5 ■ Hand-crafted metal panels for pie safes, cupboards, kitchen cabinets, and other projects; pierced metal kits and patterns; and tools and equipment, and supplies. 717–478–4127.

Christopher E. Dunham, Brassfounder, P.O. Box 423, Worthington, MA 01098: Catalog $2 ■ Hand-finished sand-cast bronze, brass, and molded pewter items. 413–238–5937.

East West DyeCom, P.O. Box 12294, Roanoke, VA 24024: Catalog $5 ■ Pre-anodized aluminum sheets and colored tubing, dyes, kits, books, and other supplies. 703–345–4241.

Ebersole Lapidary Supply, Inc., 11417 West Hwy. 54, Wichita, KS 67209: Catalog $2 ■ Gold sheet and wire, silver sheet and wire, and silversmithing supplies. 316–722–4771.

G & G's Miracle House, 5621 W. Hemlock St., P.O. Box 23234, Milwaukee, WI 53223: Catalog $1 ■ Metal findings and tools. 800–558–5513; 800–242–3403 (in WI).

T.B. Hagstoz & Son, Inc., 709 Sansom St., Philadelphia, PA 19106: Catalog $5 (refundable with $25 order) ■ Metal findings, jeweler's tools, casting equipment, gold and silver solders, and gold, silver, gold-filled metals, copper, bronze, brass nickel, silver, and pewter. 800–922–1006; 215–922–1627 (in PA).

Lydia Withington Holmes, Pewterer, Barton Hill, Stew, MA 01775: Brochure $2 ($1 refundable) ■ Pewter spoons, buttons, and ornaments cast in antique molds. 508–568–8838.

Indian Jewelers Supply Company, P.O. Box 1774, Gallup, NM 87305: Set of 4 catalogs $5 ■ Precious and base metals that include copper wire and sheet, silver wire and sheet, and silversmithing supplies; findings in precious and base metals; metalsmithing equipment, lapidary tools and supplies, and engraving tools and supplies; and semi-precious stones, shells, and coral. 505–722–4451.

K & S Engineering, 6917 W. 59th St., Chicago, IL 60638: Catalog 25¢ ■ Aluminum and other metal tubing, rods, and sheets. 312–586–8503.

Kingsley North, Inc., P.O. Box 216, Norway, MI 49870: Free information ■ Silversmithing supplies, power tools, and casting, lapidary, and glass polishing equipment. 800–338–9280.

Lonnie's, Inc., 7153 E. Apache Trail, Mesa, AZ 85207: Free information ■ Tools, equipment, and supplies for jewelers, casters, silversmiths, and lapidarists. 602–832–2641.

MBM Sales, Ltd., 18170 W. Davidson Rd., Brookfield, WI 53045: Catalog $2 ■ Hard-to-find metals and fasteners in small quantities. 800–657–0721; 414–786–4276 (in WI).

Plymouth Pewter Works, P.O. Box 1696, Plymouth, MA 02360: Free catalog with long SASE ■ Hand-finished and polished lead-free molded pewter spoons and figurines.

Pyramid of Urbana, 2107 N. High Cross Rd., Urbana, IL 61801: Free catalog ■ Kilns, tools, supplies, metal enamels, copper shapes and findings, tooling foils, other craft supplies, office accessories, art supplies, and school equipment. 217–328–3099.

Red & Green Minerals, Inc., 7595 W. Florida Ave., Lakewood, CO 80226: Free information ■ Silversmithing supplies. 303–985–5559.

Shapiro Supply Company, 1259 Delaware, St. Louis, MO 63133: Free information ■ Aluminum, brass, and stainless in angles, channels, rounds, bars, tubing, flats, pipe, sheets, and plates. 314–727–5588.

Stauffer's Pewter Shop, 707 W. Brubaker Valley Rd, Lititz, PA 17543: Brochure with long SASE ■ Handmade, early-period pewter reproductions. 717–626–7067.

Three Feathers Pewter, Box 232, Shreve, OH 44676: Catalog $3 ■ Custom cast and hand-spun original and reproduction pewter items and ornaments. 216–567–2047.

The Tinner, P.O. Box 353, Spencer, NC 28159: Catalog $1.50 ■ Handcrafted reproduction tinware. 704–637–5149.

METAL DETECTORS

Alpha Supply, Inc., 1225 Hollis St., Box 2133, Bremerton, WA 98310: Catalog $1 (refundable with $15 order) ■ Metal detectors, prospecting equipment, jewelry-making tools, and gem-finishing equipment. 206–377–5629.

Brook's Detectors, Box 25038, Montgomery, AL 36125: Free information ■ Metal detectors and accessories. 205–281–1806.

C & C Detectors, 1405 Creston Park Dr., Janesville, WI 53545: Free catalog ■ Metal detectors. 800–356–6636; 608–754–0742 (in WI).

Cal-Gold, 2569 E. Colorado Blvd., Pasadena, CA 91107: Free catalog ■ Metal detectors, supplies for miners and geologists, maps, and books. 818–792–6161.

Clevenger Detector Sales, 8206 N. Oak, Kansas City, MO 64118: Free information ■ New and used detectors. 816–436–0697.

Cochran & Associates, Inc., P.O. Box 20148, Bowling Green, KY 42102: Free information ■ Easy-to-operate metal detectors that detect ferrous and non-ferrous metals in mineralized soil areas, beaches, salt water, and other areas. 502–782–2224.

Compass Electronics Corporation, P.O. Box 366, Forest Grove, OR 97116: Free information ■ Metal detectors. 503–357–2111.

D & K Prospecting Headquarters, 13809 Southeast Division, Portland, OR 97236: Free information ■ Metal detectors and prospecting equipment and supplies. 800–542–4653; 503–761–1521 (in OR).

The Detector Warehouse, P.O. Box 381, Plainwell, MI 49080: Free catalog ■ Metal detectors, books, tapes, audio tapes, headphones, dredges, and digging tools. 800–828–1455.

Detector Electronics Corporation, 873 Concord St., Framingham, MA 01701: Free brochure ■ Metal detectors. 508–626–0244.

Fisher Research Laboratory, 200 W. Wilmott Rd., Los Banos, CA 93635: Free information ■ Metal detectors. 209–826–3292.

JW Fishers Manufacturing, Inc., 65 Anthony St., Berkeley, MA 02779: Free information ■ Underwater metal detectors. 800–822–4644; 508–822–7330 (in MA).

Gardiner Electronics, 3131 N. 35th Ave., Phoenix, AZ 85017: Free catalog ■ Metal detectors and accessories.

Garrett Metal Detectors, 2814 National Dr., Garland, TX 75041: Free buyer's guide ■ Metal detectors. 214–278–6151.

Golddigger, 253 N. Main, Moab, UT 84532: Catalog $1 ■ Metal detectors. 801–259–5150.

House of Treasure Hunters, 5712 El Cajon Blvd., San Diego, CA 92115: Free information ■ Metal detectors and gold prospecting equipment. 619–286–2600.

Kansas/Texas Detector Sales, P.O. Box 17015, Fort Worth, TX 76102: Free information with long SASE ■ Metal detectors. 800–876–3463; 817–498–2228 (in TX).

Kellyco Detector Distributors, 1085 Belle Ave., Winter Springs, FL 32708: Free information with long SASE ■ Metal detectors. 407–699–8700.

Metal Detectors of Minneapolis, 3746 Cedar Ave, South, Minneapolis, MN 55407: Free information ■ Metal detectors, books and maps, accessories, recovery tools, and audio-video tapes. 612–721–1901.

Mid-America Sales, 5550 Stage Rd., Bartlett, TN 38134: Free information ■ Metal detectors, books, and accessories. 800–345–6515.

Mid-West Metal Detectors, 8338 Pillsbury Ave. South, Bloomington, MN 55420: Free information ■ Metal detectors, books, and accessories. 612–881–5254.

Mississippi River Trading Company, Inc., 2980 Austin Peay, Memphis, TN 38128: Free information ■ Metal detectors, books, and accessories. 800–535–6868.

Northwoods General Store, 163 Nob Hill East, Colgate, WI 53711: Free price list ■ Metal detectors. 414–628–0400.

Pacific Detectors, P.O. Box 51158, Pacific Grove, CA 93950: Free information ■ Metal detectors, books, and accessories. 800–637–6601.

Tesoro Electronics, 5289 W. Montebello Ave., Glendale, AZ 85301: Free information ■ Easy-to-use, light-weight metal detectors with high gain sensitivity. 602–934–3999.

Thomas Electroscopes, P.O. Box 5058, South Williamsport, PA 17701: Free catalog ■ Long-range induction metal detectors for treasure hunting and prospecting. 800–323–9275.

White's Electronics, 1011 Pleasant Valley Rd., Sweet Home, OR 97386: Free information ■ Metal detectors. 800–547–6911.

MICROSCOPES

Edmund Scientific Company, Edscorp Bldg., Barrington, NJ 08007: Free catalog ■ Microscopes, magnifiers, weather forecasting instruments, magnets, telescopes, binoculars, lasers, and other science equipment. 609–573–6260.

Mineralogical Research Company, 15840 E. Alta Vista Way, San Jose, CA 95127: Free list with long SASE and 2 first class stamps ■ Microscopes, rare mineral specimens, meteorites, micromounts, specimen boxes, and other supplies. 408–923–6800.

MILITARY MEMORABILIA

General

Avalon Forge, 409 Gun Rd., Baltimore, MD 21227: Catalog $1 ■ Reproductions of 18th-century military collectibles. 410–242–8431.

British Collectibles, Ltd., 1727 Wilshire Blvd., Santa Monica, CA 90403: Catalog $8 ■ Authentic collectibles from the 1800s through World War II. 310–453–3322.

The Bunker, 1842 E. 17th, P.O. Box 14196, Tulsa, OK 74159: Catalog $8 (refundable) ■ World War I and II German and Japanese uniforms, helmets, and equipment.

Collectors Antiquities, Inc., 60 Manor Rd., Staten Island, NY 10310: Catalog $10 ■ Military antiques, memorabilia, and other collectibles. 212–981–0973.

Collector's Armoury, 800 Slaters Ln., P.O. Box 59, Alexandria, VA 22313: Catalog $2 ■ Replica model guns, medals, armour, swords, helmets, and military collectibles. 800–544–3456.

Collectors Heritage, Inc., P.O. Box 355, Bernardsville, NJ 07924: Catalog $5 (refundable) ■ Reproduction museum-quality military swords, knives, and bayonets. 908–953–0938.

N. Flayderman & Company, Inc., P.O. Box 2446, Fort Lauderdale, FL 33303: Catalog $10 ■ Antique guns, swords, and knives; and nautical, western, and military collectibles from the Civil War through World War II. 305–761–8855.

Galvanized Yankee, 918 Caroline St., Fredericksburg, VA 22401: Annual catalog subscription $6 ■ Military collectibles from the Civil War through World War II. 703–373–1886.

Dennis Heath Civil War Collectibles, Rt. 1, Box 55, Deep Run, NC 28525: Annual catalog subscription $5 ■ Civil War weapons, relics, and accouterments. 919–569–8781.

Historical Military Art & Collectibles, P.O. Drawer 1806, Lafayette, CA 94549: Free catalog ■ Collector books, limited edition military art, and military, espionage and controversial political collectibles. 510–283–1771.

Jacques Noel Jacobsen, 60 Manor Rd., Ste. 1000, Staten Island, NY 10310: Catalog $10 ■ Antiques and military collectibles, insignia, weapons, photos and paintings, band instruments, and Indian and Western items. 718–981–0973.

C & D Jarnagin Company, Rt. 3, Box 217, Corinth, MS 38834: Catalog $2 ■ Replica uniforms and equipment from 1800 to 1871. 601–287–4977.

Legendary Arms, Inc., P.O. Box 20198, Greeley Square Station, New York, NY 10001: Free information ■ Reproduction military period knives and swords. 212–532–9055.

Meehan Military Posters, P.O. Box 477, New York, NY 10028: Catalog $10 (refundable) ■ Genuine war posters. 212–634–5683.

Museum Replicas Limited, P.O. Box 840, Conyers, GA 30207: Catalog $1 ■ Reproductions of authentic museum-quality, historically accurate replicas of weapons and period battle wear.

Pieces of History, Box 1580, Wildomar, CA 92395: Catalog $1 ■ Hundreds of medals from around the world. 714–244–5971.

Red Lancer, P.O. Box 8056, Mesa, AZ 85214: Catalog $6 ■ Original 19th-century military art, rare books, Victorian era campaign medals and helmets, and toy soldiers. 602–964–9667.

Soldier Shop, Inc., 1222 Madison Ave., New York, NY 10128: Catalog $5 ■ Antique and new toy soldiers, painted miniatures and kits, military collectibles, paintings, weapons, medals, books, and prints. 212–535–6788.

Theme Prints, Ltd., P.O. Box 123, Bayside, NY 11361: Free brochure ■ Books, antique arms, historic documents, letters and autographs from the early Revolutionary era to early Hollywood. Includes Civil War memorabilia. 718–225–4067.

Zalkin Military Collectibles, P.O. Box 1585, Homestead, FL 33090: Catalog $5 ■ War relics from the Civil War to the present. 305–271–5690.

Civil War

ABCDEF Bookshop, 726 N. Hanover St., Carlisle, PA 17013: Catalog $1 (refundable) ■ Civil War books. 717–243–5802.

Dale C. Anderson Company, 4 W. Confederate Ave., Gettysburg, PA 17325: Annual catalog subscription (6 issues) $12 ■ Military arms, accouterments, and collectibles.

Armchair General's Merchantile, 1008 Adams, Bay City, MI 48708: Catalog $2 (refundable) ■ Games, miniatures, and books for Civil War enthusiasts. 517–892–6177.

Bohemian Brigade Book Shop & Publishers, 8705 Vultee Ln., Knoxville, TN 37923: Catalog $1 ■ Civil War books and military collectibles. 615–694–8227.

Bonnet Brigade, Pat Wullenjohn, P.O. Box 28, Fremont, CA 94537: Catalog $3 ■ Civil War period clothing, equipment, accouterments, weapons, and camping equipment.

Broadfoot Publishing Company, 1907 Buena Vista Cir., Wilmington, NC 28405: Free catalog ■ Old and new books about the Civil War. 919–686–4816.

Cedar Creek Relic Shop, P.O. Box 232, Middletown, VA 22645: Annual catalog subscription $6 ■ Civil War relics. 703–869–5207.

Civil War Antiques, David W. Taylor, P.O. Box 87, Sylvania, OH 43560: Catalog $5 ■

Civil War antiques for collectors. 419–882–5547.

Civil War Shop, 408 LaFayette Rd., Fort Oglethorpe, GA 30742: Price list $3 ■ Civil War collectible muskets, swords, relics, and documents. 404–866–9779.

Collector's Armoury, Inc., 800 Slaters Ln., P.O. Box 59, Alexandria, VA 22313: Free catalog ■ Civil War memorabilia, World War II medals, Samurai swords, flags, and replica model guns. 800–544–3456.

Crescent City Sutler, 17810 Hwy. 57, Evansville, IN 47711: Catalog $2 ■ Reproduction and original Civil War uniforms and equipment. 812–983–4217.

Der Dienst, P.O. Box 221, Lowell, MI 49331: Catalog $2 ■ Replica Civil War medals.

Fall Creek Suttlery, P.O. Box 92, Whitestown, IN 46075: Catalog $2 (refundable) ■ Authentic mid-19th century military and civilian clothing and accessories, reproduction Civil War guns, accouterments, tents, and uniforms. 317–769–5355.

Farnsworth Military Gallery, 401 Baltimore St., Gettysburg, PA 17325: Free information ■ New, used, and rare books on the Civil War and art prints. 717–334–8838.

Gibson's Paper Antiques, 303 Sequoyah Dr., Blountville, TN 37617: Free information with long SASE ■ Authentic Civil War newspapers. 615–323–2427.

Will Gorges Antiques, 308 Simmons St., New Bern, NC 28560: Catalog $10 ■ Authentic, original Civil War uniforms, weapons, and photographs. 919–636–3039.

Gart Hendershott, P.O. Box 22520, Little Rock, AR 72221: Catalog $3 ■ Autographs, photographs, and imprints of the Civil War era. 501–224–7555.

Heritage Militaria, P.O. Box 3449, Truckee, CA 95734: Free catalog ■ Uniforms, medals, headgear, and other military memorabilia.

The Historical Shop, Box 73244, Metairie, LA 70003: Catalog $1 ■ Confederate photos, documents, postal items, autographs, currency, slavery items, and other collectibles. 504–467–2532.

Historical Store, Ltd., 203 Harrison St. SE, Leesburg, VA 22075: Free information ■

Civil War collectible reprints, books, currency, photos, and miniatures. 703–771–1110.

Indian Hollow Antiques, 298 W. Old Cross Rd., New Market, VA 22844: Free information with long SASE ■ Weapons, uniforms, equipment, documents, money, buttons, and other Civil War militaria. 703–740–3959.

Kennesaw Mountain Military Antiques, 1810 Old Hwy. 41, Kennesaw, GA 30144: Catalog subscription $6 ■ Civil War collectibles. 404–424–JACK.

L & G Early Arms, P.O. Box 113, Amelia, OH 45102: Free list with long SASE ■ Authentic Civil War guns.

Bob Lurate Civil War Material, P.O. Box 1428, Lexington, VA 24450: Free information ■ Civil War memorabilia. 703–463–2615.

Northern Map Company, 103 Cherokee Cir., Dunnellon, FL 32630: Catalog $1 ■ Maps from the Civil War; old state, city, railroad, and county maps, from 70 to 120 years old; maps from Canada; and map kits. 904–489–3967.

Olde Soldier Books, Inc., 18779 N. Frederick Ave., Gaithersburg, MD 20879: Free information ■ Civil War books, documents, autographs, prints, and Americana. 301–963–2929.

Old Sutler John, P.O. Box 174, Westview Station, Binghamton, NY 13905: Catalog $2 ■ Reproduction Civil War guns, bayonets, swords, uniforms, leather items, and other collectibles. 607–775–4434.

Owens Civil War Books, P.O. Box 13622, Richmond, VA 23225: Free catalog and search service ■ New, used, and rare books on the Civil War era. 804–272–8888.

Rapine Bullet Manufacturing Company, P.O. Box 1119, East Greenville, PA 18041: Catalog $2 ■ Civil War bullet molds. 215–679–5413.

The Regimental Quartermaster, P.O. Box 553, Hatboro, PA 19040: Catalog $2 ■ Civil War era reproductions. 215–672–9020.

Sword & Saber, P.O. Box 4417, Gettysburg, PA 17325: Catalog $5 ■ Confederate and Union documents, covers, letters, newspapers, photographs, and other slavery-related items. 717–334–0205.

United States Cavalry Museum, P.O. Box 2160, Fort Riley, KS 66442: Free catalog ■

Limited edition prints, books, and other collectibles. 913–239–2737.

Upper Mississippi Valley Mercantile Company, 1505 W. 17th St., Davenport, IA 52804: Catalog $2 (refundable) ■ Uniforms, tinware, tents, leather goods, hand-forged items, camp furniture, and other collectibles. 319–322–0896.

Wildman's Civil War Surplus, 2879 S. Main St., Kennesaw, GA 30144: Price list $2 ■ Rare and antique guns, books, and other Civil War collectibles. 404–422–1785.

Zalkin Military Collectibles, P.O. Box 1585, Homestead, FL 33090: Catalog $5 ■ Collectibles from the Civil War to the present. 305–271–5690.

War Medals & Souvenirs

Collector's Armoury, Inc., 800 Slaters Ln., P.O. Box 59, Alexandria, VA 22313: Free catalog ■ Collectible World War II medals, Samurai swords, flags, Civil War memorabilia, and replica model guns. 800–544–3456.

Der Dienst, P.O. Box 221, Lowell, MI 49331: Catalog $2 ■ Replicas of Civil War medals.

R. Andrew Fuller Company, Box 2071, Pawtucket, RI 02861: Free catalog ■ Medals and ribbons and display cases.

W.D. Grissom, P.O. Box 12001, Chula Vista, CA 91912: Free list with long SASE ■ United States and foreign military medals.

Historical Military Art & Collectibles, Postal Drawer 1806, Lafayette, CA 94549: Free catalog ■ World War II and older military collectibles that include medals, flags, badges, pins, and patches. 510–283–1771.

Peter Hlinka, Historical Americana, P.O. Box 310, New York, NY 10028: Free catalog ■ Military and civilian decorations and medals from the United States and foreign countries, military award certificates, insignia items, books, and other Americana. 212–409–6407.

Hoover's Manufacturing Company, 4015 Progress Blvd., Peru, IL 61354: Free catalog ■ Vietnam, Korea, and World War II hat pins; dog tag key rings; and beer and coffee mugs, Zippo lighters, belt buckles, patches, flags, and custom pins and patches. 815–223–1159.

Martin Lederman, 21 Naples, Brookline, MA 02146: Free list ■ United States military medals. 617–731–0000.

The Quartermaster, 750 Long Beach Blvd., Long Beach, CA 90813: Catalog $3 ■ Medals, ribbons, patches, insignia, badges, flight jackets, and display boxes.

Quincy Sale, P.O. Box 700113, Tulsa, OK 74170: Catalog $2.50 ■ United States medals and ribbons, shoulder patches, wings, badges, insignia, and identification books.

S. Vernon, Box 1560, Wildomar, CA 92395: Catalog $1 ■ Military medals and related collectibles. 516–536–5287.

MODELS & MODEL BUILDING

Aircraft Models

Ace R/C, 116 W. 19th St., P.O. Box 472, Higginsville, MO 64037: Catalog $2 ■ Radio controlled glider. 816–584–7121.

Aerocraft, P.O. Box 553, East Northport, NY 11731: Free information ■ Radio controlled and electric-powered, easy-to-assemble airplanes. 516–754–6628.

Aerodrome Models, Ltd., 2623 S. Miller Rd., Saginaw, MI 48603: Free information ■ Airplane models and accessories. 517–781–3000.

Aerotech, Inc., 1955 S. Palm St., Ste. 15, Las Vegas, NV 89104: Free information ■ Rocket launched, radio controlled aerobatic glider. 702–641–2301.

Air Flair Manufacturing Company, Box 11702, Kansas City, MO 64138: Free information ■ Radio controlled model jet airplanes. 816–353–7854.

The Airplane Factory, Inc., 1880 Pineview, Mandeville, LA 70448: Free information ■ Quick-building, radio controlled sport-flying airplanes. 800–264–7840.

Airtronics, Inc., 11 Autry, Irvine, CA 92718: Free information ■ Electric sailplane with folding propeller and removable plug-in wing tips. 714–830–8769.

Altech Marketing, P.O. Box 391, Edison, NJ 08818: Free information ■ Ready-to-fly models. 908–248–8738.

America's Hobby Center, Inc., 146 W. 22nd St., New York, NY 10011: Catalog $3

■ Model airplanes, radio control equipment, accessories, and tools. 212–675–8922.

Astro Flight, Inc., 13311 Beach Ave., Marina Del Ray, CA 90292: Free information ■ Electric powered airplanes and engines. 310–821–6242.

B.I.M. Marketing, 4510 NW 41st, Fort Lauderdale, FL 33319: Free information ■ Radio controlled model airplane kits. 305–735–7392.

Bridi Aircraft Designs, 23625 Pineforest Ln., Harbor City, CA 90710: Free information ■ Radio controlled model airplane kits and gliders. 213–549–8264.

Byron Originals, Inc., P.O. Box 279, Ida Grove, IA 51445: Product line catalog $4; information packet $3 ■ Easy-to-assemble model airplanes and jet engines. 712–364–3165.

Cambridge Model Aircraft, P.O. Box 26, Norwood, NJ 07648: Free information ■ Quick-assembly radio controlled airplanes. 914–429–3484.

Carden Corporation, 1731 NW Madrid Way, Boca Raton, FL 33432: Free information ■ Radio controlled model airplane kits. 407–367–7744.

Century Jet Models, Inc., P.O. Box 111, Rantoul, IL 61866: Free information ■ Radio controlled model jet airplane kits and accessories. 217–893–0707.

Chicago Model International, 124 Messner Dr., Wheeling, IL 60090: Free information ■ Ready-to-fly radio controlled model airplanes. 708–215–6262.

Cleveland Model & Supply Company, 9800 Detroit Ave., Cleveland, OH 44102: Catalog $2 ■ Airplane models and accessories. 216–961–3600.

Colorado Discount Hobbies, 2495 W. Hampden Ave., Englewood, CO 80110: Free information ■ Model airplanes, helicopters, gliders, cars, boats, radio control equipment, building supplies, and accessories. 303–761–3600.

Combat Models, Inc., 8535 Arjons Dr., Ste. R, San Diego, CA 92126: Free information ■ Radio controlled gliders and almost ready-to-fly radio controlled model airplanes. 619–536–9922.

Coverite, 420 Babylon Rd., Horsham, PA 19044: Free information ■ Radio controlled

model airplane kits, building materials, tools, and supplies. 215–672–6720.

Cox Hobbies, Inc., 350 W. Rincon St., Corona, CA 91720: Free information ■ Radio controlled model airplanes and cars. 714–278–2551.

Culpepper Models, Inc., 2526 Washington, Dubuque, IA 52001: Free information ■ Sailplanes and electric-powered airplanes. 319–583–4830.

D & R Aircraft Manufacturing, P.O. Box 299, Gonzales, TX 78629: Free information ■ Radio controlled model airplane kits and accessories. 512–672–7023.

Davey Systems Corporation, 675 Tower Ln., West Chester, PA 19380: Free information ■ Airplane models with electric engines. 215–430–8645.

Douglas Aircraft Model Aviation, P.O. Box 92472, Long Beach, CA 90809: Free information ■ Radio controlled gliders. 310–498–1737.

Doylejet, 4015 San Jacinto St., Houston, TX 77004: Free information ■ Jet engines. 713–440–4744.

Duracraft, 1007 Orchard Grove Dr., Royal Oak, MI 48067: Free information ■ Radio controlled model airplane kits. 313–547–5082.

Evers Toy Store, 204 1st Ave. East, Dyersville, IA 52040: Free information ■ Airplane models and miniature die-cast automobiles. 319–875–2438.

Flyline Models, Inc., P.O. Box 2136, Fairfax, VA 22031: Catalog 50¢ ■ Rubber-powered flying models. 703–273–9593.

G & P Sales, 410 College Ave., Angwin, CA 94508: Information $3 ■ Radio controlled model airplane kits. 707–965–3866.

Global Hobby Distributors, 10725 Ellis Ave., Fountain Valley, CA 92728: Free information ■ Radio controlled model airplane kits, gliders, and accessories. 714–963–0133.

G.M. Precision Products, 510 E. Arrow Hwy., San Dimas, CA 91773: Free information ■ Radio controlled model airplane kits, sailplanes, and thermal gliders. 714–592–5144.

Carl Goldberg Models, Inc., 4734 W. Chicago Ave., Chicago, IL 60651: Free information ■ Radio controlled model airplane kits, electric powered planes, gliders, accessories, and building materials. 312–626–9550.

Gorham Model Products, Inc., 23961 Craftsman Rd., Calabasas, CA 91302: Catalog $2 ■ Radio controlled helicopters and accessories. 818–992–0195.

Great Planes Model Distributors Company, P.O. Box 9021, Champaign, IL 61826: Free information ■ Ready-to-fly airplane models. 217–398–6300.

Hobby Barn, Box 17856, Tucson, AZ 85731: Free catalog ■ Airplanes and boat models and accessories. 602–747–3633.

Hobby Dynamics, 4105 Fieldstone Rd., Champaign, IL 61821: Free information ■ Radio controlled model airplane kits, helicopters, electric powered gliders, and sailplanes. 217–355–0022.

Hobby Horn, 15173 Moran St., P.O. Box 2212, Westminster, CA 92684: Catalog $2 ■ Electric and fuel-operated airplanes, sailplanes, and radio controlled models. 714–893–8311.

Hobby Lobby International, Inc., 5614 Franklin Pike Cir., Brentwood, TN 37027: Free catalog ■ Airplane models and accessories. 615–373–1444.

Hobby Shack, 18480 Bandilier Cir., Fountain Valley, CA 92728: Free catalog ■ Ready-to-assemble airplanes and automobiles and radio control systems and accessories. 800–854–8471.

Hobby Surplus Sales, P.O. Box 2170, New Britain, CT 06050: Catalog $2 ■ Airplanes, cars, ships, model trains, radio control equipment, and other craft supplies and accessories. 203–223–0600.

Bob Holman Plans, P.O. Box 741, San Bernardino, CA 92402: Catalog $5 ■ Radio controlled model airplane kits and accessories. 714–885–3959.

Ikon N'wst, P.O. Box 306, Post Falls, ID 83854: Catalog $4 ■ Giant scale and radio controlled model airplane kits. 208–773–9001.

Impact Engineering, 2100 Stonehill Ct., Arlington, TX 76012: Free information ■ Easy-to-install shock absorbing struts for retractable or fixed landing gears. 817–261–8130.

Indy R/C Sales, Inc., 10620 N. College Ave., Indianapolis, IN 46280: Free informa-

tion ■ Pre-assembled airplane kits. 800–338–4639.

Jet 'n' More, 1088 Banyan Way, P.O. Box 342, Pacifica, CA 94044: Free information ■ Radio controlled model jet airplanes. 415–355–2085.

J'Tec, 164 School St., Daly City, CA 94014: Free catalog ■ Model engine mounts, mufflers, engine test stands, power sticks, and other accessories. 415–756–3400.

K & B Manufacturing, Inc., 2100 College Dr., Lake Havasu City, AZ 86403: Free information ■ Airplane and marine engines.

L & R Aircraft, Ltd., 13645 Fisher Rd., Burton, OH 44021: Free information ■ High-performance sport and aerobatic airplanes. 216–834–1578.

Lanier RC, P.O. Box 458, Oakwood, GA 30566: Free catalog ■ Radio controlled model airplane kits, almost ready-to-fly models, and gliders. 404–532–6401.

Bob Martin R/C Models, 1520–C Acoma Ln., Lake Havasu City, AZ 86403: Free information ■ Radio controlled gliders and accessories. 602–855–6900.

Midwest Products Company, Inc., 400 S. Indiana St., P.O. Box 564, Hobart, IN 46342: Free information ■ Giant scale model airplanes. 219–942–1134.

Max Mills Models, 3820 Cheraz NE, Albuquerque, NM 87111: Free information ■ Radio controlled gliders and sailplanes. 505–292–3510.

Milo Model Products, Box 236, Nester, CA 92053: Free information ■ Radio controlled gliders. 619–429–8281.

Minimax Enterprise, P.O. Box 2374, Chelan Falls, WA 98816: Free information ■ Radio controlled gliders. 509–683–1288.

Model Expo, Inc., P.O. Box 1000, Mt. Pocono, PA 18344: Free catalog ■ Airplane models and accessories, tools, automobile and boat kits, and trains. 800–222–3876.

Morley Helicopters, P.O. Box 6026, San Pedro, CA 90734: Free information ■ Radio controlled model helicopters and sailplanes. 509–683–1288.

Walt Moucha Models, P.O. Box 112, Menominee, MI 49858: Free information ■ Radio controlled model airplane kits and accessories. 906–863–1225.

MRC Models, 200 Carter Dr., Edison, NJ 08817: Free information ■ Ready-to-fly airplanes. 908–248–0400.

Mutchler's Hobbies, Inc., 4620 Crandall-Lanesville Rd., Corydon, IN 47112: Free information with long SASE ■ Remote control model airplanes and accessories. 812–366–3141.

NorthEast Sailplane Products, 18 Kirby Lane, Willston, VT 05495: Catalog $3 ■ Radio controlled sailplanes. 802–658–9482.

Pacific Aircraft, 14255 N. 79th St., Scottsdale Airpark, AZ 85260: Free information ■ Handcarved and painted solid mahogany model airplanes. 800–950–9944.

Parrish Aircraft, 1125 SW 49th, Plantation, FL 33317: Free information ■ Radio controlled model airplane kits. 305–581–4477.

Paul's Flying Stuff, P.O. Box 121, Escondido, CA 92025: Free information ■ Radio controlled model jet airplanes. 619–743–5458.

Peck-Polymers, Box 710399, Santee, CA 92072: Catalog $2 ■ Rubber-powered flying model kits, plans, and accessories. 619–448–1818.

Penn Valley Hobby Center, 837 W. Main St., Lansdale, PA 19446: Catalog $1 ■ Rubber- and engine-powered models and accessories. Includes free flight and control line planes, kits, and engines. 215–368–0770.

Pica Enterprises, 2657 NE 188th St., Miami, FL 33180: Free information ■ Radio controlled model airplane kits. 305–935–1436.

Polk's Model-Craft Hobbies, 346 Bergen Ave., Jersey City, NJ 07304: Catalog $2 ■ Tools, radio control equipment, accessories, and airplane, car, and boat models, and building supplies. 201–332–8100.

Proctor Enterprises, 25450 NE Eilers Rd., Aurora, OR 97002: Catalog $4 ■ Radio controlled model airplane kits, accessories, and hardware. 503–678–1300.

R.C. Buyers Warehouse, 99 Pines St., Box 646, Nashua, NH 03060 : Free information ■ Helicopter models and building components and supplies, engines, radio systems, tools, and accessories. 603–595–2494.

RC Systems, Inc., 5400 Cornell Rd., Cincinnati, OH 45242: Free information ■ Miniature airplanes, helicopters, boats, gyroplanes, jets, radio control accessories, and building supplies. 513–489–3232.

Robbe Model Sport, 170 Township Line Rd., Belle Mead, NJ 08052: Catalog $5 ■ Radio controlled model airplane kits, almost ready-to-fly models, gliders, helicopters, electrical supplies, and accessories. 908–359–2115.

Royal Products Corporation, 790 W. Tennessee Ave., Denver, CO 80223: Free information ■ Radio controlled model airplane kits, jet airplane kits, gliders, and accessories. 303–778–7711.

Scale Aviation, 2425 Ivanhoe Dr., Los Angles, CA 90039: Free information ■ Radio controlled model airplane kits and accessories. 213–666–3156.

SIG Manufacturing Company, Inc., 401 S. Front St., Montezuma, IA 50171: Catalog $3 ■ Radio controlled, control line, and rubber-powered model planes. 515–623–5154.

Skyline Hobby's Manufacturing, 49 Treebeard Cir., St. Charles, MO 63303: Free information ■ Radio controlled model airplane kits and accessories. 314–928–7777.

Southeast Model Products, 3815 N. Hwy. US 1, Unit 29, Cocoa, FL 32926: Information $2 with long SASE ■ Radio controlled ducted fan model airplanes. 407–639–0465.

Spirit Jets, 9255 Survey Rd., #12, Elk Grove. CA 95624: Free information ■ Radio controlled model jet airplanes. 916–685–1009.

Square Roundhouse, 1468 Lander, Turlock, CA 95381: Free information with long SASE ■ Model planes, radio controlled cars, and Lionel trains. 209–668–4454.

Standard Hobby Supply, P.O. Box 801, Mahwah, NJ 07430: Catalog $3 ■ Ready-to-fly airplanes, off-road buggies and cars, racing cars, and parts and accessories. 201–825–2211.

C.B. Tatone, Inc., 21658 Cloud Way, Hayward, CA 94545: Free information ■ Aluminum motor mounts for two- and four-cycle engines, engine mounts, and other accessories. 510–783–4868.

Technopower II, Inc., 610 North St., Chagrin Falls, OH 44022: Catalog $3 ■ Radial-style gas engines. 216–564–9787.

Top Flite Models, Inc., 2635 S. Wabash, Chicago, IL 60616: Free information ■ Radio controlled, almost ready-to-fly model airplanes, electric-powered models, and building materials. 312–842–3388.

Tower Hobbies, Box 9078, Champaign, IL 61826: Catalog $3 ■ Model airplanes, cars, boats, radio control equipment, engines, and building supplies. 800–637–6050.

U.S. Quadra, Rt, 1, Neidesha, KS 66757: Catalog $1 ■ Quadra engines, parts, and accessories. 316–325–2821.

Vailly Aviation, 18 Oakdale Ave., Farmingville, NY 11738: Free information ■ Radio controlled model airplane kits. 516–732–4715.

Bob Violett Models, Inc., 1373 Citrus Rd., Winter Springs, FL 32708: Catalog $2 ■ Radio controlled model jet airplanes and accessories. 407–365–5869.

Wing Manufacturing, 306 E. Simmons, Galesburg, IL 61401: Free information ■ Radio controlled model airplane kits, accessories, and building materials. 309–342–3009.

World Engines, Inc., 8960 Research Ave., Cincinnati, OH 45236: Free information ■ Ready-to-fly models. 513–793–5900.

Automobile Models

Accent Models, Inc., 26 Diamond Spring Rd., Denville, NJ 07834: Catalog $2 ■ Collectible car models. 201–625–0997.

Alexandre's Autos, 13020 SW 80th Ave., Miami, FL 33156: Free information ■ Die cast model cars. 800–779–0576.

America's Hobby Center, Inc., 146 W. 22nd St., New York, NY 10011: Catalog $3 ■ Car model kits and accessories. 212–675–8922.

Autofanatics, Ltd., P.O. Box 55158, Sherman Oaks, CA 91413: List $1 ■ Miniature scale model automobiles, in kits or assembled. 818–788–5440.

Automobiles in Scale, 6822 Foxborough Ct., Yorba Linda, CA 92686: Catalog $5 (refundable with $25 order) ■ Domestic and imported automobile kits, books, super detail products, and wheel and tire kits. 714–970–8328.

Automobilia, 44 Glendale Rd., Park Ridge, NJ 07656: Catalog $3 ■ Authentic scale

models of cars, trucks, fire engines, and military vehicles. Includes working steam-powered models. 201–573–0173.

Auto Motif, Inc., 2968 Atlanta Rd., Smyrna, GA 30080: Catalog $1 ■ Car models, gifts, and collectibles with an automotive theme, books, prints, puzzles, office accessories, lamps, original art, and posters. 404–435–5025.

Auto World Model Shoppe, 10 Green Ridge St., Scranton, PA 18509: Catalog $3.95 ■ Model cars, trucks, slot racing models, radio controlled cars, scratch building supplies, and decals. 717–344–7258.

C & S Distributors, Rt. 113, Blue Hen Mall, Dover, DE 19901: Free information ■ Ertl diecast cars, other models, decals, paints, accessories, and show cases. 302–674–4042.

California Mini Wheels, 1417 S. Robertson Blvd., Los Angeles, CA 90035: Catalog $3 (refundable) ■ Assembled scale classic, vintage, contemporary, racing models, and other models. 310–276–4433.

Colorado Discount Hobbies, 2495 W. Hampden Ave., Englewood, CO 80110: Free information ■ Model airplanes, helicopters, gliders, cars, boats, radio control equipment, and building supplies. 303–761–3600.

Cox Hobbies, Inc., 350 W. Rincon St., Corona, CA 91720: Free information ■ Radio controlled model airplanes and cars. 714–278–2551.

Crawley Distributing, 4012 Benchmark Trail, Springhill, FL 34609: Free information ■ Slot cars and accessories. 904–799–4139.

Dahm's Automobiles, P.O. Box 360, Cotati, CA 94931: Catalog $2 ■ Racing bodies for radio controlled cars and trucks. 800–232–4679; 707–792–1316 (in CA).

Edgewood Engineering, 24313 Ox Bow Lane North, Sonora, CA 95370: Catalog $2 ■ Die cast, resin, plastic kits, and built-up ¹⁄₄₃ to ¹⁄₈ scale race car models. 209–586–2819.

Evers Toy Store, 204 1st Ave. East, Dyersville, IA 52040: Free information ■ Model cars and airplanes. 319–875–2438.

Great Northern Hobbies, 328 5th Ave., Troy, NY 12182: Free information ■ Parts and accessories for radio controlled model cars, replacement bodies, and kits. 518–233–1300.

High Speed Miniatures, P.O. Box 1011, Taylor, MI 48180: Free list with long SASE ■ American racing car kits.

Hobby Heaven, P.O. Box 3229, Grand Rapids, MI 49501: Free catalog with long SASE and two 1st class stamps ■ Ready-to-build kits for model automobile, from the 1950s, 1960s, and 1970s. 616–453–1094.

Hobby House, Inc., 8208 Merriman Rd., Westland, MI 48185: Free information ■ Model cars and supplies by Burago, Testor, Merry Yard, Revell, Solido, Tamiya, Monogram, and others. 313–425–9720.

Hobby Shack, 18480 Bandilier Cir., Fountain Valley, CA 92728: Free catalog ■ Ready-to-assemble airplanes and automobiles, and radio controlled systems and accessories. 800–854–8471.

Hobby Surplus Sales, P.O. Box 2170, New Britain, CT 06050: Catalog $2 ■ Planes, cars, ships, model trains, radio controlled models, and other craft supplies and accessories. 203–223–0600.

Hobby Warehouse of Sacramento, P.O. Box 5058, Fair Oaks, CA 95628: Free information ■ Radio control automobile equipment, accessories, and kits. 800–333–3640.

Long Island Train & Hobby Center, 192 Jericho Turnpike, Mineola, NY 11501: Price list $2 with long SASE ■ Car models that include Batman, Green Hornet, Super Modifieds, Chargers, Toronados, Torinos, Vibrators, AFX-Tyc, and All Track collectibles. 516–742–5621.

Merkel Model Car Company, P.O. Box 689, Franklin Park, IL 60131: Catalog $2.75 each (specify type of car model) ■ Car models that include collectible and current kits, promotional and pre-assembled cars, die-cast and other pre-assembled models, other kits, building accessories, and supplies. 708–455–1495.

Mile High Mini Autos, 2002 Spring Dr., Rio Rancho, NM 87124: List $1 ■ Metal scale models of modern and classic automobiles. 505–892–2124.

Miniature Cars USA, P.O. Box 188, Berkeley Heights, NJ 07922: Catalog $3 ■ Die-cast models, metal and plastic kits, and other model cars. 908–665–7811.

Miniatures of the World, Inc., 104 May Dr., Harrison, OH 45030: Catalog $2 ■ Race, performance, exotic, and sports cars; trucks; motorcycles; fire trucks; farm and construction equipment; and other collectibles. 513–367–1746.

MK Model Products, 7209 Balboa Blvd., Van Nuys, CA 91406: Free information ■ Off-road and on-road car models, accessories, chargers, speed controls, and batteries. 800–446–6335; 818–787–5851 (in CA).

Model Car Collectables, 5743 S. Willowbrook Dr., Morrison, CO 80465: Free list with long SASE ■ Die-cast 1:43 and 1:24 model cars.

Model Empire, 7116 W. Greenfield Ave., West Allis, WI 53214: Catalog $3 (refundable with $20 order) ■ Cars, trucks, figures, racers, space and military models, boats, airplanes, and diecast models. 414–453–4610.

Model Expo, Inc., P.O. Box 1000, Mt. Pocono, PA 18344: Free catalog ■ Detailed, accurately scaled models of legendary automobiles, in kits or assembled. 800–222–3876.

Munchkin Motors, 20 Westford Rd., P.O. Box 266, Eastford, CT 06242: Free information ■ Collectible miniature cars. 203–974–2545.

Polk's Model-Craft Hobbies, 346 Bergen Ave., Jersey City, NJ 07304: Catalog $2 ■ Tools, radio control equipment, accessories, and airplane, car, and boat models and building supplies. 201–332–8100.

Race Prep, 20115 Nordhoff St., Chatsworth, CA 91311: Catalog $2 ■ Off-road and on-road car kits, accessories, motors, electronics, chargers, and battery packs. 818–709–6800.

Runabout, Inc., P.O. Box 8400, Red Bank, NJ 07701: Free information ■ Die cast models by Dinky, Solido, Corgi, Lledo, Ertl, and others. 908–747–5754.

Sinclair's Auto Miniatures, P.O. Box 8403, Erie, PA 16505: Catalog $3 ■ Die-cast and handcrafted miniature cars. 814–838–2274.

Merrill Smith Company, Miniature Motors Division, 12634 Angling Rd., Edinboro, PA 16412: Free catalog ■ Die-cast 1:43 scale automobiles. 814–734–5631.

Specialty Diecast Company, 370 Miller Rd., Medford, NJ 08055: Free information ■ Die cast model cars. 800–432–1933.

Square Roundhouse, 1468 Lander, Turlock, CA 95381: Free information with long SASE ■ Radio controlled cars, Lionel equipment and service, model planes, rocket equipment, and supplies. 209–668–4454.

Standard Hobby Supply, P.O. Box 801, Mahwah, NJ 07430: Catalog $3 ■ Ready-to-fly airplanes, off-road buggies and cars, racing cars, parts, and accessories. 201–825–2211.

Stormer Racing, 23 High Speed Rd., P.O. Box 126, Glasgow, MT 59230: Free information ■ Kits, parts, and accessories for radio controlled automobiles. 800–255–7223.

Tower Hobbies, Box 9078, Champaign, IL 61826: Catalog $3 ■ Model airplanes, cars, boats, radio control equipment, engines, and building supplies. 800–637–6050.

Valley Plaza Hobbies, 2211 Mouton Dr., Carson City, NV 89706: Catalog $6.50 ■ Miniature car models. 702–887–1131.

Walt's Hobby, 2 Dwight Park Dr., Syracuse, NY 13209: Free information ■ Radio control equipment and kits. 315–453–2291.

James Wieland, Box 927–130, Litchfield, CT 06759: Catalog $2 ■ Model cars. 203–266–7387.

Paper Airplanes

International Paper Airplane Company, P.O. Box 061179, Palm Bay, FL 32906: Free information ■ Paper airplanes.

Radio Control Equipment

Ace R/C, 116 W. 19th St., Box 472, Higginsville, MO 64037: Catalog $2 ■ Radio controlled model airplane equipment and supplies. 816–584–7121.

Aerocell, 407 Commerce Way, Jupiter, FL 33458: Free information ■ Flight pack batteries and charger. 407–575–0422.

America's Hobby Center, Inc., 146 W. 22nd St., New York, NY 10011: Catalog $2 ■ Model airplanes, radio control equipment, accessories, and tools. 212–675–8922.

B & P Associates, P.O. Box 22054, Waco, TX 76702: Free information ■ Starter batteries. 817–662–5587.

Futaba Corporation of America, 4 Studebaker, Irvine, CA 92716: Free information ■ Radio control systems for cars, trucks, and buggies. 714–455–9888.

Hobby Shack, 18480 Bandilier Cir., Fountain Valley, CA 92708: Free catalog $1 ■ Radio control equipment and accessories. 800–854–8471.

SR Batteries, Inc., Box 287, Bellport, NY 11713: Information $3 ■ Batteries. 516–286–0079.

Walt's Hobby, 2 Dwight Park Dr., Syracuse, NY 13209: Free information ■ Radio control kits, parts, and accessories for cars. 315–453–2291.

Rocket Models

Acme Rocket Company, P.O. Box 28283, Tempe, AZ 85282: Catalog $1 ■ Rocket supplies, kits, and accessories. 602–838–3629.

Belleville Hobby, 1827 N. Charles St., Belleville, IL 62221: Catalog $1.50 ■ Rocket supplies and accessories, engines, parts, and books. 618–234–5989.

Branchville Hobby Shop, 51 Ethan Allen Hwy., Ridgefield, CT 06877: Free information with long SASE ■ Rocket equipment and supplies, airplane models and ships, and plastic models. 203–544–8031.

Centuri Engineering Company, Inc., P.O. Box 1988, Phoenix, AZ 85001: Catalog $1 ■ Supplies and equipment for building, launching, and tracking model rockets. 602–264–0325.

Estes Industries, P.O. Box 227, Penrose, CO 81240: Free catalog ■ Model rocket kits, engines, supplies, control equipment, and accessories. 719–372–6565.

Merrell Scientific/World of Science, 1665 Buffalo Rd., Rochester, NY 14624: Catalog $2 ■ Rockets, engines, and igniters. Other items include chemicals, laboratory glassware and equipment, equipment and supplies for biology, chemistry, physical and earth science, and astronomy experiments. 716–426–1540.

North Coast Rocketry, 13011 Branscomb Rd., Huntsville, AL 35803: Free information ■ Rocket model kits. 800–877–6032.

Square Roundhouse, 1468 Lander, Turlock, CA 95381: Free information with long SASE ■ Rocket equipment and supplies, radio controlled cars, Lionel train equipment

and accessories, and model planes. 209–668–4454.

Teleflite Corporation, 11620 Kitching St., Moremo Valley, CA 92387: Catalog $2 ■ Information on how to build rocket motors using simple equipment and supplies.

Tiffany Hobbies of Ypsilanti, P.O. Box 467, Ypsilanti, MI 48197: Free information ■ Rocket model kits. 800–232–3626.

Ship Models

Action Hobbies, 105 Pickwick Ave., Colonial Heights, VA 23834: Free information ■ Ready-to-run boats and accessories and parts for radio controlled cars. 804–520–7406.

America's Hobby Center, Inc., 146 W. 22nd St., New York, NY 10011: Catalog $1.50 ■ Model ship-building kits. 212–675–8922.

Bluejacket Ship Crafters, P.O. Box 425, Stockton Springs, ME 04981: Catalog $2 (refundable) ■ Kits, fittings and supplies, accessories, and tools for building ship models. 800–448–5567; 800–834–7608 (in ME).

Branchville Hobby Shop, 51 Ethan Allen Hwy., Ridgefield, CT 06877: Free information with long SASE ■ Ship models, airplanes, rocket equipment and supplies, plastic models, and HO, N, and Lionel trains and equipment. 203–544–8031.

Coles' Power Models, Inc., P.O. Box 788, Ventura, CA 93001: Catalog $4 ■ Operating steam engines for model ships. 805–643–7065.

Colorado Discount Hobbies, 2495 W. Hampden Ave., Englewood, CO 80110: Free information ■ Model airplanes, helicopters, gliders, cars, boats, radio control equipment, and building supplies. 303–761–3600.

Dumas Boats, 909 E. 17th St., Tucson, AZ 85719: Free catalog ■ Radio controlled boat models. 602–623–3742.

Dynamic Models, P.O. Drawer C, Port Jefferson Station, NY 11776: Catalog $5 ■ Boat kits, hulls, fittings, and accessories. 516–928–8200.

A.J. Fisher, Inc., 1002 Etowah Ave., Royal Oak, MI 48067: Catalog $3 ■ Scale brass ship and yacht model fittings.

Hobby Barn, Box 17856, Tucson, AZ 85731: Free catalog ■ Boat and airplane models and accessories. 602–747–3633.

Hobby House, Inc., 8208 Merriman Rd., Westland, MI 48185: Free information ■ Model boats, fittings and supplies, accessories, and tools. 313–425–9720.

Hobby Surplus Sales, P.O. Box 2170, New Britain, CT 06050: Catalog $3 ■ Planes, cars, ships, and model trains, and radio controlled models. 203–223–0600.

K & B Manufacturing, Inc., 2100 College Dr., Lake Havasu City, AZ 86403: Free information ■ Airplane and marine engines.

Laughing Whale, 174 Front St., Bath, ME 04530: Catalog $2 ■ Kits for building classic wooden ships. 207–443–5732.

Model Expo, Inc., P.O. Box 1000, Mt. Pocono, PA 18344: Free catalog ■ Boat kits, airplane models and accessories, tools, automobile kits, and trains. 800–222–3876.

Octura Models, Inc., 7351 N. Hamlin Ave., Skokie, IL 60076: Free information with long SASE ■ Radio controlled power boats. 708–674–7351.

Performance Models, 1866 NW 22nd Pl., Miami, FL 33125: Information $2 ■ Ready-to-run radio controlled boats. 305–634–8145.

The Pipeline, 8389 Canyon Oak Dr., Citrus Heights, CA 95610: Catalog $3 (refundable with $15 order) ■ Competition boats, hardware, and accessories. 916–623–4124.

Pirate's Cove, Ltd., 156 Talley Dr., Palm Harbor, FL 34684: Free information ■ Radio controlled, ready-to-run sailboats. 813–787–8033.

Polk's Model-Craft Hobbies, 346 Bergen Ave., Jersey City, NJ 07304: Catalog $2 ■ Tools, radio control equipment, accessories, and airplane, car, and boat models and building supplies. 201–332–8100.

Prather Products, Inc., 1660 Ravenna Ave., Wilmington, CA 90744: Catalog $2 ■ High performance, epoxy glass boats. 310–835–4764.

Preston's, Main Street Wharf, Greenport, NY 11944: Free catalog ■ Ship models and accessories. 516–477–1990.

Robbe Model Sport, Inc., 170 Township Line Rd., Belle Mead, NJ 08502: Catalog $8.50 ■ Boats, airplanes, cars, and accessories. 908–359–2115.

The Scale Shipyard, 5866 Orange Ave., Long Beach, CA 90805: Catalog $4 ■ Fittings, fiberglass model ship hulls, and accessories.

Seacraft Classics, 6615 N. Scottsdale Rd., Scottsdale, AZ 85250: Free catalog ■ Hand-carved, ready-to-display, detailed classic 19th century model sailing ships and boats with hardwood display stands and brass name plates. 800–356–1987; 602–951–9518 (in AZ).

Ships N' Things, P.O. Box 605, Somerville, NJ 08876: Catalog $5 (refundable with $25 order) ■ Competition boats, hardware, props, and accessories. 908–722–0075.

Superboat Marine Products, 320 Convery Blvd., Perth Amboy, NJ 08861: Free information ■ Powerboat parts and accessories. 908–826–6625.

Tower Hobbies, Box 9078, Champaign, IL 61826: Catalog $3 ■ Model airplanes, cars, boats, radio control equipment, engines, and building supplies. 800–637–6050.

Trinity Products, Inc., 1901 E. Linden Ave., Linden, NJ 07036: Free information ■ Electric motors and cooling units for model boats. 908–862–1705.

Victor Model Products, 12258–1/2 Woodruff Ave., Downey, CA 90241: Free brochure ■ Radio controlled sailing yachts. 310–803–1897.

R. Michael Wall's American Marine Model Gallery, Derby Square, Salem, MA 01970: Catalog $10 ■ Collectible ship models. 508–745–5777.

Supplies

Aerotrend Products, 31 Nichols St., Ansonia, CT 06401: Free information ■ Radio controlled model airplane accessories and hardware. 203–734–0600.

Balsa USA, P.O. Box 164, Marinette, WI 54143: Free information ■ Balsa wood, tools, and accessories. 906–863–6421.

Dave Brown Products, 4560 Layhigh Rd., Hamilton, OH 45013: Free information ■ Radio controlled airplane accessories and building materials. 513–738–1576.

Charlie's Aircraft Accessories, 2828 Cochran St., Ste. 281, Simi Valley, CA 93065: Catalog $1 ■ Radio controlled airplane accessories and building materials. 805–581–5061.

Chrome-Tech U.S.A., 2314 Ravenswood Rd., Madison, WI 53711: Free brochure with long SASE ■ Chrome plating for model cars. 608–274–9811.

Colorado Discount Hobbies, 2495 W. Hampden Ave., Englewood, CO 80110: Free information ■ Building supplies, equipment and accessories, model airplanes, helicopters, gliders, cars, boats, and radio control equipment. 303–761–3600.

Coverite, 420 Babylon Rd., Horsham, PA 19044: Free information ■ Radio controlled model airplane kits, building materials, tools, and supplies. 215–672–6720.

Du-Bro Products, P.O. Box 815, Wauconda, IL 60084: Catalog $1 ■ Model building hardware, accessories, tools, and supplies. 312–526–2136.

Euro-Chrome, 201 9th Ave., LaSalle, Quebec, Canada H8P 2N7: Free information with long SASE ■ Chrome and gold plating for modelers and collectors of model cars, trucks, and old toys. 514–363–5857.

Carl Goldberg Models, 4734 W. Chicago Ave., Chicago, IL 60651: Free information ■ Radio controlled model airplane kits, electric powered planes, gliders, accessories, and building materials. 312–626–9550.

Hobby Hardware, 7903 S. Grandview Ave., Tempe, AZ 85264: Free catalog ■ Standard and metric sizes of 1/4 scale hardware.

Hobby Shack, 18480 Bandilier Cir., Fountain Valley, CA 92728: Free catalog ■ Model-making supplies, tools, and equipment. 800–854–8471.

Hobby Woods, 2031 Larkin, Clovis, CA 93612: Free catalog with long SASE ■ Custom cut balsa for model building. 209–292–WOOD.

K & S Engineering, 6917 W. 59th St., Chicago, IL 60638: Catalog 25¢ ■ Aluminum and other metal tubes, rods, and sheets for model building. 312–586–8503.

Lone Star Models, 1623 57th St., Lubbock, TX 79412: Free information ■ Custom cut balsa. 806–745–6394.

Northeastern Scale Models, Inc., P.O. Box 727, Methuen, MA 01844: Catalog $1 (refundable) ■ Basswood and supplies for model and doll house building. Includes carving blocks, decking, strips and sheets, pre-cut pieces, and hardware. 508–688–6019.

Pacer Technology, 9420 Santa Anita Ave., Rancho Cucamonga, CA 91730: Free information ■ Model airplane building materials. 714–987–0550.

Proctor Enterprises, 25450 NE Eilers Rd., Aurora, OR 97002: Catalog $4 ■ Radio controlled model airplane kits, accessories, and hardware. 503–678–1300.

Robart Manufacturing, P.O. Box 1247, St. Charles, IL 60174: Free information ■ Model airplane accessories, supplies, and tools. 708–584–7616.

Robbe Model Sport, 180 Township Line Rd., Belle Mead, NJ 08052: Catalog $5 ■ Radio controlled model airplane kits, almost ready-to-fly models, gliders, helicopters, electrical supplies, and accessories. 908–359–2115.

SIG Manufacturing Company, Inc., 401 S. Front St., Montezuma, IA 50171: Catalog $3 ■ Airplane balsa. 515–623–5154.

Sullivan Products, P.O. Box 5166, Baltimore, MD 21224: Free information ■ Model airplane hardware.

Superior Aircraft Materials, 12020 Centralia, Hawaiian Gardens, CA 90716: Free information ■ Balsa, birch, plywood, and other materials. 310–865–3220.

Top Flite Models, Inc., 2635 S. Wabash, Chicago, IL 60616: Free information ■ Electric-powered models, and building materials, and almost ready-to-fly radio controlled model airplanes. 312–842–3388.

Tools

Badger Air-Brush Company, 9128 W. Belmont, Franklin Park, IL 60131: Catalog $1 ■ Tools and supplies for building model airplanes. 312–678–3104.

Campbell Tools Company, 2100 Selma Rd., Springfield, OH 45505: Catalog $2 ■ Lathes, mills, taps, dies, micrometers, cutting tools, miniature screws, other supplies, and brass, aluminum, and steel. 513–322–8562.

Coverite, 420 Babylon Rd., Horsham, PA 19044: Free information ■ Radio controlled model airplane kits, building materials, tools, and supplies. 215–672–6720.

Dremel Manufacturing Corporation, 4915 21st St., Racine, WI 53406: Free information ■ Power tools for modelers and home craftsmen. 414–554–1390.

Du-Bro Products, P.O. Box 815, Wauconda, IL 60084: Catalog $1 ■ Hardware, accessories, tools, and supplies for building model airplanes. 312–526–2136.

Hobby Hardware Supply, P.O. Box 243, Hillside, NJ 07205: Catalog $2 ■ Model building tools. 908–353–8552.

Hobby Products Company, 2757 Scioto Pkwy., Columbus, OH 43026: Free catalog ■ Lathes for metal, wood, or plastics, milling machines, saws, hand tools, and power woodworking tools. 614–771–5996.

International Hobby Corporation, 350 E. Tioga St., Philadelphia, PA 19134: Free information ■ Battery powered hobby tools. 215–426–2873.

K & S Engineering, 6917 W. 59th St., Chicago, IL 60638: Catalog 25¢ ■ Precision tools. 312–586–8503.

Marc's Modelers Tools, 809 Sansom St., Philadelphia, PA 19107: Free catalog ■ Precision tools. 215–925–4566.

Micro-Mark, 340 Snyder Ave., Berkeley Heights, NJ 07922: Catalog $1 ■ Miniature and standard size tools. 800–225–1066.

Model Expo, Inc., P.O. Box 1000, Mt. Pocono, PA 18344: Free catalog ■ Modeling tools and accessories, train sets, automobile kits and collectibles, wood and plastic ship model kits, and airplane kits. 800–222–3876.

Polk's Model-Craft Hobbies, 346 Bergen Ave., Jersey City, NJ 07304: Catalog $2 ■ Modeling tools and supplies, radio control equipment, and airplanes, cars, boats, and other models. 201–332–8100.

Robart Manufacturing, P.O. Box 1247, St. Charles, IL 60174: Free information ■ Model airplane accessories, supplies, and tools. 708–584–7616.

Sherline Products, Inc., 170 Navajo St., San Marcos, CA 92069: Free catalog ■ Precision-made, miniature power-operated tools. 800–541–0735; 619–744–3674 (in CA).

Train Models

Allied Model Trains, 4411 S. Sepulveda Blvd., Culver City, CA 90230: Free information with long SASE ■ Lionel, American Flyer, LGB, Marklin, Brass rolling stock, and equipment and accessories. 213–313–9353.

American Models, 10088 Colonial Industrial Dr., South Lyon, MI 48178: Catalog $1.25 ■ S gauge trains.

America's Hobby Center, Inc., 146 W. 22nd St., New York, NY 10011: Catalog $3 ■ Kits, accessories, and equipment for building trains and other models for train layouts. 212–675–8922.

Amro Ltd., 121 Lincolnway West, New Oxford, PA 17350: Free information ■ Foreign railway models. 717–624–8920.

Antique Toy Trains, David Laughridge, 1 Belfry Terrace, Lexington, MA 02173: Catalog $3 ■ Lionel O gauge train parts and accessories.

Aristo-Craft, Polk's Model Craft Hobbies, 346 Bergen Ave., Jersey City, NJ 07304: Catalog $2 ■ True-to-scale and true-to-life buildings, trestle sets, water towers, and bridges. 201–332–8100.

Arttista Accessories, 1616 S. Franklin St., Philadelphia, PA 19148: Free information with long SASE ■ Handmade and painted O and O27 gauge accessories.

Barillaro Toy Trains, Inc., 19 Sillimanville Rd., Colchester, CT 06415: Brochure $1 ■ Expandable modular train layouts. 203–267–7616.

Janice Bennett, P.O. Box 178, Closter, NJ 07624: Catalog $1.50 with long SASE ■ Decals for American Flyer, Ives, and Lionel trains.

Bookbinder's Trains Unlimited, 84–20 Midland Pkwy., Jamaica, NY 11432: Catalog $5 ■ Lionel standard and O gauge trains and accessories. 718–657–2224.

Bragdon Enterprises, 2960 Garden Tower Ln., Georgetown, CA 95634: Free information with long SASE ■ Trees and foliage materials for model train layouts.

Caboose Hobbies, 500 S. Broadway, Denver, CO 80209: Free information ■ Model trains, accessories, books, and supplies, from Z to G scale. 303–777–6766.

Lou Cantafio & Sons, 6 Como Trail, RD 3, Box 472, Lake Hopatcong, NJ 07849: Free information with long SASE ■ Lionel O gauge train parts and accessories.

Champion Decal Company, P.O. Box 1178, Minot, ND 58702: Catalog $7 ■ HO and O scale decals.

Charlie's Trains, P.O. Box 158, Hubertus, WI 53033: Parts list $1 ■ Train parts and accessories. 404–628–1544.

Choo Choo Works, 9734 Southwest Hwy., Oak Lawn, IL 60453: Free information with long SASE ■ Prewar and postwar model trains, equipment, and accessories. Includes Lionel equipment with some limited quantities. 708–425–1137.

Classic Model Trains, P.O. Box 179, Hartford, OH 44424: Price list $2 ■ Paints for American Flyer, Ives, and Lionel trains. 216–772–5177.

Collector's Corner, 33 Palace Pl., Port Chester, NY 10573: Free information ■ Pre- and postwar Lionel trains and accessories. 914–939–5511.

Continental Hobby House, P.O. Box 193, Sheboygan, WI 53082: Catalog $5 ■ Lionel and American Flyer trains.

Alison Cox Trains, 18025 8th Ave. NW, Seattle, WA 98177: Lionel catalog $5; Marx catalog $1.50 ■ Parts for Lionel and Marx trains.

Dallee Electronics, 4246 Oregon Pike, P.O. Box 280, Brownstone, PA 17508: Catalog $2 ■ Electronic control equipment for model railroad operation. 717–859–6673.

Discount Train Warehouse, Inc., 777 W. Imperial Hwy., Brea, CA 92621: Free information ■ Trains and scenic accessories. 714–255–0185.

Doug's Train World, c/o Valley Junction Train Station, 401 Railroad Pl., West Des Moines, IA 50265: Free price list ■ Lionel and LGB trains and accessories, O gauge straight and curved track, remote switches, and other accessories. 800–247–5096; 515–274–4424 (in IA).

Anthony F. Dudynski Supply Company, 2036 Story Ave., Bronx, NY 10473: Free information with long SASE ■ Trains and scenic accessories. 212–863–9422.

Express Station Hobbies, Inc., 640 Strander Blvd., Tukwila, WA 98188: Free information ■ Rolling stock, accessories, books, video rentals, finishing and detailing supplies, and scenery. 206–228–7750.

The Freight Yard, 725 S. Alvy St., Anaheim, CA 92802: Price list $1 ■ N scale trains and accessories. 714–956–1355.

GarGraves Trackage Corporation, RD 1, Box 255, North Rose, NY 14516: Free information ■ Track for realistic model railroad layouts, complete with wood ties and steel rails. 315–483–6577.

R.F. Giardina Company, P.O. Box 562, Oyster Bay, NY 11771: Catalog $2 ■ Replacement, restoration, and repair parts for American Flyer Trains.

Golden Spike International, 1700 Grand Concourse, Bronx, NY 10457: Catalog $2 ■ Vintage train models for collectors. 212–294–1614.

Grand Central, Ltd., 6929 Seward Ave., P.O. Box 29109, Lincoln, NE 68507: Free information with long SASE ■ Collectible Lionel classics, new Lionel equipment and sets, operating and layout accessories, and other large gauge items and rolling stock. 402–467–3668.

Hobby Depot, 1721 Buttermilk Hill Rd., Delaware, OH 43015: Price list $2 ■ Rolling stock and layout accessories in HO, N, G, and O scales. 614–363–7986.

Hobbyland, 343 Lincolnway West, South Bend, IN 46601: Catalog $2 ■ Trains and scenic accessories. 800–225–6509.

Hobby Surplus Sales, P.O. Box 2170, New Britain, CT 06050: Catalog $2 ■ Accessories and equipment for Lionel, American Flyer, HO and N gauge trains; tools; scenery; and other hobby and craft supplies. 203–223–0600.

International Hobby Corporation, 350 E. Tioga St., Philadelphia, PA 19134: Free information with long SASE ■ Trains and scenic accessories. 215–426–2873.

Island Trains, 4041 Hylan Blvd., Staten Island, NY 10306: Free information with long SASE ■ Lionel trains and accessories. 718–317–0762.

John's Train Shop, 8151 Delmar, St. Louis, MO 63130: Free list with long SASE ■ New and used equipment for all gauges. 314–721–2939.

Kadee, P.O. Box 1726, Medford, OR 97501: Free information ■ N-gauge table top and Z-gauge desktop locomotives, cars, and track. 800–545–4899.

Leventon's Hobby Supply, P.O. Box 1525, Chehalis, WA 98532: Free train list with long SASE; parts catalog $2 ■ HO, S, O

trains, and standard gauge parts and rolling stock. 206–748–3643.

Lionel Classics Service Center, 9693 Gerwig Ln., Columbia, MD 21046: Catalog $2 ■ Pre-war tinplate parts for Lionel trains. 410–381–2588.

Little Hobby's, 22 Turntable Junction, Church St., Flemington, NJ 08822: Free information with long SASE ■ Lionel, HO, N, and LGB equipment and accessories. 908–782–3474.

Longs Model Railroad Supply, 25070 Alessandro Blvd., Moreno Valley, CA 92553: Free information ■ Trains and scenic accessories. 714–242–5060.

Donald B. Manlick, 2127 S. 11th St., Manitowoc, WI 54220: Free list with long SASE ■ Custom decals for HO, N, O, and S scales.

MDK, Inc., P.O. Box 2831, Chapel Hill, NC 27515: Catalog $5 ■ K-Line electric trains. 800–866–9986.

Mike's Train House, 9693 Gerwig Ln., Columbia, MD 21046: Catalog $2 ■ Locomotives and cars; sets by Lionel, Williams, and others; and accessories. 410–381–2580.

Mike's Trainland, Inc., 5661 Shoulder's Hill Rd., Suffolk, VA 23435: Free price list ■ Model trains, supplies, and operating equipment. 800–955–4224.

Model Engineering Works, P.O. Box 1188, Ramona, CA 92065: Catalog $3.50 ■ Standard gauge parts and decals.

Model Expo, Inc., P.O. Box 1000, Mt. Pocono, PA 18344: Free catalog ■ Train sets, ship model kits, automobile and airplane kits, and modeling tools and accessories. 800–222–3876.

Model Railway Post Office, Box 426, Hewitt, NJ 07421: Free information ■ Trains and scenic accessories. 800–328–6776.

Model Rectifier Corporation, 200 Carter Dr., Edison, NJ 08817: Free information ■ Power control units. 908–248–0400.

Stanley Orr, P.O. Box 97, Stromville, NY 12582: Catalog $1.70 ■ Lionel repair parts and decals for standard, O, and O–27 gauges.

P & P Lines, P.O. Box 102, Easton, CT 06612: Catalog $2 ■ Scenic system-making supplies and accessories. 203–268–3243.

Red Caboose, 16 W. 45th St., 4th Floor, New York, NY 10036: Free information ■ HO, N gauge, and O gauge equipment; European scales; and American Flyer and Lionel trains and accessories. 212–575–0155.

Right-of-Way Industries, P.O. Box 13036, Akron, OH 44313: Information $1 ■ O gauge switches, double crossovers, yard routing track sections, magnetic uncouplers, curved track, controllers, diesel sound effect mechanisms, and other layout accessories. 216–867–5361.

Charles Ro Supply Company, 662 Cross St., P.O. Box 100, Malden, MA 02148: Free price list with long SASE ■ Lionel and LGB trains and accessories, HO rolling stock, and other equipment and accessories. 617–321–0090.

Roundhouse South, 146 Broadway, Daytona Beach, FL 32118: Free information with long SASE ■ Lionel and LGB trains and accessories. 904–238–7391.

Roundhouse Trains, 12804 Victory Blvd., North Hollywood, CA 91606: Free information with long SASE ■ LGB, Lionel, American Flyer, Marklin, HO, and N gauge equipment. 818–769–0403.

San Antonio Hobby Shop, 2550 W. El Camino, Mountain View, CA 94040: Free information ■ HO, N, O, Lionel, LGB, Z and other narrow gauge equipment, scratch building and brass supplies, accessories, and books. 415–941–1278.

Joe Schwingl, 92–61 246th St., Bellerose Terrace, NY 11001: Catalog $3]1 ■ Lionel O gauge train parts and accessories.

Charles Siegel's Train City, 3133 Zuck Rd., Erie, PA 16506: Price list $10 ■ Trains and accessories by American Flyer, Lionel, MPC, Marx, and others. 814–833–8313.

Nicholas Smith Trains, 2343 W. Chester Pike, Broomall, PA 19008: Free catalog with long SASE ■ Pola, LGB, and other equipment and supplies. 215–353–8585.

Square Roundhouse, 1468 Lander, Turlock, CA 95381: Free information with long SASE ■ Lionel equipment, other equipment and accessories, model planes, rocket equipment and supplies, and radio controlled cars. 209–668–4454.

Standard Hobby Supply, P.O. Box 801, Mahwah, NJ 07430: Catalog $3 ■ Model railroad equipment and accessories. 201–825–2211.

George Tebolt, 130 E. Chester Rd., New Rochelle, NY 10801: Catalog $1 ■ Lionel O and O–27 gauge parts.

Town & Country Hobbies & Crafts, 28 Dewey Ave., Totowa Boro, NJ 07512: Free list with long SASE ■ Lionel accessories and parts. 201–942–5176.

Train Express, 4365 W. 96th St., Indianapolis, IN 46268: Free information ■ Lionel train sets, engines, boxcars, rolling stock, operating cars, operating accessories, building kits, track, and American Flyer equipment. 800–428–6177.

Train 99, 333 Wilmington Westchester Pike, Glen Mills, PA 19342: Free information with long SASE ■ Cars and engines, sets, and accessories by Lionel, American Flyer, Williams, and others. 215–TRAIN–99.

Train World, 751 McDonald Ave., Brooklyn, NY 11218: Free information ■ Model railroading equipment and accessories. 718–436–7072.

T-Reproductions, 227 W. Main St., Johnson City, TN 37603: Catalog $2 (refundable) ■ Buddy "L" train reproductions. 615–926–4287.

Underground Railroad Shoppe, 1906 Wilmington Ave., New Castle, PA 16105: Free list with long SASE ■ Lionel and American Flyer trains and equipment. 412–652–4912.

Owen Upp Railroader's Supply Company, P.O. Box 773, Brookfield, WI 53008: Free list with first class stamp ■ Lionel, K-Line and Williams equipment, Gargraves track, books, videos, and accessories. 414–771–2353.

Watts' Train Shop, 9180 Hunt Club Rd., Zionsville, IN 46077: Free information ■ Trains and scenic accessories. 800–542–7652.

West Coast Interconnect, Inc., 3217 Winona Dr., Burbank, CA 91504: Free information with long SASE ■ Lionel model trains and accessories in all scales. 800–477–8724.

Whistle Stop, 24900 E. Colorado Blvd., Pasadena, CA 91107: Free information with long SASE ■ Rolling stock, kits, parts, detailing supplies, tools, scratch building supplies, and brass imports. 818–796–7791.

Williams Parts & Service, 6046 Cedarwood Dr., Columbia, MD 21044: Free brochure ■ Lionel classics and accessories, train controllers, track and accessories, and sets. 410–964–2262.

Charles C. Wood, P.O. Box 179, Hartford, CT 44424: Catalog $2 ■ Standard gauge equipment, classic model trains, and other supplies. 216–772–5177.

Woodland Scenics, P.O. Box 98, Linn Creek, MD 65052: Catalog $1.25 ■ Trees, turf, foliage, ballast, and scenery detailing supplies. 314–346–5555.

World of Trains, 105–18 Metropolitan Ave., Forest Hills, NY 11375: Free information ■ Trains and scenic accessories. 718–520–9700.

MOTORCYCLES & MOTOR BIKES

Clothing & Helmets

AGV USA, Intersport, 5711 Industry Ln., Unit 38, Frederick, MD 21701: Catalog $3 ■ Leather clothing for motorcyclists. 800–726–2065; 310–604–4221 (in CA).

Arai Helmets, Ltd., P.O. Box 9485, Daytona, FL 32120: Brochure $2 ■ Helmets. 800–766–ARAI.

Bates Leather Shop, P.O. Box 2668, Long Beach, CA 90801: Free catalog ■ Leather clothing and accessories. 310–435–6551.

Bieffe USA, Inc., 1746 Junction Ave., San Jose, CA 95112: Free information ■ Reinforced helmets. 408–436–8098.

Chaparral, 889 W. Mill St., San Bernardino, CA 92410: Free catalog ■ Clothing, boots, goggles, and soft luggage. 800–841–2960.

Cycle Racer, Inc., 2921 E. Miraloma, Anaheim, CA 92806: Catalog $2 ■ Leather clothing, gloves, and boots. 800–423–7070; 714–632–7393 (in CA).

Fieldsheer Clothing, 2939 Pacific Commerce Dr., Rancho Dominguez, CA 90221: Free information ■ Leather clothing for motorcyclists. 800–726–2065; 310–604–4221 (in CA).

FirstGear Clothing, Intersport Fashions West, 333 S. Anita, Ste. 1025, Orange, CA 92668: Free information ■ Hein Gericke clothing for motorcyclists. 714–978–7718.

Harley-Davidson Catalog, P.O. Box 92218, Milwaukee, WI 53201: Catalog $2 ■ Clothing for men and women bikers.

Langlitz Leathers, 2446 Southeast Division, Portland, OR 97202: Catalog $1 (refundable) ■ Custom leather clothing. 503–235–0959.

Lockhart-Phillips, 991 Calle Negocio St., San Clemente, CA 92672: Free information ■ Leather jackets in small to extra-large sizes. 800–822–6005; 714–498–9090 (in CA).

Motoport USA, 7720 El Camino Real, Ste. 504, Rancho LaCosta, CA 92009: Catalog $4.95 ■ Touring and biker clothing and accessories for men and women. 800–777–6499; 619–591–0568 (in CA).

Moto Race, P.O. Box 861, Wilbraham, MA 01095: Catalog $3 ■ Boots, vests, gloves, and sportswear; motorcycle accessories and parts; and tires. 800–628–4040; 413–734–6211 (in MA).

Rider Wearhouse, 8 S. 18th Ave., Duluth, MN 55805: Free catalog ■ Motorcycle clothing with weatherproof seam-sealed protection against abrasion. 800–222–1994.

Malcom Smith Products, 850 Marlborough, Riverside, CA 94403: Free information ■ Motorcycle helmets. 800–854–4742; 714–686–1006 (in CA).

Thurlow Leatherworld, 4807 Mercury St., San Diego, CA 92111: Catalog $2 ■ Handcrafted deerskin leather clothing. 619–279–9004.

Tour Master Riding Gear, 2360 Townsgate Rd., Westlake Village, CA 91361: Free catalog ■ Sport gloves, Spandex fingerless gloves, knit and leather fingerless gloves, summer gloves, gauntlet gloves, tail and tank bags, clothing, rain suits, rain boots, and dry-knit socks. 800–421–7247; 805–373–6868 (in CA).

Vanson Leathers, Inc., 434 Hancock, Quincy, MA 02171: Free information ■ Custom and ready-made leather clothing. 617–328–9291.

Vetter Products, Division Bell Helmets, Inc., P.O. Box 927, Rantout, IL 61866: Free information ■ Helmets with aerodynamic face shield, ventilation vents, and terrycloth foam padded inner liner. 217–893–9300.

Z Custom Leathers, 7501 Slater Ave., Unit R, Huntington Beach, CA 92647: Free information ■ Leather clothing for motorcyclists. 714–848–5285.

Parts & Accessories

Advanced Styling, Box 210, Makawao, HI 96768: Catalog $3 ■ Sport fairings, clear fairings, racing fairings, tank bags, and other styling accessories. 800–FAS–LANE.

American Jawa, Ltd., 185 Express St., Plainview, Long Island, NY 11803: Free information ■ Motorcycle side cars. 516–938–3210.

Antique Cycle Supply, RR 1, Cedar Springs, MI 49319: Catalog $5 ■ Harley Davidson parts, accessories, tools and literature for all Flathead, Knucklehead, Panhead, and Shovelhead models. Specializes in obsolete parts. 616–636–8200.

A–1 Used Cycle Parts, Inc., 106 E. Arlington, St. Paul, MN 55117: Free information ■ Save from 40 to 60 percent on used parts for Honda, Suzuki, Yamaha, and Kawasaki cycles. 800–522–7891; 612–487–2841 (in MN).

Bartels Performance Products, 9461 Jefferson Blvd., Culver City, CA 90232: Free information ■ Harley-Davidson accessories and parts. 800–747–1151; 310–842–8081 (in CA).

Baxter Cycle, 400 Lincoln St., Marne, IA 51552: Free information ■ New and used parts, 1950 and later Triumph, Norton, BSA, and Moto Guzzi motorcycles. 712–781–2351.

Beach Yamaha, 19721 Beach Blvd., Huntington Beach, CA 92648: Free information ■ Yamaha parts and accessories. 714–536–7555.

Brickhouse Cycles, 7819 N. Military Hwy., Norfolk, VA 23518: Free information ■ Used parts for late model Japanese bikes. 800–877–4804; 804–480–4800 (in VA).

British Cycle Supply Company, P.O. Box 119, Wolfville, Nova Scotia, Canada B0P 1X0: Free information ■ Original Triumph, BSA, and Norton replacement, speed and custom parts, and accessories. 902–542–7478.

British Parts Old & New, 13428 E. Telegraph Rd., Whittier, CA 90605: Free information ■ New, used, and reconditioned parts for Norton, Triumph, and BSA motorcycles. 310–941–4440.

California Side Car, 15159 Golden West Circle, Westminster, CA 92683: Free information ■ Motorcycle side cars. 800–824–1523; 714–891–1033 (in CA).

Capital Cycle Corporation, P.O. Box 528, Sterling, VA 22170: Free catalog ■ BMW parts and accessories. 703–444–2500.

Carl's Honda, 9920 Farragut Rd., Brooklyn, NY 11236: Free information ■ Honda parts and accessories. 800–221–7508; 718–257–0602 (in NY).

Chaparral, 889 W. Mill St., San Bernardino, CA 92410: Free catalog ■ Tires by Dunlop, Metzeler, Michelin, Continental, Bridgestone, Cheng Shin, and others; clothing, boots, and goggles; and soft luggage. 800–841–2960.

Charleston Custom Cycle, 211 Washington, Charleston, IL 61920: Free information ■ N.O.S. parts for Harley Davison Lightweights, American, and other motorcycles, from 1948 to 1978. 217–345–2577.

Classic Cycles, 50 Broad Ave., Edison, NJ 08820: Free information ■ British parts and accessories. 908–548–7975.

Clet's Motorcycle, 4329 Centennial Ave., Radcliff, KY 40160: Free information ■ Japanese salvage parts for most bikes, from 1960 to 1986. 800–367–8402; 502–351–5918 (in KY).

Clinton Cycle & Salvage, Inc., 6709 Old Branch Ave., Camp Springs, MD 20748: Free price list ■ Used parts for Honda, Kaw, Yam, and Suz 250 to 1300cc street bikes. 800–332–8264; 301–449–3550 (in MD).

Competition Accessories, Inc., Rt. 68 North at Rt. 235, Xenia, OH 45385: Catalog $5 (refundable) ■ Accessories for BMW, Moto Guzzi, Triumph, Yamaha, and Ducati motorcycles. 800–543–3535.

Covr-Larm, 2554 Lincoln Blvd., Ste. 218, Marina Del Rey, CA 90291: Free information ■ Security sensor systems for vehicle protection. 310–821–7800.

Cycle Re-Cycle, 2117 E. 10th St., Indianapolis, IN 46201: Free information ■ Used cycle parts. 317–634–6645.

Cycle Recyclers, 1538 Park Ave., Chico, CA 95928: Free information ■ Used motorcycle parts and accessories. 800–356–4735.

Cycle Sports, RD 1, Box 151A, Mt. Pleasant, PA 15666: Free information ■ Kawasaki parts. 412–423–4553.

D & S Cycle, Rt. 73, Berlin, NJ 08009: Free information ■ Yamaha parts and accessories. 609–767–1310.

Dai Distributing, P.O. Box 1602, Springfield, OH 45501: Free catalog ■ N.O.S. and reproduced parts for Indian Chief motorcycles. 513–322–5909.

Daytona Yamaha, 324 11th St., Holly Hill, FL 32017: Free information ■ Yamaha parts and accessories. 904–258–0354.

Donelson Cycles, Inc., 3328 Woodson Rd., St. Louis, MO 53114: Free catalog ■ BMW, Triumph, Norton, and Yamaha parts and accessories; clothing, helmets, boots, and rain suits; and saddlebags and tank. 314–427–5523.

East Coast Suzuki Warehouse, 687 Rt. 1, Edison, NJ 08817: Free information ■ Suzuki and Honda motorcycles, parts, and accessories. 800–544–4814.

Eastern Cycle Salvage, Inc., 87 Park St., Beverly, MA 01915: Free information ■ Used parts for most makes and models of motorcycles. 617–922–3707.

Eurosport Cycle, 5200 Airport Freeway, Fort Worth, TX 76117: Free information ■ Triumph/Moto Guzzi parts and accessories. 817–838–8135.

Freedom Cycles, 12505 South Hwy. 71, Grandview, MO 64030: Free information ■ Parts and accessories for Kawasaki, Honda, Cagiva, Husqvarna, and KTM cycles. 816–761–6621.

G.P. Cycle Works, 75 Executive Ave., Rohnert Park, CA 94928: Free information with long SASE ■ Parts for most models of BSA and Triumph motorcycles, from 1947 and later. 707–586–0214.

Gustafson Plastics, P.O. Box 3567, St. Augustine, FL 32085: Free information ■ Replacement and custom windscreens for cafe, racing, and touring fairings. 904–824–2119.

Hartco, 716 Parkway, Servierville, TN 37862: Free information ■ Lambskin seat covers. 800–446–7772; 615–428–5263 (in TN).

H-D Sales, 4016 N. Detroit Ave., Toledo, OH 43612: Free information with long

SASE ■ Parts and accessories for Harley-Davidson motorcycles. 219–476–5655.

Honda Parts, Rt. 166 South, Toms River, NJ 08757: Free information ■ Honda parts and accessories. 800–443–5828.

Hugh's Bultaco, RD 1, Box 205, Craryville, NY 12521: Free information ■ Bultaco bikes, parts, and accessories. 512–851–7184.

Don Hutchinson Cycle, 116 Foundry St., P.O. Box 445, Wakefield, MA 01880: Free information ■ New and used parts for Triumph motorcycles. 617–245–9663.

Hy-Tech, 16844 Ceres Ave., Fontana, CA 92335: Free information ■ Used parts for dirt bike. 714–822–1656.

Indian Motorcycle Supply, Inc., 264 S. Main St., Sugar Grove, IL 60554: Free information ■ New parts and accessories for Indian Chief, Four Sport Scout, Arrow, VT Scout, and Warrior motorcycles. 708–466–4601.

Innovation Specialties, 1900 Powell St., Ste. 1135, Emeryville, GA 94608: Free information ■ Radar detector for motorcycles and Nady motorcycle anti-theft alarms. 800–222–8228; 800–624–1784 (in CA).

Kart World, 1488 Mentor Ave., Painesville, OH 44077: Catalog $3 (refundable) ■ Parts, engines, and accessories for mini-cars and mini-bikes. 216–357–5569.

Kawasaki of Pittsburgh, 611 Butler St., Pittsburgh, PA 15223: Free information ■ Kawasaki parts and accessories. 412–781–8611.

Kawasaki Parts Warehouse, P.O. Box 1120, Freehold, NJ 07728: Free information ■ Kawasaki parts and accessories. 800–848–2609.

Dennis Kirk, 955 Southfield Ave., Rush City, MN 55069: Free catalog ■ Motorcycle tires and tubes, general accessories and equipment, gloves, helmets, luggage racks, carryall bags, and boots. 800–328–9280.

Kiwi Indian Parts, Box 7783, Riverside, CA 92513: Catalog $5 ■ Indian parts and accessories. 714–780–5400.

Klempf's British Parts Warehouse, 204 20th St. SW, Rochester, MN 55902: Free information with long SASE ■ Triumph, BSA, and Norton parts and accessories from the 1960s to the present. 507–288–8393.

Laurel Highlands Accessories Plus, P.O. Box 383, Norvelt, PA 15674: Free information ■ Motorcycle accessories and clothing. 412–437–8035.

Lockhart-Phillips USA, 991 Calle Negocio, San Clemente, CA 92672: Catalog $5 ■ Motorcycle accessories and windscreens. 800–822–6005; 714–498–9090 (in CA).

M.A.P. Cycle Enterprises, 7165 30th Ave. North, St. Petersburg, FL 33710: Catalog $3 ■ New, used, stock, and N.O.S. parts and accessories for BSA cycles. 813–381–1151.

Joe Martin's Antique Motorcycle Parts, P.O. Box 3156, Chattanooga, TN 37404: Catalog $3 ■ Parts for Indian and Harley motorcycles.

Midwest Action Cycle, 617 W. Wise Rd., Schaumberg, IL 60193: Free information ■ Suzuki parts and accessories. 800–323–0078; 708–894–4661 (in IL).

Mike's Cycle Parts, 3511 Boone Rd. SE, Salem, OR 97301: Free information ■ Used Japanese motorcycle parts. 800–327–7304.

Miller Specialties, Inc., 204 E. Main St., Clinton, CT 06413: Free information ■ Restored Ducato motorcycles and parts. 203–669–5307.

Moores Cycle Supply, 49 Custer St., West Hartford, CT 06110: Catalog $4 ■ Triumph and BSA parts. 203–953–1689.

Moto Race, P.O. Box 861, Wilbraham, MA 01095: Catalog $3 ■ Tires, brakes, accessories, and clothing. 800–628–4040; 413–734–6211 (in MA).

Motorcycle Accessory Warehouse, 2 Venture Ln., P.O. Box 3629, Sunriver, OR 97707: Free catalog ■ Tires, helmets, batteries, seats, saddlebags, accessories, and sportswear. 503–593–3633.

Pen Argyl Cycle, Inc., 506 E. Main St., Pen Argyl, PA 18072: Free information ■ Parts and accessories for Honda and Yamaha motorcycles. 215–863–5000.

Pensacola Motorcycle Salvage, 101 South F St., Pensacola, FL 32501: Free information with long SASE ■ Late model parts and accessories for Japanese motorcycles. 800–888–3010.

Performance Motorcycle Center, 7645 Carrol Rd., San Diego, CA 92121: Free information ■ Motorcycle parts and accessories. 619–271–7731.

Performance Speedway, 2810–C Algonquin Ave., Jacksonville, FL 32210: Catalog $5 ■ Mopeds, electric cars, and golf cars. Includes hard-to-find parts for gas to electric conversion, conversion manuals, moped parts, repair manuals, and other books.

Pichler Fairings, 196 S. Van Buren Ave., Barberton, OH 44203: Catalog $2 ■ Half and full fairings for touring, cruising, and sport bikes. 216–745–3156.

Racepart, 92 Bogart St., Garfield, NJ 07026: Free catalog with long SASE ■ High performance motorcycle accessories. 201–684–0711.

Ray's Yamaha-Suzuki-Kawasaki, Inc., 959 S. Telegraph, Monroe, MI 48161: Free information ■ Yamaha, Suzuki, and Kawasaki parts. 313–241–8444.

Rifle Fairings, 3140 El Camino Real, Atascadero, CA 93422: Free information ■ Rifle windshields for all popular sport bikes. 800–262–1237; 805–239–4235 (in CA).

RKA Accessories, Box 1006, Windsor, CA 95492: Free information ■ Soft luggage for motorcycles, with design options for all bikes. 707–579–5045.

Sam's Motorcycles, 605 Silver, Houston, TX 77007: Free information ■ Save from 40 to 75 percent on used parts for most makes and models of motorcycles. 713–862–4026.

Satellite Parts Locating System, 3511 Boone Rd. SE, Salem, OR 97301: Free information ■ New and used Japanese cycle parts. 800–327–7304.

Sky Cycle, Inc., Rt. 13, Lunenburg, MA 01462: Free information ■ Used Honda, KAW, Suzuki, and Yamaha parts and accessories. 800–345–6115; 508–345–4647 (in MA).

Spec II, 9812 Glen Oaks, Sun Valley, CA 91352: Catalog $3 ■ High performance parts and accessories and full fairings. 800–235–1236; 818–504–6364 (in CA).

StaRider, 3317 Hwy. 70 East, Building E, New Berlin, NC 28560: Free information ■ Parts and accessories for Honda, KAW, and Yamaha bikes. 800–TOY–PLAY.

Steve's Cycle, Rt. 5, Box 109, Tifton, GA 31794: Free information ■ Used parts and accessories. 912–386–8666.

Storz Performance, 1445 Donlon St., #18, Ventura, CA 93003: Catalog $2 ■ Performance accessories for motorcycles. 805–654–8816.

Suzuki Motorcycle Parts & Accessories, 687 Rt. 1, Edison, NJ 08817: Free information ■ Suzuki parts and accessories. 800–544–4814.

Targa Accessories, Inc., 23561 Ridge Route Dr., Laguna Hills, CA 92653: Catalog $3 ■ Motorcycles, parts, and accessories. 800–521–7845; 714–472–1022 (in CA).

Tri-City Kawasaki, 1410 Tilghman St., Allentown, PA 18102: Free information ■ Kawasaki parts and accessories. 215–434–7111.

Vance & Hines Motorcycle Center, 9007 Sunland Blvd., Sun Valley, CA 91352: Catalog $2 ■ Performance products. 818–768–9026.

Wolf Cycles, 5413 East Dr., Baltimore, MD 21227: Free information ■ New and used Amal and Lucas parts. 410–247–7420.

MOUNTAIN & ICE CLIMBING

Adventure 16, Inc., 4620 Alvarado Canyon Rd., San Diego, CA 92120: Free information ■ Clothing, carabiners and crampons, axes, hammers, pitons, packs, ropes, and other equipment. 800–854–2672; 800–854–0222 (in CA).

Alpine Research, Inc., 1803 S. Foothills Pkwy., Boulder, CO 80303: Free catalog ■ Backcountry ski equipment, tents, sleeping bags, frame packs, books, videos, rock and ice climbing gear, caving equipment, and winter survival equipment. 303–499–4466.

Blue Water Ropes & Equipment, 209 Lovvorn Rd., Carrolton, GA 30117: Free information ■ Carabiners, pitons, and ropes. 404–834–7515.

Climb High, Inc., 1861 Shelburne Rd., Shelburne, VT 05482: Free information ■ Mountain climbing boots and clothing, carabiners and crampons, axes, hammers, pitons, packs, ropes, and other equipment. 802–985–5056.

Lowe Alpine Systems, P.O. Box 1449, Broomfield, CO 80020: Free information ■ Mountain climbing boots and clothing, carabiners and crampons, axes, hammers, pi-

tons, packs, ropes, and other equipment. 303–465–3706.

Mountain Tools, P.O. Box 222295, Carmel, CA 93922: Free catalog ■ Equipment and hardware and soft goods for mountain and ice climbing. 408–625–6222.

Outdoor Sports Headquarters, Inc., 967 Watertower Ln., Dayton, OH 45449: Free information ■ Mountain climbing boots and clothing, axes, hammers, ropes, and other equipment. 515–865–5855.

SMC Mountain Climbing Equipment, 12880 Northrup Way, Bellevue, WA 98005: Free information ■ Carabiners, pitons, ropes, and axes. 206–883–0334.

MOVIE & THEATRICAL MEMORABILIA

American Archive, P.O. Box 10448, Zephyr Cave, NV 89448: Free information ■ Movie posters, lobby cards, other movie memorabilia, and 8mm and 16mm films. 702–588–2192.

American Arts & Graphics, Inc., P.O. Box 2067, Everett, WA 98203: Free catalog ■ Giant posters, fun posters for kids, aerodynamic posters, all-star pinup posters, sports posters, and art and photo posters; and humorous, animal, art and photo, and scenic calendars. 800–524–3900.

American Comic Book Company, 3972 Atlantic Blvd., Long Beach, CA 90807: Free information with long SASE ■ Vintage movie posters. 310–426–0393.

Artrock Posters, 45 Sheridan St., San Francisco, CA 94103: Catalog $2 ■ Original rock concert posters. 415–255–7390.

Backlot Books & Movie Items, 7278–A Sunset Blvd., Los Angeles, CA 90046: Free information with long SASE ■ Posters, photographs, and autographs. 310–274–0160.

Loraine Burdick Movie Memorabilia, 5 Court Pl., Puyallup, WA 98372: Catalog 75¢ ■ Movie memorabilia. 206–845–0340.

Celebrity Graphics, P.O. Box 385, Flushing, MI 48433: Free information with long SASE ■ Original one-sheets, color still sets and singles, lobby cards, black-and-white still sets, and posters. 313–659–8751.

Dean Chapman Collectable Toys, 7111 Amundsonn Ave., Edina, MN 55439: Free list ■ Character, western, and TV-related toys, games, premiums, and other movie memorabilia. 612–925–0156.

Cinema City, Box 1012, Muskegon, MI 49443: Catalog $3 ■ Movie posters, photos, autographs, and scripts. 616–722–7760.

Cinema Graphics, Box 10761, Denver, CO 80210: Catalog $3 ■ Movie posters, photos, magazines, and press books. 303–744–3855.

Cinemonde, 1932 Polk St., San Francisco, CA 94109: Free information ■ Original movie one-sheets. 415–776–9988.

Dwight Cleveland, 1815 N. Orchard St., Chicago, IL 60614: Free information ■ Lobby cards, one-sheets, window cards, glass slides, motion picture heralds, exhibitor's books, and studio annuals. 312–266–9152.

Collectors Originals, P.O. Box 17522, Memphis, TN 38117: Free information ■ Movie posters, lobbies, stills, and other memorabilia. 901–682–6761.

Collectors Warehouse, Inc., 5437 Pearl Rd., Cleveland, OH 44129: Free information with long SASE ■ Rare movie posters. 216–842–2896.

Fiesta Arts, Inc., Eastview Ln., Glen Head, NY 11545: Catalog $2.50 ■ Turn-of-the-century movie posters and memorabilia. 516–671–6888.

Framex, 4054 Laurel Canyon Blvd., Studio City, CA 91604: Free information ■ One-sheets complete with glass, frame, vacuum mounting, cardboard, and wire. Museum mounts and mats available. 818–509–0700.

Front Row Photos, Box 484, Nesconset, NY 11767: Catalog $2 ■ Exclusive concert photos. 516–585–1918.

Gifted Images Gallery, P.O. Box 34, Baldwin, NY 11510: Free catalog ■ Animation art. Includes cels, drawings, and backgrounds. 800–726–6708; 516–536–6886 (in NY).

Gone Hollywood, 172 Bella Vista Ave., Belvedere, CA 94920: Free information ■ Vintage movie posters. 415–435–1929.

The Good Old Days, 40 Cottage St., P.O. Box 1235, Easthampton, MA 01027: Free information with long SASE ■ Lobby cards, window cards, inserts, one-sheets, and other movie memorabilia. 413–527–3163.

Granada Posters, P.O. Box 64980, Dallas, TX 75206: Free information ■ Movie posters, lobby cards, black and white stills, and press books. 214–373–3012.

Jim's TV Collectibles, P.O. Box 4767, San Diego, CA 92164: Catalog $2 ■ Television and theatrical collectibles, from the 1950s through 1990s.

La Belle Epoque, 11661 San Vincente Blvd., Ste. 211, Los Angeles, CA 90024: List $4 ■ Rare posters. 310–442–0054.

Last Moving Picture Company, 6307 Hollywood Blvd., Hollywood, CA 90028: Free information with long SASE ■ Window cards, lobby cards, inserts, one-sheets, stills, and posters. 213–467–0838.

Werner H. Lehmann, 16 Alden Pl., Bronxville, NY 10708: Catalog $1 ■ European movie memorabilia from 1950 through 1985.

Alan Levine Movie & Book Collectibles, 292 Glenwood Ave., Bloomfield, NJ 07003: Lists $1 with long SASE ■ Movie magazines from 1915 to 1970; movie posters and lobby cards; and celebrity autographs. 201–743–5288.

Rick Lipp, 427 Broadway, Jackson, CA 95642: Free information with long SASE ■ Stills, lobby sets, inserts, and press kits. 209–296–4754.

Little Shop of Posters, 244 Ridgefield Rd., Endicott, NY 13760: Free information ■ Press books, posters, and other movie memorabilia. 609–267–0277.

Matinee Idol, 8650 Melrose Ave., Los Angeles, CA 90069: Free information ■ Autographs, celebrity photographs, vintage sheet music, movie magazines, movie posters, movie programs, lobby cards, and campaign books. 310–659–5569.

Mauro's Nostalgia, 457 Main St., Ste. 206, Farmingdale, NY 11735: Four catalogs $8 (refundable) ■ Original movie posters and non-sports cards from the 1930s to present.

Memory Shop West, 519 Fleming St., Key West, FL 33040: Free information with long SASE ■ Posters, lobby cards, and stills. 305–296–1441.

Miscellaneous Man, P.O. Box 1900, New Freedom, PA 17349: Catalog $5 ■ Specializes in anything printed before the 1970s. Includes posters, circus and travel collectibles, movies, World War I and II memorabilia, and collectibles from expositions. 717–235–4766.

Moe's Movie Madness, 3526 N. Main, P.O. Box 246, Toms Brook, VA 22660: Free information ■ Movie posters and memorabilia. 703–436–9181.

Motion Picture Arts Gallery, 133 E. 58th St., New York, NY 10022: Free brochure ■ Movie memorabilia, vintage posters, and lobby cards. 212–223–1009.

Movie Gallery, 2072 Front St., East Meadow, NY 11554: Free information ■ Movie posters, sheets, lobby cards, and inserts. 516–794–0294.

Movie Memories, 131 Parker Ave., Hawthorne, NJ 07506: Free information with long SASE ■ Movie posters and lobby cards. 201–427–0709.

Movie Memories Poster Shop, 502 Waverley St., Palo Alto, CA 94301: Free poster catalog with long SASE; movie still catalog $3.50 ■ Movie posters and stills. 415–328–6265.

Movie Poster Place, Inc., P.O. Box 128, Lansdowne, PA 19050: Catalog $1 (refundable) ■ Movie posters, stills, press books, and trailers. 215–622–6062.

Movie Poster Service, Box 517, Canton, OK 73724: Free information ■ One-sheets, lobby sets, lobby cards, and movie posters. 405–886–2248

Movie Poster Shop, 3600 21st St. NE, Calgary, Alberta, Canada T2E 6V6: Catalog $2 ■ Movie posters and movie star photos. 403–250–7588.

Movie Poster Warehouse, 32 Kern Rd., Don Mills, Ontario, Canada M3B 1T1: Free information ■ Nostalgic and current movie posters and movie star photos. 414–444–8461.

Movie Star News, 134 W. 18th St., New York, NY 10011: Illustrated brochure $1 ■ Movie star photos. 212–620–8160.

Jerry Ohlinger's Movie Material Store, Inc., 1507 Wilcox Ave., Hollywood, CA 90028: Free catalog ■ Stills, movie posters, star photos, magazines, and books. 213–461–6516.

Jerry Ohlinger's Movie Material Store, Inc., 242 W. 14th St., New York, NY 10011: Free catalog ■ Stills, movie posters, star photos, magazines, and books. 212–989–0869.

One Shubert Alley, 346 W. 44th St., New York, NY 10036: Free information ■ T-shirts, posters, mugs, jewelry from Broadway shows, and other theatrical memorabilia. 800–223–1320; 212–586–7610 (in NY).

Paper Chase, 4073 LaVista Rd., Ste. 363, Tucker, GA 30084: Free information ■ Movie posters, used videos, baseball cards, and comics. 800–433–0025.

Tom Peper, 32 Shelter Cove Lane, #109, Hilton Head Island, SC 29928: Price list $1 ■ Autographs, lobby cards and posters, original comic art, and animation art and cels. 800–628–7497.

Poster Emporium, P.O. Box 16681, Raytown, MO 64133: Free information ■ Sets, inserts, half sheets, press kits, two-sheets, and three-sheets. 816–353–7300.

Poster Gallery, Box 2745, Ann Arbor, MI 48106: Catalog $3 ■ Original movie posters and photos of stars. 313–665–3151.

Poster Service, 255 Northland Blvd., Cincinnati, OH 45246: Catalog $2 ■ Imported and domestic music, and psychedelic, movie, and artprint posters.

Poster World, 14 Bolton Pl., Fairlawn, NJ 07410: Free information with long SASE ■ Movie posters from the 1940s to the 1980s. 201–791–1073.

Rick's Movie Posters, P.O. Box 23709, Gainesville, FL 32602: Catalog $3 ■ Foreign scripts and movie poster originals from the 1950s through the 1980s. 904–373–7202.

Noel Dean Schiff, 6975 N. Sheridan, Chicago, IL 60626: Free information ■ Vintage movie posters and lobby cards. 312–262–6011.

Murray A. Summers, 10670 Cliff Mills Dr., Marshall, VA 22115: Catalog $3 (refundable) ■ Scarce movie magazines from the 1920s to the 1970s, movie posters, and other memorabilia. 703–364–1275.

Toy Scouts, Inc., 330 Merriman Rd., Akron, OH 44303: Catalog $3 ■ Movie posters, Disney collectibles, and other movie memorabilia. 216–836–0668.

Triton Theatre Posters, 323 W. 45th St., New York, NY 10036: Catalog 50¢ ■ Current hits and rare collectible theatrical posters. 800–626–6674.

S. Wallach, Box 428, Ste. S., Toronto, Ontario, Canada M5M 4M9: Catalog $2 ■ Original posters. 416–444–8461.

World of Cinema, 488 Henley Ave., New Milford, NJ 07646: Catalog $2 ■ Movie posters from the 1940s to the present, cinema books, rock posters, foreign material, and sound tracks. 201–262–3513.

MOVIE & TV SCRIPTS

Cinema City, Box 1012, Muskegon, MI 49443: Catalog $3 ■ Movie scripts, posters, photos, and autographs. 616–722–7760.

Rick's Movie Posters, P.O. Box 23709, Gainesville, FL 32601: Brochure $2 ■ Foreign scripts and movie posters from the 1950s through the 1980s. 904–373–7202.

Script City, 8033 Sunset Blvd., Hollywood, CA 90046: Catalog $2 ■ Movie scripts, TV scripts, film and media books, photos, and posters. 213–871–0707.

MOVIE PROJECTION EQUIPMENT

International Cinema Equipment Company, 6750 NE 4th Ct., Miami, FL 33138: Free information ■ Professional 35mm projectors, 16mm and 35mm telecine equipment, miscellaneous audio visual equipment, cinema sound equipment and accessories, portable projectors, 16mm and 35mm cameras, 16mm portable sound projectors, professional auditorium 16mm projection equipment, and film editing equipment. 305–756–0699.

Surplus Audio Visual & Electronics, 2570 E. Medicine Lake Blvd., Plymouth, MN 55441: Free information ■ Super 8mm and 16mm projectors and miscellaneous equipment. 612–546–4377.

Vita Theatre Supply, 145 Munroe St., Ste. 400, Lynn, MA 01901: Free information ■ New and used movie projection equipment and supplies. 617–599–9506.

MOVIES (FILMS)

American Archive, P.O. Box 10448, Zephyr Cave, NV 89448: Free information ■ Movie posters, lobby cards, other movie memorabilia, and 8mm and 16mm films. 702–588–2192.

Canyon Cinema, 2325 3rd St., #338, San Francisco, CA 94107: Catalog $15 ■ Slides and documentary movies. 415–626–2255.

The Cinema Center, Botsford, CT 06404: Free information ■ Super 8mm and 16mm movies in most categories and vintage movie memorabilia.

Ray Courts, P.O. Box 5040, Spring Hill, FL 34606: Free information ■ Classic color and black-and-white films. 904–683–5110.

Walt Disney Home Movies, 500 S. Buena Vista, Burbank, CA 91521: Free catalog ■ Super 8mm movie films. 818–560–5151.

Excalibur Films, 3621 W. Commonwealth, Fullerton, CA 92633: Catalog $6.95 ■ Movie reels and video cassettes. 800–BUY–MOVIES.

Green Mountain Post Films, P.O. Box 229, Turners Falls, MA 01376: Catalog $2 ■ Nonfiction films and videos. 413–863–4754.

National Cinema Service, P.O. Box 43, Ho-Ho-Kus, NJ 07423: Free list ■ New and used 16mm full-length features, shorts, and cartoons. 201–445–0776.

National Gallery of Art, Extension Program, Washington, DC 20565: Free catalog ■ Operates a program that lends art appreciation films to individuals, schools, and community groups. 202–646–6466.

Pyramid Film & Video, 2801 Colorado Ave., Santa Monica, CA 90406: Free catalog ■ Educational and entertainment films and videos. 800–421–2304; 213–828–7577 (in CA).

Barry Siegel Movies, 2221 Dwight Way, Berkeley, CA 94704: Free information with long SASE ■ Movie shorts in 16mm format. 510–849–4868.

Thornhill Entertainment, 2143 Statesville Blvd., Ste. 168, Salisbury, NC 28144: Free information ■ Most categories of 16mm films. 704–636–1116.

Trailers on Tape, 1576 Fell St., San Francisco, CA 94117: Free catalog ■ Preview trailers of musicals, comedies, horror, science fiction, and dramas. 415–921–TAPE.

Video Communications, Inc., 6535 E. Skelly Dr., Tulsa, OK 74145: Free information ■ Classic movie serials. 800–331–4077.

MUSICAL INSTRUMENTS

Accordion-O-Rama, 16 W. 19th St., New York, NY 10011: Free catalog ■ Save up to 40 percent on new and rebuilt accordions and concertinas. 212–206–8344.

Altenburg Piano House, Inc., 1150 E. Jersey St., Elizabeth, NJ 07201: Free information with long SASE ■ Organs and pianos. 800–526–6979; 800–492–4040 (in NJ).

American Guitar Center, 2446 Reedie Dr., Wheaton, MD 20902: Free catalog ■ Used guitars and amplifiers, new equipment, and accessories. 301–946–3043.

Sam Ash Music Corporation, P.O. Box 9047, Hicksville, NY 11802: Free catalog ■ Save up to 50 percent on musical equipment. 800–472–6274; 516–333–8700 (in NY).

Bari Associates, Inc., 788 NE 40th Ct., Fort Lauderdale, FL 33334: Free brochure ■ Bari mouthpieces. 305–564–2733.

Fred Bernardo's Music, 212 W. Lancaster, Shillington, PA 19607: Catalog $1 ■ Strings for most fretted instruments. 215–777–3733.

Black Mountain Instruments, Calistoga, CA 94515: Free information ■ Ready-to-use dulcimers or kits. 707–942–4240.

R.E. Brune, Luthier, 800 Greenwood St., Evanston, IL 60201: Free catalog ■ Handmade harpsichords, lutes, classical guitars, and baroque guitars. 708–864–7730.

Capri Taurus Folk Music, P.O. Box 153, Felton, CA 95018: Catalog $3 ■ Ethnic and folk musical instruments. 408–335–4478.

Caruso Music, 20 Bank St., New London, CT 06320: Free information ■ New and used keyboards, drum machines, digital sequencers, cases, and sound and recording equipment. 203–442–9600.

Carvin, 1155 Industrial Ave., Escondido, CA 92025: Catalog $2 ■ Guitars, amplifiers, recording mixers, equalizers, crossovers, speakers, microphones, other musical instruments, and accessories. 800–854–2235.

Castiglione Accordion, P.O. Box 40, Warren, MI 48090: Catalog $3 ■ New and used accordions and concertinas. 313–755–6050.

Conn Music Centers, 1385 Deerfield Rd., Highland Park, IL 60035: Free information with long SASE ■ Pianos and organs. 708–831–3250.

Al Corey Music Center, 99 Main St., Waterville, ME 04901: Free information ■ Pianos, organs, and other instruments. 207–872–5622.

Digital Arts & Technologies, Inc., 21 Glen Ridge Rd., Mahopac, NY 10541: Catalog $5 ■ Software and accessories for amateur and professional musicians. 914–628–7949.

Discount Music Supply, 41 Vreeland Ave., Totowa, NJ 07512: Free catalog ■ Guitars, accessories, and electronic equipment. 201–942–9411.

Discount Reed Company, P.O. Box 6010, Sherman Oaks, CA 91403: Free price list with long SASE ■ Save up to 40 percent on reeds for clarinets, saxophones, bassoons, oboes, and other instruments. 818–990–7962.

Drummer's World, 133 W. 45th St., New York, NY 10036: Free brochure ■ Percussion instruments and accessories. 212–840–3057.

Dulcimers by J.R., Rt. 1, C.R. 21, Newcomerstown, OH 43832: Free information with long SASE ■ Tap dulcimers, hammer dulcimers and stands, and other instruments. 614–498–7753.

Elderly Instruments, 1100 N. Washington, P.O. Box 14210, Lansing, MI 48901: Free catalog ■ Musical instruments, strings, straps, pickups, records, books, and accessories. 517–372–7890.

Fiddlepicker, Box 1033, Mountainside, NJ 07092: Free list ■ Fiddles and bows, acoustic-electric violins, violectras, violas, and transducers for string instruments. 201–379–9034.

Freeport Music, 41 Shore Dr., Huntington Bay, NY 11743: Catalog $1 (refundable) ■ Save from 20 to 60 percent on musical instruments, electronics, and accessories. 516–549–4108.

Geoffrion Keyboards & Hickory Ridge Dulcimer Works, Rt. 1, Box 273, Pomona, IL 62975: Brochure $3 ■ Keyboards and dulcimers. 618–687–2159.

Giardinelli Band Instrument Company, Inc., 7845 Maltlage Dr., Liverpool, NY 13090: Free catalog ■ Brass and woodwind instruments and accessories. 800–288–2334; 212–575–5959 (in NY).

Hubbard Harpsichords Incorporated, 144 W. Moody St., Waltham, MA 02154: Catalog $1 ■ Ready-to-play harpsichords or kits. 617–894–3238.

Hughes Dulcimer Company, 4419 W. Colfax Ave., Denver, CO 80204: Free brochure ■ Dulcimer kits, books, recordings, strings, tools, and supplies. 303–572–3753.

Instrument Workshop, 8023 Forest Dr. NE, Seattle, WA 98115: Catalog $3 ■ Kits and parts for harpsichords. 206–523–6129.

International Violin Company, 4026 W. Belvedere Ave., Baltimore, MD 21215: Catalog $1 ■ European violins and bows, strings, imported tone wood, tools, varnishes, and parts. 410–542–3535.

K Music, 608 Mohawk St., Utica, NY 13501: Free catalog ■ Guitars. 315–733–2848.

Lark in the Morning, P.O. Box 1176, Mendocino, CA 95460: Catalog $2.50 ■ Dulcimers, Irish harps, bagpipes, and musical antiques. 707–064–5569.

Ledford Musical Instruments, 125 Sunset Heights, Winchester, KY 40391: Free catalog ■ Appalachian dulcimers. 606–744–3974.

Robert Levine Importer, 80 Blenheim Dr., Easton, PA 18402: Free brochure ■ Precision mouthpieces for alto, tenor, and baritone saxophones in Sheffield stainless steel or ebonite and ebonite clarinet and soprano saxophone mouthpieces. 215–258–4266.

Victor Litz Music Center, 305 N. Frederick Ave., Gaithersburg, MD 20877: Free catalog ■ Musical instruments and equipment. 301–948–7478.

Lone Star Percussion, 10611 Control Pl., Dallas, TX 75238: Free catalog with long SASE ■ Percussion instruments and accessories. 214–340–0835.

Luthiers Mercantile, 412 Moore Ln., P.O. Box 774, Healdsburg, CA 95448: Catalog $3 ■ Banjo and guitar kits and accessories. 707–433–1823.

Mandolin Brothers, 629 Forest Ave., Staten Island, NY 10310: Free catalog ■ Mandolins, guitars, autoharps, and banjos in electronic and acoustic models. 718–981–3226.

Manny's Musical Instruments & Accessories, Inc., 156 W. 48th St., New York, NY 10036: Free information ■ Musical instruments and accessories. 212–819–0577.

McSpadden Musical Instruments, The Dulcimer Shoppe, P.O. Box E, Mountain View, AR 72560: Free catalog ■ Dulcimers, dulcimer kits, accessories, parts, plans, books, and recordings. 501–269–4313.

Metropolitan Music Store, Mountain Rd., P.O. Box 1415, Stowe, VT 05672: Free catalog ■ Violins, violas, cellos, luthier supplies, tools, and wood. 802–253–9834.

Michael's Music, 32 W. Merrick Rd., Freeport, NY 11520: Free information ■ Used guitars. 516–379–4111.

Musicmakers Kits, Inc., 423 S. Main, Stillwater, MN 55082: Catalog $1 ■ Ready-to-use musical instrument blueprints and pre-cut kits. 612–439–9120.

Nadine's Music, 18136 Sherman Way, Reseda, CA 91335: Free information ■ Keyboards, guitars, amplifiers, and recording accessories. Includes used equipment. 800–525–5149.

National Educational Music Company, Ltd., 1181 Rt. 22, P.O. Box 1130, Mountainside, NJ 07092: Free catalog ■ Brass, woodwind, and percussion instruments; imported violins and violas; and stands, cases, and strings; and bows. 908–232–6700.

Player Piano Company, 704 E. Douglas, Wichita, KS 67202: Free catalog ■ Player piano restoration supplies and music rolls. 316–263–1714.

Rayburn Musical Instrument Company, 283 Huntington Ave., Boston, MA 02115: Free information ■ Mouthpieces, reeds, and used woodwind and brass instruments. 617–266–4727.

Robinson's Harp Shop, P.O. Box 161, Mt. Laguna, CA 92048: Free brochure ■ Harpmaking parts and accessories, plans, strings, hardware, and books. 619–473–8556.

Rolls Music Center, Inc., 1065 W. Broad St., Falls Church, VA 22046: Free information ■ Keyboards, sound systems, percussion instruments, guitars, amplifiers, lights, and accessories. 703–533–9510.

Runyon Products, Inc., P.O. Box 590, Lewisburg Rd., Opelousas, LA 70570: Free information ■ Mouthpieces for soft playing and big band sounds. 800–843–4078; 318–948–6252 (in LA).

St. Croix Kits, 423 S. Main, Stillwater, MN 55082: Catalog $1 ■ Kits for harps, guitars, dulcimers, banjos, harpsichords, and bagpipes. 800–439–9120.

Sawmill, Martin Guitar Company, Nazareth, PA 18064: Free information ■ Guitar kits, parts and accessories, and exotic and domestic hardwoods. 800–345–3103; 215–759–2064 (in PA).

Schober Organ Corporation, 43 W. 61st St., New York, NY 10023: Free catalog ■ Build-them-yourself electric organ kits.

Shar Products Company, P.O. Box 1411, Ann Arbor, MI 48106: Free catalog ■ Violins, violas, cellos, accessories, and music for string instruments. 800–248–7427; 313–665–7711 (in MI).

Shining Mountain Workshop, 12804 Country Rd. 29, Dolores, CO 81323: Free brochure ■ Handmade cherry and mahogany Toltec Talking Drums. 303–565–3508.

Stewart-MacDonalds Guitar Shop Supply, 21 N. Shafer St., P.O. Box 900, Athens, OH 45701: Free catalog ■ Parts, tools, and supplies for building and repairing guitars, violins, banjos, dulcimers, and mandolins. 800–848–2273; 614–592–3021 (in OH).

Synthony Music, 3939 E. Campbell, Phoenix, AZ 85018: Free information ■ Electronic music instruments, midi peripherals, and other equipment. 800–221–KEYS; 602–955–3590 (in AZ).

Thoroughbred Music, 2204 E. Hillsborough Ave., Tampa, FL 33610: Free information ■ Keyboards, electronics, drum machines, and accessories. 800–800–4654.

Weinkrantz Musical Supply Company, 2519 Bomar Ave., Dallas, TX 75235: Free price list ■ Violins, violas, cellos, and accessories. 214–350–4883.

West Manor Music, 831 E. Gun Hill Rd., Bronx, NY 10467: Free price list ■ Brass, woodwind, string, and percussion instruments. 212–655–5400.

Wichita Band Instruments Company, 2525 E. Douglas, Wichita, KS 67211: Free information with long SASE ■ Musical instruments and accessories. 800–835–3006.

Sylvia Woods Harp Center, P.O. Box 816, Montrose, CA 91021: Free catalog ■ Harps, electronic tuners, metronomes, cassette recorders, harp and dulcimer recordings, books, harp novelties, art books, greeting cards, clothing, rubber stamps, and jewelry. 818–249–0325.

Woodwind & Brasswind Musical Instruments, 19880 State Line Rd., South Bend, IN 46637: Free catalog ■ Brass and woodwind musical instruments and accessories. 219–272–8266.

World of Music, 20015 Steven's Creek Blvd., Cupertino, CA 95014: Free price list with long SASE ■ Musical instruments, accessories, and sound equipment. 408–252–8264.

Yamaha Music Corporation, P.O. Box 6600, Buena Park, CA 90622: Free information ■ Electronic keyboards.

Zeta Systems, 2230 Livingston Ave., Oakland, CA 94606: Free information ■ Electronic guitars and violins and controllers. 800–622–6434; 510–261–1702 (in CA).

MUSIC BOOKS & SHEET MUSIC

Boston Music Company, 172 Tremont St., Boston, MA 02116: Free catalog ■ Sheet music. 617–426–5100.

Chinaberry Book Service, 2830 Via Orange Way, Ste. B, Spring Valley, CA 92078: Free catalog ■ Books and music for children and adults. 619–670–5200.

Empire Publishing Service, 7645 Le Berthon St., Tujunga, CA 91042: Free catalog ■ Entertainment industry and performing art books, other books, plays and musicals, and musical scores. 818–784–8918.

Fun Publishing Company, 2121 Alpine Pl., Cincinnati, OH 45206: Free information ■ Teach-yourself books for the portable keyboard, piano, and xylophone. Others include the How to Coach Soccer books. 513–533–3636.

Mail Box Music, P.O. Box 341, Rye, NY 10580: Free catalog ■ Guitar and keyboard folk music, pop, and rock song books. 800–331–5269.

Player Piano Company, 704 E. Douglas, Wichita, KS 67202: Free catalog ■ Player piano music rolls and restoration supplies. 316–263–1714.

Shar Products Company, P.O. Box 1411, Ann Arbor, MI 48106: Free catalog ■ Music and accessories for violins, violas, and cellos. 800–248–7427; 313–665–7711 (in MI).

Willis Music Company, 7380 Industrial Rd., Florence, KY 41042: Free catalog ■ Sheet music. 606–283–2250.

World Around Songs, Inc., 5790 Hwy. 80 South, Burnsville, NC 28714: Free catalog ■ American folk music, country music, party music, international folk music, and religious music song books. 704–675–5343.

MUSIC BOXES

Klockit, P.O. Box 636, Lake Geneva, WI 53147: Free catalog ■ Swiss music box movements in 144-notes, 72-notes, 50-notes, 36-notes, and 18-notes; music box kits; and clock-building parts and supplies. 800–556–2548.

Music Box World, P.O. Box 7577, Rego Park, NY 11374: Catalog $2 ■ Music boxes and movements. 718–626–8153.

Richter's Music Boxes, 900 N. Point, San Francisco, CA 94109: Free catalog ■ Music boxes from around the world. 415–441–2663.

San Francisco Music Box Company, Mail Order Dept., P.O. Box 7817, San Francisco, CA 94120: Free catalog ■ Reproduction antique music boxes and other music boxes. 510–653–3022.

Shaker Shops West, 5 Inverness Way, Inverness, CA 94937: Catalog $3 ■ Reproduction Shaker music boxes and other country-style crafts. 415–669–7256.

Smocking Bonnet, P.O. Box 555, Cooksville, MD 21723: Catalog series: Big book $5; medium book $3; small book $2 ■ Regular size and miniature music box movements. 800–524–1678.

Unicorn Studios, Box 370, Seymour, TN 37865: Catalog $1 ■ Easy-to-install windup and electronic music box movements, winking light units, and voice units for talking dolls and bears. 615–984–0145.

West Coast Music Box Company, 3924 Camphor Ave., Newbury Park, CA 91320: Free information ■ Electronic and other music boxes. 805–499–9336.

NAMEPLATES

Engraving Place, Rt. 94, Franklin, NJ 07416: Free brochure ■ Engraved solid brass nameplates. 800–828–4378.

Landmark Brass, P.O. Box 150507, Van Brunt Station, Brooklyn, NY 11215: Brochure $1 ■ Custom-engraved brass architectural plaques. 718–499–0984.

Taylor Graphics, P.O. Box 492, Greencastle, IN 46135: Free catalog ■ Nameplates, award and recognition plaques, deskplates and doorplates, photo charm products, card cases, and luggage tags. 800–777–1836; 317–653–8481 (in IN).

NEEDLE CRAFTS

Alabama Needle Arts, 105 S. Main, Enterprise, AL 36330: Catalog $2 ■ Military designs in cross-stitch kits. 205–393–2758.

American Needlewomen, 2946–50 SE Loop 820, Fort Worth, TX 76140: Catalog $1 ■ Needle crafts, accessories, and supplies from Europe and the United States. 800–433–2231.

Annie's Attic, 106. W. Groves, Big Sandy, TX 75755: Catalog $2 ■ Sewing and needle craft patterns. Includes patterns for toys. 903–636–4303.

Batik & Weaving Supplier, P.O. Box 451, Lexington, MA 01273: Catalog $2 ■ Weaving, knitting, spinning, dyeing, and batiking supplies. 617–646–4453.

Braid-Aid, 466 Washington St., Rt. 53, Pembroke, MA 02359: Catalog $4 ■ Braided rug kits and braiding accessories; wool by the pound or yard; and hooking, basketmaking, shirret, spinning, and weaving supplies and accessories. 617–826–6091.

Cal Feather Pillow Products, P.O. Box 1117, Armona, CA 93202: Free price list ■ Polyester pillow filler forms.

California Stitchery, 6015 Sunnyslope Ave., Van Nuys, CA 91401: Free catalog ■ Judaic-design needle craft kits in needlepoint, embroidery, and latch hook. In-

cludes tallit bags, challah and matzo covers, table linens, pillows, yamulkes, pictures, rugs, and holiday items. 818–781–9515.

The Cotton Patch, 1025 Brown Ave., Lafayette, CA 94549: Catalog $5 ■ Quilting books and supplies. 800–835–4418.

Craft Basket, B 5000, Plover, WI 54467: Free catalog ■ Needle craft kits and accessories. 800–343–5118.

Craft Gallery, Ltd., P.O. Box 145, Swampscott, MA 01907: Catalog $2 ■ Threads, fibers, books, fabrics, and accessories for stitchery, crochet, and other needle crafts.

Craft King Mail Order Dept., P.O. Box 90637, Lakeland, FL 33804: Catalog $2 (refundable) ■ Save from 40 to 60 percent on needle craft, art and craft, and macrame supplies. 813–686–9600.

Craft Resources, Inc., Box 828, Fairfield, CT 06430: Catalog $1 ■ Latch-hooking, needlepoint, crewel, cross-stitching kits, and supplies for string art, basket-making, metal and wood crafts, stained glass, and other crafts. 800–243–2874.

Crafts by Donna, P.O. Box 1456, Costa Mesa, CA 92626: Catalog $2 ■ Threads, other supplies, and how-to books for Brazilian embroidery. 714–545–8567.

Craftways, 4118 Lakeside Dr., Richmond, CA 94806: Catalog $2 ■ Quilt, applique, cross-stitching patterns, and iron-on transfers. 510–223–3144.

Creative Yarns, 9 Swan St., Asheville, NC 28803: Catalog $3.50 ■ Knitting yarns, handpainted canvases, silks, metallics, ribbons, and other supplies. 704–274–7769.

Cross Creek, 4114 Lakeside Dr., Richmond, CA 94806: Free catalog ■ Crossstitching supplies, kits, books, folk art dolls, soft sculpture patterns, and iron-on transfers. 800–538–4942; 800–421–9948 (in CA).

The Cross Eyed Owl, 1552 Rhode Island Ave. North, Golden Valley, MN 55427: Catalog $2.50 ■ Counted cross-stitch kits. 800–955–1843.

Cross 'N Patch, Box 132, Millville, UT 84326: Catalog $2 ■ Needle craft kits and supplies. 801–753–1748.

Curriculum Resources, Inc., P.O. Box 828, Fairfield, CT 06430: Catalog $1 ■ Needlepoint, crewel, latch hook, and other

stitchery kits. 800–243–2874; 203–254–7702.

Custom Cross-Stitch, Box 15565, Chesapeake, VA 23328: Catalog $2 (refundable) ■ Cross-stitch and plastic canvas supplies. 804–547–8424.

Custom Needlework Designs, Inc., P.O. Box 9, Oreland, PA 19075: Free information ■ Needle craft patterns and kits. 800–767–6313.

Daisy Chain, P.O. Box 1258, Parkersburg, WV 26102: Catalog $2 (refundable) ■ Needlework supplies, kits, and books. 304–428–9500.

The DMC Corporation, P.O. Box 5308–J, Clinton, IA 52736: Free information with long SASE ■ Cross-stitch embroidery thread.

Edinburgh Court Designs, 1321 Edinburgh Ct., Concord, CA 94518: Brochure and yarn samples $5 (refundable) ■ Designer knitting kits. 510–689–9227.

Embroidery Machine, P.O. Box 599, Pawtucket, RI 02862: Free information ■ Automatic, easy-to-use embroidery machine, with 3 needle sizes, instant threader, and pattern book. 800–642–9606.

Essamplaire, 4126 44th St., Red Deer, Alberta, Canada T4N 1H2: Catalog $2 ■ Counted thread sampler kits. 403–347–3574.

Kathleen Fell Needle Crafts, Box 158333, Nashville, TN 37215: Catalog $2 ■ Counted cross-stitch kits and supplies. 615–665–0275.

For Generations, 3056 Castro Valley Blvd., Ste. 190, Castro Valley, CA 94546: Catalog $2 ■ Children's sweater kits with soft, handdyed mohair yarn. 510–582–2205.

Garden Fairies Trading Company, P.O. Box 5770, Santa Rosa, CA 95402: Catalog $4 ■ Handmade collar patterns, French lace, Swiss embroideries, Battenberg lace supplies, smocking patterns, soft toy patterns, books, and designer fabrics. 800–925–9919.

Glorafilia, Ltd., 533 Kings Croft, Cherry Hill, NJ 08034: Catalog $4 ■ Needle crafts from England. Includes pictures, footstools, embroidery samplers, crewel cushions, and cross-stitch rugs. 609–779–3733.

Martha Hall, 46 Main St., Yarmouth, ME 04096: Catalog $1 ■ Easy-to-knit sweaters in silk, mohair, linen, cotton, cashmere, alpaca, and natural Maine wool. 207–846–9746.

Herrschners, Inc., Hoover Rd., Stevens Point, WI 54492: Catalog $1 ■ Needle craft supplies, kits, yarns, and knitting accessories. 800–441–0838.

Sue Hillis Designs, P.O. Box 2263, Petersburg, VA 23804: Free information ■ Counted cross-stitch kits. 800–622–5353.

Keepsake Quilting, Dover St., P.O. Box 1459, Meredith, NH 03253: Free catalog ■ Quilting books, patterns, notions, fabrics, quilting accessories, and batting.

Sue Lentz Needlework, Star Rt., Box 228, Athelstane, WI 54104: Catalog $2.75 ■ Fabrics, fibers, patterns and graphs, and other supplies.

LHL Enterprises, Box 241, Solebury, PA 18963: Catalog $3 (refundable) ■ Needlework and art and craft supplies. 215–348–3611.

Love & Money Crafts, 221 Jackson Industrial Dr., Ann Arbor, MI 48106: Catalog $1 (refundable) ■ Needle craft supplies. 800–521–1538; 313–665–2966 (in MI).

Carolyn Lowy Needlecraft, 630 Sun Meadows Dr., Kernersville, NC 27284: Free information with long SASE ■ Needlepoint, knitting, embroidery, and counted cross-stitch patterns. 919–784–7576.

Mary Maxim, Inc., 2001 Holland Ave., P.O. Box 5019, Port Huron, MI 48061: Free catalog ■ Needle craft kits, yarn, and accessories. 313–987–2000.

Claire Murray, Inc., P.O. Box 1089, North Charlestown, NH 03630: Catalog $5 (refundable) ■ Hand-hooked rugs and kits. 800–323–YARN.

The Needlecraft Shop, 23 Old Pecan Rd., Big Sandy, TX 75755: Free catalog ■ Plastic canvas supplies and patterns.

Ouran Industries, P.O. Box 24102, Apple Valley, MN 55124: Catalog $2 (refundable) ■ Hand-printed designs on Belgium canvasses.

Patterncrafts, Box 25370, Colorado Springs, CO 80936: Catalog $2 ■ Quilt patterns and hoops, counted stitch and sewing projects, stencils, country crafts, wall hangings, needle crafts, dolls, and stuffed animals. 719–574–2007.

Peacock Alley Needlepoint Crafts, 650 Croswell SE, Grand Rapids, MI 49506: Cata-

log $2 ■ Needle craft kits, supplies, accessories, and canvasses. 616–454–9898.

Shay Pendray's Needle Arts, Inc., 2211 Monroe, Dearborn, MI 48124: Catalog $2 ■ Japanese embroidery supplies. 313–278–6266.

Eva Rosenstand, P.O. Box 185, Clovis, CA 93613: Catalog $3 ■ Embroidery supplies and accessories. 207–985–7089.

Samplers by Virginia Colby, 205 Richmond Ave., Amityville, NY 11701: Free brochure with long SASE ■ Miniature counted-thread samplers. 516–264–5529.

The Scarlet Letter, P.O. Box 397, Sullivan, WI 53178: Catalog $3 ■ Museum reproduction counted thread sampler kits; handwoven linens and silks; sewing accessories; and books and custom maple frames.

Shillcraft, P.O. Box 7770, Baltimore, MD 21221: Catalog $2 ■ Needle craft supplies and latch hook kits for rugs, wall hangings, and other crafts. 410–682–3064.

Jane Snead Samplers, 4015 Yerkes Rd., Collegeville, PA 19426: Free catalog ■ Samplers, needlepoint kits, embroidery kits, and frames.

Snowgoose, P.O. Box 27805, Denver, CO 80227: Catalog $1 ■ Lace kits for beginners. 303–934–5168.

Stitchery, 120 N. Meadows Rd., Medfield, MA 02181: Catalog 50¢ ■ Crewel, needlepoint, cross-stitch, and latch hook kits. 800–225–4127.

Stitches East, 55 E. 52nd St., New York, NY 10022: Free information ■ Supplies for knitting and needle crafts. 212–421–0112.

Things Japanese, 9805 NE 116th St., Ste. 7160, Kirkland, WA 98034: Catalog $4 ■ Japanese needlework supplies. Includes brocade threads and yarns, silk-blend and metallic threads, needlework kits, silk ribbons, and embroidery supplies. 206–821–2287.

Thumbelina Needlework Shop, P.O. Box 1065, Solvang, CA 93463: Catalog $1 ■ Books, fabrics, threads, yarns, kits, and accessories. 805–688–4136.

Vermont Patchworks, P.O. Box 229, Shrewsbury, VT 05738: Catalog $2 (refundable) ■ Quilting fabrics, supplies, and books.

George Wells Rugs, 565 Cedar Swamp Rd., Glen Head, NY 11545: Catalog $2 ■ Rug

hooking supplies, yarn, and dyes. 516–676–2056.

Yarn Country, P.O. Box 6500, Concord, CA 94524: Catalog and yarn samples $10.99 ■ Yarns for crochet, cross-stitch, and canvas crafts; books; and other supplies. 800–441–YARN.

NEWSPAPERS & MAGAZINES

American Family Publishers, P.O. Box 4824, Chicago, IL 60680: Free information ■ Magazine subscriptions. 800–237–2400.

Sherry Balantich Movie Magazines, 10410 Penny Lane, Indianapolis, IN 46229: List $3 ■ Movie magazines, from the 1930s through 1960s.

Cardinal Gifts, 306 W. Johnson, Cary, NC 27513: Free information with long SASE ■ Authentic historic newspapers.

Gibson's Paper Antiques, 303 Sequoyah Dr., Blountville, TN 37617: Free information with long SASE ■ Authentic Civil War newspapers. 615–323–2427.

Historic Newspaper Archives, 1582 Hart St., Rahway, NJ 07065: Free catalog ■ Newspapers for the day on which you were born. 800–221–3221; 908–381–2332 (in NJ).

Timothy Hughes, P.O. Box 3636, Williamsport, PA 17701: Catalog $1 ■ Rare and early edition newspapers. 717–326–1045.

Jay-Bee Magazines, Henry Greenbaum, 134 W. 26th St., New York, NY 10001: Catalog $1 ■ Magazines from 1889–1989. 212–675–1600.

Alan Levine Movie & Book Collectibles, P.O. Box 1577, Bloomfield, NJ 07003: Catalog $2 with long SASE ■ Books on collecting; old-time movie posters and lobby cards; and old radio, television, and movie magazines. 201–743–5288.

MultiNewspapers, Box DE, Dana Point, CA 92629: Free brochure ■ English language magazines and newspapers from over 60 countries.

Publishers Clearing House, 101 Winners Cir., Port Washington, NY 11050: Free information ■ Magazine subscriptions. 516–883–5432.

Steven S. Raab, 2033 Walnut St., Philadelphia, PA 19103: Free catalog ■ Autographs, signed books and photos, historic newspapers, World War I posters, and other historic memorabilia. 215–446–6193.

Murray A. Summers, 10670 Cliff Mills Dr., Marshall, VA 22115: Catalog $3 ■ Movie magazines from the 1920s to the 1970s, movie posters, and other memorabilia. 703–364–1275.

Teaneck Book Store, 838 Palisade Ave., Teaneck, NJ 07666: Free information with long SASE ■ Vintage books and magazines. 201–217–9675.

Way It Was, P.O. Box 48621, Los Angeles, CA 90048: Free catalog ■ Original back issue newspapers. 213–374–1766.

OFFICE & BUSINESS SUPPLIES

Business Forms & Booklets

Adams Business Forms, P.O. Box 91, Topeka, KS 66601: Free information ■ Manifold books; unit, bank, and computer forms; guest checks; and other forms. 800–444–3508.

Apple Label, 1120 Old Country Rd., Plainview, NY 11803: Free catalog ■ Business forms, labels, and other supplies. 212–786–0100.

Business Forms of America, Division of BFT, Inc., 9321 Kirby, Houston, TX 77054: Free catalog ■ Business forms, stationery, and signs. 800–231–0329; 713–790–1926 (in TX).

Caprock Business Forms, Inc., 1211 Ave. F, Lubbock, TX 79401: Free information ■ Continuous computer forms, letterheads and envelopes, snap-apart sets, manifold books and pads, and scratch pads. 800–666–3322.

Champion Printing Company, 3250 Spring Grove Ave., Cincinnati, OH 45225: Free information ■ Self-mailers and bind-ins. 800–543–1957; 513–541–1100 (in OH).

Franz Stationery Company, Inc., 1601 Algonquin Rd., Arlington Heights, IL 60005: Free catalog ■ Office stationery and forms, and other office equipment, furniture, and supplies. 800–323–8685.

HG Professional Forms Company, 2020 California St., Omaha, NE 68102: Free catalog ■ Pre-printed forms and supplies, accounting accessories, computer paper and forms, record-keeping systems, general use forms and pads, ruled writing pads, pad holders, binders, report covers, and envelopes. 800–228–1493.

Hubing Business Forms, Inc., 138 Hansen Access Rd., King of Prussia, PA 19406: Free information ■ Custom business forms. 215–265–7340.

Mattick Business Forms, Inc., 333 W. Hintz Rd., Wheeling, IL 60090: Free catalog ■ Stationery, office and business forms, and labels. 708–541–7345.

Moore Business Products, Catalog Division, P.O. Box 5000, Vernon Hills, IL 60061: Free catalog ■ Business forms, typewriter and printer ribbons, print wheels, copier supplies, laser printer paper and toner cartridges, fax paper, computer accessories, printer stands, and other supplies. 800–323–6230.

Paulton Corporation, 130 Waukegan Rd., Deerfield, IL 60015: Free catalog ■ Business forms, sales books, and office supplies. 708–948–7270.

Rapidforms, Inc., 301 Grove Rd., Thorofare, NJ 08086: Free catalog ■ Business forms and labels. 800–257–8354.

RJM Business Forms, Box 383, Garden City, NY 11530: Free information ■ Short-run carbonless business forms. 516–538–1838.

Salesbook Service, P.O. Box 8310, Rolling Meadows, IL 60008: Free catalog ■ Sales books, register forms, and snap-out forms. 708–359–3812.

Shipman Printing Industries, P.O. Box 157, Niagara Falls, NY 14302: Free information ■ Business forms, letterheads, padded forms, window-style and other envelopes, and custom printing. 800–462–2114.

Stationery House, 1000 Florida Ave., Hagerstown, MD 21740: Free catalog ■ Business stationery, business forms, supplies, and gifts. 301–739–4487.

Triangle Printing Company, P.O. Box 100854, Nashville, TN 37210: Free information ■ Booklets in small orders. 800–843–9529.

General Office Supplies

Accountants' Supply House, 518 Rockaway Ave., P.O. Box 310, Valley Stream, NY 11582: Free catalog ■ Custom stationery and envelopes; forms and labels; and adding machines, shipping materials, disk storage cabinets, typewriter and data processing ribbons, and furniture. 800–DIAL–ASH; 516–561–7700 (in NY).

Alfax Wholesale Furniture, 370 7th Ave., Ste. 1101, New York, NY 10001: Free catalog ■ General office equipment, supplies, and office furniture. 212–947–9560.

American Thermoplastic Company, 622 2nd Ave., Pittsburgh, PA 15219: Free catalog ■ Custom binders and index sets, sheet protectors, clipboards, conference kits, report and presentation folders, data processing and catalog binders, and cassette binders and albums. 800–456–6602.

Artistic Greetings, Inc., 409 Williams St., P.O. Box 1623, Elmira, NY 14902: Free catalog ■ Stationery and office accessories. 607–733–6313.

Browncor International, 14101 NW 4th St., Sunrise, FL 33325: Free catalog ■ Mailing and shipping supplies. 800–327–2278.

The Business Book, One E. 8th Ave., Oshkosh, WI 54906: Free catalog ■ Pressure sensitive labels, mailing labels, stampers, personalized business envelopes, custom business stationery, speed letters, memo pads, business cards and forms, greeting cards, books, and other office supplies. 800–558–0220.

Copen Press, Inc., 100 Berriman St., Brooklyn, NY 11208: Free catalog ■ Envelopes, order forms, catalog printing, reply cards, and binding and mailing services. 718–235–4270.

Day-Timers, Allentown, PA 18001: Free catalog ■ Stationery and business cards. 215–395–5884.

Frank Eastern Company, 599 Broadway, New York, NY 10012: Catalog $1 ■ Office equipment, furniture, and supplies. 212–219–0007.

Fidelity Products Company, 5601 International Pkwy., P.O. Box 155, Minneapolis, MN 55440: Free catalog ■ Office equipment and supplies. 800–328–3034; 800–862–3765 (in MN).

Franz Stationery Company, Inc., 1601 Algonquin Rd., Arlington Heights, IL 60005: Free catalog ■ Stationery, business forms, other supplies, office equipment, and furniture. 800–323–8685.

Grayarc, P.O. Box 2944, Hartford, CT 06104: Free catalog ■ Office equipment and supplies. 203–379–9941.

HG Professional Forms Company, 2020 California St., Omaha, NE 68102: Free catalog ■ Pre-printed forms and supplies, computer paper and forms, record-keeping systems, forms and pads, ruled writing pads, pad holders, binders, report covers, and envelopes. 800–228–1493.

Jacobs Gardner Office Products & Furniture, 5121 Buchanan St., Hyattsville, MD 20781: Free catalog ■ Computer supplies, binders, report covers, calculators, electronic notebook recorders, filing accessories, bookends, postage and mailing accessories, presentation aids, pens and pencils, and office furniture. 800–638–0983.

Robert James Company, Inc., P.O. Box 2726, Birmingham, AL 35202: Free catalog ■ Office supplies. 800–633–8296; 205–251–5154 (in AL).

Moore Business Products, Catalog Division, P.O. Box 5000, Vernon Hills, IL 60061: Free catalog ■ Business forms, typewriter and printer ribbons, print wheels, copier supplies, laser printer paper and toner cartridges, fax paper, computer printout paper, and binders. 800–323–6230.

The Penn Press, Inc., 325 Hendrickson Ave., Lynbrook, NY 11563: Free information ■ Letterheads, envelopes, announcements, and business cards. 516–887–7800.

Pyramid of Urbana, Box 877, Urbana, IL 61801: Free catalog ■ Office supplies and furniture, craft supplies, art supplies, and school equipment. 800–637–0955; 800–252–1363 (in IL).

Quo Vadis, 120 Elmview Ave., Hamburg, NY 14075: Free catalog ■ Agenda planning diaries and gifts. 716–648–2602.

Sears, Roebuck & Company, Catalog Division, 925 S. Homan Ave., Chicago, IL 60607: Free catalog ■ Office supplies, accessories, and equipment. (Catalog also available from local stores.) 312–875–2500.

Specialty Mailers, Inc., P.O. Box 80126, Chamblee, GA 30341: Free price list ■ Envelopes and other mailing supplies. 404–455–3188.

Staples, Inc., P.O. Box 160, Newton, MA 02195: Free catalog ■ Office supplies, accessories, furniture, computer supplies and

paper, drafting equipment, fax machines, and typewriters. 617–965–7030.

SYNC, Unique Merchandise Mart, Building 42, Hanover, PA 17333: Free catalog ■ Electronic and technological products and supplies for the office, home, or other personal use. 717–633–3311.

Tic-La-Dex, 3443 Camino Del Rio South, Ste. 326, San Diego, CA 92108: Free catalog ■ Organizers, portfolios, plastic divider cards, Night Writer pens, recycled plastic envelopes and book covers. 800–827–9467; 619–281–7242.

Viking Office Products, 13809 S. Figueroa St., P.O. Box 61144, Los Angeles, CA 90061: Free information ■ Office supplies. 800–421–1222.

Vulcan Binder & Cover, P.O. Box 29, Vincent, AL 35178: Free catalog ■ Ring binders. 205–672–2241.

J. Williams Company, Attn: Morning Mail, P.O. Box 72, Covington, GA 30209: Catalog $1 ■ Office supplies, calculators, and custom stationery and notes. 800–241–0854.

Labels & Tags

A–1 Business Supplies, Inc., 101 Rt. 46 East, P.O. Box 405, Pine Brook, NJ 07058: Free information ■ Pressure-sensitive labels, marking pens, shrink-wrap systems, price markers, and other supplies. 201–882–1066.

Apple Label, 1120 Old Country Rd., Plainview, NY 11803: Free catalog ■ Labels, business forms, and other office supplies. 212–786–0100.

Continental Data Forms, 69 Veronica Ave., Somerset, NJ 08873: Free information ■ Pinfeed pressure-sensitive labels. 800–323–0973.

Data Label, Inc., 1000 Spruce St., Terre Haute, IN 47807: Free information ■ Stock and custom labels. 800–457–0676.

Ennis Express Label Service, Tag & Label Division, P.O. Box E, Wolfe City, TX 75496: Free information ■ Custom labels. 800–527–1008; 800–442–1297 (in TX).

Five Star Publications, P.O. Box 3142, Scottsdale, AZ 85271: Free catalog ■ Labels. 602–941–0770.

Flamingo Label Company, Inc., 3741 E. Ten Mile Rd., Warren, MI 48091: Free infor-

mation ■ Custom labels in rolls, sheets, and pinfeed for computers. 800–535–6399.

C.J. Fox Company, 2 Fox Pl., P.O. Box 6186, Providence, RI 02940: Free information ■ Labels. 800–556–6868.

Grayarc, P.O. Box 2944, Hartford, CT 06104: Free catalog ■ Stationery, business cards, forms, labels, envelopes, and other supplies. 203–379–9941.

Hawks Tag Service, P.O. Box 44187, Cincinnati, OH 45244: Free price list ■ Custom tags in short run orders. 800–752–5765.

Jet Label, 1100 Woodmere, Traverse City, MI 49684: Free information ■ Short-run labels. 800–622–3883; 616–947–2002 (in MI).

Kay Toledo Tag, 6050 Benore Rd., Toledo, OH 43612: Free brochure ■ Custom tags in Tyvek, fluorescent, cloth, vinyl, and other materials. 800–822–8247.

Lancer Label, 301 S. 74th St., P.O. Box 6256, Omaha, NE 68114: Free catalog ■ Custom bumper stickers and labels in rolls, sheets, and pinfeed. 800–228–7074.

New York Label, 56 Pentaquit Ave., Bay Shore, NY 11706: Free catalog ■ Self-adhesive labels in singles, rolls, or sheets. 800–257–2300; 516–968–6300.

PrintProd, Inc., 419 Bainbridge St., Dayton, OH 45410: Free information ■ Custom multi-color tags. 800–322–TAGS.

Short Run Labels, Division Far West Marketing, Inc., 1681 Industrial Rd., San Carlos, CA 94070: Free catalog ■ Self-adhesive custom labels in small amounts. 415–592–7683.

Sunshine B/F, 20 Peachtree Ct., Holbrook, NY 11741: Free catalog ■ Tags, tickets, snap-apart sets, envelopes, and sales and receipt books. 800–331–3841; 516–585–3841 (in NY).

U.S. Tag & Label Corporation, 2217 Robb St., Baltimore, MD 21218: Free catalog ■ Stock and custom tags and labels. 800–638–1018; 410–467–2633 (in MD).

Writewell Company, Inc., 5850 W. 80th St., Indianapolis, IN 46278: Free catalog ■ Stationery and envelopes, note cards, memo pads, and labels. 317–871–6710.

Receipt Books

Cook Receipt Book Manufacturing Company, Box 2005, Dothan, AL 36302: Free catalog ■ Receipt books. 800–842–0444.

Herald Multiforms, Inc., P.O. Box 1288, Dillon, SC 29536: Free information ■ Receipt books. Includes continuous forms, checks, and snap outs. 800–845–5050; 803–774–9051 (in SC).

Rapidforms, Inc., 301 Grove Rd., Thorofare, NJ 08086: Free catalog ■ Labels and standard business forms. 800–257–8354.

Rush Receipt Book Company, 457 Houston South, Mobile, AL 36606: Free price list ■ Receipt books. 205–478–9662.

Sunshine B/F, 20 Peachtree Ct., Holbrook, NY 11741: Free catalog ■ Sales and receipt books, tags, tickets, snap-apart sets, and envelopes. 800–331–3841; 516–585–3841 (in NY).

Superior Receipt Book Company, 215 S. Clark St., P.O. Box 326, Centreville, MI 49032: Free information ■ Custom receipt books. 800–624–2887; 616–467–8265 (in MI).

ORIGAMI (Paper Folding)

The Friends of the Origami Center of America, Room ST–1, 15 W. 77th St., New York, NY 10024: Free list with long SASE and two 1st class stamps ■ Books, supplies, and origami papers.

OSTOMY SUPPLIES

AARP Ostomy Care Center, 3557 Lafayette Rd., Indianapolis, IN 46222: Free catalog ■ Ostomy supplies. 800–284–4788.

American Ostomy Supplies, 6013 W. Bluemound Rd., Milwaukee, WI 53213: Free catalog ■ Colostomy supplies. 800–858–5858.

A-Z Ostomy Supply, 321 W. Main, Marshall, MN 56258: Free catalog ■ Ostomy supplies. 800–237–4555; 507–532–5754 (in MN).

B & K Prescriptions, 601 E. Iron, Salina, KS 67401: Free information ■ Ostomy supplies ■ 800–831–5219; 800–432–0224 (in KS).

Blanchard Ostomy Products, 1510 Raymond Ave., Glendale, CA 91201: Free

information ■ Stoma seals, faceplates, pouches and accessories for ileostomies, urostomies, or non-irrigated colostomies. 818–242–6789.

Bruce Medical Supply, 411 Waverly Oaks Rd., P.O. Box 9166, Waltham, MA 02154: Free catalog ■ Ostomy supplies. 800–225–8446.

Coloplast, Inc., 5610 W. Sligh Ave., Ste, 100, Tampa, FL 33634: Free information ■ Conseal Colostomy System. 800–237–4555.

Convatec, Bristol-Myers Squibb Company, P.O. Box 5254, Princeton, NJ 08543: Free information ■ Convatec appliance for ostomates. 800–422–8811.

Edgepark Surgical, Inc., 4791 Turney Rd., Garfield Heights, OH 44125: Free catalog ■ Ostomy supplies. 800–321–0591.

Fairs' OPS, Inc., Ostomy Prosthesis Support, P.O. Box 5760, Greenway Station, Glendale, AZ 85306: Free information ■ Undergarments designed by ostomates for ostomates. 602–978–4435.

Family Medical Pharmacy, 851 S. Harbor Blvd., Anaheim, CA 92085: Free information ■ Ostomy supplies and accessories. 714–772–4840; 800–292–3300 (in CA).

Georgetown Health Care Center, 9338 W. 75th St., Shawnee Mission, KS 66204: Free information ■ Ostomy, urological, and home medical supplies. 800–346–3026.

Gricks, Division of Q-T Products, Inc., 100 Minnesota Ave., Unit #4, Warwick, RI 02888: Free catalog ■ Ostomy supplies and accessories. 401–732–3402.

Healthcare Prescription Services, 3830 E. Southport Rd., Indianapolis, IN 46237: Free catalog ■ Ostomy supplies. 800–382–9799; 317–782–3478 (in IN).

Healthfirst Pharmacy, 1000 S. Beckham St., Tyler, TX 75701: Free catalog ■ Ostomy supplies. 903–531–8830.

Health Supplies of America, P.O. Box 1059, Burlington, NC 27834: Free catalog ■ Ostomy supplies. 800–334–1187.

Home Health Express, Division EFS Medical Supplies, Inc., 49 Walnut St., Unit #4, Norwood, NJ 07648: Free information ■ Ostomy supplies. 800–828–7123.

Home Medical Center Hospital Supplies, 7173 W. Cermack, Irwin, IL 60402: Free in-

formation ■ Ostomy supplies. 800–323–2828.

Hospital Drug Store, 1509 Tulane Ave., New Orleans, LA 70112: Free information ■ Ostomy supplies. 800–826–1450; 504–524–2254 (in LA).

King Ostomy Products, 431 W. 13th Ave., Ste. 4, Eugene, OR 97401: Free information ■ Ostomy deodorant tablets. 503–345–0391.

Malloy's Prescription Pharmacy, 901 S. La Brea Blvd., Inglewood, CA 90301: Free information ■ Ostomy and convalescent supplies. 213–671–6144.

Marc Medical Pharmacy, 6200 Wilshire Blvd., Los Angeles, CA 90048: Free information ■ Ostomy supplies. 213–938–7131.

Marlen Manufacturing & Development Company, 150 Richmond Rd., Bedford, OH 44146: Free information ■ Protective adhesive skin barriers for ileostomies, colostomies, and urostomies. 216–292–7060.

Mason Laboratories, Inc., P.O. Box 334, Horsham, PA 19044: Free information ■ Ostomy pouches, pouch odor deodorant, and other supplies. 215–675–6044.

Medic Pharmacy & Surgical, 5100 W. Commercial Blvd., Fort Lauderdale, FL 33319: Free information ■ Ostomy and medical supplies. 800–888–9417.

Nihan & Martin Pharmacy, 1417 Myott Ave., Rockford, IL 60619: Free catalog ■ Ostomy appliances and accessories. 815–963–8594.

Nu-Hope Laboratories, Inc., P.O. Box 3638, Pacoima, CA 91333: Free information ■ Urostomy pouches. 818–899–7711.

Ostomed Healthcare, 3116 S. Oak Park Ave., Berwyn, IL 60402: Free information ■ Ostomy supplies. 800–323–1353; 708–795–7701 (in IL).

Ostomy Discount of America, 3600 Laketon Rd., Pittsburgh, PA 15235: Free catalog ■ Ostomy supplies at discount prices. 800–443–7828.

Ostomy Supply & Care Center, Inc., 502 6th Ave. North, Fargo, ND 58102: Free information ■ Ostomy supplies. 701–293–0277.

Palidsades Pharmaceuticals, Inc., 219 County Rd., Tenafly, NJ 07670: Free information ■ Internal deodorant for patients with colostomies, ileostomies, and incontinence. 800–237–9083.

Parthenon Company, Inc., 3311 W. 2400 South, Salt Lake City, UT 84119: Free information ■ Ostomy supplies. 800–453–8898.

Penny Saver Medical Supply, 1851 W. 52nd Ave., Denver, CO 80221: Free information ■ Ostomy supplies. 800–748–1909.

Salk Company, Inc., 119 Braintree St., P.O. Box 452, Boston, MA 02134: Free information ■ Natural-looking undergarments for active ostomates. 800–343–4497; 617–782–4030 (in MA).

Shield Healthcare Centers, 9688 B East Alameda Ave., Denver, CO 80231: Free information ■ Ostomy supplies. 800–332–3614; 303–343–9838 (in CO).

Tennessee Home Medical, 117 7th Ave. West, Springfield, TN 37172: Free information ■ Ostomy supplies. 800–542–2005; 615–384–6093 (in TN).

Torbot Ostomy Center, 1185 Jefferson Blvd., Warwick, RI 02886: Free brochure ■ Ostomy appliances and accessories. 800–545–4254.

Undercover Cover Company, HC 79, 104 BB, Melba, ID 83641: Free information ■ Appliance undercovers. 208–896–4716.

United Division of Pfizer, 11775 Starkey Rd., Largo, FL 33540: Free catalog ■ Ostomy supplies. 813–392–1261.

VPI, A Cook Group Company, 127 S. Main St., P.O. Box 266, Spencer, IN 47460: Free information ■ Non-adhesive systems for colostomy, urostomy, and ileostomy patients. 800–843–4851; 812–829–4891 (in IN).

Worldwide Home Health Center, Inc., 926 E. Tallmadge Ave., Akron, OH 44310: Free catalog ■ Ostomy and incontinence supplies, mastectomy breast forms, and clothing. 800–223–5938; 800–621–5938 (in OH).

Yentl's Secrets, 4415 Mockingbird Ln., Toledo, OH 43623: Free brochure ■ Pouch covers in varied sizes and fabrics. 419–841–1752.

PADDLEBALL

Adventure 16, Inc., 4620 Alvarado Canyon Rd., San Diego, CA 92120: Free information ■ Paddles and balls. 800–854–2672; 800–854–0222 (in CA).

Cannon Sports, P.O. Box 11179, Burbank, CA 91510: Free information ■ Paddles and balls. 800–223–0064; 818–503–9570 (in CA).

Spalding & Brothers, 425 Meadow St., P.O. Box 901, Chicopee, MA 01021: Free information ■ Paddles and balls. 413–536–1200.

Sunstar International, Ltd., Sunsport Sporting Goods, 24–16 Queens Plaza South, Long Island City, NY 11101: Free information ■ Paddles and balls. 718–706–0611.

Wa-Mac, Inc., Highskore Products, Inc., 178 Commerce Rd., P.O. Box 128, Carlstadt, NJ 07072: Free information ■ Paddles and balls. 800–447–5673; 201–438–7200 (in NJ).

PAPER COLLECTIBLES

Arlington Card, 140 Gansett Ave., Cranston, RI 02910: Free information ■ Non-sports cards collectibles and paper wrappers. 401–942–3188.

Buck Hill Associates, 23 Catallon Dr., Waterford, NY 12188: Free catalog ■ Posters, handbills, historical documents and Americana from America's past, and other paper collectibles. 518–583–1166.

18th Century Collectibles, Edward J. Craig, 41 3rd St., Newport, RI 02840: Free catalog ■ Early American autographs, postal history, fiscal paper, slavery and Judaica memorabilia, and other collectibles. 401–847–6498.

Evergreen Press, 3380 Vincent Rd., Pleasant Hill, CA 94523: Free brochure ■ Late 19th- and early 20th-century paper memorabilia. Includes children's books, greeting cards, book marks and bookplates, wedding certificates, calendars, ornaments, paper dolls, and postcards. 510–933–9700.

Hi-De-Ho Collectibles, P.O. Box 2841, Gaithersburg, MD 20886: Free information ■ Antique movie posters, lobby cards, and cartoon memorabilia; television toys, games, puzzles, and dolls; advertising signs; 3–D figures; and stand-ups. 301–926–4438.

John Heleva Paper Collectibles, Box 375, Fair Oaks, CA 95628: Catalog $4.50 ■ Old stocks, bonds, and other paper collectibles. 916–448–4060.

Howling Moon, P.O. Box 9050, Austin, TX 78766: Free catalog ■ Autographs and paper

collectibles that include cartoon and celebrity art. 512–499–8504.

June Moon Collectibles, 7 S. Fairview, Park Ridge, IL 60068: Free information ■ Non-sports cards collectibles. 708–825–1411.

Kenrich Company, 9418 E. Las Tunas Dr., Temple City, CA 91780: Free information ■ Non-sports cards collectibles and paper wrappers. 818–286–3888.

Henri LaBelle, 1162 Lesage St., P.O. Box 561, Prevost, Quebec, Canada J0R 1T0: Free information ■ Non-sports cards collectibles. 514–224–2813.

Legacy Antiques, P.O. Box 531, Burlingame, CA 94011: Free information ■ Old postcards, stocks and bonds, stereopticon views, trading cards, timetables, and Wells Fargo items.

Mauro's Nostalgia, 457 Main St., Ste. 206, Farmingdale, NY 11735: Four catalogs $8 (refundable) ■ Original movie posters and non-sports cards from the 1930s to present.

Original Paper Collectibles, 700 Clipper Gap Rd., Auburn, CA 95603: Free brochure with long SASE ■ Paper labels and used stock certificates. 916–878–0296.

Out West, 2231 Creekside Rd., Santa Rosa, CA 95405: Free information ■ Old postcards, photographs, stereopticon views, and other paper Americana. 707–575–5406.

Postmarks Unlimited, Rt. 2, Box 110, Hurdle Mills, NC 27541: Free price list ■ Specialized collections and grab bag assortments of postmarks.

Ken Prag Americana Collectibles, P.O. Box 531, Burlingame, CA 94011: Free information with long SASE ■ Stocks and bonds, postcards, trading cards, timetables, passes, Wells Fargo collectibles, stereopticon views, and other paper Americana. 415–566–6400.

Steven S. Raab, 2033 Walnut St., Philadelphia, PA 19103: Free catalog ■ Autographs, signed books and photos, historic newspapers, World War I posters, and other historic paper memorabilia. 215–446–6193.

Stampede Investments, Scott G. Kalcik, 1533 River Rd., Wisconsin Dells, WI 53965: Free information ■ Autographs, historical documents, old stocks and bonds, and other paper collectibles. 608–254–7751.

Tally Ho Studio, 639 Park Ave. SW, Canton, OH 44706: Free information ■ Non-sports cards collectibles. 216–452–4488.

Tattered Cover, 2023 Boston Pike, Richmond, IN 47374: Free information with long SASE ■ Rare and used paper collectibles and hardback books. 317–935–6293.

Yesterday's Paper, P.O. Box 819, Concrete, WA 98237: Free information ■ Financial, territorial, and western paper collectibles, documents, and other memorabilia. 206–853–8228.

PAPER MAKING & SCULPTING

Aiko's Art Materials Import, 3347 N. Clark St., Chicago, IL 60657: Catalog $1.50 ■ Japanese handmade paper, Oriental art supplies, fabric dyes, and other art supplies. 312–404–5600.

Gerlachs of Lecha, P.O. Box 213, Emmaus, PA 18049: Catalog $2.25 ■ Paper sculpting kits. 215–965–9181.

Gold's Artworks, Inc., 2100 N. Pine St., Lumberton, NC 28358: Free information with long SASE ■ Paper-making pigments and chemicals, pulp materials, kits, and other supplies. 800–356–2306; 919–739–9605 (in NC).

Holcraft Collection, 211 El Cajon Ave., P.O. Box 792, Davis, CA 95616: Catalog $2 ■ Molds for papier mache and chalkware crafts and other craft supplies. 916–756–3023.

Lake City Crafts, Rt. 2, Box 637, Highlandville, MO 65669: Catalog $2 ■ Supplies and accessories for paper quilling, crafting, and filigree projects.

Little Goodies, P.O. Box 1004, Lewisville, TX 75067: Catalog $2 ■ Pre-cut paper flower kits.

Peter Michael Martin Paper Designs, P.O. Box 1085, Mattapoisett, MA 02739: Brochure $1 ■ Framed cut-paper designs. 508–758–9620.

MPR Associates, Inc., P.O. Box 7343, High Point, NC 27264: Free idea sheets with long SASE and 75¢ postage ■ Paper ribbon for crafting.

Papercutting by Alison, 404 Partridge Center, Sarasota, FL 34236: Catalog $1.50 ■ Paper-cutting patterns and supplies.

The Paper Potpourri, P.O. Box 5575, Portland, OR 97228 ■ Catalog $2 ■ Old-time Victorian-style paper crafts.

Pyramid of Urbana, Box 877, Urbana, IL 61801: Free catalog ■ Paper-sculpting and paper-making supplies and materials, other craft supplies, office accessories and supplies, art supplies, and school equipment. 800–637–0955; 800–252–1363 (in IL).

Quill-It, P.O. Box 1304, Elmhurst, IL 60126: Catalog $1 (refundable) ■ Quilling papers, paper-snipping supplies, kits, books, tools, plaques, frames, fringes, and other supplies.

Stillwaters Early America, 438 Cedar Ave., Brighton, CO 80601: Brochure $1 with long SASE ■ Watercolor paper cuttings and patterns. 303–659–3098.

Terrific Little Crafts, 4140 Oceanside Blvd., Oceanside, CA 92056: Catalog $1 ■ Quilling supplies, jewelry findings, paper clay, and other craft items.

Tree Toys, Box 492, Hinsdale, IL 60521: Catalog $1 ■ Silhouette paper-snipping designs on antique parchment or black paper. 708–323–7474.

Twinrocker Papermaking Supplies, P.O. Box 413, Brookston, IN 47923: Free catalog ■ Paper-making supplies and ready-to-use handmade paper. 317–563–3119.

PAPERWEIGHTS

Alberene Crystal, 221 W. Main, Charlottesville, VA 22901: Free information ■ Perthshire paperweights, Thomas Webb crystal, and Edinburgh crystal. Includes discontinued items. 800–843–9078.

Gem Antiques, 1088 Madison Ave., New York, NY 10028: Free information ■ Antique and contemporary paperweights from Britain, France, and the United States. 212–535–7399.

Petri's, 731 Bridgeway, Sausalito, CA 94965: Catalog $2 ■ Paperweights, perfume bottles, vases, art glass collectibles, kaleidoscopes, and Lladro, Chilmark, and Swarovski items. 415–332–6477.

L.H. Selman, Ltd., 761 Chestnut St., Santa Cruz, CA 95060: Catalog $15 ■ Antique, modern, and contemporary paperweights. 800–538–0766.

PARTY DECORATIONS

Anderson's, 4875 White Bear Pkwy., White Bear Lake, MN 55110: Free catalog ■ Party and prom decorations and supplies. 800–328–9640; 612–426–1667 (in MN).

The Cracker Box, Solebury, PA 18963: Catalog $4.50 ■ Ornament kits. 215–862–2100.

Essentials Unlimited, Inc., P.O. Box 5137, Oak Brook, IL 60522: Free catalog ■ Coordinated paper plates and other party supplies. 708–916–9006.

Hearth Song, P.O. Box B, Sebastopol, CA 95473: Free catalog ■ Party decorations and supplies, children's books, doll house miniatures, art supplies, kites, and games. 800–533–4397.

Novelties Unlimited, 410 W. 21st St., Norfolk, VA 23517: Free list ■ Clown supplies, props, and gags; magic; balloons; make-up; party decorations; and other supplies. 804–622–0344.

Paper Wholesaler, 795 NW 72nd St., Miami, FL 33150: Catalog $3 (refundable) ■ Paper and plastic table wear, party supplies, and gift wrappings. 305–285–9229.

Paradise Products, P.O. Box 568, El Cerrito, CA 94530: Catalog $2 ■ Party decorations and favors. 510–524–8300.

Under the Big Top, P.O. Box 807, Placentia, CA 92670: Catalog $4 ■ Party supplies, costumes, clown props, and balloons. 714–579–1144.

U.S. Toys, 2008 W. 103rd Terrace, Leawood, KS 66206: Free catalog ■ Decorations and supplies for holidays, celebrations, parties, and other festive occasions; magic equipment and novelties; and carnival supplies. 913–642–8244.

PATIOS & WALKWAYS

Stone Company, Inc., Rt. 1, Eden, WI 53019: Free information ■ Natural building and landscape cobblers, granite boulders, wall stone, steppers, and flagstone. 414–477–2521.

PENS & PENCILS

Altman Luggage, 135 Orchard St., New York, NY 10001: Free information ■ Fine writing instruments, luggage, and other leather goods. 800–372–3377.

Bertram's Inkwell, 11301 Rockville Pike, Kensington, MD 20895: Free catalog ■ Pens and pencils, desk sets, and other gifts. 800–782–7680; 410–468–6939 (in MD).

A.T. Cross Company, One Albion Rd., Lincoln, RI 02865: Free catalog ■ Pens and pencils and desk sets. 800–282–7677; 401–333–1200 (in RI).

Fahrney Pens, Inc., 8329 Old Marlboro Pike, Upper Marlboro, MD 20772: Free catalog ■ Writing instruments. 800–624–PENS.

Hunt Manufacturing Company, 230 S. Broad St., Philadelphia, PA 19102: Free information ■ Calligraphy papers, markers, kits, and other supplies; fountain pens, pen sets, nibs, and inks; and acrylics, oil paints, and water colors. 215–732–7700.

Koh-I-Noor Rapidograph, Inc., 100 North St., Bloomsbury, NJ 08804: Free information ■ Mont Blanc writing instruments. 800–631–7646.

Menash, 462 7th Ave., New York, NY 10018: Free catalog ■ Writing instruments, refills, and accessories. 800–344–PENS.

PERFUMERY SUPPLIES

Aphrodesia Products, 282 Bleeker St., New York, NY 10014: Catalog $3 ■ Herbs, essential oils, and perfumery supplies. 800–221–6898; 212–989–6440 (in NY).

Candlechem Products, P.O. Box 705, Randolph, MA 02368: Catalog $2 ■ Oils, essential oils, dyes, and other scenting materials for use in making candles and perfumes. 617–986–7541.

Caswell-Massey Company, Ltd., Catalog Division, 100 Enterprise Pl., Dover, DE 19901: Free catalog ■ Herbs, essential oils, and perfumery supplies. 800–326–0500.

The Essential Oil Company, P.O. Box 88, Sandy, OR 97055: Free information ■ Essential oils and other aromatherapy supplies. 503–695–2400.

The Faith Mountain Company, P.O. Box 199, Sperryville, VA 22740: Catalog 50¢ (refundable) ■ Herbs, essential oils, and perfumery supplies. 800–822–7238.

Good Hollow Greenhouse & Herbarium, Rt. 1, Box 116, Taft, TN 38488: Catalog $1 ■ Herbs, perennials, wildflowers, scented geraniums, essential oils and potpourris,

teas, and dried herbs and spices. 615–433–7640.

Heaven's Herbal Creations, 8202 West M.L. Ave., Kalamazoo, MI 49009: Catalog $2 ■ Essential oils, herbal body care products, potpourris, and exclusive scents. 616–375–2934.

Indiana Botanic Gardens, P.O. Box 5, Hammond, IN 46325: Catalog 50¢ ■ Herbs, fragrances, and essential oils. 800–348–6434; 219–931–2480 (in IN).

Little Shepherds, 9658 W. Chatfield Ave., Littleton, CO 80123: Catalog $1 ■ Potpourri, incense oils, bath salts, and spices. 303–933–1296.

Meadowbrook Herb Gardens, Rt. 138, Wyoming, RI 02898: Catalog $1 ■ Herbs, essential oils, fragrances, and perfumery supplies. 401–539–7603.

Nature's Herb Company, 281 Ellis St., P.O. Box 40604, San Francisco, CA 94102: Free catalog ■ Herbs, spices, essential oils, perfumery supplies, and supplies for potpourris and sachets. 415–474–2756.

Penn Herb Company, 603 N. 2nd St., Philadelphia, PA 19123: Catalog $1 ■ Herbs, essential oils, and perfumery supplies. 800–523–9971; 215–925–3336 (in PA).

Raven's Nest, 4539 Iroquois Trail, Duluth, GA 30136: Catalog $1 ■ Essential oils, spices, potpourris and extracts, and herbal gifts.

Soap Opera, 319 State St., Madison, WI 55703: Free price list ■ Essential oils, rare oils, designer fragrances, herbs, perfume base, and cosmetics and toiletries. 800–251–SOAP.

Tom Thumb Workshops, P.O. Box 357, Mappsville, VA 23407: Catalog $1 (refundable) ■ Potpourri, herbs and spices, essential oils, and dried flowers. 804–824–3507.

Varney's Chemist Laden, 310 E. Main St., Fredericksburg, TX 78624: Catalog $1 ■ Herbs and oils, dried flowers, toiletries, seasonings and spices, and books. 800–284–0526.

PERSONALIZED & PROMOTIONAL PRODUCTS

Achievement Products, Inc., 294 Rt. 10, P.O. Box 388, East Hanover, NJ 07936:

Free information ■ Cloisonne lapel pins, plaques and awards, business gifts, and other promotional items. Can be imprinted with custom logos. 201–887–5090.

Advertising Ideas Company, 3281 Barber Rd., Barberton, OH 44203: Free catalog ■ Luggage, desk accessories, flashlights, disposable lighters, caps and T-shirts, pens, magnets, badges and holders, toys, mugs, self-adhesive notes, and other advertising and promotional novelties. 800–323–6359.

Amsterdam Printing & Litho Corporation, 55 Wallins Corners Rd., Amsterdam, NY 12010: Free catalog ■ Advertising novelties with custom printing. 800–543–6882.

B & F/Maxam, P.O. Box 660036, Dallas, TX 75266: Free catalog ■ Kitchen aids, tools, telephones, luggage, hunting knives, cutlery, cameras, leather briefcases, and other promotional merchandise. 214–333–2111.

Best Impressions Company, 348 N. 30th Rd., P.O. Box 800, LaSalle, IL 61301: Free catalog ■ Advertising specialties for promotions, incentives, and year-round gift giving. 815–223–6263.

Crestline Company, Inc., 22 W. 21st St., New York, NY 10010: Free catalog ■ Badges and ribbons, stickers, buttons, portfolios and binders, presentation folders and clipboards, cases and portfolios, note bags, pens and pencils, gifts and novelties, mugs and steins, and other novelties. 800–221–7797.

Hudson Incentives & Imprints, Inc., P.O. Box 396, Hudson, OH 44236: Free catalog ■ Advertising novelties with custom printing. 800–942–5372; 216–656–1746 (in OH).

The Jompole Company, Inc., 330 7th Ave., New York, NY 10001: Free information ■ Save up to 50 percent on balloons and lollipops to diamonds and furs, and other incentive merchandise. 212–594–0440.

N & D Novelty Company, 13 Hamden Park Dr., Hamden, CT 06517: Free information ■ Balloons, inflatable toys, advertising specialties, official licensed sports souvenirs, plush and plastic toys, carnival supplies, and circus items. 203–287–9990.

Namark Cap & Emblem Company, 6325 Harrison Dr., Las Vegas, NV 89120: Free information ■ Specialty caps, T-shirts, jackets, and screen-printed emblems. 800–634–6271.

Novelties Unlimited Advertising Specialties, P.O. Drawer 15159, Hattiesburg, MS 39404: Free catalog ■ Advertising novelties with custom logos. 800–647–1652; 800–536–7709 (in MS).

Prestige Promotions, 4875 White Bear Pkwy., White Bear Lake, MN 55110: Free information ■ Pens, coffee mugs, calendars, buttons, key tags, bumper stickers, magnets, and other novelties. 800–328–9351.

Sales Guides, Inc., 10510 N. Port Washington Rd., Mequon, WI 53092: Free catalog ■ Promotional merchandise that includes pens and pencils, key fobs, memo cubes, desk top items, giveaways, food and candy, games, hardware, executive gifts, binders, time pieces, and others. 800–654–6666.

N.G. Slater Corporation, 220 W. 19th St., New York, NY 10011: Free catalog ■ Advertising novelties that include T-shirts, tote bags, pins, shopping bags, coat room checks, coins and medallions, bumper stickers, and jewelry, and equipment and supplies for making buttons. 212–924–3133.

J.T. Townes, Inc., P.O. Box 760, Danville, VA 24543: Free information ■ Scratch pads. 800–437–PADS; 804–792–3711 (in VA).

Weisenbach Specialty Printing, Inc., 342 S. Washington Ave., Columbus, OH 43215: Free catalog ■ Promotional products made from recycled materials. Includes items made from plastic and paper, reusable ceramic mugs, and advertising novelties. 614–464–2223.

PETS

Bird Supplies

Advanced Avian Designs, 12021 Wilshire Blvd., Ste. 516, Los Angeles, CA 90025: Free catalog (specify bird type) ■ Playgyms for indoor freedom and exercising. 213–826–9536.

Animal Environments, 2270 Camino Vida Roble, Carlsbad, CA 92009: Free information ■ Bolt-free cages with extra-large doors and a maximum safety environment. 800–438–4442.

Audubon Workshop, 1501 Paddock Dr., Northbrook, IL 60062: Booklet 25¢ ■ Bird supplies. 800–325–9464.

AVP/Animal Veterinary Products, Division of U.S. Pet, Inc., P.O. Box 1326, Galesburg, IL 61402: Free catalog ■ Bird supplies. 800–962–1211.

Bear Mountain Enterprises, P.O. Box 1080, Altaville, CA 95221: Free information ■ Handcrafted oak cabinet cages. 209–785–3065.

Century Cages, 4107 Fruit Valley Rd., Vancouver, WA 98660: Free catalog ■ Nickel plated all-steel bird cages. 206–694–9947.

Chaparral Manufacturing, P.O. Box 2761, Turlock, CA 95381: Free information ■ Walk-in aviaries, breeding modules, and cages, small enough for finches, and large enough for macaws. 209–668–3080.

Dakota Quality Bird Food, Box 3084, Fargo, ND 58108: Free catalog ■ Niger thistle, small black sunflower seeds, wild birdseed mixes, royal finch mix, and safflower seed. 800–356–9220.

Elite Aviaries, Ltd., P.O. Box 207, Bronxville, NY 10708: Free information ■ Parrot cages and aviaries with coordinating fluorescent light fixtures above the cage. 914–963–CAGE.

Feed, Feather & Farm Supply, 4531–9 St. Augustine Rd., Jacksonville, FL 32207: Catalog $1 ■ Birdseed and supplies. 904–396–4273.

For Birds Only, 176 Jericho Tpk., Mineola, NY 11501: Free information ■ Seed for parrots, cockatiels, parakeets, finches, and canaries; sunflower seed, millet spray, and corn cob litter; and cages, books, and medications. 516–746–3657.

Greeson's Baby Parrots, 4201 SW 25th Ave., Fort Lauderdale, FL 33312: Free information ■ Cheese, corn, and red apple flavored total nutrition bird foods. 305–792–5657.

Inglebrook Forges, 151 N. San Dimas Canyon Rd., San Dimas, CA 91773: Free information ■ Bird cages. 714–599–3715.

Jones Seed Company, Rt. 2, Box 114, Lawton, OK 73501: Free brochure (specify if breeder, retailer, or hobbyist) ■ Fortified or standard birdseed mixtures for parakeets, cockatiels, finches, canaries, parrots, wild birds, and pigeons. 405–248–0051.

Just for the Birds, 3766 E. Broad St., Columbus, OH 43213: Catalog $4 (refundable) ■ Exotic bird supplies, Avian Nutritional Products, and diet pellets with essential nutrients. 614–237–2473.

Kester's Birdseed, Inc., P.O. Box 516, Omro, WI 54963: Catalog $2 ■ Custom birdseed mixes for cockatiels, lovebirds, parakeets, parrots, canaries, and finches. 800–558–8815; 414–685–2929 (in WI).

King's Aviary, 256–08 Craft Ave., Rosedale Queens, NY 11422: Free information ■ Wrought-iron bird cages that are convertible into playpens. 718–527–9281.

Lake's Minnesota Macaws, Inc., 639 Stryker Ave., St. Paul, MN 55107: Free information ■ Nutritionally balanced bird foods for adult macaws, cockatoos, parakeets, conures, lories, cockatiels, and lovebirds; hand-rearing formulas; and feeding syringes. 800–634–2473; 612–290–0606 (in MN).

Lexacon Pet Products, P.O. Box 1091, Kent, OH 44240: Free information ■ Cage-top playgyms. 800–752–4589.

Mellinger's, Inc., 2310 W. South Range Rd., North Lima, OH 44452: Free catalog ■ Thistle, safflower, finch mix, and sunflower birdseed. 216–549–9861.

Michael's Bird Paradise, Inc., 3925 Investment Ln., Riviera Beach, FL 33404: Free brochure with long SASE ■ Wrought-iron cages. 407–842–1050.

Mid-Wisconsin Seed & Supplies, 226 W. Mansion St., Mauston, WI 53948: Catalog $1.50 (refundable) ■ Spray millet, sun seed, specialty seeds, and cages. 800–553–8009.

Pet Warehouse, P.O. Box 20250, Dayton, OH 45420: Catalog $1 ■ Bird, tropical fish, dog, and cat supplies. 800–443–1160.

Pipe Dreams, 1824 Tawakoni Ln., Plano, TX 75075: Free information ■ Cage-top gyms.

Polly's Pleasures, 26530 Harper Ave., St. Clair Shores, MI 48081: Free information ■ Cage-top gyms. 313–776–3551.

Safeguard Bird Cages, 114–116 Earland Dr., New Holland, PA 17557: Free catalog ■ Exotic bird and parrot breeding and flight cages. 800–433–1819; 717–354–4586 (in PA).

Scarlet Oak Aviaries, Inc., 27935 Pergl Rd., Glenwillow, OH 44139: Free information ■ Easy-to-assemble bird cages. 216–439–5106.

Star Pet Supply, 1500 New Horizons Blvd., Amityville, NY 11701: Free catalog ■ Supplies and grooming aids for dogs, cats, birds, and other pets. 800–274–6400.

Sunshine Bird Seed Company, 502 E. 1st St., Meridian, ID 83642: Free information ■ Custom and premium birdseed mixtures. 208–888–1885.

Swelland's Cage & Supply Company, 1414 Barnett Rd., Ramona, CA 92065: Free information ■ Bird supplies and ready-made and custom breeding cages. 619–789–3572.

UPCO, P.O. Box 969, St. Joseph, MO 64502: Free catalog ■ Cages, birdseed, supplies, books, toys, and remedies for birds. 816–233–8800.

Volkman Bird Seed, 1616 SE Woodward, Portland, OR 97202: Free information ■ Premium birdseed and cuttlebone. 510–261–7780.

Wingnut Supply, 58 Providence Hwy., East Walpole, MA 02032: Catalog $5 (refundable) ■ Bird supplies. 800–999–PETI.

Dog & Cat Supplies

Abeta Pet Supply, 503 Miltwood Dr., Greensboro, NC 27408: Catalog $1 ■ Solid wood furniture for cats. 919–288–5391.

Animal Pet Care Products, 2515 E. 43rd St., Box 23547, Chattanooga, TN 37422: Free catalog ■ Leather collars, sweaters, carriers, feeding dishes, doggie beds, puppy comfort stations, rawhide bones, kennel enclosures, pooper scoopers, grooming aids, flea and other pest control products, pet doors for dogs, and other supplies for birds, tropical fish, and cats. 800–446–4932.

Animal Town, Inc., P.O. Box 485, Healdsburg, CA 95448: Free catalog ■ Dog, cat, and other pet supplies. 800–445–8642.

AVP/Animal Veterinary Products, Division of U.S. Pet, Inc., P.O. Box 1326, Galesburg, IL 61402: Free catalog ■ Health care supplies for dog and cat breeders, groomers, and kennels. 800–962–1211.

Care-A-Lot, 1617 Diamond Springs Rd., Virginia Beach, VA 23455: Free catalog ■ Dog and cat supplies. 804–460–9771.

Cedar-al Products, Inc., Rt. 1, Box 6, Clallam Bay, WA 98326: Free brochure ■ Pet pillows and cage floor coverings; deodorizer and freshener for carpets, pet beds, and around the home; and pet shampoo. 800–431–3444; 206–963–2601 (in WA).

Drs. Foster & Smith, Inc., 2253 Air Park Rd., P.O. Box 100, Rhinelander, WI 54501: Free catalog ■ Pet and equine products and healthcare supplies. 800–826–7206.

Dog-Master Systems, Division Environmental Research Labs, P.O. Box 1250, Agoura Hills, CA 91301: Free catalog ■ Supplies for raising and training puppies and dogs.

Du-Say's, 215 7th St., Picayune, MS 39466: Free catalog ■ Clothing, treats, convenience products, playtime toys, bedding, collars and leads, grooming and health aids, travel accessories, and other items for dogs and cats. 601–798–9308.

Feed, Feather & Farm Supply, 4531–9 St. Augustine Rd., Jacksonville, FL 32207: Catalog $1 ■ Supplies for dogs and cats. 904–396–4273.

Felix, 3623 Fremont Ave. North, Seattle, WA 98103: Free catalog ■ Cat toys, mouse houses, climbers, combs, and scratching posts.

G & H Pet Supplies, P.O. Box 3213, Simi Valley, CA 93063: Free catalog ■ Equipment and supplies for dog grooming and care. 805–527–8718.

J-B Wholesale Pet Supplies, 289 Wagaraw Rd., Hawthorne, NJ 07506: Free catalog ■ Supplies for cats and dogs. 800–526–0388; 201–423–2222 (in NJ).

Jeffers Vet Supply, P.O. Box 100, Dothan, AL 36302: Free catalog ■ Instruments, books, medications, and supplies for livestock and pets. 800–633–7592.

Just Cats, 244 E. 60th St., New York, NY 10022: Free information ■ Jewelry, collectibles, clothing, and unique objects for cat lovers and their cats. 212–888–CATS.

Ka-trene Products, P.O. Box 476, Montour Falls, NY 14865: Free brochure ■ Cat shelters, boxes, grooming aids, carriers, and toys. 607–535–7581.

Kennel Vet Corporation, P.O. Box 835, Bellmore, NY 11710: Free catalog ■ Vaccines and biologicals, vitamins and nutritional supplements, remedies for common medical conditions, cages, kennels, pet doors, deodorizers and repellents, flea and tick control aids, leashes and leads, toys and rawhide bones, and books about dogs, cats, birds, and horses. 516–783–5400.

Leather Brothers, Inc., P.O. Box 1077, Conway, AR 72032: Free catalog ■ Leather and nylon collars and leads, other collars, wire muzzles, dog harnesses, name tags, and training leads. 800–442–5522.

Leatherrite Manufacturing, Inc., 262 2nd St. SW, Carmel, IN 46032: Free catalog ■ Leather, nylon, and vinyl leads, collars, and harnesses. 800–722–5222; 317–844–7241 (in IN).

Nite Lite Company, P.O. Box 8210, Little Rock, AR 72221: Free catalog ■ Kennel, training, and hunting supplies for dogs, and clothing and accessories for the hunter. 800–648–5483; 800–632–6895 (in AR).

Omaha Vaccine Company, Inc., 3030 L St., Omaha, NE 68107: Free catalog ■ Health, grooming, and training supplies for dogs, cats, other house pets, and horses. 800–367–4444; 402–731–9600 (in NE).

Our Best Friends Pet Catalog, 79 Albertson Ave., Albertson, NY 11507: Catalog $2 ■ Pet foods, health and grooming supplies, and pet clothing. 800–852–PETS; 516–742–7400 (in NY).

Pedigrees Pet Catalog, P.O. Box 905, Brockport, NY 14420: Free catalog ■ Pet clothing, name tags, collars, leads, feeders, carriers, toys, books, and T-shirts for owners. 716–637–1434.

Pet Warehouse, P.O. Box 20250, Dayton, OH 45420: Catalog $1 ■ Dog, cat, bird, and tropical fish supplies. 800–443–1160.

Pro Kennel Supply, P.O. Box 25226, Little Rock, AR 72221: Free catalog ■ Dog and kennel supplies. 800–762–7049.

Sporting Dog Specialties, Box 900, Brockport, NY 14420: Free catalog ■ Gun dog training dummies, game scents, books, collars, leads, camouflage gear, gifts for sportsmen, and art prints. 716–352–1232.

Star Pet Supply, 1500 New Horizons Blvd., Amityville, NY 11701: Free catalog ■ Supplies and grooming aids for dogs, cats, birds, and other pets. 800–274–6400.

R.C. Steele Dog Equipment, 1989 Transit Way, Brockport, NY 14420: Free catalog ■ Dog equipment and kennel supplies. 800–872–4506.

United Pharmacal Company, Inc., P.O. Box 969, St. Joseph, MO 64502: Free catalog ■ Save from 30 to 50 percent on health and medical supplies for dogs, cats, and horses. 816–233–8800.

Wholesale Veterinary Supply, Inc., P.O. Box 2256, Rockford, IL 61131: Free catalog ■ Supplies for dogs, cats, rabbits, other household pets, horses, and cattle. 800–435–6940.

Tropical Fish Supplies

Acrylic Creations, 5517 Roan Rd., Sylvania, OH 43560: Free price list ■ Custom acrylic tanks, reef filters, skimmers, lighting, and other aquarium supplies. 419–882–1287.

Anchor Bay Aquarium, Inc., 37017 Green St., New Baltimore, MI 48047: Free price list with long SASE ■ Rare cichlids, catfish, and other exotic tropical fish; books; supplies; and live plants. 313–725–1383.

Aquarium Design & Engineering, Inc., 372 River Edge Rd., Jupiter, FL 33477: Free information ■ Water pumps and filtration systems. 407–743–0707.

Aquarium Instruments, Inc., 249 Grove St., Shelton, CT 06484: Catalog $2 ■ Aquarium monitoring products. 203–924–1014.

Aquarium Lights, Inc., 1317 Colony Way Ct., Chesterfield, MO 63017: Free price list ■ Liquid and freeze-dried nutritional products and aquarium lighting accessories. 800–745–0848.

The Aquarium Mail Order, 4300 Clarcona-Ocose Rd., Ste. 211, Orlando, FL 32810: Free information ■ Tropical fish supplies. 407–298–1129.

Aquarium Products, 180 Penrod Ct., Glen Burnie, MD 21061: Free information ■ Medications and water conditioners for tropical fish. 410–761–2100.

Aquatic Specialists, 5201 Kingston Pike, Knoxville, TN 37919: Catalog $5 (refundable) ■ Net-caught marine fish, marine invertebrates and macro algae, and cured live rock. 615–584–1084.

Aquatic Supply House, 42 Hayes St., Elmsford, NY 10523: Free catalog ■ Tropical fish supplies and accessories, foods and automatic feeding devices, medications, heaters, air pumps, filters, sterilizers, water changers, and books. 800–777–PETS.

Buckaroo Marine, 1319 N. Main, Tucson, AZ 85705: Free brochure ■ Saltwater fish and invertebrates. 800–927–1050.

J.P. Burleson, Inc., P.O. Box 32, Frederick, MD 21701: Catalog $3 ■ Aquarium testing

kits, cleansing solutions, water stabilization products, filter media, water conditioners, conductivity meters, and other items. 301–846–4800.

By-Rite Pet Supplies, 23450 Kidder St., Hayward, CA 94545: Catalog $2 ■ Aquarium supplies and accessories. 800–321–3448.

California Reef Specialists, 740 Tioga Ave., Sand City, CA 93955: Catalog $5 (refundable) ■ Cold water reef fish and invertebrates, aquarium chiller units, wet/dry filters, acrylic aquariums, protein skimmers, and pumps. 408–394–7271.

Daleco Master Breeder Products, 3340 Land Dr., Fort Wayne, IN 46809: Catalog $4 ■ Tropical fish supplies and accessories, live food cultures, power filters, purification equipment, medications, lighting and temperature controls, fresh and salt water support systems, and aquariums. 219–747–7376.

Delaware Aquatic Imports, 18 Anderson Rd., Newark, DE 19713: Catalog $1 (refundable) ■ Water-grown aquatic plants. 302–738–4042.

Desert Aquatics, 3355 E. Tropicana Ave., Las Vegas, NV 89121: Free information ■ Filtration systems for fresh and salt water tropical fish aquariums. 702–459–6000.

Energy Savers Unlimited, Inc., 22138 S. Vermont, Bldg. C, Torrance, CA 90502: Free information ■ Aquarium lighting systems. 800–678–8844.

Exotic Aquaria, Inc., 1672 NE 205th Terrace, North Miami Beach, FL 33179: Free information ■ Tropical fish, algae, and corals. 800–622–5877.

Exotic Fish, 406 Northside Dr., Valdosta, GA 31602: Free information ■ Tropical fish supplies and aquarium accessories. 800–736–0473.

Hamilton Technology Corporation, 14902 S. Figueroa St., Gardena, CA 90248: Free information ■ Reef tank lights, digital electronic pH computer, and accessories. 800–447–9797.

Hawaiian Marine Imports, Inc., 10801 Kempwood, Ste. 2, Houston, TX 77043: Free information ■ Filters, hoses, and accessories. 713–460–0236.

Imperial Discus, P.O. Box 770106, Lakewood, OH 44107: Free information ■ Tropical fish. 216–234–2320.

Island Eco-Systems, P.O. Box 1102, Tavernier, FL 33070: Free information ■ Net-collected Atlantic Caribbean fish. 305–852–4385.

Dale Jordan, 71 Melon Lea Cove., Winnipeg, Manitoba, Canada R2G 2L4: Free information ■ Tropical fish. 204–668–9780.

Kent Marine, 915 Raleigh Ct., Marietta, GA 30064: Free information ■ Saltwater aquarium supplies. 404–427–8870.

Kordon, Division of Novalek, Inc., 2242 Davis Ct., Hayward, CA 94545: Free information ■ Live and frozen brine shrimp, brine shrimp eggs, brine shrimp food, and a salt water mix for brine shrimp.

Lifereef Filter Systems, 4628 S. Ward Way, Morrison, CO 80465: Free catalog ■ Aquarium filter systems, skimmers, controllers, air dryers, light fixtures, chillers, water pumps, and other accessories. 303–978–0940.

Living Reef, 9309 Narnia Dr., Riverside, CA 92503: Catalog $2.50 ■ Tropical fish supplies and accessories. 800–788–REEF.

Living Sea Aquarium, 811 W. Devon Ave., Park Ridge, IL 60068: Free information ■ Tropical and marine fish and invertebrates. 708–698–SALT.

Mail Order Pet Shop, 1338 N. Market Blvd., Sacramento, CA 95834: Free catalog ■ Filters, heaters, medications, marine supplies, plastic plants, air pumps, and water conditioners for tropical fish, and supplies for dogs, cats, birds, and hamsters. 800–366–7387.

Majestic Pet Supply, P.O. Box 88484, Carol Stream, IL 60188: Catalog $2.50 ■ Tropical fish supplies and accessories. 800–245–2389; 708–682–8867 (in IL).

Marine Invertebrates, 784 Boston Post Rd., Milford, CT 06460: Catalog $2.50 ■ Ozone generators, protein skimmers, controllers, water and air pumps, and other accessories and supplies. 203–878–9297.

Marine Products, 678 E. Broadway, Milford, CT 06460: Catalog $2 ■ Aquarium supplies and accessories. 203–877–5002.

Mark's Aquarium & Pet World, 7019 3rd Ave., Brooklyn, NY 11209: Free information ■ Custom tanks, filtration systems, splash guards, stands, and other accessories. 718–745–4001.

Now Playing with Fish, 2007 Independence, Cape Girardeau, MO 63701: Free information ■ Live corals, invertebrates, saltwater fish, and acrylic aquarium accessories. 314–335–1955.

Pet Warehouse, P.O. Box 20250, Dayton, OH 45420: Catalog $2 ■ Tropical fish, bird, dog, and cat supplies. 800–252–7388.

Reef Aquarium Designs, Inc., 509 Herbert St., Port Orange, FL 32119: Free brochure ■ Custom marine, reef, and fresh water aquarium systems. 904–760–0738.

Reef Concepts, 1965 Lake Dr., Winston-Salem, NC 27127: Free information ■ Ozone generators, pH controllers, trace elements, and other accessories. 919–788–3017.

Reef Displays, 10925 Overseas Hwy., Marathon, FL 33050: Free catalog ■ Net-caught Atlantic fish and invertebrates, macro algae, algae snails, Carribean live rock, and fresh and cured reef rock. 305–743–0070.

Reef Encounter, 1040 River Rd., Edgewater, NJ 07020: Free information ■ Aquarium accessories. 800–732–9435; 201–947–7333 (in NY & NJ).

Reef Tech, 6908 Cole St., Arvada, CO 80004: Free information ■ Aquariums, filters, canopies, and stands. 303–422–3882.

Regal Discus, 2321 N. 9th St., Phoenix, AZ 85006: Free brochure ■ Aquarium reverse osmosis filter system. 602–531–7532.

Sanders Brine Shrimp Company, 1180 W. 4600 South, Ogden, UT 84405: Free price list ■ Brine shrimp eggs. 801–393–5027.

Sea-Thru, 790 Court St., Franklin Lakes, NJ 07417: Free information ■ Marine filtration equipment. 201–652–5282.

Spectacular Sea Systems, 600 NE 42nd St., Pompano Beach, FL 33064: Free information ■ Aquarium systems and accessories. 305–941–3792.

That Fish Place, 237 Centerville Rd., Lancaster, PA 17603: Free catalog ■ Aquarium supplies and accessories. 800–733–3829.

Tropical Pumps Company, P.O. Box 11342, Spring, TX 77391: Free information ■ Saltwater-safe pumps, pH testers and controllers, and chemical test kits. 800–866–5273; 800–580–5273 (in TX).

World Class Aquarium, 2015 Flatbush Ave., Brooklyn, NY 11234: Free information ■ Aquarium systems and accessories, marine and fresh water fish, custom cabinets, and lighting accessories. 718–258–0653.

Carriers

Collapsible Wire Products, 5120 N. 126th St., Butler, WI 53007: Free brochure ■ Crates for transporting pets. 414–781–6125.

DAFCO, 2411 Grear St., Salem, OR 97301: Free brochure ■ Lightweight collapsible dog carrier. 800–458–1562.

Kennels & Enclosures

Cal-Formed Plastics Company, 2050 E. 48th St., Los Angeles, CA 90058: Free information ■ Easy-to-clean, interlocking two-piece dog house with 5-way flow-through ventilation. 800–772–7723.

Central Metal Products, Inc., State Rd. 213, North Edge, Windfall, IN 46076: Free catalog ■ Wire cages for dogs. 317–945–7677.

Horst Company, 101 E. 18th St., Greely, CO 80631: Free catalog ■ Kennels and runs. 303–353–7724.

Keipper Cooping Company, 3235 W. Burnham St., P.O. Box 15138, Milwaukee, WI 53215: Free information ■ All-wire collapsible coops. 414–672–8966.

Kennel-Aire Manufacturing Company, 6651 Hwy. 7, St. Louis Park, MN 55426: Free catalog ■ Wire animal enclosures. 800–346–0134.

Manson Industries, Inc., Rt. 8, Huntoon & Auburn Rd., Topeka, KS 66605: Free folder ■ Runs, enclosures, cages, pens, and accessories for dogs and cats. 913–478–4662.

Mason Company, 260 Depot St., Box 365, Leesburg, OH 45135: Free catalog ■ Kennels and cages for dogs. 800–543–5567.

Pet Castle, P.O. Box 1059, Brownwood, TX 76801: Free information ■ One-piece molded dog house for indoors and outside. 800–351–1363; 915–643–2517 (in TX).

Pet Logs, 6514 Chapel Hill Rd., Raleigh, NC 27607: Free information ■ Easy-to-clean cedar log dog houses. 800–334–5530.

Pet Doors

Borwick Innovations, Inc., P.O. Box 30345, Santa Barbara, CA 93130: Free information ■ Easy-to-install pet screen door that snaps into any screen without screws or bolts. 800–365–5657.

Falcon Pet Doors, 418 Wendy, Mill Valley, CA 94941: Free information ■ Safe, easy-to-install pet entrances for sliding doors. 415–383–5368.

Featherer Pet Emporium, 862 Southampton Rd., Benicia, CA 94510: Free brochure ■ Easy-to-lock, weatherproof, electronic (9-volt battery-operated) cat entry that fits most doors. 707–745–5016.

Hale Security Pet Door, 5622 N. 52nd Ave., Glendale, AZ 85301: Free information ■ Pet doors for walls, French doors, and wood doors. 800–888–8914.

Mar-Jo Industries, Inc., 18425 Via De Palmas, Higley, AZ 85236: Free brochure ■ Electronically controlled, air tight and weatherproof cat door for sliding glass doors. 602–987–9559.

Patio Pacific, Inc., 1931 N. Gaffey St., San Pedro, CA 90731: Free catalog ■ Pet door panels for sliding glass doors. 800–826–2871.

Petdoors U.S.A., 4523 30th St. West, Bradenton, FL 34207: Free brochure ■ Easy-to-install, self-closing, energy-efficient pet doors with a security lock see-through panel. 800–749–9609.

Pet-Eze, 862 Southhampton Rd., Benicia, CA 94510: Free brochure ■ Pet doors with energy-conserving glass and aluminum insert panel with flexible flap for any size sliding door. 800–331–6702; 707–745–5026 (in CA).

Turen, Inc., Etna Rd., Lebanon, NH 03766: Free brochure ■ Energy-efficient oval pet doors. 603–448–2990.

PHONOGRAPHS

Kenny Bunny, 480 S. Fair Oaks, Pasadena, CA 91105: Free information ■ Antique phonographs and parts. 213–733–7733.

Kurluff Enterprises, 4331 Maxson Rd., El Monte, CA 91732: Free information ■ Antique phonographs and parts. 818–444–7079.

Victorian Talking Machine Company, 261 Robinson Ave., Newburgh, NY 12550:

Free information ■ Antique phonographs and parts. 914–561–0132.

PHOTOGRAPHY
Albums & Photo Mounts

Albums, Inc., Box 81757, Cleveland, OH 44181: Free catalog ■ Wedding albums, photo mounts, plaques, and frames. 800–662–1000.

Camille Company, Inc., 828 Bergen St., Brooklyn, NY 11238: Free catalog ■ Photo albums. 718–789–0100.

Crown Products, 2142 Superior Ave., Cleveland, OH 44114: Free catalog ■ Albums, folios and photo mounts for presentation of wedding, portrait, and other photos. 216–781–6000.

Exposures, 2800 Hoover Rd., Stevens Point, WI 54481: Catalog $1 ■ Photo mounting supplies, albums, and frames. 800–572–5750.

Memories, Inc., P.O. Box 17526, Raleigh, NC 27619: Free information ■ Handmade wedding books and albums. 800–462–5069; 919–571–1648 (in NC).

Merit Albums, Inc., 19438 Business Center Dr., Northridge, CA 91324: Free catalog ■ Wedding albums, photo mounts, proof books, and folios. 818–886–5100.

Michel Company, 4672 N. Pulaski, Chicago, IL 60630: Free catalog ■ Albums, photo mounts, and frames. 800–621–6649.

Penn Photomounts, Concord & Tryens Rd., Ashton, PA 19014: Free catalog ■ Photo mounts, albums, and folios. 800–228–7366; 800–227–7366 (in PA).

Pierce Company, 9801 Nicollet, Minneapolis, MN 55420: Catalog $1 (refundable) ■ Hand-painted backgrounds for portrait photography, mounts, albums, drapes, and printed forms. 612–884–1991.

TLC, 9800 Topanga Cyn Blvd., Chatsworth, CA 91311: Catalog $2 ■ Hand-cut mats, frames, equipment cases, archival storage systems, slide viewers and light boxes, and flash accessories. 818–998–8889.

Backgrounds

Denny Manufacturing Company, Inc., P.O. Box 7200, Mobile, AL 36607: Free catalog ■ Background scenes and professional backdrops. 800–235–7012.

Photek Backgrounds, 909 Bridgeport Ave., Shelton, CT 06484: Free information ■ Featherlite, reversible, and washable backgrounds. 203–926–1811.

Photographic Products, 13535 Crenshaw Blvd., Hawthorne, CA 90250: Free brochure ■ Hand-painted backgrounds, motorized roller systems, stools and tables, umbrellas, background cases and stands, strobe lights, and Victorian-style chairs. 800–821–5796; 310–973–8488 (in CA).

Photo-Tech, Inc., P.O. Box 9326, North St. Paul, MN 55109: Free information ■ Easy-to-use background system. 612–771–4438.

Pierce Company, 9801 Nicollet, Minneapolis, MN 55420: Catalog $1 (refundable) ■ Hand-painted backgrounds for portrait photography, photo supplies, mounts, albums, drapes, and printed forms. 612–884–1991.

Bags & Camera Cases

The Camjacket Company, 2610 Adams Ave., San Diego, CA 92116: Free catalog ■ All-weather cases for cameras and lenses. 800–338–8759.

Coast Manufacturing Company, 200 Corporate Blvd. South, Yonkers, NY 10701: Free information ■ Camera bags. 914–271–5365.

Diamond/LeMans by Beseler, Beseler Photo Marketing Company, Inc., 1600 Lower Rd., Linden, NJ 07036: Free information ■ Bags for cameras, video equipment, and camcorders. 800–678–8324.

Domke, Division Saunders Group, 21 Jet View Dr., Rochester, NY 14624: Free catalog ■ Camera bags and other photo equipment. 716–328–7800.

GMI Photographic, Inc., 1776 New Hwy., P.O. Drawer U, Farmingdale, NY 11735: Free information ■ Camera bags and equipment cases. 516–752–0053.

LowePro, 620 Compton St., Bloomfield, CO 80302: Free information ■ Camera bags. 303–465–3706.

Photoflex, 541 Capitola Rd., Ste. G, Santa Cruz, CA 95062: Free information ■ Camera bags. 800–826–5903.

Tamrac, 9240 Jordan Ave., Chatsworth, CA 91311: Free catalog ■ Camera and video bags. 800–662–0717.

Tenba, 503 Broadway, New York, NY 10012: Free information ■ Camera equipment bags. 212–966–1013.

Tundra Camjacket, Satter, Inc., 4100 Dahlia St., P.O. Box 7234, Denver, CO 80207: Free information ■ Camera bags. 303–399–7493.

Books

Aperture Foundation, Inc., 20 E. 23rd St., New York, NY 10010: Free information ■ Books on photography for amateur and professional photographers. 212–505–5555.

John S. Craig, 111 Edward Ave., P.O. Box 1637, Torrington, CT 06790: Free information ■ Hard-to-find instruction manuals for photography equipment. 203–496–9791.

Eastman Kodak Company, Information Center, 343 State St., Rochester, NY 14650: Free brochure ■ Books and other publications on photography. 800–462–6495.

Hudson Hills Press, 230 5th Ave., Ste. 1308, New York, NY 10001: Free information ■ Books on photography and art. 212–889–3090.

Light Impressions, 439 Monroe Ave., Rochester, NY 14607: Free catalog ■ Books and supplies for archival storage of negatives and prints. 800–828–6216.

Strand Bookstore, 828 Broadway, New York, NY 10003: Free information ■ Books on photography. 212–473–1452.

Camera Manufacturers

Ampac, Inc., Horseman Building, 910 Sahara Dr. NW, Cleveland, TN 37320: Catalog $5 ■ Monorail view cameras and accessories. 615–478–1405.

Ansco Photo Optical Products, 1801 Touhy Ave., Elk Grove, IL 60007: Free information. 800–323–6697.

Bronica, GMI Photographic, Inc., 1776 New Hwy., P.O. Drawer U, Farmingdale, NY 11735: Free information. 516–752–0053.

Calumet Photographic, 890 Supreme Dr., Bensenville, IL 60106: Free information. 800–225–8638.

Canon, One Canon Plaza, Lake Success, NY 11042: Free brochure. 516–488–6700.

Chinon America, Inc., 1065 Bristol Rd., Mountainside, NJ 07092: Free information. 908–654–0404.

Contax, 100 Randolph Rd., CN 6700, Somerset, NJ 08875: Free information. 201–560–0600.

Eastman Kodak Company, Information Center, 343 State St., Rochester, NY 14650: Free information. 800–462–6495.

Foto-Care, Ltd., 170 5th Ave., New York, NY 10010: Free information ■ Large format Wista cameras. 212–741–2990.

Fuji Photo Film USA, Inc., 555 Taxter Rd., Elmsford, NY 10523: Free information. 914–789–8100.

Garfield & Berk Optometrists, 175 5th Ave., New York, NY 10010: Free information. 212–254–0450.

Peter Gowland Cameras, 609 Hightree Rd., Santa Monica, CA 90402: Free information. 310–454–7867.

Victor Hasselblad, Inc., 10 Madison Rd., Fairfield, NJ 07004: Free brochure. 800–338–6477.

Kalimar, Inc., 622 Goddard Ave., Chesterfield, MO 63017: Free information. 800–525–4627.

Keystone Camera Products Corporation, 468 Getty Ave., Clifton, NJ 07015: Free information. 201–546–2800.

Konica USA, Inc., 440 Sylvan Ave., Englewood Cliffs, NJ 07632: Free information. 201–568–3100.

Leica USA, Inc., 156 Ludlow Ave., Northvale, NJ 07647: Free information. 201–767–7500.

Mamiya America Corporation, 8 Westchester Plaza, Elmsford, NY 10523: Free information. 914–347–3300.

Minolta, 101 Williams Dr., Ramsey, NJ 07446: Free information. 201–825–4000.

Nikon, 1300 Walt Whitman Rd., Melville, NY 11747: Free brochure. 800–NIKON–US.

Nikonos Cameras, 1300 Walt Whitman Rd., Melville, NY 11747: Free brochure. 800–NIKON–US.

Olympus Corporation, 145 Crossways Park, Woodbury, NY 11797: Free information. 800–221–3000.

Pentax Corporation, 35 Inverness Dr. East, Englewood, CO 80112: Free brochure. 303–799–8000.

Polaroid Corporation, 549 Technology Square, Cambridge, MA 02139: Free information. 617–577–2000.

Ricoh Consumer Products Group, 180 Passaic Ave., Fairfield, NJ 07004: Free brochure. 201–882–7762.

Ritz Camera Centers, 6711 Ritzway, Beltsville, MD 20705: Free catalog. 301–953–9600.

Rollei Cameras, HP Marketing, 16 Chapin Rd., Pine Brook, NJ 07470: Free brochure. 201–808–9010.

Samsung Optical America, Inc., 40 Seaview Dr., Secaucus, NJ 07094: Free information. 201–902–0347.

Sigma Corporation of America, 15 Fleetwood Ct., Ronkonkoma, NY 11779: Free information. 516–585–1144.

Tamron Industries, Inc., P.O. Box 388, Port Washington, NY 11050: Free brochure. 800–827–8880.

Tokina Optical Corporation, 1512 Kona Dr., Compton, CA 90220: Free information. 310–537–9380.

Vivitar Corporation, 9350 DeSoto Ave., P.O. Box 2193, Chatsworth, CA 91311: Free brochure. 818–700–9380.

Wisner Large Format Cameras, Wisner Classic Manufacturing Company, Inc., P.O. Box 21, Marion, MA 02738: Free information. 800–848–0448.

WISTA Large Format Cameras, Foto-Care, Ltd., 170 5th Ave., New York, NY 10010: Free information. 212–741–2990.

Yashica, Inc., 100 Randolph Rd., P.O. Box 6802, Somerset, NJ 08875: Free information. 908–560–0060.

Darkroom Equipment

Acufine, Brandess Kait Company, 5441 N. Kedzie Ave., Chicago, IL 60625: Free information ■ Darkroom chemicals. 312–588–8601.

Alta Photographic, Inc., 11526 Sorrento Valley Rd., San Diego, CA 92121: Free information ■ Darkroom chemicals. 800–688–8688.

Bencher, Inc., 333 W. Lake St., Chicago, IL 60606: Free information ■ Enlargers and darkroom accessories. 312–263–1808.

Bogen Photo Corporation, 565 E. Crescent St., P.O. Box 506, Ramsey, NJ 07446: Free information ■ Dry-mount presses. 201–818–9500.

Bostick & Sullivan, P.O. Box 2155, Van Nuys, CA 91404: Catalog $1 (refundable) ■ Platinum and palladian photographic chemicals. 818–785–4130.

Darkroom Products, Ltd., 2949 11th St., Rockford, IL 61109: Free information ■ Darkroom accessories. 815–399–0301.

Daylab, 400 E. Main, Ontario, CA 91761: Free information ■ All-in-one, self-contained color enlarger, exposure meter, timer, and developing system. 800–235–3233.

Delta 1, 10830 Sanden Dr., Dallas, TX 75238: Free information ■ Temperature-regulated sinks. 214–349–9779.

Dimco-Gray, 8200 S. Suburban Rd., Centerville, OH 45459: Free brochure ■ Darkroom timers. 513–433–7600.

Empire West Plastics, P.O. Box 511, Graton, CA 95444: Free information ■ Darkroom equipment and supplies. 707–823–1190.

Freestyle, 5124 Sunset Blvd., Los Angeles, CA 90027: Free information ■ Darkroom supplies and equipment. 213–660–3460.

GMI Photographic, Inc., 1776 New Highway, P.O. Drawer U, Farmingdale, NY 11735: Free information ■ Darkroom chemicals and enlarging papers. 516–752–0066.

Heico Chemicals, Whittaker Corporation, Delaware Water Gap, PA 18327: Free information ■ Darkroom chemicals. 717–476–0353.

Helix, 310 S. Racine Ave., Chicago, IL 60607: Free catalog ■ Cameras and accessories, darkroom equipment and supplies, video equipment, and underwater photo equipment. 800–621–6471.

Jobo Fototechnic, Inc., P.O. Box 3721, Ann Arbor, MI 48106: Free information ■ Photo processing chemicals and color retouching dyes for color and black-and-white photography. 313–995–4192.

Leedal, Inc., 1918 S. Prairie Ave., Chicago, IL 60616: Free brochure ■ Stainless steel darkroom sinks with plumbing and back splash, stands, and shelves. 800–441–6663.

Omega/Arkay, P.O. Box 2078, 197 Schaeffer Ave., Westminster, MD 21157: Free information ■ Darkroom accessories and enlargers. 410–857–6353.

Photo-Therm, 110 Sewell Ave., Trenton, NJ 08610: Free catalog ■ Temperature controls and temperature baths, modular controls, and film processors. 609–396–1456.

Photographers Formulary, P.O. Box 950, Condon, MT 59826: Catalog $1 ■ Photographic chemicals. 800–922–5255.

Porter's Camera Store, Inc., Box 628, Cedar Falls, Iowa 50613: Free catalog ■ Picture-taking equipment and accessories, darkroom supplies, and photography novelties and accessories. 800–553–2001.

Seal Products, 550 Spring St., Naugatuck, CT 06770: Free information ■ Dry-mounting presses. 203–729–5201.

Solar Cine Products, Inc., 4247 S. Kedzie Ave., Chicago, IL 60632: Catalog $1.50 ■ Darkroom and other photographic equipment and supplies. 312–254–8310.

TheNewLab, 22 Cleveland, San Francisco, CA 94103: Free brochure ■ Photo processing equipment. 800–526–3165; 415–626–6996 (in CA).

Yankee Photo Products, Inc., 4024 E. Broadway Rd., Phoenix, AZ 85040: Free information ■ Darkroom equipment, accessories, and slide trays for most 35mm slide projectors. 602–275–7696.

Zone VI Studios, Inc., 698 Elm St., Newfane, VT 05345: Free catalog ■ Picture-taking equipment and darkroom equipment. 800–457–1114.

Enlargers

Aristo Grid Lamp, 35 Lumber Rd., Roslyn, NY 11576: Free information ■ Enlarger accessories. 516–484–6141.

Bencher, Inc., 333 W. Lake St., Chicago, IL 60606: Free information ■ Enlargers and darkroom accessories. 312–263–1808.

Charles Beseler Company, 1600 Lower Rd., Linden, NJ 07036: Free brochure ■ En-

largers, accessories, color heads and electronic controls, and modular units for color or black-and-white photo enlarging. 908–862–7999.

Omega/Arkay, P.O. Box 2078, 197 Schaeffer Ave., Westminster, MD 21157: Free information ■ Darkroom accessories and enlargers. 410–857–6353.

Paterson, Division Saunders Group, 21 Jet View Dr., Rochester, NY 14624: Free catalog ■ Darkroom accessories and enlargers. 716–328–7800.

The Saunders Group, 21 Jet View Dr., Rochester, NY 14624: Free brochure ■ Exposure and flash meters, medium format dichroic enlargers and accessories, strobe brackets, tripods, and other equipment. 716–328–7800.

Testrite Instrument Company, Inc., 133 Monroe St., Newark, NJ 07105: Free catalog ■ Enlargers, accessories, and other equipment. 201–589–6767.

Exposure Meters

Bogen Photo Corporation, 565 E. Crescent St., P.O. Box 506, Ramsey, NJ 07446: Free information ■ Multi-purpose exposure meters, tripods, enlargers, and other equipment and accessories. 201–818–9500.

Minolta, 101 Williams Dr., Ramsey, NJ 07446: Free brochure ■ Exposure meters and accessories. 201–825–4000.

Pentax Corporation, 35 Inverness Dr. East, Englewood, CO 80112: Free brochure ■ Exposure meters. 303–799–8000.

The Saunders Group, 21 Jet View Dr., Rochester, NY 14624: Free brochure ■ Exposure and flash meters, medium format dichroic enlargers and accessories, strobe brackets, tripods, and other equipment. 716–328–7800.

Sekonic, 40–11 Burt Dr., Deer Park, NY 11729: Free brochure ■ Standard and full-function digital readout exposure meters. 516–242–6801.

Sinar Bron, 17 Progress St., Edison, NJ 08820: Free information ■ A three-in-one meter that includes a color temperature meter for both flash and continuous light sources, a flash-duration meter, and a lux meter. 908–754–5800.

Smith-Victor Shepherd, Victor Corporation, 301 N. Colfax St., Griffith, IN 46319:

Free information ■ Light meters. 219–924–6136.

Film

Agfa Corporation, 100 Challenger Rd., Ridgefield Park, NJ 07660: Free information ■ Color slide, color print, and black-and-white film. 201–440–2500.

Eastman Kodak Company, Information Center, 343 State St., Rochester, NY 14650: Free information ■ Color slide, color print, black-and-white, infrared, and special process films. 800–462–6495.

Forte Film, GMI Photographic, Inc., 1776 New Highway, P.O. Drawer U, Farmingdale, NY 11735: Free information ■ Black-and-white film. 516–752–0066.

Fuji Photo Film USA, Inc., 555 Taxter Rd., Elmsford, NY 10523: Free information ■ Color slide, color print, and black-and-white film. 914–789–8100.

Ilford Photo Corporation, W. 70 Century Blvd., Paramus, NJ 07652: Free information ■ Chromogenic black-and-white film. 201–265–6000.

Konica USA, Inc., 440 Sylvan Ave., Englewood Cliffs, NJ 07632: Free information ■ Color print film. 201–568–3100.

MicroTec, P.O. Box 9424, San Diego, CA 92109: Free information ■ Film for the Minox camera and photo processing. 619–272–8820.

Polaroid Corporation, 549 Technology Square, Cambridge, MA 02139: Free information ■ Color slide, black-and-white slide, color print pack, and black-and-white pack film. 617–577–2000.

3M Photo Color Systems Division, 3M Center, Building 223–2S–05, St. Paul, MN 55144: Free information ■ Color slide and color print film. 800–695–FILM.

Filters

Aetna Optix, 44 Alabama Ave., Island Park, NY 11558: Free information ■ Rokunar filters and accessories.

Cambridge Camera Exchange, 7th Ave. & 13th St., New York, NY 10011: Free information ■ Cambron filters and accessories. 212–255–3744.

Cokin Creative Filters, P.O. Box 243, Whippany, NJ 07981: Free brochure ■ Cokin filters and accessories. 516–783–4880.

Eastman Kodak Company, Information Center, 343 State St., Rochester, NY 14650: Free information ■ Wratten filters and accessories. 800–462–6495.

Kenko Filters, 17801 Sky Park Cir., Irvine, CA 92714: Free information ■ Kenko filters and accessories. 714–251–9646.

Photo Systems, Inc., 7200 W. Huron River Dr., Dexter, MI 48130: Free information ■ Ambico filters and accessories.

Schneider Corporation, 400 Crossways Park Dr., Woodbury, NY 11797: Free information ■ Filters for black-and-white photography, neutral density filters, star and diffraction filters, lens shades, masks for matte boxes, lens reversal rings, tele-converters, and auto-extension tubes. 516–496–8500.

Tiffen Manufacturing, 90 Oser Ave., Hauppage, NY 11788: Free brochure ■ Filters and accessories. 516–272–2500.

Uniphot Corporation, P.O. Box 429, Woodside, NY 11377: Brochure $1 ■ Filters and accessories. 718–779–5700.

Flash Units & Lighting

Agnew Photo Products, P.O. Box 1474, Thousand Oaks, CA 91358: Free information ■ Easy-to-use bounce light system with reflector, fasteners, and tripod mount. 805–492–9756.

Bogen Photo Corporation, 565 E. Crescent St., P.O. Box 506, Ramsey, NJ 07446: Free information ■ Compact studio electronic flash systems and Metz Mecablitz flash units with a choice of power sources and system accessories. 201–818–9500.

Britek, Inc., 12704 Marquardt Ave., Santa Fe Springs, CA 90670: Free information ■ Professional studio flash and lighting equipment. 800–925–6258.

Brite White Lite, P.O. Box 26663, Richmond, VA 23261: Free brochure ■ Photographic equipment for creative control of light. 804–752–7647.

Paul C. Buff, Inc., 2725 Bransford Ave., Nashville, TN 37204: Free information ■ Compact, lightweight, studio flash equipment. 800–443–5542; 615–383–3982 (in TN).

Canon, One Canon Plaza, Lake Success, NY 11042: Free brochure ■ Flash units for the Canon cameras. 516–488–6700.

Chimera, 1812 Valtec Ln., Boulder, CO 80301: Free catalog ■ Portable lighting units and strobe accessories. 800–424–4075.

Courtenay Solaflash, 21 Jet View Dr., Rochester, NY 14624: Free catalog ■ Professional studio lighting equipment. 800–828–6214; 716–328–7800 (in NY).

Dyna-Lite, 436 Bryant St., San Francisco, CA 94107: Free information ■ Professional studio flash and lighting equipment. 800–833–0060.

Ken Hansen Photographic, 920 Broadway, New York, NY 10010: Catalog $3 ■ Lighting equipment. 212–673–7530.

Konica USA, Inc., 440 Sylvan Ave., Englewood Cliffs, NJ 07632: Free brochure ■ Konica flash equipment and accessories. 201–568–3100.

Larson Enterprises, Inc., 365 S. Mountainway Dr., P.O. Box 2150, Orem, UT 84058: Free information ■ Compact lighting equipment. 801–225–8088.

Minolta, 101 Williams Dr., Ramsey, NJ 07446: Free information ■ Flash units for Minolta cameras. 201–825–4000.

Multiblitz Lighting Company, HP Marketing Corporation, 16 Chapin Rd., Pine Brook, NJ 07058: Free information ■ Studio electronic flash equipment for amateurs and professionals. 201–808–9010.

Nikon, 1300 Walt Whitman Rd., Melville, NY 11747: Free brochure: Free brochure ■ Flash units with accessories. 800–NIKON–US.

Nikonos Cameras, 1300 Walt Whitman Rd., Melville, NY 11747: Free brochure: Free brochure ■ Electronic flash systems for general use and underwater. 800–NIKON–US.

Novatron of Dallas, Inc., 8230 Moberly Ln., Dallas, TX 75227: Free brochure ■ Studio flash equipment. 800–527–1595; 214–381–2153 (in TX).

Olympus Corporation, 145 Crossways Park, Woodbury, NY 11797: Free information ■ Flash systems for use with Olympus cameras. 800–221–3000.

Pentax Corporation, 35 Inverness Dr. East, Englewood, CO 80112: Free brochure ■

Electronic flash units for Pentax cameras. 303–799–8000.

Photogenic Machine Company, P.O. Box 3365, Youngstown, OH 44513: Free literature ■ Soft lighting accessory equipment for use with studio or small battery-operated strobes. 800–682–7668; 216–758–6658 (in OH).

Ricoh Consumer Products Group, 180 Passaic Ave., Fairfield, NJ 07004: Free brochure ■ Flash equipment for Ricoh cameras. 201–882–7762.

Sinar Bron, 17 Progress St., Edison, NJ 08820: Free information ■ A three-in-one FCC meter that includes a color temperature meter for both flash and continuous light sources, a flash-duration meter, and a lux meter. 908–754–5800.

Speedotron Corporation, 310 S. Racine Ave., Chicago, IL 60607: Free information ■ Lighting equipment for portrait photography. 312–421–4050.

Stage Lighting Distributors, Holt Dr., Stony Point, NY 10980: Free catalog ■ Lighting equipment. 800–228–0222; 914–947–3034 (in NY).

Sunpack Division of ToCAD America, Inc., Tower One, Continental Plaza, 401 Hackensack Ave., Hackensack, NJ 07601: Free information ■ Electronic flash equipment. 201–342–1817.

Testrite Instrument Company, Inc., 133 Monroe St., Newark, NJ 07105: Free catalog ■ Portable light box systems and accessories, lightweight aluminum and chrome easels, opaque projectors, and darkroom equipment. 201–589–6767.

Tristar Photo Industrial, Inc., 9960 Indiana Ave., Riverside, CA 92503: Free information ■ Studio lighting equipment, backgrounds, lightstands, brackets and holders, soft boxes, umbrellas, video camera supports, and other equipment. 714–351–8833.

Vivitar Corporation, 9350 DeSoto Ave., P.O. Box 2193, Chatsworth, CA 91311: Free brochure ■ Electronic flash equipment, cameras, lenses, and accessories. 818–700–9380.

Wedin Products, Inc., 15 W. 25th St., Los Angeles, CA 90007: Free information ■ Flash unit accessories. 213–749–6049.

Zone VI Studios, Inc., 698 Elm St., Newfane, VT 05345: Free catalog ■ Lighting accessories and darkroom equipment. 800–457–1114.

Photo Processing

A & I Color, 933 N. Highland Ave., Los Angeles, CA 90038: Free information ■ Kodachrome film processing. 800–544–3016.

ABC Photo Service, 9016 Prince William St., Manassas, VA 22110: Free information ■ Black-and-white and color processing. 703–369–2566.

Action Photos, 1801 Dairy Ashford, Houston, TX 77077: Free information ■ Giant 20-inch x 28-inch color posters from 35mm, 120, and other negatives. 713–556–5900.

Associated Photo Company, Box 14270, Cincinnati, OH 45250: Free information ■ Custom photo Christmas cards with name imprint. 513–421–6620.

Brown & Phillips Photo Lab, 3620 St. John Ave., Kansas City, MO 64123: Free information ■ Color photo enlargements. 816–231–5990.

Castle Chrome, P.O. Box 3724, Kingston, NY 12401: Free information ■ Custom Ilford Cibachrome prints from transparencies and Kodak Ektacolor prints from negatives. 914–246–6294.

ColorChrome, P.O. Box 330318, Seattle, WA 98133: Free information kit ■ Enlargements, developing and printing, and slide and other processing services. 206–364–2485.

Custom Chrome, 150 Fox St., P.O. Box 120, Elmira, NY 14902: Free information ■ Custom Cibachrome printing. 800–433–4145; 607–732–3967 (in NY).

Custom Photo, 684 Belmont Ave., Springfield, MA 01108: Free information ■ Custom Cibachrome II processing. 413–788–7780.

Custom Quality Studio, P.O. Box 4838, Chicago, IL 60680: Free information ■ Color film developing and processing. Includes jumbo prints, enlargements, slide duplication, black and white processing, duplication and copy services, and hand-coloring of prints.

Dale Laboratories, 2960 Simms St., Hollywood, FL 33020: Free price list and mailers ■ Processes slides, prints, and negatives from Kodacolor film. 800–327–1776.

Direct Photo Service, P.O. Box 6789, Hollywood, FL 33081: Free information ■ Custom color enlargements from color negatives and C41 process. 305–985–9787.

EMCAX Photo-finishing, P.O. Box 7383, Madison, WI 53707: Free information ■ Custom hand-printed Cibachrome enlargements. 608–244–4176.

The Enlargement Works, Inc., 316 N. Milwaukee St., Ste. 406, Milwaukee, WI 53202: Free information ■ Custom, handmade color enlargements from slides or negatives. 414–278–1210.

Fuji Anaheim Color Labs, 2665 Woodland Dr., Anaheim, CA 92802: Free information ■ Fuji color slide and print processing. 800–634–2960.

G-B Color Lab, P.O. Box 562, Hawthorne, NJ 07507: Free brochure ■ Cibachrome II color prints from slides. 201–427–0460.

General Color Corporation, 604 Brevard Ave., P.O. Box 70, Cocoa, FL 32923: Free brochure ■ Custom photo processing, with print sizes up to 24 x 30 inches. 800–321–1602.

Golden Color Engineering, 10201 Washington, Blvd., Culver City, CA 90232: Free information ■ Custom color-corrected enlargements from negatives and slides. 310–559–0111.

Holland Photo, 1221 S. Lamar, Austin, TX 78704: Free information ■ Custom Ilford Cibachrome prints from slides or transparencies. 800–477–4024.

Holleman Photo Labs, Inc., 3018 N. Lamar, Austin, TX 78705: Free information ■ Black and white, and color film processing, prints and enlargements, slide duplication, and other services. 412–441–4444.

Jet Color Lab, P.O. Box 330324, Seattle, WA 98133: Free price list ■ Developing, printing, and enlarging services. 206–364–1208.

Kelly Color, Box 576, Morgantown, NC 28655: Free information ■ Proofing, custom and machine processed candid and portrait photos, package assortments, copy and restoration services, custom montages and composites, and display transparencies for light boxes. 704–433–0934.

Lakeside Photography, P.O. Box 370027, Bears Station, Tampa, FL 33697: Free information ■ Cibachrome-II color enlargements. 813–968–9307.

LaserColor Laboratories, Fairfield Dr., P.O. Box 24614, West Palm Beach, FL 33416: Free information ■ Laser beam and computer-made color prints. 800–848–2018.

Magna Photo, 14416 Biscayne Blvd., Miami, FL 33181: Free information ■ Custom, hand-made color enlargements and black and white film processing. 305–947–7272.

Master Art & Framing, 24001 Alicia Pkwy., Mission Viejo, CA 92691: Free information ■ Transfers photographs to art canvas, resulting in canvas photos that resemble oil paintings. 714–855–3003.

Melrose Photographics, 50 E. Butler Ave., Ambler, PA 19002: Free information ■ Custom Cibachrome enlargements from 35mm slides. 215–646–4022.

MicroTec, P.O. Box 9424, San Diego, CA 92109: Free information ■ Minox format film processing and film for the Minox camera. 619–272–8820.

Minox Processing Laboratories, P.O. Box 1041, New Hyde Park, NY 11040: Free information ■ Sub-miniature film processing. 800–645–8172; 516–437–5750 (in NY).

Mystic Color Lab, P.O. Box 144, Mystic, CT 06355: Free information ■ Processes black-and-white and color print film, Kodachrome and Ektachrome slide and movie film, and Kodacolor 35mm, 110, 126, and disc film. 800–367–6061.

PML Film Processing, P.O. Box 337, Menomonie, WI 54751: Free information ■ Professional black and white film processing and custom services. 715–235–2522.

Post-Pix Custom Postcard Label Company, P.O. Box 753, Brea, CA 92622: Free information ■ Makes postcards from photos. 714–529–1152.

Professional Color Labs, 306 W. 1st Ave., Roselle, NJ 07203: Free information ■ Custom photo processing. 908–241–3030.

Pro Photo Labs, 213–219 S. Tyler Ave., P.O. Drawer 777, Lakeland, FL 33802: Free price list ■ Film developing, enlarging, and other custom services. 800–237–6429; 800–282–8182 (in FL).

Shooters of U.S.A. Lab, P.O. Box 8640, Rolling Meadows, IL 60008: Free information ■ Custom color enlargements. 708–956–1010.

Silver Image, 4248 Forest Park Blvd., St. Louis, MO 63108: Free information ■ Black and white negative and print processing. 800–289–9906.

The Slideprinter, P.O. Box 9506, Denver, CO 80209: Free information ■ Custom color prints and enlargements from slides.

Sunset Color Lab, P.O. Box 46145, Los Angeles, CA 90046: Free price list ■ Color film processing and custom color prints from color transparencies and negatives.

Unique Photo, 451 S. Jefferson St., Orange, NJ 07050: Free information ■ Kodak, Agfa, Ilford, and Fuji film processing. 201–673–0100.

Photo Restoration

All Print Images, 2620 S. Parker Rd., Aurora, CO 80014: Free brochure ■ Reproduces old pictures from tintypes and daguerreotypes, and other restoration services. 303–755–9509.

Deveraux Photo Restoration, 200 W. 57th St., New York, NY 10019: Free information ■ Restoration services for photos, daguerreotypes, tin photographs, or glass negatives. 212–245–1720.

Elbinger Laboratories, Inc., 220 Albert St., East Lansing, MI 48823: Brochure $2 ■ Archival reproduction of photographs in sepia, oil coloring, and black-and-white. 517–332–1430.

Kelly Color, Box 576, Morgantown, NC 28655: Free information ■ Restoration and copy services, proofing, custom and machine-processed candids and portraits, package assortments, custom montages and composites, and display transparencies for light boxes. 704–433–0934.

Lexington Lensmasters, 1702 Main St., Lexington, MO 64067: Free information with long SASE ■ Photo restoration services. 816–259–2171.

Modernage Photographic Services, 150 Fulton St., New York, NY 10038: Free information with long SASE ■ Photo restoration services. 212–227–4767.

Retail Stores

AAA Camera Exchange, Inc., 43 7th Ave., New York, NY 10011: Free information ■ Cameras, darkroom equipment and accessories, and other equipment. 212–242–5800.

Abe's of Maine Cameras, 1957–61 Coney Island Ave., Brooklyn, NY 11223: Free information ■ Photography equipment and accessories. 718–645–1878.

Abner's by Mail, 5363 Central Ave., St. Petersburg, FL 33710: Free information ■ Camera equipment and accessories. 800–446–4148.

Adorama, 42 W. 18th St., New York, NY 10011: Catalog $1 ■ Photography, darkroom equipment and underwater photo equipment. 212–741–0052.

Alfred O's Cameras, 916 Gravier St., New Orleans, LA 70112: Free information ■ Cameras and accessories, movie and studio equipment, binoculars, and projectors. 504–523–2421.

Alkit Pro Camera, Inc., 222 Park Ave. South, New York, NY 10003: Free information ■ Camera equipment and accessories. 800–950–2500; 212–674–1515 (in NY).

All Seasons Camera, 5 Harvard Ln., P.O. Box 111, Hastings-on-Hudson, NY 10706: Free information with long SASE ■ Cameras, lenses and accessories, filters, enlargers and projectors, slide duplicators, tripods, copy equipment, flash and lighting equipment, cases, and books. 914–478–0931.

B & H Photo, 119 W. 17th St., New York, NY 10011: Free price list ■ Photo equipment and accessories. 212–807–7474.

Beach Camera of Maine, 203 Rt. 22 East, Greenbrook, NJ 08812: Free information ■ Photography equipment, binoculars, radar detectors, and video equipment. 908–424–1103.

Beach Photo & Video, Inc., 604 Main St., Daytona Beach, FL 32118: Free information ■ Photography equipment and supplies. 800–876–2115; 800–874–2115 (in FL).

Bergen County Camera, 270 Westwood Ave., Westwood, NJ 07675: Free information ■ Photography equipment, cameras, and accessories. 201–664–4113.

Berger Brothers Camera Exchange, 209 Broadway, Amityville, NY 11701: Free information ■ Photography equipment, cameras, and accessories. 800–262–4160.

Bi-Rite Photo & Electronics, 15 E. 30th St., New York, NY 10016: Free information ■ Cameras, darkroom equipment and accessories, binoculars and telescopes, and underwater photography equipment. 800–223–1970; 212–685–2130 (in NY).

Bromwell Marketing, 3 Alleghany Center, Pittsburgh, PA 15212: Free catalog ■ Large-format view cameras, lenses, tripods, and accessories. 412–321–4118.

Brooklyn Camera Exchange, 549 E. 26th St., Brooklyn, NY 11210: Free information ■ New and used cameras and accessories, and other equipment and supplies. 718–462–2892.

Cambridge Camera Exchange, Inc., 7th Ave. & 13th St., New York, NY 10011: Free catalog ■ Photography equipment and supplies. 212–675–8600.

Camera One of Sarasota, Inc., 1918 Robinhood St., Sarasota, FL 34231: Free information ■ Cameras, lenses and accessories, filters, enlargers and projectors, binoculars, tripods, cases, and books. 800–759–1302.

Cameras & Electronics of New Jersey & Maine, 982 River Rd., Edgewater, NJ 07020: Free information ■ Photography equipment, supplies, and accessories. 201–886–7400.

Camera Traders, Ltd., 1873 Ocean Pkwy., Brooklyn, NY 11223: Free information ■ Cameras, lenses and accessories, filters, enlargers and projectors, slide duplicators, tripods, copy equipment, flash and lighting equipment, cases, and books. 718–336–6667.

Camera World, 4619 W. Market St., Greensboro, NC 27407: Catalog $1 ■ Photo equipment and supplies for still, movie, video, and underwater photography. Other items include darkroom accessories and equipment. 800–634–0556.

Central Camera Company, 230 S. Wabash Ave., Chicago, IL 60604: Free information ■ Photography equipment and accessories. 800–421–1899; 312–427–5580 (in IL).

Charlotte Camera Brokers, Inc., 2400 Park Rd., Charlotte, NC 28203: Free information ■ Photography equipment, cameras and lenses, and other accessories. 704–339–0084.

Colonial Camera Shops, 104 W. Burlington, LaGrange, IL 60525: Free information ■ Photography equipment and accessories. 800–356–2748; 800–235–3422 (in IL).

Columbus Camera Group, Inc., 55 E. Blake, Columbus, OH 43202: Free information ■ Photography equipment and supplies. 614–267–0686.

Competitive Camera Corporation, 363 7th Ave., New York, NY 10001: Free information ■ Photography equipment and supplies. 212–868–9175.

Dury's Photographic, 103 White Bridge Rd., Nashville, TN 37209: Free information ■ Includes new and used cameras and accessories, and other equipment. 615–356–3275.

Executive Photo & Electronics, 120 W. 31st St., New York, NY 10001: Free information ■ Photography and video equipment, accessories, and supplies, and other electronics. 212–947–5295.

Fields & Views, Inc., P.O. Box 132, Old Catham, NY 12136: Free catalog ■ Wista cameras and accessories. 212–779–1471.

Focus Camera, Inc., 4419 13th Ave., Brooklyn, NY 11219: Catalog $3 ■ Save from 20 to 50 percent on cameras and darkroom equipment. 718–871–7608.

47th Street Photo, Mail Order Department, 455 Smith St., Brooklyn, NY 11231: Catalog $2 ■ Photography equipment, video equipment, and accessories. 800–221–7774.

FotoCell, Inc., 49 W. 23rd St., New York, NY 10010: Free information ■ Binoculars, equipment for photographers, and other equipment. 212–924–7474.

Foto Electric Supply Company, 31 Essex St., New York, NY 10002: Free information ■ Save up to 30 percent on cameras, lenses, accessories, and darkroom equipment. 212–673–5222.

Frank's Highland Park Camera, 5715 N. Figueroa St., Los Angeles, CA 90042: Catalog $3 ■ Cameras, darkroom equipment and accessories, equipment for underwater photography, video equipment, and books. 213–255–0123.

Freestyle, 5124 Sunset Blvd., Los Angeles, CA 90027: Free information ■ Photography equipment, supplies, accessories, and darkroom equipment. 213–660–3460.

Ghitelman Cameras, Inc., 166 5th Ave., New York, NY 10010: Free information ■ Photography equipment and supplies. 212–924–3020.

Gould Trading, 7 E. 17th St., New York, NY 10003: Free information ■ Professional equipment and accessories and books and videos. 212–243–2308.

Helix, 310 S. Racine Ave., Chicago, IL 60607: Free catalog ■ Cameras and accessories, darkroom equipment and supplies, video equipment, underwater equipment and accessories. 800–621–6471.

Hirsch Photo, 699 3rd Ave., New York, NY 10017: Free information ■ New and used cameras and accessories, optical equipment, darkroom equipment and supplies, and other equipment. 800–223–7957.

W.B. Hunt Company, Inc., 100 Main St., Melrose, MA 02176: Free information ■ Cameras and accessories, other optical items, darkroom equipment, and studio accessories. 617–662–6685.

Jack's Camera Shop, 300 E. Main, Muncie, IN 47305: Free information ■ New and used photography equipment and supplies. 317–282–0204.

KEH Camera Brokers, P.O. Box 94065, Atlanta, GA 30377: Free catalog ■ Cameras and accessories. 404–892–5522.

Ken-Mar Camera & Video, 6502 Jericho Tpk., Commack, NY 11725: Free information ■ Camera equipment and accessories, binocular, and video equipment. 800–864–0513; 516–482–1025 (in NY).

KOH'S Camera Sales & Service, Inc., 2 Heitz Pl., Hicksville, NY 11801: Free information ■ Cameras and accessories, studio items, and other optical equipment. 516–933–9790.

Jim Kuehl & Company, 8527 University Blvd., Des Moines, IA 50325: Free information ■ Leica cameras and accessories, and other photogaphic and optical equipment. 515–225–0110.

Le Camera, 4040 Quaker Bridge Rd., Mercerville, NJ 08619: Free information ■ Camera equipment and accessories. 609–588–9090.

Mesa Photo Supply, 1900 E. University Dr., Mesa, AZ 85203: Free information ■ Cameras and accessories, other equipment, and supplies. 602–833–6174.

Mibro Cameras, 64 W. 36th St., New York, NY 10018: Free information ■ Camera equipment and accessories. 800–223–0322; 212–967–2353 (in NY).

Midwest Photo Exchange, 3313 N. High St., Columbus, OH 43202: Free information ■ Camera equipment and accessories, darkroom equipment, lighting accessories, and collectible equipment. 614–261–1264.

Myrick Photographic, 598 Fremont St., Monterey, CA 93940: Free information ■ Photography equipment and supplies, darkroom equipment and supplies, and other optical equipment. 408–649–1900.

Olden Camera & Lens Company, Inc., 1265 Broadway, New York, NY 10001: Catalog 50¢ ■ Photography equipment, supplies, accessories, video equipment, computers, and electronics. 212–725–1234.

Peach State Photo, 1706 Chantilly Dr., Atlanta, GA 30324: Catalog $3 (refundable) ■ Camera and video equipment. 404–633–2699.

Pentagon Camera, 2900 Washington Blvd., Arlington, VA 22201: Catalog $2 (refundable) ■ Photo accessories and equipment. 703–524–5864.

Photo-Graphic Systems, 412 Central SE, Albuquerque, NM 87102: Free information ■ Used and new photography equipment and supplies. 505–247–9780.

Photron Marketing, Inc., 157 W. 30th St., New York, NY 10001: Free information ■ Cameras, other equipment, and accessories. 212–868–9455.

Porter's Camera Store, Inc., Box 628, Cedar Falls, Iowa 50613: Free catalog ■ Photo equipment and accessories, darkroom equipment, and other novelties and accessories. 800–553–2001.

Reimers Photo Materials Company, 300 E. Bay St., Milwaukee, WI 53207: Free information ■ Photography equipment and supplies. Includes used and new cameras and accessories. 800–236–5435; 414–744–4471 (in WI).

Stephen Shuart Photography, 102 Pine Ave., Kane, PA 16735: Free information ■ Photography equipment and supplies, and hard-to-find instruction guides, catalogs, and brochures. 814–837–7786.

Smile Photo, 29 W. 35th St., New York, NY 10001: Free information ■ Photography and video equipment, accessories, and supplies. 212–967–5900.

Solar Cine Products, Inc., 4247 S. Kedzie Ave., Chicago, IL 60632: Catalog $1.50 ■ Photography equipment and supplies. 312–254–8310.

Supreme Camera & Video, 2123 Utica Ave., Brooklyn, NY 11234: Free information ■ Cameras, accessories, and supplies at discount prices. 800–332–2661; 718–692–4110 (in NY).

Stan Tamarkin Cameras, 198 Amity Rd., Woodbridge, CT 06525: Free price list ■ Leica and Hasselblad camera systems and accessories. 800–289–5342.

Testrite Instrument Company, Inc., 133 Monroe St., Newark, NJ 07105: Free catalog ■ Photography equipment and accessories for the darkroom and studio. 201–589–6767.

Tri-State Camera, 160 Broadway, New York, NY 10038: Free information ■ Photography equipment and supplies. 212–349–2555.

University Camera, Inc., 2030 I–85 Service Rd., Durham, NC 27705: Free information ■ Photography equipment and supplies. 919–477–7225.

The Wall Street Camera, 82 Wall St., New York, NY 10005: Catalog $2.95 (refundable with $50 purchase) ■ Photography equipment and accessories. 212–344–0011.

Westside Camera, Inc., 2400 Broadway, New York, NY 10024: Catalog $3 (refundable) ■ Cameras, accessories, film, and darkroom equipment. 212–877–8760.

Woodmere Camera, Inc., 337 Merrick Rd., Lynbrook, NY 11563: Free information ■ Photography equipment and accessories. 516–599–6013.

Zone VI Studios, Inc., 698 Elm St., Newfane, VT 05345: Free catalog ■ Picture-taking equipment, lighting accessories, and darkroom equipment. 800–457–1114.

Slides

Cornell Laboratory of Ornithology, Visual Services, 159 Sapsucker Woods Rd., Ithaca, NY 14850: Free brochure ■ Color slides of North American birds. 607–254–2450.

Reel 3-D Enterprises, Inc., P.O. Box 2368, Culver City, CA 90231: Free information ■

Stereo slide mounts and cardboard slip-in slide mounts. 310–837–2368.

Visuals, P.O. Box 381848, Miami, FL 33138: Free list ■ Worldwide travel slides from almost 200 countries.

Worldwide, 7427 Washburn, Minneapolis, MN 55423: Catalog $1 ■ Travel slides about the United States, foreign countries, historic and scenic sites, nature settings, and others. 612–869–6482.

Storage & Filing Systems

Conservation Materials, Ltd., 1165 Marietta Way, Sparks, NV 89431: Free information ■ Archival supplies for documents and photographics. 702–331–0582.

Light Impressions, 439 Monroe Ave., Rochester, NY 14607: Free catalog ■ Books on photography and supplies for archival storage of negatives and prints. 800–828–6216.

Perma-Saf, P.O. Box 320, Denville, NJ 07834: Free information ■ Heavy-duty plastic pages for archival storage of 35mm slides and negatives.

RNI Marketing, P.O. Drawer 638, Ocala, FL 32678: Free information ■ Light- and heavyweight polyethylene pages for storing, organizing, and displaying slides, prints, and negatives. 800–451–6789; 800–622–0303 (in FL).

TLC, 9800 Topanga Cyn Blvd., Chatsworth, CA 91311: Catalog $2 ■ Archival storage systems, hand-cut mats, frames, equipment cases, slide viewers and light boxes, and flash accessories. 818–998–8889.

20th Century Plastics, Inc., 3628 Crenshaw Blvd., Los Angeles, CA 90051: Free catalog ■ Plastic pages to protect, organize, and display slides, prints, and negatives. 800–421–4662.

University Products, P.O. Box 101, Holyoke, MA 01041: Free information ■ Archival supplies for document and photographic storage and preservation. 413–532–9431.

Tripods

Bogen Photo Corporation, 565 E. Crescent St., P.O. Box 506, Ramsey, NJ 07446: Free information ■ Tripods. 201–818–9500.

Cullman, 1776 New Hwy., P.O. Drawer U, Farmingdale, NY 11735: Free information ■ Tripods. 516–752–0066.

GMI Photographic, 1776 New Hwy., P.O. Drawer U, Farmingdale, NY 11735: Free brochure ■ Cullman tripods. 516–752–0053.

Karl Heitz, Inc., P.O. Box 427, Woodside, NY 11377: Free brochure ■ Gitzo monopods. 718–565–0004.

The Saunders Group, 21 Jet View Dr., Rochester, NY 14624: Free brochure ■ Tripods, exposure and flash meters, enlargers and accessories, strobe brackets, and other equipment. 716–328–7800.

Slik America, 3 Westchester Plaza, Elmsford, NY 10523: Free information ■ Slik adjustable tripods and accessories. 914–347–2223.

Tracks Walking Staffs, 4000 1st Ave. South, Seattle, WA 98134: Free information ■ Telescoping sectioned walking staffs that convert to a camera monopod. 800–527–1527.

Velbon, 2433 Moreton St., Torrance, CA 90505: Free information ■ Tripods. 213–530–5446.

Underwater Photography Equipment

Adorama, 42 W. 18th St., New York, NY 10011: Catalog $1 ■ Underwater and other photo equipment. 212–741–0052.

B & H Photo, 119 W. 17th St., New York, NY 10011: Free price list ■ Underwater photo equipment. 212–807–7474.

Berry Scuba Company, 6674 Northwest Hwy., Chicago, IL 60631: Free catalog ■ Skin diving and scuba accessories and equipment, diving lights, and underwater camera equipment. 800–621–6019; 312–763–1626 (in IL).

Bi-Rite Photo & Electronics, 15 E. 30th St., New York, NY 10016: Free information ■ Equipment for underwater and other types of photography. 800–223–1970; 212–685–2130 (in NY).

Camera World, 4619 W. Market St., Greensboro, NC 27407: Catalog $1 ■ Equipment and supplies for still, movie, video, and underwater photography. 800–634–0556.

FotoCell, 49 W. 23rd St., New York, NY 10010: Free information ■ Underwater photo equipment. 212–924–7474.

Frank's Highland Park Camera, 5715 N. Figueroa St., Los Angeles, CA 90042: Catalog $3 ■ Cameras, darkroom equipment and accessories, and underwater photography equipment. 213–255–0123.

Fuji Photo Film USA, Inc., 555 Taxter Rd., Elmsford, NY 10523: Free information ■ Underwater camera equipment. 914–789–8100.

GMI Photographic, Inc., 1776 New Hwy., P.O. Drawer U, Farmingdale, NY 11735: Free information ■ Underwater cameras with electronic flash, close-up lenses, automatic wind and rewind, and built in film coding. 516–752–0053.

Helix, 310 S. Racine Ave., Chicago, IL 60607: Free catalog ■ Cameras, underwater photography equipment, darkroom supplies, and video equipment. 800–621–6471.

Ikelite Underwater Systems, 50 33rd St., Indianapolis, IN 46208: Catalog $1 ■ Underwater housings for most cameras. 317–923–4523.

Minolta, 101 Williams Dr., Ramsey, NJ 07446: Free information ■ Underwater camera equipment. 201–825–4000.

Nikon, 1300 Walt Whitman Rd., Melville, NY 11747: Free brochure ■ Underwater camera equipment and lenses. 800–NIKON–US.

Nikonos Cameras, 1300 Walt Whitman Rd., Melville, NY 11747: Free brochure ■ Underwater camera equipment and lenses. 800–NIKON–US.

Pioneer Marketing & Research, Inc., 216 Haddon Ave., Westmont, NJ 08108: Free information ■ Ewa-Marine underwater housings for cameras and video equipment. 800–257–7742; 609–854–2424 (in NJ).

Vivitar Corporation, 9350 DeSoto Ave., P.O. Box 2193, Chatsworth, CA 91311: Free brochure ■ Underwater camera equipment. 818–700–9300.

PINATAS

La Pinata, Number 2 Patio Market, Old Town, Albuquerque, NM 87104: Free brochure ■ Pinatas. 505–242–2400.

PINE CONES

Herbst Mountain Farms, 307 Number 9 Rd., Fletcher, NC 28732: Catalog $1 ■ Pine cones, pods, and potpourri.

International Manufacturing Company, P.O. Box 405, Lillian Springs, FL 32351: Catalog $1 ■ Pine cones, silk plants, trees and flower arrangements, flower arranging supplies, and other craft supplies. 904–875–2918.

Mountain Farms, Inc., 108 Candlewood Isle, New Fairfield, CT 06812: Catalog $1 ■ Pine cones, pods, potpourri supplies, and essential oils. 203–746–1842.

Nature Crafts, 164 Hillside Ave., Livingston, NJ 07039: Catalog $2 (refundable) ■ Pine cone crafting supplies.

J. Page Basketry, 820 Albee Rd. West, Nokomis, FL 34275: Free catalog ■ Pine needle and wheat weaving crafting supplies, dried and preserved flowers and herbs, basket-making supplies, and other craft accessories, tools, and books. 813–485–6730.

PLASTICS

Castolite, 4915 Dean, Woodstock, IL 60098: Catalog $2 ■ Liquid plastic, mold-making supplies and accessories, and how-to books. 815–338–4670.

Magic Systems, Inc., P.O. Box 23888, Tampa, FL 33623: Free information ■ Easy-to-use mold-making kits coloring materials, and plastic embedding materials. 813–886–5495.

PLATES, COLLECTIBLE

Churchills, Twelve Oaks Mall, Novi, MI 48377: Free information ■ Collectible plates by P. Buckley Moss, Fred Stone, Ray Day, Marty Bell, and Derk Hanson. 800–388–1141.

Collectibly Yours, 43 East Rt. 59, Spring Valley, NY 10977: Free information ■ Hummels, Rockwells, figurines, plates, collectible dolls, and gifts. 914–425–9244.

Danish Imports, 211 E. Main, Post, TX 79356: Free list ■ Commemorative plates. 806–495–2314.

Dexter & Company, 53 W. 49th St., New York, NY 10020: Free information ■ Collectible plates. 800–BUY–DEXT; 212–245–7460 (in NY).

Unicef, 1 Children's Blvd., P.O. Box 182233, Chattanooga, TN 37422: Free catalog ■ Stationery, postcards, gifts, and limited edition plates. 800–553–1200.

The Village Plate Collector, 217 King St., Box 1118, Cocoa, FL 32923: Free information ■ Limited edition plates. 800–752–8371; 407–636–6914 (in FL).

PLATFORM TENNIS

Cosom Sporting Goods, Grandview Ave., P.O. Box 10, Woodbury Heights, NJ 08097: Free information ■ Balls, nets, and paddles. 609–853–0300.

Moody & Company, P.O. Box 13, Milford, CT 06460: Free information ■ Paddles, balls, and nets. 800–243–4561; 203–878–1741 (in CT).

Nelson/Weather-Rite Products, Fuqua Sports, 14760 Santa Fe Trail Dr., Lenexa, KS 66215: Free information ■ Paddles, nets, and balls. 800–255–6061; 913–492–3200 (in KS).

PLAYGROUND EQUIPMENT

BigToys, 7717 New Market, Olympia, WA 98501: Free information ■ Playground equipment. 800–426–9788.

Cedar Works, Rt. 1, Box 640, Rockport, ME 04856: Free catalog ■ Wooden playsets for backyards and playgrounds. 800–233–7757.

Creative Playgrounds, Ltd., P.O. Box 10, McFarland, WI 53558: Free catalog ■ Heavy redwood playground equipment and picnic tables. 608–838–3326.

Florida Playground & Steel Company, 4701 S. 50th St., Tampa, FL 33619: Free brochure ■ Swings and other backyard/playground equipment. 800–822–4456; 813–247–2812 (in FL).

Gazebo & Porchworks, 728 9th Ave. SW, Puyallup, WA 98371: Catalog $2 ■ Outdoor swings and backyard play structures. 206–848–0502.

GYM-N-I Playgrounds, Inc., P.O. Box 310096, Laurel Bend, TX 78130: Free information ■ Modular playground structures, swing sets, and other equipment. 800–232–3398; 512–629–6000 (in TX).

Isis Innovations, 177 Thornton Dr., Hyannis, MA 02601: Free brochure ■ Playground furniture for backyard use. 508–790–5992.

PCA Industries, Inc., 5642 Natural Bridge, St. Louis, MO 63120: Free catalog ■ Aluminum playground equipment. 800–727–8180.

Rainbow Play Systems, Inc., 5980 Rainbow Pkwy., Prior Lake, MN 55372: Free information ■ Wooden play systems for backyards. 612–447–2553.

Victor Stanley, Inc., P.O. Box 144, Dunkirk, MD 20754: Free information ■ Playground equipment and outdoor furniture. 800–368–2573; 301–855–8300 (in MD).

Sun Designs, P.O. Box 6, Oconomowoc, WI 53066: Free information with long SASE ■ Idea books and plans for building gazebos, bridges, doghouses, furniture, swings and other outdoor play structures, and birdhouses. 414–567–4255.

Ultra Play Systems, Inc., 425 Sycamore St., Anderson, IN 46016: Free information ■ Outdoor gym equipment for playgrounds. 800–458–5872; 317–643–5315 (in IN).

Wood Built of Wisconsin, Inc., P.O. Box 92, Janesville, WI 53547: Free catalog ■ Hardware kits for swing and slide sets. 800–475–5051.

Woodplay, P.O. Box 27904, Raleigh, NC 27611: Free catalog ■ Redwood backyard play sets. 800–982–1822.

Woodset, Inc., P.O. Box 2127, Waldorf, MD 20601: Free catalog ■ Backyard and playground structures. 800–638–9663.

Yards of Fun, Inc., P.O. Box 119, North Manchester, IN 46962: Free catalog ■ Backyard wooden swing sets and climbing gyms. 800–228–0471.

POLITICAL MEMORABILIA

Americana Resources, 18222 Flower Hill Way, Ste. 299A, Gaithersburg, MD 20879: Price list $2 ■ Political and presidential memorabilia, postcards, advertising memorabilia, photos, books, calendars and almanacs, newspapers, posters and prints, World War I and II items, Nixon and Watergate collectibles, and other Americana. 301–926–8663.

Don Beck Collectibles, P.O. Box 15350, Fort Wayne, IN 46885: Free information with long SASE ■ Political pins, tokens, flags, and ribbons; mechanical banks and toys; World's Fair items; war relics; and marbles, old pens, character toys and items, paintings, and bronzes. 219–486–3010.

The Campaign Headquarters, P.O. Box 6661, West Palm Beach, FL 33405: Free list with two 1st class stamps ■ Political memorabilia. 407–582–4705.

Political Matchcovers, 3417 Clayborne Ave., Alexandria, VA 22306: Free information ■ Political matchbook covers. 703–768–3932.

Presidential Coin & Antique Company, 6550 Little River Tpk., Alexandria, VA 22312: Free catalog ■ Political memorabilia, medals, and tokens; antiques and coins; and other Americana. 703–354–5454.

Rex Stark-Americana, 49 Wethersfield Rd., Bellingham, MA 02019: Catalog subscription (3 issues) $5 ■ Political memorabilia, posters, flags, needlework, textiles, china, needlework, folk art, toys, and paintings. 508–966–0994.

PORCELAIN COLLECTIBLES

Collectibly Yours, 43 East Rt. 59, Spring Valley, NY 10977: Free information ■ Hummels, Rockwells, figurines, plates, collectible dolls, and gifts. 914–425–9244.

Down's Collectors Showcase, 2200 S. 114th St., P.O. Box 27904, Milwaukee, WI 53227: Free catalog ■ Figurines, mugs, miniatures and racks for collecting, thimbles, novelty items, music boxes, mugs and steins, country items, plates, art, and porcelain pieces. 800–558–4200.

Lenox Collections Gifts, One Lenox Center, P.O. Box 3029, Langhome, PA 19092: Free catalog ■ Porcelain sculptures, china, and crystal. 800–233–1885.

Royal Copenhagen Porcelain, 603 Madison Ave., New York, NY 10001: Free brochure ■ Danish porcelain statuary by the suppliers to the Royal Danish Court since 1775. 800–223–1275; 212–759–6457 (in NY).

POSTCARDS

Aladin Stamps/Postcards, 2801 Kessler Blvd. East, Indianapolis, IN 46220: Free information with long SASE ■ Postcards. 317–255–8379.

Bernard Aolin Postcards, P.O. Box 330, Bronx, NY 10475: Free information with long SASE ■ Postcards. 212–671–4575.

J.C. Ballentine Postcards, Hatcher Point Mall, P.O. Box 761, Waycross, GA 31501: Free information with long SASE ■ Postcards. 912–285–3250.

Brooklyn Collectibles, 2569 W. 2nd St. Brooklyn, NY 11223: Free information with long SASE ■ Antique postcards, photographs, and related emphemera. 718–645–3743.

George & Ellen Budd Postcards, 6910 Tenderfoot Ln., Cincinnati, OH 45249: Free information with long SASE ■ Postcards. 513–489–0518.

William W. Burt Postcards, P.O. Box 24690, Kansas City, MO 64110: Free information with long SASE ■ Postcards. 816–444–5414.

Victor L. Cox Postcards, P.O. Box 66, Keymar, MD 21757: Free catalog ■ Postcards and collecting supplies, magazines, comics, sheet music, sports cards, and old newspapers. 410–775–0188.

Dave's New/Used Cards, 9114 Warner Rd., Haslett, MI 48840 Free information with long SASE ■ Postcards. 517–675–5474.

The Dekle's, 707 32nd Ct., Hollywood, FL 33021: Free information with long SASE ■ Postcards. 305–981–6857.

Sheldon Dobres Postcards, P.O. Box 1855, Baltimore, MD 21203: Price list $1 ■ Postcards. 410–486–6569.

Ward R. Duffey Postcards, 22 East Ave., Hagerstown, MD 21740: Free information with long SASE ■ Postcards. 301–797–8672.

East End Antiques, R. Paul Saylor, East Main St., Berlin, PA 15530: Free information with long SASE ■ Postcards. 814–267–3478.

Ed's Antiques, Edward C. Schultz, 1905 Sherwood St., Allentown, PA 18103: Free information with long SASE ■ Postcards. 215–867–8143.

John & Lynne Farr Postcards, P.O. Box 6086, Omaha, NE 68106: Free information with long SASE ■ Pre-1920 and other postcards. 402–334–0284.

Foreign Cards Ltd., P.O. Box 123, Guilford, CT 20320: Free catalog ■ Postcards from worldwide sources. 203–453–5813.

Tracy Garrett, P.O. Box 18000-52, Las Vegas, NV 89114: Free information with long SASE ■ Views, topicals, transportation, military, entertainment, and other postcards. 702–737–3218.

Gordie's Used Cards, 1235 Vista Superba, Glendale, CA 91205: Free information with long SASE ■ Automobile-related postcards. 818–246–6686.

Clay Griffin Postcards, 1100 Merriman Rd., Akron, OH 44303: Free information with long SASE ■ Postcards. 216–867–7290.

John & Betty Henel, 79 Fruehauf Ave., Snyder, NY 14226: Free information with long SASE ■ Postcards from worldwide locations. 716–839–4174.

Frank E. Howard Postcards, 856 Charlotte St., Macon, GA 31206: Free information with long SASE ■ Postcards. 912–788–1514.

Fred N. Kahn Postcards, 258 Stratford Rd., Asheville, NC 28804: Free information with long SASE ■ Postcards. 704–252–6507.

Bob Karrer Postcards, P.O. Box 6094, Alexandria, VA 22306: Free information with long SASE ■ Panama Canal and Canal Zone postcards. 703–360–5105.

Alan R. Lavendler Postcards, 139 E. Clinton St., New Bedford, MA 02740: Free information with long SASE ■ Postcards. 508–997–6227.

Fred H. Lego Postcards, 6506 Kipling Pkwy., Forestville, MD 20747: Free information with long SASE ■ Postcards. 301–735–6556.

Dick Lightle Postcards, P.O. Box 2562, Kansas City, KS 66110: Free information with long SASE ■ Postcards. 913–334–3186.

Ed McAllister Postcards, 3413 W. Jefferson, Joliet, IL 60435: Free information with long SASE ■ Postcards. 815–725–2504.

Mac's Used Cards, 3306 Ave. D, Fort Worth, TX 76106: Free information with long SASE ■ Postcards. 817–535–3961.

Mary Martin Postcards, 231 Rock Ridge Rd., Millersville, MD 21108: Free brochure with long SASE ■ Postcard storage boxes and postcards that include United States views, topicals, greetings, foreign cards, and rarities. 410–987–7550.

National Postcard Exchange, 225 3rd St., Macon, GA 31202: Free information with long SASE ■ Foreign postcards, topicals, and postcards from the early 1900s to the present. 912–743–8951.

Terry & Noreen Pavey Postcards, P.O. Box 10614, Glendale, AZ 85315: Free information with long SASE ■ Postcards. 602–439–2156.

William & Patti Peterson Postcards, P.O. Box 398, Plainfield, CT 06374: Free information with long SASE ■ Postcards. 203–564–1494.

Postcards Etc., P.O. Box 4318, Thousand Oaks, CA 91359: Free information with long SASE ■ Postcards. 805–497–1725.

Postcards International, P.O. Box 2930, New Haven, CT 06515: Free information with long SASE ■ Postcards. 203–865–0814.

Michael G. Price Postcards, P.O. Box 7071, Ann Arbor, MI 48107: Free information with long SASE ■ Postcards. 313–668–7388.

Arlene Raskin Postcards, 2580 Ocean Pkwy., Apt. 2L, Brooklyn, NY 11235: Free information with long SASE ■ Postcards. 718–998–1910.

Mike E. Rasmussen Postcards, P.O. Box 726, Marina, CA 93933: Free information with long SASE ■ Postcards. 408–384–5460.

Ruggiero's Postcards, 359 Silver Sands Rd., East Haven, CT 06512: Free information with long SASE ■ Postcards and stamps. 203–469–7083.

C. Michael Smith Postcards, P.O. Box 12092, Huntsville, AL 35815: Free information with long SASE ■ Postcards. 205–498–3834.

Shirley Stonesifer Postcards, 483 Sullivan Rd., Westminster, MD 21157: Free information with long SASE ■ Postcards. 410–775–0188.

Tippett Postcards, Inc., P.O. Box 49257, Sarasota, FL 33578: Free information ■ Postcards. 813–377–8886.

JoAnn Van Scotter Postcards, 208 E. Lincoln St., Mt. Morris, IL 61054: Free information with long SASE ■ Postcards. 815–734–6971.

Harry A. Victor Postcards, 1408 18th Ave., San Francisco, CA 94122: Free list with long SASE and two first class stamps ■

Postcards that include the poster series, railroads, cigarettes, foods, beverages, and other subjects. 415–664–4286.

Martha J. Walton Postcards, 707 Collegewood Dr., Ypsilanti, MI 48197: Free information with long SASE ■ Postcards. 313–482–8354.

Michael B. Wasserberg Postcards, 1025 Country Club Dr., Margate, FL 33063: Free information with long SASE ■ Postcards. 305–972–3789.

Writewell Company, 5850 W. 80th St., Indianapolis, IN: 46278: Free information ■ Loose-leaf postcard albums with leather-grained vinyl padded covers and optional personalization. 317–871–6710.

POTPOURRI

Caswell-Massey Company, Ltd., Catalog Division, 100 Enterprise Pl., Dover, DE 19901: Catalog $1 ■ Potpourri and pomander mixes, dried flowers, and herb plants. 800–326–0500.

Farmer's Daughter, P.O. Box 1071, Nags Head, NC 27959: Catalog $2 ■ Country decor accessories, pottery potpourri burner, replacement candles, and electric candle lamps. 800–423–2196.

Frontier Cooperative Herbs, P.O. Box 299, Norway, IA 52318: Free information ■ Potpourris and herbs, essential oils, and fragrances. 319–227–7991.

The Gathered Herb & Greenhouse, 12114 N. State Rd., Otisville, MI 48463: Catalog $2 ■ Potpourri supplies, herbs and herb teas, perennials, and dried flowers. 313–631–6572.

Good Hollow Greenhouse & Herbarium, Rt. 1, Box 116, Taft, TN 38488: Catalog $1 ■ Herbs, perennials, wildflowers, scented geraniums, essential oils and potpourris, teas, and dried herbs and spices. 615–433–7640.

Hartman's Herb Farm, Old Dana Rd., Barre, MA 01005: Catalog $1 ■ Potpourris, sachets, bath herbs and oils, herbal pillows, dried flowers, spices, teas, essential oils, and pomander balls. 508–355–2015.

Heaven's Herbal Creations, 8202 West M.L. Ave., Kalamazoo, MI 49009: Catalog $2 ■ Potpourris, herbal body care products, exclusive scents, and essential oils. 616–375–2934.

Herb & Spice Collection, P.O. Box 118, Norway, IA 52318: Free catalog ■ Potpourris, culinary herbs and spices, herbs and teas, and natural herbal body care products. 800–365–4372.

International Manufacturing Company, P.O. Box 405, Lillian Springs, FL 32351: Catalog $1 ■ Silk plants, trees, flower arrangements and arranging supplies, potpourris, and other craft supplies. 904–875–2918.

Little Shepherds, 9658 W. Chatfield Ave., Littleton, CO 80123: Catalog $1 ■ Wholesale potpourris, incense, aromatic oils, bath salts, and spices. 303–933–1296.

Keeping Room & Gardens, P.O. Box 64, Williston Park, NY 11596: Free brochure ■ Flower and herb potpourris. 800–866–1022; 516–294–4257 (in NY).

Meadow Everlastings, 149 Shabbona Rd., Malta, IL 60150: Catalog $2 (refundable) ■ Dried flowers, wreath kits, and potpourri supplies. 815–825–2539.

Mountain Farms, Inc., 108 Candlewood Isle, New Fairfield, CT 06812: Catalog $1 ■ Potpourri materials, essential oils, and other supplies. 203–746–1842.

Nature's Finest, P.O. Box 10311, Burke, VA 22009: Catalog $2.50 (refundable) ■ Dried flowers, herbs, spices, oils, fixatives, bottles, books, equipment, and other potpourri supplies.

Petals & Buds, 10798 County Rd. 3101, Winona, TX 75792: Free information ■ Dried rose buds in pink, burgundy, yellow, red-orange, and white; potpourris; and rose petals. 903–877–3724.

Raven's Nest, 4539 Iroquois Trail, Duluth, GA 30136: Catalog $1 ■ Potpourris and extracts, herbs, spices, essential oils, and herbal gifts.

San Francisco Herb Company, 250 14th St., San Francisco, CA 94103: Free catalog ■ Potpourri supplies and cooking herbs and spices. 800–227–4530; 800–622–0768 (in CA).

Tom Thumb Workshops, P.O. Box 357, Mappsville, VA 23407: Catalog $1 ■ Potpourris, herbs and spices, essential oils, dried flowers, and craft supplies. 804–824–3507.

The Ultimate Herb & Spice Shoppe, 111 Azalea, P.O. Box 395, Duenweg, MO 64841: Catalog $2 ■ Herbs and spices, tea blends, potpourris, soaps, and sundries. 417–782–0457.

Well-Sweep Herb Farm, 317 Mt. Bethel Rd., Port Murray, NJ 07865: Catalog $2 ■ Potpourri and pomander mixes, dried flowers, and herb plants. 908–852–5390.

PRINTING PRESSES

Barco, 237 S. Evergreen, Bensenville, IL 60106: Catalog $2 (refundable) ■ Type fonts, rubber stamps, and other supplies. 708–766–1230.

Dickerson Press Company, P.O. Box 8, South Haven, MI 49090: Free information ■ Printing presses for etching, lithography, and intaglio stone or plate reproductions. 616–637–4251.

Graphic Chemical & Ink Company, P.O. Box 27, Villa Park, IL 60181: Free catalog ■ Printing supplies. 708–832–6004.

Kelsey Presses, 30 Cross St., P.O. Box 941, Meriden, CT 06450: Catalog $1 ■ Printing presses, hot stamping equipment, and supplies. 203–235–1695.

Turnbaugh Printers Supply, 104 S. Sporting Hill Rd., Mechanicsburg, PA 17055: Catalog $1 ■ Type fonts, printing presses, and supplies. 717–737–5637.

PROSPECTING & ROCKHOUNDING

Alpha Supply, 1225 Hollis St., Box 2133, Bremerton, WA 98310: Catalog $1 (refundable) ■ Prospecting and rockhounding equipment and supplies, jewelry-making tools, gem finishing equipment, and metal detectors. 206–377–5629.

B & J Rock Shop, 14744 Manchester Rd., Ballwin, MO 63011: Catalog $3 ■ Rockhounding equipment and supplies, quartz crystals, amethyst crystal clusters, Brazilian agate nodules, and other imported and domestic stones. 314–394–4567.

Bourget Bros., 1636 11th St., Santa Monica, CA 90404: Catalog $5 ■ Rockhounding, treasure hunting, and prospecting equipment; gemstones and cabochons; wax patterns; beads and bead-stringing supplies; and lapidary tools and equipment. 800–828–3024; 310–450–6556 (in CA).

Cal-Gold, 2569 E. Colorado Blvd., Pasadena, CA 91107: Free catalog ■ Metal detectors, mining and geology equipment, maps, books, and ultraviolet light equipment. 818–792–6161.

Contempo Lapidary, 12273 Foothill Blvd., Sylmar, CA 91342: Free information ■ Rockhounding and lapidary equipment. 800–356–2441; 818–899–1973 (in CA).

Crystallite Corporation, 13449 Beach Ave., Marina Del Ray, CA 90291: Free catalog ■ Rockhounding and lapidary equipment. 310–821–6632.

D & K Prospecting Headquarters, 13809 Southeast Division, Portland, OR 97236: Free information ■ Prospecting equipment and supplies, metal detectors, and accessories. 800–542–4653; 503–761–1521 (in OR).

E.F. Domine Company, Inc., Greenwood Ave., Tracy, MN 56175: Free literature ■ Mining loaders, gold placers and concentrators, conveyors, and spinners. 507–629–3758.

East Coast Prospecting & Mining Supplies, Rt. 3, Box 321J, Ellijay, GA 30540: Free information ■ Dredges, high bankers, tumblers, micro-sluices, gold wheels, sluice boxes, trommels, and lapidary equipment and supplies. 404–276–4433.

Ebersole Lapidary Supply, Inc., 11417 West Hwy. 54, Wichita, KS 67209: Catalog $2 ■ Rockhounding equipment and supplies, lapidary and jewelry-making tools, findings, mountings, cabochons, and rocks. 316–722–4771.

Eloxite Corporation, 806 10th St., Wheatland, WY 82201: Catalog 75¢ ■ Prospecting and rockhounding equipment, cut stones, beads, cabochons, and clock-making supplies and equipment. 307–322–3050.

Fisher Research Laboratory, 200 W. Wilmott Rd., Los Banos, CA 93635: Free information ■ Metal detectors. 209–826–3292.

Fortyniner Mining Supply, 16238 Lakewood Blvd., Bellflower, CA 90706: Free information ■ Gold dredges, dry washers, treasure hunting supplies, metal detectors, magazines, and books. 310–925–2271.

Golddigger, 253 N. Main, Moab, UT 84532: Catalog $1 ■ Prospecting equipment and metal detectors. 801–259–5150.

Graves Company, 1800 Andrews Ave., Pompano Beach, FL 33069: Free catalog ■

Rockhounding equipment, ultraviolet light equipment, and accessories. 800–327–9103.

Herkimer Diamond Mines, P.O. Box 510, Herkimer, NY 13350: Free information ■ Petrified wood products, rockhounding equipment and supplies, mineral specimens and rocks, and quartz crystals. 315–891–7355.

House of Treasure Hunters, 5712 El Cajon Blvd., San Diego, CA 92115: Free information ■ Gold prospecting equipment and metal detectors. 619–286–2600.

Jeanne's Rock & Jewelry, 5420 Bissonet, Bellaire, TX 77401: Free information ■ Rockhounding equipment and supplies, seashells, petrified wood products, and beads and bead-stringing supplies. 713–664–2988.

Keene Engineering, 9330 Corbin Ave., Northridge, CA 91324: Free catalog ■ Portable mining equipment. 818–993–0411.

Kingsley North, Inc., P.O. Box 216, Norway, MI 49870: Free catalog ■ Rockhounding equipment, jewelry-making tools, casting equipment, tumblers, and opals. 800–338–9280.

Lentz Lapidary, Inc., 11740 S. Oliver, Rt. 2, Box 135, Mulvane, KS 67110: Catalog $2 ■ Buckles, jewelry, mountings, clocks and motors, bookends, desk sets, rough rock specimens, cabochons, and rockhounding and lapidary equipment. 316–777–1372.

Miners Geological Equipment, P.O. Box 1301, Riggins, ID 83549: Free catalog ■ Geology equipment and supplies. 208–628–3247.

Placer Equipment Mfg., Inc., 3068 N. 30th Ave., Phoenix, AZ 85017: Catalog $2.50 ■ Dredges, dry washers, sluice boxes, gold pans, and other mining and prospecting equipment. 602–278–1266.

Pro-Mac Mining Supplies, P.O. Box 47, Happy Camp, CA 96039: Catalog $3 ■ Mining and treasure hunting supplies and equipment. 916–493–2014.

Pro-Mac South, 900 W. Apache Trail, Apache Junction, AZ 85220: Catalog $3 ■ Mining and treasure hunting supplies and equipment. 602–983–3484.

PUPPETS & MARIONETTES

Books by Mail, 1750 California Ave., Ste. 114, Corona, CA 91719: Send two first class stamps for catalog ■ Books and novelties for puppeteers, clowns, magicians, face painters, and balloon artists. 909–273–0900.

Freckles Clown Supplies, 4231 Timuquana Rd., Jacksonville, FL 32210: Catalog $5 ■ Puppets, make-up, clown supplies, costumes, how-to books on clowning and ballooning, and other theatrical supplies. 904–778–3977.

Ken's Illusionarium, 3288 Main St., Vancouver, British Colombia, Canada V5V 3M5: Free newsletter ■ Books, magic equipment, and supplies for magicians, mentalists, clowns, jugglers, ventriloquists, and puppeteers. 604–875–9712.

Maher Studios, P.O. Box 420, Littleton, CO 80160: Catalog $1 ■ Ventriloquist dummies, scripts and dialogues, puppets, and how-to books. 303–798–6830.

Mastercraft Puppets, P.O. Box 39, Branson, MO 65616: Free information ■ Handcrafted puppets. 800–762–4514; 417–561–8100 (in MO).

Mecca Magic, Inc., 49 Dodd St., Bloomfield, NJ 07003: Free brochure ■ Puppets, juggling supplies, theatrical make-up, clown equipment, balloons, and magic tricks. 201–429–7597.

Puppets on Parade, 4310 Cathay Ct., Louisville, KY 40219: Catalog $2 (refundable) ■ Handcrafted puppets. 502–964–3485.

PURSES & WALLETS

Bally of Switzerland for Ladies, 689 Madison Ave., New York, NY 10021: Free information ■ Women's shoes, clothing, luggage, small leather goods, and accessories. 212–751–2163.

Bally of Switzerland for Men, 711 5th Ave., New York, NY 10022: Free information ■ Men's shoes, clothing, luggage, small leather goods, and accessories. 212–751–9082.

Bottega Veneta, 635 Madison Ave., New York, NY 10022: Free catalog ■ Wallets, purses and bags, credit card cases, and luggage. 212–371–5511.

Burberry's Limited, 9 E. 57th St., New York, NY 10022: Free catalog ■ Clothing,

handbags, luggage, silk scarves and shawls, belts, hats, shoes, tennis accessories, sports bags, and toiletries. 212–371–5010.

Coach Leatherware Company, 300 Chubb Ave., Lyndhurst, NJ 07071: Free catalog ■ Leather handbags, gloves, belts, wallets, briefcases, and accessories. 201–460–4716.

Sarah Coventry, P.O. Box 1387, Elk Grove Village, IL 60009: Free catalog ■ Small leather goods, belts, bags, costume jewelry, watches, hair ornaments, sunglasses, and nail care sets. 800–252–8770.

Creative House, 100 Business Pkwy., Richardson, TX 75081: Free catalog ■ Luggage, briefcases and attache cases, handbags, wallets, and accessories. 800–527–5940; 214–231–3461 (in TX).

Deerskin Place, 283 Akron Rd., Ephrata, PA 17522: Free brochure ■ Save up to 50 percent on cowhide, sheepskin, and deerskin clothing and accessories. 717–733–7624.

Deerskin Trading Post, 119 Foster St., Box 6008, Peabody, MA 01961: Free catalog ■ Leather clothing for men and women, shoes and slippers, gloves, shoulder bags, and women's boots. 508–532–4040.

Gucci, CSB 3168, Department 846, Melville, NY 11747: Free catalog ■ Shoes, fashions, leather goods, and accessories. 800–221–2590.

Latonas Luxuries in Leather, P.O. Box 407, Blaistown, NJ 07825: Free catalog ■ Wallets, frames, desk accessories, handbags, attache cases, jewel cases, diaries and memorandum books, and luggage. 201–383–6681.

National Luggage Dealers Association, 245 5th Ave., New York, NY 10018: Free catalog ■ Small leather goods and handbags. 212–684–1610.

New England Leather Accessories, P.O. Box 127, Rochester, NH 03867: Brochure $2 (refundable) ■ Leather card cases, diary covers, briefcases and portfolios, handbags and purses, and accessories. 603–332–0707.

PUZZLES

Aardvark Puzzles, 37772 Sunset Ln., Oconomowoc, WI 53066: Free catalog ■ Handcrafted, interlocking, one-of-a-kind wooden jigsaw puzzles. 414–567–0952.

J.C. Ayer & Company, 42 Chestnut St., Salem, MA 01970: Free brochure ■ Computer-designed jigsaw puzzles. Includes puzzles made from photographs. 508–741–1522.

Bits & Pieces, 1 Puzzle Pl., Stevens Point, WI 54481: Free catalog ■ Jigsaw puzzles and gifts for adults and children. 800–544–7297.

F.A. Bourke, Inc., P.O. Box 726, Middlebury, VT 05753: Free information ■ Individually crafted puzzles with whimsical silhouettes and intricate interlocking pieces. 802–388–3648.

The Cordage, P.O. Box 863, Doylestown, PA 18901: Brochure $1 ■ Hand-forged reproduction and original puzzles.

Elms Puzzles, Inc., 8 Beech Leaf Ct., Towson, MD 21204: Free information ■ Wooden jigsaw puzzles personalized with shapes and silhouettes. 410–583–7535.

Lucretia's Pieces, RFD 1, Box 501, Windsor, VT 05089: Free information ■ Challenging puzzles designed with special shapes and unexpected surprises. 802–436–3006.

Pacific Puzzle Company, 378 Guemes Island Rd., Anacortes, WA 98221: Free catalog ■ Educational puzzles for children. 206–293–7034.

Parliament Puzzles, RR 2, P.O. Box 848, Woodstock, VT 05091: Free brochure ■ Antique wooden jigsaw puzzles from Great Britain and other puzzles. 802–457–3877.

The Puzzle People, Inc., 22719 Tree Farm Rd., Colfax, CA 95713: Free brochure ■ Children's educational puzzles. 916–637–4823.

Rainy Lake Puzzles, 4255 Garfield Ave. South, Minneapolis, MN 55409: Free catalog ■ Intricately handcut wood jigsaw puzzles. 612–827–5757.

Stave Puzzles, Box 329, Norwich, VT 05055: Free catalog ■ Hand-cut jigsaw puzzles. 802–295–5200.

QUILTS & QUILTING

Authentic Amish, 1602 Walnut Bottom Rd., Newville, PA 17241: Catalog $3 ■ Handcrafted Amish quilts and wall hangings. 717–776–7814.

The Cotton Patch, 1025 Brown Ave., Lafayette, CA 94549: Catalog $5 ■ Fabrics, quilting books, and supplies. 800–835–4418.

Craftways, 4118 Lakeside Dr., Richmond, CA 94806: Catalog $2 ■ Designs for quilts, appliques, and cross-stitching designs. 510–223–3144.

Dover Street Booksellers, 39 E. Dover St., P.O. Box 1563, Easton, MD 21601: Catalog $2 ■ Books on quilting, fabric piecing, appliques, and other crafts. 410–822–9329.

The Garden Patch, 1228 NW Dixon St., Corvallis, OR 97330: Brochure $1 ■ Hand-stitched and appliqued cotton quilts. 503–754–7285.

Hancock Fabrics, 3841 Hinkleville Rd., Paducah, KY 42001: Free information ■ Quilting supplies, fabrics, and sewing notions. 800–626–2723.

Hearthside Quilts, Rt. 7, Box 429, Shelburne, VT 05482: Catalog $3 ■ Traditional and modern quilt designs in easy-to-sew pre-cut kits. 800–451–3533.

Hinterberg Design, Inc., 2100 N. Western Ave., West Bend, WI 53095: Free information ■ Quilting frame with adjustable height and tilt, ratchet wheel tensioning, and optional extension or shorter poles. 800–443–5800.

Keepsake Quilting, Dover St., P.O. Box 1459, Meredith, NH 03253: Catalog $1 ■ Quilting books, patterns, notions, fabrics, quilting aids, scrap bags, and batting.

Lancaster Towne Quilts, P.O. Box 277, Strasburg, PA 17579: Catalog $5 ■ Handmade Dutch country-style Amish quilts.

Claire Murray, Inc., P.O. Box 1089, North Charlestown, NH 03630: Catalog $5 (refundable) ■ Quilts, handpainted ceramics, and hand-hooked rugs. 800–323–YARN.

New England Quilt Supply, 158 Center St., P.O. Box 633, Pembroke, MA 02359: Free information with long SASE ■ Quilting fabrics, notions, hoops, and stands. 617–293–6401.

Norton House, 1836 Country Store Village, Wilmington, VT 05363: Catalog $3 ■ Fabrics in 100 percent cotton, quilting how-to books, and supplies. 802–464–7213.

Pangles's Fabric & Craft Center, Inc., 138 E. Main, Box 1098, Wise, VA 24293: Free information ■ Quilting supplies, Pandapuff and Kodofill polyester stuffing in a

double-bonded thickness, and other craft supplies. 703–328–6606.

Quilting Books Unlimited, 1911 W. Wilson, Batavia, IL 60510: Catalog $1 ■ Quilting books. 708–406–0237.

Quilt Patch, 208 Brigham St., Marlboro, MA 01752: Catalog $2 ■ Kits for quilts, wallhangings, and pillows; stencils, ready-to-use handcrafted quilts, and supplies; and supplies. 508–480–0194.

Quilts of America, Inc., 431 E. 73rd St., New York, NY 10021: Free information ■ Antique American quilts and folk art from the 19th- and 20th-century. 212–535–1600.

Quiltwork Patches, P.O. Box 724, Corvallis, OR 97339: Catalog $1 ■ Quilting kits, supplies, tools, stencils, hoops, fabrics, and books. 503–752–4820.

That Patchwork Place, Inc., P.O. Box 118, Bothell, WA 95041: Catalog $2 (refundable) ■ Quilting supplies and projects, books, and other craft supplies. 800–426–3126; 206–483–3313 (in WA).

RACQUETBALL & SQUASH

Clothing

Alchester Mills Company, Inc., 314 S. 11th St., Camden, NJ 08103: Free information ■ Gloves, socks, sweatbands, and eyeguards. 609–964–9700.

Dorson Sports, Inc., 195 Lauman Ln., P.O. Box 606, Hicksville, NY 11802: Free information ■ Gloves. 800–645–7215; 516–822–2424 (in NY).

Ektelon, 12540 Spindletop Rd., San Diego, CA 92129: Free information ■ Clothing and gloves, socks, sweatbands, bags and balls, racquets, eyeguards, and thongs. 619–560–0066.

Foot-Joy, Inc., 144 Field St., Brockton, MA 02403: Free information ■ Gloves, shoes, socks, and balls. 508–586–2233.

Franklin Sports Industries, Inc., 17 Campanelli Parkway, P.O. Box 508, Stoughton, MA 02072: Free information ■ Gloves. 617–344–1111.

Head Sports, Inc., 4801 N. 63rd St., Boulder, CO 80301: Free information ■ Gloves, shoes, sweatbands, bags, balls, and racquets. 800–257–5100; 303–530–2000 (in CO).

Holabird Sports Discounters, 9004 Yellow Brick Rd., Rossville Industrial Park, Baltimore, MD 21237: Free brochure ■ Save up to 40 percent on sports equipment and clothing. 410–687–6400.

Johar, Inc., P.O. Box 10, Forrest City, AR 72335: Free information ■ Gloves. 800–248–1232; 501–633–8161 (in AR).

Moody & Company, Inc., P.O. Box 13, Milford, CT 06460: Free information ■ Clothing, gloves, shoes, socks, sweatbands, bags and balls, eyeguards, and thongs. 800–243–4561; 203–878–1741 (in CT).

Olympia Sports, School Tech, Inc., 745 State Circle, Ann Arbor, MI 48108: Free information ■ Gloves. 313–761–5135.

Pennsylvania Sporting Goods, 1360 Industrial Hwy., P.O. Box 451, Southhampton, PA 18966: Free information ■ Gloves, sweatbands, balls, eyeguards, and racquets. 800–535–1122.

Pony Sports & Leisure, Inc., Meadows Office Complex, 7th Floor, 201 Rt. 17, Rutherford, NJ 07070: Free information ■ Shoes, socks, and sweatbands. 800–654–7669; 201–896–0101 (in NJ).

Puma USA, Inc., 147 Centre St., Brockton, MA 02403: Free information ■ Clothing, shoes, socks, and balls. 508–583–9100.

Reebok International, Ltd., 100 Technology Center Dr., Stoughton, MA 02072: Free information ■ Clothing, shoes, and socks. 800–382–3823; 617–341–5000 (in MA).

Regent Sports Corporation, 45 Ranick Rd., Hauppage, NY 11787: Free information ■ Gloves. 516–234–2948.

Spalding & Brothers, 425 Meadow St., P.O. Box 901, Chicopee, MA 01021: Free information ■ Clothing, gloves, shoes, socks, sweatbands, bags, balls, and racquets. 413–536–1200.

Squash Services, P.O. Box 491, Richboro, PA 18954: Free information with long SASE ■ Shoes, racquets, safety gear, gloves, and bags. 215–364–4999.

Wa-Mac, Inc., Highskore Products, Inc., 178 Commerce Rd., P.O. Box 128, Carlstadt, NJ 07072: Free information ■ Gloves, socks, sweatbands, balls, bags, eyeguards, and racquets. 800–447–5673; 201–438–7200 (in NJ).

Equipment

Alchester Mills Company, Inc., 314 S. 11th St., Camden, NJ 08103: Free information ■ Eyeguards, gloves, socks, sweatbands, and grips. 609–964–9700.

Austad's, 4500 E. 10th St., P.O. Box 1428, Sioux Falls, SD 57196: Free catalog ■ Racquetball and other sports equipment. 800–444–1234.

Bard Sports Corporation, 14516 SW 119th Ave., Miami, FL 33186: Free information ■ Bags, racquets, and grips. 800–433–1022.

Brine, Inc., 47 Sumner St., Milford, MA 01757: Free information ■ Bags, balls, and grips. 800–227–2722; 800–982–6842 (in MA).

Cannon Sports, Inc., P.O. Box 11179, Burbank, CA 91510: Free information ■ Balls, racquets, and eyeguards. 800–223–0064; 818–503–9570.

Ektelon, 12540 Spindletop Rd., San Diego, CA 92129: Free information ■ Bags and balls, racquets, eyeguards, thongs, clothing and gloves, socks, and sweatbands. 619–560–0066.

Faber Brothers, 4141 S. Pulaski Rd., Chicago, IL 60632: Free information ■ Balls, bags, and racquets. 312–376–9300.

Foot-Joy, Inc., 144 Field St., Brockton, MA 02403: Free information ■ Balls, gloves, shoes, and socks. 508–586–2233.

Head Sports, Inc., 4801 N. 63rd St., Boulder, CO 80301: Free information ■ Bags and balls, racquets, gloves, shoes, and sweatbands. 800–257–5100; 303–530–2000 (in CO).

Holabird Sports Discounters, 9004 Yellow Brick Rd., Rossville Industrial Park, Baltimore, MD 21237: Free brochure ■ Save up to 40 percent on equipment and clothing for basketball, tennis, running, and jogging, golf, exercising, racquetball, and other sports. 410–687–6400.

M.W. Kasch Company, 5401 W. Donges Bay Rd., Mequon, WI 53092: Free information ■ Bags, balls, and racquets. 414–242–5000.

Las Vegas Discount Golf & Tennis, 5325 S. Valley View Blvd., Ste. 10, Las Vegas, NV 89118: Free catalog ■ Equipment, shoes, and clothing for tennis, racquetball, golf, running, and jogging. 702–798–7777.

Leisure Marketing, Inc., 2204 Morris Ave., Ste. 202, Union, NJ 07083: Free information ■ Bags and racquets. 908–851–9494.

Lombard's Sporting Goods, 1840 NE 164th St., North Miami, FL 33162: Catalog $1 ■ Racquets and racquetball accessories. 305–944–1166.

Moody & Company, Inc., P.O. Box 13, Milford, CT 06460: Free information ■ Bags, balls, eyeguards, racquets, grips, and thongs. 800–243–4561; 203–878–1741 (in CT).

Pennsylvania Sporting Goods, 1360 Industrial Hwy., P.O. Box 451, Southhampton, PA 18966: Free information ■ Balls, eyeguards, and racquets. 800–535–1122.

Professional Golf & Tennis Suppliers, 7825 Hollywood Blvd., Pembroke Pines, FL 33024: Free catalog ■ Equipment and accessories. 305–981–7283.

Puma USA, Inc., 147 Centre St., Brockton, MA 02403: Free catalog with long SASE ■ Balls and bags. 508–583–9100.

Spalding & Brothers, 425 Meadow St., P.O. Box 901, Chicopee, MA 01021: Free information ■ Bags, balls, and racquets. 413–536–1200.

Sport World Distributors, 3060 Clermont Rd., P.O. Box 27131, Columbus, OH 44327: Free information ■ Bags, balls, eyeguards, and racquets. 614–838–8511.

Squash Services, P.O. Box 491, Richboro, PA 18954: Free information with long SASE ■ Shoes, racquets, safety gear, gloves, and bags. 215–364–4999.

Trans Global Sports Company, 13104 S. Avalon Blvd., Los Angeles, CA 90061: Free information ■ Balls and racquets. 213–321–9714.

USTech, Inc., 17720 NE 65th St., Redmond, WA 98052: Free information ■ Bags and balls, racquets, eyeguards, and thongs. 206–881–8989.

Voit Sports, 1451 Pittstand-Victor Rd., 100 Willow Office Park, Fairport, NY 14450: Free information ■ Bags, balls, eyeguards, and racquets. 800–367–8648; 716–385–2390 (in NY).

Wa-Mac, Inc., Highskore Products, Inc., 178 Commerce Rd., P.O. Box 128,

Carlstadt, NJ 07072: Free information ■ Balls, bags, eyeguards, and racquets. 800–447–5673; 201–438–7200 (in NJ).

Wild World of Sporting Goods, 220 S. University Dr., Plantation, FL 33324: Free price list ■ Tennis, racquetball, and squash racquets. 305–475–9800.

Wilson Sporting Goods, 2233 West St., River Grove, IL 60171: Free information ■ Bags, balls, and racquets. 800–323–1552.

RADIATOR ENCLOSURES

Arsco Manufacturing Company, Inc., 3564 Blue Rock Rd., Cincinnati, OH 45247: Free brochure ■ Steel radiator enclosures. 800–543–7040; 513–385–0555 (in OH).

Deco-Trol, 802 N. I–35 East, Denton, TX 76201: Free information ■ Brass, chrome, and antique brass plated; flat and semi-gloss colored; all-aluminum; and unfinished wood grills and registers. 800–678–1977.

Monarch Radiator Enclosures, 2744 Arkansas Dr., Brooklyn, NY 11234: Brochure $1 (refundable) ■ Easy-to-assemble all-steel radiator enclosures. 201–796–4117.

The Reggio Register, P.O. Box 511, Ayer, MA 01432: Catalog $1 ■ Solid brass and cast-iron registers and grills. 508–772–3493.

RADIOS

Amateur Radio Equipment

Alinco Electronics, Inc., 438 Amapola Ave., Torrance, CA 90501: Free information ■ Hand-held transceivers. 310–618–8616.

Aluma Tower Company, Box 2806, Vero Beach, FL 32961: Free information ■ Telescoping crank-up, guyed stack-up, tilt-over, rooftop, and mobile antenna towers. 407–567–3423.

Amateur Electronics Supply, 5710 W. Good Hope Rd., Milwaukee, WI 53223: Free information ■ Amateur radio equipment. 414–358–0333.

American Radio Relay League, 225 Main St., Newington, CT 06111: Free information ■ Books on how to become a ham radio operator, get a license, learn Morse code, organize equipment, set up a station, and other amateur radio subjects. 203–666–1541.

Antennas West, Box 50062, Provo, UT 84605: Free information ■ Easy-to-install indoor antennas for apartments, motels, attics, and portable use. 801–373–8425.

Astron Corporation, 9 Autry, Irvine, CA 92718: Free information ■ Heavy-duty power supplies. 714–458–7277.

Austin Amateur Radio Supply, 5325 North I–35, Austin, TX 78723: Free information ■ Amateur radio equipment. 512–454–2994.

Barker & Williamson, 10 Canal St., Bristol, PA 19007: Free information ■ Easy-to-install portable antennas. 215–788–5581.

Barry Electronics Corporation, 512 Broadway, New York, NY 10012: Free information ■ Amateur, professional, and commercial electronics equipment. 212–925–7000.

Bilal Company, 137 Manchester Dr., Florissant, CO 80816: Free information ■ Antennas from 10 to 160 meters. 719–687–0650.

Burghardt Amateur Center, 182 N. Maple, P.O. Box 73, Watertown, SD 57201: Free information ■ Amateur radio equipment. 605–886–7314.

Butternut Electronics, P.O. Box 123, Olmito, TX 78575: Free catalog ■ Vertical and compact, two-element beam butterfly antennas.

Byers Chassis Kits, 5120 Harmony Grove Rd., Dover, PA 17315: Free information ■ Chassis and cabinet kits, assembled cabinets, slope box kits, rack shelves and equipment cabinets, dipole hangers, other enclosures, and aluminum and brass sheets. 717–292–4901.

Comm Pute, Inc., 1057 E. 2100 South, Salt Lake City, UT 84106: Free information ■ Amateur radio and computer interfacing equipment. 800–942–8873.

Comtelco Industries, Inc., 501 Mitchell Rd., Glendale Hts., IL 60139: Free information ■ Mobile antennas, magnet mounts, and accessories. 800–634–4622.

Delaware Amateur Supply, 71 Meadow Rd., New Castle, DE 19720: Free information ■ Amateur radio equipment. 302–328–7728.

GAP Antenna Products, 6010 Bldg. B, N. Old Dixie Hwy., Vero Beach, FL 32967:

Free information ■ Antennas for limited space. 407–778–3728.

Gateway Electronics, 8123 Page Blvd., St. Louis, MO 63130: Free information ■ New and surplus electronics equipment for amateurs, industry, experimenters, and others. 800–669–5810.

Jo Gunn Enterprises, Hwy. 82, Box 32–C, Ethelsville, AL 35461: Catalog $2 ■ Mobile antennas, coaxial equipment, and other electronics equipment. 205–658–2229.

Ham Radio Outlet, Inc., 2620 W. La Palma, Anaheim, CA 92801: Catalog $1 ■ Radio amateur transceivers, receivers, mobile units, mini hand held units, hardware and software for computers, and antennas and rotators. 800–854–6046.

Ham Station, 220 N. Fulton Ave., P.O. Box 6522, Evansville, IN 47719: Free information with long SASE ■ New and used amateur radio equipment. 800–729–4373; 812–422–0231 (in IN).

Hamtronics, Inc., 65 Moul Rd., Hilton, NY 14468: Catalog $1 ■ Amateur radio equipment. 716–392–9430.

Heights Tower Systems, Ltd., 1721 Indian Rd., Lapeer, MI 48446: Free information ■ Manual and electrically operated antenna towers. 313–667–1700.

Hustler, One Newtronics Pl., Mineral Wells, TX 76067: Free information ■ Antennas for amateur radio. 817–325–1386.

Jun's Electronics, 3919 Sepulveda Blvd., Culver City, CA 90230: Free information ■ Scanners and communications equipment for amateur, two-way, marine, and cellular mobile phone installation. 310–390–8003.

Kantronics, 1202 E. 23rd St., Lawrence, KS 66046: Free information ■ Amateur and professional radio equipment. 913–842–7745.

KW Litho, P.O. Box 17390, Fort Worth, TX 76102: Free samples with long SASE ■ QSL cards. 817–332–3658.

Larsen Antennas, 11611 NE 50th Ave., P.O. Box 1799, Vancouver, WA 98668: Free catalog ■ Professional antennas for amateurs. 206–573–2722.

Madison Electronics Supply, 12310 Zavalla St., Houston, TX 77085: Free information ■ Hard-to-find parts and other equipment for amateur radio, electronics hobbyists, and others. 800–231–3057; 713–729–7300 (in TX).

Maggiore Electronic Lab, 600 Westtown Rd., West Chester, PA 19382: Free catalog ■ Amateur and professional radio equipment. 215–436–6051.

Memphis Amateur Electronics, 1465 Wells Station Rd., Memphis, TN 38108: Free information ■ Amateur radio equipment. 800–238–6168.

Missouri Radio Center, 102 NW Business Park Ln., Kansas City, MO 64150: Free information ■ Amateur radio equipment, hand-held transceivers, remote controllers, preamplifiers, and accessories. 800–821–7323; 816–741–8118 (in MO).

Mobile Mark, Inc., 3900 River Rd., Schiller Park, IL 60176: Free information ■ Easy-to-mount mobile and window antennas. 708–671–6690.

National Tower Company, P.O. Box 15417, Shawnee Mission, KS 66215: Free information ■ Amateur radio equipment and antennas. 913–888–8864.

Network QSL's Cards, P.O. Box 13200, Alexandria, LA 71315: Samples $1 ■ QSL cards. 800–354–0830.

Wm. M. Nye Company, Inc., 1614 130th Ave. NE, Bellevue, WA 98005: Free catalog ■ Antennas and tuners for amateur radio, phone patch equipment, code practice sets, and other equipment. 206–454–4524.

R & L Electronics, 1315 Maple Ave., Hamilton, OH 45011: Free catalog ■ Amateur radio equipment and antennas. 800–221–7735; 513–868–6399 (in OH).

Reno Radio, 12 Glen Carran Cir., Sparks, NV 89431: Free information ■ Amateur and professional radio equipment. 702–331–7373.

RF Enterprises, Box 43, Merrifield, MN 56465: Free information ■ Amateur radio equipment and antennas. 218–765–3254.

Rivendell Electronics, 8 Londonberry Rd., Derry, NH 03038: Free information ■ Amateur radio equipment. 603–434–5371.

Smiley Antenna Company, Inc., 408 La Cresta Heights Rd., El Cajon, CA 92021: Free information ■ Antennas for amateur radio. 619–579–8916.

Telecom, Inc., 675 Great Rd., Rt. 119, Littleton, MA 01460: Free information ■

Amateur radio and other electronics equipment. 508–486–3400.

Telex/Hy-Gain Communications, Inc., 9600 Aldrich Ave. South, Minneapolis, MN 55420: Free information ■ Antenna rotators with large load capacity and braking power. 612–887–5528.

Texas Towers, Division Texas RF Distributors, Inc., 1108 Summit Ave., Plano, TX 75074: Free information ■ Antennas and towers, rotors, and other amateur radio equipment. 214–422–7306.

US Tower, 1220 Marcin St., Vasalia, CA 93291: Free catalog ■ Antenna towers, motor drives, and accessories. 209–733–2438.

VHF Communications, 280 Tiffany Ave., Jamestown, NY 14701: Free information ■ New and used electronics equipment for amateur radio. 716–664–6345.

W & W Associates, 29–11 Parsons Blvd., Flushing, NY 11354: Free information ■ Communication batteries. 800–221–0732; 718–961–2103 (in NY).

Will-Burt Company, P.O. Box 900, Orrville, OH 44667: Free information ■ Telescoping antenna masts. 216–682–7015.

Wilson Antenna, Inc., 1181 Grier Dr., Ste. A, Las Vegas, NV 89119: Free information ■ CB and mobile antennas. 800–541–6116.

Yaesu USA, 17210 Edwards Rd., Cerritos, CA 90701: Free information ■ Amateur radio base station equipment. 310–404–2700.

E.H. Yost, 7344 Tetiva Rd., Sauk City, WI 53583: Free catalog ■ Batteries for radios, computers, and other equipment. 608–643–3194.

Antique Radios

Antique Electronic Supply, 6221 S. Maple St., Tempe, AZ 85238: Catalog $2 ■ Hard-to-find tubes, parts, and supplies for antique radio restoration and repair. 602–820–5411.

Antique Radios, David & Nancy Snow, 6392 Pepper Tree, Jackson, MI 49203: Free information ■ Antique radios.

Bob Barnes Radios, 511 N. Chestnut, Monroe City, MO 63456: Free information with long SASE ■ Crystal set parts. 314–735–2945.

Daily Electronics, P.O. Box 5029, Compton, CA 90224: Free information with long SASE ■ Antique radio tubes. 213–774–1255.

Don Diers, 4276 N. 50th St., Milwaukee, WI 53216: Price list $1 with long SASE ■ Tubes and parts for antique radio restoration. 414–445–9927.

L. Gardner, 458 Two Mile Creek Rd., Tonawanda, NY 14150: Free information with long SASE ■ Crystal set parts. 716–873–0447.

Charles Martin Radio Parts, 602 Duque Rd., Lutz, FL 33549: Free information with long SASE ■ Crystal set parts. 813–949–1835.

Midwest Supply Electronics, 1165 Lafayette Ave., Terre Haute, IN 47804: Free information ■ Antique radio tubes. 812–232–0187.

The Olde Tyme Radio Company, 2445 Lyttonsville Rd., Silver Spring, MD 20910: Free information with long SASE and two 1st class stamps ■ Antique radios, parts, tubes, schematics, and restoration supplies. 301–585–8776.

Play Things of Past, 9511 Sunrise Blvd., Cleveland, OH 44133: Free information with long SASE ■ Pre-1928 parts and literature and parts for wireless equipment to modern transistor radios.

Harry Poster, P.O. Box 1883, South Hackensack, NJ 07606: Free information ■ Vintage television sets and radios. 201–794–9606.

Gary Schneider, 9511 Sunrise Blvd., #J–23, North Royalton, OH 44133: Free information ■ Parts for battery-operated antique radios.

Vintage TV & Radio, 3498 W. 105th St., Cleveland, OH 44111: Free information ■ Tubes, parts, books, and refinishing supplies. 216–671–6712.

Waves Antiques Early Radios & Phonographs, 32 E. 13th St., New York, NY 10003: Free list with long SASE ■ Antique radios, phonographs, and other equipment. 212–989–9284.

Citizen Band Equipment

CBC International, Inc., P.O. Box 31500, Phoenix, AZ 85046: Catalog $2 ■ Parts for CB radios, 10–meter and FM conversion kits, books, plans, and accessories.

Cobra, 6500 W. Cortland St., Chicago, IL 60635: Free information ■ Fixed-installation and portable citizen band radios. 312–889–8870.

Fox Electronics, 4518 Taylorsville Rd., Dayton, OH 45424: Free information ■ Portable citizen band radios. 513–236–3591.

Maxon Electronics, 10828 NW Air World Dr., Kansas City, MO 64153: Free information ■ Hand-held mobile radios. 816–891–6320.

Nady Systems, Inc., 6701 Bay St., Emeryville, CA 94608: Free information ■ UHF and VHF hand-held transceivers. 510–652–2411.

Radio Shack, Division Tandy Corporation, 1500 One Tandy Center, Fort Worth, TX 76102: Free catalog ■ Portable and fixed-installation citizen band radios, electronics components, science kits, computers and accessories, stereo equipment, and toys and games. 817–390–3700.

Transcrypt International, Inc., 1620 N. 20th St., Lincoln, NE 68503: Free information ■ Portable, including hand-held models, two-way radios. 800–228–0226.

Wilson Antenna, Inc., 1181 Grier Dr., Ste. A, Las Vegas, NV 89119: Free information ■ CB and amateur mobile antennas. 800–541–6116.

RADON TESTING

First Alert, 780 McClure Rd., Aurora, IL 60404: Radon detectors. 708–851–7330.

Home Diagnostics, Inc., 230 Park Ave., New York, NY 10169: Free catalog ■ Home products for radon testing, water analysis, carbon monoxide and formaldehyde testing, blood pressure monitoring, and diabetes screening. 212–490–7977.

RAFTING & WHITEWATER RUNNING

Bermudes USA, Inc., P.O. Box 810, Sag Harbor, NY 11963: Free catalog ■ Dry gear for whitewater kayaking and canoeing. 516–725–9545.

Cascade Outfitters, 145 Pioneer Pkwy. East, P.O. Box 209, Springfield, OR 97477: Free catalog ■ Whitewater river running equipment. 800–223–7238.

Colorado Kayak, P.O. Box 3059, Buena Vista, CO 81211: Free catalog ■ Paddles, sports clothing, and accessories. 800–535–3565.

Easy Rider Canoe & Kayak Company, P.O. Box 88108, Seattle, WA 98138: Information package $5 ■ Whitewater and sea cruising paddles and single and double seater kayaks and canoes, rowing trainers, paddles, and accessories. 206–228–3633.

Hyside Inflatables, P.O. Box Z, Kernville, CA 93238: Free brochure ■ River running inflatable rafts, self-bailing kayaks, and other equipment. 619–376–3723.

Mitchell Paddles, Inc., RD 2, P.O. Box 922, Canaan, NH 03741: Free information ■ Canoe and kayak paddles, boats, and dry suits. 603–523–7004.

Nantahala Outdoor Center, US 19 West, Box 41, Bryson City, NC 28713: Free catalog ■ Supplies and equipment for whitewater paddling. 800–367–3521; 704–488–8785 (in NC).

Northwest River Supplies, Inc., 2009 S. Main, Moscow, ID 83843: Free catalog ■ Rafts, waterproof bags, paddles, boats, and supplies. 800–635–5202.

Wildwater Designs, 230 Penllyn Pike, Penllyn, PA 19422: Free catalog ■ Gear for whitewater, lake, or ocean travel in kayaks or canoes. 215–646–5034.

Wyoming River Raiders, 601 SE Wyoming Blvd., Casper, WY 82609: Free catalog ■ Outdoor clothing, camping and river expedition equipment, fishing gear, hiking equipment, books, and other supplies. 800–247–6068; 307–235–8624 (in WY).

RECIPES

The publications below were prepared by food companies to provide consumers with information and suggestions for ways to use their products. Sometimes, publications are available only for a limited time or in limited quantities. If an offer has expired, you can generally expect your money to be returned or to receive a similar, substitute publication. To be on the safe side, however, it's usually best to send any payment requested as a money order or check.

Almond Board of California, P.O. Box 15920, Sacramento, CA 95852: Free brochures ■ *Super Special Almond Cookies, Cooking with California Almonds and Fresh*

Produce, Fast and Healthy Recipes with California Almonds, and *Good Health with California Almonds.* 916–338–2225.

American Lamb Council, Dept. COC, 6911 S. Yosemite St., Englewood, CO 80112: Free order blank ■ All-time favorite recipes with lamb. 303–771–3500.

American Mushroom Institute, 907 E. Baltimore Pike, Kennett Square, PA 19348: Free brochures ■ *Fresh Mushrooms* describes how to pick, store, prepare, and cook them. *Taste the International Flavor of Pennsylvania Fresh Mushrooms* includes prized recipes from America's leading chefs and restaurateurs. 215–388–7806.

American Pop Corn Company, Box 178, Sioux City, IA 51102: Booklet 50¢ ■ *The American Pop Corn Story and Recipe Collection* describes recipes for all-time favorites made with Jolly Time Pop Corn.

American Spice Trade Association, P.O. Box 1267, Englewood Cliffs, NJ 07632: Free publications list with long SASE ■ Offers the American Spice Association's Publications Guide. Includes: audio-visual presentations; technical manuals; article reprints from industrial food publications, technical publications, food-service publications, and nutrition publications; general interest literature; cooking and health; and other pamphlets.

Angostura International Limited, 20 Commerce Dr., Ste. 100, Cranford, NJ 07016: Free booklets ■ *Canyon Ranch Spa's Angostura Cookbook* contains recipes using Angostura Low Sodium Worcestershire Sauce, Low Sodium Soy Sauce, and Angostura Bitters. *Low Sodium Information You Can Bank On* includes examples of how Angostura Low Sodium Worcestershire Sauce, Angostura Low Sodium Teriyaki Sauce, Angostura Low Sodium Soy Sauce, and Angostura Bitters can be used to prepare foods without using salt. *Professional Mixing Guide* contains recipes for cocktails and mixed drinks. 908–272–2200.

Best Foods Baking Group, 100 Passaic Ave., Fairfield, NJ 07004, ATTN: Consumer Services Department: Brochure 50¢ ■ *Brownberry Ten Simple Ways to Make Great Bread A Spectacular Treat* includes easy ways to change a simple bread, Brownberry bread, into entrees and desserts. Also ask for *Thomas' Best* that's available for $1.50. Contains a collection of award-winning recipes that use Thomas' English

Muffins. *PITA the Great,* for $6.95, includes recipes for pita and yogurt, dips and other snacks, sandwiches, soups and salads, barbecue ideas, holiday buffets, and vegetarian suppers. 800–533–9598; 201–808–3176 (in NJ).

Brown-Forman Beverage Company, P.O. Box 1080, Louisville, KY 40201: Free brochures ■ *Delicious Comforts for Every Occasion* includes ideas for using Early Times to prepare party-time and other occasion drinks. *All that Comfort* includes recipes for mixed drinks prepared with Southern Comfort. 800–753–4567.

California Apricot Advisory Board, 1280 Boulevard Way, Walnut Creek, CA 94595: Free booklet with long SASE ■ *Simply Sensational California Apricots* describes how apricots can be used in the preparation of poultry, salads, ice cream, cakes and pies, curried frittata, meats, fish, drinks, and cheesecake.

California Artichoke Advisory Board, 10719 Merritt St., P.O. Box 747, Castroville, CA 95012: Free brochures with long SASE ■ *Baby California Artichokes* includes recipes for a dip, serving with sausage and parmesan cheese, stir-frying, french frying, marinating, and others. *Artichokes California* describes recipes for serving artichokes hot or cold.

California Fig Advisory Board, 3425 N. 1st St., P.O. Box 109–CC, Fresno, CA 93726: Free brochures with long SASE ■ *Buyer's Guide to Dietary Fiber* simplifies the selection of fruits, nuts, and vegetables high in dietary fiber. *Fabulous Figs, The Fitness Fruit* contains recipes for making chewy, sweet finger-foods to use as snacks and wholesome nutritious dishes. *Low-fat Recipes Featuring California Figs* contains easy-to-prepare, healthy and nutritious breads, entrees, salads, muffins, and cookies. 209–445–5626.

California Prune Board, 5990 Stoneridge Dr., Ste. 101, Pleasanton, CA 94588: Free brochures ■ *Sweet Delicious California Prunes* describes nutritious, low-fat recipes that include a compote of prunes and port, prune-apple butter, prune-orange-cranberry juice breakfast drink, and others. *Prune that Fat* shows how to cut the fat from brownies, cakes, cookies, muffins, and other bakery favorites.

California Table Grape Commission, P.O. Box 5498, Fresno, CA 93755: Free information ■ Recipe ideas, nutrition information, and conservation information.

Canned Fruit Promotion Service, CFPS, Inc., P.O. Box 7111, San Francisco, CA 94120: Free brochure with long SASE ■ Consumer recipes with U.S. canned Bartlett pears, cling peaches, and fruit cocktail. Includes nutritional evaluation. 415–495–7714.

Carolina Brown Rice Recipes, P.O. Box 2636, Houston, TX 77252: Brochure 50¢ ■ Describes 14 easy-to-prepare recipes with nutritional analysis of each recipe. Includes salads, side dishes, entrees, and desserts.

Carolina Light, Lean & Low Fat Recipe Book, P.O. Box 2636, Houston, TX 77252: Book $2.50 ■ Contains 97 versatile rice recipes using white and brown rice that reflect today's nutritional and taste preferences.

Carolina 30 Minute Meals, P.O. Box 2636, Houston, TX 77252: Booklet 50¢ ■ Describes recipes that use Carolina Enriched Rice to prepare 12 different menus.

Cherry Marketing Institute, 2220 University Park Dr., Ste. 200, Okemos, MI 48864; Free brochures ■ *The Extraordinary Cherry* contains recipes for using cherries with chicken, salads, relishes and sauces, vegetables, and bakery favorites. *Cherry Good for You!* describes low-fat, low-calorie cherry recipes. *The Extraordinary Cherry Recipe Cards* contains recipes for more cherry favorites. 517–347–0010.

Chicken Cookbook, Dept. NBC, Box 307, Coventry, CT 06238: Book $1.75 ■ Contains hundreds of recipes from the 39th National Chicken Cooking Contest, and includes the top five winners.

Cruzan Rum Recipe Offer, P.O. Box 218, Frederiksted, St. Croix, U.S. Virgin Islands 00841: Free booklet ■ *Create a Cruzan Delight with Cruzan Rum* includes recipes for making a daiquiri, pina colada, mai tai, screwdriver, Caribbean sunrise, rum tonic, gimlet, martini, Amalie punch, hot buttered rum, and apple sizzle, and recipes for salads, desserts, and main dishes.

The Fitness Formula, P.O. Box 2636, Houston, TX 77252: Booklet $3 ■ Contains 80 pages of health ideas, including 16 pages of nutritional information and recipes with Success and Mahatma Brown Rice.

Florida Dept. of Agriculture, Commissioner, 2051 E. Dirac Dr., Tallahassee, FL 32310: Free brochures ■ Offers free Florida seafood brochures that contain recipes with *Oysters, Shrimp, Lobster,* and *Fish.* Other brochures include *Microwave Recipes* and *Soups and Stews.* 904–488–0163.

Florida Tomato Committee, P.O. Box 140635, Orlando, FL 32814–0635: Book $7 ■ *Cooking with Fresh Tomatoes* includes over 100 pages of recipes with fresh Florida tomatoes. 407–894–3071.

Frieda's, Inc., P.O. Box 58488, Los Angeles, CA 90058: Free brochures with long SASE ■ *Fiesta Foods* describes Mexican-inspired foods and suggests ways to use them. *Foods of the Orient* explains the secrets of successful Oriental cooking and includes several recipes. *Fresh Herb Know-How* includes a fresh herb recipe guide and some suggested recipes for their use. *Guide to Exotic Fruits* explains how to incorporate exotic fruits into menus and contains an exotic fruits reference chart. *Guide to Exotic Mushrooms* includes buying and storing tips for mushrooms, and recipes. *Microwaveable* is a guide to microwaving new and unusual produce. *Slim Line Vegetable Guide* includes a reference guide to low-calorie vegetables and contains recipes. 213–627–2981.

Goya Foods, Inc., 100 Seaview Dr., Secaucus, NJ 07096: Free booklets with long SASE ■ *The Seasoning Goyas* includes recipes for cooking with Goya Adobo, Goya Alcaparrado, Goya Recaito, Goya Sofrito, and Goya Extra Virgin Spanish Olive Oil. *Goya Introduces TAPAS* describes recipes for Spanish hors d'oeuvres, appetizers, and elegant Spanish noshes. 201–348–4900.

Goya Foods, Inc., 100 Seaview Dr., Secaucus, NJ 07096: Booklets $1 with two Goya labels ■ *Delicious Starts with Coco Goya* contains recipes for making exotic drinks, ice creams and sauces, pies and other desserts, main meal dishes, and others. *Goya Bean Book* explores different ways to prepare 12 kinds of beans. *Goya's Caribbean Cook's Book* features Caribbean-inspired recipes for nibbling foods, soups and stews, side dishes, entrees, mixed drinks, and more. *Latin Barbeque a La Goya* contains a collection of special recipes and ideas from Master Chef Felipe Rojas-Lombardi and the Kitchens of Goya that will change your barbecue from now on. *The Goya Cook's Tour of Spain* includes recipes from different regions of Spain and from the Kitchen of Goya for seafoods, omelets, kabobs, soups, turnovers, Paella, and others. 201–348–4900.

Hegg & Hegg, 801 Marine Dr., Port Angeles, WA 98362: Free recipe cards ■ *Seafood Recipes* includes recipes for different ways to prepare seafood. 800–435–3474; 206–457–3344 (in WA).

Hillshire Farm & Kahn's, P.O. Box 25111, Cincinnati, OH 45225: Free booklet ■ *Easy & Delicious Dinners from Hillshire Farm* describes how sausage can be used in salads and soups, in stir-fry entrees, on the grill and stove top, in baked entrees, in the microwave, with pasta, and other ways.

Idaho Fresh Pack, Inc., Number One Potato Pl., Lewisville, ID 83431: Free booklets ■ *Idahoan Recipes with Potatoes* "dressing up" a potato and *Idahoan Recipe Collection* that contains easy-to-prepare recipes with potatoes, including breakfast dishes, side dishes, main dishes, breads, rolls, and desserts. 800–547–4577.

International Olive Oil Council, P.O. Box 2197, J.A.F. Station, New York, NY 10116: Free booklet ■ *From Asia to the Mediterranean: Cultural Models for Healthy Eating Recipes.* A collection of international favorites, including gazpacho and soups, appetizers, salads, vegetables, fish, main dishes, and desserts.

Kellogg Company, Food & Nutritions Communications, P.O. Box 3447, Department P–2, Battle Creek, MI 49016: Free recipe booklets ■ Free brochures available include: *Favorite Corn Flake Crumb Recipes (#6230530), Favorite Microwave Recipes (#6230525), Favorite Rice Krispies Recipes (#6230505),* and Kellogg's Favorite Recipe Collection (#6230520).

Kikkoman Kitchens, P.O. Box 420784, San Francisco, CA 94142: Free brochures with long SASE ■ *Spice Up Your Meals with Kikkoman Teriyaki Sauces, A Rainbow of Flavors with Kikkoman Stir-Fry Sauce,* and *The Art of Stir-Frying with Kikkoman Sauces.*

Knouse Foods, Fruit'N Sauce Recipes, 800 Peach Glen/Idaville Rd., Peach Glen, PA 17375: Free brochure ■ *Fruit'N Sauce Recipes* contains recipes for cakes, salads, muffins, desserts, vegetable side dishes, and drinks using Fruit'N Sauce. 717–677–8181.

Thomas J. Lipton, Inc., P.O. Box 1100, Grand Rapids, MN 55745: Free brochures ■ Describes recipes using Lipton teas. In-

cludes: *Family Fun Beverages; Herbal Teas... What's in It for Me; Savor the Moment, Lipton Herbal Teas; Tea Time, A Guide from Lipton to the Pleasures of Tea; Tea, A Natural Fitness Beverage;* and *Naturally Decaffeinated Tea...It's Right for Today's Lifestyle.*

Thomas J. Lipton, Inc., P.O. Box 1100, Grand Rapids, MN 55745: Free brochures ■ Offers several publications on nutrition and health. Includes: *A Diet for Life; Diet and Disease Prevention; Snacking, The Great American Pastime; Feeding Baby; The Healthy Appetite Guide from Healthy Sensation Dressings; Lite'n Up, A Guide to Healthy Living; Pregnancy, A Time for Good Nutrition; Tea as a Fitness Beverage;* and *Cholesterol and Fats: Getting to the Heart of the Matter.*

Thomas J. Lipton, Inc., P.O. Box 1100, Grand Rapids, MN 55745: Booklet $1.75 ■ *Wish-Bone Salads Plus Much More Cookbook* explains how to use Wish-Bone salad dressings to make appetizers, vegetables, pasta, salads, meat, poultry, fish and seafood, sandwiches and breads, relishes, sauces, and glazes.

Thomas J. Lipton, Inc., P.O. Box 1100, Grand Rapids, MN 55745: Booklet 50¢ ■ *The Lite Guide to Fitness* describes simple and effective ways to exercise and how to prepare savory, reduced-calorie recipes with Wish-Bone Lite Dressings.

Thomas J. Lipton, Inc., P.O. Box 1100, Grand Rapids, MN 55745: Booklet $1.25 ■ *Knox Light to Luscious Cookbook* includes recipes for appetizers, salads, low-calorie dishes, desserts, jams and jellies, salads, vegetables, cakes and pies, beverages, and others.

Lucky Leaf Test Kitchens, Dept. 2 (Microwave Cookbook), Peach Glen, PA 17375: Free booklet ■ *Cooking with Microwave* contains recipes that use applesauce to make appetizers, salads, vegetable dishes, main dishes, desserts, and dessert sauces. 717–677–8181.

Lucky Leaf Test Kitchens, Dept. 2 (Regular Cookbook), Peach Glen, PA 17375: Free booklet ■ *Kitchen Tested Recipes* explains how apples and apple juice can be used to prepare appetizers, salads, vegetable dishes, main dishes, and desserts. 717–677–8181.

Mahatma Brown Rice Recipes, P.O. Box 2636, Houston, TX 77252: Brochure 50¢ ■

Describes recipes for salads, side dishes, entrees, and desserts with Mahatma Brown Rice.

Mahatma Light Lean & Low Fat Recipe Book, P.O. Box 2636, Houston, TX 77252: Book $2.50 ■ Contains 97 versatile rice recipes using white and brown rice that reflect today's nutritional and taste preferences.

Mahatma Magic Touch Rice Dishes, P.O. Box 2636, Houston, TX 77252: Brochure 35¢ (Available nationally, except Northeast) ■ Describes recipes from the Riviana Kitchens that use Mahatma Seasoned Rice mixes to make side dishes, entrees, and salads. 713–525–9550.

Maine Sardine Council, 470 N. Main St., P.O. Box 337, Brewer, ME 04412: Free brochure ■ *The Maine Sardine Story* explains how to use sardines from the can to make cucumber and sardine sandwiches, Maine sardine pesto and pasta, sardine spread, other sandwiches, casseroles, and others. 207–989–2180.

Marin French Cheese Company, P.O. Box 99, Petaluma, CA 94953: Free brochure ■ *Rouge et Noir Fancy Cheeses* includes recipes for canapes, Camembert appetizer mold, Camembert rounds, Camembert Mousse, dips, and others. 707–762–6001.

Musselman's Test Kitchens, Dept. 2 (Microwave Cookbook), Division of Knouse Foods, Biglerville, PA 17307: Free booklet ■ *Microwave Recipes* explains how Musselman's fruits and fruit juices can be used to prepare appetizers, beverages, vegetable dishes, stuffing, main dishes, desserts, and fruit sauces. 717–677–8181.

Musselman's Test Kitchens, Dept. 2 (Regular Cookbook), Division of Knouse Foods, Biglerville, PA 17307: Free booklet ■ *Musselman's Favorite Recipes* contains recipes that use Musselman's fruits and fruit juices. Includes beverages, breads, main dishes, salads and dressings, vegetables, cookies, cakes and pies, and desserts. Also recipes that use Musselman's sugar-free natural products. 717–677–8181.

National Broiler Council, Communications Division, P.O. Box 5806, Columbia, SC 2250: Free brochures with long SASE ■ *Chicken How to Cut and Bone It* contains main-course recipes with boned chicken and shows how to cut and bone chicken. Other brochures include *Chicken Food for Fitness, Chicken, An International Favorite, Chicken*

Microwaves in Minutes, Chicken Great on the Grill, and *Chicken, for Special Occasions.* 803–254–8158.

The National Live Stock & Meat Board, Order Processing Department, 444 N. Michigan Ave., Chicago, IL 60611: Booklet 50¢ ■ *Facts about Versatile Veal* ■ Contains information that covers the selection and storage, step-by-step descriptions of basic cooking methods, cookery timetables and nutrition, and taste-tempting recipes with veal. 312–670–9440.

The National Live Stock & Meat Board, Order Processing Department, 444 N. Michigan Ave., Chicago, IL 60611: Free brochures ■ *Versatile Veal* describes delicious, easy-to-prepare recipes. *Veal, It's Worth Going Out For* describes different cuts of veal and basic cooking methods. *Veal, A Lean Alternative* provides facts about veal with the most recent information on veal's nutritional content and gourmet recipes. *Favorite Veal* describes winning recipes from the Beef Industry Council's recipe contest. 312–670–9440.

National Turkey Federation, 11319 Sunset Hills Rd., Reston, VA 22090: Brochures 15¢ with long SASE ■ Offers many publications with tips and recipes for cooking turkeys. Includes: *User-Friendly Microwave Turkey Recipes, Grill Thrills, Low-fat Turkey Cuisine for Singles and Duets, Roasting a Whole Turkey: As Simple As 1-2-3, Eat to Your Heart's Content, Turkey Deli! Makes Meals Fast as a Heartbeat, Turkey Planned Overs, Turkey for Today's Low-fat Lifestyle, Uncover the Facts About Ground Turkey, Turkey Burgers, Turkey Makes Meals Fast and Fit,* and *Turkey A Quality Product.* 703–435–7209.

North American Blueberry Council, P.O. Box 166, Marmora, NJ 08223: Brochure 50¢ with long SASE ■ *The Blueberry Bulletin* includes facts on the North American Blueberry Industry - where blueberries are grown, nutritional news, how they are used and how to buy, prepare, and freeze blueberries; and how to use them in six recipes.

North American Blueberry Council, P.O. Box 4, Ocean City, NJ 08226: Cookbook $4.95 ■ *Let Blueberries Reign* is a collection of famous blueberry recipes.

North American Blueberry Council, P.O. Box 538, Tuckahoe, NJ 08250: Folder 50¢ with long SASE ■ *Traditional Recipe Folder* that describes how to make blueberry muf-

fins, sauce, cheese tart, cobbler, lattice-topped pie, and coffeecake.

Oklahoma Peanut Commission, Box D, Madill, OK 73446: Free Free brochures ■ *How to Cook a Peanut* explains how to blanch, french fry, oil roast, dry roast, and sugar-coat peanuts, and includes recipes. *It's Easy to Be a Gourmet with Peanuts...The Good Buys in Many Ways* contains recipes for main dishes, vegetables, soups, salads, fruit dressings, breads, sandwiches, cakes and frostings, pies, cookies, and others, using peanut butter. *Microwave Magic* describes how to use the microwave to prepare peanut main dishes, cakes and frostings, cookies, muffins, pies, and candies. *Recipes from Your Oklahoma Peanut Commission* explains how to make peanut brittle, cream candies using peanut butter, peanut butter fudge, no-bake peanut butter cookies, peanut butter milkshake, and others. 405–795–3622.

Peanut Advisory Board, 1950 N. Park Pl., Ste. 525, Atlanta, GA 30339: Free brochures ■ *Ready Recipes* is a collection of time-saving recipes that feature peanut butter. *Peanut Butter Lovers* contains recipes for peanut butter cookies. 404–933–0357.

Pickle Packers International, Inc., P.O. Box 606, St. Charles, IL 60174: Free brochures ■ *Perk Up Meals with Pickle Power* describes how to make better tasting burgers, chicken, cheesedogs, and sandwiches. *Shape Up with Pickles* contains 13 recipes that have 250 or fewer calories. *Sweet & Dill Pickle Salad Cubes* includes 10 recipes that use sweet pickle salad cubes. 708–584–8950.

Recipes for Success, P.O. Box 2636, Houston, TX 77252: Brochure 50¢ ■ Contains 23 recipes using Success White, Brown, and Mixes.

River Brown Rice Health & Diet Tips, P.O. Box 2636, Houston, TX 77252: Brochure 50¢ (Available in Northeast) ■ Contains recipes for preparing brown rice custard, raisin-nut-rice dessert, brown rice surprise casserole, creole shrimp and rice, and others.

River Brown Rice Recipes, P.O. Box 2636, Houston, TX 77252: Brochure 50¢ (Available in Northeast) ■ Describes 14 easy-to-prepare recipes with nutritional analysis of each recipe. Includes salads, side dishes, entrees, and desserts.

Roman Meal Company, Dept. PRF, P.O. Box 11126, Tacoma, WA 98411: Free booklets ■ *12 Sandwiches Under 200 Calories with Roman Meal Light Bread* includes special sandwich recipes for calorie counters. *Diet & Nutrition Plan* describes a 14–day balanced menu plan for dieting. *Roman Meal Low Cholesterol Sandwich Tips* offers nutritional tips on lowering dietary cholesterol, with recipes for turkey and smoky salmon sandwiches.

San-J International, Inc., 2880 Sprouse Dr., Richmond, VA 23231: Free brochures ■ *Tamari Soy Sauce Guide & Recipes* includes recipes that use Tamari Soy Sauce to prepare peanut chicken, potato bread, almond rice salad, macadamia nut ice cream, mustard sauce, and others. *Quick Tips for San-J Sauces* describes how to make foods more flavorful. *Tamari Soy Sauce Guide and Recipes* includes recipes for a mustard sauce, mayonnaise, salad dressings, potato bread, peanut chicken, macadamia nut ice cream, and almond rice salad. *Sizzling Szechuan Tips and Recipes* shows how to make Szechuan corn muffins, Szechuan hot peppered beef, and Szechuan guacamole. 804–226–8333.

Sioux Honey Association, 301 Lewis Blvd., P.O. Box 388, Sioux City, IA 51102: Free booklets ■ *Bake in Freshness with Sue Bee Honey* has recipes for bagels, pies, bread, muffins, carrot cake, honey yogurt cheesecake, honey frosting, and candy. *Microwave Magic Recipes with Sue Bee Honey* contains a collection of recipes for microwave cooking. *Pantry Pleasers from Sue Bee Honey* includes recipes that show how honey can be used to prepare jams, jellies, and marmalades. *Recipes for Preserving with Sue Bee Honey* explains how honey can be used to prepare pickles and preserves. *Sue Bee Honey Recipes for Health-Conscious Actives* includes recipes for "natural" meals. *Sue Bee "Life-Style" Recipes* presents over 60 recipes as proof that honey can be used to make entrees, salads, vegetables, pastries, treats, and snacks delicious and exciting.

The Sugar Association, 1101 15th St. NW, Ste. 600, Washington, DC 20005: Free booklet ■ Describes the functional role of sugar in baking and preserving, as well as its use in dairy products, confectionery, cereals, beverages, and processed foods. Includes 20 recipes. 202–785–1122.

The Sugar Association, 1101 15th St. NW, Ste. 600, Washington, DC 20005: Booklet

$2 ■ Features the best recipes from the national 1991 Chef's Sugar Secrets Contest. Premier chefs share how they use sugar in their favorite entrees, appetizers, sauces, and breads. 202–785–1122.

Sunkist Growers, Inc., Consumer Affairs Department, Box 7888, Van Nuys, CA 91409: Free booklets with long SASE (enclose separate envelope with each booklet requested) ■ *Sunkist Mock Cocktails* contains ideas for party themes and non-alcoholic drink recipes. *Put the Squeeze on Salt, Fat and Cholesterol with Sunkist Lemons* describes how fresh citrus enhances flavor and reduces sodium, fat, and cholesterol. Also contains several fresh citrus recipes. *Grab Your Slice of Life* contains fitness and nutrition information, along with some delicious lower calories fresh citrus recipes. *Fresh-Squeezed Tips for Diabetics* explores the role of fresh citrus fruits in a diabetic meal plan and includes recipes for persons on diabetic diets. 818–986–4800.

Sweet Adelaide Enterprises, Inc., 12918 Cerise Ave., Hawthorne, CA 90250: Free recipes ■ *Paula's California Herb Vinegars, Oils, and Herb Seasonings* includes suggestions for creating imaginative and subtly flavored tastes. 310–970–7840.

Sweet Potato Council of the U.S., Harold Hoecker, SPC-EdP 2, P.O. Box 14, McHenry, MD 21541: Booklet 50¢ with long SASE ■ *Cooking with Sweet Potatoes* includes 57 different ways to prepare sweet potatoes.

Texas Peanut Producers Board, P.O. Box 398, Gorman, TX 76454: Free brochure with long SASE ■ *Santa's Peanuts* contains hints for peanut storage and instructions for making "Old Fashioned" peanut butter, plus recipes for the holidays, including appetizers, soup, meats, pies, cakes, cookies, and candies. 817–734–2853.

Texasweet Citrus Advertising, Inc., Consumer Facts Brochures, P.O. Box 2497, McAllen, TX 78502: Free brochures with long SASE ■ *Stop and Rediscover the Sweeter, Juicier Grapefruit from Texas* includes nutritional information, easy steps to sectioning grapefruit, quick and easy meal ideas, selection and storage tips, and helpful hints for measuring and preparing Texas Citrus. *Ruby-Sweet Recipe Leaflet* contains mouth-watering recipes, other tidbits, "how to build a gift basket," and an order form to order grapefruit spoons. 512–682–2861.

Timber Crest Farms, 4791 Dry Creek Rd., Healdsburg, CA 95448: Free brochures ■ *Cooking with Dried Tomato Halves, Cooking with Dried Tomato Bits, Cooking with Marinated Dried Tomatoes,, Organically Grown Apricot Recipe Booklet,* and *California Prunes, Plum Good Recipes.* 707–433–8251.

USA Dry Pea & Lentil Council, 5071 Hwy. 8 West, Moscow, ID 83843: Free brochures ■ *Six Heart-Healthy Recipes Using Lentils and Split Peas* includes cooking instructions for split peas and lentils, and describes how these products can be used in healthful menu planning. *Lentils & Split Peas Recipes for the '90s* describes the nutritional benefits that lentils and split peas provide and includes a variety of new recipes. 208–882–3023.

Virginia-Carolina Peanut Promotions, P.O. Box 1709, Rocky Mount, NC 27802: Free booklet ■ *Peanut Classics Traditional Recipes* contains recipes for peanut butter, sugar-coated peanuts, peanut candies, including brittles and crunch, pies, cookies, cakes, frostings, soup, and sandwiches. 919–446–3097.

Washington Apple Commission, P.O. Box 18–ROF, Wenatchee, WA 98807: Free brochure with long SASE ■ *Washington Apples* explains how to store and choose apples, and includes recipes for apple pie, apple cobbler, quick apple tarts, spicy baked apples, Waldorf salad, and apple fruit salad. 509–663–9600.

Washington Apple Commission, P.O. Box 18–ROF, Wenatchee, WA 98807: Free brochure with long SASE with 75¢ postage ■ *The Romance of Flavors* includes recipes from America's master chefs. 509–663–9600.

Washington Red Raspberry Commission, Marketing & Promotion Office, 1626 N. Atlantic Office, Spokane, WA 99205: Free brochure with long SASE ■ Red Raspberry Recipe Brochure and Nutritional Information. Other publications include the *Raspberry Recipe of the Month* brochure for 25¢ with a long SASE, and *The Remarkable Red Raspberry Cookbook* for $9.95.

Wisconsin Milk Marketing Board, 8418 Excelsior Dr., Madison, WI 53717: Free brochures with long SASE ■ Includes: *Cheese Lover's Recipes from Wisconsin, Naturally Delicious Cottage Cheese, Creativity with Cottage Cheese, Wisconsin Cheese and California Wine - A Natural Pair, 24 Easy Ways with Wisconsin Cold Pack Cheese, Wisconsin Cheese - Your Grand Finale, Showcase of Premier Pizza Chefs, Showcase of Premier Supermarket Chefs, Pass it On...Milk, It Does a Body Good! Wisconsin Cheese in a Flash - A Guide to Choosing and Using Wisconsin Cheese,* and *A Slice of Lifestyle.*

RECORDS, CASSETTES & CDs

Children's Recordings

Audiofidelity Enterprises, Inc., P.O. Box 86, Rahway, NJ 07065: Free information ■ Children's videos and records, and vintage video movie and jazz classics. 908–388–5000.

Children's Recordings, P.O. Box 1343, Eugene, OR 97440: Free catalog ■ Children's music and stories on records and tapes. 503–485–1634.

A Gentle Wind, P.O. Box 3103, Albany, NY 12203: Free information ■ Music and story cassettes for children ages 1 to 12. Includes selections from the American Library Association's Notable Children's Recording Program. 518–436–0391.

Music for Little People, Box 1460, Redway, CA 95560: Free catalog ■ Musical cassettes and videos, and musical instruments for children. Includes famous stories, favorite songs, lullabies, nature stories, and folk and classical music. 707–923–3991.

Video Revolution, 97 Thoreau St., Concord, MA 01742: Free catalog ■ Audio and video tapes for children. 800–342–3436.

Collectible Recordings

Aardvark Music, P.O. Box 69441, Los Angeles, CA 90069: Catalog $1 ■ Hard-to-find and old records.

American Pie, Box 66455, Los Angeles, CA 90066: Catalog $2 ■ Hard-to-find 45s from the past 40 years. 213–821–4005.

A–1 Record Finders, 5639 Melrose Ave., Los Angeles, CA 90038: Free information ■ Hard-to-find and old records and vintage sounds. 213–RECORDS.

Benedikt & Salmon Record Rarities, 3020 Meade Ave., San Diego, CA 92116: Free catalogs (indicate choice of (1) classical (2) jazz, big bands, and blues (3) personalities, soundtracks, and country music) ■ Hard-to-find rare records from 1890 to date, early phonographs, cylinders, autographed memorabilia, and rare books on music and the performing arts. 619–281–3345.

Beverly Records & Costumes, 111612 S. Western Ave., Chicago, IL 60643: Free information ■ Long-playing old records and 45s. 312–779–0066.

Bornand Music Box Company, 139 4th Ave., Pelham, NY 10803: Free list ■ Rare music box recordings, and restored Swiss cylinder and disk type music boxes. 914–738–1506.

Broadway-Hollywood Recordings, P.O. Box 496, Georgetown, CT 06829: Catalog $2 ■ Rare, out-of-print soundtrack show albums and other recordings. 203–748–1266.

Chad & Jeremy Music, 2527 W. Kennewick Ave., Kennewick, WA 99336: Free information with long SASE ■ Hard-to-find and old recordings. 509–783–3114.

Collectables Records, Box 35, Narberth, PA 19072: Free catalog ■ Rhythm and blues records from the 1970s.

Compact Disc Collectibles, 29555 Northwestern Hwy., #613, Southfield, MI 48034: Catalog $3 ■ Rare and hard-to-find compact disks. 313–681–1161.

Cosmopolitan Bookshop, 7007 Melrose Ave., Los Angeles, CA 90064: Free information with long SASE ■ Hard-to-find records. 213–938–7119.

C.C. Crowe's Recollections, P.O. Box 6006, Woodland Park, CO 80866: Free catalog ■ Picture sleeves, 45s, and children's records, from the 1950s to the 1980s. 719–687–6896.

Final Decade, P.O. Box 1693, Old Chelsea Station, New York, NY 10011: Catalog $2 ■ Hard-to-find compact disks. 212–929–5462.

Finest Records, 2400 8th Ave., Greeley, CO 80631: Free information ■ Radio shows, 12-inch records, compact disks, and long-playing records from the 1960s, 1970s, and 1980s. 303–352–5390.

Flip Side Records & Collectables, 215 Arch St., Meadville, PA 16335: Free information ■ Music and other vintage sounds from the 1920s to the 1980s, and later. 914–333–9403.

Forty-Fives, P.O. Box 358, Lemoyne, PA 17043: Catalog $2 ■ Hard-to-find long-playing vinyl records and vintage 45s from 1950 to the present. 212–877–5020.

G & A Rare Records, 139 W. 72nd St., New York, NY 10024: Free information ■ Records and other vintage sounds. 212–877–5020.

Gurley's Records, Box 995, Princeton, NC 27569: List $2 (refundable) ■ Rare and old 33s, 45s, 78s and soundtracks.

The House of Music, 2057 W. 95th St., Chicago, IL 60643: Free information with long SASE ■ Hard-to-find records, tapes, and compact disks. 312–239–4114.

Don Maris, Box 20075, Arlington, TX 76007: Free list ■ Superman, Batman and Robin, and other 1940s radio shows on cassettes. 817–261–8745.

Metro Music, P.O. Box 10004, Silver Spring, MD 20904: Free information with long SASE ■ Recordings from the 1960s and modern garage and psych sounds. 301–622–2473.

Midnight Recordings, P.O. Box 390, Old Chelsea Station, New York, NY 10011: Free catalog ■ Hard-to-find and rare issues vinyl records and compact disks. 212–675–2768.

Music Machine, 10367 Reisterstown Rd., Owings Mills, MD 21117: Free information with long SASE ■ Rock rarities, collectibles, oddities, and other recordings. 410–356–4567.

Music Mailorder, P.O. Box 20708, Milwaukee, WI 53220: Free catalog ■ Rare and imported records, tapes, compact disks, videos, books and magazines, posters, and other collectibles. 414–321–SPIN.

1940 Jukebox & Record Company, 8919 N. Washington, Thornton, CO 80229: Free information ■ Hard-to-find and rare 45s and 78s. 303–288–4230.

Nodomestix CD Importers, P.O. Box 399, River Edge, NJ 07661: Free catalog ■ Hard-to-find compact disks. 201–599–9714.

Old Homestead Records, P.O. Box 100, Brighton, MI 48116: Free information ■ New and used long-playing records and used 45s and 78s. 313–227–1997.

Oldies Unlimited, Box 17122, Cleveland, OH 44117: Free list with long SASE ■ Original label 45s. Includes rockabilly, doo-

wops, 1960s garage, girl groups, Beatles, Elvis, and others.

Old Tyme Music Scene, 915 Main St., Boonton, NJ 07005: Free information ■ Long-playing records, 78s, and 45s, from Elvis to other oldies. 201–335–5040.

Bill Orenstein Recordings USA, P.O. Box 1665, Studio City, CA 91604: Free information with long SASE ■ Out-of-print modern jazz, big bands, and vocals on long-playing records. 818–985–3728.

Roger C. Ott, P.O. Box 2095, Oak Lawn, IL 60455: Free catalog ■ Albums, cassettes, and singles from the 1950s, 1960s, 1970s, and 1980s. 708–598–0270.

Pack Central, Inc., 6745 Denny Ave., North Hollywood, CA 91606: Catalog $2 ■ Records and cassettes from the 1950s, 1960s, 1970s, and 1980s. 818–760–2828.

Park Avenue Record & CD Exchange, 532 Queen Ave. North, Seattle, WA 98109: Free information with long SASE ■ Compact disks, imports, and out-of-print and rare long-playing records, 45s, and 78s. 206–284–2390.

Pete's Records, 203 E. Morris St., Dalton, GA 30721: Free information with long SASE ■ Out-of-print long-playing records and 45s; rock, country, and soul compact disks and cassettes; and old rock magazines. 404–226–7112.

Record Affair, P.O. Box 351553, Los Angeles, CA 90035: Free price list ■ Rare jazz and vocal long-playing records. 213–937–8776.

Record Collector, 1158 N. Highland, Los Angeles, CA 90038: Free information ■ Rare classical and jazz long-playing records. 213–467–2875.

Record Gems, 486 Merrick Rd., Oceanside, NY 11572: Free catalog ■ Hard-to-find records in all categories, from the 1920s to the 1980s. 516–764–3355.

ReRun Records, P.O. Box 680267, Orlando, FL 32668: Free information ■ Hard-to-find 45s and long-playing soul, R & B, jazz, and blues records. 407–293–8329.

Ed Schreiber, P.O. Box 2704, Huntington Beach, CA 92647: Beatles catalog $2 ■ Original Beatles memorabilia and recordings.

Sound Track Album Retailers, P.O. Box 487, New Holland, PA 17557: Free catalog

■ Sound tracks, cast recordings, compact disks, long-playing records, and imports. 717–656–0121.

Sun TV Records, 1202 Pine Island Rd., Cape Coral, FL 33909: Free information with long SASE ■ Hard-to-find and rare long-playing records and 45s. 813–574–7372.

John Tefteller, P.O. Box 1727, Grants Pass, OR 97526: Free information ■ Rare 45s, 78s, and a few long-playing records. Includes rhythm and blues, rockabilly, rock 'n roll, and country music. 503–476–1326.

Ten Thousand Hits, P.O. Box 365, Bellmawr, NJ 08099: Free catalog ■ Original recordings of hits on 45s, from the 1950s to the present.

Yesterday Sounds, Box 852, Richboro, PA 18954: Catalog $2.50 ■ Hard-to-find original 45s and long-playing records and new re-issues. 215–364–7832.

Current Recordings

Arhoolie Records, 10341 San Pablo Ave., El Cerrito, CA 94530: Catalog $1 ■ Old-time folk lyric blues and classics, specializing in roots and regional music. 510–525–1494.

Art on Video, 12 Havemeyer Pl., Greenwich, CT 06830: Information $1 ■ Classic and newly released VHS and Beta videos of artists, exhibitions, museum collections, art and craft techniques, photography, and fashions. 203–869–4694.

Audio Editions, Books on Cassette, 1133 High St., Auburn, CA 95603: Free catalog ■ Best sellers, business and management, classics, drama and poetry, all-time favorites, books for young people, personal growth subjects, and language cassette recordings. 916–888–7803.

Audio-Forum, 96 Broad St., Guilford, CT 06437: Free catalog ■ Full-length courses for teaching yourself a foreign language. 800–551–6300.

Audiofidelity Enterprises, Inc., P.O. Box 86, Rahway, NJ 07065: Free information ■ Children's videos and music, vintage video movie classics, and jazz classics. 908–388–5000.

Audio House Compact Disk Club, 4304 Brayan, Swartz Creek, MI 48473: Free information ■ Used compact disks. 313–655–8639.

Baltimore CD Connection, 5720 Pimlico Rd., Baltimore, MD 21209: Catalog $6 ■ Imported titles and other compact disks. 410–444–7332.

Barnes & Noble, 126 5th Ave., New York, NY 10011: Free catalog ■ Records, cassettes, and books. 800–242–6657.

The Beautiful Music Company, 155 E. Main St., Smithtown, NY 11787: Free catalog ■ Bluegrass and country, marches, instrumentals, jazz, gospel, big bands and favorite artists, classics and opera, and barbershop quartet recordings.

Berkshire Record Outlet, Inc., Rt. 102, Pleasant St., Lee, MA 01238: Free catalog ■ Classical music recordings. 413–243–4080.

Book of the Road, 7175 SW 47th St., Ste. 202, Miami, FL 33155: Free information ■ Popular novels on audio cassettes. 305–667–5762.

Caedmon Records, Inc., 1995 Broadway, New York, NY 10023: Free catalog ■ Classical music on cassettes and records. 212–580–3400.

Classic Recordings, 2054 28th St. SE, Southridge Center, Grand Rapids, MI 49512: Free information Compact and laser disks. 800–433–8979; 616–957–3614 (in MI).

Compact Disc Warehouse, 456 El Camino Real, Sunnyvale, CA 94087: Free information ■ Domestic and imported compact disks. 800–899–1017; 408–730–1017 (in CA).

Compact Music, 1105 Webster, Sandy, UT 84094: Free catalog ■ Used compact disks. 801–571–9767.

Concord Records, Inc., P.O. Box 845, Concord, CA 94522: Free catalog ■ Classical recordings on compact disks. 510–682–6770.

Coronet, 311 Bainbridge, Philadelphia, PA 19147: Free information ■ Save up to 30 percent on compact disks and cassettes. 215–925–2762.

Country Music Hall of Fame, 4 Music Square East, Nashville, TN 37203: Free catalog ■ Cajun, bluegrass, old-time and early country classics, country fiddling, western swing and cowboy, Elvis Presley and rock, gospel, and Christmas albums, cassettes, compact disks, books, and song books. 800–255–2357.

Ken Crane's, 14260 Beach Blvd., Westminster, CA 92683: Free catalog ■ Pioneer laser disks. 800–624–3078; 800–626–1768 (in CA).

Critics' Choice Video, P.O. Box 549, Elk Grove Village, IL 60009: Free catalog ■ Records, tapes, video cassettes, and books. 800–544–9852.

Crystal Records, 2235 Willida Ln., Sedro Woolley, WA 98284: Free catalog ■ Chamber music recordings on records, compact disks, or cassettes. 206–856–4779.

Dercum Audio, 910 Waltz Rd., P.O. Box 1425, West Chester, PA 19380: Free information ■ Mysteries, science fiction, classic literature, and other books for adults and children on cassettes. 215–430–8889.

Digital Sounds, 1378 S. Rangeline Rd., Carmel, IN 46032: Free information ■ Pop, rock, jazz, classical, New Age, country music, soul, easy listening, and other compact disks. 317–846–3734.

Dove Books on Tape, Inc., 12711 Ventura Blvd., Studio City, CA 91604: Free catalog ■ Books recorded on tape. 800–762–6662.

Down Home Music Company, 10341 San Pablo Ave., El Cerrito, CA 94530: Free sample newsletters; blues, country, and vintage rock and roll catalogs, $5 each ■ Records, tapes, compact disks, music books, and videos, from around the world. 510–525–1494.

Peter Dunn's Vinyl Museum, 2000 Gulf-To-Bay Blvd., Clearwater, FL 34625: Free information with long SASE ■ All types of music on records. 813–442–4656.

Express Music Catalog, 175 5th Ave., New York, NY 10010: Catalog $10 ■ Tapes, compact disks, long-playing records, and video cassettes. 800–233–6357; 212–254–6161 (in NY).

Final Decade, P.O. Box 1693, Old Chelsea Station, New York, NY 10011: Catalog $1 ■ Hard-to-find and current compact disks. 212–929–5462.

Folk-Legacy Records, Inc., Box 1148, Sharon, CT 06069: Free information ■ Country folk music on records, compact disks, and cassettes. 800–836–0901; 364–5661 (in CT).

Gambler's Bookstore, 135 N. Sierra St., Reno, NV 89501: Free information ■ Cassettes on achieving personal success, succeeding in the stock market, business, and finance. Others describe how to win at sports betting, poker, blackjack, keno, baccarat, craps, roulette, and other games. 702–786–6209.

Gasparo, P.O. Box 120069, Nashville, TN 37212: Free catalog ■ Classical recordings on compact disks. 615–254–8460.

Graceland Records, c/o Joe Carter, 209 Main St., Marlboro, MA 01752: Free information with long SASE ■ Elvis Presley records. 508–485–0884.

Haverstick & Bally, 4040 W. Kennedy Blvd., Tampa, FL 33609: Free catalog ■ Classical compact disks. 800–222–6872; 813–882–0104 (in FL).

Hear Records, 921 Eastwind Dr., Ste. 114, Westerville, OH 43081: Free catalog ■ Recordings for all moods and interests. 800–432–7365.

Heartland Music, 1341 Ocean Ave., Box 106, Santa Monica, CA 90401: Free catalog ■ Big-band, nostalgic, patriotic, romantic, inspirational, gospel, be-bop, rock n' roll, country, and easy listening music. 800–788–2400.

Hot Wax Records, 722 Rue Orleans, New Orleans, LA 70116: Free information with long SASE ■ Records for all moods and interests. 504–834–6114.

It's Only Rock 'N Roll, 49 West 8th St., New York, NY 10011: Free information ■ Long-playing records, cassettes, videos, books, and magazines

J & R Music World, 59–50 Queens-Midtown Expy., Maspeth, NY 11378: Free catalog ■ Records, cassettes, and video tapes. 800–221–8180.

Keep the Faith, Inc., 810 Belmont Ave., P.O. Box 8261, North Haledon, NJ 07508: Free catalog ■ Audio tapes, video tapes, and books on Catholicism. 800–221–1564; 201–423–5395 (in NJ).

Kicking Mule Records, P.O. Box 158, Alderpoint, CA 95411: Free catalog ■ Compact disks, cassettes, music books, long-playing records, and teaching tapes for guitar, banjo, dulcimer, fiddle, harp, harmonica, and other instruments. 800–262–5312.

Klavier Records, Box 177, San Juan Capistrano, CA 92675: Free catalog ■ Professional recordings of band organs and calliopes on compact disks, records, and cassettes.

Kromer, 53 Louella Ct., Wayne, PA 19087: Free list with long SASE ■ Carrousel organ music, tapes, records, and music rolls; new and rebuilt organs. 215–687–0172.

Laser House, 1409 W. 14 Mile Rd., Ste. 264, Madison Heights, MI 48071: Catalog $2 (refundable) ■ Compact disks and laser video disks. 313–875–6040.

Lyric Distribution, Inc., P.O. Box 235, Roslyn Heights, NY 11577: Catalog $1 ■ Operatic treasures on video tapes, cassettes, and compact disks. 516–625–0588.

The Mechanical Maestro, 1300 3rd St., St. Paul, MN 55106: Free information ■ Traditional and contemporary Christian songs played on a circus calliope. 512–774–2590.

Media Exchange, Box 126, South Milwaukee, WI 63172: Free catalog ■ New and used compact disks. 414–762–9235.

Metro Music, P.O. Box 10004, Silver Spring, MD 20904: Free New Wave or 1960s catalog with two 1st class stamps ■ Records from the 1960s and New Wave recordings. 301–622–2473.

Metronome, 1531 Piedmont Ave. NE, Atlanta, GA 30324: Free information with long SASE ■ New, used, and imported long-playing records, cassettes, and compact disks. 404–488–9800.

Midnight Recordings, P.O. Box 390, Old Chelsea Station, New York, NY 10011: Catalog $3 ■ Rock compact disks, long-playing records, imports and U.S. pressings from the 1960s, blues, and other recordings from the 1950s. 212–675–2768.

Mobymusik, 14410 Ventura Blvd., Sherman Oaks, CA 91423: Catalog $1 ■ Rock, heavy metal, New Wave recordings, jazz, and independent labels on imported and domestic long-playing records, tapes, and compact disks. 818–881–9908.

Music Machine, 10367 Reistertown Rd., Owings Mills, MD 21117: Free information with long SASE ■ Rock, record rarities and oddities, and other recordings. 410–356–4567.

Old Homestead Records, P.O. Box 100, Brighton, MI 48116: Free information ■ New and used long-playing records and used 45s and 78s. 313–227–1997.

Olsson's Books & Records, 1239 Wisconsin Ave. NW, Washington, DC 20007: Free information ■ Classical, rock, jazz, folk music, and New Age recordings; other compact disks and cassettes; and books. 202–338–9544.

Roger C. Ott, P.O. Box 2095, Oak Lawn, IL 60455: Free catalog ■ Albums, cassettes, and singles from the 1950s, 1960s, 1970s, and 1980s. 708–598–0270.

Overseas Shopper, Box 22354, Portland, OR 97222: Free catalog ■ Rock, pop, and jazz music from Canada, Europe, and Japan. 503–652–7573.

OZ Warehouse, 1575 Hwy. P, Lawrenceville, GA 30245: Free catalog plus monthly updates ■ Compact disks. 404–962–6180.

Pack Central, Inc., 6745 Denny Ave., North Hollywood, CA 91606: Catalog $2 ■ Records and cassettes from the 1950s, 1960s, 1970s, and 1980s. 818–760–2828.

Park Avenue Record & CD Exchange, 532 Queen Ave. North, Seattle, WA 98109: Free information with long SASE ■ Compact disks, imports, out-of-print, and rare long-playing records, 45s, and 78s. 206–284–2390.

Performers' Choice, Box 560, Cazenovia, NY 13035: Free catalog ■ Home learning programs and classical music on compact disks and tapes. 315–655–9796.

Princeton Record Exchange, 20 Tulane St., Princeton, NJ 08542: Free information ■ New and used rock, jazz, and classical records and compact disks. 609–921–0881.

Putnam Supply, Inc., P.O. Box 1013, Putnam, TX 76469: Free catalog ■ Country music cassettes and records. 915–622–3213.

Radio Memories, Box 193, Yorktown Heights, NY 10598: Free information ■ Radio programs, many with the original commercials, from the 1930s, 1940s, and 1950s. 914–245–6609.

Raven Records, 1725 Cumberland Ave., Knoxville, TN 37916: Free information ■ Compact disks, long-playing records, and cassettes. 615–523–3898.

Reach Out, 7324 Noah Reid Rd., Chattanooga, TN 37421: Free catalog ■ Recordings with a Christian theme. 615–892–6814.

Record Hunter, 507 5th Ave., New York, NY 10017: Free catalog ■ Records, tapes, and cassettes. 212–697–8970.

Record-Rama Sound Archives, 4981 McKnight Rd., Pittsburgh, PA 15237: Free information ■ Albums, 45s, and compact disks. 412–367–7330.

Right Hemisphere, 19 S. Jackson St., Media, PA 19063: Free information ■ Records from the 1960s, 1970s, and out-of-print records, tapes, and compact disks. 215–566–1322.

Rockaway Records, 2390 N. Glendale Blvd., Los Angeles, CA 90039: Free information with long SASE ■ Recordings by the Beatles and Elvis Presley. 213–664–2135.

Marion Roehl Recordings, 3533 Stratford Dr., Vestal, NY 13851: Free catalog ■ Carrousel organ, player piano, music box, and saloon piano recordings. 607–797–9062.

ROIR, 611 Broadway, New York, NY 10012: Free catalog ■ New Wave and heavy metal recordings on cassettes. 212–477–0563.

Rose Records, 214 S. Wabash, Chicago, IL 60604: Free catalog ■ New releases, imports, and overstocks of classical, folk, blues, pop, jazz, soul, and country music records. 800–955–ROSE.

Sound Source, P.O. Box 35780, Los Angeles, CA 90035: Free information ■ Imported compact disks. 213–857–5701.

Stamford Records, 2331 Summer St., Ridgeway Center, Stamford, CT 06905: Free information with long SASE ■ New and used records for all listening interests. 203–356–0014.

Time-Warner Video, 100 Enterprise Pl., P.O. Box 7023, Dover, DE 19903: Free catalog ■ Hard-to-find videos on many subjects. 800–624–9909.

Walking Tapes, Box 767364, Roswell, GA 30076: Free catalog ■ Marches, Latin, country, swing, classical, and new age recordings to play while walking. 404–993–4233.

The Wax Museum, 1505 Elizabeth Ave., Charlotte, NC 28204: Free information ■ Hard-to-find recordings.

Windham Hill Records, P.O. Box 9388, Stanford, CA 94309: Free catalog ■ Jazz, guitar, and children's records. 415–329–0647.

Radio Recordings

Adventures in Cassettes, 5353 Nathan Ln., Plymouth, MN 55442: Free information ■ Old radio shows on cassettes as originally aired in the 1930s and 1940s. 612–553–2000.

Adventures Recordings, P.O. Box 4822, Inglewood, CA 90302: Catalog $1 ■ Radio programs from yesteryear. 213–641–3180.

George Brehm, 13402 Liebacher Ave., Norwalk, CA 90650: Free information ■ Recordings of radio programs.

BWP Radio, Inc., 1105 N. Main St., Ste. 9–E, Gainesville, FL 32601: Catalog $5 (refundable) ■ Cassette recordings of famous old-time radio shows from the 1930s, 1940s, and 1950s. 904–377–7480.

Carl R. Froelich, Heritage Farm, New Freedom, PA 17349: Free catalog ■ Old-time radio programs on cassettes. 717–235–6122.

McCoy's Recording, Inc., P.O. Box 1069, Richland, WA 99352: Catalog $2 (refundable) ■ Music, drama, comedies, westerns, and mysteries, from the 1920s to the 1960s, on audio cassettes.

Postings, P.O. Box 8001, Hilliard, OH 43026: Free catalog ■ Recordings of radio programs. 800–262–6604.

Radio/Video Yesteryear, Box C, Sandy Hook, CT 06482: Free information ■ Recordings of radio programs.

Soundtracks

Broadway-Hollywood Recordings, P.O. Box 496, Georgetown, CT 06829: Catalog $2 ■ Rare, out-of-print soundtrack show albums and other recordings. 203–748–1266.

Disc-Connection-Records, Tapes, CDs, 10970 W. Pico Blvd., Los Angeles, CA 90064: Free information with long SASE ■ Rare movie and Broadway soundtracks. 310–208–7211.

Conrad J. Doerr, 3973 Glenfeliz, Los Angeles, CA 90039: List $2.50 (refundable) ■ Broadway show soundtracks with featured vocalists and big bands. 213–663–6416.

Sound Track Album Retailers, P.O. Box 487, New Holland, PA 17557: Free catalog ■ In-print and out-of-print foreign and domestic soundtracks and cast recordings. 717–656–0121.

World of Cinema, 488 Henley Ave., New Milford, NJ 07646: Catalog $2 ■ Sound tracks, movie posters, cinema books, and other memorabilia. 201–262–3513.

Storage Cabinets

Davidson-Whitehall Company, 555 Whitehall St., Atlanta, GA 30303: Free information ■ Compact disk storage cabinets. 404–524–4534.

Hills Products, Inc., P.O. Box 1015, Hillsboro, NH 03244: Free information ■ Compact disk storage cabinets. 800–247–2018.

HY-Q Enterprises, 3003 Arapahoe St., Denver, CO 80205: Free information ■ Storage cabinets for compact disks, VHS video cassettes, and audio tapes. 800–878–7458.

Lorentz Design, Inc., 287 S. Jackson St., Denver, CO 80209: Free information ■ Compact disk storage cabinets. 800–933–0403.

Mallard Pond Creations, P.O. Box 722, Cherryville, NC 28021: Free information ■ Cassette player/recorder tape storage cabinets. 704–732–4708.

The Market Tree, Ltd., P.O. Box 609, Boone, NC 28607: Free information ■ Compact disk and cassette storage cabinets. 800–344–5116.

Per Madsen Design, P.O. Box 330101, San Francisco, CA 94133: Free brochure ■ Stackable, portable units for disk and tape storage. 415–928–4509.

Sorice, P.O. Box 747, Nutley, NJ 07110: Free information ■ Audio and video disk and cassette storage cabinets. 800–432–8005.

Univenture, P.O. Box 570, Dublin, OH 43017: Free catalog ■ Binder-type compact disk storage organizers. 614–761–2669.

RECYCLED & ENVIRONMENTALLY SAFE PRODUCTS

Alte Schule U.S.A., 704 E. Palace Ave., Santa Fe, NM 87501: Free information ■ Recycled pads, notebooks, diaries, sketchbooks, gift wrap, envelopes, stationery, and other paper products. 505–983–2593.

Atlantic Recycled Paper Company, P.O. Box 11021, Baltimore, MD 21212: Free catalog ■ Office and restroom paper supplies. 410–323–2676.

Bio-Pax Division, Diversified Packaging Products, 1265 Pine Hill Dr., Annapolis, MD 21401: Free catalog ■ Recycled paper packaging supplies. 410–974–4411.

Borlin Industries, 11960 Wilshire Blvd., Los Angeles, CA 90025: Free catalog ■ Non-ecotoxic and biodegradable household cleaners and detergents, baby care products, and natural body care products. 800–825–4540.

Canusa Corporation, 1616 Shakespeare St., Baltimore, MD 21231: Free catalog ■ Computer and copier paper. 410–522–0110.

Clothcrafters, Inc., P.O. Box 176, Elkhart Lake, WI 53020: Free catalog ■ Reusable kitchen supplies and cotton bags, 100 percent cotton diapers, and other environmentally sensitive products. 414–876–2112.

Conservatree Paper Company, 10 Lombard St., Ste. 250, San Francisco, CA 94111: Free catalog ■ Office paper supplies. 415–433–1000.

Co-Op America Catalog, 2100 M St. NW, Ste. 403, Washington, DC 20063: Free catalog ■ Environmentally sensitive products, from reusable coffee filters to hi-tech items, and recycled paper items. 202–223–1881.

Diamond Paper, P.O. Box 7000, Sterling, VA 22170: Free catalog ■ Office paper supplies. 703–450–0000.

DMP (Direct Mail Press), 9335 Fraser Ave., Silver Spring, MD 20910: Free catalog ■ Recycled paper products. 301–585–7077.

Earth Care Paper, Inc., P.O. Box 14140, Madison, WI 53714: Free catalog ■ Note cards, stationery, gift wrappings and holiday cards, office paper supplies, and other recycled paper products. 608–277–2900.

Earthforms, P.O. Box 65303, Baltimore, MD 21209: Free information ■ Recycled business cards, notepads, stationery and envelopes, and other paper products. 410–486–4099.

Ecco Bella, 6 Provost Square, Ste. 602, Caldwell, NJ 07006: Free catalog ■ Environmental-related products. Includes cosmetics and skin care items, personal care products, health and healing products, hair care

preparations, household products, pet products, energy savers, and recycled paper items. 800–888–5320.

Ecover, Inc., P.O. Box 1576, Norwalk, CT 06852: Free information ■ Biodegradable household cleaning products.

Energy Savers, RD Associates, Box 99, New Rochelle, NY 10804: Free catalog ■ Innovative products that conserve energy. 800–228–6500.

Graphic Advantage, Inc., P.O. Box 1711, Paramus, NJ 07653: Free information ■ Recycled memo pads. 201–652–0725.

Real Goods, 966 Mazzoni St., Ukiah, CA 95482: Free catalog ■ Solar electricity-operated lighting, tankless water heating, water-saving appliances, composting toilets, gas appliances, and recycled paper products. 800–762–7325.

The Recycled Paper Company, 185 Corey Rd., Boston, MA 02146: Free catalog ■ Stationery and copier paper. 617–277–9901.

Save Energy Company, 2410 Harrison St., San Francisco, CA 94110: Free catalog ■ Products for home and garden that save energy, resources, and money. 800–326–2120.

Seventh Generation, Colchester, VT 05446: Free catalog ■ Facial tissues, paper towels, other recycled paper products; biodegradable garbage bags, soap, diapers, and household cleaners; solar powered watches, radios, and flashlights; and other recycled and biodegradable items. 800–456–1197.

Tic-La-Dex, 3443 Camino Del Rio South, Ste. 326, San Diego, CA 92108: Free catalog ■ Recycled plastic envelopes and book covers. 800–827–9467; 619–281–7242.

ROCKS, MINERALS & FOSSILS

Display Cases & Lights

Blacklight Specialties, 1854 Alcatraz, Berkeley, CA 94703: Free information ■ Ultraviolet lamps, fluorescent minerals, accessories and supplies, papers, paints, and inks. 510–653–4424.

Display Case Company, P.O. Box 880, Exmore, VA 23350: Free catalog ■ Crystal clear boxes and display cases. 804–442–2299.

Fluorescent Minerals Company, 5106 Walnut Grove Ave., San Gabriel, CA 91776: Free brochure ■ Fluorescent lamps for minerals. 800–833–6757.

Hot Springs Souvenir & Rock Company, 805 E. Grand Ave., Hot Springs National Park, AR 71901: Free information ■ Display stands and light boxes. 501–624–4672.

Lustig International, P.O. Box 2051, San Leandro, CA 94577: Free information ■ Display stands. 800–221–4456.

O'Brien Manufacturing, 2081 Knowles Rd., Medford, OR 97501: Free information ■ Oak show cases with tempered glass, built-in plunger locks, halogen lighting, and roller bearing doors. 503–773–2410.

Sylmar Sales, 670 Corral Cir., Dewey, AZ 86327: Free information ■ Display stands for slabs, shells, fossils, minerals and rocks, and geodes.

Fossils

Ackley's Rock & Stamps, 3230 N. Stone Ave., Colorado Springs, CO 80907: Catalog $1 (refundable) ■ Fossils, lapidary and silversmith supplies, jewelry boxes and trays, and mountings and findings. 719–633–1153.

Adirondack Gem & Rock Shop, 64 Petroua Ave., P.O. Box 668, Saranac Lake, NY 12983: Free information with long SASE ■ Mineral specimens, fossils, slabs, cabochons, and other rockhound and gemstone items. 518–891–3390.

The Amber Company, 5643 Cahuenga Blvd., North Hollywood, CA 91601: Free price list ■ Amber, beads, fossils, ethnic jewelry, books, faceting and cabbing rough, lapidary supplies, decor accessories, and gemstones. 818–509–5730.

B & B Jewelcraft, Box 80, Quartzsite, AZ 85346: Free list with long SASE ■ Rocks, minerals, and fossils. 602–927–6329.

Hal Bach's Rock Shop, 137 Marne Rd., Cheektowage, NY 14215: Free information ■ Fossils, minerals, and rock specimens. 716–896–6559.

Bitner's, 42 W. Hatcher, Phoenix, AZ 85021: Free information ■ Rocks, minerals, and fossils. 602–870–0075.

Black Hills Institute of Geological Research, Inc., 217 Main St., P.O. Box 643, Hill City, SD 57745: Free information ■ Cretaceous ammonites, eocene fishes, oligocene mammals, dinosaurs, and other fossils. 605–574–4289.

Bourget Bros., 1636 11th St., Santa Monica, CA 90404: Catalog $5 ■ Fossils, gemstones, cabochons, wax patterns, beads, and bead-stringing and jewelry-making supplies. 800–828–3024; 310–450–6556 (in CA).

Box Elder Trading Post, 300 Box Elder Rd., Box Elder, SD 57719: Price list $1 ■ Fossils, minerals, and other rock specimens. 605–923–4390.

Ebersole Lapidary Supply, Inc., 11417 West Hwy. 54, Wichita, KS 67209: Catalog $2 ■ Fossils, petrified woods, rock specimens, tools, jewelry findings, mountings, cabochons, and jewelry kits. 316–722–4771.

Extinctions, 303 Carlisle Ave., York, PA 17404: Free catalog ■ Trilobites, crinoids, vertebrates, ferns, and other specimens. 717–846–4111.

Frances' Stones, 13101 Spring Run Rd., Midlothian, VA 23112: Free information with long SASE ■ Mineral specimens, geodes, fossils, cabochons, and other supplies. 804–739–3981.

Geo-Impressions, P.O. Box 989, Pelham, NH 03076: Catalog $1 ■ Common to rare vertebrates and invertebrates. 603–635–7923.

Jeanne's Rock & Jewelry, 5420 Bissonet, Bellaire, TX 77401: Free information ■ Petrified wood products, fossils, seashells, lapidary supplies, and gifts. 713–664–2988.

Malick's Fossils, 5514 Plymouth Rd., Baltimore, MD 21214: Catalog $3 ■ Fossils and other artifacts. 410–426–2969.

Maruskiya's of Nome, 100 Front St., Nome, AK 99762: Free price list ■ Mastodon ivory, teeth, and bones; fossilized walrus ivory and teeth; oosiks; reindeer and moose antlers; and Alaskan ivory carvings.

Prehistoric Journeys, P.O. Box 3376, Santa Barbara, CA 93130: Catalog $3 ■ Rare vertebrate fossils and dinosaur bones. 805–685–7825.

Rare Earths, 5511 W. Buffalo, Chandler, AZ 85226: Free information with long SASE ■ Rocks, minerals, and fossils. 602–940–0856.

J.F. Ray, P.O. Box 1364, Ocala, FL 32678: Catalog $3 (refundable) ■ Shark teeth, al-

ligator and dinosaur parts; tribolites, insects, amber, mammal teeth and bones; crinoid calyxes, echinoids, achipods, starfishes, ammonites, protozoans, corals, plants, and bryozoans; and marine items. 904–595–4721.

The Rock Hut, 706 Harrison Ave., Leadville, CO 80461: Free information with long SASE ■ Thumbnail mineral specimens, fossils, tools and supplies, and ultraviolet lamps. 719–486–2313.

Rock Shop, 5511 Todville Rd., Box 444, Seabrook, TX 77586: Price list $3 ■ Faceted gemstones, cabochons, rock and mineral specimens, geodes, artifacts, and fossils. 713–474–2488.

Skullduggery, 621 South B St., Tustin, CA 92680: Catalog $2 ■ Fossil replicas. 800–336–7745.

Stratagraphics, 63 Knolltop Dr., Rochester, NY 14610: Catalog $1 ■ Fish, mammals, reptiles, other vertebrate fossils, and petrified wood specimens.

Village Rock Shop, 346 S. Chicago, Hot Springs, SD 57747: Free price list ■ Petrified wood specimens and prepared and unprepared fossils. 605–745–5446.

Warfield Fossil Quarries, Box 316, HRC 61, Thayne, WY 83127: Catalog $2 ■ Fish, leaves, turtles, reptiles, tribolites, ammonites, and other fossils. 307–883–2445.

Meteorites

Bethany Sciences, P.O. Box 3726, New Haven, CT 06525: Catalog $2 ■ Stones, irons, stony-iron meteorites, display stands, jewelry, and books. 203–393–3395.

Robert Haag Meteorites, P.O. Box 27527, Tucson, AZ 85726: Catalog $5 (refundable) ■ Buys, sells, and trades meteorites. 602–882–8804.

Martin's Star Tracker, 633 S. Broadway, Boulder, CO 80301: Free information ■ Meteorites, telescopes, and accessories. 303–449–0805.

Mineralogical Research Company, 15840 E. Alta Vista Way, San Jose, CA 95127: Free list with long SASE and 2 first class stamps ■ Meteorites, rare mineral specimens, microscopes, micro mounts, and specimen boxes. 408–923–6800.

David New, P.O. Box 278, Anacortes, WA 98221: Free list ■ Meteorites, tektites, and

minerals from worldwide sources. 206–293–2255.

Ward's Natural Science, P.O. Box 92912, Rochester, NY 14692: Free information with long SASE ■ Meteorites, telescopes and accessories, audio-visual aids, and books. 716–359–2502.

Miscellaneous Varieties

Ace's Rock Shop, 3914 Washington, Kansas City, MO 64111: Free information with long SASE ■ Mineral specimens, cabochons, crystal specimens, lapidary equipment, silversmith and jeweler supplies, and ultraviolet equipment. 816–561–2004.

Adirondack Gem & Rock Shop, 64 Petroua Ave., P.O. Box 668, Saranac Lake, NY 12983: Free information with long SASE ■ Mineral specimens, fossils, slabs, cabochons, and other rockhound and gemstone items. 518–891–3390.

Aleta's Rock Shop, 1515 Plainfield NE, Grand Rapids, MI 49505: Catalog $1.50 (refundable with $10 order) ■ Mineral specimens, rocks for cutting and tumbling, lapidary equipment, and silversmith supplies. 616–363–5394.

Allen's Rocks & Gifts, 26513 Center Ridge Rd., Cleveland, OH 44145: Free information with long SASE ■ Minerals, findings, silversmith supplies, casting and lapidary equipment, tools, and other supplies. 216–871–6522.

Arizona Gems & Minerals, Inc., 414 5th St., P.O. Box 1432, Safford, AZ 85546: Catalog $1 ■ Geodes, silversmithing and lapidary tools, jewelry-making supplies, and mineral sets. 602–428–5164.

Arrow Gems & Minerals, Inc., P.O. Box 9068, Phoenix, AZ 85068: Free catalog ■ Pewter figurines, pendants, buckles, bolas, beads and findings, minerals, and faceted stones. 602–997–6373.

Aurora Mineral Corporation, 16 Niagara Ave., Freeport, NY 11520: Free information ■ Amethyst, geodes, fossil fishes, quartz crystals, and mineral specimens from around the world. 516–623–3800.

B & B Jewelcraft, Box 80, Quartzsite, AZ 85346: Free list with long SASE ■ Rocks, minerals, and fossils. 602–927–6329.

Bitner's, 42 W. Hatcher, Phoenix, AZ 85021: Free information ■ Rocks, minerals, and fossils. 602–870–0075.

Blacklight Specialties, 1854 Alcatraz, Berkeley, CA 94703: Free information ■ Ultraviolet lamps and accessories and fluorescent minerals. 510–653–4424.

Box Elder Trading Post, 300 Box Elder Rd., Box Elder, SD 57719: Price list $1 ■ Minerals, rocks, and fossils. 605–923–4390.

Carousel Gems & Minerals, 1202 Perion Dr., Belen, NM 87002: Free information with long SASE ■ Thumbnail and cabinet mineral specimens and rare gemstones. 505–864–2145.

Charlie's Rock Shop, 620 J St., Penrose, CO 81240: Catalog $3 (refundable) ■ Mineral specimens, jewelry supplies and findings, tools, and beads. 800–336–6923.

Colorado Gem & Mineral Company, P.O. Box 424, Tempe, AZ 85281: Free list with long SASE ■ Crystals and faceted gemstones that include tourmaline and amethyst from Brazil, Pakistan, Uruguay, and Bolivia. 602–966–6626.

Crystal Cavern Minerals, Inc., 1800 Arnold Palmer Dr., El Paso, TX 79935: Free price list ■ Mineral specimens. 915–593–1800.

Cureton Mineral Company, P.O. Box 5761, Tucson, AZ 85703: Free information ■ Rare minerals and meteorites. 602–743–7239.

Desert Discoveries, 12131 Boron Ave., Boron, CA 93516: Free information with long SASE ■ Mineral specimens, sets, and supplies and accessories.

Frances' Stones, 13101 Spring Run Rd., Midlothian, VA 23112: Free information with long SASE ■ Mineral specimens, geodes, fossils, cabochons, and supplies and accessories. 804–739–3981.

Galas Minerals, 6000 Fulkerth Rd., Turlock, CA 95380: Free information with long SASE ■ Mineral specimens. 209–634–4292.

Gemco International, P.O. Box 833, Fayston, VT 05673: Free information ■ Facet rough gemstones and small cut stones. Save on some slightly or moderately flawed. 802–496–2770.

Girdauskas Minerals, 2 Cleveland Dr., Poughkeepsie, NY 12601: Free list ■ Native minerals and unusual specimens in micro and cabinet sizes. 914–298–9216.

Margo Sara Gitlin, P.O. Box 2644, Glenville, NY 12325: Price list $1 ■ Mineral specimens and cutting rough.

Kenneth Glasser, P.O. Box 441, Monsey, NY 10952: Catalog $12 ■ All types, sizes, and qualities of rough diamonds. 914–426–1241.

Grayson Lapidary, Inc., 5135 Washington St., Hillside, IL 60162: Free information ■ Micromounts from the United States, Italy, Germany, South Africa, and Greece. Thumbnail to cabinet size specimens from the United States, India, Russia, Norway, England, and Scotland. 708–449–1399.

Grieger's, P.O. Box 93070, Pasadena, CA 91109: Free catalog ■ Minerals and rare stones from around the world, lapidary equipment, jewelry supplies and findings, and mountings. 800–423–4181; 800–362–7708 (in CA).

HRM Minerals, Assay Office, Marshall Mint, 98 North C St., P.O. Box 888, Virginia City, NV 89440: Catalog $2 (refundable) ■ Minerals, metals, and nuggets from remote and hidden mines. 702–847–0777.

India Nature's Statement, P.O. Box 1533, Bellflower, CA 90706: Free information ■ Thumbnail and cabinet size specimens of Apophyllite and zeolite from India. 310–920–2614.

International Gems & Minerals Corporation, P.O. Box 3017, Long Island City, NY 11103: Free information ■ Mineral specimens. 718–204–7439.

Knight's Gem Stones, Box 411, Waitsfield, VT 05673: Free information with long SASE ■ Gem rough stones in different grades. 802–496–3707.

MACAJAC Mineral Specimens, 6088 S. Clayton St., Littleton, CO 80121: Free list ■ Thumbnail to cabinet size American and foreign crystal and mineral specimens.

Mineralogical Research Company, 15840 E. Alta Vista Way, San Jose, CA 95127: Free list with long SASE and 2 first class stamps ■ Mineral specimens and meteorites, microscopes, micromounts, specimen boxes, and supplies. 408–923–6800.

North American Minerals, 10710 Kenwood Rd., Ste. 122, Cincinnati, OH 45242: Free information ■ Cave-in-rock fluorite specimens, octahedrons, and other mineral specimens. 513–271–8307.

H. Obodda Mineral Specimens, P.O. Box 51, Short Hills, NJ 07078: Free list ■ Afghan and Pakistani pegmatite minerals and other specimens. 201–467–0212.

Oceanside Gem Imports, Inc., P.O. Box 222, Oceanside, NY 11572: Free price list ■ Mineral specimens, gemstones, and faceting rough. 516–678–3473.

Donald K. Olson & Associates, P.O. Box 858, Bonsall, CA 92003: Free information ■ Mineral specimens from worldwide locations. 619–758–2388.

The Outcrop, P.O. Box 2171, Springfield, IL 62705: Free list with 1st class stamp ■ Thumbnail to small cabinet size mineral specimens from around the world. 217–787–6149.

Gene Paul Minerals, Division of the Redhead, Inc., 2 Shadow Ln., Montvale, NJ 07645: Free information ■ Mineral specimens. 201–391–5955.

Precam Minerals, P.O. Box 1371, Huntington Beach, CA 92647: Free information ■ Mineral specimens and lapidary equipment. 800–331–0774.

Precious Earth Company, P.O. Box 39, Germantown, WI 53022: Free list ■ Iron, copper, and lead specimens from Wisconsin and Michigan mines, and other minerals from worldwide sources. 800–558–8558; 414–255–4540 (in WI).

Rare Earths, 5511 W. Buffalo, Chandler, AZ 85226: Free information with long SASE ■ Rocks, minerals, and fossils. 602–940–0856.

The Rock Hut, 706 Harrison Ave., Leadville, CO 80461: Free information with long SASE ■ Thumbnail mineral specimens, fossils, tools and supplies, and ultraviolet lamps. 719–486–2313.

Russell's Rock Shop, 27911 North St., North Liberty, IN 46554: Free information ■ Gem trees and supplies, bookends, agate slabs, amethyst, cabs, findings, slabs, and lucite stands. 219–289–7446.

Rusty's Rock Shop, 4106 Buckingham Dr., Decatur, IL 62526: Free price list ■ Fluorite octahedrons, pyrite suns, and other mineral specimens. 217–877–7122.

Salt Minerals, 540 Beaverbrook St., Winnipeg, Manitoba, Canada R3N 1N4: Free list ■ Specimens from worldwide locations.

Star Minerals, P.O. Box 610–243, North Miami, FL 33161: Free list ■ Thumbnail to cabinet size mineral specimens from worldwide sources.

Les Tolonen Mineral Specimens, P.O. Box 581, Baraga, MI 49908: Cave-in-Rock fluorite and other minerals, Michigan copper and silver minerals, and Missouri lead minerals, and plastic mineral bases and mounting putty. 906–353-7285.

V–Rock Shop, 4760 Portage St. NW, North Canton, OH 44720: Free information ■ Cabochons, beads, pearls, faceted stones, display stands, pyramids, enhydros, citrine, and Brazilian agate; quartz specimens; and amethyst geodes and plates. 800–45V–ROCK; 216–494–1759 (in OK).

Western Minerals, Gene & Jackie Schlepp, P.O. Box 43603, Tucson, AZ 85733: Free information ■ Mineral collections, mining and mineralogical books, microscopes, goniometers, and alidades. 602–325–4534.

What on Earth, The Continent Shopping Center, 6262 Busch Blvd., Columbus, OH 43229: Free information with long SASE ■ Mineral specimens, fossils, and gemstones. 614–436–1458.

Whole Earth Minerals, P.O. Box 50058, Reno, NV 89503: Free information with long SASE ■ Rare minerals, other thumbnail specimens, and old and out-of-print books. 702–786–6432.

Willis' Earth Treasures, 116 Prospect St., Stewartsville, NJ 08886: Free information with long SASE ■ Mineral specimens. 908–859–0643.

Wright's Rock Shop, Rt. 4, Box 462, Hot Springs, AR 71913: Catalog $2 ■ Quartz, tourmaline and healing crystals; marcasite; other minerals and fossils; and lapidary equipment. 501–767–4800.

Petrified Wood

Beaver-Hood Company, P.O. Box 177, Prineville, OR 97754: Free price list ■ Polished specimens of exotic, rare, tropical, ancient, and extinct woods; and petrified seeds, ferns, cones, and leaves.

Burnett Petrified Wood, Inc., 37420 Sodaville Cutoff Dr., Lebanon, OR 97355: Free information ■ Petrified wood specimens. 503–258–3320.

Ebersole Lapidary Supply, Inc., 11417 West Hwy. 54, Wichita, KS 67209: Catalog

$2 ■ Tools, findings, mountings, cabochons, rocks, and petrified wood. 316–722–4771.

Herkimer Diamond Mines, P.O. Box 510, Herkimer, NY 13350: Free information ■ Petrified wood, mineral and rock specimens, quartz crystals, and gifts. 315–891–7355.

Jeanne's Rock & Jewelry, 5420 Bissonet, Bellaire, TX 77401: Free information ■ Petrified wood, seashells, lapidary supplies, and gifts. 713–664–2988.

Red & Green Minerals, Inc., 7595 W. Florida Ave., Lakewood, CO 80226: Free information ■ Petrified wood, faceting rough, crystal specimens, books, and magazines. 303–985–5559.

Riviera Lapidary Supply, 30192 Mesquite, Riviera, TX 78379: Catalog $3 ■ Petrified wood, cabochons, slabs, cabbing rough, gemstones, crystals, beads, and bead-stringing supplies. 512–296–3958.

ROLLER SKATES & SCOOTERS

Chicago Roller Skate Company, 4245 W. Lake St., Chicago, IL 60624: Free information ■ Roller skates. 312–826–1177.

Dominion Skate Company, Ltd., 45 Railroad St., Brampton, Ontario, Canada L6X 1G4: Free information ■ Roller skates and scooters. 416–453–9860.

Kryptonics, Inc., 5660 Central Ave., Boulder, CO 80301: Free information ■ Roller skates and skateboards. 303–442–9173.

National Sporting Goods Corporation, 25 Brighton Ave., Passaic, NJ 07055: Free information ■ Roller skates, scooters, and skateboards. 201–779–2323.

Roller Derby Skate Company, 311 W. Edwards St., Litchfield, IL 62056: Free information ■ Roller skates, scooters, and skateboards. 217–324–3961.

Saucony/Hyde, P.O. Box 6046, Centennial Industrial Park, Peabody, MA 01961: Free information ■ Roller skates, scooters, and skateboards. 508–532–9000.

Variflex, Inc., 5152 N. Commerce Ave., Moorpark, CA 93021: Free information ■ Roller skates and skateboards. 805–532–0322.

RUBBER STAMPS

Aladdin Stamps & Celebrations, P.O. Box 354, Elk Grove, CA 95759: Free catalog with two 1st class stamps ■ Alphabet, flower, animal and teddy bear, butterfly, and shell rubber stamps. 916–686–5970.

Arben Stamp Company, 413 Main St., P.O. Box 353, Evansville, IN 47703: Catalog $2.50 ■ Rubber stamps and accessories. 800–223–3086; 812–423–4269 (in IN).

Bizzaro Rubber Stamps, P.O. Box 16160, Rumford, RI 02916: Catalog $1 ■ Rubber stamps and accessories. 401–728–9560.

Critter Prints, P.O. Box 630, Newport, WA 99156: Catalog $3 (refundable) ■ Animal and other rubber stamps and supplies.

Design Rubber Stamps, 55 7th Ave. South, New York, NY 10014: Catalog $2 (refundable with $10 order) ■ Custom and in-stock rubber stamps and accessories. 212–243–0357.

Embossing Arts, P.O. Box 626, Sweet Home, OR 97386: Catalog $2 ■ Rubber stamps and easy-to-use embossing powders.

Evermark Impressions, P.O. Box 9957, Canoga Park, CA 91309: Catalog $2 (refundable) ■ Fantasy stamps and accessories.

Festive Images, P.O. Box 566, Lomita, CA 90717: Free information with long SASE and two 1st class stamps ■ Rubber stamps and accessories. 310–519–9314.

Five Star Publications, P.O. Box 3142, Scottsdale, AZ 85271: Free catalog ■ Custom self-inking stamps, daters, and other rubber stamps and supplies. 602–941–0770.

Good Stamps..Stamp Goods, 30901 Timberline Rd., Willits, CA 95490: Catalog $2 (refundable) ■ Rubber stamps with an environmental theme. 707–459–9124.

Graphic Rubber Stamp Company, 11250 Magnolia Blvd., North Hollywood, CA 91601: Catalog $3.50 ■ Rubber stamps and accessories. 818–782–9443.

ImaginAir Designs, 1007 Woodland NW, Albuquerque, NM 87107: Catalog $2 ■ Aviation stamps and other designs. 505–345–2308.

Imprints Graphic Studio, Inc., P.O. Box 3656, Carmel, CA 93921: Catalog $3 ■ Rubber stamps and accessories. 408–373–7337.

Jackson Marketing Products, Brownsville Rd., Mt. Vernon, IL 62864: Free information ■ Supplies and equipment for making regular and pre-inked rubber stamps. 618–242–1334.

Kidstamps, Inc., P.O. Box 18699, Cleveland Heights, OH 44118: Free catalog ■ Rubber stamps and accessories. 800–727–5437.

The Lew Company, P.O. Box 3038, Montebello Hills, CA 90640: Catalog $2 (refundable) ■ Personalized rubber stamps.

Loving Little Rubber Stamps, 2 Spring St., Stoneham, MA 02180: Free catalog ■ Rubber stamps and accessories. 617–438–8396.

Luv 'N Stuff, P.O. Box 85, Poway, CA 92074: Catalog $2 (refundable) ■ Rubber stamps and accessories. 619–748–8060.

Museum of Modern Rubber, 102 S. Kraemer Blvd., Ste. 211, Placentia, CA 92670: Free catalog ■ Rubber stamps and accessories. 800–626–2408.

National Stampagraphic, 1952 Everett St., North Valley Stream, NY 11580: Subscription $16 a year ($18/Canada; $20/foreign) ■ Published quarterly, includes articles and information of interest to rubber stamp users, and advertisements from rubber stamp hobbyists, manufacturers, and distributors. 516–285–5587.

Neato Stuff, P.O. Box 4066, Carson City, NV 89702: Catalog $2 ■ Rubber stamps, accessories, rubber stamp jewelry, and card kits. 702–883–9351.

Once Upon a Stamp, P.O. Box 551, Forest Knolls, CA 94933: Catalog $2 (refundable) ■ Mounted and unmounted rubber stamps and accessories. 415–488–4223.

100 Proof Press, RR 1, Box 136, Eaton, NY 13034: Catalog $2 ■ Rubber stamps and accessories. 315–684–3547.

Outstamping, P.O. Box 2571, Anaheim, CA 92814: Catalog $3 (refundable) ■ Rubber stamps, fabric stamps, paper, pads, markers, embossing powders, and paper punches. 714–535–1593.

Paper Angel, Box 608, Mossyrock, WA 98564: Free brochure ■ Personalized calligraphy style rubber stamps. 206–983–8330.

Penny Black Rubber Stamps, P.O. Box 11496, Berkeley, CA 94701: Free catalog ■

Rubber stamps, accessories, and paper supplies. 510–849–1883.

Personal Stamp Exchange, 345 S. McDowell Blvd., Ste. 324, Petaluma, CA 94952: Catalog $4 ■ Rubber stamps and accessories. 707–763–8058.

P.O. Box Rubberstamps, 740 E. 19th St., Houston, TX 77008: Catalog $3.50 ■ Rubber stamps and accessories.

Purple Wave Stamp Designs, P.O. Box 5340, Ventura, CA 93005: Catalog $2.50 ■ Mounted and unmounted rubber stamps and accessories.

Purry Patterns Precious Pets, P.O. Box 1180, Penn Valley, CA 95946: Catalog $2 (refundable) ■ Animal rubber stamps and other stamps. 916–432–4932.

Quarter Moon Rubber Stamps, P.O. Box 611585, San Jose, CA 95161: Catalog $2.50 (refundable) ■ Rubber stamps and accessories. 408–272–0211.

Raindrops on Roses Rubber Stamp Company, 4808 Winterwood Dr., Raleigh, NC 27613: Catalog $2 ■ Country stamp sets, brush markers, and supplies. 919–846–8617.

Rubber Stamp Emporium, 4516 Lander Way, Salt Lake City, UT 84118: Catalog $2 (refundable with $10 order) ■ Rubber stamps and supplies that include animals, people, flowers and hearts, holidays and festive occasions, and miniatures; ink pads; and blank cards with envelopes.

The Rubberstampler, 1945 Wealthy SE, Grand Rapids, MI 49506: Catalog $2 (refundable) ■ Over 500 rubber stamps.

Rubberstampmadness, P.O. Box 6585, Ithaca, NY 14851: Sample copy $4; annual subscription (6 issues) $18; $20 Canada ■ Contains ideas on how to use rubber stamps, reviews on recent catalogs, articles about rubber stamp users, and sources for rubber stamps.

Rubber Stamp Romance, 1050 7th Ave., Santa Cruz, CA 95062: Catalog $2 (refundable) ■ Rubber stamps and accessories. 408–475–7391.

Rubber Stamps of America, P.O. Box 474, Saxtons River, VT 05154: Catalog $1 ■ Rubber stamps and accessories. 802–869–2622.

SonLight Impressions, 17517 Fabrica Way, Cerritos, CA 90701: Catalog $3 ■ Rubber stamps and accessories. 805–925–8182.

Stampberry Farms, 1952 Everett St., North Valley Stream, NY 11580: Catalog $2 (refundable) ■ Rubber stamps and accessories. 516–285–5587.

Stampendous, Inc., 1357 S. Lewis St., Anaheim, CA 92805: Catalog $3 ■ Rubber stamps, ink pads, brush markers, glitter glue, and other supplies. 800–869–0474; 714–773–9550 (in CA).

Stamp Francisco Rubber Stamps, 466 8th St., San Francisco, CA 04103: Catalog $2 ■ Rubber stamps and accessories. 415–252–5975.

Stampians, 5120 Whispering Oak Way, Paso Robles, CA 93446: Catalog $2.50 ■ Rubber stamps and accessories. 805–239–1717.

Stamp in the Hand, P.O. Box 5160, Long Beach, CA 90805: Catalog $3 ■ Rubber stamps and accessories. 310–403–7137.

Stamp Magic, P.O. Box 60874, Longmeadow, MA 01116: Catalog bear stamps $1; general interest stamps $1 ■ Rubber stamps and accessories.

Stamp Mill, 414 S. Mill Ave., Tempe, AZ 85281: Catalog $2 (refundable) ■ Rubber stamps and accessories. 602–894–6467.

Stamp Pad Company, Inc., P.O. Box 43, Big Lake, MN 55309: Free catalog ■ Rubber stamps with a country theme and accessories. 800–534–3717.

Stamps 'N' Such, 25412 S. Crenshaw Blvd., Torrance, CA 90505: Catalog $1 (refundable) ■ Rubber stamps and accessories. 310–539–6441.

Stewart-Superior Corporation, 1800 W. Larchmont Ave., Chicago, IL 60613: Free information ■ Rubber stamps, inks and ink pads, rollers, cleaners, sponge rubber, cements, and rubber stamp gum. 800–621–1205; 312–935–6025 (in IL).

Unique Impressions, 215 Clarose Ln., Jefferson City, MO 65109: Catalog $2 ■ Folk art rubber stamps and accessories. 314–893–4576.

Wildlife Enterprises, 2721 Mosquito Rd., Placerville, CA 95667: Catalog $2 ■ Patriotic rubber stamps. 916–626–5924.

Wood Cellar Graphics, RR 1, Box 146, Carroll, NE 68723: Catalog $2 ■ Rubber stamps with country designs. 402–585–4771.

Works of Art, P.O. Box 15007, Portland, OR 97215: Catalog $2 ■ Dual-use stamps for fabric and paper, paints, inks, and accessories.

RUGBY

Mitre Sports, Genesco Park, Room 609, Nashville, TN 37202: Free information ■ Balls and boots. 800–626–9380; 615–367–74754 (in TN).

Rugby Imports, Ltd., 885 Warren Ave., East Providence, RI 02914: Free information ■ Balls and uniforms. 401–438–2727.

Rugby & Soccer Supply, P.O. Box 565, Merrifield, VA 22116: Catalog $3 ■ Balls, boots, jerseys, and shorts. 703–280–5540.

RUG MAKING

Braid-Aid, 466 Washington St., Rt. 53, Pembroke, MA 02359 Catalog $4 ■ Braided rug kits and braiding accessories; hooking, basket-making, shirret, spinning, and weaving supplies and accessories; and wool by the pound or yard. 617–826–6091.

Edgemont Yarn Services, Inc., P.O. Box 205, Washington, KY 41086: Free price list ■ Weaving and rug-making supplies. 606–759–7614.

Harry M. Fraser Company, Rt. 3, Box 254, Stoneville, NC 27048: Catalog $2.50 ■ Rug-hooking and braiding supplies. 919–573–9830.

Great Northern Weaving, Box 3611, Augusta, MI 49012: Catalog $1 ■ Cotton and wool rags, warp, loopers, fillers and braiding equipment. 616–731–4487.

Suzanne McNeil, 401 N. Bailey, Fort Worth, TX 76107: Catalog $1 ■ Rug-making kits. 817–625–2627.

Claire Murray, Inc., P.O. Box 1089, North Charlesytown, NH 03630: Catalog $5 (refundable) ■ Ready-to-use hand-hooked rugs or kits. 800–323–9276.

Oriental Rug Company, P.O. Box 205, Washington, KY 41086: Free information ■ Rug-weaving supplies and equipment. Includes wools, floor and table looms, frames, cutters, shears and trimmers, rack shuttles threading hooks, loom stretchers, and counters. 606–759–7614.

OR Rug Company, P.O. Box 205, Washington, KY 41086: Free price list ■

Rug-weaving looms, loom parts and accessories, rags, prints, and looper clips, carpet warp, rug fillers, shears, rag cutter, and counters. 606–759–7614.

Ruggery, 565 Cedar Swamp Rd., Glen Head, NY 11545: Catalog $2 ■ Yarns, accessories, and other rug-making supplies. 516–676–2056.

Shillcraft, P.O. Box 7770, Baltimore, MD 21221: Catalog $2 ■ Latch-hooking kits and supplies for rugs, wall hangings, and other crafts. 410–682–3064.

RUGS & CARPETS

Abingdon Rug Outlet, 246 W. Main St., Abingdon, VA 24210: Free information with long SASE ■ Save up to 70 percent on hand-made rugs. 703–628–9821.

Adams & Swett, 964 Massachusetts Ave., Boston, MA 02118: Catalog $2 ■ Hand- and machine-braided wool rugs in early American and contemporary styles. 617–268–8000.

American Broadloom Braided Rug & Furniture Company, 404 Roosevelt Ave., Central Falls, RI 02863: Free information ■ Hand-braided wool rugs. 401–722–2017.

Armstrong World Industries, P.O. Box 3001, Lancaster, PA 17604: Free information ■ Carpets and rugs. 800–233–3823.

At Home in the Valley, Box 7303, Van Nuys, CA 91409: Catalog $1 ■ Braided rugs, chair pads, placemats, curtains, rocker sets, and rounds. 818–780–4663.

Aunt Philly's Toothbrush Rugs, P.O. Box 36335, Denver, CO 80236: Catalog $2 ■ Patterns, kits, and supplies for making rugs out of scrap materials.

Bearden Brothers Carpet & Textiles, 3200 Dug Gap Rd., Dalton, GA 30720: Free information with long SASE ■ Carpet, padding, and other floor coverings. 800–433–0074.

Betsy Bourdon, Weaver, Scribner Hill, Wolcott, VT 05680: Brochure $3 ■ Rugs, linens, and handwoven blankets. 802–472–6508.

Braid-Aid, 466 Washington St., Rt. 53, Pembroke, MA 02359: Catalog $2 ■ Rug braiding, hooking, quilting, shirret, spinning, and weaving supplies. 617–826–6091.

J.R. Burrows & Company, P.O. Box 522, Rockland, MA 02370: Catalog $5 ■ Custom period carpet reproductions by special order, and artistic wallpaper and fabrics. 617–982–1812.

Cabistan Oriental Imports, P.O. Box 1951, Dalton, GA 30722: Free catalog ■ Machine woven and handmade oriental wool rugs, and area and braided rugs. 800–252–6612.

Cameo Carpets, Dalton, GA 30722: Free information ■ Save up to 50 percent on carpet and vinyl floor covering. 800–343–4914.

Carpet Outlet, Box 417, Miles City, MT 59301: Free information ■ Carpets and rugs. 800–225–4351; 800–233–0208 (in MT).

Cooke Textile Company, P.O. Box 254, Angola, IN 46703: Free information with long SASE ■ Wool rugs. 219–665–2201.

Country Braid House, 29 Clark Rd., Tilton, NH 03276: Free brochure ■ Custom braided wool rugs. 603–286–4511.

Country Manor, Mail Order Department, Rt. 211, P.O. Box 520, Sperryville, VA 22740: Catalog $2 ■ Hand-woven cotton rugs, kitchen utensils and accessories, and other country crafts. 800–344–8354.

Country Rugs, RD 1, Box 99, Kintnersville, PA 18930: Brochure $1 ■ Hand-loomed wool and cotton rugs using methods of the early 1800s. 215–346–7068.

Custom Hooked Rugs, RFD 2, Box 213, Middle Jam Rd., Sebago Lake, ME 04075: Free information ■ Custom handmade wool rugs. 207–892–8660.

Dalton Paradise Carpets, P.O. Box 2488, Dalton, GA 30722: Free information ■ Carpets, rugs, and other floor coverings. 800–338–7811.

El Paso Saddleblanket Co., 601 N. Oregon, El Paso, TX 79901: Free catalog ■ Rugs handwoven by Indians in Mexico, plus U.S. wool rugs. 800–351–7847; 915–544–1000.

Ewesful Crafts-The Yorks, Rt. 1, 1041 7 Mile Rd., Athens, MI 49011: Free information ■ Handwoven rag rugs in cotton, cotton blends, and denim. 517–741–7949.

Family Heir-loom Weavers, RD 3, Box 59E, Red Lion, PA 17356: Catalog $3 ■ Carpets with historic patterns. 717–246–2431.

Folkheart Rag Rugs, 18 Main St., Bristol, VT 05443: Brochure $1 ■ Hand-stencilled cotton rag rugs. 803–453–4101.

Galaxy Carpet Mills, Inc., 850 Arthur Ave., Elk Grove Village, IL 60007: Free information ■ Stain-proof carpets with a rope-loop texture. 708–593–0555.

Gazebo of New York, 127 E. 57th St., New York, NY 10022: Catalog $6 ■ Handmade braided rugs and quilted pillows. 212–832–7077.

F.J. Hakimian, Inc., 136 E. 57th St., Ste. 201, New York, NY 10022: Free information ■ European and Oriental carpets, antique rugs, and period tapestries. 212–371–6900.

Heirloom Rugs, 28 Harlem St., Rumford, RI 02916: Catalog $2 ■ Hand-hooked rugs. 401–438–5672.

Heritage Rugs, P.O. Box 404, Bucks County, PA 18931: Catalog $1 ■ Custom wool rugs. 215–343–5196.

Charles W. Jacobsen, Inc., 401 N. Salina St., Syracuse, NY 13203: Free brochure ■ Hand-woven Oriental rugs. 315–422–7832.

Johnson's Carpets, 3239 S. Dixie Hwy., Dalton, GA 30720: Free information ■ Carpets and rugs. 800–235–1079; 404–277–2775 (in GA).

K & D Supply Company, 1440 Industrial Dr., Matthews, NC 28105: Catalog $3 ■ Authentic flat-braided rugs. 800–477–1400; 704–841–8003 (in NC).

Kaoud Brothers Oriental Rugs, 17 S. Main St., West Hartford, CT 06107: Catalog $5 ■ Oriental rugs. 203–233–6211.

Tom E. Knisely, Handweaver, 1785 York Rd., Dover, PA 17315: Brochure $1 ■ Traditional handwoven rugs and fabrics. 717–938–9920.

Larchmont Woolcrafters, 2630 Brannon Rd., Micholasville, KY 40356: Brochure $2 ■ Custom hand-hooked rugs. 606–223–2896.

Mills River, 713 Old Orchard Rd., Hendersonville, NC 28739: Catalog $2 ■ Flat-braided oval and round rugs. 800–874–4898.

Claire Murray, Inc., P.O. Box 1089, North Charlestown, NH 03603: Catalog $5 (refundable) ■ Hand-hooked rugs and hand-sewn quilts. Available in kits. 800–323–9276.

National Carpet, 1384 Coney Island Ave., Brooklyn, NY 11230: Catalog $3 ■ Reproduction Turkish antique carpets, hand-loomed Hungarian and Colonial Williamsburg rugs, Persian and Oriental rugs, Berbers, hand-hooked rugs, braided ovals, and others. 718–253–5700.

Network Floor Covering, 3200 Dug Gap Rd., Dalton, GA 30720: Free brochure ■ Save up to 80 percent on carpet. 800–442–2013.

Northstar Rag Rugs, P.O. Box 85, Bristol, VT 05443: Brochure $1 ■ Custom rugs. 802–453–2443.

Olde Mill House Shoppe, 105 Strasburg Pike, Lancaster, PA 17602: Catalog $1 ■ Braided rugs, country-style handcrafted furniture, homespun table linens, and bathroom accessories. 717–299–0678.

Paradise Carpets, Dalton, GA 30722: Free information ■ Factory direct carpet. 800–338–7811.

Peerless Imported Rugs, 3033 Lincoln Ave., Chicago, IL 60657: Catalog $1 ■ Hand- and machine-woven Oriental rugs, rag rugs, Navajo rugs, colonial braids, grass rugs, and tapestries from Europe. 800–621–6573.

Quality Discount Carpet, 1207 W. Walnut Ave., Dalton, GA 30720: Free brochure ■ Save up to 50 percent on carpets. 800–233–0993; 404–226–7611 (in GA).

Rastetter Woolen Mill, 5802 Star Rt. 39, Millersburg, OH 44654: Free information ■ Hand-woven rag rugs, throw rugs, stair runners and treads, area rugs, and wall-to-wall carpets. 216–674–2103.

Rug Factory Store, 560 Mineral Spring Ave., P.O. Box 249, Pawtucket, RI 02860: Catalog $2 ■ Braided rugs, rugs with contrasting borders, tweeds, Scandinavians, and multicolored Early American and traditional rugs. 401–724–6840.

S & S Carpet Mills, 2650 Lakeland Rd., Dalton, GA 30722: Free information ■ Save up to 50 percent on carpets. 800–241–4013.

Shillcraft, P.O. Box 7770, Baltimore, MD 21221: Catalog $2 ■ Supplies and patterns for latch hooking rugs, wall hangings, and pillow covers. 410–682–3064.

Southern Rug, 2325 Anderson Rd., Crescent Springs, KY 41017: Catalog $5 ■ Hand-

crafted, flat-braided rugs in blended wool yarns. 800–541–RUGS.

Southern Rug-Home Shopping, 6822 22nd Ave. North, Unit 124, St. Petersburg, FL 33702: Oriental rug catalog $5 ■ Hand-crafted braided rugs. 813–847–3894.

Sunbelt Flooring Brokers, Inc., Box 45063, Baton Rouge, LA 70895: Free information ■ Save up to 50 percent on carpet and vinyl floor coverings. 800–749–1804.

Traditional Country Crafts, Inc., Box 111, Landisville, PA 17538: Brochure $1 ■ Hand-loomed rag rugs and candles. 717–653–5969.

Trott Furniture Company, P.O. Box 7, Richlands, NC 28574: Catalog $5 ■ Oriental rugs and 18th-century solid mahogany, cherry, and walnut furniture. 800–682–0095; 919–324–3660 (in NC).

Village Carpet, 1114 Conover Blvd. West, Conover, NC 28613: Free brochure ■ Save up to 50 percent on carpet. 704–465–6818.

Warehouse Carpets, Inc., Box 3233, Dalton, GA 30721: Free information ■ Save up to 40 percent on rugs and carpets. 404–226–2229.

Weavery, Harriet Giles, 2305 Delong Rd., Lexington, KY 40515: Free information ■ Custom, handwoven cotton or wool rag rugs in historic and contemporary designs. 606–272–1910.

Thomas K. Woodard American Antiques & Quilts, 835 Madison Ave., New York, NY 10021: Catalog $5 ■ Classic American-style room-size area rugs and runners. 212–988–2906.

Yankee Pride, 29 Parkside Cir., Braintree, MA 02184: Catalog $3 (refundable) ■ Wool, hand-braided, hooked, and rag rugs; hand-crafted quilts; Dhurries; and comforters and bedspreads. 617–848–7610.

York Interiors, Inc., 2821 E. Prospect Rd., York, PA 17402: Free brochure ■ Oriental rugs. 800–723–7029.

RUNNING, JOGGING & WALKING

Clothing & Shoes

Academy Broadway Corporation, 5 Plant Ave., Vanderbilt Industrial Park, Smithtown,

NY 11787: Free information ■ Rainsuits. 516–231–7000.

Adidas USA, 15 Independence Blvd., Warren, NJ 07060: Free information ■ Shoes, shorts, singlets, socks, sweatbands, and warm-up suits. 908–580–0700.

Alchester Mills Company, Inc., 314 S. 11th St., Camden, NJ 08103: Free information ■ Socks, sweatbands, and safety vests. 609–964–9700.

Asics Tiger Corporation, 10540 Talbert Ave., Fountain Valley, CA 92708: Free information ■ Shoes, shorts, rainsuits, singlets, and warm-up suits. 714–962–7654.

California Best, 970 Broadway, Ste. 104, Chula Vista, CA 91911: Free information ■ Shoes and clothing. 800–438–9327.

Carlsen Import Shoes Corporation, 524 Broadway, New York, NY 10012: Free catalog ■ Shoes, clothing, and other sporting equipment. 212–431–5940.

Champion Products, Inc., 3141 Monroe Ave., Rochester, NY 14618: Free information ■ Shorts, singlets, socks, and warm-up suits. 716–385–3200.

Converse, Inc., One Fordham Rd., North Reading, MA 01864: Free information ■ Shoes, shorts, singlets, socks, sweatbands, and warm-up suits. 800–225–5079; 508–664–1100 (in MA).

Cook & Love, 114 S. Main St., Memphis, TN 39103: Free catalog ■ Walking shoes in hard-to-find sizes. 800–858–3364; 800–367–3006 (in TN).

Dolfin International Corporation, P.O. Box 98, Shillington, PA 19607: Free information ■ Shorts, rainsuits, singlets, and warm-up suits. 215–775–5500.

Eastbay Running Store, Inc., 427 3rd St., Wausau, WI 54401: Free information ■ Shoes and clothing. 800–826–2205; 800–472–4406 (in WI).

Empire Sporting Goods Manufacturing Company, 443 Broadway, New York, NY 10013: Free information ■ Rainsuits. 800–221–3455; 212–966–0880 (in NY).

Faber Brothers, 4141 S. Pulaski Rd., Chicago, IL 60632: Free information ■ Pedometers, rainsuits, and safety vests. 312–376–9300.

Finish Line, Ltd., 528 West Ave., Norwalk, CT 06850: Free information ■ Shoes. 203–853–4367.

Kaz of California, 8945 Quartz Ave., Northridge, CA 91324: Free information ■ Shorts, rainsuits, singlets, and warm-up suits. 818–341–9034.

Kellsport Industries, 125 Sockanossett Cross Rd., P.O. Box 8399, Cranston, RI 02920: Free information ■ Shoes. 800–341–4600.

Las Vegas Discount Golf & Tennis, 5325 S. Valley View Blvd., Ste. 10, Las Vegas, NV 89118: Free catalog ■ Shoes and clothing. 702–798–7777.

Leisure Unlimited, P.O. Box 308, Cedarburg, WI 53012: Free information ■ Pedometers and rainsuits. 800–323–5118; 414–377–7454 (in WI).

NaturalSport, 2510 S. Broadway, Salem, IL 62881: Free catalog ■ Aerobic walking shoes, other shoes, shorts, pants, and jackets. 800–678–9138.

New Balance Athletic Shoe, Inc., 38 Everett St., Boston, MA 02134: Free information ■ Shoes, shorts, singlets, raincoats, sweatbands, and warm-up suits. 800–253–SHOE.

North Face, 999 Harrison St., Berkeley, CA 94710: Free information ■ Rain suits. 510–527–9700.

Okun Brothers Shoes, 356 E. South St., Kalamazoo, MI 49007: Free catalog ■ Shoes for men, women, and children. 616–342–1536.

Puma USA, Inc., 147 Centre St., Brockton, MA 02403: Free information ■ Shoes, shorts, singlets, rainsuits, socks, and warm-up suits. 508–583–9100.

Red Tag Sports, P.O. Box 29069, San Diego, CA 92129: Free information ■ Men's and women's clothing and shoes. 619–530–2372.

Road Runner Sports, 6310 Nancy Ridge Rd., Ste. 101, San Diego, CA 92121: Free price list ■ Shoes and clothing. 800–662–8896.

Safesport Manufacturing Company, 1100 W. 45th Ave., Denver, CO 80211: Free information ■ Pedometers, rainsuits, and safety vests. 303–433–6506.

Sheldon Shoes, Inc., 1415 N. Lilac Dr., Minneapolis, MN 55422: Free catalog ■ Walking shoes for women. 800–328–4827; 612–544–3349 (in MN).

Spalding & Brothers, 425 Meadow St., P.O. Box 901, Chicopee, MA 01021: Free information ■ Shoes, shorts, singlets, sweatbands, and warm-up suits. 413–536–1200.

Spiegel's Ultimate Outlet, P.O. Box 6340, Chicago, IL 60680: Catalog $2 ■ Men's and women's walking shoes. 800–345–4500.

Sportnit, 25 Briarcrest Square, Hershey, PA 17033: Catalog $1 ■ Running shoes, warm-up suits, and cold weather gear for men and women. 800–233–2336.

Tel-a-Runner, P.O. Box 1323, Morristown, NJ 07960: Free information ■ Men's and women's shoes and clothing. 201–366–9426.

Tennis Gear & Running Center, 137 Baltimore St., Cumberland, MD 21502: Free price list ■ Clothing and shoes. 800–638–3578; 301–722–6252 (in MD).

Terramar Sports, Ltd., 10 Midland Ave., Port Chester, NY 10573: Free information ■ Thermal silk glove liners, sock liners, and balaclavas. 914–934–8000.

Valcour Shoes, 52 Margaret St., Plattsburgh, NY 12901: Free information ■ Walking shoes for women, sizes 7 to 12, widths AAAA to EE. 518–561–7246.

Venus Knitting Mills, Inc., 140 Spring St., Murray Hill, NJ 07974: Free information ■ Shorts, singlets, sweatbands, and warm-up suits. 800–955–4200; 201–464–2400 (in NJ).

Wyoming Woolens, P.O. Box 3127, Jackson, WY 83001: Free information ■ Rainsuits and safety vests. 307–733–2889.

Pedometers & Stopwatches

Accusplit, 2290–A Ringwood Ave., San Jose, CA 95131: Free information ■ Pedometers and sports watches. 408–432–8228.

Air Design Limited, 8809 148th Ave. NE, Redmond, WA 98053: Free information ■ Pedometers. 800–247–0800; 206–867–9227 (in NE).

Aristo Import Company, Inc., 15 Hunt Rd., Orangeburg, NY 10962: Free information ■ Pedometers for step counting, walking, or jogging. 914–359–0720.

Compass Industries, Inc., 104 E. 25th St., New York, NY 10010: Free information ■ Pedometers. 212–473–2614.

Creative Health Products, 5148 Saddle Ridge Rd., Plymouth, MI 48170: Free catalog ■ Pedometers and pulse monitors. 800–742–4478.

Crown Health Equipment Company, Inc., P.O. Box 751, Mt. Vernon, OH 43050: Free information ■ Pedometers. 614–397–1060.

Dynamic Classics, Ltd., 230 5th Ave., New York, NY 10001: Free information ■ Pedometers. 212–571–0267.

Faber Brothers, 4141 S. Pulaski Rd., Chicago, IL 60632: Free information ■ Pedometers, rainsuits, and safety vests. 312–376–9300.

Free Style USA, 21025 Osborne St., Canoga Park, CA 91304: Free information ■ Pedometers. 818–882–6350.

General Sportcraft Company, Ltd., 140 Woodbine St., Bergenfield, NJ 07621: Free information ■ Pedometers. 201–384–4242.

Gutman Cutlery, Inc., 120 S. Columbus Ave., Mt. Vernon, NY 10553: Free information ■ Walking and walking/jogging pedometers. 800–CUTLERY; 914–699–4044 (in NY).

Innovative Time Corporation, 6054 Corte Del Cedro, Carlsbad, CA 92008: Free information ■ Pedometers. 800–854–3831; 619–438–0595 (in CA).

KNR Associates, 1307 Hickory St., Onalaska, WI 54650: Brochure $1 ■ Pedometers. 800–234–1770.

Leisure Unlimited, P.O. Box 308, Cedarburg, WI 53012: Free information ■ Pedometers and rainsuits. 800–323–5118; 414–377–7454 (in WI).

Peak Marketing, Inc., P.O. Box 68, Suffern, NY 10901: Free information ■ Pedometer with digital readout and stride adjustment. Clips to waistband. 800–772–8862.

Precise International, 3 Chestnut St., Suffern, NY 10901: Free information ■ Walking and walking/jogging pedometers. 914–357–6200.

Safesport Manufacturing Company, 1100 W. 45th Ave., Denver, CO 80211: Free information ■ Pedometers, rainsuits, and safety vests. 303–433–6506.

Sportline, 847 McGlincey Ln., Campbell, CA 95008: Free information ■ Pedometers. 408–377–8900.

SAIL BOARDS

Sailboard Warehouse, Inc., 300 S. Owasso, St. Paul, MN 55117: Catalog $1.50 ■ Sail boards, sails and masts, wet suits, roof tracks, harnesses, books, videos, and other accessories. 800–992–SAIL; 612–482–9995 (in MN).

Windsurfing by Mail, 6043 NW 167th St., Miami, FL 33015: Free catalog ■ Sailboards and accessories. 800–THE–SURF.

SCIENCE KITS & PROJECTS

Edlie Electronics, 2700 Hempstead Tpk., Levittown, NY 11756: Free catalog ■ Electronics kits, parts, and supplies. 516–735–3330.

Edmund Scientific Company, Edscorp Bldg., Barrington, NJ 08007: Free catalog ■ Microscopes, magnifiers, weather forecasting instruments, magnets, telescopes, lasers, and other optical, scientific, and educational products. 609–573–6260.

The Electronic Goldmine, P.O. Box 5408, Scottsdale, AZ 85261: Free information ■ Science kits and supplies. 602–451–7454.

Jack Ford Science Projects, P.O. Drawer 1009, Duluth, GA 30136: Catalog $1 ■ Science projects for amateur experimenters.

J.L. Hammett Company, 30 Hammett Pl., Braintree, MA 02184: Free catalog ■ Science kits and projects, microscopes, laboratory apparatus, rock collections, magnets, astronomy charts, and anatomical models. 800–672–1932; 617–848–1000 (in MA).

Heath Company, P.O. Box 8589, Benton Harbor, MI 49023: Free catalog ■ Computers and robots, television sets, home devices, educational projects, and other electronics kits. 800–44–HEATH.

Hubbard Scientific Company, P.O. Box 104, Northbrook, IL 60065: Free catalog ■ Science equipment and supplies for life, earth, and introductory physical science; energy experiments; health and physiology experiments; and topography projects. 800–323–8368.

Information Unlimited, Inc., Box 716, Amherst, NH 03031: Catalog $1 ■ Lasers, communication equipment, Tesla coils and experiments, mini radios, rocket equipment, flying saucers, and other kits. 603–673–4730.

Joy of Nature, 9 Hingham Cove, San Rafael, CA 94901: Free information ■ Science discovery kits for nature-curious individuals. 415–453–6169.

Krystal Kits, P.O. Box 445, Bentonville, AR 72712: Free catalog ■ Electronics projects, kits, and plans. 501–273–5340.

Merrell Scientific/World of Science, 1665 Buffalo Rd., Rochester, NY 14624: Catalog $2 ■ Chemicals, glassware, laboratory equipment, and supplies for biology, nature, physical and earth science, astronomy experiments, and model rocketry. 716–426–1540.

Nasco, 901 Janesville Ave., Fort Atkinson, WI 53538: Free science catalog ■ Science supplies and equipment, science activity kits and projects, microscopes and dissection kits, rock collections, magnets, electric motors, ultraviolet light equipment, astronomy charts and star maps, and anatomical models. 800–558–9595.

PAIA Electronics, Inc., 3200 Teakwood Ln., Edmond, OK 73013: Free catalog ■ Electronics kits and books. 405–340–6300.

Radio Shack, Division Tandy Corporation, 1500 One Tandy Center, Fort Worth, TX 76102: Free catalog ■ Electronics science projects and kits. 817–390–3700.

Dick Smith Electronics, P.O. Box 8021, Redwood City, CA 94063: Catalog $1 ■ Electronics kits. 415–368–1066.

Things of Science, 1950 Landings Blvd., Ste. 202, Sarasota, FL 34231: Free information ■ Biology, chemistry, physics, mathematics, astronomy, optics, fossils, and other science kits for 9– to 14–year olds. 813–923–1465.

Uptown Sales, Inc., 33 N. Main St., Chambersburg, PA 17201: Catalog $1 ■ Science kits and projects for amateur scientists. 800–548–9941.

SCOUTING

Boy Scouts of America, P.O. Box 909, Pineville, NC 28134: Free catalog ■ Scouting, outdoor sports, boating, hunting, camping, and archery equipment and supplies. 800–323–0732.

Girl Scout Catalog, 830 3rd Ave., New York, NY 10022: Free catalog ■ Uniforms and insignia, camping equipment, sportswear, books, jewelry, and gifts. 212–940–7500.

SEASHELLS

Benjane Arts, P.O. Box 298, West Hempstead, NY 11552: Catalog $5 ■ Seahells. 516–483–1330.

Bourget Bros., 1636 11th St., Santa Monica, CA 90404: Catalog $5 ■ Seashells, jewelry-making tools and supplies, gemstones, and beads and bead-stringing supplies. 800–828–3024; 310–450–6556 (in CA).

Ebersole Lapidary Supply, Inc., 11417 West Hwy. 54, Wichita, KS 67209: Catalog $2 ■ Shark teeth, cameo shells, murex or fox shells, tiger cowries, mushroom corals, other seashells from worldwide sources, and lapidary equipment and supplies. 316–722–4771.

Ed's House of Gems, 7712 NE Sandy Blvd., Portland, OR 97213: Free information with long SASE ■ Seashells, crystals, minerals, gemstones, lapidary equipment and tools, mountings, and Indian relics. 503–284–8990.

Herkimer Diamond Mines, P.O. Box 510, Herkimer, NY 13350: Free information ■ Petrified wood products, seashells, craft supplies, minerals and rocks, quartz crystals, and gifts. 315–891–7355.

Indian Jewelers Supply Company, P.O. Box 1774, Gallup, NM 87305: Set of 4 catalogs $5 ■ Precious and base metals; findings in precious and base metals; metalsmithing and lapidary tools and supplies; and semi-precious stones, seashells, and coral. 505–722–4451.

Jeanne's Rock & Jewelry, 5420 Bissonet, Bellaire, TX 77401: Free information ■ Seashells, petrified wood products, lapidary supplies, and gifts. 713–664–2988.

Riviera Lapidary Supply, 30192 Mesquite, Riviera, TX 78379: Catalog $3 ■ Seashells, beads, cabochons, slabs, cabbing rough gems, and crystals. 512–296–3958.

Shell-A-Rama, Box 291327, Fort Lauderdale, FL 33318: Catalog $1 ■ Seashells for craft projects, decorations, and collections. 305–434–2818.

SEWING

Dress Forms

Dress Rite Forms, 3817 N. Pulaski, Chicago, IL 60641: Free information ■ Professional forms in all sizes and shapes. 312–588–5761.

Home Makers Supply Company, 2300 NE Broadway, Portland, OR 97232: Free information ■ Dress forms. 503–282–0908.

Pattern Bodiform, 161 7th Ave., San Francisco, CA 94118: Free brochure ■ Adjustable dress form for average and not-average measurements. 415–752–2215.

Wolf Form Company, Inc., 39 W. 19th St., New York, NY 10011: Free information ■ Men's, women's, and children's garment forms, for newborns to size 52, and larger. 212–255–4508.

Notions

Badhir Trading, Inc., 8429 Sisson Hwy., Eden, NY 14057: Catalog $2.50 (refundable) ■ Beaded, sequined, and jeweled appliques and trims and fringes for dresses, costumes, and bridal fashions. 716–992–3195.

Banasch, 426 E. 6th St., Cincinnati, OH 45202: Free catalog ■ Beads, pearls, notions, and buttons. 800–543–0355; 800–582–0330 (in OH).

Baubanbea Enterprises, P.O. Box 1205, Smithtown, NY 11787: Catalog $1 ■ Rhinestones, sequins, beads, jewels, lace, appliques, fringes, trim, feathers, imported and domestic fabrics, and silk flowers. 516–724–4661.

Barbara Bauer Buttons, P.O. Box 385, Lexington, GA 30648: Brochure $1 ■ Porcelain buttons. 404–743–3268.

Bee Lee Company, Box 36108, Dallas, TX 75235: Free catalog ■ Notions, belt buckles and snaps, trims, zippers, interfacings, threads, and other notions. 214–351–2091.

B. Black & Sons, 548 S. Los Angeles St., Los Angeles, CA 90013: Free price list ■ Tailoring supplies. 213–624–9451.

Bridal-By-The-Yard, P.O. Box 2492, Springfield, OH 45501: Free information ■ Lace, satins, taffeta, organza, millinery supplies, trims, and notions. 513–325–2847.

Button Creations, 3801 Stump Rd., Doylestown, PA 18901: Catalog $2 ■ Wood, mother-of-pearl, pottery, hand-painted porcelain, leather, military, pewter, and cloisonne buttons and thimbles. 800–346–0223.

Button Hole, Rt. 1, Box 263–B, Madison Heights, VA 24572: Brochure $1 ■ Handcrafted porcelain buttons. 804–384–0539.

Button Shop, P.O. Box 1065, Oak Park, IL 60304: Free catalog ■ Buttons, closures, trims, sewing machine accessories and parts, notions, and tools. 708–795–1234.

Campbells, P.O. Box 400, Gratz, PA 17030: Catalog $4.50 ■ Historic and ethnic garment patterns, sewing accessories, books, and other hard-to-find supplies.

Clotilde, 1909 SW 1st Ave., Fort Lauderdale, FL 33315: Catalog $1 ■ Notions, books, patterns, and videos. 800–772–2891.

Craft Gallery, Ltd., P.O. Box 145, Swampscott, MA 01907: Catalog $2 ■ Threads, fibers, books, fabrics, and accessories for sewing, crochet, and other stitchery crafts.

DK Sports, Division Daisy Kingdom, 134 NW 8th Ave., Portland, OR 97209: Free information ■ Rainwear and outerwear fabrics and notions. 800–288–5223.

Dogwood Lane Buttons, Box 145, Dugger, IN 47848: Catalog $2.50 ■ Handmade porcelain buttons. 800–648–2213.

Dritz Corporation, P.O. Box 5028, Spartanburg, SC 29304: Free information ■ Marking pens, awls, cutting mats, cutters, scissors, needles, straight and safety pins, zipper glides, craft tape, glue sticks, tape measures, and other notions. 800–845–4948.

Fashion Touches, P.O. Box 1541, Bridgeport, CT 06604: Free catalog ■ Custom-covered belts and buttons. 203–333–7738.

Fiskars Corporation, 7811 W. Stewart Ave., Wausau, WI 54401: Free catalog ■ Scissors, sharpeners, and safety scissors for children. 715–842–2091.

Garden Fairies Trading Company, P.O. Box 5770, Santa Rosa, CA 95402: Catalog $4 ■ Handmade collar patterns, French lace, Swiss embroideries, Battenberg lace supplies, smocking patterns, soft toy patterns, books, designer fabrics, and cottons. 800–925–9919.

Gettinger Feather Corporation, 16 W. 36th St., New York, NY 10033: Information $2 ■ Raw or dyed feathers from ostriches, marabou, turkeys, and other birds. 212–695–9470.

The Ghent Needlecrafter, 220 Colonial Ave., Norfolk, VA 23518: Free information ■ Imported and domestic fabrics, laces, books and patterns, and notions for smocking and other sewing crafts. 804–623–2777.

L.A. Glitz, 4520 Van Nuys Blvd., Box 744, Sherman Oaks, CA 91403: Catalog $2 ■ Rhinestones, gems, studs and nailheads, and sequined and beaded appliques.

Greenberg & Hammer, Inc., 24 W. 57th St., New York, NY 10019: Free catalog ■ Tailoring supplies. 800–955–5135; 212–246–2835 (in NY).

Green Pepper, 3918 W. 1st Ave., Eugene, OR 97402: Catalog $2 ■ Buckles, velcro and velcro fasteners, zippers, buttons, other notions, and kits for coats and jackets, ski wear, water-repellent clothing, and duffel bags. 503–345–6665.

Hancock Fabrics, 3841 Hinkleville Rd., Paducah, KY 42001: Free information ■ Quilting supplies, fabrics, and notions. 800–626–2723.

Hearthside Quilters Nook, 10731 W. Forest Home Ave., Hales Corner, WI 53130: Catalog $2 ■ Sewing and smocking supplies, patterns, notions, fabrics, and laces. 414–425–2474.

Hemming's Sewing Center, 2645 White Bear Ave., Maplewood, MN 55109: Free catalog ■ Bernina sewing machine accessories, notions, and books. 612–770–4130.

Home-Sew, Inc., P.O. Box 4099, Bethlehem, PA 18018: Catalog $1 ■ Sewing supplies, notions, and other craft supplies. 215–867–3833.

Jacquart's, 505 E. McLeod, Ironwood, MI 49938: Catalog $2 ■ Notions, hardware, zippers, and other fasteners. 906–932–1339.

Kreinik Manufacturing Company, P.O. Box 1966, Parkersburg, WV 26102: Free information ■ Gold and silver metallic thread. 800–624–1928; 304–422–8900 (in WV).

The Lace Place, Ann Smith Herring, P.O. Box 404, Chappaqua, NY 10513: Catalog $2 ■ Smocking and sewing supplies and accessories. 914–238–8581.

Ledgewood Studio, 6000 Ledgewood Dr., Forest Park, GA 30050: Catalog $2 with long SASE and two 1st class stamps ■ Dress patterns for antique dolls and supplies for authentic period costumes, and other supplies that include braids, French laces, silk ribbons, silk taffeta, China silk, Swiss batiste, trims, and notions.

Donna Lee's Sewing Center, 25234 Pacific Hwy. South, Kent, WA 98032: Catalog $4 ■ Swiss batiste, imperial batiste, China silk, silk charmeuse, French val laces, English laces, Swiss embroidery, trim and yardage fabrics, silk ribbon, and embroidered ribbon. 206–941–9466.

Linda's Silver Needle, P.O. Box 2167, Naperville, IL 60567: Catalog $5 (refundable) ■ Sewing and smocking supplies and accessories. 800–SMOCK–IT.

Madeira USA, Ltd., 30 Bayside Ct., P.O. Box 6068, Laconia, NH 03246: Free information ■ Gold and silver metallic thread. 800–225–3001.

Nancy's Notions, P.O. Box 683, Beaver Dam, WI 53916: Free catalog ■ Notions, threads, books, patterns, and fabrics that include interlock knits, fleece, gabardines, sweater knits, and challis. 800–833–0690.

National Thread & Supply, 695 Red Oak Rd., Stockbridge, GA 30281: Free catalog ■ Cone threads and other sewing supplies and notions. 800–331–7600.

Newark Dressmaker Supply, 6473 Ruch Rd., P.O. Box 20730, Lehigh Valley, PA 18002: Catalog $1 ■ Supplies and accessories for sewing, other crafts, and needlework. 215–837–7500.

Northwest Sewing, P.O. Box 25826, Seattle, WA 98125: Free catalog ■ Threads and needles for sewing machines and sergers, sewing supplies and notions, knitting supplies, and books. 800–745–7539.

Oregon Tailor Supply, P.O. Box 42284, Portland, OR 97242: Free information with long SASE ■ Zippers, other notions, and buttons. 503–232–6191.

Outdoor Wilderness Fabrics, 16195 Latah Dr., Nampa, ID 83651: Price list $4 ■ Coated and uncoated nylon fabrics, fleece and blends in coat weights, waterproof fabrics, hardware, webbing, zippers, patterns, and notions. 208–466–1602.

Park East Sewing Center, 1358 3rd Ave., New York, NY 10021: Free information ■

Serger threads, books, fabrics for sewing and quilting, and notions. 212–737–1220.

Perfect Notion, 566 Hoyt St., Darien, CT 06820: Catalog $1 ■ Notions, scissors, serger accessories, and threads. 203–968–1257.

Quintessence, P.O. Box 723544, Atlanta, GA 30339: Catalog $3 ■ Beads, rhinestones, hand-carved sea shells, beaded appliques, exotic leathers, lamb suedes, snakeskin, fabrics, belt buckles, dressmaker accessories, and other notions. 404–264–1759.

Rainshed Outdoor Fabrics, 707 NW 11th, Corvallis, OR 97330: Catalog $1 ■ Rainwear and outerwear fabrics, notions, webbing, and patterns. 503–753–8900.

Serge & Sew, Zachary Square Mall, 11285 96th Ave. North, Maple Grove, MN 55369: Free catalog ■ Save on serging supplies, notions, and fabrics. 612–493–2449.

Sewing Emporium, 1079 3rd Ave., Chula Vista, CA 92010: Catalog $1.50 ■ Sewing machines and accessories, cutting equipment, pressing equipment, threads, and other supplies. 619–420–3490.

Sewing Machine Discount Sales, 5960 Florence Ave., P.O. Box 2277, Bell Gardens, CA 90201: Free catalog with long SASE ■ Woolly nylon, pearl cotton, and silk thread; embroidery thread; polyester thread; and polyester cone thread for sergers and sewing machines. 213–560–8177.

Sew Smart, 1124 John Sims Pkwy., Niceville, FL 32578: Free information ■ Fabrics, smocking supplies, patterns, laces, and books. 904–678–9656.

Signal Thread Company, 521 Airport Rd., Chattanooga, TN 37421: Color card catalog $5 ■ Spun polyester thread in mini cones. 800–THREADS.

Ben Silver, 149 King St., Charleston, SC 29401: Free catalog ■ College crests, monograms, and other blazer buttons. 800–221–4671.

Singer Sewing Center, 1669 Texas Ave., College Station, TX 77840: Free information with long SASE ■ Sewing equipment and accessories and sewing machine serger attachments. 800–338–5672.

Specialties, 236 Cotton Hanlon Rd., Montour Falls, NY 14865: Catalog $2 ■ Lingerie fabrics, notions, and patterns. 607–535–4105.

The Stitching Bear, 915 N. Main St., Findlay, OH 45840: Free information with long SASE ■ Smocking and sewing supplies, patterns, books, and fabrics. 419–424–2040.

Stretch & Sew Fabrics, 19725 40th Ave. West, Lynnwood, WA 98036: Information $2 with long SASE ■ Stretch and sew fabrics, patterns, notions, interfacing, and elastic. 206–774–9678.

Things Japanese, 9805 NE 116th St., Ste. 7160, Kirkland, WA 98034: Information $4 ■ Silk filament sewing thread. 206–821–2287.

Thread Discount Sales, P.O. Box 2277, Bell Gardens, CA 90201: Free catalog with long SASE ■ Polyester thread in cones. 213–562–3438.

Threads-West, 430 E. State St., Redlands, CA 92373: Free color list with long SASE ■ Polyester thread in 6,000– and 12,000–yard cones. 714–793–4405.

Utex Trading, 710 9th St., Ste. 5, Niagara Falls, NY 14301: Free price list with long SASE ■ Sewing supplies and accessories and imported silk fabrics. 716–282–8211.

Victorian Treasures, 12148 Madison St. NE, Blaine, MN 55434: Catalog $3.50 (refundable) ■ Imported laces, fabrics, Swiss embroideries, notions, and sewing supplies. 612–755–6302.

Patterns

Altra, 100 E. Washington St., New Richmond, IN 47967: Free information ■ Fabrics, notions, and pre-cut sewing kits for outdoor clothing, nylon and bunting jackets, insulated clothing, parkas, and rainwear. 800–443–8714; 317–339–4653 (in IN).

Amazon Drygoods, 2218 E. 11th St., Davenport, IA 52803: Catalog $5 ■ Victorian and Edwardian clothing patterns from the 1920s and 1930s. 319–322–6800.

Annie's Attic, 106 W. Groves, Big Sandy, TX 75755: Catalog $1.95 ■ Sewing and needle craft patterns and supplies. 903–636–4303.

Bonnie's Crafts, 9800 W. 113th Ave., Cedar Lake, IN 46303: Catalog $1.50 ■ Soft sculpture patterns and kits.

Butterick Pattern Service, P.O. Box 729, Altoona, PA 16603: Free information ■ Patterns for clothing.

Campbells, P.O. Box 400, Gratz, PA 17030: Catalog $4.50 ■ Historic and ethnic garment patterns, sewing accessories, books, and other hard-to-find supplies.

Daisy Kingdom, 134 NW 8th Ave., Portland, OR 97209: Catalog $2 ■ Nursery ensembles and children's fashions in kits or ready-made.

Donner Designs, P.O. Box 7217, Reno, NV 89510: Catalog $1 ■ Ski wear sewing kits and patterns. 702–358–5281.

Fair Winds Pattern Company, 819 N. June St., Hollywood, CA 90038: Brochure $1 ■ Classic clothing patterns, from 1900 to 1945.

Folkwear, Customer Service Dept., P.O. Box 5506, Newtown, CT 06470: Catalog $2 ■ Never out of style original patterns.

Friends Pattern Company, 50305 State Rd. 145, Woodsfield, OH 43793: Catalog $3.50 ■ Amish clothing patterns. 614–472–0444.

Frostline Kits, 2525 River Rd., Grand Junction, CO 81505: Free catalog ■ Ready-to-sew kits for jackets, vests, comforters, luggage, camping gear, and ski wear. 800–KITS–USA.

Green Pepper, 3918 W. 1st Ave., Eugene, OR 97402: Catalog $2 ■ Buckles, velcro and velcro fasteners, zippers, buttons, and other notions, and kits for coats and jackets, ski wear, water-repellent clothing for cold weather, and duffel bags. 503–345–6665.

Heidi's Pages & Petticoats, Heidi M. Marsh, 810 El Caminito, Livermore, CA 94550: Catalog $3 ■ Authentic clothing patterns, from 1855 to 1865.

Little Memories, P.O. Box 170145, Arlington, TX 76003: Brochure $1.75 ■ Smocking plates, duplicate stitch designs, and patterns. 817–451–8582.

Old World Enterprises, 29036 Kepler Ct., Cold Spring, MN 56320: Catalog $2 ■ Patterns for reproduction 19th-century clothing for men and women.

Past Patterns, P.O. Box 7587, Grand Rapids, MI 49510: Catalog $3 ■ Patterns for historically authentic clothing for men, women, and children. 616–245–9456.

Pauliwog, Rt. 1, Box 249, Sand Springs, OK 74063: Free brochure with long SASE ■ Soft sculpture patterns.

Prairie Clothing Company, 3732 Tanager Dr. NE, Cedar Rapids, IA 52402: Catalog $1 ■ Clothing patterns. 319–378–0125.

Rainshed Outdoor Fabrics, 707 NW 11th, Corvallis, OR 97330: Catalog $1 ■ Rainwear and outerwear fabrics, notions, webbing, and patterns. 503–753–8900.

The Ready Wear Company, 391 3rd Ave., Troy, NY 12181: Free catalog ■ Print, paint, bead, or embroider on one-size-fits-all women's blouses, jogging suits, jackets, and skirts. 800–342–2400; 518–235–1700 (in NY).

Seams Sew Easy, P.O. Box 2189, Manassas, VA 22110: Free information ■ Patterns and instructions for Christmas ornaments and decorations. 703–330–1727.

Servant & Company, c/o Centennial General Store, 237 Steinweir Ave., Gettysburg, PA 17325: Catalog $1 ■ Patterns from the Civil War years for military and civilian clothing, for men, women, and children. 717–334–9712.

Sew/Fit Company, Brewet Sewing Supplies, 3800 W. 42nd St., Chicago, IL 60632: Free catalog ■ Patterns and other supplies and accessories. Includes the Sew/Fit Rotary Cutting Mat. 312–579–3222.

Specialties, 236 Cotton Hanlon Rd., Montour Falls, NY 14865: Catalog $2 ■ Lingerie fabrics, notions, and patterns. 607–535–4105.

Staley's, 710–C Caroline St., Fredericksburg, VA 22401: Catalog 50¢ ■ Clothing patterns for men, women, and children, from the 19th-century. 703–899–6464.

Stuffins by Pat, P.O. Box 5226, Lake Wylie, SC 29710: Brochure $1 with long SASE ■ Soft sculpture patterns.

Sewing Machines

Bernina, 534 W. Chestnut, Hinsdale, IL 60521: Free information ■ Sewing machines. 312–654–4136.

Discount Appliance Centers, 2908 Hamilton St., Hyattsville, MD 20782: Free information with long SASE ■ Sewing machines, belts, attachments, and vacuum cleaners and accessories. 301–559–6801.

Pfaff American Sales Corporation, 610 Winters Ave, Paramus, NJ 07653: Free brochure ■ Sewing machines.

Sewing Supplies, 75 E. Main St., Patchogue, NY 11772: Free information ■ Sewing machines, notions, and accessories. 516–475–8282.

Sewin' in Vermont, 84 Concord Ave., St. Johnsbury, VT 05819: Free price list ■ Save up to 40 percent on sewing machines and accessories. 800–451–5124; 1–748–3803 (in VT).

Sew-Knit Distributors, 9789 Florida Blvd., Baton Rouge, LA 70815: Free price list with long SASE ■ Sewing and knitting machines and knitting accessories. 800–289–5648.

Singer Sewing Center, 1669 Texas Ave., College Station, TX 77840: Free information with long SASE ■ Sewing machines, accessories, and sewing machine serger attachments. 800–338–5672.

Stuffing & Fill

Air-Lite Synthetics Manufacturing, 342 Irwin St., Pontiac, MI 48053: Free information ■ Batting, fiber fill, and pillow forms. 800–521–1267 313–335–8131 (in MI).

Brewer Sewing Supplies, 3800 W. 42nd St., Chicago, IL 60632: Free information ■ Sewing machines, parts, and accessories, quilting supplies, and batting and stuffing. 800–621–2501; 800–621–1354 (in IL).

Buffalo Batt & Felt Corporation, Craft Product Division, 3307 Walden Ave., Depew, NY 14043: Catalog $1 ■ Stuffing, polyester fiber fill, and patterns. 716–683–4100.

Frugal Fox, Box 369, Fontana, WI 53125: Free price list with long SASE ■ Pillow forms, quilt batting, and fiberfill.

Hobb's Bonded Fibers, Craft Products Division, P.O. Box 151, Groesbeck, TX 76642: Free information with long SASE ■ Celanese and Fortrel polyester battings. 817–729–3223.

Lee's Mills, 2317 Center Ave., Janesville, WI 53545: Free information ■ Long and short pile, light and heavy density craft pile fabrics, and super-soft stuffing. 608–754–0404.

Oklee Quilting Company, P.O. Box 277, Oklee, MN 56742: Free information with long SASE ■ Polyester bonded batting for quilts, outerwear, and other crafts. 218–796–5151.

Oriental Rug Company, P.O. Box 205, Washington, KY 41086: Free information ■ Polyester fiberfill, and polyester quilt batting, and pillow inserts. 606–759–7614.

Pangle's Fabric & Craft Center, 138 E. Main, Box 1098, Wise, VA 24293: Free information ■ Quilting supplies and Pandapuff, Kodofill polyester stuffing in a double-bonded thickness. 703–328–6606.

Royal Processing Company, Inc., 3445 N. Spencer St., Charlotte, NC 28205: Free information ■ Kapok and polyester fill for pillows, quilts, and stuffed dolls and toys. 800–451–8487.

Tags & Labels

Alpha Impressions, Inc., 4161 S. Main St., Los Angeles, CA 90037: Free brochure ■ Woven labels and hang tags. 213–234–8221.

Bach Label Company, 1212 S. San Pedro St., Los Angeles, CA 90015: Free information ■ Printed and woven labels with logo reproductions. 213–744–1021.

Charm Woven Labels, Box 30027, Portland, OR 97230: Free brochure ■ Custom silk, linen, wool, polyester, and cotton labels. 503–252–5542.

Dana Labels, Inc., 7778 SW Nimbus Ave., Beaverton, OR 97005: Free information ■ Custom garment labels, size tags, shipping labels, care/content labels, cosmetic labels, and pressure-sensitive labels. 800–255–1492; 503–646–7933 (in OR).

IDENT-IFY Label Corporation, P.O. Box 204, Brooklyn, NY 11214: Free information with long SASE ■ Sew-on labels and name tapes. 718–436–3126.

L & L Stitchery, P.O. Box 43821, Atlanta, GA 30378: Free brochure ■ Woven labels and name tapes. 404–691–2239.

Name Maker, Inc., P.O. Box 43821, Atlanta, GA 30378: Catalog $1 ■ Custom labels and name tapes with signature, logo, or custom artwork, in nylon, taffeta, or satin. 404–691–2237.

NewsTech, 12447 Pinebrook, South Lyon, MI 48178: Catalog $2 ■ Hang tags, self-stick labels, and business cards.

Northwest Tag & Label, Inc., 110 Foothills Rd., Ste. 237, Lake Oswego, OR 97034: Brochure $1 ■ Iron-on and washable printed fabric tags and labels in nylon, satin, and woven edge. 503–636–6456.

Sterling Name Tape Company, P.O. Box 1056, Winsted, CT 06098: Label sample kit $1 ■ Custom labels. 800–654–5210; 203–379–5142 (in CT).

SHEDS

Country Designs, Box 774, Essex, CT 06426: Catalog $5 ■ Building plans for barns, sheds, and garages.

Hammond Barns, 3130 Hardacre Ct., P.O. Box 584, New Castle, IN 47362: Brochure $2 ■ Plans for storage sheds, tool sheds, workshops, and other structures. 317–529–7822.

SHOES & BOOTS
Men's & Women's Shoes

Alp Sports Sandals, 244 North Hwy. 101, Encinitas, CA 92024: Free information ■ Men's and women's sandals. 619–436–2222.

Ampersand's, 2510 S. Broadway, Salem, IL 62881: Free catalog ■ Women's casual, dress, and walking shoes. 800–678–9138.

Arnold's Shoe Salon, Beachwood Pl., Beachwood, OH 44122: Free information ■ Women's shoes, from sizes 4½ to 11, AAAA to B. 216–464–6767.

Aussie Connection, 825 NE Broadway, Portland, OR 97232: Free catalog ■ Washable Australian sheepskin slippers and boots. 800–950–2668.

Backstreet Boots, P.O. Box 618, Verdale, WA 99037: Catalog $2 ■ Boots. 800–444–5432.

Bally of Switzerland for Ladies, 689 Madison Ave., New York, NY 10021: Free information ■ Women's shoes, clothing, luggage, small leather goods, and accessories. 212–751–2163.

Bally of Switzerland for Men, 711 5th Ave., New York, NY 10022: Free information ■ Men's shoes, clothing, luggage, small leather goods, and accessories. 212–751–9082.

G.H. Bass by Mail, 301 US Rt. 1, Scarborough, ME 04074: Free catalog ■ Loafers and shoes for the entire family and men's and women's casual clothing. 800–333–0386.

Belgian Shoes, 60 E. 56th St., New York, NY 10022: Brochure $2 ■ Handcrafted casual shoes. 212–755–7372.

Bencone Casuals, 121 Carver Ave., Westwood, NJ 07675: Free catalog ■ Women's shoes, all-weather boots, athletic walking shoes, casual shoes, loafers, and pumps. 800–521–8668.

Birkenstock Footwear, 301 SW Madison Ave., Corvalis, OR 97333: Free catalog ■ Waterproof clogs, in sizes 4 to 11 for women, and 5 to 13 for men. 800–231–6740.

J.W. Bray Company, Inc., P.O. Box 189, 305 E. Hawthorne St., Dalton, GA 30722: Free catalog ■ Terry cloth and satin-style boudoir slippers. 404–226–2729.

Carlsen Import Shoe Corporation, 524 Broadway, New York, NY 10012: Free catalog ■ Shoes for running and track, hiking and walking, basketball, aerobics, physical training and exercising, tennis, and baseball. 212–431–5940.

Cartan's Shoes, 2120 W. Vickery, Fort Worth, TX 76102: Free catalog ■ Women's shoes, in sizes 4 to 13, AAAAA to EEE. 800–541–8052.

Chernin's Shoes, 1001 S. Clinton St., Chicago, IL 60607: Free catalog ■ Shoes and loafers for men, women, and children. 312–922–5900.

Church's English Shoes, 428 Madison Ave., New York, NY 10017: Free brochure ■ Handcrafted all-leather shoes, in sizes 6 to 14, AA–EEE. 800–221–4540; 212–755–4313 (in NY).

Clover Nursing Shoe Company, 1948 E. Whipp Rd., Kettering, OH 45440: Free brochure ■ Shoes with all-leather uppers, sizes 5 to 12 and slim to double-wide widths. 513–435–0025.

Coward Shoes, Mail Order Division, 362 5th Ave., New York, NY 10001: Free catalog ■ Leather shoes for men and women, in sizes 5 to 12, AA to EEE. 800–759–8899.

Elite Petite Shoes, 11441 Stemmons Freeway, Dallas, TX 75229: Catalog $2 ■ Women's shoes, sizes 2 to 5½, AAA to WW. 800–634–3975; 214–241–7307 (in TX).

Essex Shoe Company, 32 Brunswick Ave., Edison, NJ 08817: Free catalog ■ Women's shoes, in sizes up to 12, widths 4A to EE.

Executive Shoes, P.O. Box 9128, Hingham, MA 02043: Free catalog ■ Handcrafted athletic and walking shoes in hard-to-fit sizes. 800–934–1022.

Fabiano Shoe Company, 850 Summer St., South Boston, MA 02127: Brochure 50¢ ■ Thinsulate-insulated Telemark boots. 617–268–5625.

Footprints, The Birkenstock Store, 1339 Massachusetts, Lawrence, KS 66044: Free catalog ■ Birkenstock sandals and sandal repair. 800–827–1339.

Giordano's, 1118 1st Ave., New York, NY 10021: Catalog $3 ■ Designer shoes in small and narrow sizes, 3 to 6, AA to medium. 212–688–7195.

Gucci, CSB 3168, Department 846, Melville, NY 11747: Free catalog ■ Shoes, clothing, leather goods, and accessories. 800–221–2590.

Hanover Shoe Company, 118 Carlisle St., Hanover, PA 17331: Catalog $1 ■ Men's shoes, in sizes 6 to 15, AA to EEE. 800–426–3708.

Hill Brothers, 99 9th St., Lynchburg, VA 24504: Free catalog ■ Women's pumps, sandals, athletic shoes, and casuals, in sizes 3 to 13, AAAAA to EEEE. 804–847–6555.

Hitchcock Shoes, Inc., Hingham, MA 02043: Free catalog ■ Men's shoes, in sizes 5 to 13, EE to EEEEEE. 617–749–3260.

Johansen Bros. Shoe Company, RR 1, US Hwy. 67 West, Corning, AR 72422: Free catalog ■ Women's fashion shoes. 800–624–9079.

Koson's, P.O. Box 3663, St. Augustine, FL 32085: Free brochure ■ Swedish clogs for men, women, and children. 904–829–1975.

L.A. Gear, 4221 Redwood, Los Angeles, CA 90066: Free information ■ Children's shoes. 800–252–4327; 800–423–79032 (in CA).

Bruno Magli Shoes, 535 Madison Ave., New York, NY 10022: Free catalog ■ Men's shoes. 800–MAGLI–22.

Maryland Square, 2510 S. Broadway, Salem, IL 62881: Free catalog ■ Women's footwear in full and half sizes. 800–678–9138.

Mason Shoe Manufacturing Company, 1251 1st Ave., Chippewa Falls, WI 54729: Free catalog ■ Shoes for men and women, in sizes 4 to 16, AA to EEEE. 715–723–1871.

Masseys, Direct Footwear Merchants, 601 12th St., Lynchburg, VA 24504: Free catalog ■ Casual, dress, athletic shoes, boots, and slippers. 800–462–7739.

Minnetonka by Mail, P.O. Box 444, Bronx, NY 10458: Free catalog ■ Leather moccasins for men, women, and children, with soft, crepe, and polyurethane soles, and shoes and boots for casual wear. 212–365–7033.

Nancy's Choice, 34th & Palo Verde, P.O. Box 27800, Tucson, AZ 85726: Free catalog ■ Shoes in hard-to-find sizes, from 9 to 13, widths N to WW, plus some slims. 602–748–8600.

Naturalizer Shoes, Mail Order Division, 112 E. Burlington Ave., La Grange, IL 60525: Free catalog ■ Shoes for women, in regular, hard-to-fit, and special sizes. 800–888–5958.

Nierman's, 316 N. Michigan Ave., Chicago, IL 60602: Free catalog ■ Shoes for hard-to-fit persons whose feet very wide or narrow. 312–346–9797.

Okun Bros. Shoes, 356 E. South St., Kalamazoo, MI 49007: Free catalog ■ Walking shoes for men, women, and children. 616–342–1536.

Old Pueblo Traders, Palo Verde at 34th, P.O. Box 27800, Tucson, AZ 85726: Catalog $1 ($2 refundable) ■ Genuine glove leather pants boots for women. 602–748–8600.

Ortho-Vent Division, Inc., 115 Brand Rd., Salem, VA 24156: Free catalog ■ Shoes in 105 sizes, in widths AA to EEEE. 800–848–2929; 703–389–3698 (in VA).

Reyers, Sharon City Centre, Sharon, PA 16146: Free information ■ Shoes, from size 2½ to 14, in widths AAAAAA to EE. 800–245–1550.

Richlee Shoe Company, P.O. Box 3566, Frederick, MD 21701: Free catalog ■ Elevator shoes for men, sizes 5 to 11, B to EEE. 800–343–3810.

Shoecraft Corporation, Box 129, Accord, MA 02018: Free information ■ Dress shoes, sandals, sport shoes, and flats, in sizes 10 to 13. 800–225–5848.

Shoes & Socks, 1281 Andersen Dr., Ste. D, San Rafael, CA 94901: Free catalog ■ Children's dress, casual, athletic shoes, and socks. 800–228–1820.

Standard Shoes, 48 Main St., Bangor, ME 04401: Free catalog ■ Arch-supporting shoes for women in sizes 2A to 3A; 6 to 12, A and B; 5 to 12, C and D; 5 to 12, E and EE, and some half sizes. 800–284–8366.

Talbots, 175 Beal St., Hingham, MA 02043: Free catalog ■ Women's shoes in regular, petite, and extended sizes. 800–992–9010.

Norm Thompson, P.O. Box 3999, Portland, OR 97208: Free catalog ■ Wood Ducks and other casual shoes. 800–547–1160.

Tog Shop, Lester Square, Americus, GA 31710: Free catalog ■ Women's footwear in full and half sizes and slim (AAA), narrow (AA), or medium (B) widths. 912–924–4800.

A.J. Valenci, Designer Cir., Salem, VA 24156: Free catalog ■ Designer shoes, up to size 12; in AA, B, and D widths. 703–375–3420.

Vasque Boots, Red Wing Shoe Company, 314 Main St., Red Wing, MN 55066: Free brochure ■ Hiking boots for men and women. 800–972–5220.

Wissota Trader, 1313 1st Ave., Chippewa Falls, WI 54729: Free catalog ■ Regular and hard-to-find sizes of shoes and clothes for men and women. 800–833–6421.

Wolverine Boots & Shoes, 9341 Courtland Dr., Rockford, MI 49351: Free information ■ Footwear for men and women. 616–866–5500.

Western Boots

Abilene Boot Company, Division B.B. Walker Company, Asheboro, NC 27204: Free information ■ Men's and women's boots in soft genuine elk.

Allen's Boot Center, 1522 S. Congress, Austin, TX 78704: Free information with long SASE ■ Save up to 50 percent on cowboy boot seconds. 512–447–1413.

Amado's Boot Company, 710 2nd St., Mercedes, TX 78570: Free information with long SASE ■ Custom leather cowboy boots. 512–565–9641.

Armando's Boot Shop, 169 N. 7th St., P.O. Box 328, Raymondville, TX 78580: Free in-formation with long SASE ■ Custom leather cowboy boots. 512–689–3521.

Austin-Hall Boot Company, 491 N. Resler Dr., P.O. Box 220990, El Paso, TX 79913: Catalog $3 ■ Made-to-order, wood-pegged, brass-nailed, leather-lined boots. 915–581–3847.

Bell Custom Boots, 2118 N. Treadaway Blvd., Abilene, TX 79601: Free information with long SASE ■ Custom leather cowboy boots. 915–677–0632.

Blucher Boot Company, 350 N. Main, Fairfax, OK 74637: Catalog $2 ■ Individually custom crafted boots. 918–642–3205.

Boot Town, 10838 N. Central Expy., Dallas, TX 75231: Free catalog ■ Western boots. 800–222–6687.

The Cowhand, 200 W. Midland Ave., P.O. Box 743, Woodland Park, CO 80863: Free information ■ Gloves, spurs, bits, belts, buckles, and Western-style boots for men, women, and children. 800–748–DUDS.

The Dehner Company, Inc., 3614 Martha Street, Omaha, NE 68105: Free catalog ■ Custom boots.

Drysdales Catalog, 3220 S. Memorial Dr., Tulsa, OK 74145: Free catalog ■ Men's Justin Ropers in sizes 6–12, 13, and 14, in A, B, D, E, and EE widths (full and half sizes). Women's Justin Ropers in sizes 4 to 9, and A, B, and C widths. 800–444–6481.

Lucchese Boots, 4025 Broadway, San Antonio, TX 78209: Free information ■ Handmade boots and shoes. 800–548–9755.

Luskey's Western Stores, Inc., 101 N. Houston St., Fort Worth, TX 76102: Free catalog ■ Western-style clothing, boots, and hats for men, women, and children. 817–335–5833.

Chris Romero Boot Company, 5819 NW Loop 410, Ste. 157, San Antonio, TX 78238: Free information with long SASE ■ Custom leather cowboy boots. 512–522–9622.

Tonto Rim Trading Company, P.O. Box 463, Salem, IN 47167: Catalog $3 ■ Western boots and hats. 800–253–4287; 812–883–3023 (in IN).

Western Boot Company, 1065 W. Mariposa Rd., P.O. Drawer 1949, Nogales, AZ 85621: Free catalog ■ Custom western-style boots. 602–287–3322.

Wilson Boot Company, 110 E. Callender St., Livingston, MT 59047: Brochure $1 ■ Handmade leather boots. 406–222–3842.

SHUFFLEBOARD

Activity Aids International, P.O. Box 54, Shakopee, MN 55379: Free information ■ Cues, disks, and sets. 612–445–2718.

Allen R. Shuffleboard Company, Inc., 6585 Seminole Blvd., Seminole, FL 34642: Free information ■ Cues, disks, and sets. 813–397–0421.

Chesal Industries, 2120 W. Florist Ave., P.O. Box 09281, Milwaukee, WI 53209: Free information ■ Cues, disks, and sets. 414–228–7920.

Dom Sports & Games, Dom Enterprises Mfg., Ltd., 957 Roselawn Ave., Toronto, Ontario, Canada M6B 1B6: Free information ■ Cues, disks, and sets. 416–781–2338.

General Sportcraft Company, Ltd., 140 Woodbine St., Bergenfield, NJ 07621: Free information ■ Cues, disks, and sets. 201–384–4242.

International Billiards, Inc., 2311 Washington Ave., Houston, TX 77007: Free information ■ Cues, disks, and sets. 800–255–6386; 713–869–3237 (in TX).

Dick Martin Sports, Inc., 185 River Rd., P.O. Box 931, Clifton, NJ 07014: Free information ■ Cues, disks, and sets. 800–221–1993; 201–473–0757 (in NJ).

Palmer Billiard Corporation, 307 Morris Ave., Elizabeth, NJ 07208: Free information ■ Cues, disks, and sets. 908–289–4741.

SGD Company, Inc., P.O. Box 5445, Akron, OH 44313: Free information ■ Cues, disks, and sets. 800–321–3411.

Ultra Play Systems, Inc., 425 Sycamore St., Anderson, IN 46016: Free information ■ Cues, disks, and sets. 800–458–5872; 317–643–5315 (in IN).

SIGNS & SIGN-MAKING

Americraft Corporation, 904 4th St. West, Palmetto, FL 34221: Free catalog ■ Injection molded and formed letters. 800–237–3984; 813–722–6631 (in FL).

Barclay Leaf Imports, Inc., 21 Wilson Terrace, Elizabeth, NJ 07208: Free information ■ Gold leaf. 908–353–5522.

Dick Blick Company, P.O. Box 1267, Galesburg, IL 61401: Catalog $3 ■ Sign-making supplies and equipment. 800–447–8192.

C.A.C. Banners, 50 N. Madison Ave., Spring Valley, NY 10977: Free information ■ Custom banners with ropes, velcro fasteners, corner loops, grommets, and pipe sleeves. 914–425–1461.

Cambridge Metalsmiths, Box 1400, Lynden, Ontario, Canada L0R 1T0: Free brochure ■ Cast metal signs, hand-enamelled on heavy metal relief, with a choice of over 250 emblems. 519–647–3326.

Erie Landmark Company, 90 W. Montgomery Ave., Ste. 211, Rockville, MD 20850: Free brochure ■ Custom outdoor and indoor bronze or redwood markers and signs. 301–460–9575.

Geer & Company, Rt. 22A, Bridport, VT 05734: Free brochure ■ Gold leaf signs and graphic designs hand-chiseled in wood, stone, slate, marble, and granite. 802–758–2492.

N. Glantz & Son, 218 57th St., Brooklyn, NY 11220: Free information ■ Supplies and equipment for sign painters. 718–439–7707.

Gold Leaf & Metallic Powders, 74 Trinity Pl., Ste. 1807, New York, NY 10006: Free information ■ Genuine and composition leaf in rolls, sheets, books, and boxes. 800–322–0323; 212–267–4900 (in NY).

John Hinds & Company, 81 Greenridge Dr. West, Elmira, NY 14905: Free catalog ■ Custom aluminum and bronze plaques and signs. 607–733–6712.

Hodgins Engraving, P.O. Box 597, Batavia, NY 14020: Free information ■ Engraved plastic signs. 800–666–8950.

Homestead Plaques, 9389 N. Oak Rd., Otisville, MI 48463: Free information ■ Custom signs with a choice of artwork, lettering, and background colors. 313–631–4092.

HTD Incorporated, 420 Pearl St., Malden, MA 02148: Free information ■ Sign-making systems and components. 800–553–3025.

Kaufman Supply, Rt. 1, Centertown, MO 65023: Free catalog ■ Supplies and equipment for sign painters. 314–893–2124.

Kimball Sign Company, 2602 Whitaker St., Savannah, GA 31401: Information packet $1 ■ Woodcarving machines for signs, pictures, and other arts and crafts. 912–232–6561.

La Haye Bronze, Inc., 1346 Railroad St., Corona, CA 91720: Free catalog ■ Sandcast, hand-chased bronze signs. 800–523–9544; 714–734–1371 (in CA).

Lake Shore Industries, P.O. Box 59, Erie, PA 16512: Free information ■ Cast aluminum and bronze signs and plaques. 800–458–0463; 814–456–4277 (in PA).

Landmark Brass, P.O. Box 150507, Van Brunt Station, Brooklyn, NY 11215: Brochure $1 ■ Custom-engraved brass architectural plaques, name plaques, circa plaques, and kickplates. 718–499–0984.

Letters Unlimited, 32 W. Streamwood Blvd., Streamwood, IL 60103: Free catalog ■ Vinyl letters. 800–422–4231.

MaDaNa Manufacturing, 947 N. Cole Ave., Los Angeles, CA 90038: Free catalog ■ Genuine gold leaf and composition metal leaf and accessories. 213–469–0856.

Marlin Industries, Inc., Rt. 70, Box 191, Cashiers, NC 28717: Brochure $1 ■ Woodcarving machines for making signs, decoys, statues, and gun stocks. 704–743–5551.

Max-Cast, 611 B Ave., Kalona, IA 52247: Free information ■ Bronze, aluminum, and iron letters. 319–656–5365.

Mayfair Signs, P.O. Box 2955, Sumas, WA 98295: Free brochure ■ Custom, hand-painted cast aluminum signs. 604–823–4141.

Earl Mich Company, 806 N. Peoria St., Chicago, IL 60622: Free information ■ Vinyl and reflecting sign letters. 800–MICH–USA; 312–829–1552 (in IL).

Mossburg's Foam Products, 103 N. Alabama Ave., Chesnee, SC 29323: Free information ■ Easy-to-install foam, plastic, and vinyl letters. 800–845–6140; 803–461–8116 (in SC).

National Banner Company, Inc., 11938 Harry Hines Blvd., Dallas, TX 75234: Free information ■ Blank banners hemmed and roped, or grommeted, with heavy duty rope sewn top and bottom. 800–527–0860.

Newman Brothers, Inc., 5607 Center Hill Ave., Cincinnati, OH 45216: Free catalog ■ Handcrafted cast bronze and aluminum plaques. 513–242–0011.

Rayco Paint Company, 2535 N. Laramie, Chicago, IL 60639: Free information ■ Supplies and equipment for sign painters. 800–421–2327.

Reich Supply Company, Inc., 811 Broad St., Utica, NY 13501: Free information ■ Sign-making and screen-printing materials and equipment. 800–338–3322; 315–732–6126 (in NY).

Ryther-Purdy Lumber Company, Inc., 69 Elm St., P.O. Box 622, Old Saybrook, CT 06475: Free information ■ Handcrafted wooden signs. 203–388–4405.

Sepp Leaf Products, Inc., 381 Park Ave. South, New York, NY 10016: Free information ■ Gold and palladium leaf, rolled gold, tools, and kits. 212–683–2840.

Sign-Mart, 1657 N. Glassell, Orange, CA 92667: Free information ■ Hemmed banners with grommets. 800–533–9099; 714–998–9470 (in CA).

Smith-Cornell, Inc., P.O. Box 686, Auburn, IN 46706: Free catalog ■ Brass and aluminum historic markers. 800–325–0248; 219–925–1172 (in IN).

Southern Sign Supply, Inc., 127 Roesler Rd., Glen Burnie, MD 21061: Free information ■ Supplies and equipment for sign painters. 800–638–5008; 800–445–1108 (in MD).

Joseph Struhl Company, Inc., 195 Atlantic Ave., P.O. Box N, Garden City Park, NY 11040: Free information ■ Ready-made window signs for retail stores. 800–552–0023.

Sun Energy, Inc., P.O. Box 177, Princeton, NJ 08542: Free information ■ Wireless, solar-powered house number signs. 609–799–8800.

Leo Uhlfelder Company, 420 S. Fulton Ave., Mt. Vernon, NY 10553: Free information ■ Natural hair brushes for painting and lettering and synthetic brushes for oils and acrylics. 914–664–8701.

Variety Art & Sign Supply, 912 Silver Lily St., Marrero, LA 70072: Catalog $4 ■ Sign-making supplies, accessories, and books. 504–341–9816.

John Voss Signs, Box 553, Manluss, NY 13104: Free catalog ■ Aluminum and plastic signs. 315–682–6418.

Wensco Sign Supplies, P.O. Box 1728, Grand Rapids, MI 49501: Catalog $5 ■ Supplies and equipment for sign painters. 800–253–1569; 800–632–4629 (in MI).

SILK-SCREENING

Advance Process Supply Company, 400 N. Noble St., Chicago, IL 60622: Free catalog ■ Supplies and equipment for silk-screening. 312–829–1400.

Chaselle, Inc., 9645 Gerwig Ln., Columbia, MD 21046: Catalog $4 ■ Art software and books, brushes and paints, tempera colors, acrylics and sets, pastels, ceramic molds and kilns, sculpture equipment, and silk-screen painting supplies. 800–242–7355.

Crown Art Products Company, Inc., 90 Dayton Ave., Passaic, NJ 07055: Free catalog ■ Silk-screening supplies and equipment and section frames. 201–777–6010.

Decart, Inc., Morrisville, VT 05661: Free brochure ■ Water-based enamels and paints for transfer techniques, glass crafting, and silk-screening. 802–888–4217.

Guildcraft Company, 3158 Main St., Buffalo, NY 14214: Catalog $1 ■ Supplies and accessories for silk-screening, batik, tie dying, stenciling, block printing, and foil crafts. 716–837–9346.

Ivy Crafts Imports, 122113 Distribution Way, Beltsville, MD 20705: Catalog $2.95 ■ Paints, resists, applicators, and other supplies. 301–595–0550.

Naz-Dar Company, 1087 Branch St., Chicago, IL 60622: Free catalog ■ Silk-screening and graphic arts equipment and supplies. 312- 943–8338.

Pyramid of Urbana, 2107 N. High Cross Rd., Urbana, IL 61801: Free catalog ■ Screen-printing films, supplies, kits, frames, tools, inks, and printers; other craft supplies; office accessories and supplies; art supplies; and school equipment. 217–328–3099.

Reich Supply Company, Inc., 811 Broad St., Utica, NY 13501: Free information ■ Sign-making and screen-printing materials and equipment. 800–338–3322; 315–732–6126 (in NY).

SILVER & FLATWARE

Atlantic Silver, 5223 Ehrlich Rd., Tampa, FL 33624: Free information ■ New and estate flatware and hollowware. 800–288–6665.

Barrons, P.O. Box 994, Novi, MI 48376: Free information ■ Save up to 65 percent on china, crystal, and silver. 800–538–6340.

Beverly Bremer Silver Shop, 3164 Peachtree Rd. NE, Atlanta, GA 30305: Free information ■ Save up to 75 percent on new and used obsolete and hard-to-find patterns. 404–261–4009.

Buschemeyer's Silver Exchange, 515 S. 4th Ave., Louisville, KY 40202: Free information ■ New and used silver patterns and sterling. 800–626–4555.

Walter Drake Silver Exchange, Drake Building, Colorado Springs, CO 80940: Free pattern directory ■ Sterling and silver plate in active, inactive, and obsolete patterns. 719–596–3853.

Fortunoff Fine Jewelry, P.O. Box 1550, New York, NY 10022: Catalog $2 ■ Sterling flatware, silver plate and stainless steel serving pieces and accessories, and china. 800–937–4376.

Graham Silver, P.O. Box 6021, Omaha, NE 68106: Free information with long SASE ■ Place settings, serving pieces, tea services, and other silver items. 800–228–2294.

Greater New York Trading, 81 Canal St., New York, NY 10002: Free information with long SASE ■ Silver, china, and glassware. 800–336–4012.

Hagan's Sterling & Silverplate, P.O. Box 25487, Tempe, AZ 85282: Free information ■ Discontinued and current sterling and silver plate. 800–528–7425.

Kaiser Crow, Inc., 3545 S. Platte River Dr., Englewood, CO 80110: Free information ■ Save up to 60 percent on stainless, silver flatware, and other silver patterns. 800–468–2769; 303–781–6888 (in CO).

Lanac Sales, 73 Canal St., New York, NY 10002: Free information ■ China, crystal, sterling, and gifts. 212–925–6422.

Helen Lawler, 5400 E. Country Rd., Blytheville, AR 72315: Free information ■ Discontinued silver patterns. 314–720–8502.

Littman's Sterling, 151 Granby St., Norfolk, VA 23510: Free information ■ Individual sterling pieces and place settings. 800–368–6348.

Locators, Inc., 908 Rock St., Little Rock, AR 72202: Free information ■ Discontinued china, crystal, and silver. 800–367–9690.

Michele's Silver Matching Service, 805 Crystal Mountain Dr., Austin, TX 78733:

Free information ■ Over 750 inactive and active silver patterns. 800–332–4693.

Midas China & Silver, 4315 Walney Rd., Chantilly, VA 22021: Free catalog ■ Save up to 60 percent on silverware, table settings, china, and gifts. 800–368–3153.

Past & Presents, 65–07 Fitchett St., Rego Park, NY 11374: Free information ■ Flatware, china, and crystal. 718–897–5515.

Robin Importers, 510 Madison Ave., New York, NY 10022: Free brochure with long SASE ■ China, crystal, and stainless steel flatware. 800–223–3373; 212–753–6475 (in NY).

Rogers & Rosenthal, 22 W. 48th St., Room 1102, New York, NY 10036: Free information with long SASE ■ Crystal, china, silver, silverplate, and stainless steel flatware. 212–827–0115.

Wilma Saxton, Inc., 37 Clementon Rd., Berlin, NJ 08009: Free price list ■ Sterling silver, silverplate, and stainless matching service. 609–767–8640.

Silverladies & Nick, 5650 W. Central Ave., Toledo, OH 43615: Free information ■ Sterling and silver plate in old, inactive, and obsolete patterns. 800–423–4390.

Silver Lane, P.O. Box 322, San Leandro, CA 94577: Free information ■ Discontinued crystal and china patterns, and current and obsolete silver. 510–483–0632.

The Sterling Shop, P.O. Box 595, Silverton, OR 97381: Free list with long SASE ■ Inactive and obsolete American-made sterling and discontinued silverplate patterns. 503–873–6315.

Thurber's, 14 Minnesota Ave., Warwick, RI 02888: Free information ■ Sterling and china. 800–848–7237.

SKATEBOARDS

Better Board Company, 1106 2nd St., Box 124, Encinitas, CA 92024: Free information ■ Skateboards and accessories. 619–598–0248.

Cal Hot Products, 2795 W. Lincoln Ave., Anaheim, CA 92801: Catalog $1 ■ Skateboards, accessories, foot gear, protective gear, and stickers. 800–HOT–3233.

California Hot Products, 2511 W. La Palma Ave., Anaheim, CA 92801: Catalog $1 ■ Skateboards, parts, clothing, helmets, stickers, and safety gear. 800–HOT–3233; 800–4CALHOT (in CA).

Cali4nia Skate Express, 4629 N. Blythe, Fresno, CA 93722: Free information ■ Ready-to-use and custom skateboards, T-shirts, stickers, and shoes. 800–426–9177.

FTC Skate Shop, 1586 Bush at Franklin, San Francisco, CA 94109: Price list $1 ■ Skateboards, accessories, clothing, and shoes. 415–673–8363.

Grind King, P.O. Box 535, Venice, CA 90294: Catalog $2 ■ Skateboards, trucks, and stickers.

Intensity Skates, P.O. Box 1037, College Park, MD 20740: Catalog $1 ■ Ready-to-use and custom skateboards and skating accessories, clothing, and hightops. 800–47–SKATE.

Kryptonics, Inc., 5660 Central Ave., Boulder, CO 80301: Free information ■ Skateboards and roller skates. 303–442–9173.

National Sporting Goods Corporation, 25 Brighton Ave., Passaic, NJ 07055: Free information ■ Skateboards, roller skates, and scooters. 201–779–2323.

Roller Derby Skate Company, 311 W. Edwards St., Litchfield, IL 62056: Free information ■ Skateboards, roller skates, and scooters. 217–324–3961.

Saucony/Hyde, P.O. Box 6046, Centennial Industrial Park, Peabody, MA 01961: Free information ■ Skateboards, roller skates, and scooters. 508–532–9000.

Sessions Skateboard Mail Order, 989 E. California Ave., Ste. 3, Sunnyvale, CA 94086: Free catalog ■ Skateboards, shoes, and clothing. 408–735–1138.

Skates on Haight, 384 Oyster Point Blvd., South San Francisco, CA 94080: Catalog $2 ■ Skateboards and accessories, snowboards, bodyboards, shoes, stickers, helmets, and clothing. 415–244–9800.

Skate Ware-House, 4035 S. Higuera St., San Luis Obispo, CA 93401: Free information ■ Ready-to-use and custom skateboards and components parts, and canvas and suede high-tops, and T-shirts. 800–666–7723.

Skully Brothers, 4629 N. Blythe, Fresno, CA 93722: Catalog $2 ■ Skateboards, accessories, shoes, clothing, stickers, and safety gear. 209–275–4002.

Stylin', P.O. Box 233, Osage Beach, MO 65065: Catalog $1 ■ Skateboards, accessories, clothing, shoes, and stickers. 314–348–0726.

Tracker Designs, Ltd., P.O. Box 217, Cardiff, CA 92007: Free information ■ Skateboards, trucks, and wheels. 800–282–8722; 619–722–1455 (in CA).

Valterra Products, Inc., 720 Jessie St., San Fernando, CA 91340: Free information ■ Skateboards, trucks, wheels, and helmets. 818–898–1671.

Variflex, Inc., 5152 N. Commerce Ave., Moorpark, CA 93021: Free information ■ Skateboards and roller skates. 805–532–0322.

Z Products, P.O. Box 5397, Santa Monica, CA 90405: Free information ■ Skateboards, trucks, and wheels. 310–476–4857.

SKIING

Clothing

Action Sports Gear, Inc., 150 N. Farms Rd., Northampton, MA 01060: Free information ■ Men's and women's ski clothing. 413–586–8844.

Adventure International Corporation, Adventure Gear, 8039 Deering Ave., Canoga Park, CA 91304: Free information ■ Hats, gloves and mittens, pants, jackets, parkas, suits, separates, sweaters, underwear, and wind shirts. 818–594–0380.

Alafoss of Iceland, 499 7th Ave., New York, NY 10018: Free information ■ Men's and women's ski clothing. 212–564–3500.

All Weather Outerwear Company, 1270 Broadway, Ste. 701, New York, NY 10001: Free information ■ Jackets, pants, parkas and suits, separates, vests, and wind shirts. 212–244–2690.

Alpine Designs, 197 Longview St., Newport, VT 05855: Free information ■ Jackets and pants, parkas and suits, separates, vests, and wind shirts. 800–451–4348; 802–334–5033 (in VT).

Alpine Research, Inc., 1803 S. Foothills Pkwy., Boulder, CO 80303: Free catalog ■ Back country ski equipment and clothing, tents, sleeping bags, frame packs, books, videos, rock and ice climbing gear, caving equipment, and winter survival equipment. 303–499–4466.

Eddie Bauer, P.O. Box 3700, Seattle, WA 98124: Free catalog ■ Men's and women's ski clothing, natural fiber sportswear, down outerwear, footwear, and luggage. 800–426–8020.

L.L. Bean, Inc., Freeport, ME 04033: Free catalog ■ Men's and women's clothing for skiing, back country travel, and snowshoeing, and camping and workout gear. 800–221–4221.

Bissig Sport Fashions, Ski Dept., P.O. Box 1267, Aspen, CO 81612: Free information ■ Hats, gloves and mittens, jackets, parkas, pants, suits, vests, and wind shirts. 303–925–8324.

Bogner of America, Bogner Dr., Newport, VT 05855: Free information ■ Gloves and mittens, hats, parkas, jackets, pants, suits, separates, sweaters, wind shirts, and vests. 800–451–4417; 802–334–6507 (in VT).

Columbia Sportswear Company, 6600 N. Baltimore, P.O. Box 03239, Portland, OR 97203: Free information ■ Men's, women's, and children's hats, gloves, mittens, jackets, pants, suits, parkas, underwear, vests, and wind shirts. 800–622–6953.

Competitive Edge, 1400 N. Shoreline Dr., P.O. Box 7211, Mountain View, CA 94039: Free catalog ■ Clothing, goggles and glasses, watches, gloves, ski equipment, books, luggage, carryall bags, videos, and T-shirts. 800–627–0600.

Descente America, Inc., Descente, Ltd., 601 Madison Ave., New York, NY 10022: Free information ■ Hats, mittens and gloves, parkas and suits, jackets, pants, underwear, socks, sweaters, wind shirts, and vests. 800–221–4990; 212–888–7710 (in NY).

Detail Ski Wear, Inc., P.O. Box 200, Bondville, VT 05340: Free information ■ Jackets and pants, hats, parkas and suits, separates, vests, and wind shirts. 802–297–1045.

Donner Designs, P.O. Box 7217, Reno, NV 89510: Catalog $1 ■ Sewing kits and patterns for ski clothing. 702–358–5281.

Eagle River Nordic, P.O. Box 936, Eagle River, WI 54521: Free catalog ■ Boots, gloves, hats, videos, books, and ski equipment. 715–479–2208.

Early Winters, Inc., P.O. Box 4333, Portland, OR 97208: Free catalog ■ Men's and women's ski clothing, leisure separates for men and women, gifts, and equipment. 800–821–1286.

Ellesse USA, Inc., 1430 Broadway, New York, NY 10018: Free information ■ Gloves and mittens, hats, jackets and parkas, suits, sweaters, wind shirts, and vests. 212–840–6111.

Faeth Outdoor Sales, R.J.F. Enterprises, Inc., 1151 S. 7th St., P.O. Box 118–A, St. Louis, MO 63166: Free information ■ Hats, mittens and gloves, parkas and suits, jackets, underwear, socks, sweaters, wind shirts, and vests. 314–421–0030.

Fila Sports, Inc., 145 Park Ln., Brisbane, CA 94006: Free information ■ Gloves and mittens, hats, jackets and parkas, suits, separates, sweaters, wind shirts, and vests. 415–468–6800.

Gart Brothers Denver Sportscastle, 1000 Broadway, Denver, CO 80203: Free information ■ Skis, boots, and men's and women's clothing. 800–426–1399; 303–861–1122 (in CO).

Gorsuch, Ltd., 263 E. Gore Creek Dr., Vail, CO 81657: Free catalog ■ Men's and women's ski and other clothing. 303–949–4005.

Head Sportswear, 9189 Red Branch Rd., Columbia, MD 21045: Free information ■ Men's and women's ski clothing. 410–730–8300.

Liberty Mountain Sports, P.O. Box 306, Montrose, CA 91020: Free information ■ Hats, mittens and gloves, jackets, socks, underwear, and sweaters. 818–248–0618.

Marker International, P.O. Box 26548, Salt Lake City, UT 84126: Free brochure ■ Men's and women's ski clothing. 801–972–2100.

Marmot Mountain Works, Ltd., 2321 Circadian Way, Santa Rosa, CA 95407: Free information ■ Men's and women's ski clothing. 707–544–4590.

North Face, 999 Harrison St., Berkeley, CA 94710: Free information ■ Hats, mittens and gloves, jackets, parkas and suits, underwear, sweaters, vests, and wind shirts. 800–654–1751.

Scandia Trading Company, Skyr Skiwear, P.O. Box 486, Winchester, MA 01890: Free information ■ Hats, jackets, pants and suits, parkas, socks, sweaters, underwear, and wind shirts. 617–729–4141.

Scandinavian Ski & Sport Shop, 40 W. 57th St., New York, NY 10019: Free information ■ Men's and women's ski clothing and equipment. 212–757–8524.

Slalom Skiwear, Inc., Longview St., Newport, VT 05855: Free information ■ Men's and women's ski clothing. 802–334–7958.

WASCO Sports, 890 Cowan Rd., Ste. C, Burlingame, CA 94010: Free information ■ Men's and women's ski clothing and other outdoor fashions. 800–247–9933.

Equipment & Accessories

Akers Ski, Inc., Andover, ME 04216: Free catalog ■ Nordic skis, ski boots, bindings, poles, and transportation and storage gear. 207–392–4582.

Allsop, 4201 Meridian, Box 23, Bellingham, WA 98227: Free information ■ Nordic skis and poles, boot trees, and carriers. 206–734–9090.

Alpina Sports Corporation, P.O. Box 23, Hanover, NH 03755: Free information ■ Boot bags, alpine and nordic boots, and nordic bindings and skis. 603–448–3101.

B & G Wholesale, 47–09 30th St., Long Island City, NY 11101: Free information ■ Boot bags, alpine and nordic boots, and alpine and nordic skis. 718–706–0100.

Ballco Products, Inc., P.O. Box 25346, San Mateo, CA 94402: Free information ■ Boot bags, goggles, alpine and nordic ski poles, and ski bags. 415–343–2918.

Brenco Enterprises, Inc., 7877 S. 180th St., Kent, WA 98032: Free information ■ Alpine and nordic boots, and apres ski boots. 206–251–5020.

Caber USA, 50 Jonergin Dr., Swanton, VT 05488: Free information ■ Alpine ski poles, boots, and nordic skis. 802–868–2761.

Climb High, Inc., 1861 Shelburne Rd., Shelburne, VT 05482: Free information ■ Nordic boots. 802–985–5056.

Collins Ski Products, Inc., P.O. Box 11, Bergenfield, NJ 07621: Free information ■ Ski carriers, goggles, and alpine ski poles. 800–526–0369; 201–384–6060 (in NJ).

Daleboot USA, 2150 S. 3rd West St., Salt Lake City, UT 84115: Free information ■ Boot bags, and alpine ski poles and boots. 801–487–3649.

Eagle River Nordic, P.O. Box 936, Eagle River, WI 54521: Free catalog ■ Ski equipment, clothing, boots, gloves, hats, and videos. 715–479–2208.

Elan-Monark, 208 Flynn Ave., P.O. Box 4279, Burlington, VT 05401: Free information ■ Boot bags, ski bags, alpine ski poles, bindings, boots, and alpine and nordic skis. 802–863–5593.

Fabiano Shoe Company, 850 Summer St., South Boston, MA 02127: Free information ■ Nordic boots and bindings, and apres ski boots. 617–268–5625.

Igloo Viksi, Inc., P.O. Box 180, St. Agathe Des Monts, Quebec, Canada J8C 3A3: Free information ■ Boot bags and trees, alpine and nordic ski poles, ski bags, and nordic skis, boots, and bindings. 819–326–1662.

Johar, Inc., P.O. Box 10, Forrest City, AR 72335: Free information ■ Nordic ski poles. 800–248–1232; 501–633–8161 (in AR).

Karhu USA, Inc., P.O. Box 4249, South Burlington, VT 05401: Free information ■ Ski carriers and bags, and nordic skis. 800–222–1833; 802–864–4519 (in VT).

Kenko International, Inc., 8141 West I–70, Frontage Rd. North, Arvada, CO 80002: Free information ■ Nordic boots and bindings. 303–425–1200.

Koflach/Blizzard USA, 4699 Nautilus Court St., Boulder, CO 80301: Free information ■ Boot bags, nordic and alpine ski poles, ski bags, nordic and alpine skis, and alpine boots. 303–530–2668.

Maska USA, Inc., Pierson Industrial Park, Rt. 25, P.O. Box 381, Bradford, VT 05033: Free information ■ Nordic skis, poles, and boots. 800–451–4600; 802–222–4751 (in VT).

J. Miller Industries, 3334 W. Castor St., Santa Ana, CA 92704: Free information ■ Nordic ski poles. 714–754–6851.

Miller Ski Company, Inc., N. 1200 West, Orem, UT 84057: Free information ■ Nordic and alpine skis, poles, bindings and boots, boot bags, and apres ski boots. 801–225–1100.

Nyberg Sports Distributors, Inc., 6217 22nd Ave., Kenosha, WI 53140: Free information ■ Nordic skis and boots. 414–654–6268.

O.U. Sports, Inc., 220 S. Jackson St., Seattle, WA 98104: Free information ■ Alpine and nordic skis. 206–624–6948.

Paradise International Trading, P.O. Box 11583, Tahoe Paradise, CA 95708: Free information ■ Alpine and nordic skis, nordic boots, and apres ski boots. 916–577–5646.

Pro Advantage, Inc., 2030 N. Redwood Rd., Ste. 10, Salt Lake City, UT 84116: Free information ■ Boot bags, goggles, and alpine ski poles, bags, and skis. 801–532–4822.

Rax Works, Inc., 7775 Arjons Dr., San Diego, CA 92126: Free information ■ Nordic skis. 714–271–7500.

Reflex Sport Products, Easton Aluminum, 1971 S. 4490 West, Salt Lake City, UT 84104: Free information ■ Boot bags, alpine and nordic ski poles, ski bags, and alpine skis. 800–755–6651; 801–973–9770 (in UT).

Reliable Racing Supply, Inc., 630 Glen St., Queensbury, NY 12804: Free catalog ■ Ski equipment. 518–793–0526.

Rossignol Ski Company, Industrial Ave., P.O. Box 298, Williston, VT 05495: Free information ■ Alpine and nordic skis. 802–863–2511.

Salomon/North America, 400 E. Main St., Georgetown, MA 01833: Free information ■ Alpine and nordic bindings and boots. 800–225–6850; 508–352–7600 (in MA).

Skis Dynastar, Inc., Hercules Dr., P.O. Box 25, Colchester, VT 05446: Free information ■ Alpine and nordic skis, alpine boots, and boot and ski bags. 802–655–2400.

Spalding & Brothers, 425 Meadow St., P.O. Box 901, Chicopee, MA 01021: Free information ■ Nordic and alpine skis and poles. 413–536–1200.

Swix Sport USA, Inc., 261 Ballardvale St., Wilmington, MA 01887: Free information ■ Boot and ski bags, goggles, alpine and nordic ski poles, and nordic bindings and boots. 508–657–4820.

Tristar Sports, Inc., 475 Smith St., Middletown, CT 06457: Free information ■ Nordic and alpine skis, poles, bindings, and boot and ski bags. 800–624–7827; 203–632–2000 (in CT).

Yamaha Sporting Goods Division, 6600 Orangethorpe Ave., Buena Park, CA 90622: Free information ■ Alpine skis. 800–851–6514; 714–522–9011 (in CA).

Goggles

American Optical Corporation, 14 Mechanic St., Southbridge, MA 01550: Free information ■ Ski goggles. 508–765–9711.

B.J. Plastic Molding Company, Inc., 3803 North Mt. Prospect Rd., Franklin Park, IL 60131: Free information ■ Ski goggles. 708–766–3200.

Brigade Quartermasters, Inc., 1025 Cobb International Blvd., Kenesaw, GA 30144: Catalog $3 ■ Ski goggles. 404–428–1234.

Carrera Ski & Sport Division, 35 Maple St., Norwood, NJ 07648: Free information ■ Ski goggles. 201–767–3820.

Jones & Company, 325 E. Massasoit Ave., East Providence, RI 02914: Free information ■ Ski goggles. 401–434–4010.

Martin Sunglasses, Jack Martin Company, Inc., 9830 Baldwin Pl., El Monte, CA 91731: Free information ■ Ski goggles. 800–423–4465; 213–686–1100 (in CA).

Nelson/Weather-Rite Products, Inc., Fuqua Sports, 14760 Santa Fe Trail, Lenexa, KS 66215: Free information ■ Ski goggles. 800–255–6061; 913–492–3200 (in KS).

SKIN DIVING & SCUBA EQUIPMENT

Ador-Aqua, 42 W. 18th St., New York, NY 10011: Free information ■ Consoles, snorkels, diver's watches, back packs, lights, pneumatic guns, knives, masks, and equipment packages. 212–645–1234.

Aqua-Leisure Industries, Inc., Avon Industrial Park, P.O. Box 25, Avon, MA 02322: Free information ■ Diving masks, fins, and flippers. 508–587–5400.

Aquarius, 51 Lake St., Nashua, NH 03060: Free information ■ Skin diving equipment. 800–435–8974; 603–889–4346 (in NH).

Atlantis, 3558 S. Orange Ave., Orlando, FL 32806: Free information ■ Wet suits for divers, surfers, and water skiers. 407–851–8025.

Bare Sportswear Corporation, 1600 Kentucky St., Bellingham, WA 98226: Free information ■ Wet suits. 206–676–2700.

Bermudes USA, Inc., P.O. Box 810, Sag Harbor, NY 11963: Free information ■ Wet suits. 516–725–9545.

Berry Scuba Company, 6674 N. Northwest Hwy., Chicago, IL 60631: Free catalog ■ Skin diving and scuba equipment, inflatable boats, watches, clothing, diving lights, and underwater camera equipment. 800–621–6019; 312–763–1626 (in IL).

Big Foot Products, P.O. Box 575, Rosemead, CA 91770: Free information ■ Wet suits. 818–280–1492.

Body Glove International, Inc., Dive N' Surf, Inc., 530 6th St., Hermosa Beach, CA 90254: Free information ■ Wet and skin diving suits, fins and flippers, and other equipment. 213–374–4074.

Central Skin Divers, 160–09 Jamaica Ave., Jamaica, NY 11432: Free information with long SASE ■ Save up to 40 percent on skin diving equipment and clothing. 718–739–5772.

Competitive Aquatic Supply, Inc., 15131 Triton Ln., Huntington Beach, CA 92649: Free information ■ Fins and flippers, diving masks, wet suits, and waterproof watches. 800–421–5192; 310–633–3333 (in CA).

Depth Perception of Nevada, Inc., 4660 S. Eastern, Ste. 209, Las Vegas, NV 89119: Free information ■ Wet suits, vests, and soft backpacks. 702–456–2634.

Divers Supply, 5208 Mercer University Dr., Macon, GA 31210: Free information ■ Skin diving equipment and clothing. 800–474–6790.

Eagle Watersports, Inc., 500 Century Plaza Dr., Ste. 190, Houston, TX 77073: Free information ■ Wet suits. 800–231–0379.

EP Sports, 319 S. Park Dr., St. Marys, OH 45885: Free information ■ Wet suits, gloves, ropes, bags, hats, and vests. 800–231–0379.

HO Sports, 17622 NE 67th, Redmond, WA 98052: Free information ■ Slalom skis, knee boards, ski boards, and wet suits. 206–885–3505.

Hot Sports, 2151 Sampson Ave., Corona, CA 91720: Free information ■ Wet suits. 714–279–2884.

M & E Marine Supply Company, P.O. Box 601, Camden, NJ 08101: Catalog $2 ■ Skin diving equipment. 609–858–1010.

Mobby's USA, 4625 Nevso Ave., Ste. 1, Las Vegas, NV 89103: Free information ■ Wet suits. 800–662–2979.

Ocean Ray Wet Suits, 289–G Suburban Ave., Deer Park, NY 11729: Free brochure ■ Wet suits, hoods and mitts, and gloves. 800–645–5554; 516–667–7249 (in NY).

O'Neill, 1071 41st Ave., Santa Cruz, CA 95062: Free information ■ Wet suits. 408–475–7500.

Parkway/Imperial, 241 Raritan St., South Amboy, NJ 08879: Free information ■ Wet suits, tanks, gauges, and regulators. 908–721–5300.

Skin Diver Wet Suits, 1632 S. 250th St., Kent, WA 98032: Free information ■ Wet suits, boots, gloves, and hoods. 206–878–1613.

Sport Europa, 7871 NW 15th St., Miami, FL 33126: Free information ■ Wet suits, gloves, and hoods for men, women, and children. 800–327–7031.

Sports Merchandizers, 1696 Cobb Pkwy. SE, Box 1262, Marietta, GA 30061: Free catalog ■ Skin diving equipment. 800–241–1856; 404–952–3259 (in GA).

Tanks D'Art, Inc., 350 Easy St., Simi Valley, CA 93065: Free information ■ Diving tanks. 800–635–5815.

3 Little Devils, Rt. 4, Hwy. 123, Baraboo, WI 53913: Catalog 25¢ ■ Scuba equipment. 800–356–9016; 800–872–4244 (in WI).

Waterworks Wet Suits, 9123 I–45 South, Conroe, TX 77385: Free information ■ Wet suits. 713–367–2526.

Wenoka Sea Style, 1134 53rd Ct. North, P.O. Box 8238, West Palm Beach, FL 33407: Catalog $4 ■ Skin diving equipment. 407–845–6155.

SLEDS & TOBOGGANS

Dorman-Pacific Company, Inc., 7900 Edgewater Dr., Oakland, CA 94621: Free information ■ Sleds, snowmobile boots, and clothing. 800–DORFMAN; 800–4DP–HATS (in CA).

Faber Brothers, 4141 S. Pulaski Rd., Chicago, IL 60632: Free information ■ Sleds. 312–376–9300.

Faeth Outdoor Sales, R.J.F. Enterprises, Inc., 1151 S. 7th St., P.O. Box 118–A, St. Louis, MO 63166: Free information ■ Snowmobiles, bobsleds, snowmobile boots, and clothing. 314–421–0030.

Fulton & Fulton, 1701 Venable St., Richmond, VA 23223: Free information ■ Toboggans. 804–648–1222.

Intex Recreation Corporation, Sporting Goods Division, 4130 Santa Fe Ave., P.O. Box 1440, Long Beach, CA 90801: Free information ■ Toboggans. 310–549–5400.

M.W. Kasch Company, 5401 W. Donges Bay Rd., Mequon, WI 53092: Free information ■ Sleds and snowboards. 414–242–5000.

Julius Levenson, Inc., 1107 Broadway, Ste. 400, New York, NY 10024: Free information ■ Sleds, snowboards, and toboggans. 212–255–8770.

Life Industries, Inc., 381 Congress St., Boston, MA 02210: Free information ■ Toboggans. 617–542–5764.

Miller Ski Company, Inc., N. 1200 West, Orem, UT 84057: Free information ■ Toboggans, sleds, insulated clothing, snow shoes, snowmobile boots, and clothing. 801–225–1100.

National Pro Industries, Inc., 91 De La Barre, Boucherville, Quebec, Canada J4B 2X6: Free information ■ Toboggans, bobsleds, sleds, and snow shoes. 514–641–1634.

Nelson/Weather-Rite Products, Inc., Fuqua Sports, 14760 Santa Fe Trail Dr., Lenexa, KS 66215: Free information ■ Sleds, toboggans, and ski sleds. 800–255–6061; 913–492–3200 (in KS).

Paradise International Trading, P.O. Box 11583, Tahoe Paradise, CA 95708: Free information ■ Sleds and toboggans. 916–577–5646.

Paris Company, Inc., P.O. Box 250, South Paris, ME 04281: Free information ■ Sleds and toboggans. 207–743–5111.

Sevylor USA, 6651 E. 26th St., Los Angeles, CA 90040: Free information ■ Sleds. 213–727–6013.

SLM, Inc., P.O. Box 1070, Patch Rd., RD 1, Gloversville, NY 12078: Free information

■ Sleds, snowboards, and toboggans. 518–725–8101.

Toddboggan Manufacturing Company, 1214 N. 3000 West, Vernal, UT 84078: Free information ■ Toboggans. 801–789–3497.

Wellington Leisure Products, Inc., P.O. Box 244, Madison, GA 30650: Free information ■ Bobsleds. 404–342–4915.

ZIFFCO, 333–B W. Alondra Blvd., Gardena, CA 90248: Free information ■ Toboggans. 800–532–2241; 800–532–2242 (in CA).

SLIPCOVERS

Fabric Shop, 120 N. Seneca St., Shippensburg, PA 17257: Free information with long SASE ■ Antique satins, custom draperies, and drapery, slipcover, and upholstery fabrics. 800–233–7012; 800–692–7345 (in PA).

Fabric Wholesalers, Inc., P.O. Box 20235, Portland, OR 97220: Free price list ■ Fabrics and notions for clothes, draperies, curtains, and upholstering furniture. 503–666–4511.

Jack's Upholstery & Caning Supplies, 5498 Rt. 34, Oswego, IL 60543: Catalog $2 (refundable) ■ Upholstery, basket-making, and chair-caning supplies. 312–554–1045.

Rubin & Green, 290 Grand St., New York, NY 10002: Free information with long SASE ■ Upholstery and decorator fabrics, and custom bedspreads, draperies, and comforters. 212–226–0313.

Slipcovers of America, P.O. Box 590, Bethlehem, PA 18016: Free catalog ■ Slipcovers, matching draperies, and fabrics. 215–868–7788.

Tioga Mill Outlet, 200 S. Hartman St., York, PA 17403: Information $2 ■ Upholstery and drapery fabrics that include damasks, crewel, tapestry, linen, cotton, and others. 717–843–5139.

SNOWMOBILES

Faeth Outdoor Sales, R.J.F. Enterprises, Inc., 1151 S. 7th St., P.O. Box 118–A, St. Louis, MO 63166: Free information ■ Snowmobiles, bobsleds, ski bobs, snowmobile boots, and clothing. 314–421–0030.

Johar, Inc., P.O. Box 10, Forrest City, AR 72335: Free information ■ Snowmobiles. 800–248–1232; 501–633–8161 (in AR).

Dennis Kirk, Inc., 955 Southfield Ave., Rush City, MN 55069: Free catalog ■ Snowmobiles and parts. 800–328–9280.

SNOWSHOES

Buckeye Sports Supply, John's Sporting Goods, 2655 Harrison Ave. SW, Canton, OH 44706: Free information ■ Snowshoes. 800–533–8691.

Croakies, P.O. Box 2913, 1240 Huff Ln., Jackson, WY 83001: Free information ■ Snowshoes. 307–733–2266.

Deer Me Products Company, P.O. Box 34, 1208 Park St., Anoka, MN 55303: Free information ■ Snowshoes. 612–421–8971.

Fisher Sports Designs, 2209 W. Fairmont, Tempe, AZ 85282: Free information ■ Snowshoes. 602–437–0368.

Havlick Snowshoe Company, Rt. 30, Drawer QQ, Mayfield, NY 12117: Free information ■ Snowshoes. 518–661–6447.

Iverson Snowshoe Company, Maple St., P.O. Box 85, Shingleton, MI 49884: Free information ■ Snowshoes. 906–452–6370.

Leonard Joseph Company, 1100 W. 45th Ave., Denver, CO 80211: Free information ■ Snowshoes. 303–433–6506.

Longwood Equipment Company, Ltd., 1940 Ellesmere Rd., Unit 8, Scarborough, Ontario, Canada M1H 2V7: Free information ■ Snowshoes. 416–438–3710.

SOAP MAKING

Pourette Manufacturing, 6910 Roosevelt Way NE, Seattle, WA 98115: Catalog $1 (refundable) ■ Soap-making supplies and equipment, candles, and candle-making supplies and equipment. 206–525–4488.

Sunfeather Herbal Soap Company, Box 60A, Potsdam, NY 13676: Catalog $2 ■ Soap-making kits, supplies, and books. 315–265–3648.

SOCCER

Clothing

Action & Leisure, Inc., 45 E. 30th St., New York, NY 10016: Free information ■ Shoes, uniforms, gloves, shorts, shirts, shin guards, and socks. 212–684–4470.

Action Sport Systems, Inc., P.O. Box 1442, Morgantown, NC 28671: Free information ■ Uniforms, shirts, shorts, gloves, and socks. 800–631–1091; 704–874–2249 (in NC).

Active Knitting, Ltd., 89 Tycos Dr., Toronto, Ontario, Canada M6B 1W3: Free information ■ Shirts, shorts, and uniforms. 416–789–1101.

Adidas USA, 15 Independence Blvd., Warren, NJ 07060: Free information ■ Uniforms, shoes, socks, shirts, shorts, and shin guards. 908–580–0700.

Advantage Uniforms, Inc., 115 W. Main, P.O. Box 186, Manchester, MI 48158: Free information ■ Shorts and uniforms. 313–428–8522.

Alpha Sportswear, Inc., 2525 16th St., San Francisco, CA 94103: Free information ■ Uniforms, shin guards, and shoes. 800–227–4266.

Andia Progress Company, Inc., 47 Soundview Ave., White Plains, NY 10606: Free information ■ Shin guards, shirts, shorts, and custom and ready-to-wear uniforms. 800–431–2775; 914–948–2685 (in NY).

Asics Tiger Corporation, 10540 Talbert Ave., Fountain Valley, CA 92708: Free information ■ Shoes, socks, shorts, and shin guards. 714–962–7654.

B & G Wholesale, 47–09 30th St., Long Island City, NY 11101: Free information ■ Uniforms, gloves, shoes, shin guards, shirts, and shorts. 718–706–0100.

Bike Athletic Company, Kazmaier Associates, Inc., 2801 Red Dog Dr., P.O. Box 666, Knoxville, TN 37901: Free information ■ Shin guards, shirts, shorts, and uniforms. 800–251–9230; 615–546–4703 (in TN).

Champion Products, Inc., 3141 Monroe Ave., Rochester, NY 14618: Free information ■ Uniforms, shoes, socks, and shirts. 716–385–3200.

Continental Sports Supply, Inc., P.O. Box 1251, Englewood, CO 80150: Free information ■ Gloves, shin guards, shirts, shorts, and uniforms. 303–934–5657.

Doss Shoes, Soccer Sport Supply Company, 1745 1st Ave., New York, NY 10128: Free information ■ Gloves, shin guards, shirts, shorts, and uniforms. 212–427–6050.

Foremost Athletic Apparel, 1307 E. Maple Rd., Troy, MI 48083: Free information ■ Shin guards, shirts, shorts, and uniforms. 800–433–9486; 800–882–4333 (in MI).

Genesport Industries, Ltd., Hokkaido Karate Equipment Manufacturing Company, 150 King St., Montreal, Quebec, Canada H3C 2P3: Free information ■ Gloves, shin guards, shirts, and shorts. 514–861–1856.

Holabird Sports Discounters, 9004 Yellow Brick Rd., Rossville Industrial Park, Baltimore, MD 21237: Free brochure ■ Save up to 40 percent on soccer and other sports equipment and clothing. 410–687–6400.

Lotto Italioa, Inc., 2301 McDaniel Dr., Carrollton, TX 75006: Free information ■ Soccer shoes. 800–527–5126; 214–351–2537 In TX).

Matchfit Athletic Apparel, P.O. Box 13100, Charlotte, NC 28211: Free information ■ Uniforms, shoes, shorts, shin guards, socks, and gloves. 704–847–0896.

Pegasus Sportswear, Inc., P.O. Box 2963, Torrance, CA 90509: Free information ■ Gloves, shin guards, shirts, shorts, and custom uniforms. 310–539–4734.

Puma USA, Inc., 147 Centre St., Brockton, MA 02403: Free information ■ Uniforms, gloves, shorts and shirts, socks, shoes, and shin guards. 508–583–9100.

Soccer International, Inc., P.O. Box 7222, Arlington, VA 22207: Catalog $2 ■ Soccer equipment, uniforms, balls, gifts, T-shirts, and books. 703–524–4333.

Soccer Kick, 2130 Henderson Mill Rd., Atlanta, GA 30345: Free catalog ■ Soccer equipment and gifts. 800–533–KICK; 404–939–6355 (in GA).

Union Jacks, 3525 Roanoke Rd., Kansas City, MO 64111: Free information ■ Uniforms, shin guards, shirts, shorts, shoes, and socks. 800–288–5550; 816–561–5550 (in MO).

Equipment

Action & Leisure, Inc., 45 E. 30th St., New York, NY 10016: Free information ■ Soccer balls, cleats, and wrenches. 212–684–4470.

Action Sport Systems, Inc., P.O. Box 1442, Morgantown, NC 28671: Free information ■ Soccer balls. 800–631–1091; 704–874–2249 (in NC).

Adidas USA, 15 Independence Blvd., Warren, NJ 07060: Free information ■ Soccer balls, cleats, and other equipment. 908–580–0700.

Andia Progress Company, Inc., 47 Soundview Ave., White Plains, NY 10606: Free information ■ Soccer balls, goals, and nets. 800–431–2775; 914–948–2685 (in NY).

Audero Sports Supply, Inc., 4935 McConnell Ave., Ste. 11, Los Angeles, CA 90066: Free information ■ Goals, nets, and soccer balls. 310–822–3637.

B & G Wholesale, 47–09 30th St., Long Island City, NY 11101: Free information ■ Soccer balls. 718–706–0100.

Buckeye Sports Supply, John's Sporting Goods, 2655 Harrison Ave. SW, Canton, OH 44706: Free information ■ Goals, nets, and soccer balls. 800–533–8691.

Champion Sports Products Company, Inc., P.O. Box 138, Sayreville, NJ 08872: Free information ■ Soccer balls, goals, and nets. 908–238–0330.

Continental Sports Supply, Inc., P.O. Box 1251, Englewood, CO 80150: Free information ■ German Bundesliga soccer balls. 303–934–5657.

Cosom Sporting Goods, Grandview Ave., P.O. Box 10, Woodbury Heights, NJ 08097: Free information ■ Goals, nets, and soccer balls. 609–853–0300.

Doss Shoes, Soccer Sport Supply Company, 1745 1st Ave., New York, NY 10128: Free information ■ Goals, nets, and soccer balls. 212–427–6050.

Gamemaster Athletic Company, 582 Goddard Ave., Chesterfield, MO 63107: Free information ■ Soccer balls, goals, and nets. 800–325–4141; 314–532–4646 (in MO).

General Sportcraft Company, Ltd., 140 Woodbine St., Bergenfield, NJ 07621: Free

information ■ Soccer balls, goals, and nets. 201–384–4242.

Holabird Sports Discounters, 9004 Yellow Brick Rd., Rossville Industrial Park, Baltimore, MD 21237: Free brochure ■ Save up to 40 percent on soccer equipment and clothing. 410–687–6400.

Irwin Sports, 43 Hanna Ave., Toronto, Ontario, Canada M6K 1X6: Free information ■ Soccer balls, goals, and nets. 416–533–3521.

Jayfro Corporation, Unified Sports, Inc., 976 Hartford Tpk., P.O. Box 400, Waterford, CT 06385: Free catalog ■ Portable goals, nets, and practice equipment. 203–447–3001.

Kwik Goal, 140 Pacific Dr., Quakertown, PA 18951: Free information ■ Soccer balls, goals, nets, wrenches and cleats, training equipment, referee supplies, and video cassettes. 800–531–4252; 215–536–2200 (in PA).

Markwort Sporting Goods Company, 4300 Forest Park Ave., St. Louis, MO 63108: Free information ■ Soccer balls, goals, and nets. 314–652–3757.

Matchfit Athletic Apparel, P.O. Box 13100, Charlotte, NC 28211: Free information ■ Soccer balls, goals, nets, cleats, and wrenches. 704–847–0896.

Regent Sports Corporation, 45 Ranick Rd., Hauppage, NY 11787: Free information ■ Soccer balls, goals, and nets. 516–234–2948.

Soccer International, Inc., P.O. Box 7222, Arlington, VA 22207: Catalog $1 ■ Soccer balls, uniforms, gifts, T-shirts, and books. 703–524–4333.

Soccer Kick, 2130 Henderson Mill Rd., Atlanta, GA 30345: Free catalog ■ Soccer equipment, clothing, and shoes. 800–533–KICK; 404–939–6355 (in GA).

Spalding & Brothers, 425 Meadow St., P.O. Box 901, Chicopee, MA 01021: Free information ■ Soccer balls. 413–536–1200.

Winston Sports Corporation, 200 5th Ave., New York, NY 10010: Free information ■ Soccer balls. 212–255–6870.

SOLAR & WIND ENERGY

Applied Photovoltaic, Box 2773, Staunton, VA 24401: Catalog $3 ■ Solar components and parts. 301–963–0141.

ARCO Solar, P.O. Box 6032, Camarillo, CA 93010: Free information ■ Solar panels for energy systems. 800–ARCO–SOL.

Atlantic Solar Products, 9351 Philadelphia Rd., P.O. Box 70060, Baltimore, MD 21237: Free catalog ■ Solar powered systems for the home. 410–686–2500.

Balmar, 1537 NW Ballard Way, Seattle, WA 98107: Free information ■ Wind-driven alternator. 206–789–4970.

Bramen Company, P.O. Box 70, Salem, MA 01970: Free information ■ Automatic solar-vent for cold frames and greenhouses. 508–745–7765.

Enertech Corporation, P.O. Box 420, Norwich, VT 05055: Free information ■ Wind-operated power systems and parts. 802–649–1145.

Everfair Enterprises, 10131 NW 46th St., Sunrise, FL 33351: Free information ■ Wind-operated electric generating systems. 305–572–4592.

Haines Solar Energy, 2720 N. 68th St., Scottsdale, AZ 85257: Free information ■ Solar battery chargers. 602–481–6974.

Hamilton Ferris Company, Generator Products, P.O. Box 126, Ashland, MA 01721: Free information ■ Solar panels for battery chargers and power inverters for converting 12 volts DC to 110 volts AC. 508–881–4602.

Hitney Solar Products, 2655 North Hwy. 89, Chino Valley, AZ 86323: Free information ■ Solar powered systems for homes. 602–636–2201.

International Energy Supply Company, P.O. Box 70060, Baltimore, MD 21237: Free information ■ Solar battery chargers. 800–537–1566.

Jade Mountain, P.O. Box 4616, Boulder, CO 80306: Free information ■ Hydropower equipment. 303–449–6601.

Kallwall Solar Components Center, 88 Pine St., Manchester, NH 03103: Catalog $1 ■ Solar energy heating equipment. 603–668–8186.

Kansas Wind Power, Rt. 1, Holton, KS 66436: Catalog $4 ■ Sun ovens, wind generators, composting toilets, tankless water heaters, air cooler, and other solar energy equipment and parts. 913–364–4407.

Kirkby Solar Electric, P.O. Box 12455, Scottsdale, AZ 85267: Free pamphlet ■ Solar battery chargers. 602–443–8520.

LVM Electric, 34 Industrial Way East, Eatontown, NJ 08742: Free information ■ Wind-powered electric generating systems. 908–389–0114.

Photocomm, Inc., Solar Electric Systems, 930 Idaho Maryland Rd., Grass Valley, CA 95945: Catalog $5 ■ Solar energy systems for homes, recreational vehicles, boats, and cabins. 800–544–6466.

PowerTel Corporation, 28561 Front St., Temecula, CA 92390: Free information ■ Solar electric generators and solar panels. 800–736–9036.

Real Goods, 966 Mazzoni St., Ukiah, CA 95482: Free catalog ■ Alternative energy products. Solar energy components, solar educational toys, and environmental books and games. 707–468–9214.

Save Energy Company, 2410 Harrison St., San Francisco, CA 94110: Free catalog ■ Energy-saving devices for homes and gardens. 800–326–2120.

Solar Components Corporation, 121 Valley St., Manchester, NH 03103: Catalog $1 ■ Solar components and energy systems, for homes, greenhouses, and other applications. 603–668–8186.

Solar Depot, 61 Paul Dr., San Rafael, CA 94903: Free information ■ Solar electric power systems, solar water heaters, solar electric and solar thermal systems, and other equipment and accessories. 415–499–1333.

Solar Electric, Inc., 1450 Harbor Island Dr., Ste. 204A, San Diego, CA 92101: Free information ■ Solar panels. 800–842–5678.

Solar Electric Systems, Box 1562, Cave Creek, AZ 85331: Catalog $2 ■ Solar energy equipment for generating 12 volts DC and 120 volts AC. 602–488–3708.

Solarex Electric Generators, Consumer Products Division, 1335 Piccard Dr., Rockville, MD 20850: Free catalog ■ Solar panels and battery chargers, and other equipment. 800–521–SOLAR; 301–948–0202 (in MD).

Solar Power International, 729 53rd St. SW, Everett, WA 98203: Free information ■ Compact solar electric generating system. 206–347–0788.

Solarwest Electric, Inc., 232 Anacapa St., Santa Barbara, CA 93101: Catalog $5 ■ Photovoltaic products. 805–963–9667.

Sunelco, P.O. Box 1499, Hamilton, MT 59840: Free catalog ■ Solar modules, controllers, batteries, inverters, water pumps, and propane-operated appliances. 800–338–6844.

The Sun Electric Company, P.O. Box 1499, Hamilton, MT 59840: Free cataog ■ Solar energy equipment and components for recreational vehicles, cabins, or homes. 800–338–6844.

Sunlight Energy Corporation, 4411 W. Echo Ln., Glendale, AZ 85302: Free information with long SASE ■ Solar battery chargers. 800–338–1781.

Sunnyside Solar, RD 4, Box 808, Brattleboro, VT 05301: Free information ■ Hydropower equipment and photovoltaic solar electric systems for homes. 800–346–3230; 802–257–1482 (in VT).

Sun Quest, Inc., 1555 Rankin Ave., Newton, NC 28603: Free information ■ Solar water heaters for connection to existing hot water heaters. 704–465–6805.

SunWatt Corporation, RFD Box 751, Addison, ME 04606: Free information ■ Solar battery chargers. 207–497–2204.

Thermax, P.O. Box 3128, Burlington, VT 05401: Free information ■ Easy-to-install wind-operated electric generators. 802–658–1098.

UtilityFree Batteries, P.O. Box 228, Basalt, CO 81621: Free list ■ New and reconditioned nickel-cadmium, new fiber nickel-cadmium, and new or reconditioned nickel-iron batteries for homes, recreational vehicles, and other uses. 800–766–5550.

Watsun Corporation, P.O. Box 751, 614 2nd St. SW, Albuquerque, NM 87103: Free information ■ Solar trackers. 505–242–8024.

World Power Technologies, Inc., 19 N. Lake Ave., Duluth, MN 55802: Free brochure ■ Easy-to-install wind-operated electric generators. 218–722–1492.

Zoneworks Corporation, P.O. Box 25805, Albuquerque, NM 87125: Free information ■ Passive solar trackers and fixed racks for top-of-pole, side-of-pole, or roof/ground/wall mounts. 800–776–6718.

SOLARIUMS & SUN ROOMS

Amdega, Inc., Boston Design Center, 1 Design Center Pl., Ste. 624, Boston, MA 02210: Free brochure ■ Modular system for sun room designing. 617–951–2755.

American Solar Systems, 31740 Enterprise, P.O. Box 2865, Livonia, MI 48150: Catalog $3 ■ Greenhouses and solariums.

Appropriate Technology Corporation, P.O. Box 975, Brattleboro, VT 05362: Free information ■ Sun rooms. 800–257–4501.

Arctic Glass & Window Outlet, Rt. 1 West, Hammond, WI 54015: Catalog $2 ■ Sun rooms, windows, entryway and patio doors, and skylights. 715–796–2292.

Atria, Inc., 10301 N. Enterprise Dr., Mequon, WI 53092: Free information ■ Motorized roof systems for sun rooms. 414–242–1920.

BDG North America, Ltd., The Business Park at Cambridge, P.O. Box 8, Cambridge, VT 05444: Free information ■ Victorian style sun rooms. 802–644–2103.

Brady & Sun, 97 Webster St., Worcester, MA 01603: Free information ■ Pre-assembled, two-story, wood frame solariums. 800–888–7177.

California Solariums, 5300 N. Irwindale Ave., Irwindale, CA 91706: Free catalog ■ Sun rooms. 818–969–6767.

Creative Structures, 1765 Walnut Ln., Quakerstown, PA 18951: Free information ■ Sun room and greenhouse kits. 800–873–3966.

C-Thru Industries, Inc., 2285 Fleetwood Dr., Riverside, CA 92509: Free information ■ Sun rooms. 714–369–8777.

Florian Greenhouses, Inc., 64 Airport Rd., West Milford, NJ 07480: Catalog $5 ■ Solariums for installation by do-it-yourselfers. 800–356–7426.

Four Seasons Solar Products, 5005 Veterans Memorial Hwy., Holbrook, NY 11741: Free catalog ■ Modular solarium kits. 800–368–7732.

Glasswalls Porch Enclosures, Mon-Ray Windows, 2720 Nevada Ave., Minneapolis, MN 55427: Free literature ■ Supplies for converting a screened porch or enclosing a patio into an all-season room. 800–544–3646; 612–544–3646 (in MN).

Habitat Solar Rooms, 123 Elm St., South Deerfield, MA 01373: Information $10 ■ All-cedar kits for solar rooms. 800–992–0121.

Habitek, 102 Queens Dr., King of Prussia, PA 19406: Free brochure ■ Window greenhouses, solariums, and solar enclosures. 215–962–0240.

Janco Greenhouses, 9390 Davis Ave., Laurel, MD 20707: Catalog $5 ■ Solariums with optional variable pitch roofs. 800–323–6933.

Lindal Cedar Homes, P.O. Box 24426, Seattle, WA 98124: Information $15 ■ Sun rooms. 800–426–0536.

Machin Designs USA, Inc., P.O. Box 713, Glenview, IL 60025: Brochure $5 ■ Sun rooms. 800–922–0110.

Pella Information Center, P.O. Box 308, Moline, IL 61265: Free information ■ Sunrooms.

Progressive Building Products, P.O. Box 866, East Longmeadow, MA 01028: Design package $5.95 ■ Greenhouse and solarium components. 800–776–2534.

Skytech Systems, P.O. Box 763, Bloomsburg, PA 17815: Catalog $3 ■ Freestanding and window greenhouses, solariums, and sunrooms. 717–752–1111.

Solar Additions, Inc., Box 241, Greenwich, NY 12834: Preliminary information $1; complete information kit $5 ■ Do-it-yourself kits and custom components for add-on solar rooms. 800–833–2300; 518–692–9673 (in NY).

Solarium Systems International, 333 N. Mead, Wichita, KS 67219: Free information ■ Solariums with optional variable pitch roofs. 800–225–6423.

Southeastern Insulated Glass, 6477–B Peachtree Industrial Blvd., Atlanta, GA 30360: Free information ■ Greenhouse and sun room kits, sliding glass doors, and skylights. 800–841–9842; 404–455–8838 (in GA).

Sturdi-Built Manufacturing Company, 11304 SW Boones Ferry Rd., Portland, OR 97219: Free catalog ■ Greenhouses, cold frames, and sunrooms. 503–244–4100.

Sun Room Company, 322 E. Main St., P.O. Box 301, Leola, PA 17540: Free information ■ Sun rooms, window box greenhouses, skylights and window walls, and custom windows. 800–426–2737; 717–656–9391 (in PA).

Sunshine Rooms, Inc., Box 4627, Wichita, KS 67204: Free information ■ Add-on or free-standing sun rooms. 800–222–1598.

Under Glass Manufacturing Corporation, Market Street Industrial Park, P.O. Box 323, Wappingers Falls, NY 12590: Free information ■ Greenhouses, solariums, and greenhouse accessories. 914–298–0645.

SPELEOLOGY (CAVE EXPLORATION)

Bent Arrow Caving Supply, 7888 W. Eller Rd., Bloomington, IN 47401: Free information with long SASE ■ Equipment, supplies, and gear for cavers. 812–825–7990.

Bob & Bob Enterprises, P.O. Box 441, Lewisburg, WV 24901: Free information ■ Gear and safety equipment for cavers. 304–772–5049.

W. Born & Associates, 2438 Blacklick-Eastern Rd., Millersport, OH 43046: Free information with long SASE ■ Equipment and supplies for cavers. 614–467–2676.

Cadwell Caving Supplies, 2267 Blackrock Rd., Plainfield, IN 46168: Free information with long SASE ■ Equipment and supplies for cavers. 317–839–6996.

Caving Connection, Rt. 4, Box 2114, Lafayette, GA 30728: Free information with long SASE ■ Equipment and supplies for cavers. 404–764–1640.

Inner Mountain Outfitters, 102 Travis Cir., Seaford, VA 23696: Free information with long SASE ■ Equipment and supplies for cavers. 804–898–2809.

Pathfinder Sporting Goods, 6932 E. 1st St., P.O. Box 30670, Tucson, AZ 85751: Free information with long SASE ■ Equipment and supplies for cavers. 602–327–1952.

Pigeon Mountain Industries, P.O. Box 803, Lafayette, GA 30728: Free information ■ Gear and supplies for cavers. 800–282–7673; 404–764–1437 (in GA).

Quest Outdoors, 128 Breckenridge Ln., Louisville, KY 40207: Free information

with long SASE ■ Equipment and supplies for cavers. 502–893–5746.

Speleoshoppe, P.O. Box 297, Fairdale, KY 40118: Free information ■ Equipment, supplies, and gear for cavers. 800–626–5877; 502–367–6292 (in KY).

Summit Rescue Group, 1515 NE White Dr., Lee's Summit, MO 64063: Free information with long SASE ■ Equipment and supplies for cavers. 314–445–5686.

J.L. Waters & Company, Inc., 109 N. College Ave., P.O. Box 3217, Bloomington, IN 47401: Free information with long SASE ■ Equipment and supplies for cavers. 812–334–4050.

J.E. Weinel, Inc., P.O. Box 203, Valencia, PA 16059: Free information with long SASE ■ Equipment and supplies for cavers. 800–346–7673; 412–898–2335 (in PA).

SPINNING WHEELS & LOOMS

AE Textiles, Bradyville, TN 37026: Brochure and samples $2 (refundable) ■ Tabletop and free-standing frame looms for hooking, speed tufting, and sculpting; speed needles; and rug yarn and foundation cloth. 615–765–5682.

AVL Looms, 601 Orange St., Chico, CA 95928: Catalog $2 ■ Looms and supplies. 800–626–9615; 916–893–4915 (in CA).

Ayotte's Designery, P.O. Box 287, Center Sandwich, NH 03227: Catalog $1 ■ Spinning and weaving supplies. 603–284–6915.

Batik & Weaving Supplier, P.O. Box 451, Lexington, MA 02173: Catalog $2 ■ Supplies for weaving, knitting, spinning, fabric dyeing, and batik supplies. 617–646–4453.

Braid-Aid, 466 Washington St., Rt. 53, Pembroke, MA 02359: Catalog $4 ■ Braided rug kits, braiding supplies, spinning and weaving accessories, and wool by the pound or yard. 617–826–6091.

Crystal Palace Yarns, 3006 San Pablo Ave., Berkeley, CA 94702: Free brochure ■ Yarns, natural fibers, and spinning wheels.

Edgemont Yarn Services, Inc., P.O. Box 205, Washington, KY 41096: Free price list ■ Weaving supplies and 2–harness looms, 4–harness looms, tabletop looms, loom parts, and rug-making supplies. 606–759–7614.

Essenich Looms, P.O. Box 4253, Greensboro, NC 27404: Free brochure ■ Handcrafted 4– and 8–harness table and floor looms. 919–230–1293.

Ewe's Cottage, P.O. Box 672, Roundup, MT 59702: Catalog $3 (refundable) ■ Custom wool processing, books, dyes, fibers, spinning wheels, looms, and yarns. 406–323–1708.

Fiber Studio, 9 Foster Hill Rd., Box 637, Henniker, NH 03242: Catalog $1 ■ Spinning, weaving, and knitting equipment; natural fibers in cotton, mohair, wool, alpaca, silk, and linen; spinning fibers; and mill ends and close outs. 603–428–7830.

Gilmore Looms, 1032 N. Broadway, Stockton, CA 95205: Free brochure ■ Looms and accessories. 209–463–1545.

Glimakra Looms & Yarns, Inc., 133 Ross St., Petaluma, CA 94954: Catalog $2 ■ Looms and yarns. 800–289–9276; 707–762–3362 (in CA).

Harrisville Designs, Harrisville, NH 03450: Catalog $10 (refundable) ■ Yarns, looms, and accessories.

J-Made Looms, P.O. Box 452, Oregon City, OR 97045: Catalog $2 ■ Looms in 45–, 60–, and 72–inch models. 503–631–3973.

LACIS, 2982 Adeline St., Berkeley, CA 94703: Free information ■ Hairpin lace looms.

Leesburg Looms & Supply, 113 W. Van Buren St., Leesburg, IN 46538: Free brochure ■ Easy-to-operate 2– and 4–harness looms. 219–453–3554.

Louet Sales, RR 4, Prescott, Ontario, Canada K0E 1T0: Catalog $2 ■ Spinning, weaving, carding, felting, and lace-making equipment; books; dyestuffs; and yarns and fibers. 613–925–4502.

Macomber Looms, P.O. Box 186, York, ME 03909: Free catalog ■ Looms. 207–363–2808.

Mannings Creative Crafts, P.O. Box 687, East Berlin, PA 17316: Catalog $1 ■ Spinning wheels and looms, yarns and spinning fibers, books, and dyes and mordants. 717–624–2223.

Mountain Loom Company, Box 115, Midway, British Columbia, Canada V0H 1M0:

Free brochure ■ Sampler, table, pique, tapestry, and floor looms. 800–665–2779.

Norwood Looms, P.O. Box 167, Freemont, MI 49412: Brochure $1 ■ Looms, quilting hoops, and frames. 616–924–3901.

Pendleton Shop, Jordan Rd., P.O. Box 233, Sedona, AZ 86336: Catalog $1 ■ Looms and weaving supplies. 602–282–3671.

Real Ewe, 411 N. Rodney, Helena, MT 59601: Free information ■ Supplies for weavers, knitters, and spinners. 406–443–3359.

Rio Grande Weaver's Supply, 216 Pueblo Norte, Taos, NM 87571: Catalog $1 ■ Spinning wheels, looms, and loom kits; hand-dyed rug, tapestry, and clothing yarns; and yarns, dyes, fleeces, books, and videos. 505–758–0433.

River Farm, Rt. 1, P.O. Box 401, Timberville, VA 22853: Brochure $1 ■ Spinning wheels, looms, and American fleece for spinning. 800–USA–WOOL.

Schacht Spindle Company, Inc., 6101 Ben Pl., Boulder, CO 80301: Catalog $2.50 ■ Looms and accessories. 800–228–2553.

School Products Company, Inc., 1201 Broadway, New York, NY 10001: Catalog $2 ■ Spinning wheels and accessories. 212–679–3516.

Shannock Tapestry Looms, 10402 NW 11th Ave., Vancouver, WA 98685: Free brochure ■ Weaving supplies and tapestry looms with roller beams. 206–573–7264.

Bonnie Triola, 34 E. Gore Rd., Erie, PA 16509: Catalog $10 ■ Cone and stock yarns. Includes natural fibers, synthetics, blends, and discontinued designer yarns. 814–825–7821.

Weavers' Store, 11 S. 9th St., Columbia, MO 65201: Catalog $2 ■ Looms, spinning wheels, yarns, and mill ends. 314–442–5413.

Weaving Works, 4717 Brooklyn Ave. NE, Seattle, WA 98105: Catalog $1 ■ Looms, spinning wheels, hand and machine knitting supplies, yarns, and books. 206–524–1221.

Webbs, 18 Kellogg Ave., P.O. Box 349, Amherst, MA 01004: Price list $2 ■ Yarns for spinning and weaving, looms, spinning wheels, drum carders, and knitting machines. 413–253–2580.

Wool Room, Laurelton Rd., Mt. Kisco, NY 10549: Free brochure with long SASE ■

Spinning fibers, weaving yarns, and equipment. 914–241–1910.

SPORTS CARDS

A & J Sportscards, 2570 Hwy. 10 NE, Moundsview, MN 55112: Free price list ■ Baseball and football sports cards. 612–784–4821.

Ace Cards, Inc., 4100 N. Powerline Rd., Ste. A–3, Pompano Beach, FL 33073: Free information ■ Baseball card singles, sets, and cases; other sports memorabilia; and autographs. 305–968–6270.

Johnny Adams, Jr., Box 12763, Green Bay, WI 54307: Free information ■ Sports cards. 414–499–3485.

American Wholesalers, Inc., 2530 Superior Ave., Cleveland, OH 44114: Free information ■ Sports cards collecting supplies. 800–241–2606; 216–241–2606 (in OH).

B & E Collectibles, Inc., 12 Marble Ave., Thornwood, NY 10594: Free information ■ Sports cards. Hard-to-find sports cards singles. 914–769–1304.

B & J Sports Cards, Box 693, Skokie, IL 60076: Free information with long SASE ■ Baseball, football, basketball, soccer, and non-sports cards mint sets, traded and updated sets, and umpire sets. 708–699–9770.

B & O Wholesale, 1630 Marinette Dr., Springfield, OH 45503: Free information with long SASE ■ Sports cards, card storage boxes, card cases, albums, plastic sheets, and ball holders. 513–325–5054.

B & R Distributors, 55 Garibaldi Ave., Lodi, NJ 07644: Free information ■ Sports cards singles and sets. 201–472–4515.

Ball Four Cards, 4732 N. Royal Atlanta Dr., Tucker, GA 30084: Free information ■ All-star sports cards, card cases, storage boxes, polyethylene sheets, albums, card holders, plastic ball holders, and card sleeves. 800–677–5457; 404–621–0369 (in GA).

Ball Park Heroes, 1531 J St., Bedford, IN 47421: Free information with long SASE ■ Hard-to-find sports cards singles and sets. 812–275–2717.

Barnetts Sports Cards, P.O. Box 964, Hartville, OH 44632: Free information with long SASE ■ Hard-to-find sports cards singles and sets. 216–877–4270.

Bart's Baseball Cards, 2299 Belvidere St., Waukegan, IL 60085: Free information ■ Sports cards. 708–623–3737.

Baseball Barons Sportscards, 1295 Boardman Canfield Rd., Boardman, OH 44512: Free information ■ Basketball, baseball, and hockey sports cards. 800–437–7814.

Baseball Card City, 4 Deal Lane, Livingston, NJ 07039: Free information with long SASE ■ Rare and hard-to-find sports cards singles and sets. 201–994–1831.

Baseball Card Corner, Duffy Square, 10756 Montgomery Rd., Cincinnati, OH 45242: Free information ■ Sports cards. 513–489–5676.

Baseball Card Kingdom, 323 Jersey St., Harrison, NJ 07029: Free information with long SASE ■ Baseball card sets, minor league sets, sports impression figurines, Star Company platinum and gold edition sets, and other memorabilia. 201–481–9630.

Baseball Card World, P.O. Box 970, Anderson, IN 46015: Free information with long SASE ■ Sports cards hobby supplies. 317–644–2033.

Beverly Hills Baseball Card Shop, 109 N. Robertson, Beverly Hills, CA 90211: Free information ■ Baseball cards, sports memorabilia, and sports novelties. 310–652–CARD.

Big Bob's Baseball Cards, Inc., 282L Quarry Rd., Milford, CT 06460: Free information with long SASE ■ Sports cards singles and sets and hard-to-find items. 203–876–2847.

Bill's Cards & Supplies, 25 N. Colonial Dr., Hagerstown, MD 21742: Free information with long SASE ■ Sports cards and hobby supplies. 301–797–2992.

Bradford's Sportscards, Box 22455, Minneapolis, MN 55422: Free information with long SASE ■ Sports cards. 612–533–4804.

Brewart Coins & Stamps, 403 W. Katella, Anaheim, CA 92802: Free information with long SASE ■ Rare and hard-to-find sports cards singles and sets. 714–533–2521.

Broadway Rick's Strike Zone, 1848 N. Federal Hwy., Boynton Beach, FL 33435: Free information with long SASE ■ Hard-to-find baseball, football, hockey, and basketball sports cards singles and sets. 407–364–0453.

Lou Brown Cards & Sam, 6504 28th St. SE, Grand Rapids, MI 49506: Free information ■ Sports cards. 616–940–2738.

California Sports Card Exchange, 1091 Gayley Ave., Los Angeles, CA 90024: Free information with long SASE ■ Hard-to-find sports cards singles and sets. 310–208–7210.

Card Collectors Company, 105 W. 77th St., New York, NY 10024: Catalog $2 ■ Sports cards and other collectibles. 212–873–6999.

The Cardsmith, 2224 S. Guthrie Dr., Los Angeles, CA 90034: Free information ■ Sports cards singles and sets. 310–559–0177.

Carolina Cards, 139 Whitfield, St., P.O. Box 157, Enfield, NC 27823: Free information ■ Sports cards singles and sets. 919–445–3323.

Jim Carr, Inc., P.O. Box 385, Pelham, NH 03076: Free information with long SASE ■ Hard-to-find sports cards singles and sets. 603–635–2821.

Cee-Jay Sports Card Company, Sunset Industrial Park, 52 20th St., Brooklyn, NY 11232: Free information with long SASE ■ Hard-to-find football, basketball, hockey, golf, and tennis sports cards singles and sets. 718–83–CJAY6.

Center Field, 10746 France Ave. South, Bloomington, MN 55431: Free information with long SASE ■ Baseball, football, basketball, hockey, non-sports cards, old records, and comics. 612–884–0355.

Champion Sports, 702 W. Las Tunas, San Gabriel, CA 91776: Free information ■ Sports cards hobby supplies. 818–570–1106.

CJ's Sports Cards, 14627 58th Pl. West, Edmonds, WA 98020: Free information with long SASE ■ Hard-to-find sports cards singles. 206–742–8450.

Classic Cards, 41 Long Acre Dr., Huntington, NY 11743: Free information with long SASE ■ Sports cards singles and sets. 516–424–5792.

Conroe Collectibles, Rt. 5, Box 1257, Conroe, TX 77304: Free catalog ■ Sports cards and supplies. 409–588–2907.

Diamond King Sports Cards, 221 Park Ave., Merrick, NY 22566: Free information with long SASE ■ Rare and hard-to-find sports cards singles and sets. 516–795–9551.

Durta Enterprises, 235 S. Lindberg, Griffith, IN 46319: Free information with long SASE ■ Plastic and vinyl sheets, sleeves, albums, album slip cases, ball cubes, ball holders, storage boxes, and counting organizers and sorting trays. 800–451–2615; 219–922–1133 (in IN).

Empire Sports Cards, 15253 Hesperian Blvd., Ste. 3–48, San Leandro, CA 94578: Free information ■ Sports cards. 510–481–9584.

Extra Base Sports Collectibles, 16 Belgrade, Youngstown, OH 44505: Free information ■ Sports cards. 216–759–0043.

First Base Sports Nostalgia Shop, Audelia Plaza, 10729 Audelia Rd., #102, Dallas, TX 75238: Free information with long SASE ■ Baseball, football, and other sports cards, memorabilia, and souvenirs. 214–341–9919.

Flip Cards & Supplies, 181 Rt. 46 West, Lodi, NJ 07844: Free information ■ Sports cards collecting supplies. 800–WOW–FLIP; 201–472–8077 (in NJ).

4 Bagger Sport Cards, 18701 Dixie Hwy., Homewood, IL 60430: Free information with long SASE ■ Comic books and baseball, football, and hockey sports cards. 708–799–8175.

Larry Fritsch Cards, 735 Old Wausau Rd., P.O. Box 863, Stevens Point, WI 54481: Free catalog ■ Baseball, football, basketball, and hockey sports cards sets and singles. 715–344–8687.

Georgia Music & Sports, 1867 Flat Shoals Rd., Riverdale, GA 30296: Free information with long SASE ■ Sports cards singles and sets. 404–996–3385.

Golden Gems, P.O. Box 455, Westwood, MA 02090: Free information ■ Sports cards. 617–762–8848.

Grand Slam Sports Collectibles, Lakeview Plaza, 23 Mile Rd., New Baltimore, MI 48047: Catalog $1 ■ Sports cards hobby and archival supplies. 313–725–5550.

Gerry Guenther, 7521 Patchin Rd., Pardeeville, WI 53954: Free information ■ Superstar sports cards. 608–742–2201.

Hall's Nostalgia, 25 Mystic St., P.O. Box 408, Arlington, MA 02174: Free information ■ Sports cards. 800–367–4255; 617–646–7757 (in MA).

Bruce Harris Sportscards, 1291 Steeple Run Dr., Lawrenceville, GA 30243: Free information ■ Sports cards. 404–822–0988.

Hartford Sports, 400 60th Ave., Hartford, MI 49057: Free information with long SASE ■ Football cards in singles and team sets. 616–621–2070.

Bill Henderson's Cards, 2320 Ruger Ave., Janesville, WI 53545: Free information with long SASE ■ Rare and hard-to-find sports cards singles and sets. 608–755–0922.

H.L.T. & T. Sports, 5429–A S. Braeswood Rd., Houston, TX 77096: Free information ■ Baseball cards, programs and yearbooks, pro caps, pro jerseys, and pro satin jackets. 713–728–3111.

Hobby Supplies, P.O. Box 372, Marlboro, NJ 07746: Free information with long SASE ■ Sports cards collecting supplies. 908–780–3689.

Howard's Sports Collectibles, 128 E. Main St., P.O. Box 84, Leipsic, OH 45856: Catalog $5 ■ Baseball and football cards in sets or singles. 800–457–9974.

International Collectors, Box 12763, Green Bay, WI 54307: Free information ■ Baseball, boxing, basketball, football, and hockey sports cards. Includes starter sets. 800–226–9991; 414–499–3485 (in WI).

J & J Sports Cards & Comics, 7760 Monterrey St., Gilroy, CA 95020: Free information with long SASE ■ All-star sports cards. 408–848–4415.

JDM Sports Products, 24831 Alicia Pkwy., Laguna Hills, CA 92653: Free information ■ Sports cards. 714–380–4828.

Jim & Steve's Baseball & Football Card Shop, 2716 Grand Ave., Waukegan, IL 60085: Free information ■ Hard-to-find sports cards singles and limited editions. 708–244–1981.

Stephan R. Juskewycz Company, 5650 Wattsburg Rd., Erie, PA 16509: Free information with long SASE ■ Rare and hard-to-find sports cards singles and sets. 814–825–8837.

Kenrich Company, 9418 E. Las Tunas Dr., Temple City, CA 91780: Free information with long SASE ■ All-star sports cards singles and sets and sports memorabilia. 818–286–3888.

Robert Klevens, 12260 NW 29th Pl., Sunrise, FL 33323: Free information with long SASE ■ Buys, sells, and trades Japanese baseball cards. 305–741–6025.

Koinz & Kardz-Madison, 2146 E. Johnson St., Madison, WI 53704: Free information with long SASE ■ Rare and hard-to-find sports cards singles and sets. 608–249–6669.

Legends of the Game, 322–A King St. West, Toronto, Ontario, Canada M5V 1J2: Free information ■ Football, basketball, baseball, and hockey sports cards; framed and unframed autographed photos of movie stars and sports personalities; autographed bats and balls; and comic books. 800–265–4218.

Lynchburg Coin & Collectibles, Hills Plaza, 218 Wards Rd., Lynchburg, VA 24502: Free information with long SASE ■ Baseball, football, hockey, and basketball sports cards; coins and stamps; gold and silver; and hobby supplies. 804–237–2741.

Mid-Atlantic Sports Cards, 22 S. Morton Ave., Morton, PA 19070: Free information with long SASE ■ Posters and hard-to-find sports cards singles and sets. 800–542–5345; 215–544–2171 (in PA).

The Milwaukee Kid Sports Cards & Memorabilia, 1800 Forest Hill Blvd., Ste. A–1, West Palm Beach, FL 33406: Free information with long SASE ■ Baseball, football, basketball, and hockey cards, with many rare and hard-to-find scarce singles and sets. 407–966–7653.

The Minnesota Connection, 158 Cobblestone Ln., Burnsville, MN 55337: Free information ■ Baseball, football, basketball, and hockey sports cards. 612–892–0406.

Michael Moretto, P.O. Box 960, Highland Lakes, NJ 07422: Free information ■ Hard-to-find sports cards singles, sets, and limited editions. 201–764–4682.

Steve Myland, 2530 W. Buckeye Rd., Phoenix, AZ 85009: Free information ■ Hard-to-find sports cards singles and sets. 602–272–8007.

New Jersey Sportcards, Inc., 8 Vernon Ave., Spotswood, NJ 07774: Free information with long SASE ■ Sports cards singles and sets and hard-to-find items. 908–723–1362.

New York Card Company, 614 Corporate Way, Valley Cottage, NY 10989: Free infor-

mation with long SASE ■ Sports cards singles and sets. 914–268–6262.

The 19th Inning, 3324 W. Mercury Blvd., Hampton, VA 23666: Free information with long SASE ■ Sports cards. 804–827–1667.

Northern Virginia Sports Cards Exchange, Inc., 7813 Sudley Rd., Manassas, VA 22110: Free information ■ Sports cards. 703–361–6682.

Perfect Image Sports Cards, 12003 Audubon Ave., Philadelphia, PA 19116: Free information ■ Baseball, boxing, basketball, football, golf, and hockey sports cards. 800–683–1789.

Portland Sports Card Company, 2401 NE Broadway St., Portland, OR 97232: Free information with long SASE with two 1st class stamps ■ All-star sports cards that include super stars, teams, minor league sets, factory sets, boxed sets, and umpire cards. 503–284–7126.

Power Alley, Inc., 253 Meacham Ave., Elmont, NY 11003: Free information ■ Sports cards for collectors. 516–352–5293.

Quality Baseball Cards, Inc., 106 Despatch Dr., East Rochester, NY 14445: Free information with long SASE ■ Hard-to-find sports cards singles and sets. 800–HOBBY–88; 716–248–3510 (in NY).

R & S Trading Card Company, 1236 W. Dundee Rd., Buffalo Grove, IL 60089: Free information ■ Sports cards singles, sets, and limited editions. 708–392–6868.

Ripley's Sports Cards, Inc., 1092 Baxter St., Athens, GA 30605: Free information with long SASE ■ Rare and hard-to-find sports cards singles and sets. 800–356–9052.

River City Cards & Comics, 512 Cass St., LaCrosse, WI 54601: Free information ■ Sports cards and comic books. 608–782–5540.

Roanoke Coin Exchange, Towers Mall, Roanoke, VA 24015: Free information with long SASE ■ Baseball, football, hockey, and basketball cards; coins and stamps; gold and silver; and hobby supplies. 703–982–8587.

Don Roberts Sales, 1219 Caledonia St., La Crosse, WI 54603: Free information ■ Sports cards singles and sets. 608–784–3755.

Rookies Unlimited, 106 Galway Trace, Moore, SC 29369: Free information with long SASE ■ Rare and hard-to-find sports cards singles and sets. 803–576–1942.

Rotman Collectibles, 4 Brussels St., Worcester, MA 01610: Free information with long SASE ■ Binders and plastic sheets, card cases, card holders, and boxes. 508–791–6710.

St. Louis Baseball Cards, 5456 Chatfield, St. Louis, MO 63129: Free information ■ Sports cards sets, uniforms, press pins, autographs, advertising pieces, Hartlands, Goudeys, T-cards, and baseball memorabilia. 314–892–4737.

Joe Sak, P.O. Box 71, Wilkes-Barre, PA 18703: Free information with long SASE ■ Baseball, olympic stars, golf, soccer, boxing, wrestling, and football sports cards. 717–823–6325.

Sanart Sportcards, 482 81st St., Brooklyn, NY 11209: Free information ■ Hard-to-find sports cards singles, sets, and limited editions. 718–680–0900.

San Diego Sports Collectibles, 659 Fashion Valley, San Diego, CA 92108: Catalog $2 ■ Hard-to-find sports cards singles, sets, and limited editions. 800–227–0483.

The Score Board, Inc., 1951 Old Cuthbert Rd., Cherry Hill, NJ 08034: Free information ■ Sports cards collections and sets, star cards prior to 1970, commemorative cards prior to 1942, and sports memorabilia. 609–427–3532.

Seventh Inning Stretch, 1175 Avocado Ave., Ste. 103, El Cajon, CA 92020: Free information with long SASE ■ All-star sports cards. 619–441–2700.

Southern Cards, 703 W. Main St., Charlottesville, VA 22901: Free information with long SASE ■ Hard-to-find sports cards singles and sets. 804–293–4151.

The Sports Alley, 15545 E. Whittier Blvd., Whittier, CA 90603: Free information with long SASE ■ Hard-to-find sports cards, cancelled checks by sports greats, autographed pictures, world series programs, photographs, and other memorabilia. 310–947–7383.

SportsCards Plus, 14038 Beach Blvd., Westminster, CA 92683: Free information ■ Sports cards. 714–895–4401.

Sports Collectibles, Inc., P.O. Box 11171, Chattanooga, TN 37401: Free information with long SASE ■ Sports cards, autographed

baseballs, bats, and color photos. 615–265–9366.

The Sports Depot, 14 Troy Hill Rd., P.O. Box 307, Whippany, NJ 07981: Free information ■ Baseball, football, hockey, and other sports cards. 201–887–8979.

Sports Design Products, Inc., 6841 N. Rochester Rd., Building C, Rochester Hills, MI 48306: Free catalog ■ Albums and plastic sheets, card cases, storage boxes, card holders, frames, and ball holders. 313–650–3060.

Sports Source, 4308 W. Victory Blvd., Burbank, CA 91505: Free information with long SASE ■ Sports cards singles, sets, and hard-to-find items. 818–846–4060.

Norm Stapleton, 600 W. Shiller St., Egg Harbor, NJ 08215: Free information ■ Baseball, basketball, and football singles; limited edition sports cards; and other hard-to-find cards. 609–965–0633.

Superior Sportcard, 1400 Abbott Rd., Ste. 390, East Lansing, MI 48823: Free information with long SASE ■ Hard-to-find sports cards singles and sets. 517–351–1973.

T.C. Card Company, Box 8057, F.D.R. Station, New York, NY 10150: Free information with long SASE ■ Sports cards singles, sets, and hard-to-find items. 212–980–4052.

Texas Sportcard Company, 2816 Center St., Deer Park, TX 77536: Free information ■ Hard-to-find sports cards singles and sets. 713–476–9964.

Troy Stamp & Coin Exchange, 3275 Rochester Rd., Troy, MI 48083: Free information ■ Sports cards singles and sets. 313–528–1181.

U.S. Gerslyn, Ltd., 1100 Port Washington Blvd., Port Washington, NY 11050: Free brochure ■ Sports cards hobby supplies. 516–944–3553.

Harry A. Victor Postcards, 1408 18th Ave., San Francisco, CA 94122: Free list with long SASE and two first class stamps ■ Boxing, wrestling, tennis, golf, billiards, water sports, winter sports, and track and field sports cards; postcards; paper memorabilia; and railroad, cigarette, food, and beverage cards. 415–664–4286.

T. Wall, 14 Boonton Ave., Butler, NJ 07405: Free information with long SASE ■ Hard-to-find sports cards singles, sets, and limited editions. 201–838–5565.

Brian Wallos & Company, 95 Newfield Ave., Edison, NJ 08837: Free information with long SASE ■ Hard-to-find sports cards singles and sets. 908–417–9757.

Gary Walter Baseball Cards, 561 River Terrace, Toms River, NJ 08755: Free information ■ Baseball cards. 908–286–9007.

West Coast Sports Cards, Inc., P.O. Box 1283, Kent, WA 98035: Free information with long SASE ■ Rare and hard-to-find sports cards singles and sets. 206–850–2488.

Kit Young Sportscards, 11535 Sorrento Valley Rd., Ste. 403, San Diego, CA 92121: Free information with long SASE ■ Hard-to-find sports cards singles and sets. 619–259–1300.

SQUARE DANCING

Amplifiers & Microphones

Ashton Electronics, 222 Stonegate Cir., San Jose, CA 95110: Free information ■ Amplifiers, speaker stands, and microphones. 408–995–6544.

Hilton Audio Products, 1033 Shary Cir., Concord, CA 94518: Free information ■ Amplifiers, loudspeakers, microphones, speaker stands, and cue cards for callers. 510–682–8390.

Merrbach Record Service, P.O. Box 7309, Houston, TX 77248: Free information ■ Records, tape recorders, tapes, wireless microphones, cassette decks, and sound equipment. 713–862–7077.

Random Sound, Inc., 7317 Harriet Ave. South, Minneapolis, MN 55423: Free catalog ■ Sound equipment. 512–869–9501.

Supreme Audio, P.O. Box 687, Ridgewood, NJ 07450: Free information ■ Sound equipment. 800–445–7398.

Badges & Buckles

Badge Holders, Inc., 24813 Broadmore Ave., Hayward, CA 94544: Free brochure ■ Badge holders. 510–783–8724.

D & H Engraving, 1820 Jerome Blvd., Racine, WI 53403: Free information ■ Club, fun, and mini badges. 414–637–4894.

Fawcett's Square Dance Shop, 412 W. Sam Houston, Pharr, TX 78577: Free information ■ Engraved and hot-stamped badges. 512–787–1116.

H & R Badge & Stamp Company, 2585 Mock Rd., Columbus, OH 43219: Free information ■ In-stock and custom badges and rubber stamps. 614–471–3735.

KA-MO Engravers, P.O. Box 30337, Albuquerque, NM 87190: Free catalog ■ Badges for square and round dancers. 505–352–KAMO.

J.R. Kush & Company, 7623 Hesperia St., Reseda, CA 91335: Free information ■ Handcrafted belt buckles for round dancers and square dancers. 818–344–9671.

Micro Plastics, P.O. Box 847, Rifle, CO 81650: Free information ■ Custom club badges. 303–625–1718.

Pauly's, P.O. Box 72, Wausau, WI 54402: Free information ■ Engraved and jeweled badges. 715–845–3979.

Books & Videos

American Square Dance Magazine, P.O. Box 488, Huron, OH 44839: Free information ■ Books for callers, cuers, leaders, dancers, and cloggers. 419–433–5043.

Gold Star Video Productions, P.O. Box 417802, Sacramento, CA 95841: Free information ■ Video tapes on how to square or round dance. 800–87–HINGE; 916–331–2550 (in CA).

Clothing

Andes S/D & Western Apparel, 2109 Liberty Rd., Eldersburg, MD 21784: Catalog $2 (refundable) ■ Clothing for square dancers. 410–795–0808.

Bev's Square Dance & Western Wear, 112 Depot St., Auburn, IN 46706: Free information ■ Clothing for square dancers. 219–925–3818.

Carol's Country Corner S/D, 21932 Schoenborn St., Canoga Park, CA 91304: Free information ■ Clothing for square dancers. 818–347–1207.

Catchall, 1813 9th St., Wichita Falls, TX 76301: Free information ■ Lace-trimmed petticoats. 817–766–1612.

Circles & Squares, Inc., 9047 Garland Rd., Dallas, TX 75218: Free information ■ Clothing for square dancers. 214–326–8684.

Circle W Square Dance Fashions, Rt. 1, Box 313, Sneads Ferry, NC 28460: Free information ■ Clothing for square dancers. 919–327–3337.

Dancer's Locker, P.O. Box 472, Bonita, CA 92002: Free catalog ■ Clothing for square dancers. 800–423–9046.

Doris Crystal Magic Petticoats, 437 San Mateo Ave., San Bruno, CA 94066: Free swatches and flyers ■ Petticoats for square and round dancers. 800–468–6423; 415–588–4126 (in CA).

Dorothy's Square Dance Shop, Inc., 3300 Strong Ave., Box 6004, Kansas City, KS 66106: Catalog $1 ■ Clothing and accessories for square dancers. 913–262–4240.

Fabian's Western Wear, 18th & Jefferson, Lewisburg, PA 17837: Free information ■ Square dancer's clothing. 717–523–6280.

Fawcett's Square Dance Shop, 412 W. Sam Houston, Pharr, TX 78577: Free information ■ Clothing for square dancers. 512–787–1116.

Gateway S/D Enterprises, 9040 Manchester Rd., Brentwood, MO 63144: Free information ■ Petticoats and matching pettipants for women. Shirts and pants for men. 314–963–1220.

Grand Travel Square Dance Shop, P.O. Box 690092, Tulsa, OK 74169: Free catalog ■ Clothing and sound equipment for square dancers.

Janet's Square Dance Shoppe, Rt. 9, Box 997, Lake Charles, LA 70605: Free information ■ Clothing for square dancers. 318–855–4470.

L/W Western Apparel, Rt. 4, Box 19, Elkton, VA 22827: Free information ■ Clothing for square dancers. 703–298–8676.

M & H Western Fashions, 13002 Lorain Ave., Cleveland, OH 44111: Free information ■ Clothing for square dancers. 216–671–5165.

Oxbow Square Dance Shop, 8650 49th St. North, Pinellas Park, FL 34666: Free information ■ Clothing for square dancers. 813–541–5700.

Palomino Square Dance Service, S25 W26319 MacArthur Rd., Waukesha, WI 53188: Free information ■ Clothing for square dancers. 800–328–3800.

Rochester Shoe Stores, 8186 Pembroke Dr., Manlius, NY 13104: Free information ■ Square and round dancing shoes. 800–688–4325.

Romie's S/D & Western Wear, 3827 El Cajon Blvd., San Diego, CA 91304: Free information ■ Square dancing and western clothing. 619–280–2150.

Ruthad, Inc., 8869 Avis, Detroit, MI 48209: Free information ■ Pettipants and single, double, or triple layer petticoats. 313–841–0586.

Sewing Specialties, 7429 4th Ave. South, Richfield, MN 55423: Free brochure ■ Easy-to-finish petticoat kits. 800–338–3289.

Shirley's S/D Shoppe, Rt. 9–D, Box 423, Hughsonville, NY 12537: Catalog $1 ■ Patterns, ready-to-wear clothing, petticoats, pantalettes, and other clothing for square dancers. 914–297–8504.

Meg Simkins, 119 Allen St., Hampden, MA 01036: Catalog $1 (refundable) ■ Clothing and accessories for square dancers. 413–566–3349.

Skyline Square Dance Shop, 9 Skyline Dr., Mankato, MN 56001: Free information ■ Clothing for square dancers. 507–345–1900.

Sky Ranch West & S/D Store, 109–111 S. Main St., Central Square, NY 13036: Catalog $1 (refundable) ■ Western and square dancing clothing. 315–668–2644.

Nita Smith, 2011 S. College Ave., Bryan, TX 77801: Free catalog ■ Clothing for square dancers. 409–822–2337.

Square Dance & Western Wear Fashions, Inc., 637 E. 47th St., Wichita, KS 67216: Free information ■ Clothing and shoes. 316–522–6670.

Square Dance Attire, 7215 W. Irving Park Rd., Chicago, IL 60634: Free information ■ Clothing for square dancers. 312–589–9220.

Steppin Out, P.O. Box 398, Humble, TX 77347: Free information ■ Square and round dancing petticoats and dresses. 713–540–3557.

Swing Thru, RD 1, Box 428, Cresco, PA 18326: Notions and badge catalog $2; clothing catalog $2 ■ Clothing. notions, and novelties for square dancers. 717–595–7474.

Triple R Western Wear, 250 W. Broad St., Falls Church, VA 22046: Catalog $3.50 (refundable) ■ Clothing for square dancers. 703–534–7273.

Western Squares, 6820 Gravois, St. Louis, MO 63116: Catalog $1 (refundable) ■ Women's clothing for square dancing. 314–353–7230.

Wheel & Deal Shop, Inc., Rt. 115, Yarmouth Rd., Gray, ME 04039: Catalog $1 (refundable) ■ Clothing for square dancers. 207–657–3412.

Yellow Rock Shoppe, 1622 S. Buckner, Dallas, TX 75217: Free catalog ■ Clothing for square dancers, country swing and ballroom dancing, and casual wear. 214–391–7040.

Records

Chaparral Records, Inc., 1425 Oakhill Dr., Plano, TX 75075: Free information ■ Square dancing records. 214–423–7389.

Cimarron Record Company, 4021 NW 61st, Oklahoma City, OK 73112: Free information ■ Records for square dancing.

Clendenin Enterprises, 7915 N. Clarendon, Portland, OR 97203: Free information ■ Records for square dancing. 503–285–7431.

Eagle Enterprises, 11220 Florissant St., Ste. 169, Florissant, MO 63032: Free information ■ Square dancing records. 314–741–7799.

Four Bar B/Quadrille Records, Box 7–11, Macks Creek, MO 65786: Free catalog ■ Square dancing records. 314–363–5432.

Kip Garvey Enterprises, P.O. Box 8045, Fremont, CA 94537: Free information ■ Square dancing records. 510–792–7099.

Hanhurst's Record Service, P.O. Box 687, Ridgewood, NJ 07451: Free information ■ Square dancing records. 800–445–7398.

Hi Hat Dance Records, 3925 N. Tollhouse, Fresno, CA 93726: Free information ■ Square dancing records. 209–227–2764.

Kalox-Belco-Longhorn, 2832 Live Oak Dr., Mesquite, TX 75150: Free information ■ Records for square dancing. 214–270–0616.

Lightning Records, P.O. Box 748, Oxford, NC 27565: Free information ■ Square dancing music. 919–693–4852.

Lou Mac & Mar-Let Records, P.O. Box 2406, Muscle Shoals, AL 35661: Free information ■ Square dancing music. 205–383–7585.

Master Record Service Mail Order, P.O. Box 82716, Phoenix, AZ 85071: Free information ■ Records for square, round, and ballroom dancing. 602–993–9932.

Merrbach Record Service, P.O. Box 7309, Houston, TX 77248: Free information ■ Records, tape recorders, tapes, wireless microphones, cassette decks, and sound equipment. 713–862–7077.

Jack Murtha Enterprises, P.O. Box 3055, Yuba City, CA 95992: Free information ■ Records for square dancing. 916–673–1120.

Palomino Square Dance Service, S25 W26319 MacArthur Rd., Waukesha, WI 53188: Free information ■ Records for square, round, and folk dancing, and for solo dancing and clogging. 800–328–3800.

Red Boot Productions, Inc., Rt. 8, College Hills, Box 28, Crest Dr., Greeneville, TN 37743: Free information ■ Square dancing records. 615–638–7784.

Reeves Records, Inc., 1835 S. Buckner, P.O. Box 17668, Dallas, TX 75217: Free information ■ Square, round, and clogging dancing records; record cases; books and manuals; plastic record jackets; and sound equipment. 214–398–7508.

Royal Records, Inc., Rt. 1, Box 33, Fairfield, IA 52556: Free information ■ Records for square dancing. 515–472–3795.

Silver Sounds Recordings, P.O. Box 229, Glastonbury, CT 06033: Free information ■ Records for square dancing. 203–633–0370.

Supreme Audio, P.O. Box 687, Ridgewood, NJ 07450: Free catalog ■ Equipment and records for square and round dancing. 800–445–7398.

Thunderbird Record Company, Rt. 1, Thompson School Rd., Corryton, TN 37721: Free information ■ Square dancing music and records. 615–687–4478.

TNT Records, RFD 2, Rt. 7, St. Albans, VT 05478: Free information ■ Square and round dancing music. 802–524–9424.

Wagon Wheel Records, 8459 Edmaru Ave., Whittier, CA 90605: Free information ■ Records for square dancing. 310–693–6976.

STAINED GLASS CRAFTING

Ameriglas, Box 27668, Omaha, NE 68127: Catalog $1 ■ Stained glass crafting supplies, tools, and kits.

Amour Products, P.O. Box 55, Midland Park, NJ 07432: Free information ■ Glass etching supplies. 201–652–8895.

Art Glass House, Inc., 3445 N. Hwy. 1, Cocoa, FL 32926: Free catalog ■ Stained glass supplies. 800–525–8009; 407–631–4477 (in FL).

Big M Stained Glass, 3201 4th Ave., Seattle, WA 98134: Catalog $5 ■ Stained glass supplies. 800–426–8307; 206–624–3962 (in WA).

Cline Glass, Inc., 1135 SE Grand Ave., Portland, OR 97214: Catalog $5 ■ Stained glass supplies. 800–547–8417.

Contempo Lapidary, 12273 Foothill Blvd., Sylmar, CA 91342: Free information ■ Stained glass and lapidary supplies and tools. 800–356–2441; 818–899–1973 (in CA).

Coran-Sholes, 509 E. 2nd, Boston, MA 02127: Catalog $3 ■ Stained glass supplies. 617–268–3780.

Crystallite Corporation, 13449 Beach Ave., Marina del Rey, CA 90291: Free information ■ Lapidary supplies, glass-working equipment, and tools. 213–821–6632.

Delphi Stained Glass, 2116 E. Michigan Ave., Lansing, MI 48912: Catalog $4.50 (refundable) ■ Stained glass supplies, tools, kits, and books. 800–248–2048.

Eastern Craft Supply, P.O. Box 341, Wyckoff, NJ 07481: Catalog $2 ■ Stained glass kits, glass etching and engraving supplies, and glass crafting supplies. 800–872–3458.

Franklin Art Glass, 222 E. Sycamore St., Columbus, OH 43206: Free information ■ Stained glass tools and supplies. 614–221–2972.

Gemstone Equipment Manufacturing Company, 750 Easy St., Simi Valley, CA 93065: Free information ■ Stained glass and lapidary supplies and tools. 805–527–6990.

Houston Stained Glass Supply, 2420 Center St., Houston, TX 77007: Free information ■ Stained glass supplies and beveled glass. 800–231–0148.

Hudson Glass, 219 N. Division St., Peekskill, NY 10566: Catalog $3 ■ Stained glass supplies. 800–431–2964; 914–737–2124 (in NY).

Kingsley North, Inc., P.O. Box 216, Norway, MI 49870: Free catalog ■ Stained glass and jewelry-making supplies and tools. 800–338–9280.

Rainbow Art Glass, 49 Shark River Rd., Neptune, NJ 07753: Brochure $2 ■ Stained glass kits and finished items that include Tiffany shades. 800–526–2356.

Sunshine Glassworks, 240 French Rd., Buffalo, NY 14227: Catalog $3 ■ Stained glass, supplies, and tools. 800–828–7159; 716–668–2918 (in NY).

Whittemore Glass, Box 2065, Hanover, MA 02339: Catalog $2 ■ Stained glass kits, tools, patterns, etching, and engraving supplies. 617–871–1743.

H.L. Worden Company, P.O. Box 519, Granger, WA 98932: Catalog $1 ■ Pattern packets and building forms for turn-of-the-century stained glass lamps. 509–854–1557.

STAIRLIFTS & ELEVATORS

Cheney Company, P.O. Box 51188, New Berlin, WI 53151: Free brochure ■ Curved and spiral stairway elevators. 800–782–1222.

Graventa, P.O. Box L–1, Blaine, WA 98230: Free information ■ Easy-to-operate, adjustable and portable wheel-chair lift for stairs. 800–663–6556.

Inclinator Company of America, P.O. Box 1557, Harrisburg, PA 17105: Free literature ■ Elevators and stairlifts for homes. 717–234–8065.

The National Wheel-O-Vator Company, Inc., P.O. Box 348, Roanoke, IL 61561: Free information ■ Wheelchair and side-riding stair lifts. 800–551–9095.

Whitakers, 1 Odell Plaza, Yonkers, NY 10703: Free brochure ■ Motorized stairlifts for homes. 800–44–LIFTS; 800–924–LIFT (in NY).

STATIONERY & ENVELOPES

American Stationery Company, 300 Park Ave., Peru, IN 46970: Free catalog ■ Regular and calligraphy stationery, wedding invitations, note cards and personal memos, envelopes, and postcards. 800–822–2577.

Amity Hallmark, Ltd., P.O. Box 929, Linden Hill Station, Flushing, NY 11354: Free catalog ■ Business cards, stationery, special occasion cards, and business forms. 718–939–2323.

Artistic Greetings, Inc., 409 William St., P.O. Box 1623, Elmira, NY 14902: Free catalog ■ Stationery, memo pads, note cards, and self-stick address labels. 607–733–6313.

Business Envelope Manufacturers, 900 Grand Blvd., Deer Park, NY 11729: Free catalog ■ Envelopes, stationery, forms, labels, business cards, and other office supplies. 516–667–8500.

Current, The Current Bldg., Colorado Springs, CO 80901: Free catalog ■ Greeting cards, stationery, and gift wrappings. 800–525–7170; 719–594–4100 (in CO).

Day-Timers, Allentown, PA 18001: Free catalog ■ Stationery and business cards. 215–395–5884.

Kristin Elliott, Inc., 6 Opportunity Way, Newburyport, MA 01950: Free catalog ■ Boxed notes, gift enclosures, Christmas cards, greeting cards, memo pads, postcards, correspondence cards, and gift wrapping. 800–922–1899; 508–465–1899 (in MA).

Envelope Sales Company, Normandy, TN 37360: Free brochure ■ Business stationery and envelopes. 615–857–3333.

Fantastic Impressions, P.O. Box 2432, North Babylon, NY 11704: Free catalog ■ Letterheads, envelopes, and cards. 516–242–9199.

Fine Stationery by Sonya Nussbaum, P.O. Box 328, Hollywood, SC 29449: Free information ■ Stationery and envelopes.

Franz Stationery Company, Inc., 1601 Algonquin Rd., Arlington Heights, IL 60005: Free catalog ■ Stationery, office forms, equipment, and furniture. 800–323–8685.

Goes Lithographing Company, 42 W. 61st St., Chicago, IL 60621: Free information ■ Stationery, envelopes, calendars, calendar pads, certificates, and other printed items. 312–684–6700.

Grayarc, P.O. Box 2944, Hartford, CT 06104: Free catalog ■ Stationery, business cards, forms, labels, envelopes, and other office supplies. 203–379–9941.

Illustrated Stationery, 3900 Jermantown Rd., Ste. 350, Fairfax, VA 22030: Free infor-

mation with 1st class stamp ■ Personalized wedding stationery.

Robert James Company, Inc., P.O. Box 2726, Birmingham, AL 35202: Free catalog ■ Stationery, furniture, and other office supplies. 800–633–8296; 205–251–5154 (in AL).

L & D Press, 78 Randall St., Box 641, Rockville Centre, NY 11570: Free price list ■ Business cards, stationery and envelopes, planning boards, calendars, and work organizers. 516–593–5058.

Mattick Business Forms, Inc., 333 W. Hintz Rd., Wheeling, IL 60090: Free catalog ■ Stationery, office and business forms, and labels. 708–541–7345.

Merrimade, Inc., 27 S. Canal St., Lawrence, MA 01843: Free catalog ■ Stationery and other printed items. 508–686–5511.

Morning Mail, P.O. Box 72, Covington, GA 30209: Free information ■ Home and business stationery. 800–241–0854.

Northeastern Envelope Company, P.O. Box T, Clarks Summit, PA 18411: Free information ■ Envelopes. 717–586–1061.

The Personal Touch, 409 William St., P.O. Box 1623, Elmira, NY 14902: Free catalog ■ Personalized stationery. 607–733–6313.

Posh Papers, 532 Elmgrove Ave., Providence, RI 02906: Free brochure ■ Note cards with envelopes.

Prolitho, Inc., 630 New Ludlow St., Ludlow, MA 01075: Free catalog ■ Business cards, stationery, and envelopes with flat and raised printing. 413–532–9473.

Reindeer House, 3409 W. 44th St., Minneapolis, MN 55410: Free catalog ■ Greeting cards and stationery. 800–328–3894.

Shipman Printing Industries, P.O. Box 157, Niagara Falls, NY 14302: Free information ■ Forms, letterheads, envelopes, and other printed items. 800–462–2114.

Specialty Mailers, Inc., P.O. Box 80126, Chamblee, GA 30341: Free price list ■ Envelopes and other mailers. 404–455–3188.

Stationery House, 1000 Florida Ave., Hagerstown, MD 21740: Free catalog ■ Business stationery and forms, office supplies, and executive gifts. 301–739–4487.

Writewell Company, Inc., 5850 W. 80th St., Indianapolis, IN 46278: Free catalog ■ Stationery and envelopes, note cards, memo pads, and labels. 317–871–6710.

STENCILS

Adele Bishop, P.O. Box 3349, Kingston, NC 28502: Catalog $3.50 ■ Decorative stencils. 802–362–3537.

American Home Stencils, Inc., 10007 S. 76th St., Franklin, WI 53132: Catalog $2.50 (refundable) ■ Precut stencils in country, traditional, romantic, floral, ribbon patterns, and designs for children; paints; and other supplies.

Great Tracers, 3 N. Schoenbeck Rd., Prospect Heights, IL 60070: Brochure $1 (refundable) ■ Lettering stencils. 708–255–0436.

Gail Grisi Stenciling, Inc., P.O. Box 1263, Haddonfield, NJ 08033: Catalog $2 (refundable) ■ Pre-cut plastic stencils, kits, sponges, acrylic paints, and how-to instructions. 609–354–1757.

Imagination Station, 1746 Broadway, Raynham, MA 02767: Catalog $3 (refundable) ■ Stencils for decorating walls. 508–823–0851.

StenArt, Inc., P.O. Box 114, Pitman, NJ 08071: Catalog $2.50 ■ Overlay stencil kits with applicators and instructions. 800–667–0033.

Stencil House of N.H., P.O. Box 109, Hooksett, NH 03306: Brochure $2.50 (refundable) ■ Cut and uncut mylar stencils, brushes, paints, stencil adhesive, and brush cleaner. 603–635–1716.

Stencil World, 1456 2nd Ave., Box 175, New York, NY 10021: Catalog $3.50 (refundable) ■ Acrylic paints, fabric dyes and paints, brushes, and pre-cut stencils. 212–517–7164.

Tempo Stencils, Box 18611, Milwaukee, WI 53218: Catalog $2 (refundable) ■ Victorian, Oriental, western, and other precut border patterns. 414–461–4640.

Yowler & Shepp Stencils, 3529 Main St., Conestoga, PA 17516: Catalog $3 (refundable) ■ Ribbons, wisteria vines, bouquets, and other stencils. 717–872–2820.

STEREOS & CD PLAYERS

Headphones

Aiwa, 800 Corporate Dr., Moonachie, NJ 07430: Free information ■ Compact disk players, surround sound processors, and headphones. 201–512–3600.

AKG, 1525 Alvarado St., San Leandro, CA 94577: Free information ■ Headphones. 510–351–3500.

Ambico, 50 Maple St., Norwood, NJ 07648: Free information ■ Headphones, loudspeakers, camcorders, video processors/enhancers, decoders, and audio controllers/processors. 201–767–4100.

Azden Corporation, 147 New Hyde Park Rd., Franklin Square, NY 11010: Free information ■ Camcorders and headphones. 516–328–7500.

Bang & Olufsen, 1150 Feehanville Dr., Mt. Prospect, IL 60056: Free information ■ Compact disk players, loudspeakers, and headphones. 708–299–9380.

Denon America, 222 New Rd., Parsippany, NJ 07054: Free information ■ Headphones, compact disk players, audio/video receivers-amplifiers, and surround sound processors. 201–575–7810.

JVC, 41 Slater Dr., Elmwood Park, NJ 07407: Free information ■ Headphones, compact disk players, and audio/video receivers-amplifiers. 201–794–3900.

Nady Systems, 6701 Bay St., Emeryville, CA 94608: Free information ■ Headphones and loudspeakers. 510–652–2411.

Onkyo, 200 Williams Dr., Ramsey, NJ 07446: Free information ■ Compact disk players, audio/video receivers-amplifiers, universal remotes, and headphones. 201–825–7950.

Panasonic, Panasonic Way, Secaucus, NJ 07094: Free information ■ Headphones, audio/video systems, compact disk players, and decoders. 201–348–7000.

Pioneer Electronics, 5000 Airport Plaza Dr., Long Beach, CA 90810: Free information ■ Headphones, loudspeakers, compact disk players, surround sound processors, audio/video receivers-amplifiers, and decoders. 310–420–5700.

Recoton, 46–23 Crane St., Long Island City, NY 11101: Free information ■ Headphones, loudspeakers, decoders, video processors/enhancers, and audio controllers/processors. 800–223–6009.

Sony Consumer Products, Sony Dr., Park Ridge, NJ 07656: Free information ■ Headphones, loudspeakers, compact disk players, camcorders, audio/video receivers-amplifiers, surround sound processors, decoders, universal remotes, and other electronics. 201–930–1000.

Teac, 7733 Telegraph Rd., Montebello, CA 90640: Free information ■ Compact disk players, surround sound processors, audio controllers, and headphones. 213–726–0303.

Technics, One Panasonic Way, Secaucus, NJ 07094: Free information ■ Loudspeakers, compact disk players, headphones, audio/video receivers-amplifiers, and surround sound processors. 201–348–7000.

Yamaha, 6660 Orangethorpe Ave., Buena Park, CA 90620: Free information ■ Headphones, loudspeakers, audio/video systems, compact disk players, and surround sound processors. 714–522–9105.

Speakers

Acoustic Research, 330 Turnpike St., Canton, MA 02021: Free information ■ Compact disk players, loudspeakers, and universal remotes. 617–821–2300.

a/d/s, One Progress Way, Wilmington, MA 01887: Free information ■ Compact disk players, loudspeakers, and audio/video receivers-amplifiers. 800–522–4434.

Altec-Lansing, P.O. Box 277, Milford, PA 18337: Free information ■ Loudspeakers. 717–296–4434.

B & W Loudspeaker, P.O. Box 653, Buffalo, NY 14240: Free information ■ Loudspeakers. 416–771–6611.

Bang & Olufsen, 1150 Feehanville Dr., Mt. Prospect, IL 60056: Free information ■ Compact disk players, loudspeakers, and headphones. 708–299–9380.

Bose Express Music, 100 Mountain Rd., Framingham, MA 01701: Free information ■ Loudspeakers. 800–233–6357.

Boston Acoustic, 70 Broadway, Lynnfield, MA 01940: Free information ■ Loudspeakers. 617–592–9000.

Curtis-Mathes, 1141 Greenway Dr., Irving, TX 75062: Free information ■

Loudspeakers, camcorders, cassette players/recorders, and television sets. 214–550–8050.

dbx, Inc., 707 E. Evelyn Ave., Sunnyvale, CA 94086: Free information ■ Loudspeakers, compact disk players, audio/video receivers-amplifiers, surround sound processors, and audio controllers. 408–720–9800.

Fisher, 21350 Lassen St., Chatsworth, CA 91311: Free information ■ Loudspeakers, cassette players/recorders, compact disk players, surround sound processors, audio/video receivers-amplifiers, and camcorders. 818–998–7322.

Infinity Systems, 9409 Owensmouth Ave., Chatsworth, CA 91311: Free information ■ Loudspeakers and television sets. 818–709–9400.

Marantz, 1150 Feehanville Dr., Mt. Prospect, IL 60056: Free information ■ Audio/video systems, loudspeakers, cassette players/recorders, compact disk players, surround sound processors, and audio controllers. 708–299–4000.

NAD, 575 University Ave., Norwood, MA 02062: Free information ■ Loudspeakers, compact disk players, and audio/video receivers-amplifiers. 617–762–0202.

Nady Systems, 6701 Bay St., Emeryville, CA 94608: Free information ■ Loudspeakers and headphones. 510–652–2411.

NEC Home Electronics, 1401 Estes Ave., Elk Grove Village, IL 60007: Free information ■ Loudspeakers, cassette players/recorders, compact disk players, audio/video receivers-amplifiers, surround sound processors, and audio controllers. 708–228–5900.

Pioneer Electronics, 5000 Airport Plaza Dr., Long Beach, CA 90810: Free information ■ Loudspeakers, compact disk players, surround sound processors, audio/video receivers-amplifiers, decoders, and headphones. 310–420–5700.

Polk Audio, 5601 Metro Dr., Baltimore, MD 21230: Free information ■ Loudspeakers. 410–358–3600.

Proton Corporation, 5630 Cerritos Ave., Cypress, CA 90630: Free information ■ Loudspeakers, compact disk players, and audio/video receivers-amplifiers. 714–952–6900.

Recoton, 46–23 Crane St., Long Island City, NY 11101: Free information ■ Loudspeakers, loudspeakers, audio controllers/processors, video processors/enhancers, and headphones. 800–223–6009.

Sansui Electronics, 1290 Wall St. West, Lyndhurst, NJ 07071: Free information ■ Loudspeakers, cassette players/recorders, compact disk players, audio/video receivers-amplifiers, surround sound processors, and audio controllers/processors. 201–460–9710.

Sony Consumer Products, Sony Dr., Park Ridge, NJ 07656: Free information ■ Loudspeakers, audio/video systems, cassette players/recorders, compact disk players, camcorders, surround sound processors, and headphones. 201–930–1000.

Speakerlab Factory, 6307 Roosevelt Way NE, Seattle, WA 98103: Free information ■ Loudspeakers. 206–523–2175.

Surround Sound, 400 S. Date Ave., Alhambra, CA 91803: Free information ■ Loudspeakers. 818–282–9419.

Technics, One Panasonic Way, Secaucus, NJ 07094: Free information ■ Loudspeakers, compact disk players, headphones, audio/video receivers-amplifiers, and surround sound processors. 201–348–7000.

Yamaha, 6660 Orangethorpe Ave., Buena Park, CA 90620: Free information ■ Loudspeakers, cassette players/recorders, laser disk players, compact disk players, audio/video receivers-amplifiers, surround sound processors, and headphones. 714–522–9105.

Stereo & CD Player Retailers

Atlantic Buyers Club, 162 Hwy. 34, Ste. 189, Matawan, NJ 07747: Free information ■ Audio and video equipment. 800–522–8937.

Audio Advisor, 225 Oakes SW, Grand Rapids, MI 49503: Catalog $1 ■ Audio and video equipment. 616–451–3868.

Audio Haven, 1937 W. 11th St., Upland, CA 91786: Free information ■ Audio equipment. 714–982–8110.

AV Distributors, 16451 Space Center Blvd., Houston, TX 77058: Free information ■ Audio, video, and stereo equipment and television sets. 800–843–3697.

Computability Consumer Electronics, P.O. Box 17882, Milwaukee, WI 53217: Free information ■ Audio, video, and stereo equipment and television sets; fax machines; copiers; and computers. 800–558–0003; 414–357–8181 (in WI).

Crutchfield, 1 Crutchfield Park, Charlottesville, VA 22906: Free information ■ Video, audio, and stereo equipment and television sets. 800–336–5566.

Electronic Wholesalers, 1160 Hamburg Tpk., Wayne, NJ 07470: Free information ■ Audio/high-fidelity receivers, audio cassette decks, compact disk players, laser disk equipment, telephones, camcorders, television sets, and cassette players/recorders. 201–696–6531.

Factory Direct, 131 W. 35th St., New York, NY 10001: Free information ■ Audio, video, and stereo equipment and television sets. 800–428–4567.

Focus Electronics, 4523 13th Ave., Brooklyn, NY 11219: Catalog $2 (refundable) ■ Audio, stereo, and video equipment; appliances; and photographic equipment. 718–436–4646.

Hi-End Audio, Rt. 6, North Dartmouth, MA 02747: Free information ■ Audio equipment. 508–996–5454.

Hi-Fi City, 145 W. 26th St., New York, NY 10001: Free information ■ Audio and video equipment. 800–443–4249; 212–691–5823 (in NY).

Highvoltage, 39 W. 32nd St., New York, NY 10001: Free information ■ Camcorders, disk players, video tape stabilizers, tripods, car stereos, tape maintenance systems, video recorders, and tapes. 212–564–4410.

Illinois Audio, 12 E. Delaware Pl., Chicago, IL 60611: Free price list ■ Audio and stereo equipment, video recorders, and tapes. 800–621–8042; 312–664–0020 (in IL).

International Electronic World, 6330 Frankford Ave., Baltimore, MD 21206: Free catalog ■ Audio and video equipment. 410–485–0511.

J & R Music World, 59–50 Queens-Midtown Expy., Maspeth, NY 11378: Free catalog ■ Audio equipment, car and portable stereos, and video recorders; telephones; video tapes, cassettes and disks; and computers. 800–221–8180.

Kief's Audio/Video, 24th & Iowa, Lawrence, KS 66044: Free information ■ Audio equipment. 913–842–1811.

Not-Just-Video, Inc., 58 Walker St., New York, NY 10013: Catalog $2.75 ■ Video equipment, television sets, audio equipment, camcorders, and other electronics. 800–856–9890.

Olden Video, 1265 Broadway, New York, NY 10001: Free information ■ Video equipment, television sets, cassette players/recorders, and other electronics. 212–725–1234.

Park Place Audio, 55 Park Pl., New York, NY 10007: Free information ■ Audio and video equipment. 212–964–4570.

Percy's, Inc., 19 Glennie St., Worcester, MA 01605: Free information ■ Save up to 50 percent on appliances and electronics. 508–755–5334.

Planet Electronics, 8418 Lilley, Canton, MI 48187: Free information ■ Audio and video equipment, television sets, and portable stereos; video recorders; telephones; batteries; and video tapes, cassettes, and compact disks. 800–222–5650; 313–453–4750 (in MI).

PowerVideo, 4413 Blue Bonnet, Stafford, TX 77477: Free information ■ Audio, video, and stereo equipment and television sets. 713–240–3202.

Saxitone Audio-Video, 1776 Columbia Rd. NW, Washington, DC 20009: Free brochure ■ Audio and video equipment and television sets. 202–462–0800.

S.B.H. Enterprises, 1678 53rd St., Brooklyn, NY 11204: Free information ■ Audio and video equipment and radar detectors. 800–451–5851; 718–438–1027 (in NY).

Sound Reproduction, 237 Bloomfield Ave., Bloomfield, NJ 07003: Free catalog ■ Car and home audio equipment. 800–932–0087.

The Sound Seller, 2808 Cahill Rd., P.O. Box 224, Marinette, WI 54143: Free information ■ Audio and video equipment. 715–735–9002.

Square Deal, 456 Waverly Ave., Patchogue, NY 11772: Free information ■ Audio equipment. 800–332–5369.

Stereo Equipment Sales, Inc., 6730 Santa Barbara Ct., Baltimore, MD 21227: Free catalog ■ Audio and video equipment, computers, telephones, telephone answering machines, recorders, and other electronics. 800–638–3920.

Tri-State Camera, 160 Broadway, New York, NY 10038: Free information ■ Audio and video equipment, camcorders, copiers, video tape cassettes, fax machines, and other electronics. 212–349–2555.

Wisconsin Discount Stereo, 2417 W. Badger Rd., Madison, WI 53713: Free information ■ Video and audio equipment and television sets. 800–356–9514.

Stereo & CD Player Manufacturers

Acoustic Research, 330 Turnpike St., Canton, MA 02021: Free information ■ Compact disk players, loudspeakers, and universal remotes. 617–821–2300.

a/d/s, One Progress Way, Wilmington, MA 01887: Free information ■ Compact disk players, loudspeakers, and audio/video receivers-amplifiers. 800–522–4434.

Aiwa, 800 Corporate Dr., Moonachie, NJ 07430: Free information ■ Compact disk players, surround sound processors, and headphones. 201–512–3600.

Akai Division, Mitsubishi Electric, 225 Old New Brunswick Rd., Piscataway, NJ 08854: Free information ■ Cassette players/recorders, compact disk players, audio/video receivers-amplifiers, television sets, surround sound processors, universal remotes, and audio controllers. 908–562–8500.

Alpine Electronics of America, 19145 Gramercy, Torrance, CA 90505: Free information ■ Compact disk players, video processors/enhancers, and decoders. 213–326–8000.

Audio Source, 1327 N. Carolan Ave., Burlingame, CA 94010: Free information ■ Surround sound processors and audio controllers. 415–348–8114.

Bang & Olufsen, 1150 Feehanville Dr., Mt. Prospect, IL 60056: Free information ■ Compact disk players, loudspeakers, and headphones. 708–299–9380.

Canon, One Canon Plaza, Lake Success, NY 11042: Free information ■ Cassette players/recorders, camcorders, surround sound processors, character/effects generators, and decoders. 516–488–6700.

dbx, Inc., 707 E. Evelyn Ave., Sunnyvale, CA 94086: Free information ■ Cassette players/recorders, loudspeakers, compact disk players, audio/video receivers-

amplifiers, surround sound processors, and audio controllers. 408–720–9800.

Denon America, 222 New Rd., Parsippany, NJ 07054: Free information ■ Compact disk players, audio/video receivers-amplifiers, surround sound processors, and headphones. 201–575–7810.

Emerson Radio Corporation, 1 Emerson Ln., North Bergen, NJ 07047: Free information ■ Camcorders, cassette players/recorders, compact disk players, and television sets. 800–922–0738.

Fisher, 21350 Lassen St., Chatsworth, CA 91311: Free information ■ Loudspeakers, cassette players/recorders, compact disk players, surround sound processors, audio/video receivers-amplifiers, camcorders, television sets, and universal remotes. 818–998–7322.

Goldstar, 1000 Sylvan Ave., Englewood, NJ 07632: Free information ■ Cassette players/recorders, compact disk players, and television sets. 201–460–8870.

Hitachi Sales Corporation, 401 W. Artesia Blvd., Compton, CA 90220: Free information ■ Cassette players/recorders, camcorders, compact disk players, audio/video receivers-amplifiers, and television sets. 310–537–8383.

International Components, 105 Maxess Rd., Melville, NY 11747: Free information ■ Surround sound processors. 516–293–1500.

JVC, 41 Slater Dr., Elmwood Park, NJ 07407: Free information ■ Audio/video systems, cassette players/recorders, camcorders, compact disk players, audio/video receivers-amplifiers, television sets, and headphones. 201–794–3900.

Harmon Kardon, 240 Crossways Park, Woodbury, NY 11797: Free information ■ Cassette players/recorders, compact disk players, audio/video receivers-amplifiers, and projection equipment. 516–496–3400.

Kenwood, P.O. Box 22745, Long Beach, CA 90801: Free information ■ Cassette players/recorders, compact disk players, television sets, audio/video receivers-amplifiers, and surround sound processors. 310–639–9000.

McIntosh, 2 Chambers St., Binghamton, NY 13903: Free information ■ Compact disk players. 607–723–3512.

Marantz, 1150 Feehanville Dr., Mt. Prospect, IL 60056: Free information ■ Audio/video systems, loudspeakers, cassette players/recorders, compact disk players, surround sound processors, and audio controllers. 708–299–4000.

Mitsubishi Electronics, 5757 Plaza Dr., Cypress, CA 90630: Free information ■ Audio/video systems, cassette players/recorders, camcorders, compact disk players, and television sets. 714–220–2500.

Multivision, 1751 Fox Dr., San Jose, CA 94538: Free information ■ Audio controllers/processors, video processors/enhancers, and character/effects generators. 510–651–2351.

NAD, 575 University Ave., Norwood, MA 02062: Free information ■ Loudspeakers, laser disk players, compact disk players, television sets, and audio/video receivers-amplifiers. 617–762–0202.

NAP Consumer Electronics, 1 Phillips Dr., Knoxville, TN 37914: Free information ■ Magnavox: cassette players/recorders, compact disk players, camcorders, television sets, and universal remotes; Philco: camcorders, television sets, cassette players/recorders, and monitors-receivers; Philips: cassette players/recorders, compact disk players, and television sets; and Sylvania: camcorders, cassette players/recorders, laser disk players, and television sets. 615–521–4391.

NEC Home Electronics, 1401 Estes Ave., Elk Grove, IL 60007: Free information ■ Loudspeakers, cassette players/recorders, compact disk players, audio/video receivers-amplifiers, television sets, camcorders, surround sound processors, and audio controllers. 708–228–5900.

Onkyo, 200 Williams Dr., Ramsey, NJ 07446: Free information ■ Compact disk players, audio/video receivers-amplifiers, universal remotes, and headphones. 201–825–7950.

Panasonic, Panasonic Way, Secaucus, NJ 07094: Free information ■ Audio/video systems, cassette players/recorders, compact disk players, television sets, camcorders, decoders, and headphones. 201–348–7000.

Pioneer Electronics, 5000 Airport Plaza Dr., Long Beach, CA 90810: Free information ■ Loudspeakers, cassette players/recorders, laser disk players, compact disk players, audio/video receivers-amplifiers,

television sets, surround sound processors, decoders, and headphones. 310–420–5700.

Proton Corporation, 5630 Cerritos Ave., Cypress, CA 90630: Free information ■ Loudspeakers, loudspeakers, compact disk players, audio/video receivers-amplifiers, television sets, and decoders. 714–952–6900.

Quasar, 1707 N. Randall Rd., Elgin, IL 60123: Free information ■ Audio/video systems, cassette players/recorders, compact disk players, camcorders, television sets, and other electronics. 708–468–5600.

Radio Shack, Division Tandy Corporation, 1500 One Tandy Center, Fort Worth, TX 76102: Free information ■ Cassette players/recorders, compact disk players, camcorders, universal remotes, computers, and other electronics. 817–390–3700.

RCA Sales Corporation, 600 N. Sherman Dr., Indianapolis, IN 46201: Free information ■ Audio/video systems, cassette players/recorders, compact disk players, television sets, camcorders, surround sound processors, character/effects generators, decoders, and audio controllers. 317–267–5000.

Recoton, 46–23 Crane St., Long Island City, NY 11101: Free information ■ Loudspeakers, decoders, audio controllers/processors, headphones, and video processors/enhancers. 800–223–6009.

Sansui Electronics, 1290 Wall St. West, Lyndhurst, NJ 07071: Free information ■ Loudspeakers, cassette players/recorders, compact disk players, camcorders, audio/video receivers-amplifiers, television sets, surround sound processors, decoders, and audio controllers/processors. 201–460–9710.

Sanyo Electronics, 1200 W. Artesia Blvd., Compton, CA 90220: Free information ■ Cassette players/recorders, compact disk players, camcorders, television sets, surround sound processors, decoders, and universal remotes. 310–537–5830.

Sharp Electronics, Sharp Plaza, Mahwah, NJ 07430: Free information ■ Cassette players/recorders, compact disk players, camcorders, television sets, audio/video receivers-amplifiers, and decoders. 800–BE–SHARP.

Sherwood, 14830 Alondra Blvd., La Mirada, CA 90638: Free information ■ Compact disk players, audio/video receivers-

amplifiers, and surround sound processors. 800–962–3203.

Shure Brothers, Inc., 222 Hartrey Ave., Evanston, IL 60202: Free information ■ Compact disk players, surround sound processors, and other electronics. 800–447–4873.

Sony Consumer Products, Sony Dr., Park Ridge, NJ 07656: Free information ■ Loudspeakers, cassette players/recorders, compact disk players, camcorders, audio/video receivers-amplifiers, television sets, camcorders, surround sound processors, decoders, universal remotes, and headphones. 201–930–1000.

Teac, 7733 Telegraph Rd., Montebello, CA 90640: Free information ■ Cassette players/recorders, laser disk players, compact disk players, surround sound processors, audio controllers, character/effects generators, and headphones. 213–726–0303.

Technics, One Panasonic Way, Secaucus, NJ 07094: Free information ■ Loudspeakers, compact disk players, surround sound processors, audio/video receivers-amplifiers, and headphones. 201–348–7000.

Toshiba, 82 Totowa Rd., Wayne, NJ 07470: Free information ■ Cassette players/recorders, compact disk players, camcorders, surround sound processors, and television sets. 201–628–8000.

Vector Research, 1230 Calle Suerte, Camarillo, CA 93010: Free information ■ Cassette players/recorders, compact disk players, and audio/video receivers-amplifiers. 805–987–1312.

Yamaha, 6660 Orangethorpe Ave., Buena Park, CA 90620: Free information ■ Loudspeakers, cassette players/recorders, laser disk players, compact disk players, audio/video receivers-amplifiers, surround sound processors, and headphones. 714–522–9105.

STICKERS

California Pacific Designs, P.O. Box 2660, Alameda, CA 94501: Free catalog ■ Nature and animal stickers. 510–521–7914.

Holly Sales, 9926 Beach Blvd., Ste. 114, Jacksonville, FL 32216: Free information ■ Clown stickers. 904–223–5828.

Stick-Em Up, P.O. Box 9108, Pleasanton, CA 94566: Catalog $2 ■ Stickers. 510–426–1040.

STONE SCULPTING & CARVING

Ebersole Lapidary Supply, Inc., 11417 West Hwy. 54, Wichita, KS 67209: Catalog $2 ■ Carving materials, beads and bead-stringing supplies, tools, findings, mountings, cabochons and rocks, and jewelry kits. 316–722–4771.

Gems by Jack, 113 Sherman, Ihlen, MN 56140: Free catalog ■ Indian gifts and catinite for carving. 507–348–8716.

Montoya/MAS International, Inc., 435 Southern Blvd., West Palm Beach, FL 33405: Catalog $3 (refundable) ■ Carving stone and sculpture tools. 407–832–4401.

Richardson's Recreational Ranch, Ltd., Gateway Route Box 440, Madras, OR 97741: Free information ■ Rock and mineral specimens from all over the world, carving materials, and lapidary equipment and supplies. 503–475–2680.

Riviera Lapidary Supply, 30192 Mesquite, Riviera, TX 78379: Catalog $3 ■ Carving materials, petrified wood, cabochons, beads, slabs, cabbing rough, gemstones, crystals, beads, and bead-stringing supplies and kits. 512–296–3958.

Steatite of Southern Oregon, Inc., 2891 Elk Ln., Grants Pass, OR 97527: Free information ■ Soapstone for sculpturing and carving. 503–479–3646.

STOVES

Barnstable Stove Shop, Rt. 149, Box 472, West Barnstable, MA 02668: Brochure $1 ■ Restored antique stoves and parts. 508–362–9913.

Bryant Stove Works, Rich Rd., Box 2048, Thorndike, ME 04986: Free catalog ■ Antique stoves for coal, gas, wood, wood and gas combination, and electricity. 207–568–3665.

C & D Distributors, 366 Middlesex Tpk., Box 766, Old Saybrook, CT 06475: Free brochure ■ Wood-burning and coal stoves. 203–388–3408.

Charmaster Products, Inc., 2307 Hwy. 2 West, Grand Rapids, MN 55744: Free brochure ■ Wood-burning, wood-gas, and wood-oil furnaces; conversion units; and fireplaces. 218–326–6786.

Dovre, Inc., 401 Hankes Ave., Aurora, IL 60505: Free information ■ Heavy-duty cast-iron stoves. 800–368–7387.

Elmira Stove Works, 22 Church St., Elmira, Ontario, Canada N3B 1M3: Catalog $2 ■ Home cooking stoves in a classical style. 519–725–5500.

HearthStone, P.O. Box 1069, Morrisville, VT 05661: Free literature ■ Automatic, clean-burning wood stoves. 802–827–8683.

Heatilator, Inc., 1915 W. Saunders St., Mt. Pleasant, IA 52641: Free brochure ■ Wood-burning stoves and fireplace inserts. 800–247–6798.

Heating Alternatives, Rt. 212, Box 970, Pleasant Valley, Quakertown, PA 18951: Free catalog ■ Coal and wood-burning stoves. 800–444–4328; 215–346–7896 (in PA).

Jotul USA, Inc., P.O. Box 1157, Portland, ME 04104: Free catalog ■ Stoves and fireplaces. 207–797–5912.

Lopi International, Ltd., Travis Industries, 10850 117th Pl. NE, Kirkland, WA 98033: Free information ■ Fireplace inserts. 800–425–3915.

Nu-Tec Incorporated, P.O. Box 908, East Greenwich, RI 02818: Free brochure ■ Wood-burning stoves and fireplace inserts. 800–822–0600.

Otis Home Center, Inc., Heartland Appliances, 312 Armstrong Rd., Rogersville, TN 37857: Free information ■ Wood, gas, or electric, country-style heating and cooking stoves. 615–272–8135.

Russo Corporation, 61 Pleasant St., Randolph, MA 02368: Free information ■ Wood-burning stoves with optional brass trim, air deflectors, brass doors, and etched glass. 617–963–1182.

Stanley Iron Works, 64 Taylor St., Nashua, NH 03060: Free information ■ Antique parlor stoves, gas stoves, and wood-gas combinations. Coal, gas, and electric conversions of antique stoves available. 603–881–8335.

Vogelzang Corporation, 400 W. 17th St., Holland, MI 49423: Free information ■ Wood-burning stove conversion kits. 800–222–6950.

Woodstock Soapstone Company, Inc., Airpark Rd., West Lebanon, NH 03784: Free catalog ■ Traditional and contemporary style woodburning stoves. 800–866–4344.

SUNDIALS

Abbey Garden Sundials, Indian Hill Rd., P.O. Box 102, Pakenham, Ontario, Canada K0A 2X0: Catalog $2 (refundable) ■ Sundials. 613–256–3973.

Betsy's Place, 323 Arch St., Philadelphia, PA 19106: Brochure $1.50 ■ Sundials and stands, brass reproduction door knockers, and trivets. 215–922–3536.

Good Directions Company, 24 Ardmore Rd., Stamford, CT 06902: Catalog $1 ■ Copper and solid brass sundials and weather vanes. 800–346–7678; 203–348–1836 (in CT).

Holst, Inc., Box 370, Tawas City, MI 48764: Catalog $2 (refundable) ■ Country items, decor accessories, sundials, weather vanes, housewares, and figurines. 517–362–5664.

Replogle Globes, Inc., 2801 S. 25th Ave., Broadview, IL 60153: Free catalog ■ Sundials. 708–343–0900.

Wind & Weather, P.O. Box 2320, Mendocino, CA 95460: Free catalog ■ Sundials, weather vanes, and weather forecasting instruments. 707–937–0323.

SUNGLASSES & EYE WEAR

American Optical Corporation, 14 Mechanic St., Southbridge, MA 01550: Free information ■ Ski goggles and other eyewear. 508–765–9711.

Blitz Optica, Inc., P.O. Box 2183, Cheyenne, WY 82003: Free catalog ■ Sunglasses and other eyewear. 800–288–8192.

Bolle America, Inc., 3890 Elm St., Denver, CO 80207: Free information ■ Eye wear and goggles. 303–321–4300.

Brigade Quartermasters, Inc., 266 Roswell St., Marietta, GA 30060: Free information ■ Ski goggles and other eyewear. 404–428–1234.

Bucci, Inc., P.O. Box 66888, Scotts Valley, CA 95066: Free brochure ■ Sunglasses for men and women. 800–767–2822.

Carrera Ski & Sport Division, 35 Maple St., Norwood, NJ 07648: Free information ■ Ski goggles and other eyewear. 201–767–3820.

Discount Sunglasses, 40–19 164th St., Ste. 580, Flushing, NY 11358: Free information with long SASE ■ Save from 30 to 50 percent on sunglasses. 800–955–2122.

Garfield & Berk Optometrists, 175 5th Ave., New York, NY 10010: Free information ■ Eyepiece correction lenses for cameras. 212–254–0450.

Gargoyles Eyewear, 19039 62nd Ave. South, Kent, WA 98032: Free brochure ■ Sunglasses that provide ultraviolet light protection. 206–251–5001.

Hidalgo, Inc., 45 La Buena Vista, Wimberley, TX 78676: Free catalog ■ Designer fashion sunglasses. 800–786–2021.

House of Eyes, P.O. Box 4366, Greensboro, NC 27404: Free information ■ Designer eye wear. 800–331–4701; 919–852–7107 (in NC).

Jones & Company, 325 E. Massasoit Ave., East Providence, RI 02914: Free information ■ Ski goggles and other eyewear. 401–434–4010.

Lens Express, Inc., 2780 Gateway Dr., Pompano Beach, FL 33069: Free information ■ Save up to 70 percent on most brands of contacts. Includes tints and disposables. 305–968–4555.

Martin Sunglasses, Jack Martin Company, Inc., 9830 Baldwin Pl., El Monte, CA 91731: Free information ■ Ski goggles and other eyewear. 800–423–4465; 213–686–1100 (in CA).

Oakley Sunglasses, 10 Holland, Irvine, CA 92718: Free information ■ Eye wear that provides protection against ultraviolet light and injury-causing blue light. 800–733–6255.

Olympic Optical Company, P.O. Box 181232, Memphis, TN 38181: Free information ■ Sunglasses that protect the eyes from ultraviolet light. 800–992–1255.

Open Range Optics, P.O. Box 1–2020, Cheyenne, WY 82003: Free information ■ Designer eyeglasses. 800–937–2020.

Precision Optical, 300 N. 6th St., Rochelle, IL 61068: Free catalog ■ Magnifiers and magnifying and regular sunglasses. 815–562–2174.

Royal Optical Company, 400 Matthew St., Santa Clara, CA 95052: Free brochure ■ Sunglasses with shatterproof lenses that provide protection against ultraviolet and infrared light. 408–727–4040.

Smith Sport Optics, P.O. Box 2999, Ketchum, ID 8334: Free information ■ Glare-reducing, eye-protection goggles. 208–726–4477.

Torelli Imports, 409 Calle San Pablo, Ste. 109, Camarillo, CA 93010: Free information ■ Sunglasses with interchangeable lenses and temple and nose pieces. 805–484–8705.

SURFBOARDS

Alvimar Manufacturing Company, Inc., 51–02 21st St., Long Island City, NY 11101: Free information ■ Surfboards and swim rings. 718–937–0404.

American Athletic, Inc., 200 American Ave., Jefferson, IA 50129: Free information ■ Surfboards and swim rings. 800–247–3978.

Body Glove International, Inc., Dive N' Surf, Inc., 530 6th St., Hermosa Beach, CA 90254: Free information ■ Surfboards. 310–374–4074.

Foam Design Consumer Products, Inc., 444 Transport Ct., Lexington, KY 40581: Free information ■ Surfboards. 606–231–7006.

The Hawaiian Island Wave Ski Company, P.O. Box 579, Kalaheo, HI 96741: Free brochure ■ Easy-to-transport surfing skis. 808–332–9364.

J & B Foam Fabricators, Inc., P.O. Box 144, Ludington, MI 49431: Free information ■ Surfboards and surfer's gear, and swim rings. 616–843–2448.

Kransco Group Company, P.O. Box 884866, San Francisco, CA 94188: Free information ■ Surfboards and swim rings. 415–433–9350.

Recreonics Corporation, 7696 Zionsville Rd., Indianapolis, IN 46268: Free information ■ Surfboards, swim rings, and diving boards. 800–428–3254; 800–792–3489 (in IN).

Rothhammer/Sprint, P.O. Box 5579, Santa Maria, CA 93456: Free information ■ Surfboards, swim rings, and equipment for divers. 800–235–2156; 800–445–8456 (in CA).

Santa Cruz Rip Grip, Inc., P.O. Box 2067, Freedom, CA 95019: Free information ■ Surfboards. 408–728–5382.

SURPLUS & LIQUIDATION MERCHANDISE

American Science & Surplus, 601 Linden Pl., Evanston, IL 60202: Catalog 50¢ ■ Surplus science and electromechanical equipment. 708–475–8440.

Burden's Surplus Center, P.O. Box 82209, Lincoln, NE 68501: Free catalog ■ Merchandise at closeout liquidation prices. 800–228–3407.

B.W. Trading Company, Box 692, Newark, OH 43055: Catalog $1 ■ Military surplus supplies and equipment. 614–344–2772.

COMB Authorized Liquidator, 720 Anderson Ave., St. Cloud, MN 56372: Free catalog ■ Liquidation merchandise. 800–328–0609.

Damark International, Inc., P.O. Box 29900, Minneapolis, MN 55430: Free information ■ Save on merchandise from over-productions, discontinued lines, or obtained through special arrangements with vendors. 800–788–7001.

Fair Radio Sales Company, Inc., P.O. Box 1105, Lima, OH 45802: Free information ■ Industrial and military surplus electronic parts. 419–227–6573.

Harbor Freight Salvage, 3491 Mission Oaks Blvd., Camarillo, CA 93010: Free catalog ■ Save up to 50 percent on hardware, tools, and other surplus merchandise. 800–444–3353.

Massachusetts Army & Navy Store, 15 Fordham Rd., Boston, MA 02134: Free catalog ■ Military surplus supplies and equipment. 617–783–1250.

Strand Surplus Center, 2202 Strand, Galveston, TX 77550: Brochure $1 ■ Government surplus merchandise. 800–231–6005.

Surplus Center, P.O. Box 82209, Lincoln, NE 68501: Free catalog ■ Hydraulics, motors, compressors, spraying equipment, pumps, and other surplus equipment. 800–488–3407.

SWIMMING POOLS & EQUIPMENT

Aquasol Controllers, Inc., P.O. Box 15334, Houston, TX 77220: Free information ■ Electronic pool sanitizer and pH monitoring and control equipment. 800–444–0675.

Chemtrol, 113 West Mission St., Santa Barbara, CA 93101: Free information ■ Electronic pool sanitizer and pH monitoring and control equipment. 800–621–2279; 805–569–1731 (in CA).

Chester Products, Inc., 1300 Lafayette Ave., Middletown, OH 45042: Free information ■ All-aluminum welded, permanently installed swimming pools. 513–424–5341.

Cover-Pools, Inc., 66 E. 3335 South, Salt Lake City, UT 84115: Free information ■ Swimming pool covers. 800–44–SAVET.

Doughboy Recreational, 10959 Jersey Blvd., Rancho Cucomonga, CA 91730: Free information ■ Above-ground pools. 714–987–4741.

Endless Pools, Inc., 200 E. Dutton's Mill Rd., Aston, PA 19014: Free information ■ Lap pool for swimming in place against a smooth, adjustable current. 800–732–8660.

Fanta-Sea Pools, 10151 Main St., Clarence, NY 14031: Free information ■ Solar energy-heated swimming pools. 800–845–5500; 800–462–8000 (in NY).

Poolsaver, 679 W. Terrace, San Dimas, CA 91773: Free brochure ■ Motorized or manually controlled pool covers. 800–22–COVER; 714–592–4355 (in CA).

Recreonics Corporation, 7697 Zionsville Rd., Indianapolis, IN 46268: Free information ■ Swimming pools and supplies. 800–428–3254; 800–792–3489 (in IN).

Solar Structures, P.O. Box 100, Wheeling, IL 60090: Catalog $5 ■ Swimming pool enclosures. 312–634–9355.

Swimex, P.O. Box 328, Warren, RI 02885: Free information ■ Compact lap pool for swimming in place, with controls for adjusting water flow. 401–245–7946.

SWITCH PLATES

Classic Accents, Inc., 12869 Eureka, Southgate, MI 48195: Catalog $1 ■ Switch cover plates, push-button light switches, and solid brass cover plates. 313–282–5525.

Hearth & Home, 3242 Severn at 17th St., Metairie, LA 70992: Free catalog ■ Switch plates, fireplace accessories, mailboxes, wall decorations, and gifts. 504–454–8907.

Prairie Town Products, Inc., P.O. Box 1426, Sedalia, MO 65301: Catalog $2 (refundable) ■ Hand-painted or walnut-stained solid wood switch plates. 816–826–4208.

TABLECLOTHS & PADS

American Table Pad Company, 8140 Zapata, Dublin, CA 94568: Free information ■ Table pads. 800–537–2364.

Best Value Table Pad Company, 1170 Stella St., St. Paul, MN 55108: Free information ■ Table pads. 800–345–9795; 612–646–6630 (in MN).

Chrisalem by Malerich, 2158 Charlton Rd., Sunfish Lake, MN 55119: Catalog $1 ■ Bedding, linens, and tablecloths. 612–451–6690.

Domestications, P.O. Box 40, Hanover, PA 17333: Catalog $2 ■ Save up to 35 percent on comforters, sheet sets, pillows, blankets, bedspreads, throws, solid or lace tablecloths, mini blinds, shower curtains, and bathroom accessories. 717–633–3313.

Factory Direct Table Pad Company, 617 Massachusetts Ave., Indianapolis, IN 46204: Free information ■ Save up to 50 percent on table pads. 800–428–4567.

Guardian Custom Products, P.O. Box A, LaGrange, IN 46761: Free information ■ Table pads. 800–444–0778.

Harris Levy, 278 Grand St., New York, NY 10002: Free information with long SASE ■ Save up to 40 percent on linens for tables, beds, and baths, with optional monogramming. 800–221–7750; 212–226–3102 (in NY).

Palmetto Linen Company, Box 109, Hardeeville, SC 29927: Free information ■ Sheets and matching dust ruffles, bath towels, blankets, comforters, pillows, tablecloths, place mats, shower curtains, kitchen towels, and oven gloves. 800–833–3506.

Pioneer Table Pad Company, P.O. Box 449, Gates Mills, OH 44040: Free information ■ Table pads. 800–541–0271.

Rue de France, 78 Thames St., Newport, RI 02840: Catalog $3 ■ Pillows, tablecloths, runners, and lace curtains. 800–777–0998.

Sentry Table Pad Company, 1170 Stella St., St. Paul, MN 55108: Free information ■ Table pads. 800–328–7237.

TABLE TENNIS

American Import Company, 1453 Mission St., San Francisco, CA 94103: Free information ■ Paddles, balls, nets, brackets, and sets. 415–863–1506.

Cannon Sports, Inc., P.O. Box 11179, Burbank CA 91510: Free information ■ Paddles, balls, nets, brackets, and sets. 800–223–0064; 818–503–9570 (in A).

Champion Sports Products Company, P.O. Box 138, Sayreville, NJ 08872: Free information ■ Paddles, balls, nets, brackets, and sets. 908–238–0330.

Designs for Leisure, Ltd., 41 Kensico Dr., Mount Kisco, NY 10549: Free information ■ Paddles, balls, nets, brackets, and sets. 914–241–4500.

Indian Industries, Inc., 817 Maxwell, P.O. Box 889, Evansville, IN 47711: Free information ■ Paddles, balls, nets, brackets, and sets. 812–426–2281.

Kempe Manufacturing Company, 98 Broadway, Freeport, NY 11520: Free information ■ Paddles, balls, nets, brackets, and sets. 516–378–2187.

Palmer Billiard Corporation, 30 Morris Ave., Elizabeth, NJ 07208: Free information ■ Paddles, balls, nets, brackets, and sets. 908–289–4741.

Pennsylvania Sporting Goods, 1360 Industrial Hwy., P.O. Box 451, Southampton, PA 18966: Free information ■ Paddles, balls, nets, brackets, and sets. 800–535–1122.

Regent Sports Corporation, 45 Ranick Rd., Hauppage, NY 11787: Free information ■ Paddles, balls, nets, brackets, and sets. 516–234–2948.

Robbins Sport, 21005 Van Dyke, Warren, MI 48091: Free information ■ Paddles, balls, nets, brackets, and sets. 313–758–6777.

Spalding & Brothers, Inc., 425 Meadow St., P.O. Box 901, Chicopee, MA 01021: Free information ■ Paddles, balls, nets, brackets, and sets. 413–536–1200.

Table Tennis America, Ltd., 4100 Will Rogers Pkwy., P.O. Box 270294, Oklahoma City, OK 73137: Free information ■ Table tennis nets and posts, rackets, and balls. 800–727–8442; 405–947–8442 (in OK).

Wa-Mac, Inc., Highskore Products, Inc., 178 Commerce Rd., P.O. Box 128, Carlstadt, NJ 07072: Free information ■ Paddles, balls, nets, brackets, and sets. 800–447–5673; 201–438–7200 (in NJ).

World of Leisure Manufacturing Company, 758 E. Edna Pl., Covina, CA 91723: Free information ■ Paddles, balls, nets, brackets, and sets. 818–332–5997.

TANNING LAMPS

Lucas Products Corporation, 5663 Opportunity Dr., P.O. Box 6570, Toledo, OH 43612: Free information ■ Tanning machines. 419–476–5992.

Pro Tan, Division Welt Industries, 175 N. Glenn Ct., Welt Towers, Atlanta, GA 30342: Free information ■ Tanning machines. 404–250–0977.

Silver Solarium USA, Inc., 379 Oyster Pt. Blvd., Ste. 3, South San Francisco, CA 94080: Free information ■ Tanning machines. 415–873–1370.

Solar Pacific, Inc., P.O. Box 5475, Kent, WA 98064: Free information ■ Tanning machines. 206–854–8664.

Suntana Sun Systems, Sun Industries, Inc., 2409 Industrial Dr., Jonesboro, AR 72402: Free literature ■ Tanning machines. 501–935–1130.

Whitland Fitness Corporation, 101 Methuen St., P.O. Box 1049, Lawrence, MA 01842: Free information ■ Tanning machines. 508–685–5109.

Wolff Suntanning Systems, P.O. Box 2538, Jonesboro, AR 72402: Free information ■ Tanning machines. 501–932–7805.

TAPESTRIES

Peerless Imported Rugs, 3033 N. Lincoln Ave., Chicago, IL 60657: Catalog $1 ■ Hand- and machine-woven Oriental rugs, Navajo rugs, colonial braids, grass rugs, and tapestries. 800–621–6573.

Allan Walker, Ltd., 3800 Ivy Rd. NE, Atlanta, GA 30305: Free information ■ Tapestries. 404–233–1926.

TATTOOING

Spaulding & Rogers Manufacturing, New Scotland Rd., P.O. Box 85, Voorheesville, NY 12186: Catalog $6 ■ Tattooing supplies. 518–768–2070.

TAXIDERMY

Dan Chase Taxidermy Supply Company, 13599 Blackwater Rd., Baker, LA 70714: Free catalog ■ Taxidermy, supplies, and how-to videos. 504–261–3795.

Clearfield Taxidermy, P.O. Box 711, Clearfield, PA 16830: Catalog $2 ■ Taxidermy supplies and tools, custom leather tanning, and supplies for leather crafting and fur-styling. 814–765–9561.

J.W. Elwood Company, Omaha, NE 68102: Free catalog ■ Taxidermy supplies. 800–228–2291.

McKenzie Taxidermy Supply, Box 480, Granite Quarry, NC 28072: Free catalog ■ Taxidermy supplies.

O.H. Mullen Sales, Inc., RR 2, Oakwood, OH 45873: Free information ■ Taxidermy supplies. 800–258–6625; 800–248–6625 (in OH).

John Rhinehart Taxidermy Supply Company, Division American Institute of Taxidermy, 3232 McCormick Dr., Janesville, WI 53545: Free information ■ Taxidermy supplies. 800–FOR–DEER; 608–755–5160 (in WI).

Touchstone Taxidermy Supply, 5011 E. Texas, Bossier City, LA 71111: Free catalog ■ Taxidermy supplies.

Van Dyke Supply Company, P.O. Box 278, Woonsocket, SD 57385: Catalog $1 ■ Taxidermy supplies. 605–796-4425.

TELEPHONES & ANSWERING MACHINES

Antique Phones

A.M. Telephone Company, Box 5, Turtle Lake, WI 54889: Catalog $1 ■ Antique telephones and parts.

Billard's Telephones, 21710 Regnart Rd., Cupertino, CA 95014: Catalog $1 ■ Antique telephones and parts. 408–252–2104.

Chicago Old Telephone Company, 327 Carthage St., Sanford, NC 27330: Free catalog ■ Old telephones, restored with authentic parts, that can be plugged into modern systems and replacement parts for most telephones. 800–843–1320.

Alexander Graham's, P.O. Box 080936, Rochester, MN 48308: Free information ■ Royal Albert, Wedgewood, Galway Crystal, Limoge, and other Victorian telephones. 800–888–2130.

Jadis Moderne, 2701 Main St., Santa Monica, CA 90405: Free information ■ Restored telephones from the 1930s. 310–396–3477.

Mahantango Manor, Box 170, Dalmatia, PA 17017: Catalog $1 ■ Working replicas of telephones from the 1900s. 800–642–3966.

Markus, P.O. Box 27612, Philadelphia, PA 19118: Free information ■ Replica country phones. 215–675–5870.

Phone Wizard, 10 S. King St., P.O. Box 70, Leesburg, VA 22075: Catalog $3 ■ Restored antique telephones and parts. 703–777–0000.

Phoneco, Inc., 207 E. Mill Rd., P.O. Box 70, Galesville, WI 54630: Free information ■ Restored antique telephones and parts. 608–582–4124.

Sweet Antiques Gallery, P.O. Box 563, Barre, VT 05648: Free brochure ■ Working, antique solid brass telephones, circa 1920. 802–479–3645.

Turtle Lake Telephone Company, P.O. Box 5, Turtle Lake, WI 54889: Catalog $1 ■ Antique hand-crank telephones and parts. 715–986–2233.

Cellular Phones

Alpine Electronics of America, 19145 Gramercy Pl., Torrance, CA 90505: Free information ■ Cellular phones. 213–326–8000.

Antel Corporation, 400 Iser Ave., Hauppage, NY 11788: Free information ■ Mobile cellular phones with conversion kits and antennas. 516–273–6800.

Audiovox, 150 Marcus Blvd., Hauppage, NY 11788: Free information ■ Portable and installation cellular phones. 516–436–6200.

Blaupunkt, Robert Bosch Corporation, 2800 S. 25th Ave., Broadview, IL 60153: Free information ■ Portable and installation cellular phones. 800–866–2022.

Cincinnati Microwave, One Microwave Plaza, Cincinnati, OH 45249: Free information ■ Portable cellular phones. 800–543–1608.

Clarion Corporation of America, 661 W. Redondo Beach Blvd., Gardena, CA 90247: Free information ■ Installation cellular phones. 310–327–9100.

Ericsson GE Mobile Communications, Mountain View Rd., Lynchburg, VA 24502: Free information ■ Cellular phones for most types of installations. 800–CARFONE.

Fujitsu America, Inc., 1100 E. Campbell Rd., Richardson, TX 75081: Free information ■ Installation and portable cellular phones. 214–690–9660.

Kraco, 503 E. Euclid Ave., Compton, CA 90224: Free information ■ Portable cellular phones. 800–421–1910.

Mitsubishi Electronics, 5757 Plaza Dr., Cypress, CA 90630: Free information ■ Portable and installation cellular phones. 714–220–2500.

Mitsubishi International, 1500 Michael Dr., Ste. B, Wood Dale, IL 60191: Free information ■ Portable, and installation cellular phones. 708–860–4200.

Motorola, 1475 W. Shure Dr., Arlington Heights, IL 60004: Free information ■ Portable cellular phones. 708–632–5000.

NEC Home Electronics, 1401 Estes Ave., Elk Grove Village, IL 60007: Free information ■ Portable and installation cellular phones. 708–228–5900.

Nokia-Mobira, 2300 Tall Pines Dr., Ste. 100, Largo, FL 34641: Free information ■ Portable and installation cellular phones. 813–536–5553.

NovAtel, P.O. Box 1233, Fort Worth, TX 76101: Free information ■ Mobile cellular phones. 817–847–2100.

Oki Telecom, 437 Old Peachtree Rd., Suwanee, GA 30174: Free information ■ Portable, briefcase-style, and installation cellular phones. 404–995–9800.

Panasonic, One Panasonic Way, Secaucus, NJ 07094: Free information ■ Portable and installation cellular phones. 201–348–7000.

Radio Shack, Division Tandy Corporation, 1500 One Tandy Center, Fort Worth, TX 76102: Free information ■ Installation and portable cellular phones. 817–390–3700.

Shintom West, 20435 South Western Ave., Torrance, CA 90501: Free information ■ Mobile cellular phones. 310–328–7200.

Shure Brothers, Inc., 222 Hartrey Ave., Evanston, IL 60202: Free information ■ Hands free cellular phones. 800–447–4873.

Technophone Corporation, 1801 Penn St., Ste. 3, Melbourne, FL 32901: Free information ■ Mobile cellular phones. 407–952–2100.

Uniden, 4700 Amon Carter Blvd., Fort Worth, TX 76155: Free information ■ Portable and installation cellular phones. 817–858–3300.

Universal Cellular, Inc., 3365 E. Miraloma Ave., Anaheim, CA 92806: Free information ■ Pocket-size, mobile cellular phones with message storage capability. 714–572–1000.

Phones & Answering Machines

Bernie's Discount Center, Inc., 821 6th Ave., New York, NY 10001: Free information with long SASE ■ Save up to 50 percent on telephones and answering machines, audio and video equipment, large and small kitchen appliances, and personal care appliances. 212–564–8758.

Bi-Rite Photo & Electronics, 15 E. 30th St., New York, NY 10016: Free information ■ Save up to 60 percent on telephones, cameras, typewriters, calculators, video equipment, and other electronics. 800–223–1970; 212–685–2130 (in NY).

Crutchfield, 1 Crutchfield Park, Charlottesville, VA 22906: Free catalog ■ Fax machines, telephones and answering machines, word processors, copiers, and computers and software. 800–336–5566.

East 33rd Street Electronics & Typewriters, 42 E. 33rd St., New York, NY 10016: Free flyer with long SASE ■ Save up to 60 percent on telephones and answering

machines, typewriters, calculators, computers and software, television sets, video equipment, and other electronics. 212–686–0930.

Electronic Wholesalers, 1160 Hamburg Tpk., Wayne, NJ 07470: Free information ■ Telephones, camcorders, television sets, cassette players/recorders, audio/hi-fi receivers, audio cassette decks, compact disk players, and other electronics. 201–696–6531.

J & R Music World, 59–50 Queens-Midtown Expy., Maspeth, NY 11378: Free catalog ■ Telephones, audio equipment, car and portable stereos, video recorders, computers, and other electronics. 800–221–8180.

Olden Video, 1265 Broadway, New York, NY 10001: Free information ■ Telephones, copiers, and photographic equipment. 212–725–1234.

Phone City, 126 E. 57th St., New York, NY 10022: Free information ■ Telephones. 212–644–6300.

Phone Control Systems, 92 Marcus Ave., Hyde Park, NY 11040: Catalog $1 ■ Telephone answering machines. 516–248–3636.

Planet Electronics, 8418 Lilley, Canton, MI 48187: Free information ■ Telephones; audio and video equipment and television sets; car and portable stereos, video players/recorders; and video tapes, cassettes, and disks. 800–222–5650; 313–453–4750 (in MI).

Stereo Equipment Sales, Inc., 6730 Santa Barbara Ct., Baltimore, MD 21227: Free catalog ■ Telephones and telephone answering machines, computers, recording equipment, and other electronics. 800–638–3920.

Teleconcepts, Inc., 36 Holly Dr., Newington, CT 06111: Free information ■ Decor telephones. 800–962–8749; 203–666–5666 (in CT).

Telephone Engineering Company, 786 Main St., Simpson, PA 18407: Free catalog ■ Rotary and push-button phones, parts, mounting equipment, cords, cables, two-line phones, business telephone systems, novelty phones, and sonic alert telephone ring signalers. 717–282–5100.

Video Depot, 1500 N. State St., Bellingham, WA 98225: Free information ■ Telephone and video equipment. 206–671–2500.

TENNIS

Clothing

Adidas USA, 15 Independence Blvd., Warren, NJ 07060: Free information ■ Dresses, sweaters, jackets, caps and sun visors, shirts and tops, shoes and socks, shorts, and warm-up suits. 908–580–0700.

Alchester Mills Company, Inc., 314 S. 11th St., Camden, NJ 08103: Free information ■ Caps and sun visors, gloves, sweatbands, and socks. 609–964–9700.

Asics Tiger Corporation, 10540 Talbert Ave., Fountain Valley, CA 92708: Free information ■ Dresses, jackets, shirts and tops, shoes and socks, and warm-up suits. 714–962–7654.

Ball Hopper Products, Inc., 559 Rodi Rd., Pittsburgh, PA 15235: Free information ■ Caps and sun visors, gloves, dresses, jackets, shirts and tops, socks, sweatbands, underwear, and warm-up suits. 800–323–5417; 412–243–0335 (in PA).

Betlin Manufacturing, 1445 Marion Rd., Columbus, OH 43207: Free information ■ Tennis jackets, shorts, and warm-up suits. 614–443–0248.

Converse, Inc., One Fordham Rd., North Reading, MA 01864: Free information ■ Caps and sun visors, jackets, shirts and tops, socks, sweatbands, and warm-up suits. 800–225–5079; 508–664–1100 (in MA).

Descente America, Inc., Descente, Ltd., 601 Madison Ave., New York, NY 10022: Free information ■ Tennis dresses, jackets, shirts and tops, shoes and socks, and warm-up suits. 800–221–4990; 212–888–7710 (in NY).

Donnay USA, P.O. Box 511, West Lebanon, NH 03784: Free information ■ Caps and sun visors, dresses, jackets, shirts and tops, shoes and socks, and warm-up suits. 800–258–8291; 603–298–8005 (in NH).

Ellesse USA, Inc., 1430 Broadway, New York, NY 10018: Free information ■ Dresses, jackets, caps and sun visors, gloves, shorts, shirts and tops, socks, sweatbands, underwear, and warm-up suits. 212–840–6111.

Fila Sports, Inc., 145 Park Ln., Brisbane, CA 94006: Free information ■ Caps and sun visors, dresses, gloves, dresses, jackets, shirts and tops, shorts, socks, sweatbands, and warm-up suits. 415–468–6800.

FTM Sports, 14500 SW 119th Ave., Miami, FL 33186: Free information ■ Caps and visors, shirts and tops, skirts, and sweaters. 800–292–5589; 305–255–2272 (in FL).

Head Sportswear, 9189 Red Branch Rd., Columbia, MD 21045: Free information ■ Dresses, shirts and tops, shorts, and sweaters. 410–730–8300.

Hill's Court, Winterbrook Corporation, Winterbrook Way, Merideth, NH 03253: Free catalog ■ Clothing for tennis players and other sportswear. 603–279–7051.

Holabird Sports Discounters, 9008 Yellow Brick Rd., Rossville Industrial Park, Baltimore, MD 21237: Free catalog ■ Tennis racquets, shoes, clothes, balls, and bags. 410–687–6400.

K-Swiss, Inc., 12300 Montague St., Pacoima, CA 91331: Free information ■ Caps and visors, shirts and tops, shorts, skirts, and sweaters. 818–897–3433.

Las Vegas Discount Golf & Tennis, 5325 S. Valley View Blvd., Ste. 10, Las Vegas, NV 89109: Free catalog ■ Equipment, shoes, and clothing for tennis, racquetball, golf, and running and jogging. 702–798–7777.

Lily's of Beverly Hills, Ltd., 12905 S. Spring St., Los Angeles, CA 90061: Dresses, jackets, caps and sun visors, shirts and tops, shorts, sweatbands, and warm-up suits. 800–421–4474; 310–770–0303 (in CA).

Moody & Company, Inc., P.O. Box 13, Milford, CT 06460: Free information ■ Caps and sun visors, jackets, gloves, shirts and tops, shorts, socks, sweatbands, sweaters, underwear, and warm-up suits. 800–243–4561; 203–878–1741 (in CT).

National Racquet Sports, Ltd., 115 Court St., Exeter, NH 03833: Free information ■ Caps and sun visors, gloves, socks, sweatbands, sweaters, and warm-up suits. 800–777–4745; 603–778–1997 (in NH).

Nike Footwear, Inc., One Bowerman Dr., Beaverton, OR 97005: Free information ■ Jackets, shirts and tops, shoes and socks, shorts, and sweatbands. 800–344–6453.

A Player, Inc., 38 Old Farm Rd., Roslyn Heights, NY 11577: Free information ■ Dresses, sweaters, jackets, shirts and tops, shoes, and warm-up suits. 516–667–0055.

Prince Manufacturing, Inc., P.O. Box 2031, Princeton, NJ 08540: Free information ■ Caps and sun visors, dresses, jackets, shirts and tops, shoes and socks, sweatbands, underwear, and warm-up suits. 800–2–TENNIS.

Professional Golf & Tennis Suppliers, 7825 Hollywood Blvd., Pembroke Pines, FL 33024: Free information ■ Tennis rackets, clothing, shoes, and racquetball equipment. 305–981–7283.

Puma USA, Inc., 147 Centre St., Brockton, MA 02403: Free information ■ Dresses, jackets, shirts and tops, socks, sweatbands, sweaters, and warm-up suits. 508–583–9100.

Samuels Tennisport, 7796 Montgomery Rd., Cincinnati, OH 45236: Free information ■ Tennis, squash, and racquetball racquets and equipment, and shoes. 800–543–1153; 800–543–1152 (in OH).

Spalding & Brothers, Inc., 425 Meadow St., P.O. Box 901, Chicopee, MA 01021: Free information ■ Caps and sun visors, gloves, dresses, jackets, shirts and tops, shorts, shoes and socks, sweatbands, underwear, and warm-up suits. 413–536–1200.

Sport Casuals, F.T.M. Sports, 14500 SW 119th Ave., Miami, FL 33186: Free catalog ■ Jackets, shirts and tops, shoes and socks, shorts, sweaters, and warm-up suits. 800–292–5589; 305–255–2272 (in FL).

Sporting Life, 1116 S. Powerline Rd., Deerfield Beach, FL 33442: Free catalog ■ Shorts, socks, headbands, wristbands, hats, tennis shoes, boat shoes, beach sandals, sport bags, tennis outfits for men and ladies, sweatshirts, and sweatsuits for tennis and other sports. 800–782–5373.

The Sporting Look, 1116 S. Powerline Rd., Deerfield Beach, FL 33442: Catalog $2 ■ Tennis clothing. 305–570–5385.

Sportline of Hilton Head, Ltd., 816 Friendly Ln., Greensboro, NC 27408: Free information ■ Tennis racquets, shoes, bags, and clothing. 800–438–6021.

Sports Express, P.O. Box 690983, Houston, TX 77269: Free information ■ Tennis racquets, court equipment, grips and wraps, shoes, bags, and clothing. 713–537–8669.

Squash Services, P.O. Box 491, Richboro, PA 18954: Free information with long SASE ■ Shoes, racquets, safety gear, and equipment for tennis, squash, and racquetball. 215–364–4999.

Sullivan Sports, P.O. Box 690906, Houston, TX 77269: Free information ■ Tennis racquets, shoes, bags, and clothing. 800–543–0926.

Tail, Inc., 3300 NW 41st St., Miami, FL 33142: Free information ■ Caps and visors, dresses, shirts and tops, shorts, and underwear. 305–638–2650.

Time Sports, Inc., 5–C S. Gold Dr., Trenton, NJ 08691: Free information ■ Caps and visors, dresses, shirts and tops, shorts, skirts, sweaters, and underwear. 609–587–1875.

Total Sports, 559 Rodi Rd., Pittsburgh, PA 15235: Free catalog ■ Tennis racquet strings, clothing, bags, and court supplies. 800–245–0208.

Equipment

Adidas USA, 15 Independence Blvd., Warren, NJ 07060: Free information ■ Composite graphite tennis racquets. 908–580–0700.

American Playground Corporation, 1801 S. Jackson, P.O. Box 2599, Anderson, IN 46011: Free information ■ Posts, nets, and other court equipment. 800–541–1602.

Associated Tennis Suppliers, 559 Rodi Rd., Pittsburgh, PA 15235: Free information ■ Tennis racquets and supplies and easy-to-use stringing machines. 800–854–7071.

Atlantic Racquet Sports, 18934 Pond Cypress Ct., Jupiter, FL 33458: Free price list ■ Strings and grips. 800–223–1540.

Austad's, 4500 E. 10th St., P.O. Box 1428, Sioux Falls, SD 57196: Free catalog ■ Equipment for tennis and other sports. 800–844–1234.

B & G Wholesale, 47–09 30th St., Long Island City, NY 11101: Free information ■ Tennis balls and aluminum, boron composite, graphite composite, ceramic, graphite, graphite composite, and wooden racquets. 718–706–0100.

Ball Hopper Products, Inc., 559 Rodi Rd., Pittsburgh, PA 15235: Free information ■ Ball retrievers and balls, posts and nets, practice machines; aluminum, boron composite, graphite composite, ceramic, graphite, graphite composite, and wooden racquets; stringing machines; and nylon, gut, and synthetic strings. 800–323–5417; 412–243–0335 (in PA).

Bard Sports Corporation, 14516 SW 119th Ave., Miami, FL 33186: Free information ■ Tennis racquets. 800–433–1022.

Cannon Sports, Inc., P.O. Box 11179, Burbank, CA 91510: Free information ■ Posts, nets, balls, ball retrievers, and other court equipment. 800–223–0064; 818–503–9570 (in CA).

Carron Net Company, P.O. Box 177, Two Rivers, WI 54241: Free information ■ Posts, nets, ball retrievers, practice machines, and other court equipment. 414–793–2217.

Donnay USA, P.O. Box 511, West Lebanon, NH 03784: Free information ■ Aluminum, boron, ceramic graphite, and graphite composite racquets; and nylon and synthetic strings. 800–258–8291; 603–298–8005 (in NH).

Dunlop Stazenger Corporation, P.O. Box 3070, Greenville, SC 29602: Free information ■ Aluminum, boron composite, ceramic, graphite, and graphite composite tennis racquets; and gut, nylon, and synthetic strings. 800–845–8794; 803–271–9767 (in SC).

Easton Aluminum, Inc., 5040 W. Harold Gatly Dr., Salt Lake City, UT 84116: Free information ■ Aluminum, ceramic, graphite, and graphite composite tennis racquets. 801–539–1400.

Edwards Sports Products, Division Brownell & Company, 429 E. Haddam, Moodus, CT 06469: Free information ■ Tennis nets, posts, and other court equipment. 800–243–2512.

Ellipse, 8565 154th Ave. NE, Redmond, WA 98052: Free information ■ Tennis racquets. 206–883–1540.

Estusa/USTech, 17720 NE 65th St., Redmond, WA 98052: Free information ■ Tennis racquets. 206–881–8989.

FEMCO Corporation, 235 Arcadia St., Richmond, VA 23225: Free information ■ Ball retrievers, nets, posts, practice machines, balls, and stringing supplies. 804–276–0011.

Gamma Sports, 559 Rodi Rd., Pittsburgh, PA 15235: Free information ■ Tennis racquets. 800–333–0337.

Guterman International, Inc., 71 Pullman St., Worcester, MA 01608: Free information ■ Portable stringers. 508–852–8206.

Hightower USA, 4691 Eagle Rock Blvd., Los Angeles, CA 90041: Free information ■ Strings, racquets, and shoes. 213–255–7186.

Holabird Sports Discounters, 9008 Yellow Brick Rd., Rossville Industrial Park, Baltimore, MD 21237: Free catalog ■ Tennis racquets, shoes, clothes, balls, bags, and other sports equipment. 410–687–6400.

Jayfro Corporation, Unified Sports, Inc., 976 Hartford Tpk., P.O. Box 400, Waterford, CT 06385: Free catalog ■ Tennis net posts, nets, portable units, windscreens, court dividers, and practice tennis standards. 203–447–3001.

Klipspringer USA, Inc., 780 Church Rd., Elgin, IL 60123: Free brochure ■ Stringing machines, hand tools, and gut strings. 708–742–1300.

L & M Distribution, Inc., 103 Jordan St., San Rafael, CA 94901: Free information ■ Ball retrievers, nets, posts, practice machines, and balls. 415–459–5565.

Las Vegas Discount Golf & Tennis, 5325 S. Valley View Blvd., Ste. 10, Las Vegas, NV 89109: Free catalog ■ Equipment, shoes, and clothing. 702–798–7777.

Leisure Marketing, Inc., 2204 Morris Ave., Ste. 202, Union, NJ 07083: Free information ■ Aluminum, boron composite, ceramic, graphite, and graphite composite tennis racquets. 908–851–9494.

Lob-ster, Inc., 1112 North Ave., Plainfield, NJ 07060: Free brochure ■ Racquets, ball machines, balls, and other equipment. 800–526–4041; 908–668–1900 (in NJ).

Lombard's Sporting Goods, 1840 NE 164th St., North Miami Beach, FL 33162: Catalog $1 ■ Tennis racquets, strings, tennis ball machines, shoes, and bags. 305–944–1166.

Matchmate, 1515 W. MacArthur, Costa Mesa, CA 92626: Free information ■ Tennis racquets. 800–854–7331.

Midwest Sports Supply, 8740 Montgomery Rd., Cincinnati, OH 45236: Free information ■ Tennis racquets, shoes for men and women, tennis bags, and strings. 800–334–4580.

Nassau Tennis, 33 Pond Rd., Gloucester, MA 01930: Free information ■ Tennis racquets. 800–255–7812.

Nevada Bob's Discount Golf & Tennis, 3333 E. Flamingo Rd., Las Vegas, NV 89121: Free catalog ■ Golf and tennis supplies and equipment. 702–451–3333.

NRC Sports, P.O. Box 331, West Boylston, MA 01583: Free information ■ Portable stringers and natural gut, synthetic, and nylon strings. 800–243–5033; 508–852–8987 (in MA).

Olympia Sports, School Tech, Inc., 745 State Circle, Ann Arbor, MI 48108–1647: Free information ■ Nets, posts, and balls. 313–761–5135.

Pennsylvania Sporting Goods, 1360 Industrial Hwy., P.O. Box 451, Southampton, PA 18966: Free information ■ Balls, ball retrievers, posts and nets, practice machines, aluminum tennis racquets, stringing machines, and nylon and synthetic strings. 800–523–1122.

Powers Court, 40 S. Main St., New City, NY 10956: Free catalog ■ Racquet stringers, strings, and other equipment. 800–431–2838; 914–634–6969 (in NY).

Prince Manufacturing, Inc., P.O. Box 2031, Princeton, NJ 08540: Free information ■ Aluminum, boron composite, ceramic, graphite, graphite composite, and wooden tennis racquets; stringing machines; and nylon and synthetic strings. 800–2–TENNIS.

Professional Golf & Tennis Suppliers, 7825 Hollywood Blvd., Pembroke Pines, FL 33024: Free information with long SASE ■ Tennis rackets, clothing and shoes, and racquetball equipment. 305–981–7283.

Pro-Kennex, 9606 Kearny Villa Rd., San Diego, CA 92126: Free information ■ Tennis racquets. 800–854–1980; 800–662–8663 (in CA).

Rackets International, 24572 La Cienega Blvd., Laguna Hills, CA 92653: Free information ■ Aluminum, boron composite, graphite composite, and wooden tennis rackets; and gut and nylon replacement strings. 714–831–8913.

Rossignol Tennis, 115 Court St., Exeter, NH 93833: Free information ■ Tennis racquets. 800–777–4745.

Samuels Tennisport, 7796 Montgomery Rd., Cincinnati, OH 45236: Free information ■ Tennis, squash, and racquetball racquets and equipment, and shoes. 800–543–1153; 800–543–1152 (in OH).

Sentra Tennis, P.O. Box 348485, Chicago, IL 60634: Free information ■ Tennis racquets. 800–524–9992.

Spalding & Brothers, Inc., 425 Meadow St., P.O. Box 901, Chicopee, MA 01021: Free information ■ Tennis balls; aluminum, boron composite, graphite, and graphite composite tennis racquets; and nylon, synthetic, and gut strings. 413–536–1200.

Sport Casuals, F.T.M. Sports, 14500 SW 119th Ct., Miami, FL 33186: Free information ■ Boron composite, ceramic, graphite, and graphite composite tennis racquets. 800–292–5589; 305–255–2272 (in FL).

Sportline of Hilton Head, Ltd., 816 Friendly Ln., Greensboro, NC 27408: Free information ■ Tennis racquets, shoes, bags, and clothing. 800–438–6021.

Sports Express, P.O. Box 690983, Houston, TX 77269: Free information ■ Tennis racquets, court equipment, grips and wraps, shoes, bags, and clothing. 713–537–8669.

Squash Services, P.O. Box 491, Richboro, PA 18954: Free information with long SASE ■ Tennis, squash, and racquetball equipment. 215–364–4999.

Sullivan Sports, P.O. Box 690906, Houston, TX 77269: Free information ■ Tennis racquets, court and training equipment, strings, grips and wraps, shoes and clothing for men and women, and tennis bags. 800–543–0926.

Tennis Company, 30610 Southfield Rd., Southfield, MI 48076: Free information ■ Tennis equipment. 313–258–9366.

Tennis Gear & Running Center, 137 Baltimore St., Cumberland, MD 21502: Free price list ■ Tennis equipment. 800–638–3578; 410–722–6252 (in MD).

Total Sports, 559 Rodi Rd., Pittsburgh, PA 15235: Free catalog ■ Tennis racquet strings, clothing, bags, and court supplies. 800–245–0208.

Tristar Sports, Inc., 475 Smith St., Middletown, CT 06457: Free information ■ Aluminum, boron composite, ceramic, and graphite composite tennis racquets and gut, nylon, and synthetic strings. 800–624–7827; 203–632–2000 (in CT).

U.S. Sports Equipment Company, 1515 W. MacArthur Blvd., Costa Mesa, CA 92626: Free information ■ Posts, nets, ball retrievers, balls, and practice machines;

stringing machines; synthetic and nylon strings; and boron composite, ceramic, graphite, and graphite composite tennis racquets. 800–854–7331; 714–549–4725 (in CA).

Wa-Mac, Inc., Highskore Products, Inc., 178 Commerce Rd., P.O. Box 128, Carlstadt, NJ 07072: Free information ■ Tennis balls and aluminum, boron composite, ceramic, graphite, graphite composite, and wooden tennis racquets. 800–447–5673; 201–438–7200 (in NJ).

Wild World of Sporting Goods, 220 S. University Dr., Plantation, FL 33324: Free price list ■ Tennis, racquetball, and squash racquets. 305–475–9800.

Wilson Sporting Goods, 2233 West St., River Grove, IL 60171: Free information ■ Aluminum, boron composite, ceramic, graphite, graphite composite, and wooden tennis racquets; nylon, gut and synthetic strings; stringing machines; balls; and nets. 800–323–1552.

Winston Sports Corporation, 200 5th Ave., New York, NY 10010: Free information ■ Aluminum, boron composite, ceramic, graphite, graphite composite, and wooden tennis racquets. 212–255–6870.

Yamaha Sporting Goods Division, 6600 Orangethorpe Ave., Buena Park, CA 90620: Free information ■ Boron composite, ceramic, graphite and graphite composite tennis racquets; and nylon and synthetic strings. 800–851–6514; 714–522–9011 (in CA).

TERM PAPERS

Academic Research, Inc., 240 Park Ave., Rutherford, NJ 02070: Free catalog ■ Over 20,000 reports and term papers. 800–47RESEARCH.

Author's Research Services, Inc., 407 S. Dearborn, Chicago, IL 60605: Catalog $2 ■ Research papers and custom writing services. 800–776–7273.

Research Assistance, 11322 Idaho Ave., Los Angeles, CA 90025: Catalog $2 ■ Over 10,000 term papers. 800–351–0222; 310–477–8226 (in CA).

TETHERBALL

American Playground Corporation, 1801 S. Jackson, P.O. Box 2599, Anderson, IN

46011: Free information ■ Balls, poles, and posts. 800–541–1602.

Franklin Sports Industries, Inc., 17 Campanelli Parkway, P.O. Box 508, Stoughton, MA 02072: Free information ■ Balls and sets. 617–344–1111.

General Sportcraft Company, Ltd., 140 Woodbine St., Bergenfield, NJ 07621: Free information ■ Balls, poles, posts, and sets. 201–384–4242.

Dick Martin Sports, Inc., 201 River Rd., P.O. Box 931, Clifton, NJ 07014: Free information ■ Balls, poles, posts, and sets. 800–221–1993; 201–473–0757 (in NJ).

Pennsylvania Sporting Goods, 1360 Industrial Highway, P.O. Box 451, Southampton, PA 18966: Free information ■ Balls, poles, posts, and sets. 800–535–1122.

Venus Knitting Mills, Inc., 140 Spring St., Murray Hill, NJ 07974: Free information ■ Balls, paddles, poles, posts, and sets. 800–955–4200; 908–464–2400 (in NJ).

THEATRICAL SUPPLIES
Make-Up

Abracadabra Magic Shop, P.O. Box 714, Middlesex, NJ 08846: Catalog $3.95 ■ Magician's supplies, clown supplies, costumes, and theatrical make-up. 908–805–0200.

Chicago Hair Goods Company, 428 S. Wabash Ave., Chicago, IL 60605: Free catalog ■ Wigs and make-up. 312–427–8600.

Eastern Costume Company, 510 N. Elm St., Greensboro, NC 27401: Free information ■ Make-up and costumes. 919–379–1026.

The Entertainers Supermarket, 21 Carol Pl., Staten Island, NY 10303: Free brochure ■ Supplies and props for face painters, clowns, magicians, balloon sculpturists, jugglers, stilt walkers, and other entertainers. 718–494–6232.

Freckles Clown Supplies, 4231 Timuquana Rd., Jacksonville, FL 32210: Catalog $5 ■ Make-up, costumes, clown supplies, puppets, how-to books on clowning and ballooning, and other theatrical supplies. 904–778–3977.

House of Costumes, 166 Jericho Tpk., Mineola, NY 11501: Free information ■ Cos-

tumes, make-up, hair goods, and novelties. 516–294–0170.

Bob Kelly Cosmetics, Inc., 151 W. 46th St., New York, NY 10036: Free brochure ■ Make-up kits. 212–819–0030.

Lynch's Clown Supplies, 939 Howard, Dearborn, MI 48124: Catalog $5 (refundable) ■ Make-up, costume accessories and trims, and clown equipment. 313–565–3425.

Mecca Magic, Inc., 49 Dodd St., Bloomfield, NJ 07003: Free brochure ■ Make-up, costumes and wigs, puppets, props, magic tricks, and juggling supplies. 201–429–7597.

Novelties Unlimited, 410 W. 21st St., Norfolk, VA 23517: Free list ■ Make-up; clown supplies, props, and gags; magic; balloons; party decorations; and other supplies. 804–622–0344.

Ben Nye Makeup, 5935 Bowcroft St., Los Angeles, CA 90016: Free catalog ■ Clown make-up. 310–839–1984.

Patsy & Blimpo, P.O. Box 2075, Huntington Beach, CA 92647: Free catalog ■ Clown make-up, wigs, and supplies. 714–897–0749.

Prolook, 489 SR 436, Ste. 109, Casselberry, FL 32707: Free information ■ Make-up kits. 407–645–2434.

Rubie's Costume Company, 120–08 Jamaica Ave., Richmond Hill, Queens, NY 11418: Free information ■ Costumes, make-up, hair goods, and special effects supplies. 718–846–1008.

Theatrical Lighting Systems, Inc., 909 Meridian St., P.O. Box 2646, Huntsville, AL 35804: Free information ■ Make-up, dimming and lighting control systems, follow spots, and other stage equipment. 205–533–7025.

Under the Big Top, P.O. Box 807, Placentia, CA 92670: Catalog $4 ■ Costumes, clown props, make-up, juggling supplies, and party supplies. 714–579–1144.

Up, Up & Away, P.O. Box 147, Beallsville, PA 15313: Free price information ■ Make-up, props, and clown equipment. 412–769–5447.

Plays

Empire Publishing Service, 7645 Le Berthon St., Tujunga, CA 91042: Free catalog ■ Entertainment industry and performing art

books, plays and musicals, musical scores, books about film and theatrical personalities, and music books. 818–784–8918.

Encore Performance Publishing, P.O. Box 692, Orem, UT 84057: Free information ■ Plays, musicals, and books on the theater and stage for children, professionals, and amateurs. 801–225–0605.

Samuel French Catalog, 45 W. 25th St., New York, NY 10010: Catalog and supplement $2.75 ■ Scripts for plays and other theatrical productions. 800–PLAY–PUB; 212–206–8990 (in NY).

Samuel French Trade, 7623 Sunset Blvd., Hollywood, CA 90046: Free catalog ■ Over 2500 plays. Includes classics made into movies. 213–876–0570.

Stage Equipment

Alcone Company, Inc., Paramount Theatrical Supplies, 5–49 49th Ave., Long Island City, NY 11101: Catalog $2.50 ■ Fabrics, make-up, hardware and rigging, lighting equipment, paint and scenery supplies, and other theatrical equipment. 718–361–8373.

Altman Stage Lighting Company, 57 Alexander St., Yonkers, NY 10701: Free information ■ Stage lighting equipment. 914–476–7987.

Avolites USA, Inc., 2385 Beryllium Rd., Scotch Plains, NJ 07076: Free information ■ Digital lighting controls. 908–654–7000.

Bandit Lites, 10624 Dutchtown Rd., Knoxville, TN 37932: Free information ■ Spots, beams, softs, commanders, color faders and rangers, and other lighting equipment. 615–675–0880.

BMI Supply, 28 Logan Ave., Glens Falls, NY 12801: Free information ■ Theatrical supplies and equipment. 800–836–0524; 518–793–6706 (in NY).

Bulbman, P.O. Box 2918, Reno, NV 89505: Free information ■ Replacement bulbs for theatrical lighting equipment. 800–648–1163.

Dazian's, Inc., 2014 Commerce St., Dallas, TX 75201: Free catalog ■ Costume farics and flame proof fabrics that include scenery canvas, ducks, theatrical gauze, muslin, duvetyne, babinettes, metallics, velours, scrims, and felt. 214–748–3450.

FM Productions, 3775 Bayshore Blvd., Brisbane, CA 94005: Free product and supplier list ■ Lighting instruments, control and dimming systems, special effects equipment, truss and hardware, and color media. 415–468–6500.

Four Star Lighting, Inc., 603 Commerce Way West, Jupiter, FL 33458: Free information ■ Scenic drapes and lighting equipment. 407–743–7367.

Gothic Scenic & Theatrical Paints, L.I. Paint Company, Box 189, Continental Hill, Glen Cove, NY 11542: Free information ■ Scenic and theatrical paints, brushes, and other supplies. 516–676–6600.

The Great American Market, 826 N. Cole Ave., Hollywood, CA 90038: Free information ■ Stage lighting equipment. 213–461–0200.

Jupiter Scenic, Inc., 603 Commerce Way West, Jupiter, FL 33458: Free information ■ Scenery drapes and lighting equipment. 407–743–7367.

Kee Industrial Products, Inc., P.O. Box 207, Buffalo, NY 14225: Free information ■ Hardware for stage platforms, multi-level sets, and backgrounds. 716–896–4900.

Kliegl Bros., 5 Aerial Way, Syosset, NY 11791: Free information ■ Computer lighting control systems. 516–937–3900.

Peavey Electronics Corporation, 711 A St., P.O. Box 2898, Meridian, MS 39302: Free information ■ Lighting equipment. 601–483–5365.

Rose Brand Fabrics, 517 W. 35th St., New York, NY 10001: Free catalog ■ Theatrical fabrics. 800–223–1624; 212–594–7424 (in NY).

Sitler's Supplies, Inc., 702 E. Washington, P.O. Box 10, Washington, IA 52353: Free information ■ Over 500 types of stage, studio, and projector lamps. 800–426–3938.

StageRight Corporation, 495 Holley Dr., Clare, MI 48617: Free information ■ Portable units and extensions for stage assemblies. 800–438–4499.

Syracuse Scenery & Stage Lighting Company, Inc., 1423 N. Salina St., Syracuse, NY 13208: Free information ■ Stage curtains, scrims, drops, borders, legs, and travelers. 315–474–2474.

Theater Magic, 6099 Godown Rd., Columbus, OH 43220: Free information ■ Special effects lighting equipment. 614–459–3222.

Theatrical Lighting Systems, Inc., 511 Church St., P.O. Box 734, Huntsville, AL 35804: Free information ■ Dimming and lighting control systems, follow spots, other lighting equipment, and make-up. 205–533–7025.

Tobins Lake Studios, 7030 Old US 23, Brighton, MI 48116: Free catalog ■ Drapes, drops, lighting equipment, and scenery paint. 313–229–6666.

Universal Manufacturing Company, 12357 E. 8 Mile Rd., Warren, MI 48089: Free information ■ Lightweight aluminum universal lighting trusses for indoors and outdoors. 313–774–4140.

Thomas J. Valentino, Inc., 151 W. 46th St., New York, NY 10036: Free catalog ■ Easy-to-use sound effects on long-playing records. 212–869–5210.

THIMBLES

Button Creations, 3801 Stump Rd., Doylestown, PA 18901: Catalog $2 ■ Buttons and thimbles in wood, mother-of-pearl, abalone, hand-painted porcelain, leather, military, pewter, and cloisonne. 800–346–0223.

Gimbel & Sons Country Store, 36 Commercial St., P.O. Box 57, Boothbay Harbor, ME 04538: Free catalog ■ Thimbles, other collectibles, and gifts. 207–633–5088.

TICKETS

All Points Tag & Ticket Company, 1330 Lloyd Rd., Wickliffe, OH 44092: Free price list ■ Raffle tickets. 800–342–2102.

Monarch Graphics, Inc., 1965 Islip Ave., Central Islip, NY 11722: Free catalog ■ Chance books and tickets. 516–232–1300.

LMN Printing, 771 W. Merrick Rd., Valley Stream, NY 11580: Free brochure ■ Chance books. 800–654–6848.

Quick Tickets, 3030 W. Pasadena, Flint, MI 48504: Free information ■ Custom tickets. 800–521–1142; 313–732–0770 (in MI).

Wholesale Ticket Company, Inc., 41 N. Parsonage St., P.O. Box 33, Saranac, MI 48881: Free information ■ Tickets and tags. 616–642–6146.

TOBACCO, PIPES & CIGARS

John Crouch Tobacconist, 128 King St., Alexandria, VA 22314: Free brochure ■ Custom-blended pipe tobaccos, cigars, pipes, and gifts. 703–548–2900.

Davidoff of Geneva, Inc., 535 Madison Ave., New York, NY 10022: Free information ■ Cigars. 800–548–4623; 212–751–9060 (in NY).

David P. Ehrlich Company, 32 Tremont St., Boston, MA 02108: Free price list ■ Cavendish and Danish blends, non-aromatic English tobaccos, American blends, and bulk tobaccos for custom blending. 617–227–1720.

Famous Smoke Shop, Inc., 55 W. 39th St., New York, NY 10018: Free catalog ■ Pipe tobaccos and premium hand-rolled and generic cigars. 800–672–5544.

Wally Frank, Ltd., 63–25 69th St., Middle Village, NY 11379: Free catalog ■ Popular and private label cigars and tobaccos, pipes, pipe tools, lighters, humidors, pouches, and pipe racks. 718–326–2233.

Georgetown Tobacco, 3144 M St. NW, Washington, DC 20007: Catalog $1 ■ Private custom blends of tobacco, pipes, imported and domestic cigars, smoking accessories, lighters, and gifts. 202–338–5100.

J-R Tobacco, 277 Rt. 46 West, Fairfield, NJ 07006: Free catalog ■ Imported cigars and pipe tobaccos. 800–JRC–IGAR; 201–882–0050 (in NJ).

Kirsten Pipe Company, P.O. Box 70526, Seattle, WA 98107: Free brochure ■ Pipes; replacement mouthpieces, valves, and bowls; pipe tools; and tobaccos. 206–783–0700.

Marks Cigars, 8th & Central Ave., Ocean City, NJ 08226: Free brochure ■ Cigars handcrafted with aged Jamaican tobaccos individually blended with Dominican long-filler leaf, rolled with clear Cuban seed and Mexican natural leaf binder, and finished with a shade-grown Connecticut wrapper. 800–257–8645.

Nat Sherman Company, 711 5th Ave., New York, NY 10022: Free catalog ■ Cigars, pipes, domestic and imported cigarettes, tobaccos, and gifts. 800–257–7850.

Fred Stoker & Sons, Inc., P.O. Box 707, Dresden, TN 38225: Catalog $1 ■ Supplies for smokers, chewing tobaccos, and gifts. 800–243–9377; 901–364–5419 (in TN).

Thompson Cigar Company, 5401 Hangar Ct., Tampa, FL 33634: Free catalog ■ Cigars, pipes, tobaccos, and smoker's accessories. 800–237–2559; 800–282–0646 (in FL).

TOLE & DECORATIVE PAINTING

Accent Products Division, Borden, Inc., 300 E. Main St., Lake Zurich, IL 60047: Free information ■ Paints for decorative painting, home decor, and other crafts. 800–323–0079.

Allen's Woodcrafts, 3020 Dogwood Ln., Sapalpa, OK 74066: Free information ■ Unfinished wood items for tole and decorative painting. 918–224–8796.

Artfare, 469 Country Club Dr., Longwood, FL 32750: Free information ■ Natural color, heavy-weight cotton items for decorative painting. 407–834–1184.

Bentwood, Inc., P.O. Box 1676, Thomasville, GA 31792: Free information ■ Hardwood products for tole and decorative painting. 912–226–1223.

Stan Brown's Arts & Crafts, Inc., 13435 NE Whitaker Way, Portland, OR 97230: Catalog $3.50 ■ Tole and decorative painting supplies and how-to books. 503–257–0559.

Cabin Craft, 2059 Atlanta Ave., Riverside, CA 92507: Catalog $3 ■ Unfinished wooden furniture, gifts, cutouts, how-to books, paints, brushes, and other tole and decorative painting supplies. 714–684–2827.

Cabin Craft Midwest, 1225 W. 1st St., P.O. Box 270, Nevada, IA 50201: Catalog $5 ■ Tole and decorative painting supplies. 800–247–3920; 800–382–8653 (in IA).

Cabin Craft Southwest, Inc., 1500 Westpark Way, Euless, TX 76040: Catalog $5 ■ Tole and decorative painting supplies. 817–571–3837.

Capri Arts & Crafts, 864 S. McGlincey Ln., Campbell, CA 95008: Free book list with long SASE ■ Books on decorative and fabric painting. 408–377–3833.

Chatham Art Distributors, 11 Brookside Ave., Chatham, NY 12037: Catalog $3 (refundable) ■ Acrylics, brushes, canvasses, oils, milk paint, tin supplies, books, and wooden items for decorating. 800–822–4747; 518–392–6300 (in NY).

Char-Lee Originals, P.O. Box 606, Somonauk, IL 60552: Catalog $5 ■ Unpainted resin figures and other ready-to-finish items.

Cupboard Distributing, Box 148, Urbana, OH 43078: Catalog $2 ■ Unfinished wood parts for tole and decorative painting, crafts, miniatures, toys, jewelry-making, and woodworking.

Dexter Tole House Distributor, 226 Spring St., Dexter, ME 04930: Catalog $3 (refundable) ■ Tole and decorative painting supplies. 207–924–3603.

Dillon's Decorative Designs, P.O. Box 2478, Newport News, VA 23609: Brochure $1 ■ Patterns packets for painting on wood.

Factory 2U, Inc., Box 250, Glenmont, NY 12077: Catalog $2 (refundable) ■ Cutouts, plaques, and ready-to-decorate items.

Heritage Craft Folk Art Studio, 520 Westnery Rd. South, Ste. 23, Ajax, Ontario, Canada L1S 6W6: Catalog $3 ■ Folk art, tole, and decorative painting supplies. 800–263–3161.

Hofcraft, P.O. Box 1791, Grand Rapids, MI 49501: Catalog $3 ■ Save up to 40 percent on how-to books and supplies for tole and decorative painting. 800–828–0359.

Hollins Enterprises, Inc., P.O. Box 148, Alpha, OH 45301: Catalog $3 ■ Tole and decorative painting supplies. 800–543–3465.

Jadvick Enterprises, Inc., 6576 Interstate 85 Ct., Norcross, GA 30093: Free information ■ Undecorated Oriental porcelain bisque.

Kerry Specialties, P.O. Box 5129, Deltona, FL 32728: Free information ■ Brushes for tole and decorative painting. 407–574–6209.

Larson Wood Manufacturing, P.O. Box 672, Park Rapids, MN 56407: Catalog $2 ■ Country-style mini cutouts, sanded smooth, and ready for decorative finishing; kits and parts; and hardware and supplies for making toys. 218–732–9121.

Liberty Design Company, Province Rd., Barrington, NH 03825: Catalog $1 ■ Sten-

cils, stencil supplies, and paints. 603–664–2705.

Ozark Art and Craft, 310 S. Ingraham Mill Rd., Springfield, MO 65802: Free catalog ■ Tole and decorative painting supplies. 417–869–8084.

Plaid Enterprises, Box 7600, Norcross, GA 30091: Free information ■ Acrylic paints and other supplies.

Robinson's Woods, 1057 Trumbull Ave., Girard, OH 44420: Catalog $3 ■ Paints, brushes, books, and wood products for tole and decorative painting. 216–759–3843.

Sandeen's, 1315 White Bear Ave., St. Paul, MN 55106: Catalog $2 (refundable) ■ Supplies for folk art crafting, rosemaling, dalmalning, and bauernmalere. Also (separate catalogs, $3 each) supplies for Norwegian stitchery, Danish cross stitching, and Swedish stitchery. 800–235–1315.

Tole Americana, Inc., 5750 NE Hassalo, Portland, OR 97220: Free information ■ Brushes, oils, acrylics and fabric paints, sealers, mediums, varnishes, unfinished wooden products, and books. 800–547–8854; 800–452–8663 (in OR).

Traditional Norwegian Rosemaking, Pat Virch, 1506 Lynn Ave., Marquette, MI 49855: Free catalog ■ Patterns, books, paints, woodenware, tinware, and other supplies for wood and tin decorators. 906–226–3931.

Unfinished Business, P.O. Box 246, Wingate, NC 28174: Catalog $3 ■ Unpainted resin figures and other ready-to-finish items.

Weston Bowl Mill, P.O. Box 218, Weston, VT 05161: Free catalog ■ Woodenware for tole and decorative painting. 800–824–6219.

TOOLS

Clamps

Addkison Hardware Company, Inc., 126 E. Amite St., P.O. Box 102, Jackson, MS 39205: Free information ■ Power-operated arm saws, other power tools, and clamps. 800–821–2750; 800–321–8107 (in MS).

Adjustable Clamp Company, 431 N. Ashland Ave., Chicago, IL 60622: Catalog $1 ■ Clamps and work-holding equipment. 312–666–0640.

Advanced Machinery Imports, P.O. Box 312, New Castle, DE 19720: Free information ■ Workshop clamps. 800–648–4264; 302–322–2226 (in DE).

American Clamping Corporation, 50 Franklin St., P.O. Box 399, Batavia, NY 14021: Free information ■ Woodworking clamps. 800–928–1004; 716–344–1160 (in NY).

American Tool Companies, Inc., P.O. Box 337, DeWitt, NE 68341: Free information ■ Workshop clamps. 402–683–2315.

Hartford Clamp Company, 466 Park Ave., P.O. Box 280131, East Hartford, CT 06128: Free information ■ Clamps for most workshop needs. 203–528–1708.

Inlet, Inc., One Saunders Ave., San Anselmo, CA 94960: Free information ■ Clamps for most workshop needs. 800–786–5665.

Universal Clamp Corporation, 15200 Stagg St., Van Nuys, CA 91405: Free information ■ Lightweight clamps. 818–780–1015.

Wetzler Clamp Company, Inc., Rt. 611, P.O. Box 175, Mt. Bethel, PA 18343: Free catalog ■ Workshop clamps. 717–897–7101.

Hand & Power Tools

Abbey Machinery, 616 N. Brookhurst St., Anaheim, CA 92801: Free information ■ Power tools. 800–225–6321; 800–252–2221 (in CA).

Acme Electric Tools, Box 1716, Grand Forks, ND 58206: Catalog $3 ■ Power tools. 800–582–6704.

Addkison Hardware Company, Inc., 126 E. Amite St., P.O. Box 102, Jackson, MS 39205: Free information ■ Power-operated arm saws, other power tools, and clamps. 800–821–2750; 800–321–8107 (in MS).

AEG Power Tool Corporation, 3 Shaw's Cove, P.O. Box 6003, New London, CT 06320: Free information ■ Woodworking power tools. 800–243–0870; 203–447–4600 (in CT).

Alley Supply Company, P.O. Box 848, Gardnerville, NV 89410: Catalog $2 ■ Precision lathes, milling machines, tools and cutter grinders, and other metal-working tools. 800–338–3326; 702–782–3800 (in NV).

American Machine & Tool Company, 4th Ave. & Spring, Royersford, PA 19468: Free

information ■ Woodworking power tools. 215–948–0400.

Bailey's Tools & Supplies, P.O. Box 550, Laytonville, CA 95454: Catalog $2 ■ Chain saws, bars, files, protective gear, forestry supplies, log splitters, books, and gifts. 707–984–6133.

Better Built Corporation, 845 Woburn St., Wilmington, MA 01887: Free brochure ■ One-man portable sawmills. 508–657–5636.

Black & Decker, P.O. Box 857, Hampstend, MD 21074: Free information ■ Woodworking power tools. 410–239–5300.

Blue Ridge Machinery & Tools, Inc., P.O. Box 536, Hurricane, WV 25526: Catalog $1 ■ Lathes, milling machines, and supplies. 304–562–3538.

Blume Supply, Inc., 3316 South Blvd., Charlotte, NC 28209: Free information ■ Woodworking power tools. 800–288–9200; 704–523–7811 (in NC).

Bosch Power Tool Corporation, 100 Bosch Blvd., New Bern, NC 28562: Free information ■ Woodworking power tools. 800–334–5730.

Bridge City Tool Works, 1104 NE 28th Ave., Portland, OR 97232: Free catalog ■ Professional hand tools.

Brookstone Company, 5 Vose Farm Rd., P.O. Box 5, Peterborough, NH 03458: Free catalog ■ Hand tools. 800–846–3000.

Cascade Tools, Inc., P.O. Box 3110, Bellingham, WA 98227: Free catalog ■ Carbide-tipped router bits and shaper cutters. 800–235–0272.

Clayton Machine Corporation, P.O. Box 513, Clawson, MI 48017: Free information ■ Oscillating spindle sanders. 313–548–2380.

Colwood Electronics, P.O. Box 940, Eatontown, NJ 07724: Free information ■ All-in-one work station that includes a woodburning and texturizing system and high speed grinding equipment. 908–544–1119.

Conestoga Wood Machinery, 987 Valley View Rd., New Holland, PA 17557: Free information ■ Woodworking power tools. 800–445–4669.

Conover Workshops, 18121 Madison Rd., Parkman, OH 44080: Free information ■ Woodworking tools. 216–548–3491.

Constantine, 2050 Eastchester Rd., Bronx, NY 10461: Catalog $1 ■ Cabinet and furniture wood and veneers, hardware, how-to books, and carving tools and chisels. 212–792–1600.

CraftWoods, 2101 Greenspring Dr., Timonium, MD 21093: Free information ■ Woodworking, woodcarving, and power tools, and kiln-dried domestic and exotic woods. 410–561–9444.

Delta International Machinery Corporation, 4290 E. Rains Rd., Memphis, TN 38118: Free information ■ Woodworking power tools. 800–438–2486; 901–363–8800 (in TN).

Dremel Manufacturing Company, 4915 21st St., Racine, WI 53406: Free information ■ Hand power tools for modelers and home craftsmen. 414–554–1390.

Eagle America, 124 Parker Ct., P.O. Box 1099, Chardon, OH 44024: Free catalog ■ Router bits and shaper cutters. 800–872–2511.

EMCO-Maier Corporation, 4757 Scioto Pkwy., Columbus, OH 43221: Free catalog ■ Woodworking power tools. 800–521–8289.

P.C. English, Inc., P.O. Box 380, Thornburg, VA 22565: Free catalog ■ Tools, cutouts, patterns, paints, woods for carving, and supplies for decoy-making and woodcarving. 800–221–9474; 703–582–2200 (in VA).

Excalibur Machine & Tool Company, 29 Passmore Ave., Unit 6, Scarborough, Ontario, Canada M1V 3H5: Free information ■ Woodworking power tools. 800–387–9789.

Farris Machinery, 309 N. 10th, Blue Springs, MO 64015: Free information ■ Space-saving combination of power tools that plane, mold, and mortise. 800–872–5489; 816–229–3055 (in MO).

The Fine Tool Shops, 170 West Rd., P.O. Box 7091, Portsmouth, NH 03801: Free catalog ■ Professional hand tools.

Foley-Belsaw Company, Box 419593, Kansas City, MO 64120: Free booklet ■ Woodworking power tools. 800–328–7140.

Force Machinery Company, 914 E. Main St., Norristown, PA 19401: Free information ■ Woodworking supplies, tools and equipment. 215–279–0950.

Freud Power Tools, 218 Feld Ave., High Point, NC 27264: Free information ■ Woodworking power tools. 800–472–7307.

Frog Tool Company, 700 W. Jackson Blvd., Chicago, IL 60606: Free catalog ■ Woodworking hand tools and books. 312–648–1270.

General Tools Manufacturing Company, 80 White St., New York, NY 10013: Free information ■ Hand tools, other workshop equipment, and measuring and calibrating tools and jigs. 212–431–6100.

Grizzly Imports, Inc., P.O. Box 2069, Bellingham, WA 98227: Free information ■ Woodworking power tools. 800–541–5537 (west of the Mississippi).

Grizzly Imports, Inc., 2406 Reach Rd., Williamsport, PA 17701: Free information ■ Woodworking power tools. 800–523–4777 (east of the Mississippi).

Gulf Central Tools, 2102 Gulf Central Dr., Houston, TX 77023: Free information ■ Woodworking power tools. 800–275–6565; 713–921–0270 (in TX).

Hida Japanese Tool, Inc., 1333 San Pablo Ave., Berkeley, CA 94702: Free information ■ Hand-forged tools for delicate work. 800–443–5512.

Highland Hardware, 1045 N. Highland Ave. NE, Atlanta, GA 30306: Free information ■ Tools for home craftsmen. 404–872–4466.

Hiller Hardware, P.O. Box 1762, Columbia, SC 29202: Catalog $1 ■ Woodworking hand and power tools. 803–779–3131.

Hitachi Power Tools, 3890 Steve Reynolds Blvd., Norcross, GA 30093: Free information ■ Woodworking power tools. 404–279–5600.

Hobby Products Company, 2757 Scioto Pkwy., Columbus, OH 43206: Free catalog ■ Small lathes for metal, wood or plastics; milling machines; saws; and hand and power woodworking tools. 614–771–5996.

Home Lumber Company, 449 Whitewater St., Whitewater, WI 53190: Free information ■ Portable power tools. 800–262–5482.

HTC Products, 120 E. Hudson, P.O. Box 839, Royal Oak, MI 48068: Free catalog ■ Mobile machine bases to put workshops on wheels. 800–624–2027.

International Tool Corporation, 1939 Tyler St., Hollywood, FL 33020: Free information ■ Power tools. 800–338–3384.

Jamestown Distributors, 28 Narragansett Ave., P.O. Box 348, Jamestown, RI 02835: Free information ■ Workshop tools. 800–423–0030; 401–423–2520 (in RI).

The Japan Woodworker, 1731 Clement Ave., Alameda, CA 94501: Catalog and supplements $1.50 ■ Japanese hand tools for craftsmen, carpenters, cabinet makers, and woodcarvers. 800–537–7820; 510–521–1810 (in CA).

W.S. Jenks & Son, 1933 Montana Ave. NE, Washington, DC 20002: Free catalog ■ Hand and power tools. 800–638–6405; 202–529–6020 (in DC).

Jensen Tools, Inc., 7815 S. 46th St., Phoenix, AZ 85044: Free catalog ■ Tools, tool kits, and cases. 602–968–6231.

JET Equipment & Tools, P.O. Box 1477, Tacoma, WA 98401: Free information ■ Woodworking power tools. 206–572–5000.

Kasco Woodworking Company, Inc., 170 W. 600 N., Shelbyville, IN 46176: Free information ■ Portable band saw mills. 317–398–7973.

Bob Kaune, 511 W. 11th, Port Angeles, WA 98362: Price list $2.50 ■ Antique and used hand tools for collectors and woodworkers. 206–452–2292.

Kimball Sign Company, 2602 Whitaker St., Savannah, GA 31401: Information packet $1 ■ Woodcarving machines for sign-making and other crafts. 912–232–6561.

Kitts Industrial Tools, 22384 Grand River Ave., Detroit, MI 48219: Free catalog ■ Precision metalworking tools and supplies. 800–521–6579; 313–538–2585 (in MI).

Klein Design, Inc., 6514 115th Pl. SE, Renton, WA 98056: Free information ■ Woodworking power tools. 206–226–5937.

Klockit, P.O. Box 636, Lake Geneva, WI 53147: Free catalog ■ Woodworking tools, wood finishing supplies, and clock-building equipment. 800–556–2548.

Laguna Tools, 2081 Laguna Canyon Rd., Laguna Beach, CA 92651: Free information ■ Space-saving, all-in-one shop that includes a table saw, joiner, planer, shaper, mortise, and sliding table. 800–234–1976; 714–494–7006 (in CA).

Leichtung Workshops, 4944 Commerce Pkwy., Cleveland, OH 44128: Free catalog ■ Tools for craftsmen and gardeners. 800–321–6840.

Lobo Power Tools, 9034 Bermudez St., Pico Rivera, CA 90660: Free information ■ Woodworking power tools. 800–786–5626.

Makita Tools, 14930 Northam St., La Mirada, CA 90638: Free information ■ Woodworking power tools. 714–522–8088.

Marlin Industries, Inc., Rt. 70, Box 191, Cashiers, NC 28717: Brochure $1 ■ Woodcarving machines. 704–743–5551.

Marwood Hardwoods, 7790 Rockwell Ave., Philadelphia, PA 19111: Free information ■ Power tools and domestic and imported hardwoods and veneers. 800–255–8363; 215–725–0700 (in PA).

Mechanick's Workbench, P.O. Box 668, Marion, MA 02738: Free information with long SASE ■ Antique woodworking tools. 508–748–1680.

Metabo Corporation, 1231 Wilson Dr., P.O. Box 2287, West Chester, PA 19380: Free information ■ Portable power tools. 215–436–5900.

Micro-Mark, 340 Snyder Ave., Berkeley Heights, NJ 07922: Catalog $1 ■ Miniature tools for hobby craftsmen. 800–225–1066.

Mighty Mite Industries, Inc., P.O. Box 20427, Portland, OR 97220: Free information ■ One-man band saw mill. 503–288–5923.

Milwaukee Electric Tool Corporation, 13135 W. Lisbon Rd., Brookfield, WI 53005: Free information ■ Woodworking power tools. 414–781–3600.

Mini-Max Tools, 5933 Peachtree Industrial Blvd., Norcross, GA 30092: Free information ■ Woodworking power tools. 404–448–1120.

MLCS Tools, Ltd., P.O. Box 4053, Rydal, PA 19046: Free information ■ Carbide-tipped router bits. 800–533–9298.

Mobile Manufacturing Company, P.O. Box 250, Troutdale, OR 97060: Free brochure ■ Portable gasoline- or electric-powered saw for cutting logs any diameter and lengths up to 60 feet. 503–666–5593.

Nibsburner, Matty Kaszuba, 381 Nut Swamp Rd., Red Bank, NJ 07701: Free information ■ Woodburning and engraving system. 908–747–5023.

Northern Hydraulics, P.O. Box 1219, Burnsville, MN 55337: Catalog $1 ■ Power tools. 800–533–5545.

Northland Woodworking Supply, 65 Wurz Ave., Utica, NY 13502: Catalog $2 (refundable) ■ Carving tools. 315–724–1299.

NSK America Corporation, 2035 S. Arlington Heights Rd., Ste. 112–113, Arlington Heights, IL 60005: Free catalog ■ Electric-powered woodcarving tool with variable speed controls, optional attachments, and foot pedal control. 708–228–1194.

Penn State Industries, 2850 Comly Rd., Philadelphia, PA 19154: Free information ■ Woodworking power tools. 800–288–7297.

Porter-Cable, P.O. Box 2468, Jackson, TN 38302: Free information ■ Woodworking power tools. 901–668–8600.

Poulan, Division White Consolidated Industries, 5020 Flournoy-Lucas Rd., Shreveport, LA 71129: Free information ■ Electric- and gas-operated chain saws. 318–687–0100.

Powermatic, Inc., Morrison Rd., McMinnville, TN 37110: Free information ■ Woodworking power tools. 800–248–0144; 615–473–5551 (in TN).

Power Tool Specialists, 3 Craftsman Rd., East Windsor, CT 06088: Free information ■ Portable power tools. Includes a hand-held nail gun. 800–243–5114.

RBIndustries, 1801 Vine St., P.O. Box 369, Harrisonville, MO 64071: Free information ■ Woodworking power tools. 800–487–2623.

Ryobi America Corporation, 5201 Pearman Dairy Rd., Anderson, SC 29625: Free information ■ Woodworking power tools. 800–323–4615; 803–226–6511 (in SC).

Santa Rosa Tool & Supply, Inc., 1651 Piner Rd., Santa Rosa, CA 95043: Free information ■ Woodworking power tools. 800–346–0387; 800–464–8665 (in CA).

Sarah Glove Company, Inc., P.O. Box 1940, Waterbury, CT 06722: Catalog $1 ■ Tools for home craftsmen. 203–574–4090.

Sears Craftsmen Tools, Catalog Division, 925 S. Homan Ave., Chicago, IL 60607: Free information ■ Woodworking power

tools. (Catalog also available from local stores.) 312–875–2500.

Seven Corners Hardware, Inc., 216 W. 7th St., St. Paul, MN 55102: Free catalog ■ Hand and power tools and supplies. 800–328–0457; 612–224–4859 (in MN).

Shopsmith, Inc., 3931 Image Dr., Dayton, OH 45414: Free information ■ Multipurpose, all-in-one power-woodworking tools. 800–543–7586; 513–898–6070 (in OH).

Shoptask, P.O. Box 7531, Tacoma, WA 98407: Free information ■ All-in-one home machine shop with mill, lathe, and drill. 800–343–5775.

Shop-Vax Corporation, 2323 Reach Rd., Williamsport, PA 17701: Free information ■ Self-contained, portable vacuum cleaner for workshops. 717–326–0502.

Silvo Hardware Company, 611 N. Broadway, Milwaukee, WI 53202: Free catalog ■ Professional hand tools.

Skil Corporation, 4300 W. Peterson Ave., Chicago, IL 60646: Catalog $1 ■ Woodworking power tools. 312–286–7330.

SMC Enterprises, 540 W. 8th St., Browerville, MN 56438: Free information ■ Power-operated carving tools, sanders, and woodburning systems. 612–594–6155.

The Source, 8815 Telegraph Rd., Lorton, VA 22079: Catalog $2 ■ Hand and power tools and cabinet-making supplies. 800–452–9999; 703–550–8600 (in VA).

Sperber Tool Works, P.O. Box 1224, West Caldwell, NJ 07007: Free literature ■ Portable sawmills. 201–744–6110.

Stanley Tools, P.O. Box 1146, Bellmore, NY 11710: Free information ■ Woodworking power tools. 203–225–5111.

Sugino Corporation, 1700 N. Penny Ln., Schaumberg, IL 60173: Free brochure ■ Compact, easy-to-use electric-operated, oscillating woodcarving tool. 708–397–9401.

Sunhill Machinery, 500 Andover Park East, Seattle, WA 98188: Free information ■ Heavy-duty routers, shapers, sanders, planers, jointers, and dust collectors. 800–544–1361; 206–575–4131 (in WA).

Tarheel Filing Company, Inc., 3400 Lake Woodard Dr., Raleigh, NC 27514: Free information ■ Power tools. 800–322–6641; 919–231–3323 (in NC).

TCM Industries, Inc., 322 Paseo Sonrisa, Walnut, CA 91789: Free information ■ Planers, table and band saws, dust collectors, jointers, sanders, and other tools. 800–654–7702; 714–594–0780 (in CA).

Tool Crib of the North, Box 1716, Grand Forks, ND 58206: Catalog $2 ■ Hand and power tools. 800–358–3096.

Tool Force, 28365 US 19 North, Clearwater, FL 34621: Free information ■ Woodworking power tools. 813–726–4177.

Toolhauz Corporation, P.O. Box 1288, Middleboro, MA 02346: Free information ■ Hand and portable power tools. 800–533–6135; 800–282–0170 (in MA).

Tools, Etc., 1567 S. Harbor Blvd., Fullerton, CA 92632: Catalog $2.50 ■ Hand and power tools. 800–327–6250; 714–525–3581 (in CA).

Total Shop, P.O. Box 25429, Greenville, SC 29616: Free catalog ■ Woodworking power tools. 800–845–9356; 803–288–4174 (in SC).

Trend-Lines, 375 Beacham St., Chelsea, MA 02150: Free catalog ■ Power tools. 800–767–9999.

Trippe Supply Company, 309 Ritchie Rd., Capitol Heights, MD 20743: Free information ■ Hand and power tools. 800–635–2127.

Vermont American, P.O. Box 340, Lincolnton, NC 28093: Free information ■ Portable power tools. 704–735–7464.

Garrett Wade Company, 161 Avenue of Americas, New York, NY 10013: Catalog $4 ■ Hand and power tools for woodworking. 800–221–2942.

Warner National Machinery & Tool Supply, 12626 Raymer St., North Hollywood, CA 91605: Free catalog ■ Metalworking power tools. 800–423–2433; 818–765–6141 (in CA).

Warren Tool Company, Inc., Rt. 9G, Rhinebeck, NY 12572: Catalog $1 ■ Whittling and woodcarving tools, woods, sharpening stones, supplies, and books. 914–876–7817.

Westchester Tool Supply Corporation, 1051 Saw Mill River Rd., Building 2, Yonkers, NY 10710: Free information ■ Machine shop tools, equipment, and supplies. 800–431–2936; 800–248–8808 (in NY).

Whole Earth Access, 822 Anthony St., Berkeley, CA 94710: Free information ■ Power tools. 800–829–6300.

Wholesale America, Inc., 4777 Menard Dr., Eau Claire, WI 54703: Catalog $1 ■ Power tools and hardware. 615–874–5000.

Wholesale Tool Company, Inc., P.O. Box 68, Warren, MI 48090: Free information ■ Power-operated machine tools, hand and portable power tools, and machine shop supplies. 313–754–9270.

Wil-Cut Company, 7113 Spicer Dr., Citrus Heights, CA 95621: Free catalog ■ Carving woods, cutters and carving tools, and books. 916–961–5400.

Wilke Machinery Company, 3230 Susquehanna Trail, York, PA 17402: Catalog $1 ■ Sanders, routers, planers, moulders, spindle sanders, machine shop supplies, and measuring, drafting, and layout tools. 717–764–5000.

Williams & Hussey, P.O. Box 1149, Wilton, NH 03086: Free information ■ Woodworking power tools. 800–258–1380; 603–654–6828 (in NH).

Woodcraft Supply, 210 Wood County Industrial Park, P.O. Box 1686, Parkersburg, WV 26102: Free catalog ■ Woodworking tools, supplies, hardware, and books. 800–542–9115.

Woodmaster Tools, Inc., 2908 Oak St., Kansas City, MO 64108: Free information ■ Multipurpose power tools that plane, finish, and sand. 800–821–6651.

Wood-Mizer Products, Inc., 8180 W. 10th St., Indianapolis, IN 46214: Catalog $2 ■ Portable sawmills. 800–553–0219.

Woodworker's Emporium, 8888 N. Milwaukee Ave., Niles, IL 60648: Catalog subscription $4 ■ Woodworking power tools. 708–824–0565.

The Woodworkers' Store, 21801 Industrial Blvd., Rogers, MN 55374: Catalog $2 ■ Hardware and ornamental woodworking supplies, tools, and finishing supplies. 612–428–2199.

Woodworker's Supply, 5604 Alameda Pl. NE, Albuquerque, NM 87113: Free catalog ■ Tools and supplies for most wood shop projects. 800–645–9292; 505–821–0578 (in NM).

Woodworking Machinery & Supplies, 290 Beaty Dr., Belmont, NC 28012: Free information ■ Woodworking power tools. 800–662–0947; 704–827–3190.

Xylophile's Company, 138 E. Loudon Ave., Lexington, KY 40505: Free information ■ Workshop tools. 800–354–9083; 606–254–9823 (in KY).

TOWELS

Chambers, Mail Order Department., P.O. Box 7841, San Francisco, CA 94120: Free catalog ■ Bed and bath linens and furnishings. 800–334–9790.

In Detail, 1633 Broadway, New York, NY 10019: Free catalog ■ Bathroom towels, designer comforters and bed coverings, linens and sheets, and decor accessories. 212–830–7484.

Leron, 750 Madison Ave., New York, NY 10021: Free catalog ■ Linens, towels, pillows and covers, and imported handkerchiefs for men and women with optional monograms. 212–753–6700.

Linen Mart, 720 Anderson Ave., St. Cloud, MN 56395: Free catalog ■ Linen, towel, and bedding ensemble closeouts and irregulars. 800–541–1252.

Palmetto Linen Company, Box 109, Hardeeville, SC 29927: Free information ■ Sheets and matching dust ruffles, bath towels, blankets, comforters, pillows, tablecloths, place mats, shower curtains, kitchen towels, and oven gloves. 800–833–3506.

TOY MAKING

Angelitos, P.O. Box 1926, Fort Collins, CO 80522: Catalog $2 (refundable) ■ Handcrafted soft fabric sculptures. 800–624–9379.

Animal Crackers Patterns, 5824 Isleta SW, Albuquerque, NM 87105: Catalog $2.50 ■ Kits, supplies, and patterns for easy-to-make stuffed toys and animals. 800–274–BEAR.

Atlanta Puffections, P.O. Box 13524, Atlanta, GA 30324: Catalog $1.50 ■ Easy-to-make stuffed animals. 404–262–7437.

Cotton Patch Crafts, Rt. 3, Box 790, Mansfield, LA 71052: Brochure $2 ■ Ready-to-stuff dolls and animals. 318–697–5745.

Creations by Suanne, P.O. Box 2064, New Market Station, Niagara Falls, NY 14301: Catalog $3 with long SASE ■ Doll sculpture kits.

Cross Creek, 4114 Lakeside Dr., Richmond, CA 94806: Free catalog ■ Soft sculpture patterns, kits, books, cross-stitching supplies, folk art dolls, and iron-on transfers. 800–538–4942; 800–421–9948 (in CA).

Double D Productions, Inc., 4110 Willow Ridge Rd., Douglasville, GA 30135: Information $1 ■ Patterns, kits, fur, eyes and noses, joints, and music boxes for stuffed toys and bears. 404–949–3648.

Gaillorraine Originals, P.O. Box 137, Tehachapi, CA 93561: Catalog $2 ■ Supplies and patterns for bears and other soft animal toys. 805–822–1857.

Garden Fairies Trading Company, P.O. Box 5770, Santa Rosa, CA 95402: Catalog $4 ■ Fabrics, trims, and soft toy patterns. 800–925–9919.

Golden Fun Kits, P.O. Box 10697, Golden, CO 80401: Catalog $1 ■ Soft toy-making supplies. Includes eyes, noses, animal joints, squeakers, musical movements, animal voices, growlers, and patterns.

Larson Wood Manufacturing, P.O. Box 672, Park Rapids, MN 56470: Catalog $2 (refundable) ■ Country-styled mini cutouts, sanded smooth and ready for decorative finishing and kits, parts, hardware, and supplies for toys. 218–732–9121.

Patterncrafts, Box 25370, Colorado Springs, CO 80936: Catalog $2 ■ Patterns for dolls and stuffed animals. 719–574–2007.

Patterns by Diane, 1126 Ivon Ave., Endicott, NY 13760: Catalog $1.50 ■ Soft toys and puppets you can make, and bear-making supplies that include furs and mohair, growlers, squeakers, music boxes, noses, eyes, and joint sets. 607–754–0391.

Pieces of Olde, P.O. Box 65130, Baltimore, MD 21209: Free information with long SASE ■ Soft sculpture toy kits. 410–366–4949.

Sonrise Soft Crafts, P.O. Box 5091, Salem, OR 97304: Brochure 50¢ ■ Information on how to make stuffed toys. 503–362–0027.

TOYS & GAMES

Character Toys

Action Toys & Collectibles, P.O. Box 102, Holtsville, NY 11742: Catalog $2 ■ TV and movie action and character toy collectibles. 516–736–8697.

All Star Comics & Toys, 3840 W. Hillsboro Blvd., Deerfield Beach, FL 33442: Catalog $2 ■ Star Wars, Star Trek, Super Powers, Secret Wars models and other comic toys.

Arthur Antonelli, 137 Littleton Rd., Westford, MA 01886: Free information with long SASE ■ Stage, screen, and television character toys and other collectibles. 508–692–9336.

Chris Arbizzani, 1225 Whitfield Dr., Geneva, IL 60134: Free list with long SASE ■ Character toys and other movie and TV collectibles. 708–232–8853.

Baker's Antiques & Collectibles, P.O. Box 558, Oakdale, NY 11769: Catalog $12 ■ Antique and collectible toys. 516–567–9295.

Dean Chapman Collectable Toys, 7111 Amundsonn Ave., Edina, MN 55439: Free list ■ Character, western, and TV-related toys, games, premiums, and related movie memorabilia. 612–925–0156.

Collectorholics, 15006 Fuller, Grandview, MO 64030: Free information ■ Character television and movie toys. 816–322–0906.

John DiCicco, 57 Bay View Dr., Shrewsbury, MA 01545: Free catalog with long SASE and two 1st class stamps ■ Character toys and other movie and TV collectibles. 508–792–0974.

Figures, P.O. Box 19482, Johnston, RI 02919: Catalog $2 ■ Science fiction and super hero action figures and playsets.

Fun House Toy Company, P.O. Box 343, Bradforwoods, PA 15015: Free list with first class stamp ■ Character toys, space toys, board games, and related collectibles. 412–935–1935.

GI Joe Nostalgia Company, c/o Joe Bodnarchuk, 62 McKinley Ave., Kenmore, NY 14217: Price list $3 ■ GI Joe dolls, uniforms, vehicles, gift sets, novelties, and artwork. 716–873–0264.

Barry Goodman, P.O. Box 218, Woodbury, NY 11797: Free information ■ Character toys, dolls, and playthings. 516–338–2701.

Half Moon Nostalgia, 2 Mead St., North Tonawanda, NY 14120: Free information ■ Television and movie character toys, from the 1950s through 1960s. 716–567–8760.

The Hobby Lobby, 26 Vista Rd., Levittown, PA 19057: Free information with long SASE ■ Action figures and vintage cars and toys, from the 1960s and 1970s. 609–871–3843.

Jim's TV Collectibles, P.O. Box 4767, San Diego, CA 92164: Catalog $2 ■ Television and theatrical collectibles, from the 1950s through 1990s.

Just Kids Nostalgia, 326 Main St., Huntington, NY 11743: Catalog $4 ■ Movie and television character dolls, other movie memorabilia, and board games. 516–423–8449.

Let's Talk Toys, 2090 S. Nova Rd., Ste. 2112, South Daytona, FL 32119: Catalog $3 ■ Character toys from the 1960s, 1970s, and 1980s. 904–788–5486.

Long Island Train & Hobby Center, 192 Jericho Tpke., Mineola, NY 11501: Price list $3 ■ Collectible toys and character dolls. 516–742–5621.

John Paquette Character Toys, 7981 SW Nyberg Rd., Tualatin, OR 97062: Catalog $2 ■ Character toys and related collectibles. 503–691–2184.

Bob Sellstedt, 9307 Hillingdon Rd., Woodbury, MN 55125: List $2 ■ Character toys and related collectibles. 612–738–1597.

Toy Scouts, Inc., 330 Merriman Rd., Akron, OH 44303: Catalog $3 ■ Baby-Boom collectibles and television cartoon and comic characters, from 1940 through 1970. 216–836–0668.

Vintage Toy Depot, Mike Frigerio, P.O. Box 206, Kenilworth, NJ 07033: Catalog $3 (refundable) ■ Character and comic collectibles. 908–276–5464.

Wex Rex Records & Collectibles, P.O. Box 702, Hudson, MA 01749: Price list $2 ■ Movie and television show character toys and collectibles. 508–568–0856.

Bruce Zalkin, P.O. Box 75579, Tampa, FL 33605: Catalog $1 ■ Character toys from movie and television shows. 813–973–4324.

Electronic Toys & Games

Access Software Incorporated, 4910 W. Amelia Earhart Dr., Salt Lake City, UT 84115: Free information ■ Video games for electronic entertainment systems. 801–359–2900.

Acclaim Entertainment, Inc., 71 Audrey Ave., Oyster Bay, NY 11771: Free information ■ Video game cartridges. 516–922–2400.

Accolade, 550 S. Winchester Blvd., San Jose, CA 95128: Free information ■ Video game cartridges. 408–985–1700.

Activision, 3885 Bohannon Dr., Menlo Park, CA 94025: Free information ■ Video game cartridges. 415–329–0500.

American Sammy, 2421 205th St., Ste. D–104, Torrance, CA 90501: Free information ■ Video game cartridges. 213–320–7167.

BRE Software, 352 W. Bedford Ave., Ste. 104, Fresno, CA 93711: Free information ■ New and used Nintendo cartridges. 209–438–4263.

Broderbund Software, Inc., P.O. Box 6125, Novato, CA 94948: Free information ■ Video game cartridges. 800–521–6263; 415–492–3200 (in CA).

Bullet-Proof Software, 8337 154th Ave. NE, Redmond, WA 98052: Free information ■ Video game cartridges. 206–861–9200.

Camerica, 230 5th Ave., Ste. 1100, New York, NY 10001: Free information ■ Video game controllers. 212–689–6320.

Capcom USA, 3303 Scott Blvd., Santa Clara, CA 95054: Free information ■ Video game cartridges. 408–727–0400.

Cape Cod Connection, 21 Pleasant View Ave., Drawer 457, Falmouth, MA 02540: Free information ■ New and used Nintendo cartridges. 800–328–WARE.

The Computer Museum Store, 300 Congress St., Boston, MA 02210: Free catalog ■ Computer-operated toys, bedroom linens, T-shirts, videos and educational toys, books, posters, mugs and coasters. 617–426–2800.

Data East USA, Inc., 1850 Little Orchard St., San Jose, CA 95112: Free information ■ Video game cartridges. 408–286–7080.

Electronic Arts, 1450 Fashion Island Blvd., San Mateo, CA 94404: Free information ■ Video game cartridges. 800–245–4525.

The Fun Club, 4948 Hwy. 169 North, New Hope, MN 55428: Free information ■ New and used video game cartridges. 612–533–8118.

Game Dude, P.O. Box 8325, Van Nuys, CA 91409: Free newsletter ■ Video game cartridges. 818–764–2442.

Gamexpress, 11390 Ventura Blvd., North Hollywood, CA 91604: Free information ■ Video game cartridges. 818–763–8697.

Hal America, Inc., 7873 SW Cirrus Dr., Building 25–F, Beaverton, OR 97005: Free information ■ Video game cartridges. 503–644–4117.

Hi Tech Expressions, 584 Broadway, Ste. 509, New York, NY 10012: Free information ■ Video game cartridges. 212–941–1224.

Hot-B USA, Inc., 1255 Post St., Ste. 1040, San Francisco, CA 94109: Free information ■ Video game cartridges. 415–567–9337.

Hudson Soft, 400 Oyster Point Blvd., Ste. 515, South San Francisco, CA 94080: Free information ■ Video game cartridges. 415–495–HINT.

Innerprise Software, 128 Cockeysville Rd., Hunt Valley, MD 21030: Free information ■ Video game cartridges. 410–785–2266.

Institutional Computer Development Corporation, 21 Walt Whitman Rd., Huntington Station, NY 11746: Free information ■ Computer chess sets. 512–424–3300.

Kaneko USA, 1370 Busch Pkwy., Buffalo Grove, IL 60089: Free information ■ Video game cartridges. 708–808–1370.

Koei Corporation, One Bay Plaza, Ste. 540, 1350 Bayshore Hwy., Burlingame, CA 94010: Free information ■ Video game cartridges. 415–348–0500.

Konami, Inc., 900 Deerfield Pkwy., Buffalo Grove, IL 60089: Free information ■ Video game cartridges. 708–215–5100.

Meldac of America, Inc., 1801 Century Park East, Ste. 2210, Los Angeles, CA 90067: Free information ■ Video game cartridges. 310–286–7040.

Natsume, Inc., 1243A Howard Ave., Burlingame, CA 94010: Free information ■ Video game cartridges. 415–342–1712.

NEC Technologies, Inc., 1414 Massachusetts Ave., Boxborough, MA 01719: Free information ■ Video game cartridges. 800–388–8888; 508–264–8000 (in MA).

Nintendo of America, 4820 150th Ave. NE, Redmond, WA 98052: Free information ■ Nintendo system, accessories, and game cartridges. 800–255–3700.

NTVIC Games, NTV International Corporation, 50 Rockefeller Plaza, New York, NY 10020: Free information ■ Video game cartridges. 212–489–8412.

Play It Again, P.O. Box 6718, Flushing, NY 11365: Free price list with three 1st class stamps ■ Buys and sells video game cartridges.

Psygnosis, 29 Saint Marys Ct., Brookline, MA 02146: Free information ■ Video game cartridges. 617–731–3553.

Radio Shack, Division Tandy Corporation, 1500 One Tandy Center, Fort Worth, TX 76102: Free catalog ■ Electronic teaching toys, musical instruments, chess games, strategy games, sports games, and radio controlled toys. 817–390–3700.

Renovation Products, Inc., 987 University Ave., Ste. 10, Los Gatos, CA 95030: Free information ■ Video game cartridges. 408–395–8375.

Sega of America, 3375 Arden Rd., Hayward, CA 94545: Free information ■ Video game cartridges. 800–USA–SEGA.

Sir-Tech., P.O. Box 245, Ogdensburg, NY 13669: Free information ■ Video game cartridges. 315–393–6633.

SNK Corporation of America, 246 Sobrante Way, Sunnyvale, CA 94086: Free information ■ Video game cartridges. 408–736–8844.

Spectrum Holobyte, 2061 Challenger Dr., Alameda, CA 94501: Free information ■ Video game cartridges. 510–522–1164.

Taito Software, 390 Holbrook Dr., Wheeling, IL 60090: Free information ■ Video game cartridges. 708–520–9280.

Taxan Corporation, 2880 San Thomas Expy., Ste. 101, Santa Clara, CA 95051: Free information ■ Video game cartridges. 408–748–0200.

Tecmo Games, 18005 S. Adria Maru Ln., Carson, CA 90746: Free information ■ Video game cartridges. 310–329–5880.

Three-Sixty Software, 2105 S. Bascom Ave., Ste. 290, Campbell, CA 95008: Free information ■ Video game cartridges. 408–879–9144.

Timeless Expectations, P.O. Box 1180, Fairfield, IA 52556: Free information ■ Scrabble, chess, bridge, backgammon, gin and cribbage electronic games; other board games; books; and gifts. 800–622–1558.

Treco USA, 2421 205th St., Ste. D–104, Torrance, CA 90501: Free information ■ Video game cartridges. 310–782–6960.

Video Game Land, 1000 Torrance Blvd., Redondo Beach, CA 90277: Free information ■ Free information ■ New and used video game cartridges. 310–792–1190.

General Toys & Games

Abilities International, Old Forge Rd., Elizabethtown, NY 12932: Catalog $1 ■ Children's learning and playing toys from around the world. 518–873–6456.

All But Grown-Ups, P.O. Box 555, Berwick, ME 03901: Free brochure ■ Challenging toys for adults and children. 800–448–1550.

American Shuffleboard Company, 210 Paterson Plank Rd., Union City, NJ 07087: Free information ■ Shuffleboard and six-pocket billiards, rocket hobby table, bumper pool table, soccer, and other table games. 201–865–6633.

Animal Town, P.O. Box 485, Healdsburg, CA 95448: Free catalog ■ Toys, novelties, games, puzzles, books, and recordings for all ages. 800–445–8642.

Aristoplay Games, P.O. Box 7529, Ann Arbor, MI 48107: Free catalog ■ Educational games for all ages. 800–634–7738.

Armchair General's Merchantile, 1008 Adams, Bay City, MI 48708: Catalog $2 (refundable) ■ Games, miniatures, and books for Civil War enthusiasts. 517–892–6177.

Back to Basics Toys, 8803 Monard Dr., Silver Spring, MD 20910: Free catalog ■ Raggedy Ann dolls, Lincoln log building sets, Lionel trains, Tinkertoy, Radio Flyer wagons, Disney classics, science sets, telescopes, Meccano construction sets, sports games, play-in doll houses, and other toys. 800–356–5360.

Childcraft, P.O. Box 29137, Overland Park, KS 66201: Free catalog ■ Educational toys and games for babies and young children. 800–222–7725.

Constructive Playthings, 1227 E. 119th St., Grandview, MO 64030: Free catalog ■ Toys, novelties, games, puzzles, books, furniture, and sports and fitness equipment. 800–448–7830; 816–761–5900 (in Kansas City).

Current, The Current Bldg., Colorado Springs, CO 80901: Free catalog ■ Toys, greeting cards, stationery, gift wrapping and decorations, and calendars. 800–525–7170; 719–594–4100 (in CO).

Discovery Toys, Inc., Martinez, CA 94553: Free catalog ■ Toys for children that encourage physical, emotional, and intellectual growth. 800–426–4777.

Early Learning Center, 40 Pepe's Farm Rd., Milford, CT 06460: Free brochure ■ Toys for children's first years, creative toys, and toys to nurture curiosity. 203–878–7999.

Enchanted Doll House, Rt. 7A, Manchester Center, VT 05255: Catalog $1 ■ Stuffed animals, dolls and accessories, books, toys and games, and miniatures. 802–362–3031.

Fasa Corporation, 1026 W. Van Buren, Chicago, IL 60607: Free information ■ Games and books on games. 312–243–5660.

Games People Played, P.O. Box 1540, Pinedale, WY 82941: Brochure $2 ■ Antique replica game boards. 307–367–2502.

Games Workshop, 1220 Key Hwy., Baltimore, MD 21230: Free information ■ Adventure games, miniature figures, books, and magazines for fantasy gaming enthusiasts. 410–727–0250.

GDW Games, P.O. Box 1646, Bloomington, IL 61702: Free catalog ■ Military and role playing, adventure, space adventure, war and science fiction, and other games that challenge. 309–452–3632.

The Great Kids Company, Division of Kaplan, P.O. Box 609, Lewisville, NC 27023: Free catalog ■ Developmental learning materials for early childhood education. 800–334–2014; 800–642–0610 (in NC).

Growing Child, P.O. Box 620, Lafayette, IN 47902: Free catalog ■ Toys, games, puzzles, books, recordings, and arts and crafts for children, from birth to age 6. 317–423–2624.

Hancock Toy Shop, 97 Prospect St., Jaffrey, NH 03452: Catalog $1 ■ Hardwood

toys and novelties for children. 603–532–7504.

Hand in Hand, Rt. 26, RR 1, Box 1425, Oxford, ME 04270: Free catalog ■ Books, toys, games, car seats, furniture, and bathroom accessories. 800–872–9745.

Hearth Song, P.O. Box B, Sebastopol, CA 95473: Free catalog ■ Toys and games that provide opportunity for creativity, challenge, discovery, and improving reading skills. 800–533–4397.

Just for Kids, P.O. Box 29141, Shawnee, KS 66201: Free catalog ■ Dolls, games, books, stuffed animals, science activities, automobiles and trucks, building blocks, party items, and games for when travelling. 800–443–5827.

Kapable Kids, P.O. Box 250, Bohemia, NY 11716: Free catalog ■ Toys for the developing child. 800–356–1564.

Miles Kimball Company, 41 W. 8th Ave., Oshkosh, WI 54901: Free catalog ■ Toys and games for children and adults. 414–231–3800.

Lankford Gameboard Collections, 15005 Howe Rd., Portland, MI 48875: Free brochure with long SASE ■ Antique reproduction game boards. 517–647–6298.

Larson Wood Manufacturing, P.O. Box 672, Park Rapids, MN 56407: Catalog $2 ■ Kits, parts, and supplies for toy-making. 218–732–9121.

LEGO Shop at Home Service, 555 Taylor Rd., P.O. Box 640, Enfield, CT 06082: Free catalog ■ LEGO play sets, extra pieces, and accessories. 203–763–4011.

Lilly's Kids, Lillian Vernon Corporation, Virginia Beach, VA 23479: Free catalog ■ Exclusive and imaginative toys for children. 804–430–1500.

Marble Man, Box 4302, Woodbridge, VA 22194: Free brochure ■ Marbles and board games that use marbles. 703–491–8729.

The Nature Company, Home Office, 750 Hearst Ave., Berkeley, CA 94710: Free catalog ■ Science- and nature-oriented items, toys, and novelties for children and adults. 800–227–1114.

Noveltoys, US Hwy. 19, Canton, TX 75103: Catalog $3 (refundable) ■ Handmade wooden toys for children. 800–342–5452.

Pied Piper, 2922 N. 35th Ave., Ste. 4, Drawer 11408, Phoenix, AZ 85061: Catalog $2 ■ Toys, books, and other learning aids for gifted children. 602–272–1853.

PlayFair Toys, 1690 28th St., Boulder, CO 80301: Free catalog ■ Toys, novelties, games, puzzles, books, and recordings. 303–440–7229.

Raisin' Cookie, 6 Commercial St., P.O. Box 992, Hicksville, NY 11802: Free catalog ■ Educational toys books, and videos for children, age 1 to 8. 800–866–6005.

R.E.A.L.IZMS, 921 Eastwind Dr., Ste. 114, Westerville, OH 43081: Free catalog ■ Skate boards and safety gear, bicycles, skooter skates, roller racers, unicycles, mini-cars, pogo sticks, trucks, cars, military toys and vehicles, high-tech games, dinosaurs, dolls, and educational toys. 614–898–5464.

Red Balloon, 1073 Wisconsin Ave. NW, Washington, DC 20007: Free catalog ■ Learning and teaching toys and games, science sets, puzzles, music toys, party games, sports equipment, construction sets, and bathtub toys. 202–965–9394.

F.A.O. Schwarz, P.O. Box 182225, Chattanooga, TN 37422: Free catalog ■ Children's toys, games, and stuffed animals. 800–426–TOYS.

Sensational Beginnings, 300 Detroit, Ste. E, P.O. Box 2009, Monroe, MI 48161: Free catalog ■ Toys and books for babies and children up to age 4. 800–444–2147; 313–242–2147 (in MI).

Through the Woods, 805 57th Ave. North, Brooklyn Center, MN 55430: Free information ■ Handmade puzzles for children that teach colors and develops eye and hand coordination. 612–561–9461.

Toad'ly Kids, 2428 Patterson Ave., Roanoke, VA 24016: Free catalog ■ Toys and games, classical and popular music tapes, and clothing for children. 703–981–0233.

Toy Park, 112 E. 86th St., New York, NY 10028: Free information ■ Toys, hobby items, and crafts. 212–427–6611.

Toys to Grow On, 2695 E. Dominguez St., P.O. Box 17, Long Beach, CA 90801: Catalog $1 ■ Games, T-shirts, backyard toys, and educational toys; party supplies; and toys for children, from birth to age 12. 800–542–8338; 310–603–8890 (in CA).

Troll Learn & Play, 100 Corporate Dr., Mahwah, NJ 07430: Free catalog ■ Children's educational toys, books, puzzles, playhouse toys, videos and other recordings, costumes, and T-shirts. 800–247–6106.

U.S. Games Systems, Inc., 179 Ludlow St., Stanford, CT 06902: Catalog $2 ■ Deluxe double bridge decks, tarot, and cartomancy decks, historical and specialty decks, antique reproductions, and other playing cards. 800–54–GAMES; 203–353–8400 (in CT).

U.S. Toys, 2008 W. 103rd Terrace, Leawood, KS 66206: Free catalog ■ Educational toys and games. 913–642–8244.

West End Games, 251 W. 30th St., New York, NY 10001: Free catalog ■ Space fantasy, adventure, war and defense, history, Star Trek, supernatural, and other games. 212–947–4828.

Windmill Hobbies, Inc., 525 N. River St., P.O. Box 460, Batavia, IL 60510: Free information ■ Games and accessories. 800–333–5963.

Wisconsin Wagon Company, 507 Laurel Ave., Janesville, WI 53545: Brochure $1 ■ Handcrafted Janesville replica solid oak coaster wagon and Janesville pine and hardwood toddler first riding 3-wheeler, circa 1900–1934; scooters, sleds, wheelbarrows, and swings; and doll furniture. 608–754–0026.

World Wide Games, 75 Mill St., Colchester, CT 06415: Catalog $1 ■ Casino games, puzzles, outdoor games, kites, and games from worldwide sources. 800–243–9342.

Special-Needs Toys & Games

Access to Recreation, Inc., 2509 E. Thousand Oaks Blvd., Thousand Oaks, CA 91362: Free catalog ■ Adaptive recreation equipment; devices to help with embroidery and knitting; games; books; video controllers; wheelchair ramps; and an environmental control system. 405–498–7535.

S & S Arts & Crafts, P.O. Box 513, Colchester, CT 06415: Free catalog ■ Craft projects and supplies. 800–243–9232.

Toys for Special Children, 385 Warburton Ave., Hastings-on-Hudson, NY 10706: Free catalog ■ Assistive communication devices, specially adapted and activity toys, capability switches, skillbuilder equipment, computer training devices, and other special

devices for children with disabilities. 800–832–8697.

Woodset, Inc., Box 2127, Waldorf, MD 20604: Free information ■ Backyard wood play equipment specially adapted for children with mobility and positioning difficulties. 800–638–9663.

World Wide Games, Dept. 2600, 75 Mill St., Colchester, CT 06415: Catalog $2 ■ Hardwood board games, puzzles, strategy and skill games, outdoor activities, and other games for all ages. 800–243–9232.

Water Toys

Sevylor USA, 6651 E. 26th St., Los Angeles, CA 90040: Free information ■ Inflatable boats, mattresses, tubes, lounges, balls, and other sports recreational products. 213–727–6013.

Ultratube, P.O. Box 244, Madison, GA 30650: Free information ■ Toys and inflatables for the water. 404–342–1916.

TOY SOLDIERS

Armchair General, Ltd., 12747 Olive Blvd., St. Louis, MO 63141: Catalog $1 ■ Military miniatures and toy soldiers.

Brunton's Barracks, 415 S. Montezuma, Prescott, AZ 86303: Free information with long SASE ■ Military figures and other miniatures. 602–778–1915.

Burlington Antique Toys, 1082 Madison Ave., New York, NY 10028: Free information with long SASE ■ Toy soldier sets and individual pieces from different historical periods. 212–861–9708.

Classic Toys, 69 Thompson St., New York, NY 10012: Free information with long SASE ■ Military miniatures and vehicles, animals, diecast and white metal cars, and wild west and historical figures. 212–941–9129.

Command Post, 117 Bramblebush Rd., Stoughton, MA 02072: Catalog $3 ■ Toy soldiers. 617–344–5258.

Counterpane Toyland, 2900 Clarendon Blvd., Arlington, VA 22201: Free information with long SASE ■ Toy soldier sets and individual pieces from different historical periods. 703–525–4551.

Cynthia's Country Store, 11496 Pierson Rd., Commerce Park-Wellington, West

Palm Beach, FL 33414: Catalog $7.50 ■ British sets and other toy soldiers. 407–793–0554.

Dunken, Box 95, Calvert, TX 77837: Free catalog ■ Civil War, World War I and World War II, Napoleonic, Germany military, and other lead soldier molds. 409–364–2020.

Dutkins' Collectables, 1019 West Rt. 70, Cherry Hill, NJ 08002: Catalog $2 ■ Hand-painted all-metal toy soldiers and mold kits. 609–428–9559.

Excalibur Hobbies, Ltd., 63 Exchange St., Malden, MA 02148: Free catalog with long SASE ■ Old and new toy soldiers, war games, plastic kits, books, and other militaria. 617–322–2959.

Gettysburg Toy Soldier, 415 Baltimore St., Gettysburg, PA 17325: Free information with long SASE ■ American Civil War and British Colonial War miniatures. 717–337–3151.

Gordon's Soldiers, 44 Page Rd., Bow, NH 03304: Catalog $20 ■ The Queen's Men military miniatures. 603–224–3924.

Gorton Toy Soldiers, P.O. Box 10632, Phoenix, AZ 85064: Free information with long SASE ■ Toy soldiers. 602–266–9619.

Tony & Jacki Grecco, P.O. Box 3490, Poughkeepsie, NY 12603: Free list ■ Toy soldiers and military toys. 914–461–8829.

Carl Hoegermeyer Toy Soldiers, P.O. Box 908, Buckingham, PA 18912: Catalog $3 ■ Toy soldiers, battlefield accessories, and other miniatures. 215–794–5606.

Holt's Hobbies, 19800 SW 280th Ave., Box 40, Miami, FL 33187: Free price list ■ World War I doughboys and German combat soldiers, motor scouts, side cars, medical figures, and other toy soldiers. 305–253–4251.

Horse Guards Limited, 500 Hilderbrand Dr., Atlanta, GA 30328: Free information with long SASE ■ Toy soldier sets and individual pieces from different historical periods. 404–252–6504.

I/R Miniatures, Inc., P.O. Box 89, Burnt Mills, NY 12077: Catalog $5.50 ■ Historically detailed 54mm and 76mm military miniatures and kits from American military history.

Jack's Gallery of Soldiers, John Jammaco, American Mail Depot, Box 180, Ave. N,

Brooklyn, NY 11234: Catalog $2 ■ Dimestore, World War II, Old West, Civil War, and other toy soldier reproductions.

King's Toy Soldiers, 4901 Broadway, Ste. 142, San Antonio, TX 78209: Free information with long SASE ■ Toy soldiers for collectors. 512–828–2292.

Labell's Toy Soldiers, Inc., Royal York Hotel, 100 Front St. West, Toronto, Ontario, Canada M5J 1E3: Free information with long SASE ■ Toy soldiers. 416–362–8697.

LLM Distributors, P.O. Box 76087, Atlanta, GA 30358: Free lists ■ Hand-painted toy soldiers and other figures. 404–394–3340.

London Bridge Toy Soldiers, East Penn Plaza, 1325 Chestnut St., Emmaus, PA 18049: Catalog $3 ■ Toy soldiers. 215–967–6887.

Memorable Things, P.O. Box 10505, Towson, MD 21204: Free list ■ Foreign and domestic toy soldiers and civilian figures and vehicles. 410–825–3117.

Mickey's House of Soldiers, 601 Capella St., Sunnyvale, CA 94086: Free information with long SASE ■ Toy soldier sets and individual pieces from different historical periods. 408–739–5465.

Midwest Miniatures, 4645 Lilac Ave., Glenview, IL 60025: Free list ■ Mignot miniatures from Paris. 708–296–5465.

Military Artists Guild, Bruce A. Roberts, 8305 Hillcrest Rd., Custer, WI 54423: Free information ■ Hand and custom painted toy soldiers. 715–341–8640.

Monarch Miniatures, P.O. Box 4195, Long Island City, NY 11104: Catalog $3 ■ Miniatures from many historical periods, including the American Civil War. 718–424–4343.

Old Toy Soldier Home, 977 S. Santa Fe Ave., Ste. 11, Vista, CA 92083: Free information with long SASE ■ Toy soldier sets and individual pieces from different historical periods. 619–758–5481.

Pageantry Products, 8571 Harrison Way, Buena Park, CA 90620: Free information with long SASE ■ Toy soldier miniatures. 714–995–5867.

Plantagenet USA, P.O. Box 5746, Marlborough, MA 01752: Free information with long SASE ■ Toy soldier sets and individual pieces from different historical periods. 508–485–5792.

Red Lancer, P.O. Box 8056, Mesa, AZ 85214: Catalog $6 ■ Original 19th-century military art, rare books, Victorian era campaign medals and helmets, old toy soldiers, and other collectibles. 602–964–9667.

Jack Scruby's Toy Soldiers, P.O. Box 1658, Cambria, CA 93428: Free list ■ Scruby 54mm and 40mm toy soldiers, Britains, and Authenticast reproductions. Includes unpainted castings. 805–927–3805.

Ship & Soldier Shop, 58 Maryland Ave., Annapolis, MD 21401: Free information with long SASE ■ Toy soldier sets and individual pieces from different historical periods. 410–268–1141.

Rodger C. Smith Collectables, 3213 W. Liberty Ave., Pittsburgh, PA 15216: Catalog $7 ■ Toy soldiers. 412–561–1001.

Soldier Shop, Inc., 1222 Madison Ave., New York, NY 10128: Catalog $5 ■ Antique and new toy soldiers, painted miniatures and kits, militaria, paintings, and weapons; military medals and arms; books; and prints.

Somerset, Ltd., 5402 Rebecca Ln., Knoxville, TN 37920: Free information with long SASE ■ Toy soldiers and other miniatures from different historical periods. 615–573–6368.

Stone Castle Imports, 804 N. 3rd St., P.O. Box 141, Bardstown, KY 40004: Free information with long SASE ■ Hand-painted 54mm soldier sets and individual pieces from different historical periods, and Imperial Productions from New Zealand. 502–897–0207.

TNC Enterprises, 318 Churchill Ct., Elizabethtown, KY 42701: Catalog $3 ■ Toy soldier sets and individual pieces from different historical periods. 502–765–5035.

The Toy Soldier, Olde Mystic Village, Mystic, CT 06355: Free information with long SASE ■ Military figures and other miniatures. 203–536–1554.

The Toy Soldier, James H. Hillestad, Paradise Falls, RR 1, Box 379, Cresco, PA 18326: Free information with long SASE ■ Toy soldier sets and individual pieces from different historical periods. 717–629–7227.

Toy Soldier Collection, 302 S. Main, Galena, IL 61036: Free information with long SASE ■ Toy soldier sets and individual pieces from different historical periods. 815–777–0383.

Toy Soldier Company, 100 Riverside Dr., New York, NY 10024: Plastics catalog $4; leads catalog $7.50 ■ United States, British, French, and German lead and plastic toy soldiers and other miniatures, from 1900 to the present. 212–799–6348.

Toy Soldier Gallery, Inc., 24 Main St., Highland Falls, NY 12928: Catalog $5 ■ Toy soldier sets and individual pieces from different historical periods. 800–777–9904.

Toy Soldier Manufacturing Company, RR 1, Box 253, Burlington, IA 52601: Catalog $3 ■ Toy soldiers cast in original factory moulds. 319–752–3840.

Toy Troops, 16928 Bolsa Chica St., Huntington Beach, CA 92649: Free information with long SASE ■ Military figures and other miniatures. 714–846–8486.

Tradition USA Toy Soldiers, 12924 Viking Dr., Burnsville, MN 55337: Free information with long SASE ■ Toy soldiers for collectors. 612–890–1634.

The Trumpeting Angel, 7654 W. Bancroft St., Toledo, OH 43617: Free information with long SASE ■ Military figures and other miniatures. 419–841–4523.

Warwick Miniatures, Ltd., P.O. Box 1498, Portsmouth, NH 03801: Catalog $3 ■ Detailed miniatures from historical periods of the United States, England, France, and Germany. Also Imperial Toy Soldiers from New Zealand. 603–431–7139.

Wiley House Toy Soldiers, 913 Sheridan Ave., Cody, WY 82414: Free information with long SASE ■ Military figures and other miniatures. 307–587–6030.

TRACK & FIELD SPORTS

Clothing

Adidas USA, 15 Independence Blvd., Warren, NJ 07060: Free information ■ Shoes and clothing. 908–580–0700.

Asics Tiger Corporation, 10540 Talbert Ave., Fountain Valley, CA 92708: Free information ■ Shoes and clothing. 714–962–7654.

B & G Wholesale, 47–09 30th St., Long Island City, NY 11101: Free information ■ Shoes. 718–706–0100.

Betlin Manufacturing, 1445 Marion Rd., Columbus OH 43207: Free information ■ Clothing. 614–443–0248.

Converse, Inc., One Fordham Rd., North Reading, MA 01864: Free information ■ Shoes. 800–225–5079; 508–664–1100 (in MA).

F & C Sportswear, 20239 W. Warren, Dearborn Heights, MI 48127: Free information ■ Clothing. 800–521–0260; 800–482–5340 (in MI).

Fab Knit Manufacturing Company, Division Anderson Industries, 1415 N. 4th St., Waco, TX 76707: Free information ■ Clothing. 800–333–4111; 817–752–2511 (in TX).

Felco Athletic Wear Company, Inc., 900 Passaic Ave., Harrison, NJ 07029: Free information ■ Clothing. 800–221–8240; 201–484–4200 (in NJ).

General Shoelace Company, 642 Starks Bldg., Louisville, KY 40202: Free information ■ Shoes. 502–585–4191.

New Balance Athletic Shoe, Inc., 38 Everett St., Boston, MA 02134: Free information ■ Shoes and clothing. 800–253–SHOE.

Nike Footwear, Inc., One Bowerman Dr., Beaverton, OR 97005: Free information ■ Shoes. 800–344–6453.

Puma USA, Inc., 147 Centre St., Brockton, MA 02403: Free information ■ Shoes. 508–583–9100.

Reebok International, Ltd., 100 Technology Center Dr., Stoughton, MA 02072: Free information ■ Shoes. 800–382–3823; 617–341–5000 (in MA).

Sport World Distributors, 3060 Clermont Rd., P.O. Box 27131, Columbus, OH 44327: Free information ■ Clothing. 614–838–8511.

Venus Knitting Mills, Inc., 140 Spring St., Murray Hill, NJ 07974: Free information ■ Clothing. 800–955–4200; 201–464–2400 (in NJ).

Equipment

Blazer Manufacturing Company, Inc., P.O. Box 266, Columbus, NE 68601: Free information ■ Crossbars, hurdles, discuses, javelins, batons, and blocks. 402–721–2525.

Cramer Products, Inc., 153 W. Warren St., P.O. Box 1001, Gardner, KS 66030: Free information ■ Crossbars, hurdles, discuses, javelins, batons, blocks, and lane markers. 800–255–6621; 913–884–7511 (in KS).

FiberSport, Inc., 6740 E. Bannister, Kansas City, MO 64134: Free information ■ Crossbars, hurdles, hammers, discuses, javelins, pits and pit bags, shot puts, and vaulting poles. 800–24–TRACK.

Hadar Manufacturing Company, 405 Main, P.O. Box 7, Dakota City, IA 50529: Free information ■ Hurdles, discuses, batons, and blocks. 515–332–5312.

Olympia Sports, School Tech, Inc., 745 State Cir., Ann Arbor, MI 48108: Free information ■ Crossbars, hurdles, lane markers, batons, and blocks. 313–761–5135.

Sports America, Inc., 101 Glover St., Barton, VT 05822: Free information ■ Crossbars, hurdles, discuses, javelins, batons, blocks, and lane markers. 802–525–3535.

Whitland Fitness Corporation, 101 Methuen St., P.O. Box 1049, Lawrence, MA 01842: Free information ■ Crossbars, hurdles, hammers, pits and pit bags, shot puts, discuses, javelins, and blocks. 508–685–5109.

TRAMPOLINES

Astronaut Trampolines, 6901 Peachtree Blvd., Norcross, GA 30092: Free information ■ Trampolines. 404–449–8690.

Austin Athletic Equipment Corporation, 705 Bedford Ave., Box 423, Bellmore, NY 11710: Free information ■ Trampolines. 516–785–0100.

Gym Equipment Company, P.O. Box 144, Ridgewood, NJ 07451: Free information ■ Trampolines. 201–447–2884.

Natural Science Industries, Ltd., 51–17 Rockaway Beach Blvd., Far Rockaway, NY 11691: Free information ■ Trampolines. 718–945–5400.

Rich Marketing Company, P.O. Box 3828, Albany, GA 31706: Free information ■ Trampolines. 912–435–2101.

Sidlinger Products, 901 W. Miller, Garland, TX 75041: Free information ■ Trampolines. 214–494–3488.

Sunstar International, Ltd., Sunsport Sporting Goods, 24–16 Queens Plaza South, Long Island City, NY 11101: Free information ■ Trampolines. 718–706–0611.

Trampoline World, P.O. Box 808, Fayetteville, GA 30214: Free literature ■ Trampolines. 404–461–9941.

Trampolking Sporting Goods, P.O. Box 3828, Albany, GA 31708: Free brochure ■ Trampolines, exercise bikes, rowers, and other physical fitness equipment. 800–841–4351; 912–435–2101 (in GA).

TVs & VCRs
Retail Sources

Audio Advisor, 225 Oakes SW, Grand Rapids, MI 49503: Catalog $1 ■ Audio and video equipment. 616–451–3868.

AV Distributors, 16451 Space Center Blvd., Houston, TX 77058: Free information ■ Audio, video, and stereo equipment, television sets, and fax machines. 800–843–3697.

Bondy Export Corporation, 40 Canal St., New York, NY 10002: Free information with long SASE ■ Household appliances, cameras, video and television equipment, office machines and typewriters, and luggage. 212–925–7785.

Cole's Appliance & Furniture Company, 4026 Lincoln Ave., Chicago, IL 60618: Free information with long SASE ■ Furniture, audio and video equipment, television sets, and household appliances. 312–525–1797.

Computability Consumer Electronics, P.O. Box 17882, Milwaukee, WI 53217: Free information ■ Audio, video, and stereo equipment and television sets; fax machines; copiers; and computers. 800–558–0003; 414–357–8181 (in WI).

Crutchfield, 1 Crutchfield Park, Charlottesville, VA 22906: Free information ■ Video, audio, and stereo equipment and television sets. 800–336–5566.

Electronic Wholesalers, 1160 Hamburg Tpk., Wayne, NJ 07470: Free information ■ Camcorders, television sets, cassette players/recorders, 8mm and Beta home decks, audio/hi-fi receivers, and other electronics. 201–696–6531.

ElectroWorks, Plaza 34, 100G Hwy. 34, Matawan, NJ 07747: Free information ■ Audio and video equipment, television sets, speakers, camcorders, cassette players/recorders, compact disk players, audio/video receivers-amplifiers, car stereos, and other home electronics. 800–662–8559.

Factory Direct, 131 W. 35th St., New York, NY 10001: Free information ■ Audio, video, and stereo equipment, television sets, and fax machines. 800–428–4567.

Focus Electronics, 4523 13th Ave., Brooklyn, NY 11219: Catalog $2 (refundable) ■ Audio, stereo, and video equipment; appliances; photographic equipment; and other electronics. 718–436–4646.

Illinois Audio, 12 E. Delaware Pl., Chicago, IL 60611: Free price list ■ Audio, stereo, and video equipment. 800–621–8042; 312–664–0020 (in IL).

International Electronic World, 6330 Frankford Ave., Baltimore, MD 21206: Free catalog ■ Audio and video equipment. 410–485–0511.

International Tele-Video Marketing, 1605 John St., Fort Lee, NJ 07024: Free information ■ Video equipment. 201–944–5727.

J & R Music World, 59–50 Queens-Midtown Expy., Maspeth, NY 11378: Free catalog ■ Audio equipment, portable stereos, video recorders, telephones, video tapes, and computers. 800–221–8180.

Not-Just-Video, Inc., 58 Walker St., New York, NY 10013: Catalog $2.75 ■ Audio and video equipment, television sets, camcorders, and other electronics. 800–856–9890.

Olden Video, 1265 Broadway, New York, NY 10001: Free information ■ Audio and video equipment, television sets, cassette players/recorders, and other electronics. 212–725–1234.

Percy's, Inc., 19 Glennie St., Worcester, MA 01605: Free information ■ Save up to 50 percent on appliances and electronics. 508–755–5334.

Planet Electronics, 8418 Lilley, Canton, MI 48187: Free information ■ Television sets, automobile and portable stereos, video recorders, video tapes and cassettes, and compact disks. 800–222–5650; 313–453–4750 (in MI).

PowerVideo, 4413 Blue Bonnet, Stafford, TX 77477: Free information ■ Audio, video, and stereo equipment and television sets. 713–240–3202.

S & S Sound City, 58 W. 45th St., New York, NY 10036: Free information ■ Video recorders and disk players, television sets, and other electronics. 212–575–0210.

Saxitone Audio-Video, 1776 Columbia Rd. NW, Washington, DC 20009: Free brochure ■ Audio and video equipment and television sets. 202–462–0800.

Sound City, Meadtown Shopping Center, Rt. 23, Kinnelon, NJ 07405: Free information ■ Audio and video equipment, cassette players/recorders, compact disk players, camcorders, television sets, processors, decoders, and other home electronics. 201–838–3444.

Stereo Equipment Sales, Inc., 6730 Santa Barbara Ct., Baltimore, MD 21227: Free catalog ■ Stereo equipment, computers, telephones, telephone answering machines, and cassette players/recorders. 800–638–3920.

Sunshine South, 2606 N. Kings Hwy., Myrtle Beach, SC 29577: Free information ■ Video equipment. 800–845–0693; 803–448–8474 (in SC).

Super Video, Inc., 93 1st St., Hackensack, NJ 07601: Free information ■ Cassette players/recorders, camcorders, television sets, and other electronics. 800–524–1596.

Tri-State Camera, 160 Broadway, New York, NY 10038: Free information ■ Audio and video equipment, camcorders, copiers, video cassettes, and fax machines. 212–349–2555.

United Video & Camera Express, 724 7th Ave., New York, NY 10019: Free information ■ Video equipment. 800–448–3738; 212–397–1081 (in NY).

Video Depot, 1500 N. State St., Bellingham, WA 98225: Free information ■ Video equipment and telephones. 206–671–2500.

Vidicomp Distributors, Inc., 16219 North Freeway, Houston, TX 77090: Free information ■ Video equipment. 713–440–0040.

Wisconsin Discount Stereo, 2417 W. Badger Rd., Madison, WI 53713: Free information ■ Video and audio equipment and television sets. 800–356–9514.

Manufacturers

Acoustic Research, 330 Turnpike St., Canton, MA 02021: Free information ■ Compact disk players, loudspeakers, and universal remotes. 617–821–2300.

Akai Division, Mitsubishi Electric, 225 Old New Brunswick Rd., Piscataway, NJ 08854: Free information ■ Cassette players/re-corders, compact disk players, television sets, audio/video receivers-amplifiers, surround sound processors, universal remotes, and audio controllers. 908–562–8500.

Canon, One Canon Plaza, Lake Success, NY 11042: Free information ■ Cassette players/recorders, camcorders, surround sound processors, character/effects generators, and decoders. 516–488–6700.

Curtis-Mathes, 1141 Greenway Dr., Irving, TX 75062: Free information ■ Loudspeakers, camcorders, cassette players/recorders, and television sets. 214–550–8050.

dbx, Inc., 707 E. Evelyn Ave., Sunnyvale, CA 94086: Free information ■ Cassette players/recorders, loudspeakers, compact disk players, audio/video receivers-amplifiers, surround sound processors, and audio controllers. 408–720–9800.

Emerson Radio Corporation, 1 Emerson Ln., North Bergen, NJ 07047: Free information ■ Camcorders, cassette players/recorders, compact disk players, and television sets. 800–922–0738.

Fisher, 21350 Lassen St., Chatsworth, CA 91311: Free information ■ Cassette players/recorders, compact disk players, surround sound processors, camcorders, television sets, and universal remotes. 818–998–7322.

G.E. Appliances, 4700 Allmond Ave., Louisville, KY 40225: Free information ■ Audio and video equipment, cassette players/recorders, camcorders, television sets, and universal remotes. 800–626–2000.

Goldstar, 1000 Sylvan Ave., Englewood, NJ 07632: Free information ■ Cassette players/recorders, compact disk players, and television sets. 201–460–8870.

Hitachi Sales Corporation, 401 W. Artesia Blvd., Compton, CA 90220: Free information ■ Audio and video equipment, cassette players/recorders, camcorders, compact disk players, and television sets. 310–537–8383.

Infinity Systems, 9409 Owensmouth Ave., Chatsworth, CA 91311: Free information ■ Loudspeakers and television sets. 818–709–9400.

Instant Replay, 2951 S. Bayshore Dr., Coconut Grove, FL 33133: Free information ■ Camcorders and cassette players/recorders. 305–854–6777.

JVC, 41 Slater Dr., Elmwood Park, NJ 07407: Free information ■ Audio and video equipment, cassette players/recorders, camcorders, compact disk players, audio/video receivers-amplifiers, television sets, and headphones. 201–794–3900.

Harmon Kardon, 240 Crossways Park, Woodbury, NY 11797: Free information ■ Cassette players/recorders, compact disk players, audio/video receivers-amplifiers, and television sets. 516–496–3400.

Kenwood, P.O. Box 22745, Long Beach, CA 90801: Free information ■ Audio and video equipment, cassette players/recorders, compact disk players, audio/video receivers-amplifiers, television sets, and surround sound processors. 310–639–9000.

Mitsubishi Electronics, 5757 Plaza Dr., P.O. Box 6007, Cypress, CA 90630: Free information ■ Audio and video equipment, cassette players/recorders, camcorders, compact disk players, and television sets. 714–220–2500.

Multivision, 1751 Fox Dr., San Jose, CA 94538: Free information ■ Audio controllers/processors, character/effects generators, and video processors/enhancers. 510–651–2351.

NAD, 575 University Ave., Norwood, MA 02062: Free information ■ Loudspeakers, laser disk players, compact disk players, television sets, and audio/video receivers-amplifiers. 617–762–0202.

NAP Consumer Electronics, 1 Phillips Dr., Knoxville, TN 37914: Free information ■ Magnavox: cassette players/recorders, laser disk players, compact disk players, camcorders, television sets, universal remotes; Philco: camcorders, television sets, cassette players/recorders, monitors-receivers; Philips: cassette players/recorders, compact disk players, television sets, projection television sets, stereo television sets; Sylvania: camcorders, cassette players/recorders, laser disk players, and television sets. 615–521–4391.

NEC Home Electronics, 1401 Estes Ave., Elk Grove Village, IL 60007: Free information ■ Audio and video equipment, cassette players/recorders, compact disk players, audio/video receivers-amplifiers, television sets, camcorders, surround sound processors, and audio controllers. 708–228–5900.

Onkyo, 200 Williams Dr., Ramsey, NJ 07446: Free information ■ Compact disk

players, audio/video receivers-amplifiers, universal remotes, and headphones. 201–825–7950.

Panasonic, Panasonic Way, Secaucus, NJ 07094: Free information ■ Audio and video equipment, cassette players/recorders, compact disk players, television sets, camcorders, decoders, and headphones. 201–348–7000.

J.C. Penney Company, Inc., Catalog Division, Milwaukee, WI 53263: Free information ■ Cassette players/recorders, television sets, audio/video systems, and other electronics. 800–222–616.

Pentax Corporation, 35 Inverness Dr. East, Englewood, CO 80112: Free information ■ Cassette players/recorders and camcorders. 303–799–8000.

Pioneer Electronics, 5000 Airport Plaza Dr., Long Beach, CA 90810: Free information ■ Audio and video equipment, cassette players/recorders, laser disk players, compact disk players, audio/video receivers-amplifiers, television sets, surround sound processors, decoders, and headphones. 310–420–5700.

Proton Corporation, 5630 Cerritos Ave., Cypress, CA 90630: Free information ■ Audio and video equipment, loudspeakers, compact disk players, audio/video receivers-amplifiers, television sets, and decoders. 714–952–6900.

Quasar, 1707 N. Randall Rd., Elgin, IL 60123: Free information ■ * Audio and video equipment, cassette players/recorders, compact disk players, camcorders, and television sets. 708–468–5600.

Radio Shack, Division Tandy Corporation, 1500 One Tandy Center, Fort Worth, TX 76102: Free information ■ Cassette players/recorders, compact disk players, camcorders, and universal remotes. 817–390–3700.

RCA Sales Corporation, 600 N. Sherman Dr., Indianapolis, IN 46201: Free information ■ Audio and video equipment, cassette players/recorders, compact disk players, television sets, camcorders, surround sound processors, character/effects generators, decoders, and audio controllers. 317–267–5000.

Samsung, 301 Mayhill St., Saddle Brook, NJ 07662: Free information ■ Cassette

players/recorders and television sets. 201–587–9600.

Sansui Electronics, 1290 Wall St. West, Lyndhurst, NJ 07071: Free information ■ Audio and video equipment, cassette players/recorders, compact disk players, camcorders, audio/video receivers-amplifiers, television sets, surround sound processors, decoders, and audio controllers/processors. 201–460–9710.

Sanyo Electronics, 1200 W. Artesia Blvd., Compton, CA 91311: Free information ■ Cassette players/recorders, compact disk players, camcorders, television sets, surround sound processors, decoders, and universal remotes. 310–537–5830.

Sears, Roebuck & Company, Catalog Division, 925 S. Homan Ave., Chicago, IL 60607: Free information ■ Cassette players/recorders, camcorders, and television sets. (Catalog also available from local stores.) 312–875–2500.

Sharp Electronics, Sharp Plaza, Mahwah, NJ 07430: Free information ■ Audio and video equipment, cassette players/recorders, compact disk players, camcorders, television sets, audio/video receivers-amplifiers, and decoders. 800–BE–SHARP.

Sony Consumer Products, Sony Dr., Park Ridge, NJ 07656: Free information ■ Audio and video equipment, cassette players/recorders, compact disk players, camcorders, audio/video receivers-amplifiers, television sets, camcorders, surround sound processors, character/effects generators, decoders, universal remotes, and headphones. 201–930–1000.

Symphonic, 6142 N. Kenmore Ave., Chicago, IL 60660: Free information ■ Cassette players/recorders and monitors-receivers. 312–338–1244.

Teac, 7733 Telegraph Rd., Montebello, CA 90640: Free information ■ Cassette players/recorders, laser disk players, compact disk players, surround sound processors, audio controllers, character/effects generators, and headphones. 213–726–0303.

Teknika, 353 Rt. 46 West, Fairfield, NJ 07006: Free information ■ Cassette players/recorders, television sets, and decoders. 201–575–0380.

Toshiba, 82 Totowa Rd., Wayne, NJ 07470: Free information ■ Cassette players/recorders, compact disk players, camcorders, surround sound processors, and television sets. 201–628–8000.

Vector Research, 1230 Calle Suerte, Camarillo, CA 93010: Free information ■ Cassette players/recorders, compact disk players, and audio/video receivers-amplifiers. 805–987–1312.

Vidicraft, SW Bancroft St., Portland, OR 97201: Free information ■ Camcorders, video processors/enhancers, and character/effects generators. 503–223–4884.

Yamaha, 6660 Orangethorpe Ave., Buena Park, CA 90620: Free information ■ Audio and video equipment, powered loudspeakers, cassette players/recorders, laser disk players, compact disk players, audio/video receivers-amplifiers, surround sound processors, and headphones. 714–522–9105.

Zenith, 1000 Milwaukee Ave., Glenview, IL 60025: Free information ■ Cassette players/recorders, camcorders, television sets, decoders, and universal remotes. 708–391–7000.

Cable TV Equipment

Ace Products, P.O. Box 582, Saco, ME 04072: Free catalog ■ Cable television equipment. 800–234–0726.

B & B Cable, Inc., 4030 Beau-D-Rue Dr., Egan, MN 55122: Free information ■ Cable television equipment. 800–826–7623.

Bay State Electronics, P.O. Box 103, Boston, MA 02188: Free information ■ Cable television equipment. 800–359–9806.

Blue Star, Rt. 3, P.O. Box 173, Williamstown, NY 13493: Free information ■ Cable television equipment. 315–964–2295.

Cable-Mate, Inc., 214 N. Main St., Algonquin, IL 60102: Free catalog with long SASE ■ Cable television equipment. 708–658–2121.

Cable Plus, 14417 Chase St., Panorama City, CA 91402: Free information ■ Cable television equipment. 800–822–9955.

Global Cable Network, 1032 Irving St., Ste. 109, San Francisco, CA 94122: Free catalog ■ Cable television equipment. 800–327–8544.

L & L Electronics, Inc., 1430 Miner St., Ste. 522, Des Plaines, IL 60016: Free catalog ■ Cable television equipment. 708–438–4056.

M.D. Electronics, 875 S. 72nd St., Omaha, NE 68114: Free catalog ■ Cable television equipment. 800–624–1150.

Midwest Electronics, Inc., P.O. Box 5000, Carpentersville, IL 60110: Catalog 60¢ ■ Cable television equipment. 800–648–3030.

Nu-Tel Electronics, 5114 Balcones Wood Dr., Austin, TX 78759: Free catalog ■ Cable TV equipment. 512–250–5031.

Pacific Cable Company, Inc., 7325–1/2 Resada Blvd., Resada, CA 91335: Free catalog ■ Cable television equipment. 800–345–8927.

Republic Cable Products, 4080 Paradise Rd., Las Vegas, NV 89109: Free information ■ Cable television equipment. 702–362–9026.

Sun Microwave International, Inc., P.O. Box 34522, Phoenix, AZ 85067: Catalog $1 ■ Wireless cable receivers and other equipment. 800–484–4190.

Swensen Electronics, 518 N. Harrison, Algonquin, IL 60102: Free catalog ■ Cable television equipment. 708–658–8643.

Trans-World Cable Company, 3958 N. Lake Blvd., Lake Park, FL 33403: Free catalog ■ Cable television equipment. 800–442–9333.

United Electronic Supply, P.O. Box 1206, Elgin, IL 60121: Free information ■ Cable television equipment. 708–697–0600.

Universal View, 520 Glenbrook Rd., Ste. 202, Stamford, CT 06906: Free catalog ■ Cable television equipment and microwave antennas. 203–975–7543.

U.S. Cable TV, Inc., 4100 N. Powerline Rd., Pompano Beach, FL 33073: Free catalog ■ Cable television equipment. 800–772–6244.

Video Tech, 3702 S. Virginia St., Reno, NV 89502: Free catalog ■ Cable television equipment. 800–562–6884.

Worldwide Cable, 7491 N. Federal Hwy., Ste. 142, Boca Raton, FL 33487: Free catalog ■ Cable television equipment. 800–772–3233.

Satellite Dishes

R.L. Drake Company, P.O. Box 112, Miamisburg, OH 45342: Free information ■ Satellite television antennas and receivers with optional remote control. 513–866–2421.

International Electronic World, 6330 Frankford Ave., Baltimore, MD 21206: Free catalog ■ Satellite television receivers and audio and video equipment. 410–485–0511.

Paraclipse, Inc., 3711 Meadowview Dr., Redding, CA 96002: Free information ■ Easy-to-assemble KU and C band compatible satellite television antennas. 916–365–9131.

Phillips-Tech Electronics, P.O. Box 8533, Scottsdale, AZ 85252: Free information ■ Satellite television antennas. 602–947–7700.

Satellite City, 4920 Topanga Canyon Blvd., Woodland Hills, CA 91364: Free information ■ Satellite television receivers and other electronics. 818–710–9348.

Satellite Television, 120 W. Centennial Ave., Muncie, IN 47303: Free information ■ Satellite television receivers. 317–288–0074.

Satman, 715 W. Glen, Peoria, IL 61614: Free buyer's guide ■ Satellite television equipment. 800–472–8626; 309–692–4140 (in IL).

Skyvision, Inc., 1010 Frontier Dr., Fergus Falls, MN 56537: Free catalog ■ Save from 30 to 60 percent on satellite television equipment for do-it-yourself installation or system upgrading. 800–543–3025; 218–739–5231 (in MN).

Sun Microwave International, Inc., P.O. Box 34522, Phoenix, AZ 85067: Catalog $1 ■ Satellite television receivers and other video equipment. 800–484–4190.

Timberville Electronics, Timberville, VA 22853: Free information ■ Satellite television receivers. 800–825–4641.

Toshiba America Electronic Components, 9740 Irvine Blvd., Irvine, CA 92718: Free information ■ Television satellite receivers and equipment for system upgrading. 714–583–3381.

Universal Antenna Manufacturing, P.O. Box 338, Ward, AR 72176: Free information ■ Satellite reflector-type antennas with optional motorized mounts. 800–843–6517; 501–843–6517 (in AR).

Xandi Electronics, Box 25647, Tempe, AZ 85282: Catalog $1 (refundable) ■ Satellite television receivers, voice disguisers, FM bugs, telephone transmitters, phone snoops, and other kits. 800–336–7389; 602–829–8152 (in AZ).

TYPEWRITERS & WORD PROCESSORS

Bondy Export Corporation, 40 Canal St., New York, NY 10002: Free information with long SASE ■ Household appliances, cameras, video and television equipment, office machines and typewriters, and luggage. 212–925–7785.

Crutchfield, 1 Crutchfield Park, Charlottesville, VA 22906: Free catalog ■ Word processors, fax machines, telephones and answering machines, and computers and software. 800–336–5566.

East 33rd Street Electronics & Typewriters, 42 E. 33rd St., New York, NY 10016: Free flyer with long SASE ■ Typewriters, computers, software, calculators, telephones and answering machines, video equipment, and television sets. 212–686–0930.

Reliable Home Office, P.O. Box 804117, Chicago, IL 60607: Free catalog ■ Word processors, calculators, computer supplies, telephones, and office furniture. 800–326–6230.

Staples, Inc., P.O. Box 160, Newton, MA 02195: Free catalog ■ Office supplies, furniture, computer supplies and paper, drafting equipment, fax machines, and typewriters. 617–965–7030.

UMBRELLAS

The Umbrella Shop, 431 S. Dearborn St., Chicago, IL 60605: Free information ■ Umbrellas for women and men. 312–341–9772.

Uncle Sam Umbrella Shop, 161 W. 57th St., New York, NY 10019: Free information ■ Umbrellas, canes, and walking sticks. 212–247–7163.

VACUUM CLEANERS

AAA-All Factory, Inc., 241 Cedar, Abilene, TX 79601: Brochure $2 (refundable) ■ Save up to 50 percent on vacuum cleaners, floor buffers, and rug shampooers. 915–677–1311.

AAA Vacuum & Sewing Center Discounters, 1357 Fruitville Park, Lancaster, PA 17601: Free information ■ Vacuum cleaners. 717–397–5776.

ABC Vacuum Warehouse, 6720 Burnet Rd., Austin, TX 78757: Free price list ■ Vacuum cleaners. 512–459–7643.

Broan Manufacturing Company, P.O. Box 140, Hartford, WI 53027: Free information ■ Vacuum cleaner systems. 800–637–1453.

Central Vac International, 3133 E. 12th St., Los Angeles, CA 90023: Free information ■ Vacuum cleaner systems. 213–268–1135.

Discount Appliance Centers, 2908 Hamilton St., Hyattsville, MD 20782: Free information with long SASE ■ Vacuum cleaners, sewing machines, and attachments. 301–559–6801.

Dust Boy, Inc., RR 2, Box 269, Milan, IN 47031: Free information ■ Portable and stationary dust collectors. 800–232–3878; 812–654–2918 (in IN).

H-P Products, Inc., 512 W. Gorgas St., Louisville, OH 44641: Free information ■ Vacuum cleaner systems. 800–822–8356.

M & S Systems, Inc., 2861 Congressman Ln., Dallas, TX 75220: Free information ■ Vacuum cleaner systems. 800–877–6631.

MidAmerica Vacuum Cleaner Supply Company, 666 University Ave., St. Paul, MN 55104: Catalog $5 ■ Vacuum cleaners and parts, floor machines, and small kitchen appliances. 612–222–0763.

NuTone, Inc., Madison & Red Bank Rds., Cincinnati, OH 45227: Free information ■ Vacuum cleaner systems. 513–527–5100.

Oreck Corporation, 100 Plantation Rd., New Orleans, LA 70123: Free catalog ■ Vacuum cleaners. 800–989–4200.

Sewin' in Vermont, 84 Concord Ave., St. Johnsbury, VT 05819: Free information ■ Vacuum cleaners and attachments. 800–451–5124; 802–748–3803 (in VT).

Shop-Vax Corporation, 2323 Reach Rd., Williamsport, PA 17701: Free information ■ Wet and dry vacuum cleaners. 717–326–0502.

VIDEO TAPES & DISCS

Absolute Beta Movie Videos, P.O. Box 130, Remington, VA 22734: Catalog $9.95 (refundable) ■ Beta video movies. 800–WER–BETA.

Audiofidelity Enterprises, Inc., P.O. Box 86, Rahway, NJ 07065: Free information ■ Vintage video movies, jazz classics, and children's videos and music. 908–388–5000.

Blackhawk Films, 5959 Triumph St., City of Commerce, CA 90040: Catalog $1 ■ Silent and sound movies on video cassettes. 800–826–2295.

Eddie Brandt's Video, 6310 Colfax Ave., North Hollywood, CA 91606: Free catalog ■ VHS and Beta vintage television shows that include B-westerns, cliffhanger serials, black movies, war and military features, foreign films, early animation, and classics. 818–506–4242.

Calibre Press, Inc., 666 Dundee Rd., Ste. 1607, Northbrook, IL 60062: Free catalog ■ Law enforcement and EMS videos, books, and survival products. 800–323–0037; 708–498–5680 (in IL).

Critics' Choice Video, P.O. Box 549, Elk Grove Village, IL 60009: Free catalog ■ VHS classics, new releases, special interest videos, and other subjects. 800–544–9852.

Down Home Music Company, 10341 San Pablo Ave., El Cerrito, CA 94530: Free sample newsletters; blues, country and vintage rock 'n' roll catalogs, $5 each ■ Records, tapes, compact disks, music books, and videos. 510–525–1494.

Excalibur Films, 3621 W. Commonwealth, Fullerton, CA 92633: Catalog $6.95 ■ Movies on video cassettes and reels. 800–BUY–MOVIES.

Express Music Catalog, 175 5th Ave., New York, NY 10010: Catalog $10 ■ Compact disks, long-playing records, and video cassettes. 800–233–6357; 212–254–6161 (in NY).

Foothill Video, P.O. Box 547, Tujunga, CA 91043: Free list with long SASE ■ Westerns, serials, and other features in VHS and Beta format. 818–353–8591.

Historic Aviation, 1401 Kings Wood Rd., Eagan, MN 55122: Free information ■ Books and videos on the history of commercial airliners, famous men in aviation, nostalgic classics, humor, military action, and other aviation topics. 800–225–5575; 612–454–2493 (in MN).

Historic Video Archives, P.O. Box 189, Cedar Knolls, NJ 07927: Catalog $3 ■ Rare, obsolete, and unusual videos.

Home Film Festival, P.O. Box 2032, Scranton, PA 18501: Free information ■ VHS and Beta videotapes. Includes hard-to-find films, independent films, limited release features, Hollywood classics, and documentaries. 800–258–3456.

Home Vision, P.O. Box 800, Concord, MA 01742: Free catalog ■ Opera, ballet, and classical video recordings. 800–262–8600; 508–263–5006 (in MA).

House of Tyrol, P.O. Box 909, Alpenland Center, Helen Highway/75 North, Cleveland, GA 30528: Free catalog ■ Travel videos, folk music videos from around the world, and language and educational videos; musical cuckoo clocks, crystal, porcelain, lamps, and music boxes; and other gifts. 800–241–5404.

International Historic Films, Inc., Box 29035, Chicago, IL 60629: Catalog $1 ■ Military, political, social history, and rare archival material in Beta, VHS, and PAL Standard for European use. 312–927–2900.

Keep the Faith, Inc., 810 Belmont Ave., P.O. Box 8261, North Haledon, NJ 07508: Free catalog ■ Audio tapes, video tapes, and books on Catholicism. 800–221–1564; 201–423–5395 (in NJ).

KLS Beta Only, 7345 Rutherford Way, North Highlands, CA 95660: Free information ■ Beta videos. 916–338–2223.

KVC Home Video, 7225 Woodland Dr., P.O. Box 68881, Indianapolis, IN 46268: Free catalog ■ Film classics and how-to videos. 800–331–1387.

Laser House, 1409 W. 14 Mile Rd., Ste. 264, Madison Heights, MI 48071: Catalog $2 (refundable) ■ Compact disks and laser video disks. 313–875–6040.

Mike LeBell's Video, 75 Fremont Pl., Los Angeles, CA 90005: Catalog $1 ■ Rare titles, horror videos, serials, westerns, and other movies from the 1920s, 1930s, and 1940s. 213–938–3333.

Lyric Distribution, Inc., P.O. Box 235, Roslyn Heights, NY 11577: Catalog $1 ■ Operatic treasures on videos, cassettes, and disks. 516–625–0588.

Metropolitan Opera Guild, 70 Lincoln Center Plaza, New York, NY 10023: Free information ■ Classical, concert, operatic, and documentary videos. 800–892–1919.

Moviecraft, Inc., P.O. Box 438, Orland Park, IL 60462: Free catalog ■ Old television shows, rare cartoons, classics, contemporary releases, war newsreels and propaganda subjects, special interest subjects, and feature films. 708–460–9082.

Movies Unlimited, 6736 Castor Ave., Philadelphia, PA 19149: Catalog $9.95 ($5 refundable) ■ Movie classics, foreign films, nostalgic television shows, rarities, new releases, music videos, and how-to information. 800–523–0823; 215–722–8298 (in PA).

Music for Little People, Box 1460, Redway, CA 95560: Free catalog ■ Children's music cassettes, videos, and musical instruments. Includes famous stories, favorite songs, lullabies, nature stories, folk music, and classical music. 707–923–3991.

Music Mailorder, P.O. Box 20708, Milwaukee, WI 53220: Free catalog ■ Rare and imported records, tapes, compact disks, videos, books and magazines, and posters. 414–321–SPIN.

Richard Nelson, P.O. Box 9155, North Hollywood, CA 91609: Free catalog ■ Westerns, mysteries, serials, action and adventure, and other video cassettes from the 1930s and 1940s.

One Video Place, 405 Lowell St., Wakefield, MA 01880: Catalog $3.95 ■ Closed-captioned movies on video cassettes.

Parent Care, Ltd., 25 Independence Ct., P.O. Box 417, Folcroft, PA 19032: Catalog $2 ■ Video tapes for parents about health and safety, making learning fun, family entertainment, baby and child care, and classics and tapes for older members of the family. 800–334–3889.

Pyramid Film & Video, 2801 Colorado Ave., Santa Monica, CA 90404: Free catalog ■ Films and videos for educational and entertainment programming. 800–421–2304; 310–828–7577 (in CA).

Quicksilver Fantasies, P.O. Box 1660, Post Falls, ID 83854: Free catalog ■ Music, art, and myth, folklore, science-fiction, and fantasy videos. 208–773–7731.

Reader's Digest, Pleasantville, NY 10570: Free catalog ■ Videos on travel, nature, drama, and movies, children's subjects, how-

to information, sports, and music. 914–241–7445.

Rose Records, 214 S. Wabash Ave., Chicago, IL 60604: Free catalog ■ Classical and opera recordings on long-playing records, CDs, cassettes, and music videos. Includes imports, new releases, and overstocks at bargain prices. 800–955–ROSE.

SemVideo Products, Inc., 2147 E. 17th St., Brooklyn, NY 11229: Free catalog ■ Laser disks. 718–998–1731.

Shokus Video, P.O. Box 8434, Van Nuys, CA 91409: Catalog $3 ■ Television releases from the 1950s. 800–325–0788; 818–704–0400 (in CA).

Special Interest Video, P.O. Box 7022, Dover, DE 19903: Free catalog ■ Videos on history and military conflicts, dancing and music, gambling, pets, automobiles, physical fitness, karate, health and cosmetics, computers, family situations, subjects for children, travel, sports, and business. 800–522–0502.

SyberVision, 7133 Koll Center Pkwy., Pleasanton, CA 94566: Catalog $2 ■ Sports, health and fitness, languages, personal relationships, and other subjects. 800–678–0877; 510–846–3388 (in CA).

The Video Catalog, P.O. Box 64428, St. Paul, MN 55164: Free catalog ■ Home videos that include all-time favorite programs and films. 800–733–2232.

Video Revolution, 97 Thoreau St., Concord, MA 01742: Free catalog ■ Audio and video tapes for children. 800–342–3436.

View Video, 34 E. 23rd St., New York, NY 10010: Free catalog ■ Art, dance, opera, jazz and pop, and classical music videos. Other special interest areas include modern lifestyles, sports, parenting, and children's interactive subjects. 212–674–5550.

Walden Video for Kids, Dept. 610, P.O. Box 9497, Stamford, CT 06907: Free catalog ■ Children's video tapes. 800–443–7359.

Yes! Videos, P.O. Box 10726, Arlington, VA 22210: Free catalog ■ Videos on opera, art, dance, classical music, musicals, and new age music. 703–276–9550.

Zenith Books, P.O. Box 1, Osceola, WI 54020: Free catalog ■ Video tapes and books on military aircraft, plastic and radio control modeling, warplanes, aviation history, flying skills, aeronautics, and other aviation subjects. 800–826–6600.

VISION IMPAIRMENT AIDS

American Council of the Blind, 1155 15th St. NW, Ste. 720, Washington, DC 20005: Free list ■ Large print list of manufacturers and distributors of low vision aids and large print materials. 202–467–5081.

American Foundation for the Blind, Product Center, 100 Enterprise Pl., P.O. Box 7044, Dover, DE 19903: Free catalog ■ Watches, clocks and timers; canes; household and personal care aids; calculators and tools; and other sensory products. 800–829–0500.

American Printing House for the Blind, 1839 Frankfort Ave., P.O. Box 6085, Louisville, KY 40206: Free catalog ■ Braille writing and embossing equipment, electronic devices, containers, low-vision simulation materials, reading readiness products, and educational aids. 502–895–2405.

Independent Living Aids/Can-Do Products, 27 East Mall, Plainview, NY 11803: Free catalog ■ Self-help products for individuals with vision impairment and physical disabilities/challenges. 800–537–2118; 516–752–8080 (in NY).

LS & S Group, Inc., P.O. Box 673, Northbrook, IL 60065: Free catalog ■ Magnifiers, watches, Braille computers, gifts, and other products for people with visual impairments. 800–468–4789; 708–498–9777 (in IL).

Maxi Aids, P.O. Box 3209, Farmingdale, NY 11735: Free catalog ■ Aids and appliances for people with visual, physical, hearing, and other impairments. 800–522–6294.

National Federation of the Blind, Materials Center, 1800 Johnson St., Baltimore, MD 21230: Free catalog ■ Aids and appliance for visually impaired and blind persons. 301–659–9314.

On the Move, Inc., 334 Franklin St., Mansfield, MA 02048: Free brochure ■ Mobility aid for visually impaired persons, from age 2 to adult. 508–339–4027.

Science Products, Box 888, Berwyn, PA 19312: Free catalog ■ Voice technology equipment, custom electronics, and other sensory aids for hearing and visually impaired persons. 800–888–7400; 215–296–2111 (in PA).

SenseSations, 919 Walnut St., Philadelphia, PA 19107: Free catalog (available in large print, Braille, and tape cassette) ■ Talking products, adaptive recorders, computer products, and other services and equipment for people with visual impairments. 215–627–0600.

VITAMINS & MINERALS

Barth Vitamins, 865 Merrick Ave., Westbury, NY 11590: Free catalog ■ Natural vitamin and mineral supplements, cosmetics, health foods, and home health aids. 800–645–2328; 800–553–0353 (in NY).

Brownville Mills, Brownville, NE 68321: Free price list ■ Natural foods and vitamins. 402–825–4131.

Freeda Vitamins, 36 E. 41st St., New York, NY 10017: Free catalog ■ Vitamins, and dietary or food supplement needs. 800–777–3737; 212–685–4980 (in NY).

General Nutrition Catalog, Puritan's Pride, 105 Orville Dr., Bohemia, NY 11716: Free catalog ■ Vitamins, health foods, natural cosmetics, books, and gifts. 800–645–1030.

Hillestad Corporation, 1545 Berger Dr., San Jose, CA 95112: Free catalog ■ Natural vitamins. 800–535–7742; 408–298–0995 (in CA).

Indiana Botanic Gardens, Inc., P.O. Box 5, Hammond, IN 46325: Catalog $1 ■ Vitamins, herbs, spices, and personal care products. 800–348–6434; 219–931–2480 (in IN).

L & H Vitamins, Inc., 37–10 Crescent St., Long Island City, NY 11101: Free catalog ■ Save from 20 to 40 percent on vitamins and nutritional supplements. 800–221–1152; 618–937–7400 (in NY).

Lee Nutrition, 290 Main St., Cambridge, MA 02142: Free information ■ Nutritional vitamin preparations and supplements. 617–661–9600.

Nature Food Centres, One Nature's Way, Wilmington, MA 01887: Free catalog ■ Vitamins, natural food products, and cosmetics. 800–225–0857; 617–657–5000 (in MA).

Nutrition Headquarters, 104 W. Jackson St., Carbondale, IL 62901: Free catalog ■ Vitamins and health food supplements. 618–457–8103.

RVP Health Savings Center, 865 Merrick Ave., Westbury, NY 11590: Free catalog ■ Vitamins, natural supplements, and cosmetics and beauty aids. 800–645–2978; 800–682–2286 (in NY).

SDV Vitamins, P.O. Box 23030, Oakland Park, FL 33307: Free information ■ Nutritional supplements and vitamin preparations. 800–535–7095.

Star Pharmaceuticals, Inc., 1500 New Horizons Blvd., Amityville, NY 11701: Free catalog ■ Save up to 60 percent on generic vitamin products, nutritional supplements, toiletries, health care products, and pet supplies. 800–274–6400.

Stur-Dee Health Products, Inc., 3497 Austin Blvd., Island Park, NY 11558: Free catalog ■ Vitamins and health food supplements. 800–645–2638; 800–632–2592 (in NY).

Vitamin Quota, Inc., 975 Bloomfield Ave., West Caldwell, NJ 07006: Free catalog ■ Private brand vitamin and mineral products, dietary supplements, health aids, and generic equivalents of name-brand vitamins and pet products. 201–227–5740.

Vitamin Specialties Company, 8200 Ogontz Ave., Wyncote, PA 19095: Free catalog ■ Vitamin supplements. 800–365–8482; 215–885–3800 (in PA).

Western Natural Products, P.O. Box 90845, Long Beach, CA 90809: Free catalog ■ Natural vitamins. 800–762–5214; 805–949–6495 (in CA).

VOLLEYBALL

Clothing

Action Sport Systems, Inc., P.O. Box 1442, Morgantown, NC 28671: Free information ■ Uniforms. 800–631–1091; 704–874–2249 (in NC).

Adidas USA, 15 Independence Blvd., Warren, NJ 07060: Free information ■ Shoes. 908–580–0700.

Asics Tiger Corporation, 10540 Talbert Ave., Fountain Valley, CA 92708: Free information ■ Shoes and uniforms. 714–962–7654.

Champion Products, Inc., 3141 Monroe Ave., Rochester, NY 14618: Free information ■ Uniforms. 716–385–3200.

Converse, Inc., One Fordham Rd., Wilmington, MA 01887: Free information ■ Shoes. 800–225–5079; 508–664–1100 (in MA).

Foot-Joy, Inc., 144 Field St., Brockton, MA 02403: Free information ■ Shoes. 508–586–2233.

Mizuno Corporation, 5125 Peachtree Industrial Blvd., Norcross, GA 30092: Free information ■ Uniforms and shoes. 800–333–7888.

Nike Footwear, Inc., One Bowerman Dr., Beaverton, OR 97005: Free information ■ Shoes. 800–344–6453.

Puma USA, Inc., 147 Centre St., Brockton, MA 02403: Free information ■ Shoes. 508–583–9100.

Sport Fun, Inc., 4621 Sperry St., P.O. Box 39150, Los Angeles, CA 90039: Free information ■ Uniforms and shoes. 800–423–2597; 818–240–6700 (in CA).

Sport World Distributors, 3060 Clermont Rd., P.O. Box 27131, Columbus, OH 44327: Free information ■ Uniforms. 614–838–8511.

Venus Knitting Mills, Inc., 140 Spring St., Murray Hill, NJ 07974: Free information ■ Uniforms. 800–526–6466; 201–464–2400 (in NJ).

Equipment

Action Sport Systems, Inc., P.O. Box 1442, Morgantown, NC 28671: Free information ■ Volleyball sets, nets, posts, and standards. 800–631–1091; 704–874–2249 (in NC).

American Athletic, Inc., 200 American Ave., Jefferson, IA 50129: Free information ■ Nets. 800–247–3978.

Andia Progress Company, Inc., 47 Soundview Ave., White Plains, NY 10606: Free information ■ Nets, balls, and protective gear. 800–431–2775; 914–948–2685 (in NY).

Cannon Sports, P.O. Box 11179, Burbank, CA 91510: Free information ■ Nets and balls. 800–223–0064; 818–503–9570.

Champion Sports Products Company, Inc., P.O. Box 138, Sayreville, NJ 08872: Free information ■ Nets, balls, and protective gear. 201–238–0330.

Franklin Sports Industries, Inc., 17 Campanelli Pkwy., P.O. Box 508, Stoughton,

MA 02072: Free information ■ Volleyball sets, balls, and nets. 617–344–1111.

Gared Sports, Inc., 1107 Mullanphy St., St. Louis, MO 63106: Free information ■ Nets, posts, standards, and balls. 800–325–2682; 314–421–0044 (in MO).

General Sportcraft Company, Ltd., 140 Woodbine St., Bergenfield, NJ 07621: Free information ■ Nets, posts, standards, balls, and protective gear. 201–384–4242.

Jayfro Corporation, Unified Sports, Inc., 976 Hartford Tpk., P.O. Box 400, Waterford, CT 06385: Free catalog ■ Nets, posts, referee stands, and equipment carriers. 203–447–3001.

Dick Martin Sports, Inc., 185 River Rd., P.O. Box 931, Clifton, NJ 07014: Free information ■ Nets, posts, balls, and protective gear. 800–221–1993; 201–473–0757 (in NJ).

Pennsylvania Sporting Goods, 1360 Industrial Hwy., P.O. Box 451, Southampton, PA 18966: Free information ■ Nets, posts, standards, and protective gear. 800–535–1122.

Regent Sports Corporation, 45 Ranick Rd., Hauppage, NY 11787: Free information ■ Nets, posts, standards, and balls. 516–234–2948.

Spalding & Brothers, 425 Meadow St., P.O. Box 901, Chicopee, MA 01021: Free information ■ Nets, posts, standards, and balls. 413–536–1200.

Voit Sports, 1451 Pittstand-Victor Rd., 100 Willowbrook Office Park, Fairport, NY 14450: Free information ■ Balls. 800–367–8648; 716–385–2390 (in NY).

Whitland Fitness Corporation, 101 Methuen St., P.O. Box 1049, Lawrence, MA 01842: Free information ■ Volleyball sets, posts, nets, and standards. 508–685–5109.

Wilson Sporting Goods, 2233 West St., River Grove, IL 60171: Free information ■ Balls. 800–323–1552.

Winston Sports Corporation, 200 5th Ave., New York, NY 10010: Free information ■ Volleyball sets, nets, posts, standards, and balls. 212–255–6870.

WATER PURIFIERS

Action Filter, Inc., 777 Wyoming Ave., Kingston, PA 18704: Free brochure ■ Easy-to-install water purifier. 800–288–4520.

Basic Designs, Inc., 5815 Bennett Valley Rd., Santa Rosa, CA 95404: Free information ■ High-flow and pocket-size water filters. 707–575–1220.

General Ecology, Inc., 151 Sheree Blvd., Exton, PA 19341: Free literature ■ Portable, base camp, and travel-type water purifiers. 800–441–8166.

Katadyn USA, Inc., 3020 N. Scottsdale Rd., Scottsdale, AZ 85251: Free information ■ Water purification equipment. 800–950–0808.

Krystal Kleen Water Corporation, P.O. Box 1276, Cape Coral, FL 33910: Free information ■ Water purification equipment for the home or business. Available in above-the-counter, below-the-counter, and whole-house system models. 813–542–8878.

Liberty Water Systems, P.O. Box 175, Delafield, WI 53018: Free information ■ Home reverse osmosis water purifiers. 414–968–5619.

Mountain Safety Research, P.O. Box 24547, Seattle, WA 98124: Free information ■ Portable water purification equipment. 800–877–9677.

National EnviroAlert Company, 297 Lake St., Waltham, MA 02154: Free brochure ■ Environmental air systems and water filtration units. 617–891–7484.

Recovery Engineering, 2229 Edgewood Ave. South, Minneapolis, MN 55426: Free information ■ Lightweight water purification equipment. 800–548–0406.

WATER SKIING

Boats

American Skier Boat Corporation, 301 Enterprise Dr., Ocoee, FL 32761: Free information ■ Inboards and stern drives. 407–656–3332.

Baja Boats, Box 151, Bucyrus, OH 44820: Free information ■ Outboards and inboards. 419–562–5377.

Brendella Boats, Inc., 3797 North Hwy. 59, Merced, CA 95348: Free information ■ Inboards. 209–384–2566.

Celebrity Boats, Inc., 451 E. Illinois Ave., P.O. Box 394, Benton, IL 62812: Free information ■ Stern drives. 618–439–9444.

Chaparral Boats, Inc., Industrial Park Blvd., P.O. Drawer 928, Nashville, GA 31639: Free information ■ Stern drives. 912–686–7481.

Cobia Boat Company, 500 Silver Lake Dr., P.O. Box 1857, Sanford, FL 32773: Free information ■ Inboards and stern drives. 407–322–3540.

Correct Craft, Inc., 6100 S. Orange Ave., Orlando, FL 32809: Free information ■ Inboards. 800–346–2092; 407–855–4141 (in FL).

Forester Boats, 25900 Fallbrook Ave., Wyoming, MN 55092: Free information ■ Stern drives. 612–462–4526.

Four Winns, Inc., 4 Winn Way, Cadillac, MI 49601: Free information ■ Stern drives. 616–775–1351.

Glasstream Boats, Hwy. 129 South, P.O. Box 943, Nashville, GA 31639: Free information ■ Stern drives. 912–686–2128.

Invader Boats, Inc., P.O. Box 420, Giddings, TX 78942: Free information ■ Stern drives. 409–542–3101.

Malibu Boats of California, Inc., 1861 Grogan Ave., Merced, CA 95340: Free information ■ Inboards. 209–383–7469.

MasterCraft Boat Company, 869 Binfield Rd., Maryville, TN 37801: Free information ■ Inboards. 615–983–2178.

Regal Marine Industries, Inc., 2300 Jetport Dr., Orlando, FL 32809: Free information ■ Stern drives. 800–US–REGAL.

Renken Boat Manufacturing Company, Inc., 1750 Signal Point Rd., Charleston, SC 29412: Free information ■ Stern drives. 803–795–1150.

Rinker Marine, 207 Chicago St., Syracuse, IN 46567: Free information ■ Stern drives. 219–457–5731.

Sea Ray Boats, Inc., 2600 Sea Ray Blvd., Knoxville, TN 37914: Free information ■ Stern drives. 800–367–1596.

Stingray Boats, P.O. Box 669, Hartsville, SC 29550: Free information ■ Stern drives. 803–383–4507.

Sunbird Boat Company, Inc., 2348 Shop Rd., Columbia, SC 29201: Free information ■ Outboards. 803–799–1125.

Supra Sports, Inc., P.O. Box C, Greenback, TN 37742: Free information ■ Inboards. 615–856–3035.

Supreme Industries, Inc., P.O. Box 789, Alcoa, TN 37701: Free information ■ Inboards. 615–984–7700.

Sylvan Boats, Calaway Church Rd., P.O. Box 1267, LaGrange, GA 30241: Free information ■ Inboards and stern drives. 404–882–1438.

Equipment & Clothing

Aamstrand Corporation, 629 Grove, Manteno, IL 60950: Free information ■ Water skiing equipment. 800–338–0557; 312–458–8550 (in IL).

Americas Cup, Inc., P.O. Box 2009, La Puente, CA 91746: Free information ■ Flotation equipment. 818–961–7121.

Aquaglide Sport Ski, Ltd., 600 S. Magnolia Ave., Dunn, NC 28334: Free information ■ Knee boards. 919–891–1299.

Barefoot Company, 7747 S. Military Trail, Lake Worth, FL 33463: Free information ■ Ropes and handles for water skiing, wet suits, and dry suits. 407–439–3668.

Barefoot International, 140 S. Main St., Thiensville, WI 53092: Free information ■ Wet suits, dry suits, barefoot suits, and ropes and handles. 800–932–0685; 414–242–3113 (in WI).

Bart's Water Ski Center, P.O. Box 294, North Webster, IN 46555: Free catalog ■ Kneeboards, ropes and handles, gloves, water toys, ski boards, T-shirts, wet suits, and dry suits. 800–348–5016.

Body Glove International, Dive N' Surf, Inc., 530 6th St., Hermosa Beach, CA 90254: Free information ■ Wet suits and barefoot suits. 310–374–4074.

L.S. Brown Company, Pawley Industries Corporation, 3610 Atlanta Industrial Dr. NW, Atlanta, GA 30331: Free information ■ Water skiing and marine sport equipment. 404–691–8200.

Buckeye Sports Supply, John's Sporting Goods, 2655 Harrison Ave. SW, Canton, OH 44706: Free information ■ Water skiing equipment. 800–321–0690.

Burbank Water Ski Company, 1861 Victory Pl., Burbank, CA 91504: Free informa-tion ■ Water skis, ski sleds, tow hooks, and ropes. 818–848–8808.

Camaro USA, P.O. Box 370, Altoona, FL 32702: Free information ■ Clothing for water skiing sports. 904–669–5060.

Casad Manufacturing Corporation, 319 S. Park Dr., St. Marys, OH 45885: Free information ■ Wet suits, skis, ski sleds, tow hooks, ropes and handles, vests, and flotation wet suits. 419–394–7478.

Colores International, Inc., 1405 132nd Ave. NE, Ste. 2, Bellevue, WA 98005: Free information ■ Water skiing equipment. 206–454–6323.

Connelly Skis, Inc., 20621 52nd West, Lynnwood, WA 98036: Free information ■ Water skis, ropes, gloves, vests, trick harnesses, boat harnesses, ski racks, and videos. 206–775–5416.

Cypress Gardens Skis, ERO Industries, Inc., 8130 N. Lehigh Ave., Morton Grove, IL 60053: Free information ■ Slalom skis, knee boards, and ski boards. 708–965–3700.

Faeth Outdoor Sales, R.J.F. Enterprises, Inc., 1151 S. 7th St., P.O. Box 118–A, St. Louis, MO 63166: Free information ■ Water skis, ski sleds, tow hooks and ropes, and vests. 314–421–0030.

Harvey's Custom Suits, 2505 S. 252nd St., Kent, WA 98032: Free information ■ Wet suits and dry suits. 206–824–1114.

Hydroslide, P.O. Box 6700, Fort Wayne, IN 46896: Free information ■ Knee boards. 800–922–4470.

Jobe Ski Corporation, 15320 NE 92nd St., Redmond, WA 98052: Free information ■ Water skis, wet suits, gloves, handles and ropes, boat and trick harnesses, vests, ski racks, and videos. 206–882–1177.

Kidder International, Inc., P.O. Box 898, Auburn, WA 98002: Free information ■ Water skis, gloves, handles and ropes, boat harnesses, videos, vests, and ski racks. 206–939–7100.

Kransco Group Company, P.O. Box 884866, San Francisco, CA 94111: Free information ■ Water skis and ski boards. 415–433–9350.

Lynton Manufacturing, 442 Higgins Ave., Winnipeg, Manitoba, Canada R3A 1S5: Free information ■ Knee boards and ski boards. 204–942–1166.

Mastercraft Skis, 4590 Pell Dr., Unit A, Sacramento, CA 95838: Free information ■ Water skis, ropes, and vests. 916–920–3993.

O'Brien International, 14615 NE 91st St., Redmond, WA 98052: Free information ■ Water skis, ropes and handles, boat harnesses, vests, ski and kneeboard racks, tubes, and videos. 206–881–5900.

Olson Boatboard Designs, 3687 Old Santa Rita Rd., Pleasanton, CA 94566: Free information ■ Ski boards. 510–847–9789.

Overton's Sports Center, Inc., P.O. Box 8228, Greenville, NC 27835: Free catalog ■ Water skis, wet suits, dry suits, and ropes and handles. 800–334–6541; 800–682–8263 (in NC).

Performance Line Company, P.O. Box 427, Drayton Plains, MI 48020: Free information ■ Water skiing and marine sport equipment. 313–674–4500.

Rampage Custom Kneeboards, 6353 Applecross Dr., Fayetteville, NC 28304: Free information ■ Fiberglass kneeboards. 919–868–5525.

RM Water Skis USA, 267 Columbia Ave., Chapin, SC 29036: Free information ■ Slalom skis and knee boards. 800–433–8313.

Sano Sports International, Division of Redline Design, Inc., 1601 Rutherford Ln., P.O. Box 49388, Austin, TX 78754: Free information ■ Knee boards and ski boards. 512–836–SANO.

Schnitz International, Inc., 8391 Bonita Isle Dr., Lake Worth, FL 33467: Free information ■ Slalom skis. 407–969–6129.

Ski Limited, 7825 South Ave., Youngstown, OH 44512: Catalog $2.50 ■ Vests, ski ropes and handles, wet suits, dry suits, and barefoot suits. 800–621–6300.

Skurfer, P.O. Box 6700, Fort Wayne, IN 46896: Free information ■ Ski boards. 800–922–4470.

Stearns Manufacturing, P.O. Box 1498, St. Cloud, MN 56302: Free information ■ Flotation equipment and water skiing vests. 612–252–1642.

Surfer House, P.O. Box 726, Lynwood, WA 98046: Free information ■ Wet suits, dry suits, and clothing for water sports. 206–778–8060.

Thruster Water Ski Boards, 1055 W. College Ave., Ste. 328, Santa Rosa, CA 95401: Free information ■ Ski boards. 707–544–5162.

Thunderwear, Inc., 1060 E. Calle Negocio, Ste. C, San Clemente, CA 92672: Free information ■ Gloves. 800–422–6565; 800–556–6363 (in CA).

Wakeski, 6810 242nd Ave., Redmond, WA 98053: Free information ■ Knee boards and ski boards. 206–868–3072.

Wavelength Wetsuits, 1140 Mark Ave., Carpintera, CA 93103: Free information ■ Slalom, barefoot, jump, and buoyancy wet suits. 805–684–6694.

Wellington Leisure Products, P.O. Box 244, Madison, GA 30650: Free information ■ Water skis, gloves, ropes and handles, kneeboards and ski boards, trick and boat harnesses, videos, and ski racks. 404–342–4915.

World Ski Lines, 25 Pamaron Way, Novato, CA 94947: Free information ■ Water skis, ski sleds, tow hooks, tournament ropes, vests, and nylon covered tubes. 415–883–3700.

Yamaha Motor Corporation, P.O. Box 6555, Cypress, CA 90630: Free information ■ Wet suits. 800–526–6650.

WEATHER FORECASTING

Alden Electronics, 40 Washington St., Westborough, MA 01581: Free information ■ Weather radar equipment, weather graphics systems, and radio facsimile weather chart recorder kits. 508–366–8851.

American Weather Enterprises, P.O. Box 1383, Media, PA 19063: Free information ■ Electronic weather stations that provide electronic readouts of barometric pressure, daily and cumulative rainfall, indoor and outdoor temperatures, and wind speed and direction. 215–565–1232.

Digitar, 3465 Diablo Ave., Hayward, CA 94545: Free information ■ Professional weather station for home use. 800–678–3669.

Edmund Scientific Company, Edscorp Bldg., Barrington, NJ 08007: Free catalog ■ Weather forecasting instruments, microscopes, magnifiers, magnets, telescopes, binoculars, and other science equipment. 609–573–6260.

HAL Communications Corporation, 1201 W. Kenyon Rd., P.O. Box 365, Urbana, IL 61801: Free information ■ Automatic weather information instruments. 217–367–1701.

Hinds Instruments, Inc., 5250 NE Elam Young Pkwy., Hillsboro, OR 97124: Free information ■ Electronic weather data display station that can be linked directly to a computer modem or printer to provide a visible or audible record. 800–688–4463.

Klockit, P.O. Box 636, Lake Geneva, WI 53147: Free catalog ■ Instruments for building weather/time stations, Swiss music box movements, and clock-building parts and supplies. 800–556–2548.

Maximum, Inc., 30 Barnett Blvd., New Bedford, MA 02745: Free catalog ■ Instruments for wind, weather, tide, and time measurement, with optional digital and analog versions. 508–995–2200.

Simerl Instruments, 238 West St., Annapolis, MD 21401: Free brochure ■ Weather-forecasting instruments. 410–849–8667.

WeatherTrac, P.O. Box 122, Cedar Falls, IA 50613: Free catalog ■ Weather forecasting instruments, weather vanes, and educational aids. 319–266–7403.

Robert E. White Instruments, Inc., 34 Commercial Wharf, Boston, MA 02110: Free catalog ■ Electronic equipment for measuring indoor and outdoor temperatures. Readings include maximum and minimum temperatures and time of occurrence. 800–992–3045.

Wind & Weather, P.O. Box 2320, Mendocino, CA 95460: Free catalog ■ Barometers, thermometers, hygrometers, psychrometers, wind direction instruments, anemometers, weather vanes, sundials, rain gauges, cloud charts, and books. 707–937–0323.

WEATHER VANES

Berry-Hill Limited, 75 Burwell Rd., St. Thomas, Ontario, Canada N5P 3R5: Free catalog ■ Weather vanes, canning equipment, cider press, and garden tools. 519–631–0480.

Cape Cod Cupola Company, Inc., 78 State Rd., North Dartmouth, MA 02747: Catalog $2 ■ Early American weather vanes and cupolas. 508–994–2119.

Copper Art, P.O. Box 1220, Claremont, NH 03743: Free brochure ■ Custom handcrafted copper and brass weather vanes and sculptures. 603–542–2324.

Copper House, RFD 1, Box 4, Epsom, NH 03234: Catalog $2 ■ Handmade copper weather vanes and indoor and outdoor copper lanterns. 603–736–9798.

Denninger Cupolas & Weathervanes, RD 1, Box 447, Middletown, NY 10940: Catalog $1 ■ Weather vanes and redwood cupolas with copper roofs. 914–343–2229.

Doe Run, Mills Rd., Box 273, Newcastle, ME 04553: Free brochure ■ Handcrafted copper weather vanes and lanterns. 207–563–5708.

David H. Fletcher, Blue Mist Morgan Farm, 68 Liberty St., Haverhill, MA 01830: Catalog $3 ■ Handcrafted copper weather vanes and lanterns. 508–374–8783.

Good Directions Company, 24 Ardmore Rd., Stamford, CT 06902: Catalog $1 ■ Antique and polished copper weather vanes with solid brass directional indicators and stainless steel chimney caps. 800–346–7678; 203–348–1836 (in CT).

Holst, Inc., Box 370, Tawas City, MI 48764: Catalog $2 (refundable) ■ Country crafts, sundials, weather vanes, housewares, figurines, and holiday decorations. 517–362–5664.

Marian Ives Weathervanes, RR 1, Box 101–A, Charlemont, MA 01339: Brochure 50¢ ■ Handmade copper weather vanes. 413–339–8534.

Ship'n Out, Rt. 22, Brewster, NY 10509: Catalog $1 ■ Copper weather vanes in an old-fashion style. 914–878–4901.

Travis Truck, Metal Sculptor, Box 1832, Martha's Vineyard, MA 02568: Brochure $1 ■ Sculpted metal weather vanes. 508–693–3914.

Weathervanes, Forget Rd., Hawlry, MA 01339: Brochure 50¢ ■ Handmade copper weather vanes for indoor and outdoor use. 413–339–8534.

Westwinds, 3540 76th, Caledonia, MI 49316: Free information ■ Weather vanes, post and mailbox signs, and hitching posts. 800–635–5262.

Wind & Weather, P.O. Box 2320, Mendocino, CA 95460: Free catalog ■ Sundials, weather vanes, and weather forecasting instruments. 707–937–0323.

WEDDING INVITATIONS & ACCESSORIES

The American Wedding Album, American Stationery Company, Inc., 300 N. Park Ave., Peru, IN 46970: Free catalog ■ Wedding invitations, stationery, and gifts. 800–428–0379.

Ann's Wedding Stationery, P.O. Box 326, Carrollton, MO 64633: Free catalog ■ Invitations and enclosures, wedding story books to record memorable moments, bridal accessories, gifts, and decor accents. 800–821–7011; 816–542–1144 (in MO).

Creations by Elaine, 6253 W. 74th St., Box 2001, Bedford Park, IL 60499: Free catalog ■ Wedding invitations and stationery, cake knives and servers, reception accessories, and jewelry. 800–323–2717.

Dawn Invitations, 300 Main St., P.O. Box 100, Lumberton, NJ 08048: Free catalog ■ Wedding invitations and gifts for attendants. 800–528–6677.

Evangel Wedding Service, P.O. Box 202, Batesville, IN 47006: Free catalog ■ Original wedding invitations, announcements, programs, napkins and coordinating accessories with a Christian theme. 800–342–4227.

Illustrated Stationery, 3900 Jermantown Rd., Ste. 350, Fairfax, VA 22030: Free information with 1st class stamp ■ Personalized wedding stationery.

Jamie Lee Stationery, P.O. Box 5343, Glendale, AZ 85312: Free catalog ■ Wedding stationery for brides. 800–288–5800.

Memories, Inc., P.O. Box 17526, Raleigh, NC 27619: Free information ■ Handmade wedding albums and picture frames, bridal garters, birdseed bags, ringbearer's pillows, and flower girl baskets. 800–462–5069; 919–571–1648 (in NC).

Now & Forever, P.O. Box 820, Goshen, CA 92227: Free catalog ■ Invitations with dramatic, romantic, and contemporary designs; accessories for the wedding ceremony and reception; and gifts for attendants. 800–451–8616.

The Precious Collection, Merchandise Mart, P.O. Box 3403, Chicago, IL 60654: Free catalog ■ Coordinated wedding invitation ensembles with traditional or contemporary designs, wedding ceremony and reception accessories. 800–284–9080.

Rexcraft, Rexburg, ID 83441: Free catalog ■ Invitations and stationery, bridal and reception accessories and thank you cards. 800–635–4653.

Sugar 'n Spice Invitations, 299 Maple, Sugar, ID 83448: Free catalog ■ Invitations and stationery, bridal and reception accessories, and thank you cards. 800–635–1433.

Wedding Invitations by After Six, P.O. Box 263, Galena, IL 61036: Free catalog ■ Wedding invitations, announcements, and stationery. 800–231–1273.

WELDING & FOUNDRY EQUIPMENT

Am-Fast Bolt, Nut & Screw Company, 406 W. Boylston St., Worcester, MA 01606: Free information ■ Foundry equipment, welding tools, power machine tools, and machine shop supplies. 508–852–8778.

Brodhead-Garrett, 4560 E. 71st St., Cleveland, OH 44105: Free information ■ Foundry equipment, welding tools, power machine tools, hand and portable power tools, machine shop supplies and measuring, drafting, and layout tools. 216–341–0248.

Edlen Machinery Company, 2524 Park St., Muskegon Heights, MI 49444: Free information ■ Foundry equipment, welding tools, power machine tools and machine shop supplies. 616–733–2695.

McKilligan, 435 Main St., Johnson City, NY 13790: Free information ■ Foundry equipment, welding tools, power machine tools, hand and portable power tools, machine shop supplies, and measuring, drafting, and layout tools. 607–729–6511.

Pyramid Products Company, 3736 S. 7th Ave., Phoenix, AZ 85041: Free literature ■ Foundry equipment and supplies for home and professional craftsmen. 602–276–5365.

WELLS

Baker Manufacturing Company, 133 Enterprise St., Evansville, WI 53536: Free information ■ Hand pump systems for water wells. 608–882–5100.

Deeprock Manufacturing Company, 7341 Anderson Rd., P.O. Box 1, Opelika, AL

36802: Free information ■ Well-digging equipment. 800–333–7762.

WHEAT WEAVING

J. Page Basketry, 820 Albee Rd. W., Nokomis, FL 34275: Free catalog ■ Wheat weaving and pine needle crafting supplies, dried and preserved flowers and herbs, basket-making supplies, and books. 813–485–6730.

Sunflower & Sunshine Company, 127 W. 30th St., Hutchinson, KS 67502: Free price list ■ Wheat-weaving supplies, kits, and video tapes; painting, applique, and sewing pattern packets; and painting books. 316–665–6256.

WHEELCHAIRS & TRANSPORTERS

Adaptive Communication Systems, Inc., 1400 Levee Dr., Coraopolis, PA 15108: Free catalog ■ Easy-mounting adaptations for wheelchair communication systems. 800–247–3433.

AM Scooters, P.O. Box 22137, Sarasota, FL 34276: Free information ■ Portable, easy-to-assemble and disassemble, offers two front wheel drive and three rear drive, battery-powered scooters and custom accessories. 813–923–5260.

Bruce Medical Supply, 411 Waverly Oaks Rd., P.O. Box 9166, Waltham, MA 02254: Free information ■ Mobility equipment, health equipment, and supplies for people with physical disabilities. 800–225–8446.

Bruno Independent Living Aids, P.O. Box 84, Oconomowoc, WI 53066: Free brochure ■ Wheelchair and scooter lifts for cars, vans, and trucks. Other items include a battery-powered rear-wheel drive scooter and battery-powered stairway elevator system. 800–882–8183.

Burke, Inc., Box 1064, Mission, KS 66222: Free information ■ Portable, easy-to-operate, rear wheel-powered mobility vehicles. 800–255–4147.

Convaid Products, Inc., P.O. Box 2458, Palos Verde, CA 90274: Free information ■ Lightweight, compact folding mobility aids for children and adults. 800–552–1020; 310–539–6814 (in CA).

Electric Mobility Corporation, #1 Mobility Plaza, Dept. 3510, Sewell, NJ 08080: Free catalog ■ Electric scooters, power chairs, water-powered lift for tubs, and other mobility accessories. 800–662–4548.

ETAC USA, 2325 Parklawn Dr., Ste. P, Waukesha, WI 53186: Free brochure ■ Wheelchairs, walking aids, bath safety equipment, and other aids to make daily living easier. 800–678–ETAC; 414–796–4600 (in WI).

Fashion Ease, Division M & M Health Care, 1541 60th St., Brooklyn, NY 11219: Free catalog ■ Wheelchair accessories and clothing with velcro closures. 800–221–8929.

Fortress, Inc., P.O. Box 489, Clovis, CA 93613: Free catalog ■ Standard powered and folding, transportable direct drive power wheelchairs; lightweight, self-powered wheelchairs, rear wheel drive scooters; and a three-wheel racing wheelchair. 800–869–4335.

Guardian Products, Inc., 12800 Wentworth St., Arieta, CA 91331: Free catalog ■ Walkers and accessories; crutches, canes, and accessories; home activity aids; beds, lifters, and ramps; and lifters and transport products. 800–255–5022; 818–504–2820 (in CA).

Health Supplies of America, P.O. Box 1059, Burlington, NC 27834: Free catalog ■ Wheelchairs, wheelchair parts, and other health care supplies. 800–334–1187.

Independent Living Aids/Can-Do Products, 27 East Mall, Plainview, NY 11803: Free catalog ■ Self-help products for individuals with vision impairment and physical disabilities/challenges. 800–537–2118; 516–752–8080 (in NY).

LARK of America, P.O. Box 1647, Waukesha, WI 53187: Free information ■ Easy-to-transport, three-wheel electric scooter. 414–542–6060.

Lumex, 100 Spence St., Bay Shore, NY 11706: Free catalog ■ Bathroom safety products, walking aids, pressure ulcer management devices, accessories to daily living, stainless steel wheelchairs, and other home health care products. 516–273–2200.

The National Wheel-O-Vator Company, Inc., P.O. Box 348, Roanoke, IL 61561: Free information ■ Wheelchair and side-riding stair lifts. 800–551–9095.

Permobil, 30 Ray Ave., Burlington, MA 01803: Free information ■ Standing seat for power based wheelchairs. 800–736–0925.

Struck Corporation, Box 307, Cedarburg, WI 53012: Free information ■ Lightweight, battery-operated scooter for indoor and outdoor use. 414–377–3300.

Triaid, Inc., P.O. Box 1364, Cumberland, MD 21502: Free brochure ■ Mobility-enhancing tricycles. 301–759–3525.

Wheelchair Institute of Kansas, P.O. Box 777, La Crosse, KS 67548: Free information ■ Wheelchairs and other transportation aids for obese patients. 800–537–6454.

WIGS

Afro World Hair Company, 7262 Natural Bridge, St. Louis, MO 63121: Free brochure with two first class stamps ■ Toupees, hairpieces, and male wigs in curly, wavy, or Afro styles. 800–325–8067.

Beauty by Spector, Inc., McKeesport, PA 15134: Free catalog ■ Save up to 50 percent on wigs and hairpieces. 412–673–3259.

Beauty Trends, P.O. Box 9323, Pembroke Pines, FL 33014: Free information ■ Adolfo wigs. 800–777–7772.

Louis Feder & Joseph Fleischer Wigs, 14 E. 38th St., New York, NY 10016: Women's catalog $10; men's color video $29.95 ■ Handmade, natural-looking hairpieces and wigs for men and women. 212–686–7701.

Franklin Fashions Corporation, 103 E. Hawthorne Ave., Valley Stream, Long Island, NY 11582: Free catalog ■ Wigs for men and women. 516–561–6260.

Gold Medal Hair Products, Inc., 1 Bennington Ave., Freeport, NY 11520: Free catalog ■ Wigs for black men and women, hair and beauty preparations, hair styling supplies, eye glasses, and jewelry. 516–378–6900.

Jacquelyn International Fashion Products, Inc., 212 5th Ave., New York, NY 10010: Free catalog ■ Women's wigs. 800–272–2424; 212–563–6930 (in NY).

Oradell International Corporation, 3 Harding Pl., Little Ferry, NJ 07643: Free catalog ■ Women's wigs. 800–223–6588; 201–440–9150 (in NJ).

Total Image Designs, 2415 Main St., Ste. 209, Stratford, CT 06497: Free catalog ■ Wigs and hairpieces.

The Wig Company, P.O. Box 12950, Pittsburgh, PA 15241: Free catalog ■ Women's wigs. 800–245–6288.

Paula Young Wigs, P.O. Box 483, Brockton, MA 02403: Free catalog ■ Wig care supplies and women's wigs. 800–472–4017.

WIND CHIMES

David Kay, Inc., One Jenni Ln., Peoria, IL 61614: Free catalog ■ Wind chimes, planters, bird houses, furniture, garden accessories, pool and backyard toys, fireplace accessories, games, and sculptures. 800–535–9917.

Keely's Kites, 240 Commercial St., Provincetown, MA 02657: Free catalog ■ Wind chimes, kites, and accessories. 310–396–KITE.

Nevada Kite Company, 1402 Nevada Hwy., Boulder City, NV 89005: Free information ■ Wind chimes, kites, and wind sox. 702–293–5483.

WINE & BEER MAKING

Ambler Woodstove & Wine Cellar, Butler & Bethlehem Pikes, Ambler, PA 19002: Free information ■ Home brewing supplies. 215–643–3565.

Andrews Home Brewing Accessories, 5740 Via Sotelo, Riverside, CA 92506: Catalog $1 ■ Home brewing supplies. 714–682–7207.

Bacchus & Barleycorn, Ltd., 8725 Johnson Dr., Merriam, KS 66202: Free catalog ■ Home brewing supplies. 913–262–4243.

The Basement Brewmaster, 4280 N. 160th St., Brookfield, WI 53005: Free information ■ Home brewing supplies. 414–781–BREW.

Beermakers of America, 1040 N. 4th St., San Jose, CA 95112: Free catalog ■ Home brewing supplies. 408–288–6647; 800–874–8200 (in CA).

Beer & Wine Hobby, 180 New Boston St., Woburn, MA 01801: Free catalog ■ Home brewing and wine-making supplies. 800–523–5423.

Beer & Winemaking Cellar, P.O. Box 33525, Seattle, WA 98133: Free catalog ■

Beer and wine making supplies. 800–342–1871.

Beer & Winemaking Supplies, Inc., 154 King St., Northampton, MA 01060: Free catalog ■ Home brewing and wine-making supplies. 413–586–0150.

The Beverage Company, P.O. Box 839, Anderson, CA 96007: Free information ■ Home brewing supplies. 916–347–5475.

Bierhaus International, Inc., 3723 W. 12th St., Erie, PA 16505: Free information ■ Anaerobic mini breweries that make up to 12 gallons of all-natural beer using only barley malt and hops. 814–833–7747.

The Brewery, 18 Main St., Potsdam, NY 13676: Free catalog ■ Home brewing supplies. 800–762–2560.

Brew & Grow, 8179 University Ave. NE, Fridley, MN 55432: Free information ■ Home brewing supplies for making beer and hydroponic gardening equipment. 612–780–8191.

Brew HA HA, Ltd., 217 High St., Pottsdown, PA 19464: Free information ■ Home brewing supplies. 215–326–7177.

Brewhaus Home Brewing Supplies, 4955 Ball Camp Pike, Knoxville, TN 37921: Free information ■ Home brewing supplies. 615–523–4615.

Brew Masters, Ltd., 12266 N. Wilkins Ave., Rockville, MD 20852: Free information ■ Home brewing supplies. 301–984–9557.

C & S Brewing Supplies, 5765 38th St., Vero Beach, FL 32960: Free information ■ Home brewing supplies. 407–567–4101.

The Cellar, 14411 Greenwood North, Seattle, WA 98113: Free information ■ Home brewing supplies. 206–365–7660.

Country Wines, 3333 Babcock Blvd., Pittsburgh, PA 15237: Free catalog ■ Malt extracts, grains, fresh hop flowers, yeast, and grape and other fruit concentrates,.

Downington Marketplace, Rt. 30, Downington, PA 19335: Free information ■ Home brewing supplies. 215–873–9734.

Flying Barrel, 111 S. Carrol St., Frederick, MD 21701: Free information ■ Home brewing supplies. 301–663–4491.

Freshops, 36180 Kings Valley Hwy., Philomath, OR 97330: Free list with long

SASE ■ Home brewing supplies. 503–929–2736.

Frozen Wort, P.O. Box 988, Greenfield, MA 01301: Free information ■ Home brewing supplies. 413–773–5920.

Gateway Homebrewing Supplies, 2051 S. Dobson Rd., Mesa, AZ 85202: Free catalog ■ Home brewing supplies. 602–892–8622.

Great Fermentations of Marin, 87 Larkspur, San Rafael, CA 94901: Free catalog ■ Home brewing and wine-making supplies. 415–459–2520.

Great Fermentations of Santa Rosa, 840 Piner Rd., Santa Rosa, CA 95403: Free information ■ Home brewing supplies. 707–544–2520.

Hennessy Homebrew, 470 N. Greenbush Rd., Rensselaer, NY 12144: Free information ■ Home brewing supplies. 800–HOBREWS.

Home Brewer's Outlet, P.O. Box 30626, Palm Beach Gardens, FL 33420: Free catalog ■ Beer brewing kits and supplies. 407–626–2899.

Home Brewery, 16490 Jurupa Ave., Fontana, CA 92335: Free catalog ■ Home brewing supplies. Includes malt extracts, grains, and hops. 714–822–3010.

Home Brew International, 1126 S. Federal Hwy., Fort Lauderdale, FL 33316: Free information ■ Home brewing supplies. 305–764–1527.

Joe & Sons, P.O. Box 11276, Cincinnati, OH 45211: Free information ■ Home brewing supplies. 513–662–2326.

Joy-Lou Home-Brew, Inc., RD 2, Box 260, Middleburgh, NY 12122: Free information ■ Home brewing supplies. 518–827–4662.

Kedco Homebrew & Wine Supply, 475 Underhill Blvd., Syosset, NY 11791: Free information ■ Home brewing supplies. 516–921–3600.

E.C. Kraus, Box 7850, Independence, MO 64053: Free catalog ■ Home brewing supplies. 816–254–0242.

Liberty Malt Supply Company, 1432 Western Ave., Seattle, WA 98101: Free information ■ Home brewing supplies. 206–622–1880.

Life Tools, 401 N. Clay St., Green Bay, WI 54301: Free information ■ Home brewing supplies. 414–432–7399.

Lil' Olde Winemaking Shoppe, 45245 Wiltshire Ln., Sugar Grove, IL 60554: Free catalog ■ Home brewing and wine-making supplies. 708–557–2523.

MCC Brewing Supplies, 707 Hwy. 175, Hopland, CA 95449: Free information ■ Home brewing supplies. 707–744–1704.

Milan Malt Shop, Rt. 1, Box 196, Red Hook, NY 12571: Catalog $3 ■ Home brewing and wine-making supplies. Includes flavors for cordials, liqueurs, whiskies, and brandies. 914–756–2741.

Napa Fermentation Supplies, 724 California Blvd., Napa, CA 94559: Free catalog ■ Home brewing supplies. 707–255–6372.

Nort's Worts, 7625 Sheridan Rd., Kenosha, WI 53140: Free catalog ■ Home brewing supplies. 414–654–2211.

Old World Home Brewing Supplies, 117 Alter Ave., Staten Island, NY 10304: Free information with long SASE ■ Home brewing supplies. 718–667–4459.

Party Creations, Rt. 2, Box 35, Red Hook, NY 12571: Free information ■ Home brewing supplies. 914–758–0661.

Premier Beer & Winemaking Supplies, 511 S. Grand East, Springfield, IL 62702: Free information ■ Home brewing supplies. 217–789–7733.

R & R Home Fermentation Supplies, 8385 Jackson Rd., Sacramento, CA 95826: Free catalog ■ Home brewing supplies. 916–383–7702.

Reno Homebrewer, 1086 S. Virginia, Reno, NV 89502: Free catalog ■ Home brewing supplies. 702–329–ALES.

Roberson's, P.O. Box 1373, Valrico, FL 33594: Free catalog ■ Home brewing supplies. 813–685–4261.

RWM Company, P.O. Box 309, Lorenzo, TX 79343: Free catalog ■ Home brewing supplies.

Sebastian Brewers Supply, 1762 Sunrise Ln., Sebastian, FL 32958: Free catalog ■ Home brewing supplies. 800–780–SUDS.

Semplex Winemakers-Beermakers, P.O. Box 11476, Minneapolis, MN 55411: Free

catalog ■ Home brewing and wine-making supplies. 612–522–0500.

Shade Tree Shop, 3712 Foothill Blvd., La Crescenta, CA 91241: Free information ■ Home brewing supplies. 707–255–6372.

S.P.I. Wine & Beer, Box 784, Chapel Hill, NC 27514: Free catalog ■ Home brewing and wine-making supplies. 800–852–9545.

F.H. Steinbart Company, 602 SE Salmon, Portland, OR 97214: Free catalog ■ Home brewing supplies. 503–232–8793.

Vynox, P.O. Box 15498, Rochester, NY 14615: Free information ■ Home brewing and wine-making supplies. 716–254–4771.

Williams' Brewing Company, Box 2195, San Leandro, CA 94577: Free catalog ■ Home brewing supplies. 415–895–BREW.

Wine Art, 5890 N. Keystone Ave., Indianapolis, IN 46220: Free price list ■ Home brewing and wine-making supplies. Includes concentrates and flavors, yeasts, sterilizers, fermenters, barrels, brewing ingredients, bottling equipment, serving accessories and glassware, books, gifts, and wine-making kits. 317–546–9940.

Wine Craft, 3400 Wooddale Dr. NE, Atlanta, GA 30326: Free information ■ Home brewing supplies. 404–266–0793.

The Wine Press & Hops, 7 Schoen Pl., Pittsford, NY 14531: Free information ■ Home brewing supplies. 716–381–8092.

WINE CELLARS & RACKS

Gironde Bros., Inc., 319 Lynnway, Lynn, MA 01901: Free brochure ■ Free-standing wine cellars with automatic temperature and humidity controls. 800–243–9355.

International Wine Accessories, 11020 Audelia Rd., Dallas, TX 75243: Free information ■ Refrigeration packages, thermal doors, wine racks, and temperature gauges and equipment for building wine cellars. 800–527–4072; 214–349–6097 (in TX).

Kedco Wine Storage Systems, 475 Underhill Blvd., Syosset, NY 11791: Free brochure ■ Credenzas, vaults, wine stewards, and storage racks for wine. 516–921–3600.

Wine Cellars USA, 134 W. 131st St., Los Angeles, CA 90061: Free information ■ Custom wine cellars. 800–777–8466; 310–719–7500 (in CA).

Wine Enthusiast, P.O. Box 39, Pleasantville, NY 10570: Catalog $2 ■ Crystal, gifts, cellars, vintage keepers, rocks, corkscrews, and wine accessories. 800–356–8466.

WINERY NEWSLETTERS

Alexander Valley Vineyards, 8644 Hwy. 128, Healdsburg, CA 95448: Free winery newsletter, *Alexander Valley Vineyards Newsletter.* 707–433–7209.

Beringer Vineyards, 2000 Main St., St. Helena, CA 94574: Free winery newsletter, *Beringer Vineyards Report.* 707–963–7114.

Cain Cellars, 3800 Langtry Rd., St. Helena, CA 94574: Free winery newsletter, *Raising Cain.* 707–963–1616.

Congress Springs Vineyards, 23600 Congress Springs Rd., Saratoga, CA 95070: Free winery newsletter, *The Grapeleaf.* 415–867–1409.

Delicato Vineyards, Hwy. 99 at French Camp Rd., Manteca, CA 95336: Free winery newsletter, *Meet Delicato.* 209–239–1215.

Fetzer Vineyards, P.O. Box 227, Redwood Valley, CA 95470: Free magazine, *Fetzer & Food Magazine.* 707–744–1250.

Foppiano Vineyards, 12707 Old Redwood Hwy., Healdsburg, CA 95448: Free winery newsletter, *Grape Tidings Newsletter.* 707–433–7272.

Frick Winery, 23072 Walling Rd., Geyserville, CA 95441: Free winery newsletter, *Frick Winery Information Letter.* 415–362–1911.

Giumarra Vineyards, 11220 Edison Hwy., Edison, CA 93220: Free winery newsletter, *Giumarra Family Grapevine.* 805–395–7153.

Grand Cru Vineyards, 1 Vintage Ln., Glen Ellen, CA 95442: Free winery newsletter, *Via the Grapevine.* 707–996–8100.

Hacienda Winery, 1000 Vineyard Ln., Sonoma, CA 95476: Free winery newsletter, *Hacienda Wine Calendar.* 707–938–3220.

Johnson's Alexander Valley Winery, 8333 Hwy. 128, Healdsburg, CA 95448: Free winery newsletter, *Johnson's Alexander Valley Wines Newsletter.* 707–433–2319.

Charles Krug Winery, 2800 St. Helena Hwy., St. Helena, CA 94574: Free winery newsletter, *Bottles and Bins.* 707–963–5057.

Leeward Winery, 2784 Johnson Dr., Ventura, CA 93003: Free winery newsletter, *Leeward Winery Newsletter.* 805–656–5054.

Mayacamas Vineyards, 1155 Lokoya Rd., Napa, CA 94558: Free winery newsletter, *Mayacamas Vineyards Newsletter.* 707–224–4030.

The Monteray Vineyard, 800 S. Alta St., Gonzales, CA 93926: Free winery newsletter, *Winemaker Notes.* 408–675–2481.

St. Francis Winery & Vineyards, 8450 Sonoma Hwy., Kenwood, CA 95452: Free winery newsletter, *Vintage Times.* 707–833–2316.

Sebastiani Vineyards, 389 4th St. East, Sonoma, CA 95476: Free winery newsletter, *Sebastiani Vineyards Newsletter.* 707–938–5532.

Simi Winery, 16275 Healdsburg Ave., Healdsburg, CA 95448: Free winery newsletter, *Simi News.* 707–433–6981.

WIRE CRAFTING

Arizona Gems & Crystals, 414 5th St., P.O. Box 1432, Safford, AZ 86314: Catalog $1 ■ Gem tree and wire crafting supplies, chip beads, other beads and findings, silversmithing and lapidary tools, jewelry-making supplies, and mineral sets. 602–428–5164.

Herkimer Diamond Mines, Box 510, Herkimer, NY 13350: Free information ■ Gem tree and wire crafting supplies, petrified wood, rockhounding equipment, and mineral and rock specimens. 315–891–7355.

Jeanne's Rock & Jewelry, 5420 Bissonet, Bellaire, TX 77401: Free information ■ Seashells, petrified wood, gem tree supplies, and rockhounding equipment and supplies. 713–664–2988.

Jems, Inc., 2293 Aurora Rd., Melbourne, FL 32935: Free price list ■ Gem trees and wire-crafting supplies, tumbled gemstones, figurines, and jewelry-making supplies. 407–254–5600.

Victoria House, 23215 Harborview Rd., Ste. 1118, Charlotte Harbor, FL 33980: Price list 50¢ ■ Wire tree supplies and

books, regular and non-tarnish wire, tools, metal leaves, and Brazilian Agate bases.

WOOD FINISHING & RESTORING

Antique Color Supply, Inc., P.O. Box 1668, Lunenburg, MA 01462: Free information with long SASE ■ Powdered milk paint for antique restoration. 508–582–6426.

Bay City Paint Company, 2279 Market St., San Francisco, CA 94114: Free information ■ Paints, brushes, glues, how-to books, and other supplies. 415–431–4914.

Formby's, Inc., Box 667, Olive Branch, MS 38654: Free information ■ Furniture refinishing products and kits. 800–FORMBYS.

Klean-Strip, P.O. Box 1879, Memphis, TN 38101: Free booklet and price list ■ Supplies for restoration of wood floors without stripping or sanding and furniture and brass refinishing; paint removers and wood preservatives; and fabric protectors and waterproofing sealer. 901–775–0100.

Minwax Company, Inc., Box 436, Little Falls, NJ 07424: Free booklet ■ Will send a booklet describing a one-step staining and sealing process using Minwax products. 201–307–4800.

Watco-Dennis Corporation, P.O. Box 426, Little Falls, NJ 07424: Free booklet ■ Danish oil finishes for furniture and woodwork that require no pre-staining or surface treatment.

Waterlox Chemical & Coatings Corporation, 9808 Meech Ave., Cleveland, OH 44105: Free catalog ■ Tung oil finishes. 800–321–0377; 216–641–4877 (in OH).

Wise Company, 6503 St. Claude Ave., P.O. Box 118, Arabi, LA 70032: Catalog $4 ■ Period and miscellaneous hardware and refinishing products to restore or repair antique furniture. 504–277–7551.

WOODWORKING

Parts & Supplies

Adams Wood Products, Inc., 974 Forest Dr., Morristown, TN 37814: Free information ■ Custom cherry, mahogany, maple, pine, cedar, and oak wood parts. 615–587–2942.

Anthony Wood Products, Inc., P.O. Box 1081, Hillsboro, TX 76645: Catalog $2 ■ Handcrafted Victorian gingerbread. 817–582–7225.

Armor Products, P.O. Box 445, East Northport, NY 11731: Catalog $1 ■ Wood turnings and parts for toys and other crafts; replacement clock movements for restoring mantel, banjos, and grandfather clocks; hardware; lamp parts; electronic music boxes; and plans for toys and children's furniture. 800–292–8296.

Artistry in Veneers, Inc., 450 Oak Tree Ave., South Plainfield, NJ 07080: Catalog $1 ■ Electric tools, veneers, furniture plans, marquetry patterns and kits, finishing products, glues, and other supplies. 908–668–1430.

Artway Crafts, Box 699, Tom Bean, TX 75489: Catalog $1 (refundable) ■ Wood cutouts, items to carve, toy parts, quartz clock movements, music boxes, wood-burning projects, tools, and books. 903–546–6755.

Barap Specialties, 835 Bellows Ave., Frankfort, MI 49635: Catalog $1 ■ Chair cane, wooden parts, lamp parts, tools, finishing materials, hardware, and plans. 616–352–9863.

Big Sky Carvers, 8256 Huffine Ln., Bozeman, MT 59715: Free information ■ Carved and sanded blanks that are ready for detailing and painting. 406–586–0008.

Birds of a Feather, 24 Dewey St., Sayville, NY 11782: Free catalog with long SASE ■ Hardwoods for woodcarvings. 516–589–0707.

Buck Run Carving Supplies, 781 Gully Rd., Aurora, NY 13026: Catalog $2 (refundable) ■ Woodcarving supplies. 315–364–8414.

Cabin Craft, 2059 Atlanta Ave., Riverside, CA 92507: Catalog $3 ■ Unfinished wooden furniture, wooden cutouts, paints, brushes, other supplies, boutique items, and books (separate catalog) on tole and decorative painting. 714–684–2827.

Cherry Tree Toys, P.O. Box 369, Belmont, OH 43718: Catalog $1 ■ Plans, kits, and unfinished hardwood parts for toys. 800–848–4363.

Chesapeake Bay Woodcrafters, 4307 Hanover Ave., Richmond, VA 23221: Free catalog ■ Woodcarving supplies. 800–388–9838.

Crafters, 11840 North US 27, Dewitt, MI 48820: Catalog $1 ■ Woodcraft patterns. 517–669–5214.

Craftsman Wood Service, 1735 W. Cortland Ct., Addison, IL 60101: Catalog $1 ■ Kiln-dried wood, imported rare woods, veneers, hand and power tools, hardware, finishing materials, clock movements and kits, and parts for lamps. 708–629–3100.

Cupboard Distributing, Box 148, Urbana, OH 43078: Catalog $2 ■ Unfinished wood parts for crafts, miniatures, toys, jewelry-making, tole and decorative painting, and woodworking.

Curt's Waterfowl Corner, 123 LeBoeuf St., Box 228, Montegut, LA 70377: Free information with long SASE ■ Woodcarving supplies. 504–594–3012.

Dupli-Tech, P.O. Box 51, Charleroi, PA 15022: Free brochure ■ Carving blanks for wildfowl, waterfowl, birds of prey, and song and game birds. 412–483–8883.

P.C. English, Inc., P.O. Box 380, Thornburg, VA 22565: Free catalog ■ Decoy, bird, and wood carving tools, cutouts, patterns, paints, and supplies. 800–221–9474; 703–582–2200 (in VA).

Forest Products, P.O. Box 12, Avon, OH 44011: Free catalog ■ Basswood carving kits and supplies.

Hobbywoods, Division Pioneer MacLea, Inc., 1305 Eastern Ave., Baltimore, MD 21231: Free information ■ Foreign and domestic hardwoods, veneers, cabinet hardware, and stains and finishes. 410–327–1116.

S & C Huber Woodcrafts, 82 Plants Dam Rd., East Lyme, CT 06333: Catalog $1.50 ■ Save up to 30 percent on craft supplies and Early American-style finished items. 203–739–0772.

Jennings Decoy Company, 601 Franklin Ave. NE, St. Cloud, MN 56304: Free catalog ■ Woodcarving cutouts and kits, tools, and supplies. 800–331–5613.

Johnson Woodworks, Inc., 1953 Airway Ct., New Lenox, IL 60451: Free catalog ■ Wood crafting kits and finished items. 815–485–4262.

J.H. Kline Carving Shop, Box 445, Forge Hill Rd., Manchester, PA 17345: Free catalog with two 1st class stamps ■ Woodcarving tools and supplies, wood for carving, and patterns for precut wood blanks. 717–266–3501.

Klockit, P.O. Box 636, Lake Geneva, WI 53147: Free catalog ■ Veneer boxes and pictures, classic wood kits, decor wood accessories, wood parts, finishing supplies, hardware, and clock-making kits and parts. 800–556–2548.

Kugler Wood Shapes, 14461 60th St. North, Clearwater, FL 34620: Free catalog ■ Unfinished wood shapes. 813–531–4471.

M.D.I. Woodcarvers Supply, 228 Main St., Bar Harbor, ME 04609: Free catalog ■ Woodcarving supplies, books, and tools. 800–TOOLS–2–U.

Meadow Craft, P.O. Box 100, Rose Hill, NC 28458: Catalog $2 ■ Unfinished wood projects for woodworkers and crafters. 919–289–3195.

Meisel Hardware Specialties, P.O. Box 70, Spring Park, MN 55364: Catalog $1 ■ Hardware, wood parts, and plans and parts for musical door harps. 800–441–9870.

Midwest Dowel Works, Inc., 4631 Hutchinson Rd., Cincinnati, OH 45248: Catalog $1 ■ Wooden dowels, plugs, and pegs, in oak, walnut, hickory, maple, cherry, mahogany, and teak. 513–574–8488.

Bob Morgan Woodworking Supplies, 1123 Bardstown, Louisville, KY 40204: Catalog $1 ■ Veneers, hardwoods, dowels, spindles, reproduced hardware, abrasives, and woodworking and wood crafting supplies and patterns. 502–456–2545.

North West Carving Supplies, P.O. Box 407, Manhattan, MT 59741: Catalog $1 ■ Woodcarving supplies and tools.

Pasternak's Emporium, 2515 Morse St., Houston, TX 77019: Catalog $1 ■ Corbels, fretwork, trim, corner brackets, interior and exterior porch railings, and other Victorian gingerbread trim. 713–528–3808.

Rainbow Woods, 29 Andrews St., Newnan, GA 30263: Free catalog ■ Hardwood turnings. 800–423–2762; 404–251–4195 (in GA).

Ritter Carvers, Inc., 1559 Dillon Rd., Maple Glen, PA 19002: Free catalog ■

Woodcarving supplies and tools. 215–646–4896.

St. Croix Kits, 423 S. Main, Stillwater, MN 55082: Catalog $1 ■ Kits for harps, guitars, dulcimers, banjos, harpsichords, and bagpipes. 612–439–9120.

Schoepfer, 138 W. 31st St., New York, NY 10001: Free price list with long SASE ■ Eyes for decoys and birds. 212–736–6939.

Ship'n Out, Rt. 2, Brewster, NY 12564: Catalog $2 ■ Brass supplies. 914–878–4901.

Timbers Woodworking, Timbers BLdg., Carnelian Bay, CA 95711: Catalog $1 ■ Woodworking supplies and patterns. 916–581–4141.

The Tool Shed, 4032 N. 13th Way, Phoenix, AZ 85014: Free catalog ■ Woodcarving supplies. 602–264–6229.

Traditional Turnings, P.O. Box 54169, Atlanta, GA 30308: Catalog $2 ■ Bedposts, table legs, and other turnings. 800–899–7411; 404–873–3307 (in GA).

Vintage Wood Works, Hwy. 34, Box R, Quinlan, TX 78624: Catalog $2 ■ Victorian gingerbread decor cutouts.

Warren Tool Company, Inc., 2209–1, Rt. 9G, Rhinebeck, NY 12572: Catalog $1 ■ Whittling and woodcarving tools, books, woods, sharpening stones, and supplies. 914–876–7817.

Winfield Collection, 1450 Torrey Rd., Fenton, MI 48430: Catalog $1 ■ Country woodcraft patterns for folk art, shorebirds, country birds, home and decor accessories, and toys. 800–466–7712.

Wood Carvers Supply, Inc., P.O. Box 8928, Norfolk, VA 23503: Catalog $2 ■ Carving tools and kits, books, and supplies. 800–284–6229.

Woodcraft Supply, 210 Wood County Industrial Park, P.O. Box 1686, Parkersburg, WV 26102: Catalog $2 ■ Tools, supplies, books, and hardware. 800–542–9115.

Wood N' Things, Inc., 601 E. 44th St., Boise, ID 83714: Free catalog ■ Carving supplies, tools, woods, and books.

Woodpenny's, 27 Hammatt St., Ipswich, MA 01938: Catalog $2 ■ Unfinished cutouts and wooden shapes for country crafts and traditional folk items. 508–356–9636.

The Woodworkers' Store, 21801 Industrial Blvd., Rogers, MN 55374: Catalog $1 ■ Wooden parts, hardwoods, veneers, knock-down fittings, finishing supplies, hardware, kits, tools, books, and plans. 612–428–2199.

WSP, Ltd., 7222 Claridge Ct., New Orleans, LA 70127: Free information with long SASE ■ Fast drying oil paint for woodcarvings.

Plans

Armor Products, P.O. Box 445, East Northport, NY 11731: Catalog $1 ■ Plans for rocking and riding horses, realistic working automobiles and trucks, and other projects. 800–292–8296.

Cherry Tree Toys, P.O. Box 369, Belmont, OH 43718: Catalog $1 ■ Plans for wooden toys and other projects. 800–848–4363.

Constantine, 2050 Eastchester Rd., Bronx, NY 10461: Catalog $1 ■ Cabinet and furniture wood, veneers, plans, hardware, how-to books, carving tools and chisels, inlay designs, and supplies. 212–792–1600.

Furniture Designs, 1827 Elmdale Ave., Glenview, IL 60025: Catalog $3 ■ Easy-to-build furniture. 708–657–7526.

Hammermark Associates, 10 Jericho Tpk., Floral Park, NY 11001: Catalog $1 (refundable) ■ Plans for replicas of country-style furniture. 516–352–5198.

Homestead Design, P.O. Box 1058, Bellingham, WA 98227: Catalog $3 ■ Plans for small barns, studios, workshops, garden sheds, and country homes. 206–676–5647.

U-Bild, P.O. Box 2383, Van Nuys, CA 91409: Catalog $3.95 Plans with step-by-step traceable patterns for woodworking and other projects. 800–828–2453.

Western Wood Products Association, Yeon Bldg., 522 SW 5th Ave., Portland, OR 97204: Free list ■ Consumer and technical information oriented toward do-it-yourself projects, and technical information for builders, engineers, and architects. 503–224–3930.

Sandpaper

Econ-Abrasives, P.O. Box 865021, Plano, TX 75086: Free information ■ Belts, cabinet paper, finishing paper, wet/dry paper, no-load paper, adhesive discs, jumbo cleaning sticks, and other sandpaper supplies. 214–377–9779.

Industrial Abrasives Company, 642 N. 8th St., Reading, PA 19612: Free information ■ Belts, cabinet paper, no load paper, sticky discs, stones, and other sanding materials. 800–428–2222.

Redhill Corporation, Box 81, Biglerville, PA 17307: Free information with long SASE ■ Hot melt glue sticks, glue guns, and sandpaper in belts, sheets, and discs. 800–822–4003.

Sans-Rite Manufacturing Company, 321 N. Justine St., Chicago, IL 60607: Free information ■ Graded sandpaper and abrasives in belts, rolls, and sleeves. 800–521–2318.

WRESTLING

Adidas USA, 15 Independence Blvd., Warren, NJ 07060: Free information ■ Shoes. 908–580–0700.

Alchester Mills Company, Inc., 314 S. 11th St., Camden, NJ 08103: Free information ■ Knee pads and braces. 609–964–9700.

Asics Tiger Corporation, 10540 Talbert Ave., Fountain Valley, CA 92708: Free information ■ Knee pads, shoes, tights and trunks, and warm-up suits. 714–962–7654.

Bike Athletic Company, Kazmaier Associates, Inc., 2801 Red Dog Dr., P.O. Box 666, Knoxville, TN 37901: Free information ■ Knee pads, knee braces, and supporters. 800–251–9230; 615–546–4703 (in TN).

The Brute Group, 2126 Spring St., P.O. Box 2788, Reading, PA 19609: Free information ■ Knee pads, knee braces, mats and mat covers, shoes, supporters, tights and trunks, uniforms, and warm-up suits. 800–397–2788; 215–678–4050 (in PA).

Cougar Sports, 7954 Wallace Rd., Eden Prairie, MN 55344: Free information ■ Knee pads, mouth and teeth protectors, and supporters. 800–445–2664; 612–934–5384 (in MN).

Cramer Products, Inc., 153 W. Warren St., P.O. Box 1001, Gardner, KS 66030: Free information ■ Knee braces and pads, mouth and teeth protectors, and other equipment. 800–255–6621; 913–884–7511 (in KS).

Genesport Industries, Ltd., Hokkaido Karate Equipment Manufacturing Company, 150 King St., Montreal, Quebec, Canada H3C 2P3: Free information ■ Knee pads, mouth and teeth protectors, supporters, tights and trunks, and mats. 514–861–1856.

Cliff Keen Athletic, 1235 Rosewood, P.O. Box 1224, Ann Arbor, MI 48106: Free information ■ Knee pads and braces, mat covers, mats, mouth and teeth protectors, shoes, supporters, tights and trunks, uniforms, and warm-up suits. 800–992–0799; 313–769–9555 (in MI).

Royal Textile Mills, Inc., Firetower Rd., P.O. Box 250, Yanceyville, NC 27379: Free information ■ Knee pads and knee braces, mouth and teeth protectors, and supporters. 800–334–9361; 919–694–4121 (in NC).

Sport World Distributors, 3060 Clermont Rd., P.O. Box 27131, Columbus, OH 44327: Free information ■ Knee pads and braces, tights and trunks, uniforms, and warm-up suits. 614–838–8511.

YARN & SPINNING FIBERS

Aurora Silk, 5806 N. Vancouver Ave., Portland, OR 97217: Color chart $15 ■ Naturally dyed silk fibers. 503–286–4149.

Ayotte's Designery, P.O. Box 287, Center Sandwich, NH 03227: Catalog $1 ■ Spinning and weaving supplies. 603–284–6915.

Babylon Wools, 95 Day St., Granby, CT 06035: Samples $3 ■ Corriedale fleece or large carded batt, in white and natural colors. 203–653–5059.

Bare Hill Studios, P.O. Bldg., Rt. 111, Box 327, Harvard, MA 01451: Catalog $3.50 ■ Alpaca, cotton, wool, mohair, and synthetic yarns.

Bartlett Yarns, P.O. Box 36, Harmony, ME 04942: Free brochure with long SASE ■ Wool yarns for knitting and weaving. 207–683–2251.

Beau Monde, Rt. 30, Box 687, Pawlet, VT 05761: Color card $10 (refundable) ■ Equipment and supplies for felters, spinners, and weavers. 802–325–3645.

Black Ram, Ltd., Bob & Sue Salsbury, 5100 Eldora Rd., Waterloo, IA 50701: Free price list ■ Cleaned Corriedale fleece in natural colors. 319–235–6181.

Black Sheep Knitting, 101 N. West St., Black Mountain, NC 28711: Free catalog ■ Natural fiber yarns for hand knitting. Includes cottons, wools, silks, and blends. 704–669–2802.

Braid-Aid, 466 Washington St., Rt. 53, Pembroke, MA 02359: Catalog $4 ■ Braided rug kits and braiding supplies; hooking, basket-making, shirret, spinning and weaving supplies; and wool by the pound or yard. 617–826–6091.

Broadway Yarn Company, P.O. Box 1467, Sanford, NC 27331: Swatch cards $3 (refundable) ■ Polyester, cotton, and nylon warp; loom selvage, wool yarns and blends, and polyester yarn; and macrame cord.

Chameleon Knitting, 6350 W. 37th St., Indianapolis, IN 46224: Catalog $2 ■ Knitting machines and accessories, and wool, cotton, mohair, linen, silk, alpaca, rayon, and acrylic yarns on cones. 317–290–1500.

Classic Elite Yarns, Inc., 12 Perkins St., Lowell, MA 01854: Free information with long SASE ■ Cones and skeins of mohair, cotton, wool, cashmere, silk, and linen fibers for knitting and weaving. 508–453–2837.

W. Cook & Company, 580 Thames St., Ste. 232, Newport, RI 02840: Free catalog ■ Mohair and mohair/silk combination yarns. 800–772–3003; 401–848–9190 (in RI).

Cotton Clouds, Rt. 2, Desert Hills, Safford, AZ 85546: Catalog with yarn samples $10 ■ Knitting, weaving, and crochet cone and skein yarns, in 100 percent cotton; looms, and spinning fibers; and kits and books. 800–322–7888; 602–428–7000 (in AZ).

Creative Yarns, 9 Swan St., Asheville, NC 28003: Catalog $3.50 ■ Knitting yarns, hand-painted needlepoint canvases, silks, metallics, and ribbons in solid and over-dyed colors. 704–274–7769.

Daisy Chain, P.O. Box 1258, Parkersburg, WV 26102: Catalog $2 (refundable) ■ Thread and yarn for machine knitting and embroidery. 304–428–9500.

Edgemont Yarn Services, P.O. Box 205, Washington, KY 41086: Color card and price sheet $2 (refundable with $20 order) ■ Cones and skeins of wools in naturals, soft naturals, heavy weights, rug yarn, boucles, wool loops, and piles. 606–759–7614.

Ewe's Cottage, P.O. Box 672, Roundup, MT 59702: Catalog $3 (refundable) ■ Books, dyes, fibers, spinning wheels, looms, and yarns. 406–323–1708.

Frederick J. Fawcett, Inc., 1304 Ross St., Petaluma, CA 94952: Free information ■ Looms, linen embroidery fabrics, macrame supplies, and linen/cotton and wool yarns and fibers. 800–289–9276.

Fiber Farm, 205 Tallwood, Georgetown, TX 78628: Free information ■ Wool, cotton, and mohair yarn. 800–527–3634.

The Fiber of Eden, Rover Rt., Box 83, West Plains, MO 65775: Catalog $8 ■ Angora, camel down, kid Mohair, silk, wool, and other yarns.

Fiber Studio, 9 Foster Hill Rd., Box 637, Henniker, NH 03242: Catalog $1 ■ Natural fibers that include pearl cottons, mohair, Andean alpaca, cotton/linen, Icelandic wools, rug linen, linens, and silk; New Zealand spinning fibers that include fleeces and carded wool, mohair, camel hair silks, flax, and wool roving; and mill ends and close outs. 603–428–7830.

Galler, Inc., 27 W. 20th St., New York, NY 10011: Free information ■ Cones and balls of imported angora, cashmere, cotton, mohair, silk, wool, and other natural yarns. 212–620–7190.

Martha Hall, 46 Main St., Yarmouth, ME 04096: Catalog $1 ■ Easy-to-knit Maine wool sweater kits and hand-dyed silk, mohair, linen, cotton, cashmere, and alpaca yarn. 207–846–9746.

Harrisville Designs, Harrisville, NH 03450: Catalog $10 (refundable) ■ Yarns, looms, and accessories.

Herrschners, Inc., Hoover Rd., Stevens Point, WI 54492: Catalog $1 ■ Yarns and knitting accessories, and crochet and hooking needle crafts. 800–441–0838.

Hub Mills, 12 Perkins St., Lowell, MA 01854: Sample package $5 ■ Mohair, wool, cotton, and silk yarns for hand and machine knitting and weaving. 508–937–0320.

JaggerSpun, Water St., P.O. Box 188, Springvale, ME 04083: Price list and samples $5 ■ One hundred percent worsted spun wool and wool-silk yarn. 207–324–4455.

La Lana Wools, 136 Paseo Norte, Taos, NM 87571: Sample card set $15 ■ Handspun, dyed yarns in wool, silk, and mohair. Includes carded blends for spinning. 505–758–9631.

Las Manos, 123 W. North St., Healdsburg, CA 95448: Catalog $2 ■ Weaving, crochet, and knitting yarns.

Mannings Creative Crafts, P.O. Box 687, East Berlin, PA 17316: Catalog $1 ■ Yarns and spinning fibers, spinning wheels and looms, dyes and mordants, and books. 717–624–2223.

Norsk Fjord Fiber, P.O. Box 271, Lexington, GA 30648: Fleece and rovings sample cards $3; Spelsau yarns sample card $3 ■ Swedish Gotland fleece, rovings and yarns. 404–743–5120.

Ogier Trading Company, 410 Nevada Ave., P.O. Box 686, Moss Beach, CA 94038: Catalog $8 (refundable) ■ Fashion and novelty yarns. 415–728–9216.

On the Inca Trail, P.O. Box 9406, Fort Worth, TX 76147: Free information ■ Alpaca yarn in cones, balls, and skeins. 800–233–6321.

John Perkins Industries, P.O. Box 8372, Greenville, SC 29604: Free information ■ Single, piled, novelty, fancy, and natural hand and machine yarns. 803–277–4240.

St. Peter Woolen Mill, 101 W. Broadway, St. Peter, MN 56082: Free brochure ■ Natural virgin wool batting. 507–931–3734.

Silk City Fibers, 155 Oxford St., Paterson, NJ 07522: Information $7.50 ■ Color-coordinated cone yarns. 201–942–1100.

Smiley's Yarns, 92–06 Jamaica Ave., Woodhaven NY 11421: Free brochure with long SASE ■ Yarn, needles, hooks, books, and tools and supplies. 718–847–5038.

Straw into Gold, 3006 San Pablo Ave., Berkeley, CA 94702: Free information ■ Ready-to-spin alpaca. 510–548–5243.

Super Yarn Mart, P.O. Box 15028, Los Angeles, CA 90015: Catalog $2 (refundable) ■ Save up to 30 percent on yarns and accessories.

Bonnie Triola, 34 E.. Gore Rd., Erie, PA 16509: Catalog $10 ■ Natural fibers, synthetics, blends, and discontinued designer yarns. 814–825–7821.

The Weaver's Knot, Inc., 1803 Augusta St., Greenville, SC 29605: Catalog $1 ■ Yarns, spinning fibers, looms, and knitting, crochet, and weaving supplies. 803–235–7747.

Weavers' Store, 11 S. 9th St., Columbia, MO 65201: Catalog $2 ■ Supplies for weavers, spinners, and knitters. 314–442–5413.

Weavers Warehouse, P.O. Box 36030, Albuquerque, NM 87176: Samples $2 (refundable) ■ Weaving and spinning equipment, and yarns in cotton, wool, silk, rayon, and blends. 505–265–6333.

Weaving Works, 4717 Brooklyn Ave. NE, Seattle, WA 98105: Catalog $1 ■ Looms, spinning wheels, hand and machine knitting supplies, and traditional and fashion yarns. 206–524–1221.

Webs Yarn, P.O. Box 349, 18 Kellogg Ave., Amherst, MA 01004: Free samples ■ Mill ends. 413–253–2580.

Wilde Yarns, P.O. Box 4662, Philadelphia, PA 19127: Information and sample cards $6 ■ Wool yarns. 215–482–8800.

WoodsEdge Wools, P.O. Box 275, Stockton, NJ 08559: Catalog and samples $10 ■ Exotic fibers and exclusive blends of soft-washed, scoured, carded, dyed, and combed fleece. 609–397–2212.

Woolstons' Woolshed, Bolton, MA 01740: Catalog $2.50 ■ Wool and silk fibers, ready-to-spin alpaca, spinning wheels, and other supplies. 508–779–5081.

The Yarn Basket, 5114 Top Seed Ct., Charlotte, NC 28226: Sample cards and price list $5 ■ Natural yarns for weaving and knitting. 704–542–8427.

Yarn by Mills, P.O. Box 28, Wallback, WV 25285: Price list $2.50 ■ Equipment and hand-spun yarns for weaving, knitting, and crochet. Includes cashmeres, silks, angoras, and other fibers. 304–587–2561.

Yarn Country, P.O. Box 6500, Concord, CA 94524: Catalog and yarn samples $10.99 ■ Yarns for crochet, cross-stitch, and canvas crafts. 800–441–YARN.

Yarn Galore, 4614 Wisconsin Ave. NW, Washington, DC 20008: Shade card $3 (refundable) ■ Yarns, knitting supplies, 100 percent wool from the Shetland Islands, and books. 202–686–5648.

YLI Corporation, P.O. Box 109, Provo, UT 84601: Color card $2.50 ■ Serging thread in solid colors and variegated color combinations and metallic thread in wool/nylon, nylon monofilament, and rayon. 800–854–1932.

YOGA

Cambridge Zen Center, 199 Auburn St., Cambridge, MA 02139: Catalog $2 ■ Pants, zafus, mats, incense, Buddhas, malas, benches, and books. 617–492–4793.

Fish Crane Yoga Props, P.O. Box 791029, New Orleans, LA 70179: Free information ■ Lightweight, sticky mats. 800–959–6115.

Gentle Yoga, Gentle Yoga 7815 Quebrada Circle, Carlsbad, CA 92009: Free catalog ■ Video tape with two thirty-minute routines to relax and improve strength and flexibility. 619–943–9374.

Harmony in Wood, 2050 S. Dayton St., Denver, CO 80231: Free catalog ■ Yoga back bench that provide for different postures to open, stretch, and relax the body. 303–337–7728.

Home Stitchery Company, P.O. Box 3526, Idyllwild, CA 92349: Free catalog ■ Meditation clothes and cushions. 714–659–3598.

Inversion Swing, P.O. 2182, La Jolla, CA 92038: Free information ■ Inversion devices and swings, complete with door mounting device. 800–383–8056; 619–456–0926 (in CA).

Mano Creations, P.O. Box 182, Vernon, British Colombia, Canada V1T 6M2: Catalog $2 (refundable) ■ Mats, sandbags, blocks, cotton bolsters, wedges, benches, multi-purpose furniture, and other yoga equipment. 604–542–7688.

Mystic River Video, P.O. Box 716, Cambridge, MA 02140: Free information ■ Yoga video tapes. 617–483–YOGA.

Oakworks, Inc., P.O. Box 221, Shrewsbury, PA 17361: Free catalog ■ Bodywork tables and accessories. 717–235–6807.

Pisces Productions, P.O. Box 208, Cotati, CA 94931: Free brochure ■ Posture tables and chairs. 800–822–5333.

Posture Rack, 8572 Freyman Dr., Chevy Chase, MD 20815: Free information ■ Posture rack for backbends. 301–587–5904.

Proprioception, Inc., Box 7612, Ann Arbor, MI 48107: Free information ■ Adjustable and interchangeable equipment for yoga. Includes straps, slings, tables, bars, and wall and ceiling mounts. 800–488–8414.

Samadhi Cushions, RFD Box 3, Barnet, VT 05821: Free information ■ Meditation cushions. 800–331–7751.

Shasta Abbey Buddhist Supplies, P.O. Box 199, Mt. Shasta, CA 96067: Catalog $2 ■ Statues, cushions, benches, bells and gongs, altar supplies, incense, scrolls, books, and tapes. 916–926–4208.

T'AI Productions, P.O. Box 25654, Los Angeles, CA 90025: Free information ■ Yoga video tapes. 310–479–3646.

Tools for Yoga, P.O. Box 99, Chatham, NJ 07928: Free information ■ Yoga mats. 201–635–0450.

White Lotus Foundation, 2500 San Marcos Pass, Santa Barbara, CA 93105: Free information ■ Aerobic yoga workout videos. 800–544–3569; 805–964–1944 (in CA).

Yoga Mats, P.O. Box 885044, San Francisco, CA 94188: Free information with long SASE ■ Handcrafted 100 percent lightweight, cotton yoga mats. 800–829–6580.

Yoga Props, 3055 23rd St., San Francisco, CA 94110: Catalog $1 ■ Wall ropes for strengthening and stretching poses. 415–285–YOGA.

Yoga Transformations, Enchanted Rabbit Mountain, 9700 Greensprings Hwy., Ashland, OR 97520: Free information ■ Tapes for private yoga lessons in the home for beginners and intermediates. 503–482–0603.

Yogaware, 1509 Kearney, Ann Arbor, MI 48104: Free information ■ Preshrunk knit shorts with reinforced leg bands and exercise wear. 313–996–0021.

Zen Home Stitchery, P.O. Box 3526, Idyllwild, CA 92549: Free catalog ■ Meditation clothes, cushions, and accessories.

CORPORATE INDEX

Crystal Lalique, 155
Crystal Match, 114, 155
Crystal Palace Yarns, 406
Crystal Records, 379
Crystal Sonics, 51
Crystalite Corporation, 305
Crystallite Corporation, 367, 412
Crystek Corporation, 171
Cuddledown of Maine, 67–68
Cuddlers Cloth Diapers, 55
Cue Stix, 75
Cuisinarts Cookware, 188, 309
Culinary Emporium, 212
Cullman, 363
Culpepper Models, Inc., 328
Culpepper Popcorn & Candy, Inc., 206
Cultured Foods Corporation, 210
Cumberland General Store, 78, 259
Cumberland Woodcraft Company, Inc., 255, 286
Cummins Garden, 233
Cupboard Distributing, 305, 428, 453
Cureton Mineral Company, 384
The Curiosity Shop , 302
Current, 267, 413, 435
Curriculum Resources, Inc., 344
Gerald Curry, Cabinetmaker , 219
Curt's Waterfowl Corner, 453
Curtain Call Costumes, 157
Elliott Curtis & Sons , 69
Curtis Canoe, 79
Curtis-Mathes, 102, 414, 439
Curvoflite, 279
Cushion-Lift of New England, 222
Custom Cards, 77
Custom Chrome, 360
Custom Coat Company, Inc., 123
Custom Cowboy Shop, 274
Custom Cross-Stitch, 344
Custom Designed Imports, 73
Custom Fiberglass Products of Florida, Inc., 85
Custom Golf Clubs, Inc., 266
Custom Hooked Rugs, 387
Custom Ironworks, Inc., 180
Custom Jigs & Spins, 184
Custom Knifemaker's Supply, 312
Custom Needlework Designs, Inc., 344
Custom Photo, 360
Custom Quality Studio, 360
Custom Windows & Walls, 155
CustomChrome Plating, Inc., 46
Customwood Manufacturing Company, 279
Cutco Cutlery, 309
Cutlery Shoppe, 312
Cutter Ceramics, Inc., 110
The Cutting Corner , 176, 179
Cycle Composites, 71
Cycle Goods, 73
Cycle Products Company, 73

Cycle Racer, Inc., 336
Cycle Re-Cycle, 337
Cycle Recyclers, 337
Cycle Sports, 337
CyclePro, 73
Cycles LaMoure, 71
Cycles Peugeot, 71
Cycles Plus, 71, 73
Cyclo Sport USA, 73
Cyma, 140
Cynthia's Country Store, 436
Cypress Gardens Skis, 446
Cypress Street Center, 218, 223
Czimer Game & Seafood, 203

D

D & A Investments, 70
D & A Merchandise Company, Inc., 121
D & G Optical, 18
D & H Engraving, 410
D & K Prospecting Headquarters, 325, 367
D & R Aircraft Manufacturing, 328
D & R Industries, 73, 75
D & S Cycle, 337
D'Ambrosia Deluxe Displays, 183
D'Anton Leathers, 176
D'Artagnan, 203
D'eja' Vu Originals, 166
D.E.A. Bathroom Machineries, 62
D.F. Enterprises, 320
D.H. Aircraft, Inc., 49
D.Y.E. Textiles Resources, 176
Dabney Herbs, 239, 241, 254
Frederick Dackloe & Bros., Inc. , 219
Dadant & Sons, Inc., 69
Daedalus Books, Inc., 87
DAFCO, 355
The Daffodil Mart , 238, 248
Dagger Canoe Company, 79
Dahlias by Phil Traff, 238
Dahm's Automobiles, 330
Dahon California, 71
Dai Distributing, 337
The Daily Planet , 259
Daily Electronics, 372
Daisy Books, 110
Daisy Chain, 344, 455
Daisy Kingdom, 393
Daisy Manufacturing Company, Inc., 268–269, 272
Daisyfresh Dairy Cultures, 200
Daiwa Corporation, 184, 265
Dakin Farm, 198, 203
Dakota Lean Meats, Inc., 200
Dakota Quality Bird Food, 77, 352
Dakota Specialties, 110
Dalbani Electronics, 171
Dalco Athletic, 58
Dale Laboratories, 360

Daleboot USA, 400
Daleco Master Breeder Products, 354
Dallas Alice, 129
Dallas Bonsai Garden, 235
Dallee Electronics, 334
Dalton Paradise Carpets, 387
Dalton Pavilions, Inc., 255
Dalverwood Art Products, 11
Damark International, Inc., 419
Damart Thermawear, 103, 121, 123
Damascus-U.S.A., 312
Dame Juliana, Inc., 184
Dan River Paddle, 81
Dan's Fly Shop, 184
Dan's Garden Shop, 249
Dan's Tackle Service, 184
Dana Designs, 105
Dana Labels, Inc., 394
Danbury Belts, 128
Dance Design, 157–158
Dance Mart, 13, 20, 90
Dance Shop, 157
Dancer's Locker, 411
Danchuk Manufacturing, Inc., 29–30, 33
Daniel's Wicker, 272
Danish Imports, 364
Danley's, 75
Danmar Products, Inc., 119, 127
Dansant Boutique, 157
Danskin, 113, 119, 157–158
Dansounds, 157
Darke & Reinhold, 259
Darkroom Products, Ltd., 357
Darowood Farms, 151
Darr Antiques & Interiors, 6
Chuck Darrow's Fun Antiques , 6
Dart Mart, Inc., 158
Dart World, Inc., 158
Darton Archery, 9
Darts Unlimited, 158
Data East USA, 140, 433
Data General Corporation, 134
Data Label, Inc., 347
Datak Corporation, 171
Datamarine International, Inc., 83
Dataworld, Inc., 134
Datrex, 81
Dauphin Technology, Inc., 134
Davard Marine, 85
Dave's Classic T-Bird Parts, 44
Dave's New/Used Cards, 365
Davey Systems Corporation, 328
David C. Andrews, 233
Davidoff of Geneva, Inc., 427
Davidson & Associates, Inc., 140
Davidson Cycles, 71
Davidson Rock Shop, 302
Davidson-Whitehall Company, 381
Davidson-Wilson Greenhouses, 232, 239, 242
Davilyn Corporation, 18, 173
Lou Davis Wholesale , 110, 153

Davis Cabinet Company, 219
Davis Citrus Farms, 196
Davis Instruments Corporation, 83
Davka Corporation, 140
Daw Books, Inc., 90
Dawa's Hopi Arts & Crafts, 294
Dawn Invitations, 448
Dawn's Artistic Treasures, 162
Steve Dawson's Magic Touch , 130
Day-Timers, 99, 346, 413
Daylab, 357
Dayna Communications, 140
Daystar, 233, 246–247, 251
Daystar Shelter Corporation, 289
Dayton Computer Supply, 146
Dayton Marine Products, 85
Dayton Wheel Products, 53
Daytona Beach Magic Shop, 321
Daytona Yamaha, 337
Dazian's, Inc., 149, 157, 176, 426
DBI Books, Inc., 90
dbx, Inc., 415–416, 439
DD's Dollhouse, 162
de Geneve Chocolatier, 191
De Long, 57, 213
De Luna Jewelers, 295
Suzanne De Pee , 66
Dean & DeLuca, 188, 212
Dean Foster Nurseries, 234
Deanie's Seafood, 208
T. DeBaggio Herbs , 241
Deborah's Attic, 149
Deborah's Country French Bread, 188
Decart, Inc., 11, 176, 398
Deco-Trol, 371
Decor Frame Company, 215
Decora, 99–100
Decorum, 62, 219
Cy Decosse Incorporated , 90
Decoys Unlimited, 160
Dee's Creations, 114
Dee's Place of Dolls, 166
DEEliteful Designs, Inc., 114
Deep River Trading Company, 219
Deeprock Manufacturing Company, 448
Deer Me Products Company, 403
Deer Run Products, Inc., 293
Deer Valley Farm, 200
John Deere & Company , 77, 228, 230, 259, 322
Deerfield Valley Woodworking, 310
Deerskin Place, 123, 368
Deerskin Trading Post, 123, 368
DeGiorgi Seed Company, Inc., 249
DeGrandchamp's Blueberry Farm, 234
The Dehner Company, Inc. , 396
deJager Bulbs, Inc., 249
The Dekle's , 365
Del-Car Auto Parts, 24
Eileen Delaney Autographs , 20

Earl May Seeds & Nursery Company, 108, 244, 247, 249, 252
Mayacamas Vineyards, 452
Maybelle's Doll Works, 167
Mayco Molds, 111
Mayfair Signs, 397
Maynard House Antiques, 220
O.V. Maynor , 240
Earl May Seeds & Nursery , 240
Maytag Dairy Farms, Inc., 194
Mayville Engineering Company, Inc., 269
Mazzoli Coffee, Inc., 131
MBM Sales, Ltd., 325
McAfee & Company, 322
Ed McAllister Postcards , 366
McB Bears, 66
MCC Brewing Supplies, 451
McCary Apiaries, 70
McClure & Zimmerman, 249
McCormick Engraving, 54
McCoy's Recording, Inc., 381
McDavid Knee Guard, Inc., 214
McDonald Ford Parts Company, 35, 38
McGee's Electronics, 171
McGowan Book Company, 95
John E. McGuire Basket Supplies , 61
McIntosh, 416
McKee's House Plant Corner, 227
McKenzie Taxidermy Supply, 421
McKilligan, 448
Rod McLellan Company , 244
MCM Electronics, 171, 173
Judi McMahon Autographs , 21
Suzanne McNeil , 387
McNultys Tea & Coffee Company, 212
McPherson Archery Company, Inc., 9
McSpadden Musical Instruments, 342
McVay's Old Wood Creations, 151
MDK, Inc., 335
MDR Manufacturing Company, 306
Me'shiwi, 295
Meade Instruments Corporation, 19, 76
Meadow Craft, 453
Meadow Everlastings, 188, 367
Meadow Farms Country Smokehouse, 204
Meadow's Chocolate & Cake Supplies, 107
Meadowbrook Herb Gardens, 242, 351
Meadowsweet Herb Farm, 242
MEB Distributing, 192
Meca Software, 142
MECC Software, 142
Mecca Magic, Inc., 56, 131, 149, 308, 321, 368, 426
The Mechanical Maestro, 380
Mechanick's Workbench, 6, 430
Mecklenburg Furniture Shops, 220

Mectel International, Inc., 134
Media Exchange, 380
Media Magic, 146
Mediaeval Miscellanea, 149
Medic Pharmacy & Surgical, 348
Medical Arts Press, 86
Medicine Bow Motors, Inc., 35
Medicool, Inc., 161
MediSense, Inc., 161
Meehan Military Posters, 326
Meengs, 115
MEI/Micro Center, 146
F.C. Meichsner Company , 19, 76
Meier Auto Salvage, 25
Meisel Hardware Specialties, 274, 453
Mel's Miniz, 164
Mel-Nor Industries, 223, 231, 272, 317, 322
Melanie Collection, 303
Melanin Graphics, 14
Meldac of America, Inc., 434
Mellinger's, 108, 224, 230, 235, 238–239, 244, 246–247, 249, 252, 254, 352
Mellow Mail, 121
Melrose Fireworks, 183
Melrose Photographics, 360
Memorable Things, 437
Memorex, 102
Memories, Inc., 356, 448
Memory Plus Distributors, Inc., 136–137
Memory Shop West, 340
Memphis Amateur Electronics, 372
Memphis Hardwood Flooring Company, 281
Men America, 124
Menash, 351
Mendelson Electronics Company, Inc., 171
Menger Boatworks, Inc., 78
Menumaster, Inc., 8
Mercantile Food Company, 201
Mercury Research Company, 38
Merganser Aircraft Corporation, 2
Merillat Industries, Inc., 100
Merit Albums, Inc., 356
Merit Golf Clubs, 265
Merit Metal Products Corporation, 274
Merkel Model Car Company, 331
Merlin Metalworks, Inc., 72
Merlite Industries, Inc., 303
Merrbach Record Service, 410, 412
Merrell Footwear, 103
Merrell Scientific/World of Science, 313, 332, 390
Merriam-Webster, Inc., 92
Merrimade, Inc., 413
Merrin, 303
Merritt's Antiques, Inc., 117
Merry Christmas Shoppe, 169

Merry Fitness Apparel, 120
Merry Gardens, 243
Merry-Go-Round Antiques, 109
Mesa Flora Nursery, 237
Mesa Garden, 237
Mesa Photo Supply, 362
Met-Tile, Inc., 282
Metabo Corporation, 430
Metacom, Inc., 87
Metal Building Components, Inc., 282
Metal Detectors of Minneapolis, 325
Metal Sales Manufacturing, 282
Metro Imagebase, Inc., 142
Metro Moulded Parts, Inc., 49
Metro Music, 378, 380
Metrobaby, 55
Metronome, 380
Metropolitan Lighting Fixture Company, Inc., 315
Metropolitan Museum of Art, 14, 257, 261
Metropolitan Music Store, 342
Metropolitan Opera Guild, 443
The Mettle Company , 215
Richard Metz Golf Studio, Inc. , 266
Metzeler Inflatable Boats, 83
David Meyer Magic Books , 92, 95, 322
Meyer's Porcelain Art Studio, 114
Meyers Industries, Inc., 79
MFJ Enterprises, Inc., 171
MG Bits & Spares, 39
Miami Clay Company, 111
Miami Cork & Supply, 306
Miami Orchids, 244
Mibro Cameras, 362
Mibro Cameras, Inc., 101
Earl Mich Company , 397
Michael's Artist Supplies, 11
Michael's Bird Paradise, Inc., 352
Michael's Classic Wicker, 224
Michael's Music, 342
Michaels of Oregon Company, 269
Michale & Company, 105
Michel Company, 356
Michele's Silver Matching Service, 398
Michelle's Clothespin Dolls, 151, 169
Michigan Bulb Company, 249
Michigan Cane Supply, 61, 112
Mickey's House of Soldiers, 437
Micrlytics, Inc., 142
Micro Express, 135
Micro Generation Computers, 135
Micro Plastics, 411
Micro Publishing Press, 92
Micro Star, 138
Micro-C, 171
Micro-Mark, 334, 430
Micro-Mart, 171
MicroIllusions, 142
Micrologic, 84

MicroMaps Software, 142
Micronics Computers, Inc., 135
Microprocessors Unlimited, 171
MicroProse Software, Inc., 142
MicroSearch, Inc., 142
Microserve, 142
Microsoft Press, 92, 142
MicroSPARC/Nibble Publications, 142
MicroTec, 358, 360
Microwave Times, 309
Mid America Corvette Supplies, 32
Mid America Designs, Inc., 32
Mid-America Sales, 325
Mid-Atlantic Performance, 32
Mid-Atlantic Sports Cards, 409
Mid County Mustang, 40
Mid-South Business Cards, 99
Mid South Pecan Company, 199, 206
Mid States Classic Cars & Parts, 47
Mid-West Metal Detectors, 325
Mid-Wisconsin Seed & Supplies, 352
MidAmerica Vacuum Cleaner Supply Company, 442
MidAmerican Parts & Equipment Company, 37
Midas China & Silver, 115, 398
Midern Computer, Inc., 135
The Midge Fly Shop, Inc. , 185
Midland Automotive Products, 53
Midnight Recordings, 378, 380
Midway Arms, Inc., 271
Midwest Action Cycle, 338
Midwest Company, 105
Midwest Dowel Works, Inc., 453
Midwest Electronics, Inc., 441
Midwest Industries, 52
Midwest Miniatures, 437
Midwest Photo Exchange, 362
Midwest Products Company, Inc., 329
Midwest Quilt Exchange, 68
Midwest Sales Group, 59, 213
Midwest Spiral Stair Company, Inc., 285
Midwest Sport Sales, Inc., 59
Midwest Sports Supply, 424
Midwest Supply Electronics, 372
Midwest Watercraft, Ltd., 301
Midwest Wildflowers, 254
Midwest Wood Products, 288
Midwestern Wood Products, 279
Miele Appliance, Inc., 8
Mighty Minis, 232
Mighty Mite Industries, Inc., 430
Mike's Auto Parts, 31–33, 37, 42
Mike's Ceramic Molds, Inc., 111
Mike's Cycle Parts, 338
Mike's Train House, 335
Mike's Trainland, Inc., 335
Mikes Fly Desk, 185
Miki's Crystal Registry, 155
Milaeger's Gardens, 247

SUBJECT INDEX